McGraw Hill

Connect. Learn. Succeed.™

Cumulative Areas under the Standard Normal Curve

z	.00	.01	.02	.03	.04	.05	.06	.07	.08	.09
−3.4	.0003	.0003	.0003	.0003	.0003	.0003	.0003	.0003	.0003	.0002
−3.3	.0005	.0005	.0005	.0004	.0004	.0004	.0004	.0004	.0004	.0003
−3.2	.0007	.0007	.0006	.0006	.0006	.0006	.0006	.0005	.0005	.0005
−3.1	.0010	.0009	.0009	.0009	.0008	.0008	.0008	.0008	.0007	.0007
−3.0	.0013	.0013	.0013	.0012	.0012	.0011	.0011	.0011	.0010	.0010
−2.9	.0019	.0018	.0018	.0017	.0016	.0016	.0015	.0015	.0014	.0014
−2.8	.0026	.0025	.0024	.0023	.0023	.0022	.0021	.0021	.0020	.0019
−2.7	.0035	.0034	.0033	.0032	.0031	.0030	.0029	.0028	.0027	.0026
−2.6	.0047	.0045	.0044	.0043	.0041	.0040	.0039	.0038	.0037	.0036
−2.5	.0062	.0060	.0059	.0057	.0055	.0054	.0052	.0051	.0049	.0048
−2.4	.0082	.0080	.0078	.0075	.0073	.0071	.0069	.0068	.0066	.0064
−2.3	.0107	.0104	.0102	.0099	.0096	.0094	.0091	.0089	.0087	.0084
−2.2	.0139	.0136	.0132	.0129	.0125	.0122	.0119	.0116	.0113	.0110
−2.1	.0179	.0174	.0170	.0166	.0162	.0158	.0154	.0150	.0146	.0143
−2.0	.0228	.0222	.0217	.0212	.0207	.0202	.0197	.0192	.0188	.0183
−1.9	.0287	.0281	.0274	.0268	.0262	.0256	.0250	.0244	.0239	.0233
−1.8	.0359	.0351	.0344	.0336	.0329	.0322	.0314	.0307	.0301	.0294
−1.7	.0446	.0436	.0427	.0418	.0409	.0401	.0392	.0384	.0375	.0367
−1.6	.0548	.0537	.0526	.0516	.0505	.0495	.0485	.0475	.0465	.0455
−1.5	.0668	.0655	.0643	.0630	.0618	.0606	.0594	.0582	.0571	.0559
−1.4	.0808	.0793	.0778	.0764	.0749	.0735	.0721	.0708	.0694	.0681
−1.3	.0968	.0951	.0934	.0918	.0901	.0885	.0869	.0853	.0838	.0823
−1.2	.1151	.1131	.1112	.1093	.1075	.1056	.1038	.1020	.1003	.0985
−1.1	.1357	.1335	.1314	.1292	.1271	.1251	.1230	.1210	.1190	.1170
−1.0	.1587	.1562	.1539	.1515	.1492	.1469	.1446	.1423	.1401	.1379
−0.9	.1841	.1814	.1788	.1762	.1736	.1711	.1685	.1660	.1635	.1611
−0.8	.2119	.2090	.2061	.2033	.2005	.1977	.1949	.1922	.1894	.1867
−0.7	.2420	.2389	.2358	.2327	.2296	.2266	.2236	.2206	.2177	.2148
−0.6	.2743	.2709	.2676	.2643	.2611	.2578	.2546	.2514	.2483	.2451
−0.5	.3085	.3050	.3015	.2981	.2946	.2912	.2877	.2843	.2810	.2776
−0.4	.3446	.3409	.3372	.3336	.3300	.3264	.3228	.3192	.3156	.3121
−0.3	.3821	.3783	.3745	.3707	.3669	.3632	.3594	.3557	.3520	.3483
−0.2	.4207	.4168	.4129	.4090	.4052	.4013	.3974	.3936	.3897	.3859
−0.1	.4602	.4562	.4522	.4483	.4443	.4404	.4364	.4325	.4286	.4247
−0.0	.5000	.4960	.4920	.4880	.4840	.4801	.4761	.4721	.4681	.4641
0.0	.5000	.5040	.5080	.5120	.5160	.5199	.5239	.5279	.5319	.5359
0.1	.5398	.5438	.5478	.5517	.5557	.5596	.5636	.5675	.5714	.5753
0.2	.5793	.5832	.5871	.5910	.5948	.5987	.6026	.6064	.6103	.6141
0.3	.6179	.6217	.6255	.6293	.6331	.6368	.6406	.6443	.6480	.6517
0.4	.6554	.6591	.6628	.6664	.6700	.6736	.6772	.6808	.6844	.6879
0.5	.6915	.6950	.6985	.7019	.7054	.7088	.7123	.7157	.7190	.7224
0.6	.7257	.7291	.7324	.7357	.7389	.7422	.7454	.7486	.7517	.7549
0.7	.7580	.7611	.7642	.7673	.7704	.7734	.7764	.7794	.7823	.7852
0.8	.7881	.7910	.7939	.7967	.7995	.8023	.8051	.8078	.8106	.8133
0.9	.8159	.8186	.8212	.8238	.8264	.8289	.8315	.8340	.8365	.8389
1.0	.8413	.8438	.8461	.8485	.8508	.8531	.8554	.8577	.8599	.8621
1.1	.8643	.8665	.8686	.8708	.8729	.8749	.8770	.8790	.8810	.8830
1.2	.8849	.8869	.8888	.8907	.8925	.8944	.8962	.8980	.8997	.9015
1.3	.9032	.9049	.9066	.9082	.9099	.9115	.9131	.9147	.9162	.9177
1.4	.9192	.9207	.9222	.9236	.9251	.9265	.9279	.9292	.9306	.9319
1.5	.9332	.9345	.9357	.9370	.9382	.9394	.9406	.9418	.9429	.9441
1.6	.9452	.9463	.9474	.9484	.9495	.9505	.9515	.9525	.9535	.9545
1.7	.9554	.9564	.9573	.9582	.9591	.9599	.9608	.9616	.9625	.9633
1.8	.9641	.9649	.9656	.9664	.9671	.9678	.9686	.9693	.9699	.9706
1.9	.9713	.9719	.9726	.9732	.9738	.9744	.9750	.9756	.9761	.9767
2.0	.9772	.9778	.9783	.9788	.9793	.9798	.9803	.9808	.9812	.9817
2.1	.9821	.9826	.9830	.9834	.9838	.9842	.9846	.9850	.9854	.9857
2.2	.9861	.9864	.9868	.9871	.9875	.9878	.9881	.9884	.9887	.9890
2.3	.9893	.9896	.9898	.9901	.9904	.9906	.9909	.9911	.9913	.9916
2.4	.9918	.9920	.9922	.9925	.9927	.9929	.9931	.9932	.9934	.9936
2.5	.9938	.9940	.9941	.9943	.9945	.9946	.9948	.9949	.9951	.9952
2.6	.9953	.9955	.9956	.9957	.9959	.9960	.9961	.9962	.9963	.9964
2.7	.9965	.9966	.9967	.9968	.9969	.9970	.9971	.9972	.9973	.9974
2.8	.9974	.9975	.9976	.9977	.9977	.9978	.9979	.9979	.9980	.9981
2.9	.9981	.9982	.9982	.9983	.9984	.9984	.9985	.9985	.9986	.9986
3.0	.9987	.9987	.9987	.9988	.9988	.9989	.9989	.9989	.9990	.9990
3.1	.9990	.9991	.9991	.9991	.9992	.9992	.9992	.9992	.9993	.9993
3.2	.9993	.9993	.9994	.9994	.9994	.9994	.9994	.9995	.9995	.9995
3.3	.9995	.9995	.9995	.9996	.9996	.9996	.9996	.9996	.9996	.9997
3.4	.9997	.9997	.9997	.9997	.9997	.9997	.9997	.9997	.9997	.9998

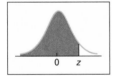

SECOND CANADIAN EDITION

BUSINESS STATISTICS

in Practice

Bruce L. Bowerman

Richard T. O'Connell

Miami University

Julie Aitken Schermer

James R. Adcock

The University of Western Ontario

with MegaStat software and other contributions by
J. Burdene Orris

Butler University

McGraw-Hill
Ryerson
Connect. Learn. Succeed.

The McGraw·Hill Companies

McGraw-Hill Ryerson
Connect. Learn. Succeed.

Business Statistics in Practice
Second Canadian Edition

ISBN-13: 978-0-07-000237-1
ISBN-10: 0-07-000237-1

1 2 3 4 5 6 7 8 9 10 TCP 1 9 8 7 6 5 4 3 2 1

Printed and bound in Canada.

Vice-President and Editor-in-Chief: Joanna Cotton
Sponsoring Editor: Kimberley Veevers
Marketing Manager: Cathie Lefebvre
Developmental Editors: Sarah Fulton and Amy Rydzanicz
Supervising Editor: Kara Stahl
Senior Editorial Associate: Christine Lomas
Copy Editor: Julia Cochrane
Production Coordinator: Emily Hickey
Cover and Interior Design: Greg Devitt Design
Cover Image Credit: © Kutay Tanir/iStock Exclusive
Page Layout: Aptara®, Inc.
Printer: Transcontinental Printing Group

Library and Archives Canada Cataloguing in Publication

Business statistics in practice / Bruce L. Bowerman ... [et al.].—
2nd Canadian ed.

Includes bibliographical references and index.
ISBN 978-0-07-000237-1

1. Commercial statistics. 2. Statistics.
I. Bowerman, Bruce L.

HF1017.B88 2011   519.502'465   C2010-905045-2

Bruce L. Bowerman
To my wife, children, sister, and other family members:
Drena
Michael, Jinda, Benjamin, and Lex
Asa and Nicole
Susan
Fiona, Radeesa, and Barney
Daphne, Chloe, and Edgar
Gwyneth and Tony
Bobby and Callie
Marmalade, Randy, and Penney

Richard T. O'Connell
To my children:
Christopher and Bradley

Julie Aitken Schermer
To my husband, Clark, my parents, Bob and Audrey,
and my mother-in-law, Diane

James R. Adcock
To my wife, Melanie, my children, Aidan and Julia,
and other family members:
Judy Adcock, Wayne Donnelly, Robert Adcock,
Jeanette Brown, Laura Adcock, Al Robson,
and Marilyn and Bob Duncan
Thank you for all your support.

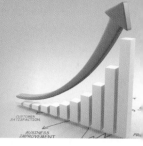

ABOUT THE AUTHORS

Bruce L. Bowerman Bruce L. Bowerman is professor of decision sciences at Miami University in Oxford, Ohio. He received his Ph.D. degree in statistics from Iowa State University in 1974, and he has over 40 years of experience teaching basic statistics, regression analysis, time series forecasting, survey sampling, and design of experiments to both undergraduate and graduate students. In 1987, Professor Bowerman received an Outstanding Teaching award from the Miami University senior class, and in 1992 he received an Effective Educator award from the Richard T. Farmer School of Business Administration. Together with Richard T. O'Connell, Professor Bowerman has written 16 textbooks. These include *Forecasting and Time Series: An Applied Approach; Forecasting, Time Series, and Regression: An Applied Approach* (also coauthored with Anne B. Koehler); and *Linear Statistical Models: An Applied Approach*. The first edition of *Forecasting and Time Series* earned an Outstanding Academic Book award from *Choice* magazine. Professor Bowerman has also published a number of articles in applied stochastic processes, time series forecasting, and statistical education. In his spare time, Professor Bowerman enjoys watching movies and sports, playing tennis, and designing houses.

Richard T. O'Connell Richard T. O'Connell is associate professor of decision sciences at Miami University in Oxford, Ohio. He has more than 35 years of experience teaching basic statistics, statistical quality control and process improvement, regression analysis, time series forecasting, and design of experiments to both undergraduate and graduate business students. He also has extensive consulting experience and has taught workshops dealing with statistical process control and process improvement for a variety of companies in the Midwest. In 2000, Professor O'Connell received an Effective Educator award from the Richard T. Farmer School of Business Administration. Together with Bruce L. Bowerman, he has written 16 textbooks. These include *Forecasting and Time Series: An Applied Approach; Forecasting, Time Series, and Regression: An Applied Approach* (also coauthored with Anne B. Koehler); and *Linear Statistical Models: An Applied Approach*. Professor O'Connell has published a number of articles in the area of innovative statistical education. He is one of the first college instructors in the United States to integrate statistical process control and process improvement methodology into his basic business statistics course. He (with Professor Bowerman) has written several articles advocating this approach. He has also given presentations on this subject at meetings such as the Joint Statistical Meetings of the American Statistical Association and the Workshop on Total Quality Management: Developing Curricula and Research Agendas (sponsored by the Production and Operations Management Society). Professor O'Connell received an M.S. degree in Decision Sciences from Northwestern University in 1973, and he is currently a member of both the Decision Sciences Institute and the American Statistical Association. In his spare time, Professor O'Connell enjoys fishing, collecting 1950s' and 1960s' rock music, and following the Green Bay Packers and Purdue University sports.

Julie Aitken Schermer   Julie Aitken Schermer (formerly Harris) is associate professor in the Management and Organizational Studies Program at The University of Western Ontario, London, Canada, where she teaches courses in the areas of business statistics, occupational health and safety, and decision making. She received her Ph.D. degree in personality psychology from The University of Western Ontario in 1999. She has over 50 published articles in peer-reviewed journals in areas of individual differences such as intelligence, personality, vocational interests, and behaviour genetics. She has also been involved in over 65 conference presentations. When not working, she spends time with her husband Clark and their dog.

James R. Adcock   James Robert Adcock is a Lecturer in the Department of Statistical and Actuarial Sciences at The University of Western Ontario, London, Canada. He has been teaching at The University of Western Ontario since 1999. He received his M.Sc. degree in statistics at The University of Western Ontario in 2001. He has a great deal of experience teaching introductory statistics to large-enrolment classes. He also has experience teaching probability and statistical computing. He has been developing courses and course material that he uses to teach statistics courses via WebCT since 2000. At The University of Western Ontario, James spends time mentoring a group of undergraduate students involved in an organization called the Actuarial and Statistical Undergraduate Association (ASUA). He is also an Academic Counsellor in the department, giving undergraduates advice and guidance in order to help them plan their personal and academic careers. In his spare time, James enjoys spending time with his wife and family and watching football.

BRIEF TABLE OF CONTENTS

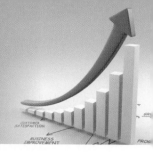

Appendices Available on **connect**

TABLE OF CONTENTS

PREFACE

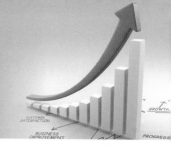

In *Business Statistics in Practice, Second Canadian Edition*, we provide a modern, practical, and unique framework for teaching the first course in business statistics. This framework features discussions, driven by case studies and examples, of all basic business statistics topics. In addition, we have endeavoured to make this book the most clearly written, motivating, and easy to use business statistics text available.

New to *Business Statistics in Practice, Second Canadian Edition*:

- New chapter introductions list learning objectives and preview the case study analysis to be carried out in each chapter.

- A new seventeenth chapter, "Process Improvement Using Control Charts," is included.

- Chapters are written in a stand-alone manner, to allow professors to use the text to match their syllabus and their preferred order for teaching.

- The emphasis on Excel and MegaStat has increased; MINITAB is no longer featured.

- New continuing cases and examples have been added to the text, including The Wine Case. As with the previous edition, each time a continuing case is revisited, there is no need to flip back to previously given computer outputs, as all of the necessary data is included with the current case discussion.

- In addition to a thorough update and refresh of the examples, data sets and end of chapter material, more advanced-level problems have been added to each chapter.

We will now discuss the attributes and features that make *Business Statistics in Practice, Second Canadian Edition*, an effective learning tool.

Business improvement through statistical analysis The ultimate goal of statistical analysis in business is business improvement. This theme is the foundation for the case studies and examples in this text, many of which are based on actual, real-world situations. For example, we evaluate the effectiveness of different training methods using experimental designs and analysis of variance, examine feedback from focus group panel members on their views about a new drink bottle design, and track DVD player sales over time.

In each of these cases, statistical analysis leads to an informed action that results in business improvement. These are highlighted by a business improvement icon in the margin. Furthermore, we continue this theme throughout the presentation of all statistical techniques in this book.

A unique continuity of presentation and use of case studies *Business Statistics in Practice, Second Canadian Edition*, features a unique continuity of presentation that integrates different statistical areas. This integration is achieved by an early emphasis (in Chapters 1 and 2) on the difference between the population and the sample and by a continuing use of practical, realistic case studies that span not only individual chapters but also groups of chapters. Specifically, Chapter 1 shows how to select random (or approximately random) samples from populations and processes by introducing case studies as examples and by presenting additional case studies as exercises. Then, in Chapter 2, we show how to use descriptive statistics to estimate the important aspects of these populations and processes. We continue to employ these case studies through the probability and sampling distribution chapters until we use confidence intervals and hypothesis testing to make statistical inferences. Furthermore, we introduce new case studies in each and every chapter. For example, we introduce several case studies in our presentation of simple linear regression and then extend these case studies when we discuss multiple regression and model building to show how regression is used in the description, prediction, and control of business variables.

A real emphasis on the importance of variation   *Business Statistics in Practice, Second Canadian Edition,* emphasizes that because businesses must satisfy individual customers, the analysis of individual population observations—which is achieved by analyzing population variation—is as important as analyzing the population mean. Our discussion of variation begins in Chapter 1, where we intuitively examine the variation of sample data. This discussion continues in Chapter 2, where we use the empirical rule to estimate tolerance intervals containing different percentages of population observations.

Our emphasis on variation continues throughout the book. For example, in Chapters 11 and 12, we show how prediction intervals can be used to evaluate the predictive capabilities of different regression models. In addition, we demonstrate how prediction intervals are used to assess whether any individual population observations are "unusual" enough to suggest the need for process improvement. Furthermore, in all of these chapters we use practical case studies to illustrate the ideas being presented.

A flexible topic flow   Although the table of contents of this book reveals a rather standard topic organization, the book utilizes a flexible topic flow that facilitates different topic choices and encourages different teaching approaches. In particular, because different courses place different amounts of emphasis on probability, hypothesis testing, regression and statistical modelling, and nonparametric statistics, this book provides great flexibility with respect to how, when, and whether to cover these topics. Furthermore, in some sections, appendices, and self-learning exercises, the book gives the student the opportunity to study more advanced topics in a concise and practical way. Thus, as we now discuss, courses with a wide variety of topic coverages and emphases can be taught using this book.

Probability   The most minimal approach to probability would cover Section 3.1 (the concept of probability), Section 4.1 (random variables), Section 5.1 (continuous probability distributions), and Section 5.3 (the normal distribution, including an intuitive example of the addition rule for mutually exclusive events). These sections are the only prerequisites for Chapters 6 through 12 (sampling distributions, confidence intervals, hypothesis testing, statistical inferences, experimental design, and regression).

Instructors who wish to also cover discrete probability distributions (Chapter 4) have the option of doing this either with a fairly minimal probability background or with a complete probability background. The fairly minimal probability background consists of Section 3.1 (the concept of probability) and Section 3.2 (using sample spaces to find probabilities). Note that this background is sufficient because, since Example 4.2 of Chapter 4 intuitively illustrates the multiplication rule for independent events and the addition rule for mutually exclusive events in the context of finding a discrete probability distribution, it is not necessary to cover the complete discussion of probability rules given in Sections 3.3 and 3.4. Of course, this complete discussion is necessary background for covering chi-square tests of independence (Chapter 14) and decision theory (Chapter 15).

Hypothesis testing   In this edition, we have used a seven-step procedure to break hypothesis testing down into small, easy to understand steps and to clearly show how to use the book's hypothesis-testing summary boxes. In addition, we have fully and concisely integrated the discussion of using rejection points and p values. The seven-step procedure shows how to use both approaches, and the hypothesis-testing boxes summarize both rejection points and p values for each test. We are aware of several courses that introduce hypothesis testing in the context of using p values to test the significance of regression coefficients. This can be done in our book by skipping Chapter 8 and by noting that every section throughout the rest of the book includes self-contained summary boxes (and examples) that fully cover any needed confidence intervals and hypothesis tests. Also, Chapter 6 (sampling distributions) intuitively illustrates the use of *p* values in the context of evaluating a claim about a population mean and evaluating a claim about a population proportion. Therefore, Chapter 6 can be used as an extremely short, intuitive introduction to *p* values.

Regression and statistical modelling This book features an innovative organization of regression analysis that simplifies the flow of the overall discussion and makes it very easy to cover whatever regression topics are desired. We have included a section on residual analysis at the end of the simple linear regression chapter (Chapter 11). In Chapter 12: Multiple Regression, we offer a modular organization of the chapter and make it easy to cover whatever portions of multiple regression instructors consider to be the most important in courses with limited time devoted to regression analysis. Similarly, because many business statistics courses do not have substantial time to devote to experimental design (Chapter 10) and time series forecasting (Chapter 16), we have put great effort into making our presentation of these topics both complete and easy to get through.

Nonparametric statistics We have placed all of the nonparametric techniques covered in the book in Chapter 13. Furthermore, at the end of the discussion of each parametric technique in Chapters 8 through 11, we refer readers to the section in Chapter 13 that discusses the nonparametric technique to use if the assumptions for the parametric technique fail to hold. Therefore, the instructor has the option of integrating the discussion of nonparametric statistics into the main flow of Chapters 8 through 11.

Advanced topics In additional sections, appendices (on *Connect*), and self-learning exercises, the book gives the student the opportunity to study more advanced topics in a concise and practical way. Examination of the table of contents reveals that many of the more advanced topics—for example, counting rules (Appendix B), the hypergeometric distribution (Section 4.5), normal probability plots (Appendix C, Part 1), and the Poisson distribution (Section 4.4)—are included in many other business statistics books. However, some of the more advanced topics, while not unique to this book, are less frequently covered in other basic statistics texts. These topics (the most advanced of which are discussed in Appendices E through J on *Connect*) are as follows:

- Properties of the Mean and Variance of a Random Variable, and the Covariance (Appendix C, Part 2).
- Derivations of the Mean and the Variance of $\bar{x}$ and $\hat{p}$ (Appendix C, Part 3).
- Confidence Intervals for Parameters of Finite Populations (Section 7.9), including sample size determination (Exercise 7.119).
- An Introduction to Survey Sampling (Section 1.6); estimation formulas, optimal allocation, and sample size determination in stratified random sampling (Appendix E, Part 1); and estimation formulas in one- and two-stage cluster sampling and ratio estimation (Appendix E, Part 2).
- A Comparison of Confidence Intervals and Tolerance Intervals (Section 7.10).
- Using Matrix Algebra to Perform Regression Calculations (Appendix F).
- The regression approach to one-way analysis of variance (Chapter 12), and the regression approach to two-way analysis of variance (Appendix G).
- Advanced Model Diagnostics and Model Building with Squared and Interaction Terms (Chapter 12).
- Logistic Regression and Discriminant Analysis (Chapter 12).
- Factor Analysis, Cluster Analysis, and Multidimensional Scaling (Appendix H).
- The Box–Jenkins methodology, a fairly complete discussion featuring nonseasonal and seasonal modelling, using autocorrelated error term models in regression analysis, intervention analysis, and transfer function models (Appendix I).
- Individual charts and *c* charts (Appendix J).

Furthermore, we have put great effort into making the discussion of all of the more advanced topics clear, concise, and easy to get through. This gives the instructor considerable flexibility in designing different business statistics courses. For example, a professor teaching a second course in business statistics can opt either to cover a variety of intermediate topics or to present a more in-depth treatment of regression analysis and forecasting.

ONLINE TECHNOLOGY

Excel and MegaStat *Business Statistics in Practice, Second Canadian Edition*, features a modern use of the statistical capabilities of the software package Excel and its add-in MegaStat. Throughout the book, we provide abundant outputs from both packages in both examples and exercises that allow students to concentrate on statistical interpretations. This use of outputs is particularly prominent in statistical areas where hand calculations are impractical and where having students run their own programs (while theoretically optimal) would, because of time constraints, not allow them to see a wide variety of applications. These areas include descriptive statistics, analysis of variance, regression, and time series forecasting. In addition, appendices for each chapter (available on *Connect*) show in detail how to use Excel and MegaStat to implement the statistical techniques discussed in the chapter. For this edition, the developer of MegaStat, Professor J. B. Orris of Butler University, has worked closely with us. MegaStat is a comprehensive, accurate, and easy to use Excel add-in package. In addition to remedying most of the computational problems associated with Excel Data Analysis Tools, MegaStat is also specifically designed to enhance the use of *Business Statistics in Practice, Second Canadian Edition.*

In addition, MegaStat is fully capable of performing analyses related to discrete and continuous probability distributions, time series forecasting, nonparametric statistics, and chi-square tests—virtually all topics covered by *Business Statistics in Practice, Second Canadian Edition.*

 **Connect™** *Connect* is a web-based assignment and assessment platform that gives students the means to better connect with their coursework, with their instructors, and with the important concepts that they will need to know for success now and in the future. *Connect* embraces diverse study behaviours and preferences with breakthrough features that help students master course content and achieve better results. The powerful course management tool in *Connect* also offers a wide range of exclusive features that help instructors spend less time managing and more time teaching. Content was developed specifically for *Connect* by Melanie Christian, St. Lawrence College.

With *Connect*, you can deliver assignments, quizzes, and tests online. A robust set of questions and problems are presented and tied to the textbook's learning objectives. Track individual student performance—by question, by assignment, or in relation to the class overall—with detailed grade reports. Integrate grade reports easily with Learning Management Systems (LMS) such as WebCT and Blackboard.

Connect helps you teach for today's needs:

Unlimited practice, instant feedback Provide instant feedback to unlimited textbook practice problems, acknowledging correct answers and pointing to areas that need more work.

Automatic grading Focus on teaching instead of administration with electronic access to the class roster and gradebook, which easily sync with your school's course management system.

Direct textbook and test bank questions Assign students online homework and test and quiz questions with multiple problem types, algorithmic variation, and randomized question order.

Integrated eBooks *Connect* directly integrates the McGraw-Hill textbooks you already use into the engaging, easy to use interface.

Dedicated Canadian support and training   The *Connect* development team and customer service groups are located in our Canadian offices and work closely together to provide expert technical support and training for both instructors and students.

***Connect*™ for Students**   *Connect* provides students with a powerful tool for improving academic performance and truly mastering course material, plus 24/7 online access to an interactive and searchable eBook. *Connect* allows students to practise important skills at their own pace and on their own schedule. Importantly, students' assessment results and instructors' feedback are all saved online—so students can continually review their progress and plot their course to success.

Visual Statistics 2.3   *Visual Statistics 2.3*, by Doane, Mathieson, and Tracy, is a software program for teaching and learning statistics concepts. It is unique in that it allows students to learn the concepts through interactive experimentation and visualization. The software and work-text promote active learning through competency-building exercises, individual and team projects, and built-in databases. Over 400 data sets from business settings are included within the package, as well as a worktext in electronic format. This software is available on *Connect*.

Course Management   McGraw-Hill Ryerson offers a range of flexible integration solutions for **WebCT** and **Blackboard** platforms. Please contact your local McGraw-Hill Ryerson *i*Learning Sales specialist for details.

Blackboard

Create Online   McGraw-Hill's Create Online places the most abundant resource at your fingertips—literally. With a few mouse clicks, you can create customized learning tools simply and affordably. McGraw-Hill Ryerson has included many of its market-leading textbooks within Create Online for eBook and print customization as well as many licensed readings and cases. For more information, please visit www.mcgrawhillcreate.com.

Coursesmart   CourseSmart brings together thousands of textbooks across hundreds of courses in an eTextbook format providing unique benefits to students and faculty. By purchasing an eTextbook, students can save up to 50 percent off the cost of a print textbook, reduce their impact on the environment, and gain access to powerful Web tools for learning, including full text search, notes and highlighting, and email tools for sharing notes among classmates. For faculty, CourseSmart provides instant access to review and compare textbooks and course materials in their discipline area without the time, cost, and environmental impact of mailing print examination copies. For further details, contact your *i*Learning Sales Specialist or visit www.coursesmart.com.

SUPERIOR SERVICE

Service takes on a whole new meaning with McGraw-Hill Ryerson and *Business Statistics in Practice, Second Canadian Edition*. More than just bringing you the textbook, we have consistently raised the bar in terms of innovation and educational research—both in operations management and in education in general. These investments in learning and the education community have helped us to understand the needs of students and educators across the country and allowed us to foster the growth of truly innovative, integrated learning.

Integrated Learning   Your Integrated Learning Sales Specialist is a McGraw-Hill Ryerson representative who has the experience, product knowledge, training, and support to help you assess and integrate any of our products, technology, and services into your course for optimum teaching and learning performance. Whether it is helping your students improve their grades, or putting your entire course online, your *i*Learning Sales Specialist is there to help you do it. Contact your *i*Learning Sales Specialist today to learn how to maximize all of McGraw-Hill Ryerson's resources!

i-Learning
ADVANTAGE
McGraw-Hill Ryerson

*i*Learning Services   McGraw-Hill Ryerson offers a unique *i*Services package designed for Canadian faculty. Our mission is to equip providers of higher education with the superior tools and resources required for excellence in teaching. For additional information, visit www.mcgrawhill.ca/highereducation/iservices.

Teaching & Learning Conference Series   The educational environment has changed tremendously in recent years, and McGraw-Hill Ryerson continues to be committed to helping you acquire the skills you need to succeed in this new milieu. Our innovative Teaching & Learning Conference Series brings faculty together from across Canada with 3M Teaching Excellence award winners to share teaching and learning best practices in a collaborative and stimulating environment. Preconference workshops on general topics such as teaching large classes and technology integration will also be offered. We will also work with you at your own institution to customize workshops that best suit the needs of your faculty.

INSTRUCTOR'S SUPPLEMENTS

Instructor's Solutions Manual   Prepared by the text authors and adapted to reflect the *Second Canadian Edition*, this manual includes worked-out solutions to all the exercises in the text.

Computerized Test Bank   Prepared by text author Julie Aitken Shermer, The University of Western Ontario, the computerized test bank has been extensively revised and technically checked for accuracy. The computerized test bank contains a variety of questions, including true/false, multiple choice, and short-answer questions requiring analysis and written answers. The computerized test bank is available through EZ Test Online—a flexible and easy to use electronic testing program that allows instructors to create tests from book-specific items. EZ Test accommodates a wide range of question types and allows instructors to add their own questions. Test items are also available in Word format (rich text format). For secure online testing, exams created in EZ Test can be exported to WebCT and Blackboard. EZ Test Online is supported at www.mhhe.com/eztest, where users can download a Quick Start Guide, access FAQs, or log a ticket for help with specific issues.

Microsoft®PowerPoint® Lecture Slides   Prepared by Peter Au, George Brown College, the PowerPoint slides draw on the highlights of each chapter and provide an opportunity for the instructor to emphasize the most relevant visuals in class discussions.

ACKNOWLEDGEMENTS

The authors are grateful to Bruce Bowerman and Richard O'Connell, authors of the U.S. text, for providing the foundation upon which this second Canadian adaptation has been built. We would also like to thank Julia Cochrane, Hristo Sendov, and Wayne Horn, as well as the following people at McGraw-Hill Ryerson for their support: Kimberley Veevers, Jeremy Guimond, Rhondda McNabb, Kara Stahl, Sarah Fulton, Amy Rydzanicz, and Cathie Lefebvre.

Reviewers for the Second Canadian Edition

Ulrieke Birner, Kwantlen Polytechnic University

Clare Chua-Chow, Ryerson University

Shari Corrigan, Camosun College

David Dobson, Simon Fraser University

Laurel Donaldson, Douglas College

Torben Drewes, Trent University

Bruno Fullone, George Brown College

Rongbing Huang, York University

Olga Kaminer, York University

Dennis Kira, Concordia University

Ata Mazaheri, University of Toronto

Peggy Ng, York University

Trien Nguyen, University of Waterloo

Jean-Paul Olivier, Red River College

Mahmut Parlar, McMaster University

Tony Quon, University of Ottawa

Andrei Semenov, York University

Victor Sousa, Centennial College

Don St. Jean, George Brown College

Sheila Steinhauer-Mozejko, Grant MacEwan University

John H. Walker, Brock University

GUIDED TOUR

Business Statistics in Practice, Second Canadian Edition, was written with students' needs in mind. Its clear and understandable explanations and use of real-world case studies and examples present content that business students can relate to.

Chapter Introductions

Each chapter opens with a preview showing how the statistical topics to be discussed apply to real business problems. The continuing case examples that run throughout the book are briefly introduced along with the techniques that will be used to analyze them.

Visual Statistics 2.3

Visual Statistics helps students learn statistics through interactive experimentation and visualization. Concepts in the text that are treated in the Visual Statistics software program are identified by this icon, with chapter reference, in the margin of the text next to the concept.

CHAPTER **4**
Discrete Random Variables

LEARNING OBJECTIVES

After reading this chapter, you should be able to

LO1 describe what is meant by a random variable

LO2 explain the difference between a discrete random variable and a continuous random variable

LO3 describe the ways in which the probability distribution of a discrete random variable can be depicted

LO4 calculate the mean (or expected value), variance, and standard deviation of discrete random variables

LO5 distinguish between the binomial distribution and the Poisson distribution

LO6 identify and understand the characteristics of a hypergeometric random variable

LO7 calculate probabilities using the hypergeometric formula

CHAPTER OUTLINE

4.1 Two Types of Random Variables

4.2 Discrete Probability Distributions

4.3 The Binomial Distribution

4.4 The Poisson Distribution

4.5 The Hypergeometric Distribution

People often struggle with the concepts of randomness and variables, but both are around us every day. If there were no randomness in our lives, and if things never varied at all, life would be pretty boring. We would always know what things would occur in our lives and when they would occur. Of course, it would be nice to know if and when some things will occur in our lives, like marriage, children, or winning the lottery. Only a journey through life can tell us whether these things will happen. In this chapter, we will deal specifically with **discrete random variables** and their probability distributions.

In Chapter 1 we introduced the idea of variables. Variables were defined as characteristics that we may be interested in analyzing. For example, we could be talking about hair colour, eye colour, sex, salary, age, or IQ. Of course, the first three characteristics in the list are qualitative (or categorical) in nature and the last three are quantitative (or numerical) in nature. In

this chapter, we will further explore the concept of variables that are numerical in nature. Specifically, we will deal with discrete random variables. Random variables that are discrete in nature will take on a finite number of values, or an infinitely countable number of values. Some examples of discrete random variables are the number of roommates you have, the number of text messages you receive in a day, and the number of questions you get correct on a multiple choice exam.

In this chapter, we will also introduce the concept of a **continuous random variable** to help you better understand discrete random variables. Examples of continuous random variables are the amount of coffee you drink every day (measured in litres), the amount of time you spend on your cell phone each day, and the time between incoming cell phone calls. Continuous random variables will be discussed in greater detail in Chapter 5.

connect Practise and learn online with *Connect*. Throughout this chapter, questions and tables with online data sets are marked with [icon].

LO1

A **random variable** is a variable that assumes numerical values that are determined by the outcome of an experiment, where one and only one numerical value is assigned to each experimental outcome.

Before an experiment is carried out, its outcome is uncertain. It follows that since a random variable assigns a number to each experimental outcome, a random variable can be thought of as *representing an uncertain numerical outcome*.

To illustrate the idea of a random variable, suppose that Sound City sells and installs satellite radio systems. One of Sound City's most popular satellite radio systems is the top-of-the-line SatStar system. Consider (the experiment of) selling the SatStar system at the Sound City store during a particular week. If we let *x* denote the number of systems sold during the week, then *x* is a random variable. That is, looked at before the week, the number of systems, *x*, that will be sold is uncertain, and, therefore, *x* is a random variable.

LO2

VS

CHAPTER 3

Notice that *x*, the number of SatStar satellite radios sold in a week, might be 0 or 1 or 2 or 3, and so forth. In general, when the possible values of a random variable can be counted or listed, then the random variable is a **discrete random variable**. That is, either a discrete random variable may assume a finite number of possible values or the possible values may take the form of a **countable** sequence or list such as 0, 1, 2, 3, 4, . . . (a **countably infinite** list).

Some other examples of discrete random variables are as follows:

1. The number, out of the next three customers entering a store, who will make a purchase. Here *x* could be 0, 1, 2, or 3.

2. The number, out of four patients taking a new antibiotic, who experience gastrointestinal distress as a side effect. Here *x* could be 0, 1, 2, 3, or 4.

3. The number of televisions in a sample of eight five-year-old televisions that have not needed a single repair. Here *x* could be any of the values 0, 1, 2, 3, 4, 5, 6, 7, and 8.

4. The rating on a 1 through 5 scale given to a song by a listener in a music survey. Here *x* could be 1, 2, 3, 4, or 5.

5. The number of major fires in a large city during the last two months. Here *x* could be 0, 1, 2, 3, and so forth (there is no definite maximum number of fires).

The values of the random variables described in (1), (2), (3), and (4) are countable and finite. In contrast, the values of the random variable described in (5) are countable and infinite (or a countably infinite list). For example, in theory there is no limit to the number of major fires that could occur in a city in two months.

Not all random variables have values that are countable. When a random variable may assume any numerical value in one or more intervals on the real number line, then the random variable is a **continuous random variable**.

Example 4.1 Happy Birthday!

Consider your age for a second. How old are you? Most of you will give answers like 19, 20, 21, and so forth, but are you really that age? When someone asks us how old we are, we do not actually tell them our exact age. Instead, we tell them our age as of our last birthday. It is very difficult to keep track of your actual age because it is *continuously changing*. In fact, you have aged a little since you starting reading this example! Your age is an example of a continuous random variable. In theory, your age could be expressed to an infinite number of

---

Case Studies

The text provides a unique use of case studies that span individual chapters and groups of chapters. Cases are used to introduce the concepts, to demonstrate the methods, and to provide students with motivating exercises. These case studies help students see how statistics is used in business and can be used to improve processes.

Student-Friendly Presentation

The authors make learning easier for students. The following examples highlight some of these improvements.

Step-by-Step Hypothesis-Testing Approach

This approach consists of a seven-step procedure designed to break hypothesis testing down into small, easy to understand steps. This procedure is used in almost all the examples in Chapters 8 and 9 and can be applied by students throughout the remainder of the text where hypothesis testing is done.

Greater Accessibility of Continuing Cases

Each time a continuing case is revisited, any needed computer output and, whenever possible, relevant background information is included with the current case discussion. Consequently, students seldom need to refer back to previously covered material in order to grasp the content included in a given case segment.

---

test hypotheses about a population mean by using the *t* **distribution.** In Section 8.5, we study *t* **tests,** and we will revisit the examples of this (and the next) section assuming that σ is unknown.

Testing a greater than alternative hypothesis by using a rejection point rule In Sections 8.1 and 8.2, we explained how to set up appropriate null and alternative hypotheses. We also discussed how to specify a value for α, the probability of a Type I error (also called the **level of significance**) of the hypothesis test, and we introduced the idea of a test statistic. We can use these concepts to begin developing a seven-step hypothesis-testing procedure. We will introduce these steps in the context of monthly cable TV subscriptions costs and testing a greater than alternative hypothesis.

A marketing company has suggested that the cost of monthly cable TV subscriptions has risen dramatically, which is causing more people to use illegal satellite dishes. Cable TV companies claim that their full cable package subscriptions cost on average \$50 a month. The marketing company wants to demonstrate that the cost is significantly greater than \$50 and randomly selects 40 cable TV subscribers and determines the price they pay for their monthly cable.

Step 1: State the null hypothesis H_0 and the alternative hypothesis H_a. In this case, we will test H_0: $\mu \leq 50$ versus H_a: $\mu > 50$. Here μ is the mean subscription cost.

Step 2: Specify the level of significance α. The marketing company will be able to support its claim that cable subscription costs have risen if we can reject H_0: $\mu \leq 50$ in favour of H_a: $\mu > 50$ by setting α equal to 0.05.

Step 3: Select the test statistic. In order to test H_0: $\mu \leq 50$ versus H_a: $\mu > 50$, we will test the modified null hypothesis H_0: $\mu = 50$ versus H_a: $\mu > 50$. The idea here is that if there is sufficient evidence to reject the hypothesis that μ equals 50 in favour of $\mu > 50$, then there is certainly also sufficient evidence to reject the hypothesis that μ is less than or equal to 50. In order to test H_0: $\mu = 50$ versus H_a: $\mu > 50$, we randomly select a sample of $n = 40$ subscribers and calculate the mean $\bar{x}$ of the monthly costs. We will then utilize the test statistic

$$z = \frac{\bar{x} - 50}{\sigma_{\bar{x}}} = \frac{\bar{x} - 50}{\sigma / \sqrt{n}}.$$

A positive value of this test statistic results from an $\bar{x}$ that is greater than 50 and thus provides evidence against H_0: $\mu = 50$ and in favour of H_a: $\mu > 50$.

Step 4: Determine the rejection point rule for deciding whether to reject H_0. To decide how large the test statistic must be to reject H_0 in favour of H_a by setting the probability of a Type I error equal to α, we do the following:

- Place the probability of a Type I error, α, in the right-hand tail of the standard normal curve and use the normal table (see Table A.3) to find the normal point z_α. Here z_α, which we call a **rejection point** (or **critical point**), is the point on the horizontal axis under the standard normal curve that gives a right-hand tail area equal to α.

- Reject H_0: $\mu = 50$ in favour of H_a: $\mu > 50$ if and only if the test statistic z is greater than the rejection point z_α. This is the **rejection point rule.**

Appendix 1.1 ■ Getting Started with Excel

Because Excel 2007 may be new to some readers, and because the Excel 2007 window looks quite different from previous versions of Excel, we will begin by describing some characteristics of the Excel 2007 window. Previous versions of Excel employed many drop-down menus. This meant that many features were "hidden" from the user, which resulted in a steep learning curve for beginners. In Excel 2007, Microsoft tried to reduce the number of features that are hidden in drop-down menus. Therefore, Excel 2007 displays all of the applicable commands needed for a particular type of task at the top of the Excel window. These commands are represented by a tab-and-group arrangement called the **ribbon**—see the right side of the illustration of an Excel 2007 window below. The commands displayed in the ribbon are regulated by a series of **tabs** located near the top of the ribbon. For example, in the illustration below, the **Home tab** is selected. If we selected a different tab, say, for example, the **Page Layout tab,** the commands displayed by the ribbon would be different.

We now briefly describe some basic features of the Excel 2007 window:

1 **Office button:** By clicking on this button, the user obtains a menu of often used commands—for example, Open, Save, Print, and so forth. This is very similar to the "File menu" in older versions of Excel. However, some menu items are unique to Excel 2007. This menu also provides access to a large number of Excel options settings.

2 **Tabs:** Clicking on a tab results in a ribbon display of features, commands, and options related to a particular type of task. For example, when the *Home tab* is selected (as in the figure below), the features, commands, and options displayed by the ribbon are all related to making entries into the Excel worksheet. As another example, if the *Formula tab* is selected, all of the features, commands, and options displayed in the ribbon relate to using formulas in the Excel worksheet.

3 **Quick access toolbar:** This toolbar displays buttons that provide shortcuts to often used commands. Initially, this toolbar displays Save, Undo, and Redo buttons. The user can customize this toolbar by adding shortcut buttons for other commands (such as, New, Open, Quick Print, and so forth). This can be done by clicking on the arrow button directly to the right of the Quick access toolbar and by making selections from the "Customize" drop-down menu that appears.

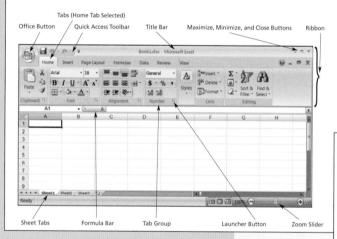

Excel and MegaStat Tutorials

The end-of-chapter appendices (available on *Connect*) contain helpful tutorials that teach students how to carry out statistical analysis using Excel and MegaStat. These tutorials include step-by-step instructions for performing almost every type of statistical method presented in the book.

Excel and MegaStat Output

Throughout the text, Excel and MegaStat outputs illustrate how statistical analysis is done electronically.

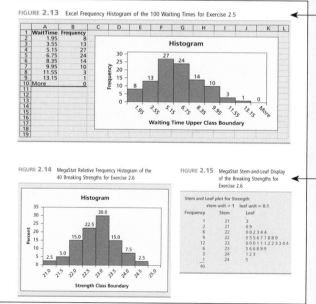

FIGURE **2.13** Excel Frequency Histogram of the 100 Waiting Times for Exercise 2.5

FIGURE **2.14** MegaStat Relative Frequency Histogram of the 40 Breaking Strengths for Exercise 2.6

FIGURE **2.15** MegaStat Stem-and-Leaf Display of the Breaking Strengths for Exercise 2.6

Exercises...

There are over 1,000 exercises in the text. Many use real data from the current business literature. Data sets on *Connect* are identified by icon in the text. Within each chapter, exercises are broken into two parts—"Concepts" and "Methods and Applications." The methods and applications exercises vary in rigour from routine calculations to fairly sophisticated case study analysis. In addition, there are Internet exercises to help students make use of the Internet for gathering and using real data, and supplementary exercises at the ends of chapters.

Exercises for Section 8.4

CONCEPTS

8.35 Suppose you are carrying out a two-sided hypothesis test about a population mean.
   a. Give the rejection point rule for rejecting $H_0: \mu = \mu_0$.
   b. Explain how the p value and α tell you whether $H_0: \mu = \mu_0$ should be rejected.

8.36 Discuss how to assess the practical importance of a statistically significant result.

METHODS AND APPLICATIONS

In Exercises 8.37 through 8.43, consider using a random sample of $n = 81$ measurements to test $H_0: \mu = 40$ versus $H_a: \mu \neq 40$. Suppose that $\bar{x} = 34$ and $\sigma = 18$.

8.37 Calculate the value of the test statistic z.

8.38 Use rejection points to test H_0 versus H_a by setting α equal to 0.10.

8.39 Use rejection points to test H_0 versus H_a by setting α equal to 0.05.

8.40 Use rejection points to test H_0 versus H_a by setting α equal to 0.01.

8.41 Use rejection points to test H_0 versus H_a by setting α equal to 0.001.
   Hint: $z_{0.0005}$ can be shown to equal 3.29.

8.42 Calculate the p value and use it to test H_0 versus H_a at each of $\alpha = 0.10, 0.05, 0.01$, and 0.001.

8.43 How much evidence is there that $H_0: \mu = 40$ is false and $H_a: \mu \neq 40$ is true?

8.44 Consider the automobile parts supplier in Exercise 8.10. Suppose that a problem-solving team will be assigned to rectify the process producing cylindrical engine parts if the null hypothesis $H_0: \mu = 3$ can be rejected in favour of $H_a: \mu \neq 3$ by setting α equal to 0.05.
   a. A sample of 40 parts yields a sample mean diameter of $\bar{x} = 3.006$ cm. Assuming σ equals 0.016, use rejection points and a p value to test H_0 versus H_a by setting α equal to 0.05. Should the problem-solving team be assigned?
   b. Suppose that product specifications state that each and every part must have a diameter between 2.95 cm and 3.05 cm—that is, the specifications are 3 cm $\pm$ 0.05 cm. Use the sample information given in part a to estimate an interval that contains almost all (99.73 percent) of the diameters. Compare this estimated interval with the specification limits. Are the specification limits being met, or are some diameters outside the specification limits? Explain.

8.45 Consider the Classic Bottling Company fill process in Exercise 8.11. Recall that the initial setup of the filler will be adjusted if the null hypothesis $H_0: \mu = 355$ mL is rejected in favour of $H_a: \mu \neq 355$ mL. Suppose that Classic Bottling Company decides to use a level of significance of $\alpha = 0.01$, and suppose a random sample of 36 fills is obtained from a test run of the filler. For each of the following sample results, determine whether the filler's initial setup should be adjusted. In each case,

...And More Exercises

Many more exercises are found on *Connect*.

Boxed Equations, Formulas, and Definitions

Each chapter contains easy to find boxes that will help students identify and understand the key ideas in the chapter.

A Hypothesis Test about a Population Mean: Testing $H_0: \mu = \mu_0$ versus a One-Sided Alternative Hypothesis When σ Is Known

Define the test statistic

$$z = \frac{\bar{x} - \mu_0}{\sigma/\sqrt{n}}$$

and assume that the population sampled is normally distributed, or that the sample size n is large. We can test $H_0: \mu = \mu_0$ versus a particular alternative hypothesis at level of significance α by using the appropriate rejection point rule or, equivalently, the corresponding p value.

Alternative Hypothesis	Rejection Point Rule: Reject H_0 if	p Value (Reject H_0 if p Value $< \alpha$)
$H_a: \mu > \mu_0$	$z > z_\alpha$	The area under the standard normal curve to the right of z
$H_a: \mu < \mu_0$	$z < -z_\alpha$	The area under the standard normal curve to the left of z

Chapter-Ending Material

The end of each chapter includes a chapter summary, a comprehensive glossary of terms, and important formula references. The examples shown here are from Chapter 2, Descriptive Statistics.

CHAPTER SUMMARY

We began this chapter by studying how to depict the shape of the distribution of a data set. We learned that **stem-and-leaf displays** and **histograms** are useful graphics for portraying a data set's distribution. We also learned about some common population shapes. We saw that data sets often have shapes that are **symmetrical**, **positively skewed (with a tail to the right)**, or **negatively skewed (with a tail to the left)**.

Next we presented and compared several measures of **central tendency**. We defined the **population mean** and we saw how to estimate it by using a **sample mean**. We also defined the **median** and **mode**, and we compared the mean, median, and mode for symmetrical distributions and for distributions that are positively or negatively skewed (to the right or left). We then studied measures of **variation** (or **spread**). We defined the **range**, **variance**, and **standard deviation**, and we saw how to estimate a population variance and standard deviation by using a sample. We learned that a good way to interpret the standard deviation when a population is (approximately) normally distributed is to use the **empirical rule**,

and we applied this rule to assess **process capability**. We next studied **Chebyshev's theorem**, which gives us intervals containing reasonably large fractions of the population units no matter what the population's shape might be. We also saw that when a data set is highly skewed, it is best to use **percentiles** and **quartiles** to measure variation, and we learned how to construct a **box-and-whiskers display** by using the quartiles.

After learning how to measure and depict central tendency and variability, we presented several methods for portraying qualitative data. In particular, we used **bar charts** for this purpose. We also discussed using a sample to estimate the proportion of population units that fall into a category of interest.

We studied using **scatter plots** to examine relationships between variables. Next we discussed misleading graphs and statistics, and we explained some of the tactics that are commonly used to try to distort the truth. We concluded with the concept of a **weighted mean** and then explained how to compute descriptive statistics for **grouped data**.

GLOSSARY OF TERMS

bar chart: A graphical display of categorical data (data in categories) made up of vertical or horizontal bars. (page 63)
box-and-whiskers display (box plot): A graphical portrayal of a data set that depicts both the central tendency and the variability of the data. It is constructed using Q_1, M_d, and Q_3. (page 59)
capable process: A process that is able to consistently produce output that meets (or conforms to) specifications (requirements). (page 51)
central tendency: A term referring to the middle of a population or sample of measurements. (page 38)
Chebyshev's theorem: A theorem that (for any population) allows us to find an interval that contains a specified percentage of the individual measurements in the population. (page 52)
coefficient of variation: A quantity that measures the variation of a population or sample relative to its mean. (page 54)
dependent variable (denoted y): A variable that we wish to describe, predict, or control. (page 68)

empirical rule: For a normally distributed population, this rule tells us that 68.26 percent, 95.44 percent, and 99.73 percent of the population measurements are within one, two, and three standard deviations, respectively, of the population mean. (page 49)
extreme outlier (in a box-and-whiskers display): A measurement located outside the outer fences. (page 59)
first quartile (denoted Q_1): A value below which approximately 25 percent of the measurements lie; the 25th percentile. (page 58)
frequency: The count of the number of measurements in a class or the number of measurements with a particular value. (page 27)
frequency distribution: A numerical summary that divides the values of a variable into classes and gives the number of values in each class. (pages 27)
grouped data: Data presented in the form of a frequency distribution or a histogram. (page 75)
histogram: A graphical portrayal of a data set that shows the data set's distribution. It divides the data into classes and gives the

CHAPTER 1
An Introduction to Business Statistics

LEARNING OBJECTIVES

After reading this chapter, you should be able to

LO1 understand how and why research samples are collected

LO2 explain what is meant by the term *random sample* and explain how a random sample may be generated

LO3 define a process and understand how a process is sampled

LO4 describe the four levels of measurement

LO5 list some of the potential problems associated with surveys

CHAPTER OUTLINE

1.1 Populations and Samples

1.2 Sampling a Population of Existing Units

1.3 Sampling a Process

1.4 Levels of Measurement: Nominal, Ordinal, Interval, and Ratio

1.5 A Brief Introduction to Surveys

1.6 An Introduction to Survey Sampling

The subject of **statistics** involves the study of how to collect, summarize, and interpret data. **Data** are numerical facts and figures from which conclusions can be drawn. Data are typically collected from a sample in order to make an inference about a population. This process is important for making decisions in many professions and organizations. For example, government officials use conclusions drawn from the latest data on unemployment and inflation to make policy decisions. Financial planners use recent trends in stock market prices to make investment decisions. Businesses decide which products to develop and market by using data that reveal consumer preferences. Production supervisors use manufacturing data to

evaluate, control, and improve product quality. Politicians rely on data from public opinion polls to formulate legislation and to devise campaign strategies. Physicians and hospitals use data on the effectiveness of drugs and surgical procedures to provide patients with the best possible treatment.

In this chapter, we begin to see how we collect and analyze data. As we proceed through the chapter, we introduce several case studies. These case studies (and others to be introduced later, many from Statistics Canada) are revisited throughout later chapters as we learn the statistical methods needed to analyze the cases. Briefly, we begin to study three cases:

The Cell Phone Case: A bank estimates its cellular phone costs and decides whether to outsource management of its wireless resources by studying the calling patterns of its employees.

The Marketing Research Case: A bottling company investigates consumer reaction to a new bottle design for one of its popular soft drinks.

The Coffee Temperature Case: A fast-food restaurant studies and monitors the temperature of the coffee it serves.

 Practise and learn online with *Connect*. Throughout this chapter, questions and tables with online data sets are marked with 🖋.

1.1 POPULATIONS AND SAMPLES

Statistical methods are very useful for learning about populations. Populations can be defined in various ways, including the following:

A **population** is a set of units (usually people, objects, or events).

Examples of populations are (1) all of last year's graduates of the Sauder School of Business at the University of British Columbia, (2) all consumers who bought a cellular phone last year, (3) all potential consumers who might purchase a house next year, (4) all accounts receivable invoices accumulated last year by Procter & Gamble, (5) all Toyota Corollas produced last year, and (6) all fires reported last month to the Ottawa fire department.

We usually focus on studying one or more characteristics of the population units.

Any characteristic of a population unit is called a **variable**.

For instance, if we study the starting salaries of last year's graduates of an MBA program, the variable of interest is starting salary. If we study the fuel efficiency obtained in city driving by last year's Toyota Corolla, the variable of interest is litres per 100 km in city driving.

We carry out a **measurement** to assign a **value** of a variable to each population unit. For example, we might measure the starting salary of an MBA graduate to the nearest dollar. Or we might measure the fuel efficiency obtained by a car in city driving to the nearest litre per 100 km by conducting a test on a driving course prescribed by the Ministry of Transportation. If the possible measurements are numbers that represent quantities (that is, "how much" or "how many"), then the variable is said to be **quantitative**. For example, starting salary and fuel efficiency are both quantitative. However, if we simply record into which of several categories a population unit falls, then the variable is said to be **qualitative** or **categorical**. Examples of categorical variables are (1) a person's sex, (2) the make of an automobile, and (3) whether a person who purchases a product is satisfied with the product.[1]

If we measure each and every population unit, we have a **population of measurements** (sometimes called **observations**). If the population is small, it is reasonable to do this. For instance, if 150 students graduated last year from an MBA program, it might be feasible to survey the graduates and to record all of their starting salaries. In general, we have the following:

If we examine all of the population measurements, we say that we are conducting a **census** of the population.

LO1

The population that we wish to study is often very large, and it is too time-consuming or costly to conduct a census. In such a situation, we select and analyze a subset (or portion) of the population.

A **sample** is a subset of the units in a population.

For example, suppose that 8,742 students graduated last year from a large university. It would probably be too time-consuming to take a census of the population of all of their starting salaries. Therefore, we would select a sample of graduates, and we would obtain and record their starting salaries. When we measure the units in a sample, we say that we have a **sample of measurements**.

We often wish to describe a population or sample.

Descriptive statistics is the science of describing the important aspects of a set of measurements.

As an example, if we are studying a set of starting salaries, we might wish to describe (1) how large or small they tend to be, (2) what a typical salary might be, and (3) how much the salaries differ from each other.

---

[1] In Section 1.4, we discuss two types of quantitative variables (ratio and interval) and two types of qualitative variables (ordinal and nominative). To remember the difference between quantitative and qualitative, remember that quantitative has the letter "n," and "n is for number." Qualitative has an "l," and "l is for letter," so you have to use words to describe the data.

When the population of interest is small and we can conduct a census of the population, we can directly describe the important aspects of the population measurements. However, if the population is large and we need to select a sample from it, then we use what we call **statistical inference**.

Statistical inference is the science of using a sample of measurements to make generalizations about the important aspects of a population of measurements.

For instance, we might use a sample of starting salaries to **estimate** the important aspects of a population of starting salaries. In the next section, we begin to look at how statistical inference is carried out.

1.2 SAMPLING A POPULATION OF EXISTING UNITS

Random samples If the information contained in a sample is to accurately reflect the population under study, the sample should be **randomly selected** from the population. To intuitively illustrate random sampling, suppose that a small company employs 15 people and wishes to randomly select two of them to attend a convention. To make the random selections, we number the employees from 1 to 15, and we place in a hat 15 identical slips of paper numbered from 1 to 15. We thoroughly mix the slips of paper in the hat and, blindfolded, choose one. The number on the chosen slip of paper identifies the first randomly selected employee. Then, still blindfolded, we choose another slip of paper from the hat. The number on the second slip identifies the second randomly selected employee.

    Of course, it is impractical to carry out such a procedure when the population is very large. It is easier to use a **random number table** or a computerized random number generator. To show how to use such a table, we must more formally define a random sample.[2]

A **random sample** is selected so that, on each selection from the population, every unit remaining in the population on that selection has the same chance of being chosen.

To understand this definition, first note that we can randomly select a sample **with or without replacement**. If we **sample with replacement**, we place the unit chosen on any particular selection back into the population. Thus, we give this unit a chance to be chosen again on any succeeding selection. In such a case, all of the units in the population remain as candidates to be chosen for every selection. Randomly choosing two employees with replacement to attend a convention would make no sense because we wish to send two different employees to the convention. If we **sample without replacement**, we do not place the unit chosen on a particular selection back into the population. Thus, we do not give this unit a chance to be selected on any succeeding selection. In this case, the units remaining as candidates for a particular selection are all of the units in the population except those that have previously been selected. *It is best to sample without replacement.* Intuitively, because we will use the sample to learn about the population, sampling without replacement will give us the fullest possible look at the population. This is true because choosing the sample without replacement guarantees that all of the units in the sample will be different (and that we are looking at as many different units from the population as possible).

    In the following example, we illustrate how to use a random number table, or computer-generated random numbers, to select a random sample.

| Example 1.1 | The Cell Phone Case: Estimating Cell Phone Costs |

Businesses and students have at least two things in common—both find cellular phones to be nearly indispensable because of their convenience and mobility, and both often rack up unpleasantly high cell phone bills. Students' high bills are usually the result of **overage**—the student

---

[2]Actually, there are several different kinds of random samples. The type we will define is sometimes called a **simple random sample**. For brevity's sake, however, we will use the term **random sample**.

uses more minutes than their plan allows. For example, on March 5, 2010, the television program *Marketplace* on CBC broadcast a show titled "Canada's Worst Cellphone Bill." According to the presenters, there was no shortage of Canadians claiming that their bill warranted the title of the "worst" bill. Businesses also lose money due to overage and, in addition, lose money due to **underage** when some employees do not use all of the (already-paid-for) minutes allowed by their plans. Because cellular carriers offer a very large number of rate plans, it is nearly impossible for a business to intelligently choose calling plans that will meet its needs at a reasonable cost. Rising cell phone costs have forced companies with large numbers of cellular users to hire services to manage their cellular and other wireless resources. These cellular management services use sophisticated software and mathematical models to choose cost-efficient cell phone plans for their clients.

In this case, we will demonstrate how a bank can use a random sample of cell phone users to study its cellular phone costs. Based on this cost information, the bank will decide whether to hire a cellular management service to choose calling plans for the bank's employees. While the bank has over 10,000 employees on a variety of calling plans, a study of the calling patterns of cellular users on 500-minute plans may help the bank accurately assess whether its cell phone costs can be substantially reduced.

The bank has 2,136 employees on a 500-minute-per-month plan with a monthly cost of $50. The overage charge is 40 cents per minute, and there are additional charges for long distance and roaming. The bank will estimate its cellular cost per minute for this plan by examining the number of minutes used last month by each of 100 randomly selected employees on this 500-minute plan. According to the cellular management service, if the cellular cost per minute for the random sample of 100 employees is over 18 cents per minute, the bank should benefit from automated cellular management of its calling plans.

In order to randomly select the sample of 100 cell phone users, the bank will make a numbered list of the 2,136 users on the 500-minute plan. This list is called a **frame**. The bank can then use a random number table, such as Table 1.1(a), to select the needed sample. To see how this is done, note that any one-digit number in the table is assumed to have been randomly selected from the digits 0 to 9. Any two-digit number in the table is assumed to have been randomly selected from the numbers 00 to 99. Any three-digit number is assumed to have been randomly selected from the numbers 000 to 999, and so forth. Note that the table entries are segmented into groups of five to make the table easier to read. Because the total number of cell phone users on the 500-minute plan (2,136) is a four-digit number, we arbitrarily select any set of four digits in the table (these digits are circled). This number, which is 0511, identifies the first randomly selected user. Then, moving in any direction from the 0511 (up, down,

TABLE 1.1   Random Numbers

(a) A portion of a random number table

33276	85590	79936	56865	05859	90106	78188
03427	90511	69445	18663	72695	52180	90322
92737	27156	33488	36320	17617	30015	74952
85689	20285	52267	67689	93394	01511	89868
08178	74461	13916	47564	81056	97735	90707
51259	63990	16308	60756	92144	49442	40719
60268	44919	19885	55322	44819	01188	55157
94904	01915	04146	18594	29852	71585	64951
58586	17752	14513	83149	98736	23495	35749
09998	19509	06691	76988	13602	51851	58104
14346	61666	30168	90229	04734	59193	32812
74103	15227	25306	76468	26384	58151	44592
24200	64161	38005	94342	28728	35806	22851
87308	07684	00256	45834	15398	46557	18510
07351	86679	92420	60952	61280	50001	94953

(b) Excel output of 100 different four-digit random numbers between 1 and 2,136

1968	1766	1350	1340	1585	1943
1717	545	974	1492	1843	647
845	1842	1575	462	1868	319
259	180	398	792	454	1147
64	321	974	2074	2026	1941
431	531	312	36	1971	1496
1863	1275	380	229	2068	1778
2024	1914	587	1772	341	77
171	1259	801	1533	380	252
517	2079	1181	1064	1648	1863
170	69	1790	1644	97	1678
207	2005	662	73	102	1129
1350	1690	99	1858	1017	56
1523	255	384	1714	2126	1220
1942	1335	503	1536	484	2041
73	1067	1344	666	2119	
785	2095	1703	1510	1940	

TABLE **1.2** A Sample of Cellular Usage (in Minutes) for 100 Randomly Selected Employees

75	485	37	547	753	93	897	694	797	477
654	578	504	670	490	225	509	247	597	173
496	553	0	198	507	157	672	296	774	479
0	822	705	814	20	513	546	801	721	273
879	433	420	521	648	41	528	359	367	948
511	704	535	585	341	530	216	512	491	0
542	562	49	505	461	496	241	624	885	259
571	338	503	529	737	444	372	555	290	830
719	120	468	730	853	18	479	144	24	513
482	683	212	418	399	376	323	173	669	611

right, or left—it does not matter which), we select additional sets of four digits. These succeeding sets of digits identify additional randomly selected users. Here we arbitrarily move down from 0511 in the table. The first seven sets of four digits we obtain are

$$0511 \quad 7156 \quad 0285 \quad 4461 \quad 3990 \quad 4919 \quad 1915$$

(See Table 1.1(a)—these numbers are enclosed in a rectangle.) Since there are no users numbered 7,156, 4,461, 3,990, or 4,919 (remember only 2,136 users are on the 500-minute plan), we ignore these numbers. This implies that the first three randomly selected users are those numbered 0511, 0285, and 1915. Continuing this procedure, we can obtain the entire random sample of 100 users. Notice that, because we are sampling without replacement, we should ignore any set of four digits previously selected from the random number table.

While using a random number table is one way to select a random sample, this approach has a disadvantage that is illustrated by the current situation. Specifically, because most four-digit random numbers are not between 0001 and 2136, obtaining 100 different four-digit random numbers between 0001 and 2136 will require ignoring a large number of random numbers in the random number table, and we will in fact need to use a random number table that is larger than Table 1.1(a). Although larger random number tables are readily available in books of mathematical and statistical tables, a good alternative is to use a computer software package, which can generate random numbers that are between whatever values we specify. For example, Table 1.1(b) gives the Excel output of 100 different four-digit random numbers that are between 0001 and 2136 (note that the leading zeros are not included in these four-digit numbers). To obtain these values, the function RANDBETWEEN(1,2136) is used in the Excel program. If used, the random numbers in Table 1.1(b) identify the 100 employees that should form the random sample.

After the random sample of 100 employees is selected, the number of cellular minutes used by each employee during the month (the employee's **cellular usage**) is found and recorded. The 100 cellular usage figures are given in Table 1.2. Looking at this table, we can see that there is substantial overage and underage—many employees used far more than 500 minutes, while many others failed to use all of the 500 minutes allowed by their plan.

Approximately random samples In general, to take a random sample we must have a list, or **frame**, of all the population units. This is needed because we must be able to number the population units in order to make random selections from them (by, for example, using a random number table). In Example 1.1, where we wished to study a population of 2,136 cell phone users who were on the bank's 500-minute cellular plan, we were able to produce a frame (list) of the population units. Therefore, we were able to select a random sample. Sometimes, however, it is not possible to list and thus number all the units in a population. In such a situation, we often select a **systematic sample**, which approximates a random sample.

Example 1.2 The Marketing Research Case: Rating a New Bottle Design[3]

The design of a package or bottle can have an important effect on a company's bottom line. For example, an article in the September 16, 2004, issue of *USA Today* reported that the introduction of a contoured 1.5-L bottle for Coke drinks played a major role in Coca-Cola's failure to meet third-quarter earnings forecasts in 2004. According to the article, Coke's biggest bottler, Coca-Cola Enterprises, "said it would miss expectations because of the 1.5-liter bottle and the absence of common 2-liter and 12-pack sizes . . . in supermarkets."[4]

In this case, a brand group is studying whether changes should be made in the bottle design for a popular soft drink. To research consumer reaction to a new design, the brand group will use the "mall intercept method," in which shoppers at a large metropolitan shopping mall are intercepted and asked to participate in a consumer survey. Each shopper will be shown the new bottle design and asked to rate the bottle image. Bottle image will be measured by combining consumers' responses to five items, with each response measured using a seven-point Likert scale.[5] The five items and the scale of possible responses are shown in Figure 1.1. Because we describe the least favourable response and the most favourable response (and we do not describe the responses between them), we say that the scale is **anchored** at its ends. Responses to the five items will be summed to obtain a composite score for each respondent. It follows that the minimum composite score possible is 5 and the maximum composite score possible is 35. Experience has shown that the smallest acceptable composite score for a successful bottle design is 25.

In this situation, it is not possible to list and number every shopper at the mall while the study is being conducted. Consequently, we cannot use random numbers (as we did in the cell phone case) to obtain a random sample of shoppers. Instead, we can select a **systematic sample**. To do this, every 100th shopper passing a specified location in the mall will be invited to participate in the survey. Here, selecting every 100th shopper is arbitrary—we could select every 200th, every 300th, and so forth. If we select every 100th shopper, it is probably reasonable to believe that the responses of the survey participants are not related. Therefore, it is reasonable to assume that the sampled shoppers obtained by the systematic sampling process make up an **approximate** random sample.

During a Saturday afternoon and evening, a sample of 60 shoppers is selected by using the systematic sampling process. Each shopper is asked to rate the bottle design by responding to the five items in Figure 1.1, and a composite score is calculated for each shopper. The 60 composite scores obtained are given in Table 1.3. Because these scores range from 20 to 35, we might infer that *most* of the shoppers at the mall on the afternoon and evening of the study would rate the new bottle design between 20 and 35. Furthermore, since 57 of the 60 composite scores are at least 25, we might estimate that the proportion of all shoppers at

FIGURE **1.1** The Bottle Design Survey Instrument

Please circle the response that most accurately describes whether you agree or disagree with each statement about the bottle you have examined.

Statement	Strongly Disagree						Strongly Agree
The size of this bottle is convenient.	1	2	3	4	5	6	7
The contoured shape of this bottle is easy to handle.	1	2	3	4	5	6	7
The label on this bottle is easy to read.	1	2	3	4	5	6	7
This bottle is easy to open.	1	2	3	4	5	6	7
Based on its overall appeal, I like this bottle design.	1	2	3	4	5	6	7

---

[3]This case was motivated by an example in the book *Essentials of Marketing Research*, by W. R. Dillon, T. J. Madden, and N. H. Firtle (Burr Ridge, IL: Richard D. Irwin, 1993). The authors also wish to thank Professor L. Unger of the Department of Marketing at Miami University for helpful discussions concerning how this type of marketing study would be carried out.

[4]Source: "Coke says earnings will come up short," by Theresa Howard, *USA Today*, September 16, 2004, p. 801.

[5]The Likert scale is named after Rensis Likert (1903–1981), who originally developed this numerical scale for measuring attitudes in his PhD dissertation in 1932. [Source: *Psychology in America: A Historical Survey*, by E. R. Hilgard (San Diego, CA: Harcourt Brace Jovanovich, 1987).]

TABLE **1.3**   A Sample of Bottle Design Ratings (Composite Scores for a Systematic Sample of 60 Shoppers) ✍

34	33	33	29	26	33	28	25	32	33
32	25	27	33	22	27	32	33	32	29
24	30	20	34	31	32	30	35	33	31
32	28	30	31	31	33	29	27	34	31
31	28	33	31	32	28	26	29	32	34
32	30	34	32	30	30	32	31	29	33

the mall on the study date who would give the bottle design a composite score of at least 25 is 57/60 = 0.95. That is, we estimate that 95 percent of the shoppers would give the bottle design a composite score of at least 25. In Chapter 2, we will see how to estimate a typical composite score, and we will further analyze the composite scores in Table 1.3.

In some situations, we need to decide whether a sample taken from one population can be employed to make statistical inferences about another, related, population. Logical reasoning is often used to do this. For instance, we might reason that the bottle design ratings given by shoppers at the mall on the afternoon and evening of the research study would be representative of the ratings given by (1) shoppers at the same mall at other times, (2) shoppers at other malls, and (3) consumers in general. However, if we have no data or other information to back up this reasoning, making such generalizations is dangerous. In practice, marketing research firms choose locations and sampling times that data and experience indicate will produce a representative cross-section of consumers. To simplify our presentation, we will assume that this has been done in the bottle design case. Therefore, we will suppose that it is reasonable to use the 60 bottle design ratings in Table 1.3 to make statistical inferences about *all consumers.*

To conclude this section, we emphasize the importance of taking a random (or approximately random) sample. Statistical theory tells us that when we select a random (or approximately random) sample, we can use the sample to make valid statistical inferences about the sampled population. However, if the sample is not random, we cannot do this. For example, television and radio stations, as well as newspaper columnists, Web sites, and restaurant comment cards, use **voluntary response samples**. In such samples, participants self-select—that is, whoever wishes to participate does so (usually expressing some opinion). These samples overrepresent people with strong (usually negative) opinions. We further discuss random sampling in Sections 1.5 and 1.6.

Exercises for Sections 1.1 and 1.2

CONCEPTS

1.1   Define a population. Give an example of a population that you might study when you start your career after graduating from university.

1.2   Define what we mean by a variable, and explain the difference between a quantitative variable and a qualitative (categorical) variable.

1.3   Below we list several variables. Which of these variables are quantitative and which are qualitative? Explain.
  a. The dollar amount on an accounts receivable invoice.
  b. The net profit for a company in 2010.
  c. The ranking of a company's stock.

  d. The national debt of Canada in 2010.
  e. The advertising medium (radio, television, Internet, or print) used to promote a product.

1.4   Explain the difference between a census and a sample.

1.5   Explain each of the following terms:
  a. Descriptive statistics.
  b. Statistical inference.
  c. Random sample.
  d. Systematic sample.

1.6   Explain why sampling without replacement is preferred to sampling with replacement.

METHODS AND APPLICATIONS

1.7   Below is the store directory for The Shops of Confederation Court Mall, in Charlottetown, Prince Edward Island. A researcher wishes to select a random sample of stores for a mall service satisfaction survey.

   a. What is the first step required to treat the list so that a random sample can be selected?

   b. Using a random number table or a random number generator, select ten stores to be included in the survey.

Mall Directory: The Shops of Confederation Court Mall

Footwear
Uptown Shoes

Women's Fashions
Bizou Accessories
Chameleon's Hanger
Cotton Ginny/Cotton Ginny Plus
Dow's Fashions for Ladies
Eclipse
Lady Slipper Lingerie & Accessories
Marianna's
TABI

Jewellery
Norton's Jewellers
Taylor's Jewellers

Pharmacy
Shoppers Drug Mart

Beauty and Health
Allison's Hair Design
Merle Norman Cosmetics Studio
Senses
Shoppers Drug Mart
Zoja's Hair Salon

Sight and Sound
CD Plus

Furniture & Home Accessories
Frameworld

The Kitchen Store
Wicker Emporium

Men's Fashions
Dow's Men's Wear

Books
The Bookmark

Home & Office
Denis Office Products
The Source

Specialty & Variety
Colleen's Elite Tailoring
Critters Pet Shop
Dollaroo
Luna Eclectic Emporium
MacAulay's Bakery & Deli
The Loto Booth/Cigar Corner
The Root Cellar
True Value General Store

Gifts & Handcrafts
Holder's Card & Gift Shop
The P.E.I. Co. Store

Sporting Goods
API Hockey & Sports

Women's & Men's Fashion
Island Beach Co.
KC Clothing Company
Roots
Vogue Optical

1.8   THE VIDEO GAME SATISFACTION RATING CASE

A company that produces and markets video game systems wishes to assess its customers' level of satisfaction with a relatively new model, the XYZ-Box. In the six months since the introduction of the model,

the company has received 73,219 warranty registrations from purchasers. The company will randomly select 65 of these registrations and conduct telephone interviews with the purchasers. Specifically, each purchaser will be asked to state their level of agreement with each of the seven statements listed on the survey instrument given in Figure 1.2. Here the level of agreement for each statement is measured on a seven-point Likert scale. Purchaser satisfaction will be measured by adding the purchaser's responses to the seven statements. It follows that for each consumer the minimum composite score possible is 7 and the maximum is 49. Experience has shown that a purchaser of a video game system is "very satisfied" if their composite score is at least 42.

   a. Assume that the warranty registrations are numbered from 1 to 73,219 on a computer. Starting in the upper left corner of Table 1.1(a) on page 4 and moving down, the first three five-digit numbers obtained that are between 1 and 73,219 are

   33276   03427   08178

   Starting with these three random numbers and moving down in Table 1.1(a) to find more five-digit random numbers between 1 and 73,219, randomly select the numbers of the first 10 warranty registrations to be included in the sample of 65 registrations.

   b. Suppose that when the 65 customers are interviewed, their composite scores are obtained and are as given in Table 1.4. Using the data, estimate limits between which most of the 73,219 composite scores would fall. Also estimate the proportion of the 73,219 composite scores that would be at least 42.

1.9   THE BANK CUSTOMER WAITING TIME CASE

A bank manager has developed a new system to reduce the time customers spend waiting to be served by tellers during peak business hours. Typical waiting times during peak business hours under the current system are roughly nine to ten minutes. The bank manager hopes that the new system will lower typical waiting times to less than six minutes.

A 30-day trial of the new system is conducted. During the trial run, every 150th customer who arrives during peak business hours is selected until a systematic

FIGURE 1.2   The Video Game Satisfaction Survey Instrument

Statement	Strongly Disagree						Strongly Agree
The game console of the XYZ-Box is well designed.	1	2	3	4	5	6	7
The game controller of the XYZ-Box is easy to handle.	1	2	3	4	5	6	7
The XYZ-Box has high-quality graphics capabilities.	1	2	3	4	5	6	7
The XYZ-Box has high-quality audio capabilities.	1	2	3	4	5	6	7
The XYZ-Box serves as a complete entertainment centre.	1	2	3	4	5	6	7
There is a large selection of XYZ-Box games to choose from.	1	2	3	4	5	6	7
I am totally satisfied with my XYZ-Box game system.	1	2	3	4	5	6	7

TABLE **1.4** Composite Scores for the Video Game Satisfaction Rating Case

39	44	46	44	44
45	42	45	44	42
38	46	45	45	47
42	40	46	44	43
42	47	43	46	45
41	44	47	48	
38	43	43	44	
42	45	41	41	
46	45	40	45	
44	40	43	44	
40	46	44	44	
39	41	41	44	
40	43	38	46	
42	39	43	39	
45	43	36	41	

TABLE **1.5** Waiting Times (in Minutes) for the Bank Customer Waiting Time Case

1.6	6.2	3.2	5.6	7.9	6.1	7.2
6.6	5.4	6.5	4.4	1.1	3.8	7.3
5.6	4.9	2.3	4.5	7.2	10.7	4.1
5.1	5.4	8.7	6.7	2.9	7.5	6.7
3.9	0.8	4.7	8.1	9.1	7.0	3.5
4.6	2.5	3.6	4.3	7.7	5.3	6.3
6.5	8.3	2.7	2.2	4.0	4.5	4.3
6.4	6.1	3.7	5.8	1.4	4.5	3.8
8.6	6.3	0.4	8.6	7.8	1.8	5.1
4.2	6.8	10.2	2.0	5.2	3.7	5.5
5.8	9.8	2.8	8.0	8.4	4.0	
3.4	2.9	11.6	9.5	6.3	5.7	
9.3	10.9	4.3	1.3	4.4	2.4	
7.4	4.7	3.1	4.8	5.2	9.2	
1.8	3.9	5.8	9.9	7.4	5.0	

sample of 100 customers is obtained. Each of the sampled customers is observed, and the time spent waiting for teller service is recorded. The 100 waiting times obtained are given in Table 1.5. The bank manager feels that this systematic sample is as representative as a random sample of waiting times would be. Using the data, estimate limits between which the waiting times of most of the customers arriving during peak business hours would be. Also estimate the proportion of waiting times of customers arriving during peak business hours that are less than six minutes.

1.10 A researcher in a large company would like to use employee identification (ID) numbers to take a random sample of 20 people from a population of 1,000 employees. In this company, ID numbers have six digits and start at 000001. In Excel, generate a potential list of numbers for the researcher (using the RANDBETWEEN function). How would you expect your list to compare to another student's list?

1.3 SAMPLING A PROCESS

LO3

A population is not always a set of *existing* units. We are often interested in studying the population of all of the units that will be or could potentially be produced by a **process**.

A **process** is a sequence of operations that takes inputs (labour, materials, methods, machines, and so on) and turns them into outputs (products, services, and the like).

Processes produce output *over time*. For example, this year's Toyota Corolla manufacturing process produces Toyota Corollas over time. Early in the model year, Toyota Canada might wish to study the population of the city fuel efficiency of all Toyota Corollas that will be produced during the year. Or, even more hypothetically, Toyota Canada might wish to study the population of the city fuel efficiency of all Toyota Corollas that could *potentially* be produced by this year's manufacturing process. The first population is called a **finite population** because only a finite number of cars will be produced during the year. Any population of existing units is also finite. The second population is called an **infinite population** because the manufacturing process that produces this year's model could in theory always be used to build one more car. That is, theoretically there is no limit to the number of cars that could be produced by this year's process. There are many other examples of finite and infinite hypothetical populations. For instance, we might study the population of all waiting times that will or could potentially be experienced by patients of a hospital emergency room. Or we might study the population of all the amounts of raspberry jam that will be or could potentially be dispensed into 500-mL jars by an automated filling machine. To study a population of potential process outputs, we sample the process—usually at equally spaced time points—over time. This is illustrated in the following case.

Example 1.3   The Coffee Temperature Case: Monitoring Coffee Temperatures

According to the Web site of the Consumer Attorneys of California,[6] Stella Liebeck of Albuquerque, New Mexico, was severely burned by McDonald's coffee in February 1992. Liebeck, who received third-degree burns over 6 percent of her body, was awarded $US160,000 in compensatory damages and $US480,000 in punitive damages. A postverdict investigation revealed that the coffee temperature at the local Albuquerque McDonald's had dropped from about 85°C before the trial to about 70°C after the trial.

This case concerns coffee temperatures at a fast-food restaurant. Because of the possibility of future litigation and to possibly improve the coffee's taste, a restaurant wishes to study and monitor the temperature of the coffee it serves. To do this, the restaurant personnel measure the temperature of the coffee being dispensed (in degrees Celsius) at half-hour intervals from 10 A.M. to 9:30 P.M. on a given day. Table 1.6 gives the 24 temperature measurements obtained in the time order that they were observed. Here time equals 1 at 10 A.M. and 24 at 9:30 P.M.

Examining Table 1.6, we see that the coffee temperatures range from 67°C to 77°C. Based on this, is it reasonable to conclude that the temperature of most of the coffee that will or could potentially be served by the restaurant will be between 67°C and 77°C? The answer is yes if the restaurant's coffee-making process operates consistently over time. That is, this process must be in a state of **statistical control**.

A process is in **statistical control** if it does not exhibit any unusual process variations. This often means that the process displays a **constant amount of variation** around a **constant**, or horizontal, **level**.

To assess whether a process is in statistical control, we sample the process often enough to detect unusual variations or instabilities. The fast-food restaurant has sampled the coffee-making process every half hour. In other situations, we sample processes with other frequencies—for example, every minute, every hour, or every day. Using the observed process measurements, we can then construct a **runs plot** (sometimes called a **time series plot**).

A **runs plot** is a graph of individual process measurements versus time.

Figure 1.3 shows the Excel output of a runs plot of the temperature data. (Some people call such a plot a **line chart** when the plot points are connected by line segments as in the Excel output.) Here we plot each coffee temperature on the vertical scale (*y*-axis) versus its corresponding time index on the horizontal scale (*x*-axis). For instance, the first temperature (73°C)

TABLE **1.6**   24 Coffee Temperatures Observed in Time Order

Time		Coffee Temperature	Time		Coffee Temperature	Time		Coffee Temperature
(10:00 A.M.)	1	73°C	(2:00 P.M.)	9	71°C	(6:00 P.M.)	17	70°C
	2	76		10	68		18	77
	3	69		11	75		19	68
	4	67		12	72		20	72
(12:00 noon)	5	74	(4:00 P.M.)	13	67	(8:00 P.M.)	21	69
	6	70		14	74		22	75
	7	69		15	72		23	68
	8	72		16	68		24	73

[6]Source: http://www.caoc.com/CA/index.cfm?event=showPage&pg=facts, Consumer Attorneys of California, August 3, 2010.

FIGURE **1.3** Excel Runs Plots of Coffee Temperatures: The Process Is in Statistical Control

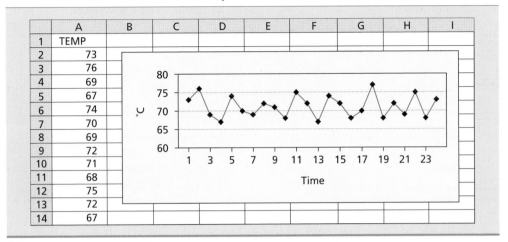

	A	B	C	D	E	F	G	H	I
1	TEMP								
2	73								
3	76								
4	69								
5	67								
6	74								
7	70								
8	69								
9	72								
10	71								
11	68								
12	75								
13	72								
14	67								

is plotted for time equals 1, the second temperature (76°C) is plotted when time equals 2, and so forth. The runs plot suggests that the temperatures exhibit a relatively constant amount of variation around a relatively constant level. That is, the centre of the temperatures can pretty much be represented by a horizontal line (constant level), and the spread of the points around the line stays about the same (constant variation). Note that the plot points tend to form a horizontal band. Therefore, the temperatures are in statistical control.

In general, assume that we have sampled a process at different (usually equally spaced) time points and made a runs plot of the resulting sample measurements. If the plot indicates that the process is in statistical control, and if it is reasonable to believe that the process will remain in control, then it is probably reasonable to regard the sample measurements as an approximately random sample from the population of all possible process measurements. Furthermore, since the process remains in statistical control, the process performance is **predictable**. This allows us to make statistical inferences about the population of all possible process measurements that will or potentially could result from using the process. For example, assuming that the coffee-making process will remain in statistical control, it is reasonable to conclude that the temperature of most of the coffee that will be or could potentially be served will be between 67°C and 77°C.

To emphasize the importance of statistical control, suppose that another fast-food restaurant observes the 24 coffee temperatures that are plotted versus time in Figure 1.4 on the next page. These temperatures range between 67°C and 80°C. However, we cannot infer from this that the temperature of most of the coffee that will be or could potentially be served by this other restaurant will be between 67°C and 80°C. This is because the downward trend in the runs plot of Figure 1.4 indicates that the coffee-making process is out of control and will soon produce temperatures below 67°C. Another example of an out-of-control process is illustrated in Figure 1.5 on the next page. Here the coffee temperatures seem to fluctuate around a constant level but with increasing variation (notice that the plotted temperatures fan out as time advances). In general, the specific pattern of out-of-control behaviour can suggest the reason for this behaviour. For example, the downward trend in the runs plot of Figure 1.4 might suggest that the restaurant's coffeemaker has a defective heating element.

Visually inspecting a runs plot to check for statistical control can be tricky. One reason is that the scale of measurements on the vertical axis can influence whether the data appear to form a horizontal band. For now, we will simply emphasize that a process must be in statistical control in order to make valid statistical inferences about the population of all possible process observations. Also, note that being in statistical control does not necessarily imply that a process is **capable** of producing output that meets our requirements. For example, suppose

FIGURE **1.4**   A Runs Plot of Coffee Temperatures:
The Process Level Is Decreasing

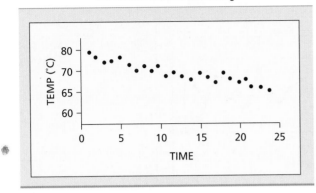

FIGURE **1.5**   A Runs Plot of Coffee Temperatures:
The Process Variation Is Increasing

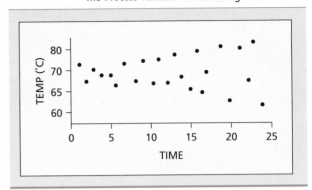

that marketing research suggests that the fast-food restaurant's customers feel that coffee tastes best if its temperature is between 67°C and 75°C. Table 1.6 on page 10 indicates that the temperature of some of the coffee it serves is not in this range (note that two of the temperatures are 67°C, one is 76°C, and another is 77°C), so the restaurant might take action to reduce the variation of the coffee temperatures. In summary, the marketing research and coffee temperature cases are both examples of using the **statistical process** to make a statistical inference. In Chapter 2, we will study more precise ways to both define and estimate a typical population value. In Chapters 3 through 7, we will study tools for assessing the reliability of estimation procedures and for estimating with confidence.

Exercises for Section 1.3

CONCEPTS

1.11 Define a process. Give an example of a process you might study when you start your career after graduating from university.

1.12 Explain what it means to say that a process is in statistical control.

1.13 What is a runs plot? What does a runs plot look like when we sample and plot a process that is in statistical control?

METHODS AND APPLICATIONS

1.14 The data below give 18 measurements of a critical dimension for an automobile part (measurements in centimetres). One part has been randomly selected each hour from the previous hour's production, and the measurements are given in time order.

Hour	Measurement	Hour	Measurement
1	3.005	10	3.005
2	3.020	11	3.015
3	2.980	12	2.995
4	3.015	13	3.020
5	2.995	14	3.000
6	3.010	15	2.990
7	3.000	16	2.985
8	2.985	17	3.020
9	3.025	18	2.985

Construct a runs plot and determine if the process appears to be in statistical control.

1.15 Table 1.7 presents the time (in days) needed to settle the 67 homeowners' insurance claims handled by an insurance agent over a year. The claims are given in time order by loss date.

a. Figure 1.6 shows an Excel runs plot of the claims data in Table 1.7. Does the claims-handling process seem to be in statistical control? Why or why not?

b. In March 2010, the region covered by the insurance company was hit by a widespread ice storm that caused heavy damage to homes in the area. Did this ice storm have a significant impact on the time needed to settle homeowners' claims? Should the agent consider improving procedures for handling claims in emergency situations? Why or why not?

1.16 In the article "Accelerating improvement," published in *Quality Progress* (October 1991), Gaudard, Coates, and Freeman describe a restaurant that caters to business travellers and has a self-service breakfast buffet. Interested in customer satisfaction, the manager conducts a survey over a three-week period and finds that the main customer complaint is having to wait too long to be seated. On each day from September 11,

TABLE **1.7** Number of Days Required to Settle Homeowners' Insurance Claims (Claims Made from July 2, 2009, to June 25, 2010)

Claim	Loss Date	Days to Settle	Claim	Loss Date	Days to Settle	Claim	Loss Date	Days to Settle
1	2009-07-02	111	24	2009-11-05	34	47	2010-03-05	70
2	2009-07-06	35	25	2009-11-13	25	48	2010-03-05	67
3	2009-07-11	23	26	2009-11-21	22	49	2010-03-06	81
4	2009-07-12	42	27	2009-11-23	14	50	2010-03-06	92
5	2009-07-16	54	28	2009-11-25	20	51	2010-03-06	96
6	2009-07-27	50	29	2009-12-01	32	52	2010-03-06	85
7	2009-08-01	41	30	2009-12-08	27	53	2010-03-07	83
8	2009-08-13	12	31	2009-12-10	23	54	2010-03-07	102
9	2009-08-20	8	32	2009-12-20	35	55	2010-03-19	23
10	2009-08-20	11	33	2009-12-23	29	56	2010-03-27	11
11	2009-08-28	11	34	2009-12-31	25	57	2010-04-01	8
12	2009-09-03	31	35	2009-12-31	18	58	2010-04-11	11
13	2009-09-10	35	36	2009-12-31	16	59	2010-04-15	35
14	2009-09-17	14	37	2010-01-05	23	60	2010-04-19	29
15	2009-09-18	14	38	2010-01-08	26	61	2010-05-02	80
16	2009-09-29	27	39	2010-01-16	30	62	2010-05-15	18
17	2009-10-04	14	40	2010-01-18	36	63	2010-05-25	58
18	2009-10-06	23	41	2010-01-22	42	64	2010-06-06	4
19	2009-10-15	47	42	2010-01-25	45	65	2010-06-12	5
20	2009-10-23	17	43	2010-01-27	43	66	2010-06-24	15
21	2009-10-25	21	44	2010-02-05	39	67	2010-06-25	19
22	2009-10-30	18	45	2010-02-09	53			
23	2009-11-02	31	46	2010-02-23	64			

1989, to October 1, 1989, a problem-solving team records the percentage of patrons who must wait more than one minute to be seated. A runs plot of the daily percentages is shown in Figure 1.7.[7] What does the runs plot suggest?

1.17 THE TRASH BAG CASE[8]

A company that produces and markets trash bags has developed an improved 130-L bag. The new bag is produced using a specially formulated plastic that is both stronger and more biodegradable than previously

FIGURE **1.6** Excel Runs Plot of the Insurance Claims Data for Exercise 1.15

FIGURE **1.7** Runs Plot of Daily Percentages of Customers Waiting More Than One Minute to Be Seated (for Exercise 1.16)

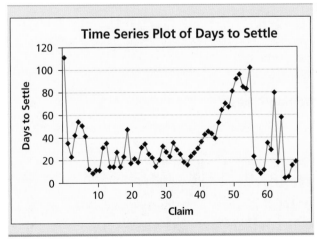

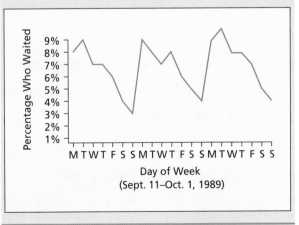

---

[7]The source of Figure 1.7 is "Accelerating improvement," by M. Gaudard, R. Coates, and L. Freeman, *Quality Progress*, October 1991, pp. 81–88. Copyright © 1991 American Society for Quality Control. Used with permission.

[8]This case is based on conversations by the authors with several employees working for a leading producer of trash bags. For purposes of confidentiality, we have withheld the company's name.

TABLE **1.8** Breaking Strengths

22.0	23.9	23.0	22.5
23.8	21.6	21.9	23.6
24.3	23.1	23.4	23.6
23.0	22.6	22.3	22.2
22.9	22.7	23.5	21.3
22.5	23.1	24.2	23.3
23.2	24.1	23.2	22.4
22.0	23.1	23.9	24.5
23.0	22.7	23.3	22.4
22.8	22.8	22.5	23.4

FIGURE **1.8** Excel Runs Plot of Breaking Strengths for Exercise 1.17

	A	B	C	D	E	F	G	H	I	J
1	Strength									
2	22.0									
3	23.8									
4	24.3									
5	23.0									
6	22.9									
7	22.5									
8	23.2									
9	22.0									
10	23.0									
11	22.8									
12	23.9									
13	21.6									
14	23.1									
15	22.6									
16	22.7									
17	23.1									
18	24.1									
19	23.1									
20	22.7									
21	22.8									

used plastics, and the company wishes to evaluate the strength of this bag. The breaking strength of a trash bag is considered to be the mass (in kilograms) of a representative trash mix that when loaded into a bag suspended in the air will cause the bag to sustain significant damage (such as ripping or tearing). The company has decided to carry out a 40-hour pilot production run of the new bags. Each hour, at a randomly selected time during the hour, a bag is taken off the production line. The bag is then subjected to a breaking strength test. The 40 breaking strengths obtained during the pilot production run are given in Table 1.8, and an Excel runs plot of these breaking strengths is given in Figure 1.8.

a. Do the 40 breaking strengths appear to be in statistical control? Explain.

b. Estimate limits between which most of the breaking strengths of all trash bags would fall.

1.18 THE BANK CUSTOMER WAITING TIME CASE

Recall that every 150th customer arriving during peak business hours was sampled until a systematic sample of 100 customers was obtained. This systematic sampling procedure is equivalent to sampling from a process. Figure 1.9 shows a MegaStat runs plot of the 100 waiting times from Table 1.5 on page 9. Does the process appear to be in statistical control? Explain.

FIGURE **1.9** MegaStat Runs Plot of Waiting Times for Exercise 1.18

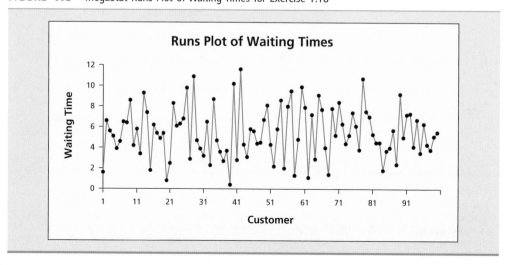

1.4 LEVELS OF MEASUREMENT: NOMINAL, ORDINAL, INTERVAL, AND RATIO

LO4

As stated in Section 1.1, a measure may be qualitative (or categorical) or quantitative. Within each of these distinctions, there are two levels of measurement. The qualitative **nominative** (or **nominal**) level is the lowest level of measurement. A nominative (or nominal) variable is used for categorizing only and has no meaningful order. For example, an individual's sex may be coded as 1 for males and 2 for females. These codes are simply labels and do not represent any other characteristic of the variable than designating group membership. Another example could be the colour of a car (with 1 = red, 2 = blue, 3 = grey, etc.). If you coded your sock drawer as 1 and your T-shirt drawer as 2, you would be engaging in a nominative (or nominal) level of measurement.

When variables are **ranked** in order, the numbers assigned have more meaning than at the nominative (or nominal) level. This ranking refers to the qualitative **ordinal** level of measurement. The measurements at the ordinal level may be nonnumerical or numerical. For example, a person may be asked to rank their favourite four colours. The person may say that yellow (1) is their most favourite colour, then green (2), red (3), and blue (4). If asked to expand further, the person may say they really adore yellow and green, red and blue are "so-so," but red is slightly better than blue. This ranking does not have equal distances between points in that 1 to 2 is not the same as 2 to 3. Only the order is meaningful. Analyzing ordinal data requires the use of **nonparametric** statistics (Chapter 13).

Within the quantitative level of measurement, the **interval** level is first. At the interval level, the distances between points are fixed and meaningful. For example, the 1 to 7 Likert scale

$$1 \quad 2 \quad 3 \quad 4 \quad 5 \quad 6 \quad 7$$

is an example of an interval scale. The distance from 2 to 3 is the same as the distance from 5 to 6. The scale could also have been written as

$$-3 \quad -2 \quad -1 \quad 0 \quad 1 \quad 2 \quad 3$$

Here the zero is the midpoint and represents the same concept as the number 4 in the 1 to 7 scale. What is of note is that the zero is arbitrary, in that it does not represent a complete absence of the variable and is not a fixed point.

When a variable has a meaningful zero and equal distances between points, then the variable is at the **ratio** level. An example of a ratio variable is money. Having \$0 is meaningful and having \$10 is twice as much as having \$5. Grades are also ratio variables. A grade of zero on an exam is meaningful, and the difference between 65 percent and 70 percent is the same as the difference between 80 percent and 85 percent.[9]

A summary of the four levels is given in the following table:

Level	Sublevel	Example
Qualitative	• Nominative or nominal • Ordinal	• Grocery aisle 3 for soup and aisle 4 for condiments • Top ten realtors in a district
Quantitative	• Interval • Ratio	• Temperature • Money

In addition to these four levels of variables, data may also take the form of **continuous** or **discrete** values. Continuous variables are typically interval or ratio scale numbers and fall along a continuum so that decimals make sense (such as salary, age, mass, and height). In contrast, discrete variables are count data in which decimals do not make sense (such as number of employees in a company).

---

[9]To remember the levels of measurement, simply remember the French word for "black" (NOIR). This acronym is useful since it also puts the levels in order from the simplest level of measurement (nominal or nominative) to the most complex (ratio).

Exercises for Section 1.4

CONCEPTS

1.19 Discuss the difference between a ratio variable and an interval variable.

1.20 Discuss the difference between an ordinal variable and a nominative (or nominal) variable.

METHODS AND APPLICATIONS

1.21 Classify each of the following qualitative variables as ordinal or nominative (nominal). Explain your answers.

Qualitative Variable	Categories					
Statistics course letter mark	A	B	C	D	F	
Heads or tails when tossing a coin	Heads	Tails				
Television show classifications	C	C8	G	PG	14+	18+
Personal computer ownership	Yes	No				
Restaurant rating	*****	****	***	**	*	
Income tax filing status	Married	Living common-law		Widowed		
	Divorced	Separated		Single		

1.22 Classify each of the following quantitative variables as interval or ratio. Explain your answer.

> **Quantitative Variable**
>
> Number of students in your class
> An answer of 7 on a nine-point Likert scale
> Salaries of five randomly selected people
> Temperature in degrees Celsius
> Years of education reported by a job candidate
> Statistics exam grade

1.5 A BRIEF INTRODUCTION TO SURVEYS

The Likert scale, introduced in Section 1.2, has proven to be a valuable method of measuring topics such as attitudes (for example, job satisfaction), values (organizational commitment), personality traits, and market research feedback. This section is a brief introduction to survey types and some issues that arise with surveys.

Surveys are also known as questionnaires. The purpose of surveys is to elicit responses from the participants. Four steps are typically involved in creating a survey. The first involves deciding upon the content (what is being studied and how the questions will be asked). Question types can vary. For example, the surveyor may want to know factual information (such as demographics of age, sex, and income). The variable of interest might be behavioural (such as what the person does on their holidays). The questions may also be opinion based (such as what fragrance a person prefers in their laundry detergent). Basically, the questions can be about anything of interest to the surveyor.

After the content has been decided upon, the questionnaire creator generates the questions. It is ideal if these questions are as short as possible and are easy to read and understand. Following the question creation, the response key has to be decided upon. Here there are two options: open and closed. Open-ended questions are ones in which the respondent can answer the question in any manner they wish. These types of responses provide rich information but are difficult to score or code. Closed-ended questions represent those that give the respondent a choice of answers. These responses are typically much easier to code and quantify.

Once the questions and the response system are determined, the questionnaire is compiled. The order of the questions is important, as questions themselves may influence people's responses to following questions. To address the quality of the survey created, the surveyor must complete the fourth step, which is to pilot test the questionnaire and address issues such as stability (reliability) and validity (whether the questions actually measure what they were intended to measure). Following the creation of the survey, the delivery of the questionnaire must be determined.

In general, surveys are delivered using one of three methods: mailed (direct or mass/bulk), telephone, and in-person. Mailed surveys are relatively inexpensive and unobtrusive, but tend to have low response rates (the number of people who complete the survey compared to the number of surveys sent out). Other concerns with mailing surveys is that you are never certain that the person who completed the survey is the person you wanted to complete the survey. As a researcher you are also never certain that the person completing the survey fully understood your questions. In general, if you plan to use mailed surveys, pretest the survey with members of your target audience. A recent trend and variation on the mailed survey is online surveys, but the same concerns with mailed surveys hold true for these as well.

Telephone surveys are also popular. Telephone interviews are less expensive than in-person interviews and tend to be faster. For example, surveys are conducted using telephones by organizations such as Environics Research Group and Ipsos Canada, which has offices across the country. Results from telephone surveys can be conveyed to the public almost immediately. Surveyors can cover a wide geographical region without having to travel. Historically, surveyors used telephone directories to contact people. Most surveyors now use random digit dialling (RDD), which uses the same logic underlying the random number table presented near the start of this chapter. When a surveyor uses RDD, there is an equal probability of any telephone number appearing (including unlisted numbers). The drawbacks are that RDD will also produce telephone numbers that are not in use, fax machine numbers, and nonresidential numbers. The other concerns that telephone surveyors have are the growing public wariness of telemarketers and reluctance to participate in telephone surveys.

LO5

Another common type of survey is the in-person interview. The face-to-face method is the richest form of communication. The participant in the survey can ask for clarification of the questions. But the in-person method is costly and may be perceived as more intrusive.

In general, there are three types of in-person interviews. The first is the structured interview, in which each respondent is given the same questions in the same order. Many businesses now use this method when interviewing job candidates. The interviewer is trained to act in the same manner for each interviewee. Answers given by respondents are then scored. The second in-person interview type is the intensive interview. Here the style is unstructured and informal. Interviewees are not given the same questions in the same order as in the structured method. This method is typically used in career counselling, performance appraisal feedback, and clinical settings. The third method is the focus group. The logic behind the focus group is that a group of people will provide more information than will individuals. The groups typically range in size from 4 to 15 people, and they will discuss approximately ten issues. This method is common for market research. In it, responses are coded by a moderator and by observers of the group.

Exercises for Section 1.5

CONCEPTS

1.23 Describe the steps involved in creating a questionnaire.

1.24 Give an example of how the content of a question might influence responses to subsequent questions.

1.25 What are the benefits and drawbacks of using each of the three methods of surveying?
  a. In-person. **b.** Mailed. **c.** Telephone.

1.26 Explain what we mean by a focus group. When would a researcher use a focus group?

1.27 Explain how you would go about requesting that people complete an online survey. How would you contact the people? How would you deal with the question of whether or not the person you contacted was the person who completed the survey?

1.6 AN INTRODUCTION TO SURVEY SAMPLING

Random sampling is not the only type of sampling. Methods for obtaining a sample are called **sampling designs**, and the sample we take is sometimes called a **sample survey**. In this section, we explain three sampling designs that are alternatives to random sampling—**stratified random sampling**, **cluster sampling**, and **systematic sampling**.

One common sampling design involves separately sampling important groups within a population. The samples are combined to form the entire sample. This approach is the idea behind **stratified random sampling**.

In order to select a **stratified random sample**, we divide the population into nonoverlapping groups of similar units (people, objects, etc.). These groups are called **strata**. A random sample is selected from each stratum, and these samples are combined to form the full sample.

It is wise to stratify when the population consists of two or more groups that differ with respect to the variable of interest. For instance, consumers could be divided into strata based on sex, age, language spoken, or income.

As an example, suppose that a department store chain proposes to open a new store in a location that would serve customers who live in a geographical region that consists of (1) an industrial city, (2) a suburban community, and (3) a rural area. In order to assess the potential profitability of the proposed store, the chain wishes to study the incomes of all households in the region. In addition, the chain wishes to estimate the proportion and the total number of households whose members would be likely to shop at the store. The department store chain feels that the industrial city, the suburban community, and the rural area differ with respect to income and the store's potential desirability. Therefore, it uses these subpopulations as strata and takes a stratified random sample.

A stratified sample takes advantage of the fact that units in the same stratum are similar to each other. It follows that a stratified sample can provide more accurate information than a random sample of the same size. As a simple example, if all of the units in each stratum were exactly the same, then examining only one unit in each stratum would allow us to describe the entire population. Furthermore, stratification can make a sample easier (or possible) to select. Recall that in order to take a random sample, we must have a frame, or list, of all of the population units. Although a frame might not exist for the overall population, a frame might exist for each stratum. For example, suppose nearly all the households in the department store's geographical region have land-line telephones. Although there might not be a telephone directory for the overall geographical region, there might be separate telephone directories for the industrial city, the suburb, and the rural area from which samples could be drawn (although recall some of the drawbacks of telephone surveying listed in the previous section).

Sometimes it is advantageous to select a sample in stages. This is a common practice when selecting a sample from a very large geographical region. In such a case, a frame often does not exist. For instance, there may not be single list of all households in Canada. In this situation, we can use **multistage cluster sampling**. To illustrate this procedure, suppose we wish to take a sample of households from all households in Canada. We might proceed as follows:

Stage 1: Randomly select a sample of counties from all of the counties in Canada.

Stage 2: Randomly select a sample of townships[10] in each county.

Stage 3: Randomly select a sample of households from each township.

We use the term **cluster sampling** to describe this type of sampling because at each stage we cluster the households into subpopulations. For instance, in Stage 1 we cluster the households into counties, and in Stage 2 we cluster the households in each county into townships. Also, notice that the random sampling at each stage can be carried out because there are lists of (1) all counties in Canada, (2) all townships in Canada, and (3) all households in each township.

---

[10]Not all parts of Canada use the term *township*. Other common terms are *canton* (Quebec) and *parish* (New Brunswick). We will continue to use *township* here for simplicity.

Consider another way of sampling the households in Canada. We might use Stages 1 and 2 above to select counties and townships within the selected counties. Then, if there is a telephone directory of the households in each township, we can randomly sample households from each selected township by using its telephone directory. Because most households today have telephones, and telephone directories are readily available, most national polls are now conducted by telephone.

It is sometimes a good idea to combine stratification with multistage cluster sampling. For example, suppose a national polling organization wants to estimate the proportion of all registered voters who favour a particular federal party. Because the federal party preferences of voters might tend to vary by geographical region, the polling organization might divide Canada into regions (say, Atlantic Canada, Quebec, Ontario, and Western Canada). The polling organization might then use these regions as strata and take a multistage cluster sample from each stratum (region).[11]

In order to select a random sample, we must number the units in a frame of all the population units. Then we use a random number table (or a random number generator on a computer) to make the selections. However, numbering all the population units can be quite time-consuming. Moreover, random sampling is used in the various stages of many complex sampling designs (requiring the numbering of numerous populations). Therefore, it is useful to have an alternative to random sampling. One such alternative is systematic sampling, which we discussed in Example 1.2 in Section 1.2. In order to systematically select a sample of n units without replacement from a frame of N units, we divide N by n and round the result down to the nearest whole number. Calling the rounded result ℓ, we then randomly select one unit from the first ℓ units in the frame—this is the first unit in the systematic sample. The remaining units in the sample are obtained by selecting every ℓth unit following the first (randomly selected) unit. For example, suppose we wish to sample a population of $N = 14{,}327$ members of an international allergists' association to investigate how often they have prescribed a particular drug during the last year. The association has a directory listing the 14,327 allergists, and we wish to draw a systematic sample of 500 allergists from this frame. Here we compute $14{,}327/500 = 28.654$, which is 28 when rounded down. Therefore, we number the first 28 allergists in the directory from 1 to 28, and we use a random number table to randomly select one of the first 28 allergists. Suppose we select allergist number 19. We interview allergist 19 and every 28th allergist in the frame thereafter, so we choose allergists 19, 47, 75, and so forth until we obtain our sample of 500 allergists. In this scheme, we must number the first 28 allergists, but we do not have to number the rest because we can count off every 28th allergist in the directory. Alternatively, we can measure the approximate amount of space in the directory that it takes to list 28 allergists. This measurement can then be used to select approximately every 28th allergist.

In this book, we concentrate on showing how to analyze data produced by random sampling. However, if the order of the population units in a frame is random with respect to the characteristic under study, then a systematic sample should be (approximately) a random sample and we can analyze the data produced by the systematic sample by using the same methods employed to analyze random samples. For instance, it would seem reasonable to assume that the alphabetically ordered allergists in a medical directory would be random (that is, have nothing to do with the number of times the allergists prescribed a particular drug). Similarly, the alphabetically ordered people in a telephone directory would probably be random with respect to many of the people's characteristics that we might wish to study.

When we employ random sampling, we eliminate bias in the choice of the sample from a frame. However, a proper sampling design does not guarantee that the sample will produce accurate information. One potential problem is **undercoverage**.

Undercoverage occurs when some population units are excluded from the process of selecting the sample.

---

[11]The analysis of data produced by multistage cluster sampling can be quite complicated. We explain how to analyze data produced by one- and two-stage cluster sampling in Appendix E (Part 2), available on *Connect*. This appendix also includes a discussion of an additional survey sampling technique called **ratio estimation**. For a more detailed discussion of cluster sampling and ratio estimation, see Scheaffer, Mendenhall, and Ott (1986).

This problem occurs when we do not have a complete, accurate list of all the population units. For example, although telephone polls today are common, some people in Canada do not have land-line telephones. In general, undercoverage usually causes some people to be underrepresented. If underrepresented groups differ from the rest of the population with respect to the characteristic under study, the survey results will be biased. A second potentially serious problem is **nonresponse**.

Nonresponse occurs when a population unit selected as part of the sample cannot be contacted or refuses to participate.

In some surveys, 35 percent or more of the selected individuals cannot be contacted, even when several callbacks are made. In such a case, other participants are often substituted for the people who cannot be contacted. If the substitute participants differ from the originally selected participants with respect to the characteristic under study, the survey will again be biased. Third, when people are asked potentially embarrassing questions, their responses might not be truthful. We then have what we call **response bias**. Fourth, the wording of the questions can influence the answers received. Slanted questions often evoke biased responses. For example, consider the following question:

Which of the following best describes your views on gun control?

1   The government should take away our guns, leaving us defenceless against heavily armed criminals.

2   We have the right to keep guns.

Exercises for Section 1.6

CONCEPTS

1.28   When is it appropriate to use stratified random sampling? What are strata, and how should strata be selected?

1.29   When is cluster sampling used? Why do we describe this type of sampling by using the term *cluster?*

1.30   Explain each of the following terms:
   a. Undercoverage.
   b. Nonresponse.
   c. Response bias.

1.31   Explain how to take a systematic sample of 100 companies from the 1,853 companies that are members of an industry trade association.

1.32   Explain how a stratified random sample is selected. Discuss how you might define the strata to survey student opinion on a proposal to charge all students a $100 fee for a new university-run bus system that will provide transportation between off-campus apartments and campus locations.

1.33   Marketing researchers often use city blocks as clusters in cluster sampling. Using this fact, explain how a market researcher might use multistage cluster sampling to select a sample of consumers from all cities with a population of more than 10,000 in a region having many such cities.

CHAPTER SUMMARY

In this chapter, we introduced the idea of using **sample data** to make **statistical inferences**—that is, drawing conclusions about populations and processes by using sample data. We began by learning that a **population** is a set of units that we wish to study. We saw that because many populations are too large to examine in their entirety, we often study a population by selecting a **sample**, which is a subset of the population units. Next we learned that if the information contained in a sample is to accurately represent the population, then the sample should be **randomly selected** from the population, and we saw how **random numbers** (obtained from a **random number table**) can be used to select a **random sample**. We also learned that selecting a random sample requires a **frame** (that is, a list of all of the population units) and that, since a frame does not always exist, we sometimes select a **systematic sample**.

We continued this chapter by studying **processes**. We learned that to make statistical inferences about the population of all possible values of a variable that could be observed when using a process, the process must be in **statistical control**. We learned that a process is in statistical control if it does not exhibit any unusual process variations, and we demonstrated how we might sample a process and how to use a runs plot to try to judge whether a process is in control.

Next, in Section 1.4, we studied different types of quantitative and qualitative variables. We saw that there are two levels of **qualitative (categorical) variables—nominative (nominal) variables**, for which there is no meaningful ordering of the categories, and **ordinal variables**, for which there is a meaningful ordering of the categories. We also learned that there are two levels of **quantitative variables—interval variables**, for which ratios are not meaningful and there is no inherently defined zero value, and **ratio variables**, which are measured on a scale such that ratios of its values are meaningful and there is an inherently defined zero value.

We concluded this chapter with Sections 1.5 and 1.6, which discuss **survey construction**, **types of survey methods**, and **survey sampling**. We introduced **stratified random sampling**, in which we divide a population into groups (**strata**) and then select

a random sample from each group. We also introduced **multistage cluster sampling**, which involves selecting a sample in stages, and we explained how to select a **systematic sample**. Finally, we discussed some potential problems encountered when conducting a sample survey—**undercoverage**, **nonresponse**, **response bias**, and slanted questions.

GLOSSARY OF TERMS

census: An examination of all of the units in a population. (page 2)

cluster sampling (multistage cluster sampling): A sampling design in which we sequentially cluster population units into subpopulations. (page 18)

descriptive statistics: The science of describing the important aspects of a set of measurements. (page 2)

finite population: A population that contains a finite number of units. (page 9)

frame: A list of all of the units in a population. This is needed in order to select a random sample. (page 4)

infinite population: A population that is defined so that there is no limit to the number of units that could potentially belong to the population. (page 9)

interval variable: A quantitative variable such that ratios of its values are not meaningful and for which there is not an inherently defined zero value. (page 15)

measurement: The process of assigning a value of a variable to each of the units in a population or sample. (page 2)

nominative (nominal) variable: A qualitative variable for which there is no meaningful ordering, or ranking, of the categories. (page 15)

nonresponse: A situation in which population units selected to participate in a survey do not respond to the survey instrument. (page 20)

ordinal variable: A qualitative variable for which there is a meaningful ordering or ranking of the categories. (page 15)

population: A set of existing or potential units (people, objects, events, or the like) that we wish to study. (page 2)

process: A sequence of operations that takes inputs and turns them into outputs. (page 9)

qualitative (categorical) variable: A variable with values that indicate in which of several categories a population unit belongs. (page 2)

quantitative variable: A variable with values that are numbers representing quantities. (page 2)

random number table: A table containing random digits that is often used to select a random sample. (page 3)

random sample: A sample selected so that on each selection from the population, every unit remaining in the population on that selection has the same chance of being chosen. (page 3)

ratio variable: A quantitative variable such that ratios of its values are meaningful and for which there is an inherently defined zero value. (page 15)

response bias: A situation in which survey participants do not respond truthfully to the survey questions. (page 20)

runs plot: A graph of individual process measurements versus time. (page 10)

sample: A subset of the units in a population. (page 2)

sampling with replacement: A sampling procedure in which we place any unit that has been chosen back into the population to give the unit a chance to be chosen on succeeding selections. (page 3)

sampling without replacement: A sampling procedure in which we do not place previously selected units back into the population and, therefore, do not give these units a chance to be chosen on succeeding selections. (page 3)

statistical control: A state in which a process does not exhibit any unusual variations. This often means that the process displays a uniform amount of variation around a constant, or horizontal, level. (page 10)

statistical inference: The science of using a sample of measurements to make generalizations about the important aspects of a population. (page 3)

strata: The subpopulations in a stratified sampling design. (page 18)

stratified random sampling: A sampling design in which we divide a population into nonoverlapping subpopulations and then select a random sample from each subpopulation (stratum). (page 18)

systematic sample: A sample taken by moving systematically through the population. For instance, we might randomly select one of the first 200 population units and then systematically sample every 200th population unit thereafter. (page 5)

undercoverage: A situation in sampling in which some groups of population units are underrepresented. (page 19)

variable: A characteristic of a population unit. (page 2)

connect Practise and learn online with *Connect*. Questions and tables with online data sets are marked with 🖊.

SUPPLEMENTARY EXERCISES

1.34 Some television stations attempt to gauge public opinion by posing a question on the air and asking viewers to call in to give their opinions. Suppose that a particular television station asks viewers whether they support or oppose the federal gun registry. Viewers are to call one of two toll-free numbers to register support or opposition.

When the results are tabulated, the station reports that 78 percent of those who called are opposed to the registry. What do you think of the sampling method used by the station? Do you think that the percentage of the entire population that opposes the registry is as high as the 78 percent of the sample that was opposed?

1.35 Classify each of the following qualitative variables as ordinal or nominative (nominal). Explain your answers.

Qualitative Variable	Categories
Personal computer operating system	Windows XP Mac OS-X Windows Vista Unix Linux Other
Movie classifications	G PG 14A 18A R
Level of education	Elementary Middle school High school University Graduate school
Rankings of top ten university hockey teams	1 2 3 4 5 6 7 8 9 10
First three characters of postal code	B3J M1J T2K V7E
Five Canadian telephone area codes	905 867 709 780 604

1.36 Table 1.9 lists the "Top 10" Canadian employers as determined by the *Financial Post* (October 21, 2009). Use random numbers to select a sample of four of these companies. Based on your knowledge of surveys, what types of questions would you ask employees at these companies to determine whether or not you would agree that they are the best Canadian employers?

TABLE **1.9**   FP 10 Best Employers—Financial Post

	Location	Full-Time Employees
Amec Americas Ltd.	Oakville, ON	4,801
Cameco Corp.	Saskatoon, SK	2,761
Digital Extremes	London, ON	96
Enbridge Inc.	Calgary, AB	3,981
Goldcorp Inc.	Vancouver, BC	2,350
Johnson Inc.	St. John's, NL	1,066
Loblaw Companies Ltd.	Brampton, ON	31,670
Mountain Equipment Co-op	Vancouver, BC	582
Research in Motion Ltd.	Waterloo, ON	8,576
Toyota Motor Manufacturing Canada Inc.	Cambridge, ON	5,954

1.37 A bank wishes to study the amount of time it takes to complete a withdrawal transaction from one of its automated banking machines (ABMs). On a particular day, 63 withdrawal transactions are observed between 10 A.M. and noon. The time required to complete each transaction is given in Table 1.10. Figure 1.10 shows an Excel runs plot of the 63 transaction times. Do the transaction times seem to be in statistical control? Why or why not?

TABLE **1.10**   ABM Transaction Times (in Seconds) for 63 Withdrawals

Transaction	Time	Transaction	Time	Transaction	Time
1	32	22	34	43	37
2	32	23	32	44	32
3	41	24	34	45	33
4	51	25	35	46	33
5	42	26	33	47	40
6	39	27	42	48	35
7	33	28	46	49	33
8	43	29	52	50	39
9	35	30	36	51	34
10	33	31	37	52	34
11	33	32	32	53	33
12	32	33	39	54	38
13	42	34	36	55	41
14	34	35	41	56	34
15	37	36	32	57	35
16	37	37	33	58	35
17	33	38	34	59	37
18	35	39	38	60	39
19	40	40	32	61	44
20	36	41	35	62	40
21	32	42	33	63	39

FIGURE **1.10**   Excel Runs Plot of ABM Transaction Times for Exercise 1.37

	A	B	C	D	E	F	G	H	I
1	ABM TIME								
2	32								
3	32								
4	41								
5	51								
6	42								
7	39								
8	33								
9	43								
10	35								
11	33								
12	33								
13	32								
14	42								

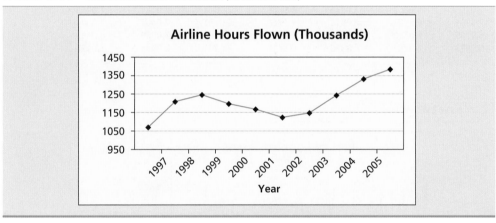

FIGURE **1.11**   Runs Plot of Airline Hours Flown (for Exercise 1.38)

Airline Hours Flown (Thousands)

1.38 Figure 1.11 gives a runs plot of the total number of hours (in thousands) Canadian airlines flew for each year from 1997 to 2006 according to the Transportation Safety Board of Canada (http://www.tsb.gc.ca/eng/stats/aviation/2006/ss06_sec2.asp#table_2). Describe the pattern of the plot. Why was there a drop in hours in 2001?

1.39   THE TRASH BAG CASE

Recall that the company will carry out a 40-hour pilot production run of the new bags and will randomly select one bag each hour to be subjected to a breaking strength test.

a. Explain how the company can use random numbers to randomly select the times during the 40 hours of the pilot production run at which bags will be tested. *Hint:* Suppose that a randomly selected time will be determined to the nearest minute.

b. Use the following random numbers (obtained from Table 1.1 on page 4) to select the times during the first five hours at which the first five bags to be tested will be taken from the production line: 61, 15, 64, 07, 86, 87, 57, 64, 66, 42, 59, 51.

1.40 In 1989, Mr. Steve Kopp, a lecturer in the Department of Statistical and Actuarial Sciences at the University of Western Ontario, decided to weigh 200 one-dollar coins (loonies) that were minted in that year. From a production standpoint, the loonie would have to be minted within strict specifications. The loonie does in fact have specific minting requirements:

Composition: 91.5% nickel with 8.5% bronze plating
Mass: 7 g
Diameter: 26.5 mm
Thickness: 1.75 mm

A person at the Royal Canadian Mint might be interested in knowing whether the minted coins fall within an acceptable tolerance. Remember that coins cannot be too light or too heavy, as vending machines are set to accept coins according to mass and size. A sample

TABLE **1.11**   Loonie Mass Data

7.0688	7.0196	7.008	7.0252	7.0912	6.9753	6.9720	7.0963
6.9651	6.9911	6.9156	7.0466	7.0948	7.0127	7.0470	7.0215
6.9605	7.0294	7.0050	7.0119	7.0929	7.0706	7.0459	6.9549
6.9797	7.0045	7.0898	7.0354	7.0186	6.9861	7.0339	6.9178
6.9861	6.9605	7.1322	6.9528	7.0648	6.9920	6.9334	7.0584
7.1227	6.9812	6.9873	7.0686	6.8479	7.0106	7.0340	7.0884
6.9861	7.0136	7.0572	6.8959	7.0079	7.0195	6.9888	7.0641
6.9692	7.0185	7.0158	7.0552	7.0478	7.0500	7.0919	7.0107
6.9018	7.1567	7.1135	6.9117	7.0346	7.0627	7.0561	6.8990
7.0574	6.9814	7.0016	7.0026	7.0212	7.0833	7.0343	7.0111
7.0467	7.0413	6.9892	7.0563	7.0374	7.0027	7.0012	7.2046
7.0386	6.9793	6.9074	7.0810	7.0076	7.0797	7.0132	6.9867
6.9799	7.0245	7.0461	6.9430	7.0934	7.0207	6.9364	6.9705
7.0326	7.0295	7.0024	6.9955	7.0184	7.0681	7.0046	7.0092
7.1380	7.0099	6.9936	6.9784	6.9475	7.0708	6.8821	7.0009
7.0908	6.9563	7.0364	6.9575	7.0118	7.0490	7.0426	7.0746
7.0335	6.9785	6.9005	7.1735	6.9034	6.9690	7.0137	6.9876
6.8788	7.0260	7.0216	7.0847	6.9481	6.9891	7.0943	6.9898
7.0654	6.9428	6.9986	6.8801	7.0640	7.0203	6.9521	7.0489
7.0610	7.0784	6.9741	6.9491	6.9541	6.9091	7.0732	6.9874
7.0057	6.9516	6.9477	7.0401	7.0017	7.0222	7.0941	6.8818
7.0277	7.0264	6.9862	7.0396	6.9685	7.0874	7.0024	7.0253
7.0438	7.0291	6.9582	7.0812	7.0780	6.9771	7.0463	7.0304
6.9977	6.9909	6.8358	7.0607	7.0652	7.0148	7.0909	6.9469
6.9531	6.9623	6.9785	6.8395	6.9618	7.0401	6.9994	7.0438

FIGURE **1.12**   Loonie Mass Plot

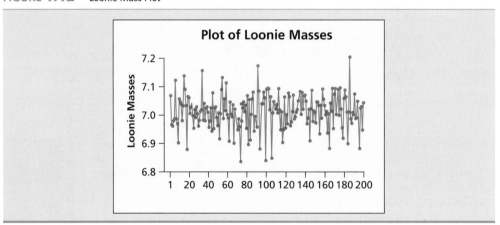

of 200 coins was obtained from a local bank in London, Ontario. The coins are packaged in rolls of 25, so eight rolls were obtained at random. These coins may or may not have come from the same production run, but they were minted in the same year (1989). Each coin was carefully weighed, and the masses are given in Table 1.11. Based on the plot of the masses in Figure 1.12, would you state that the minting process of the loonie is in statistical control? Based on the masses reported in Table 1.11, would you say the loonie is meeting the required standard of 7 g, as outlined by the Canadian Mint (http://www.mint.ca)?

1.41   INTERNET EXERCISE

The World Bank (http://www.worldbank.org/) provides data on the countries of the world in terms of their gross national income per capita. As of 2009, there were 186 member countries. Discover where Canada fits within this system. Explain what type of measurement is used to determine the relative positioning of Canada compared to the other 185 countries.

CHAPTER 2
Descriptive Statistics

LEARNING OBJECTIVES

After reading this chapter, you should be able to

LO1 describe and construct a stem-and-leaf display and explain what it demonstrates

LO2 describe how a histogram is constructed and when it should be used

LO3 know the difference between a symmetrical distribution and a positively or negatively skewed distribution

LO4 define the term *outlier*

LO5 distinguish between a mean, a median, and a mode and explain when you would report these values

LO6 compute the variance and standard deviation from raw data

CHAPTER OUTLINE

2.1 Describing the Shape of a Distribution

2.2 Describing Central Tendency

2.3 Measures of Variation

2.4 Percentiles, Quartiles, and Box-and-Whiskers Displays

2.5 Describing Qualitative Data

2.6 Using Scatter Plots to Study Relationships between Variables

2.7 Misleading Graphs and Charts

2.8 Weighted Means and Grouped Data

In Chapter 1, we saw that although we can sometimes take a census of an entire population, we must often randomly select a sample from a population. When we have taken a sample, we wish to describe the observed data set in order to make inferences about the sampled population.

In this chapter, we learn about **descriptive statistics**, which is the science of describing the important characteristics of a population or sample. Generally, we look at several important aspects of a set of measurements. One such aspect is the **central tendency**, or middle, of the data set. For instance, we might estimate a typical bottle design rating in a marketing research case. Another important aspect of a data set is the **variability**, or spread, of the data. For example, we might measure the spread of the bottle design ratings. If the ratings are clustered closely together, consumers' ratings are much the same (or are consistent). If the ratings are spread far apart, then consumers have widely varying opinions of the new bottle design. A third important aspect of a data set is the **shape** of the population or sample. Looking at a data set's shape tells us how the population or sample is distributed over various values. Still another important aspect is whether **outliers** exist. For instance, if there are outlying bottle design ratings, then some consumers have opinions about the design that are very different from the opinions of most of the sampled consumers. Descriptive statistics also involves using **graphical methods** to depict data sets and to study relationships between different variables.

In this chapter, we use a variety of methods to describe the cell phone usages, bottle design ratings, and coffee temperatures introduced in the cases of Chapter 1. In addition, we introduce two new cases:

The Electronic Articles Surveillance Case: A survey is used to study the unintended effects on consumer attitudes of false electronic article surveillance alarms.

The Marketing Ethics Case: A survey is conducted to study marketing researchers' attitudes toward violating confidentiality in marketing research studies.

 Practise and learn online with *Connect*. Throughout this chapter, questions and tables with online data sets are marked with 🔾.

2.1 DESCRIBING THE SHAPE OF A DISTRIBUTION

CHAPTER 1

Diekhoff (1992) states, "one graph is worth a thousand statistics." As mentioned in Chapter 1, we typically sample from a population and use the sample to make inferences about the population. Visually displaying the data provides a means of better understanding the sample and, by extension, the population of interest. This section begins with several graphical methods—the **stem-and-leaf display**, the **histogram**, and the **dot plot**—all of which are used to portray shapes of distributions.

LO1

Stem-and-leaf displays We illustrate how to construct stem-and-leaf displays in the following example.

Example 2.1 Cellular Telephone Usage

Recall the 100 randomly selected bank employees' usage of their cellular telephones (in minutes in one month) in Table 1.2 on page 5. From these data, we construct the stem-and-leaf display presented in Figure 2.1. The first digit constitutes the stem (using a unit of 100 minutes) and the second digit is the leaf (using ten-minute units). The first column in Figure 2.1 presents the frequency of observations that make up that line. The first row (11 cases) represents all of the cellular telephone times that are less than 100 minutes. The second row (6 cases) represents the times that fall between 100 and 199 minutes. The last row represents the single case where the number of minutes is greater than 900. As we can see in Figure 2.1, the greatest number of cases are in the 500-minute to 599-minute range, with the second-greatest number of cases between 400 and 499 minutes.

FIGURE 2.1   MegaStat Output of a Stem-and-Leaf Display of 100 Cellular Telephone Usage Cases

```
Stem and Leaf plot for Usage (minutes)
    stem unit =   100
    leaf unit =    10
       Frequency         Stem      Leaf
           11              0        0 0 0 1 2 2 3 4 4 7 9
            6              1        2 4 5 7 7 9
            9              2        1 1 2 4 4 5 7 9 9
            8              3        2 3 4 5 6 7 7 9
           15              4        1 2 3 4 6 6 7 7 7 8 8 9 9 9 9
           24              5        0 0 0 0 0 1 1 1 1 2 2 2 3 3 4 4 4 5 5 6 7 7 8 9
            9              6        1 2 4 5 6 7 7 8 9
            9              7        0 0 1 2 3 3 5 7 9
            8              8        0 1 2 3 5 7 8 9
            1              9        4
          100
```

We summarize how to set up a stem-and-leaf display in the following box:

Constructing a Stem-and-Leaf Display

1   Decide which units will be used for the stems and the leaves. As a general rule, choose units for the stems so that there will be somewhere between 5 and 20 stems.

2   Place the stems in a column with the smallest stem at the top of the column and the largest stem at the bottom.

3   Enter the leaf for each measurement into the row corresponding to the proper stem. The leaves should be single-digit numbers (these can be rounded values that were originally more than one digit).

4   If desired, rearrange the leaves so that they are in increasing order from left to right.

Frequency distributions and histograms The count of the number of measurements in a class defined by a stem is called the **frequency** of the class. One advantage of a stem-and-leaf display is that it gives the frequencies of the different classes and also lists the specific measurements in each class. However, such listings for the different classes can be unwieldy if we are portraying a large number of measurements. For example, while it is convenient to display the ratings by 60 shoppers using the stem-and-leaf display, summarizing 500 ratings with the same type of format would be difficult.

When we have many measurements, it is best to group them into the classes of a **frequency distribution** and to display the data by using a **histogram**. We illustrate this in the following example.

Example 2.2   **The Payment Time Case: Reducing Payment Times**

Major consulting firms employ statistical analysis to assess the effectiveness of the systems they design for their customers. In this case, a consulting firm has developed a computerized billing system for a trucking company. The system sends invoices electronically to each customer's computer and allows customers to easily check and correct errors. It is expected that the new billing system will substantially reduce the amount of time it takes customers to make payments. Typical payment times—measured from the date on an invoice to the date payment is received—using the trucking company's old billing system had been 39 days or more. This exceeded the industry standard payment time of 30 days.

In order to assess the system's effectiveness, the consulting firm selects a random sample of 65 invoices from the 7,823 invoices processed during the first three months of the new system's operation. The payment times for the 65 sample invoices are manually determined and are given in Table 2.1. If this sample can be used to establish that the new billing system substantially reduces payment times, the consulting firm plans to market the system to other trucking firms.

Looking at the payment times in Table 2.1, we can see that the shortest payment time is 10 days and the longest payment time is 29 days. Beyond that, it is pretty difficult to interpret the data in any meaningful way. To better understand the sample of 65 payment times, the consulting firm will form a frequency distribution of the data by first dividing the payment times into classes and then graphing the distribution by constructing a histogram.

Step 1: Find the number of classes One rule for finding an appropriate number of classes says that the number of classes should be the smallest whole number K that makes the quantity 2^K greater than the number of measurements in the data set. For the payment time data we have 65 measurements. Because $2^6 = 64$ is less than 65 and $2^7 = 128$ is greater than 65, we should use $K = 7$ classes. Table 2.2 on the next page gives the appropriate number of classes (determined by the 2^K rule) to use for data sets of various sizes.

Step 2: Find the class length We find the length of each class by computing

$$\text{Class length} = \frac{\text{largest measurement} - \text{smallest measurement}}{\text{number of classes}}.$$

TABLE 2.1   A Sample of Payment Times (in Days) for 65 Randomly Selected Invoices

22	29	16	15	18	17	12	13	17	16	15
19	17	10	21	15	14	17	18	12	20	14
16	15	16	20	22	14	25	19	23	15	19
18	23	22	16	16	19	13	18	24	24	26
13	18	17	15	24	15	17	14	18	17	21
16	21	25	19	20	27	16	17	16	21	

TABLE **2.2**   Recommended Number of Classes for Data Sets of n Measurements*

Number of Classes	Size, n, of the Data Set
2	$1 \leq n < 4$
3	$4 \leq n < 8$
4	$8 \leq n < 16$
5	$16 \leq n < 32$
6	$32 \leq n < 64$
7	$64 \leq n < 128$
8	$128 \leq n < 256$
9	$256 \leq n < 528$
10	$528 \leq n < 1056$

*For the sake of completeness we have included small values of n in this table. However, we do not recommend constructing a histogram with fewer than 16 measurements.

TABLE **2.3**   Seven Nonoverlapping Classes for a Frequency Distribution of the 65 Payment Times

Class 1	10 days to less than 13 days
Class 2	13 days to less than 16 days
Class 3	16 days to less than 19 days
Class 4	19 days to less than 22 days
Class 5	22 days to less than 25 days
Class 6	25 days to less than 28 days
Class 7	28 days to less than 31 days

Because the largest and smallest payment times in Table 2.1 are 29 days and 10 days, the class length is $(29 - 10)/7 = 2.7143$. This says that in order to include the smallest and largest payment times in the 7 classes, each class must have a length of at least 2.7143. To obtain a more convenient class length, we round this value. Often the class length is rounded to the precision of the measurements, although this is a matter of preference. For instance, because the payment times are measured in days, we will round the class length from 2.7143 to 3 days.

Step 3: Form nonoverlapping classes of equal width   We can form the classes of the frequency distribution by defining the **boundaries** of the classes. To find the first class boundary, we find the smallest payment time in Table 2.1, which is 10 days. This value is the lower boundary of the first class. Adding the class length of 3 to this lower boundary, we obtain $10 + 3 = 13$, which is the upper boundary of the first class and the lower boundary of the second class. Similarly, the upper boundary of the second class and the lower boundary of the third class are $13 + 3 = 16$. Continuing in this fashion, the lower boundaries of the remaining classes are 19, 22, 25, and 28. Adding the class length 3 to the lower boundary of the last class gives us the upper boundary of the last class, 31. These boundaries define seven nonoverlapping classes for the frequency distribution. We summarize these classes in Table 2.3. For instance, the first class—10 days to less than 13 days—includes the payment times 10, 11, and 12 days; the second class—13 days to less than 16 days—includes the payment times 13, 14, and 15 days; and so forth. Notice that the largest *observed* payment time—29 days—is contained in the last class. Generally speaking, the guidelines we have given for forming classes are not inflexible rules. Rather, they are intended to help us find reasonable classes. Finally, the method we have used for forming classes results in classes of equal length. (Example 2.3 on page 31 demonstrates a histogram with classes of unequal length.)

Step 4: Tally and count the number of measurements in each class   Having formed the classes, we now count the number of measurements that fall into each class.

After examining all 65 payment times, we find the **frequency** for each class by counting the number recorded for the class. For instance, counting the number for the class "13 to <16," we obtain the frequency 14 for this class. The frequencies for all seven classes are summarized in Table 2.4. This summary is the **frequency distribution** for the 65 payment times. Table 2.4 also gives the **relative frequency** and the **percent frequency** for each of the seven classes. The **relative frequency** of a class is the proportion (fraction) of the total number of measurements that are in the class. For example, there are 14 payment times in the second class, so its relative frequency is $14/65 = 0.2154$. This says that the proportion of the 65 payment times that are in the second class is 0.2154, or, equivalently, that $100(0.2154)\% = 21.54\%$ of the payment times are in the second class. A list of all of the classes—along with each class's

TABLE **2.4** Frequency Distributions of the 65 Payment Times

Class	Frequency	Relative Frequency	Percent Frequency
10 to < 13	3	3/65 = 0.0462	4.62%
13 to < 16	14	14/65 = 0.2154	21.54
16 to < 19	23	0.3538	35.38
19 to < 22	12	0.1846	18.46
22 to < 25	8	0.1231	12.31
25 to < 28	4	0.0615	6.15
28 to < 31	1	0.0154	1.54

FIGURE **2.2** A Frequency Histogram of the 65 Payment Times

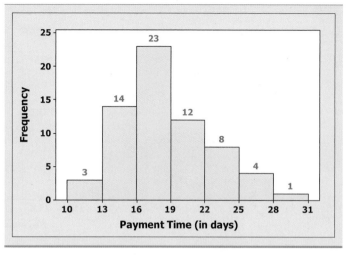

relative frequency—is called a **relative frequency distribution**. A list of all of the classes—along with each class percent frequency—is called a **percent frequency distribution**.

Step 5: Graph the histogram We can graphically portray the distribution of payment times by drawing a **histogram**. The histogram can be constructed using the frequency, relative frequency, or percent frequency distribution. To set up the histogram, we draw rectangles that correspond to the classes. The base of the rectangle corresponding to a class represents the payment times in the class. The height of the rectangle can represent the class frequency, relative frequency, or percent frequency.

We have drawn a **frequency histogram** of the 65 payment times in Figure 2.2. The first (leftmost) rectangle, or "bar," of the histogram represents the payment times 10, 11, and 12. Looking at Figure 2.2, we see that the base of this rectangle is drawn from the lower boundary (10) of the first class in the frequency distribution of payment times to the lower boundary (13) of the second class. The height of this rectangle tells us that the frequency of the first class is 3. The second histogram rectangle represents payment times 13, 14, and 15. Its base is drawn from the lower boundary (13) of the second class to the lower boundary (16) of the third class, and its height tells us that the frequency of the second class is 14. The other histogram bars are constructed similarly. Notice that there are no gaps between the adjacent rectangles in the histogram. Here, although the payment times are in days, the fact that the histogram bars touch each other emphasizes that a payment time could (in theory) be any number on the horizontal axis. In general, histograms are drawn so that adjacent bars touch each other.

Looking at the frequency distribution in Table 2.4 and the frequency histogram in Figure 2.2, we can describe the payment times:

1 None of the payment times exceed the industry standard of 30 days. (Actually, all of the payment times are less than 30—remember that the largest payment time is 29 days.)

2 The payment times are concentrated between 13 and 24 days (57 of the 65, or (57/65) × 100 = 87.69%, of the payment times are in this range).

3 More payment times are in the class "16 to < 19" than are in any other class (23 payment times are in this class).

Notice that the frequency distribution and histogram allow us to make some helpful conclusions about the payment times, whereas looking at the raw data (the payment times in Table 2.1) did not.

A **relative frequency histogram** and a **percent frequency histogram** of the payment times would both be drawn like Figure 2.2 except that the heights of the rectangles represent, respectively,

LO2

FIGURE 2.3   A Percent Frequency Histogram of the 65 Payment Times

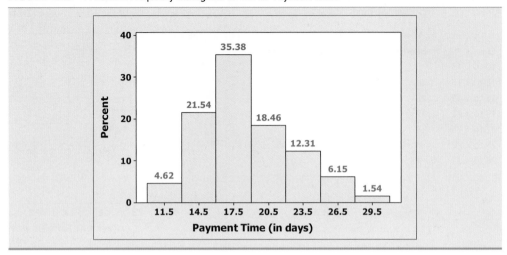

the relative frequencies and the percent frequencies in Table 2.4. For example, Figure 2.3 gives a percent frequency histogram of the payment times. This histogram also illustrates that we sometimes label the classes on the horizontal axis using the **class midpoints**. Each class midpoint is exactly halfway between the boundaries of its class. For instance, the midpoint of the first class, 11.5, is halfway between the class boundaries 10 and 13. The midpoint of the second class, 14.5, is halfway between the class boundaries 13 and 16. The other class midpoints are found similarly. The percent frequency distribution of Figure 2.3 tells us that 21.54 percent of the payment times are in the second class (which has midpoint 14.5 and represents the payment times 13, 14, and 15).

In the following box we summarize the steps needed to set up a frequency distribution and histogram:

Constructing Frequency Distributions and Histograms

1   Find the number of classes. Generally, the number of classes K should equal the smallest whole number that makes the quantity 2^K greater than the total number of measurements n.

2   Compute the **class length**:

$$\frac{\text{largest measurement} - \text{smallest measurement}}{K}.$$

If desired, round this value to obtain a more convenient class length.

3   Form nonoverlapping classes of equal length. Form the classes by finding the **class boundaries**. The lower boundary of the first class is the smallest measurement in the data set. Add the class length to this boundary to obtain the next boundary. Successive boundaries are found by repeatedly adding the class length until the upper boundary of the last (Kth) class is found.

4   Tally and count the number of measurements in each class. The **frequency** for each class is the count of the number of measurements in the class. The **relative frequency** for each class is the fraction of measurements in the class. The **percent frequency** for each class is its relative frequency multiplied by 100 percent.

5   Graph the histogram. To draw a **frequency histogram**, plot each frequency as the height of a rectangle positioned over its corresponding class. Use the class boundaries to separate adjacent rectangles. A **relative frequency histogram** and a **percent histogram** are graphed in the same way except that the heights of the rectangles are, respectively, the relative frequencies and the percent frequencies.

Although we have given a procedure for determining the number of classes, it is often desirable to let the nature of the problem determine the classes. For example, to construct a histogram describing the ages of the residents of a certain city, it might be reasonable to use classes with ten-year lengths (that is, under 10 years, 10–19 years, 20–29 years, 30–39 years, and so on), or to have narrower class lengths with an open-ended class, as is given in the next example.

Example 2.3 Age Groupings by Statistics Canada

Statistics Canada (http://www.statcan.gc.ca) provides demographic information for communities based on the most recent population census. Figure 2.4 reports the frequency of age, grouped into classes. The group labelled "85+" is considered to be an **open class** in which no upper limit is given. Figure 2.4 provides the age groupings and frequency values for London, Ontario. Also in Figure 2.4 is the corresponding histogram. Another example of a histogram with unequal class lengths would be grade distributions in a course. For example, if a professor records the distribution of grades by letters, then an F (0 percent to 49 percent) is not the same length as a D (50 percent to 59 percent).

FIGURE **2.4** Age Frequencies in London, Ontario

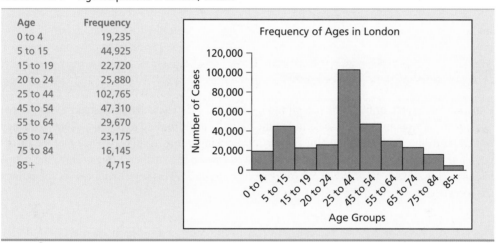

Age	Frequency
0 to 4	19,235
5 to 15	44,925
15 to 19	22,720
20 to 24	25,880
25 to 44	102,765
45 to 54	47,310
55 to 64	29,670
65 to 74	23,175
75 to 84	16,145
85+	4,715

Some common population shapes We often construct a stem-and-leaf display or histogram for a sample to make inferences about the shape of the sampled population. It is sometimes useful to describe the shape of a population by using a smooth curve. If the stem-and-leaf display and/or the histogram look quite symmetrical and bell-shaped, then it is reasonable to infer that the population can be described by a symmetrical, bell-shaped curve. Such a curve is shown in Figure 2.5 on the next page. Several different kinds of symmetrical, bell-shaped curves are used to describe populations. One such curve that is particularly useful is called the **normal curve**.

To intuitively understand the normal curve, recall from our discussion of histograms that if we use classes of equal lengths, then the height of the rectangle over a given class represents the relative proportion of measurements in the class. Similarly, *the height of the normal curve over a given point represents the relative proportion of population measurements that are near the given point.*

Many real populations are distributed according to the symmetrical, bell-shaped normal curve. We say that such populations are **normally distributed**. However, instead of being symmetrical and bell-shaped, the overall shape of a population may be **positively skewed** (with a tail to the right), as is the curve in Figure 2.6 on the next page, or **negatively skewed** (with

FIGURE 2.5
A Symmetrical,
Bell-Shaped Curve

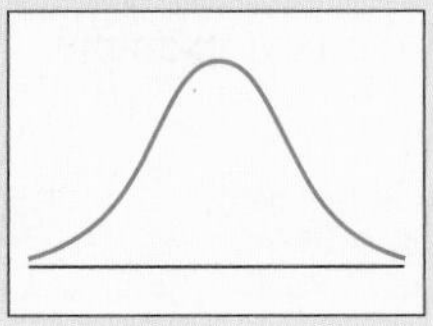

FIGURE 2.6
A Curve that Is Positively
Skewed (with a Tail to the Right)

FIGURE 2.7
A Curve that Is Negatively Skewed
(with a Tail to the Left)

LO3

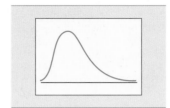

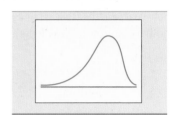

a tail to the left), as is the curve in Figure 2.7. Many other population shapes are also possible. If the stem-and-leaf display and/or the histogram of a random sample of measurements look like one of these curves, this suggests that the curve describes the overall shape of the entire population of measurements. In this case, the curve is called the **relative frequency curve** that describes the population. Said another way, *the population is distributed according to the relative frequency curve.* In a relative frequency curve, *the height of the curve over a given point represents the relative proportion of population measurements that are near the given point.* Example 2.4 demonstrates an asymmetrical distribution.

Example 2.4 The Marketing Research Case

Consider the sample of 60 bottle design ratings in Table 2.5. These bottle design ratings are the composites of responses to the scale in Figure 2.8 and range from 20 to 35. A percent frequency histogram of the ratings is shown in Figure 2.9. Looking at this display, we see that the distribution of bottle design ratings seems to be skewed toward the smaller ratings. Thus, the distribution is *skewed with a tail to the left* (or *negatively skewed*). This says that a few of the ratings are somewhat lower than the rest of the ratings.

TABLE 2.5   A Sample of Bottle Design Ratings (Composite Scores for a Systematic Sample
of 60 Shoppers)

34	33	33	29	26	33	28	25	32	33
32	25	27	33	22	27	32	33	32	29
24	30	20	34	31	32	30	35	33	31
32	28	30	31	31	33	29	27	34	31
31	28	33	31	32	28	26	29	32	34
32	30	34	32	30	30	32	31	29	33

FIGURE 2.8   The Bottle Design Survey Instrument

Please circle the response that most accurately describes whether you agree or disagree with each statement about the bottle you have examined.

Statement	Strongly Disagree						Strongly Agree
The size of this bottle is convenient.	1	2	3	4	5	6	7
The contoured shape of this bottle is easy to handle.	1	2	3	4	5	6	7
The label on this bottle is easy to read.	1	2	3	4	5	6	7
This bottle is easy to open.	1	2	3	4	5	6	7
Based on its overall appeal, I like this bottle design.	1	2	3	4	5	6	7

FIGURE **2.9**   MegaStat Output of 60 Bottle Design Ratings

Frequency Distribution—Quantitative

Rating							cumulative	
lower		upper	midpoint	width	frequency	percent	frequency	percent
20	<	22	21	2	1	1.7	1	1.7
22	<	24	23	2	1	1.7	2	3.3
24	<	26	25	2	3	5.0	5	8.3
26	<	28	27	2	5	8.3	10	16.7
28	<	30	29	2	9	15.0	19	31.7
30	<	32	31	2	14	23.3	33	55.0
32	<	34	33	2	21	35.0	54	90.0
34	<	36	35	2	6	10.0	60	100.0
					60	100.0		

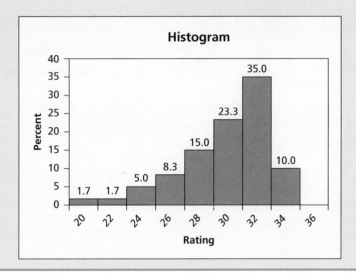

Further graphical techniques, and detecting outliers One of the authors of this book recently taught a course in business statistics to a class of 40 students. A comparison of the scores received by these students on the first two 100-point exams is given by the two **dot plots** in Figure 2.10. Note that to make each dot plot, we draw a number line on which we measure the exam scores. We then place dots above the number line to represent the exam scores. The number of dots located above a particular exam score indicates how many students received that exam score. After noticing the two-peaked appearance of the dot plot for Exam 1, the author investigated and found that most of the students who scored less than 70 on the exam had not been attending class regularly. Because of this, the author reminded the students about the importance of attending class. The dot plot for Exam 2 is single-peaked and indicates a considerable improvement in student performance. Of course, this does not prove that attending class was solely responsible for the improved performance. However, many students told the author that attending class improved their test scores.

FIGURE **2.10**   Dot Plots of the Scores on Exams 1 and 2

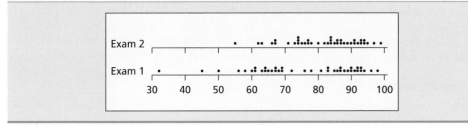

LO4   Stem-and-leaf displays and dot plots are useful for detecting **outliers**, which are unusually large or small observations that are well separated from the remaining observations. For example, the dot plot for Exam 1 indicates that the score 32 seems unusually low. How we handle an outlier depends on its cause. If the outlier results from a measurement error or an error in recording or processing the data, it should be corrected. If the error cannot be corrected, it should be discarded. If an outlier is not the result of an error in measuring or recording the data, its cause may reveal important information. For example, the outlying exam score of 32 convinced the author that the student needed a tutor. After working with a tutor, the student showed considerable improvement on Exam 2. A more precise way to detect outliers is presented in Section 2.4.

Exercises for Section 2.1

CONCEPTS

2.1   What does each population shape look like? Describe each shape and then draw a picture to illustrate.
   a. Symmetrical and bell-shaped.
   b. Double-peaked.
   c. Negatively skewed (with a tail to the left).
   d. Positively skewed (with a tail to the right).

2.2   Explain each of the following:
   a. How to construct a stem-and-leaf display, a histogram, and a dot plot.
   b. How class limits, class boundaries, and class midpoints differ.
   c. What outliers are and how they are handled.

METHODS AND APPLICATIONS

2.3   Given in Table 2.6 are the median total incomes by metropolitan areas for Canada for 2003 to 2007 as reported by Statistics Canada (http://www40.statcan.gc.ca/l01/cst01/famil107a-eng.htm). Construct stem-and-leaf plots for 2003 and 2007 (using a stem unit of $10,000). Comparing the two plots, what can you say about the median income values?

2.4   **THE VIDEO GAME SATISFACTION RATING CASE**

Table 2.7 presents the satisfaction ratings for the XYZ-Box video game system that have been given by 65 randomly selected purchasers. Figure 2.11 gives the MegaStat output of a stem-and-leaf display, and Figure 2.12 on page 36 gives the Excel output of a frequency histogram of the 65 satisfaction ratings.
   a. Verify that the classes and class frequencies given in Figure 2.12 are those obtained by using the histogram construction method discussed in this section.
   b. Using Figures 2.11 and 2.12, infer the shape of the relative frequency distribution describing the population of all possible customer satisfaction ratings for the XYZ-Box video game system.
   c. Construct a relative frequency histogram of the 65 satisfaction ratings.

2.5   **THE BANK CUSTOMER WAITING TIME CASE**

Table 2.8 on page 36 presents the waiting times for teller service during peak business hours of 100 randomly selected bank customers. Figure 2.13 on page 36 gives the Excel output of a frequency histogram of the 100 waiting times.
   a. Verify that the class boundaries and the class frequencies (in Figure 2.13) are those obtained by using the histogram construction method discussed in this section.
   b. Using Figure 2.13, infer the shape of the relative frequency distribution describing the population of all possible customer waiting times during peak business hours.

2.6   **THE TRASH BAG CASE**

Table 2.9 on page 37 presents the breaking strengths of 40 trash bags selected during a 40-hour pilot production run. Figure 2.14 on page 37 gives the MegaStat output of a relative frequency histogram and Figure 2.15 on page 37 gives the MegaStat output of a stem-and-leaf display of the 40 breaking strengths.
   a. Verify that the classes and class relative frequencies given in Figure 2.14 are those obtained by using the histogram construction method discussed in this section.
   b. Using Figures 2.14 and 2.15, infer the shape of the relative frequency distribution describing the population of all possible trash bag breaking strengths.

2.7   Babe Ruth's record of 60 home runs in a single year was broken by Roger Maris, who hit 61 home runs in 1961. The yearly home run totals for Ruth in his career as a New York Yankee are (arranged in increasing order) 22, 25, 34, 35, 41, 41, 46, 46, 46, 47, 49, 54, 54, 59, and 60. The yearly home run totals for Maris over his career in the American League are (arranged in increasing order) 8, 13, 14, 16, 23, 26, 28, 33, 39, and 61. Compare Ruth's and Maris's home run totals by constructing a back-to-back stem-and-leaf display. What would you conclude about Maris's record-breaking year?

TABLE 2.6 Median Total Income, by Family Type, by Census Metropolitan Area (All Census Families)

	2003	2004	2005	2006	2007
			All census families*		
			$		
Median total income					
Canada	56,000	58,100	60,600	63,600	66,550
St. John's (NL)	55,800	57,100	59,800	63,100	67,760
Halifax (NS)	59,200	61,400	64,700	67,600	70,610
Saint John (NB)	52,900	55,200	57,000	59,600	62,860
Saguenay (QC)	54,300	56,400	58,900	60,900	64,010
Québec (QC)	59,600	61,800	64,900	67,100	70,920
Sherbrooke (QC)	52,100	53,500	56,100	57,000	59,490
Trois-Rivières (QC)	50,500	51,600	55,100	56,900	59,640
Montréal (QC)	54,400	56,100	58,600	60,800	63,790
Ottawa–Gatineau (QC part, ON–QC)	62,800	64,700	68,500	70,900	74,670
Ottawa–Gatineau (ON part, ON–QC)	74,500	77,000	80,300	84,000	87,930
Kingston (ON)	61,900	63,700	66,400	69,100	71,980
Oshawa (ON)	72,400	75,000	76,800	78,900	81,570
Toronto (ON)	58,500	60,100	61,800	63,800	66,560
Hamilton (ON)	65,200	67,100	69,500	71,600	74,480
St. Catharines–Niagara (ON)	57,300	58,900	60,600	62,500	64,300
Kitchener (ON)	67,000	69,200	71,100	72,800	74,750
London (ON)	61,200	63,600	66,100	68,400	70,720
Windsor (ON)	67,800	68,400	69,700	70,000	70,810
Greater Sudbury / Grand Sudbury (ON)	59,200	62,300	66,100	69,700	74,840
Thunder Bay (ON)	63,400	64,600	67,200	69,400	71,480
Winnipeg (MB)	57,300	59,400	61,600	64,700	67,900
Regina (SK)	63,300	66,000	68,500	72,200	77,170
Saskatoon (SK)	57,500	59,900	63,600	68,300	72,970
Calgary (AB)	67,800	71,100	75,400	83,500	87,970
Edmonton (AB)	64,800	68,100	72,600	79,300	83,460
Abbotsford (BC)	51,000	53,700	55,700	58,900	61,970
Vancouver (BC)	54,100	56,200	58,800	62,900	66,330
Victoria (BC)	61,700	64,200	66,900	71,500	74,730

*Census families include couple families, with or without children, and lone-parent families.

Source: Statistics Canada, CANSIM, table (for fee) 111-0009. Last modified: 2010-03-29.

TABLE 2.7 Composite Scores for the Video Game Satisfaction Rating Case 🎮

39	44	46	44	44
45	42	45	44	42
38	46	45	45	47
42	40	46	44	43
42	47	43	46	45
41	44	47	48	
38	43	43	44	
42	45	41	41	
46	45	40	45	
44	40	43	44	
40	46	44	44	
39	41	41	44	
40	43	38	46	
42	39	43	39	
45	43	36	41	

FIGURE 2.11 MegaStat Stem-and-Leaf Display of the 65 Satisfaction Ratings for Exercise 2.4

Stem and Leaf plot for Rating		
stem unit = 1 leaf unit = 0.1		
Frequency	**Stem**	**Leaf**
1	36	0
0	37	
3	38	000
4	39	0000
5	40	00000
6	41	000000
6	42	000000
8	43	00000000
12	44	000000000000
9	45	000000000
7	46	0000000
3	47	000
1	48	0
65		

FIGURE 2.12   Excel Frequency Histogram of the 65 Satisfaction Ratings for Exercise 2.4

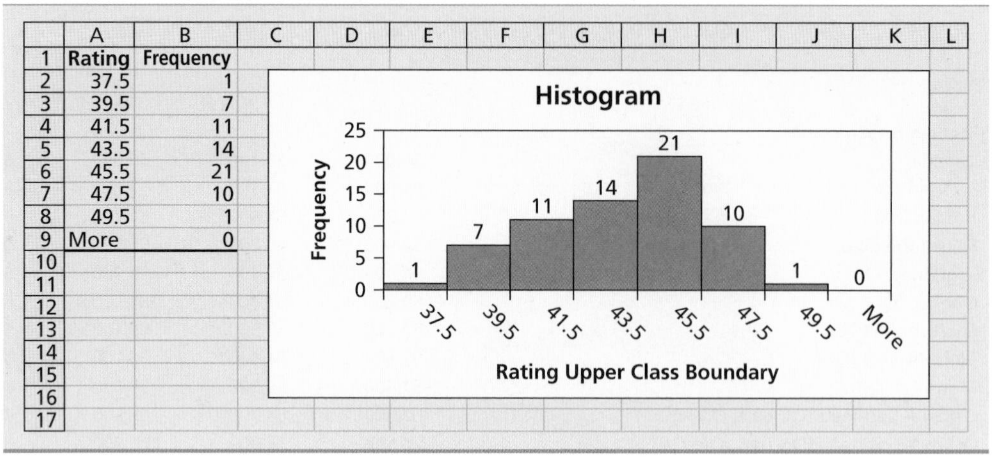

	A	B	C	D	E	F	G	H	I	J	K	L
1	Rating	Frequency										
2	37.5	1										
3	39.5	7										
4	41.5	11										
5	43.5	14										
6	45.5	21										
7	47.5	10										
8	49.5	1										
9	More	0										
10												
11												
12												
13												
14												
15												
16												
17												

Histogram

(Frequency histogram: bars at 37.5 = 1, 39.5 = 7, 41.5 = 11, 43.5 = 14, 45.5 = 21, 47.5 = 10, 49.5 = 1, More = 0; x-axis: Rating Upper Class Boundary; y-axis: Frequency)

TABLE 2.8   Waiting Times (in Minutes) for the Bank Customer Waiting Time Case

1.6	6.2	3.2	5.6	7.9	6.1	7.2
6.6	5.4	6.5	4.4	1.1	3.8	7.3
5.6	4.9	2.3	4.5	7.2	10.7	4.1
5.1	5.4	8.7	6.7	2.9	7.5	6.7
3.9	0.8	4.7	8.1	9.1	7.0	3.5
4.6	2.5	3.6	4.3	7.7	5.3	6.3
6.5	8.3	2.7	2.2	4.0	4.5	4.3
6.4	6.1	3.7	5.8	1.4	4.5	3.8
8.6	6.3	0.4	8.6	7.8	1.8	5.1
4.2	6.8	10.2	2.0	5.2	3.7	5.5
5.8	9.8	2.8	8.0	8.4	4.0	
3.4	2.9	11.6	9.5	6.3	5.7	
9.3	10.9	4.3	1.3	4.4	2.4	
7.4	4.7	3.1	4.8	5.2	9.2	
1.8	3.9	5.8	9.9	7.4	5.0	

FIGURE 2.13   Excel Frequency Histogram of the 100 Waiting Times for Exercise 2.5

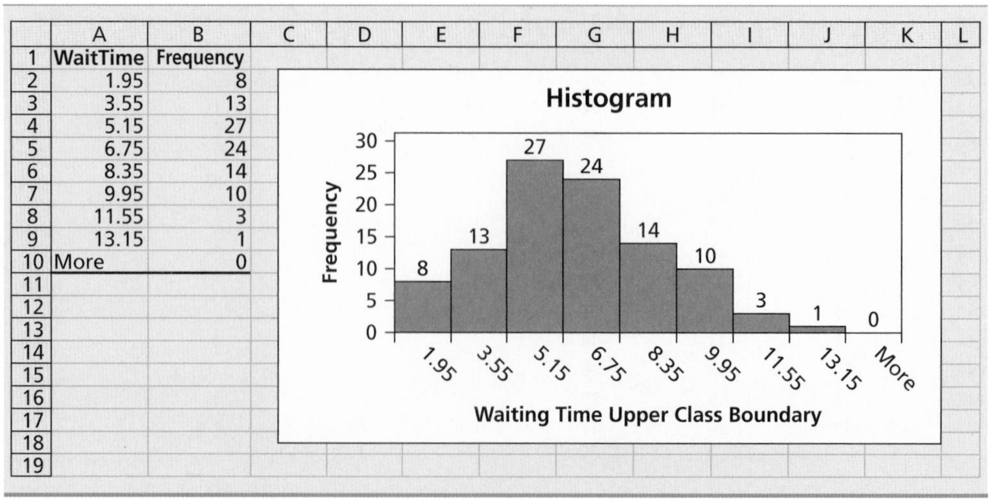

	A	B	C	D	E	F	G	H	I	J	K	L
1	WaitTime	Frequency										
2	1.95	8										
3	3.55	13										
4	5.15	27										
5	6.75	24										
6	8.35	14										
7	9.95	10										
8	11.55	3										
9	13.15	1										
10	More	0										
11												
12												
13												
14												
15												
16												
17												
18												
19												

Histogram

(Frequency histogram: bars at 1.95 = 8, 3.55 = 13, 5.15 = 27, 6.75 = 24, 8.35 = 14, 9.95 = 10, 11.55 = 3, 13.15 = 1, More = 0; x-axis: Waiting Time Upper Class Boundary; y-axis: Frequency)

FIGURE 2.14 MegaStat Relative Frequency Histogram of the 40 Breaking Strengths for Exercise 2.6

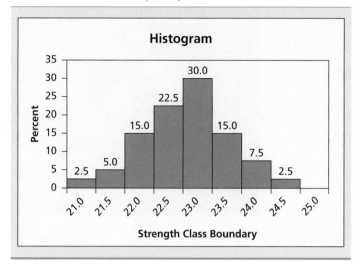

FIGURE 2.15 MegaStat Stem-and-Leaf Display of the Breaking Strengths for Exercise 2.6

Stem and Leaf plot for Strength		
	stem unit = 1	leaf unit = 0.1
Frequency	Stem	Leaf
1	21	3
2	21	6 9
6	22	0 0 2 3 4 4
9	22	5 5 5 6 7 7 8 8 9
12	23	0 0 0 1 1 1 2 2 3 3 4 4
6	23	5 6 6 8 9 9
3	24	1 2 3
1	24	5
40		

TABLE 2.9 Trash Bag Breaking Strengths

22.0	23.9	23.0	22.5
23.8	21.6	21.9	23.6
24.3	23.1	23.4	23.6
23.0	22.6	22.3	22.2
22.9	22.7	23.5	21.3
22.5	23.1	24.2	23.3
23.2	24.1	23.2	22.4
22.0	23.1	23.9	24.5
23.0	22.7	23.3	22.4
22.8	22.8	22.5	23.4

2.8 In this exercise, you will consider how to deal with class lengths that are unequal (and with open-ended classes) when setting up histograms. Data are often published in this form, and you will wish to construct a histogram. An example is provided by data concerning the benefits of ISO 9000 registration published by CEEM Information Services. According to CEEM:[1]

> ISO 9000 is a series of international standards for quality assurance management systems. It establishes the organizational structure and processes for assuring that the production of goods or services meet a consistent and agreed-upon level of quality for a company's customers.

CEEM presents the results of a Quality Systems Update/ Deloitte & Touche survey of ISO 9000–registered companies conducted in July 1993. Included in the results is a summary of the total annual savings associated with ISO 9000 implementation for surveyed companies. The findings (in the form of a frequency distribution of ISO 9000 savings) are given in the next column. Notice that the classes in this distribution have unequal lengths and that there is an open-ended class (> $500K).

To construct a histogram for these data, we select one of the classes as a base. It is often convenient to choose the shortest class as the base (although it is not necessary to do so). Using this choice, the 0 to $10K class is the base. This means that we will draw a rectangle over the 0 to $10K class with a height equal to 162 (the frequency given for this class in the published data). Because the other classes are longer than the base, the heights of the rectangles above these classes will be adjusted. Remembering that the area of a rectangle positioned over a particular class should represent the relative proportion of measurements in the class, we proceed as follows. The length of the $10K to $25K class differs from the base class by a factor of $(25 - 10)/(10 - 0) = 3/2$, and, therefore, we make the height of the rectangle over the $10K to $25K class equal to $(2/3)(62) = 41.333$. Similarly, the length of the $25K to $50K class differs from the length of the base class by a factor of $(50 - 25)/(10 - 0) = 5/2$, and, therefore, we make the height of the rectangle over the $25K to $50K class equal to $(2/5)(53) = 21.2$.

Annual Savings	Number of Companies
0 to $10K	162
$10K to $25K	62
$25K to $50K	53
$50K to $100K	60
$100K to $150K	24
$150K to $200K	19
$200K to $250K	22
$250K to $500K	21
(>$500K)	37

Note: K = 1,000.

[1]Source: *Is ISO 9000 for You?* (Fairfax, VA: CEEM Information Services).

a. Use the procedure just outlined to find the heights of the rectangles drawn over all the other classes (with the exception of the open-ended class, > $500K).

b. Draw the appropriate rectangles over the classes (except for > $500K). Note that the $250K to $500K class is a lot longer than the others. This is fine as long as we adjust its rectangle's height.

c. We complete the histogram by placing a star (*) to the right of $500K on the scale of measurements and by noting "37" next to the * to indicate 37 companies saved more than $500K. Complete the histogram by doing this.

2.9 A basketball player practises free throws by taking 25 shots each day. He records the number of shots missed each day in order to track his progress. The numbers of shots missed on days 1 through 30 are 17, 15, 16, 18, 14, 15, 13, 12, 10, 11, 11, 10, 9, 10, 9, 9, 9, 10, 8, 10, 6, 8, 9, 8, 7, 9, 8, 7, 5, 8. Construct a stem-and-leaf display and a runs plot of the numbers of missed shots. Do you think that the stem-and-leaf

display is representative of the numbers of shots that the player will miss on future days? Why or why not?

2.2 DESCRIBING CENTRAL TENDENCY

The mean, median, and mode In addition to describing the shape of the distribution of a sample or population of measurements, we also describe the data set's **central tendency**. A measure of central tendency represents the **centre** or **middle** of the data.

One important measure of central tendency for a population of measurements is the **population mean**.

CHAPTER 3

The **population mean**, which is denoted by the Greek letter μ (*mu*, pronounced *mew*) is the average of the population measurements.

More precisely, the population mean is calculated by adding all the population measurements and then dividing the resulting sum by the number of population measurements (N). For instance, consider the population of revenues for the five biggest companies in Canada in 2008 as reported by *Report on Business Magazine*. The companies and revenues (to the nearest billion dollars) are as follows:

Company	Revenue (Billions)
Royal Bank of Canada	$38
Power Corp. of Canada	37
Power Financial	36
Manulife Financial	34
Great-West Life Co.	34

The mean, μ, of this population of revenues is

$$\mu = \frac{38 + 37 + 36 + 34 + 34}{5} = \frac{179}{5} = \$35.8 \text{ billion.}$$

This population of five revenues is small, so it is possible to compute the population mean. Often, however, a population is very large and we cannot obtain a measurement for each population unit. Therefore, we cannot compute the population mean. In such a case, we must estimate the population mean by using a sample of measurements.

In order to understand how to estimate a population mean, we must realize that the population mean is a **population parameter**.

A **population parameter** is a number calculated using the population measurements that describes some aspect of the population. That is, a population parameter is a descriptive measure of the population.

There are many population parameters, and we discuss several of them in this chapter. The simplest way to estimate a population parameter is to make what is called a **point estimate**.

A **point estimate** is a one-number estimate of the value of a population parameter.

Although a point estimate is a guess of a population parameter's value, it is not a blind guess. Rather, it is an educated guess based on sample data. One way to find a point estimate of a population parameter is to use a **sample statistic**.

A **sample statistic** is a number calculated using the sample measurements that describes some aspect of the sample. That is, a sample statistic is a descriptive measure of the sample.

The sample statistic that we use to estimate the population mean is the **sample mean**, which is denoted as $\bar{x}$ (x bar) or M (M = mean, commonly used in the social sciences) and is the average of the sample measurements.

In order to write a formula for the sample mean, we employ the letter n to represent the number of sample measurements, and we refer to n as the **sample size** (N is used for the size of the population). Furthermore, we denote the sample measurements as $x_1, x_2, \ldots, x_n$. Here x_1 is the first sample measurement, x_2 is the second sample measurement, and so forth. We denote the last sample measurement as x_n. Moreover, when we write formulas we often use summation notation for convenience. For instance, we write the sum of the sample measurements

$$x_1 + x_2 + \cdots + x_n$$

as $\sum_{i=1}^{n} x_i$. Here the Greek letter Σ (*sigma*) says that we are writing out a sum of *like terms*. The general term x_i says that all the terms we are adding up look like x_i. The index $i = 1$ to n says that we let the subscript i in the general term x_i range from 1 to n, and we add up all these terms. Thus,

$$\sum_{i=1}^{n} x_i = x_1 + x_2 + \cdots + x_n.$$

The **sample mean** $\bar{x}$ is defined to be

LO5

$$\bar{x} = \frac{\sum_{i=1}^{n} x_i}{n} = \frac{x_1 + x_2 + \cdots + x_n}{n}$$

and is the **point estimate of the population mean μ.**

Example 2.5 Hourly Wages for Some Job Types in Ontario

Statistics Canada (http://www.statcan.gc.ca) provides lists of average hourly wages for types of jobs in different provinces in Canada. The September 2009 statistics for Ontario suggest that the average hourly wage for certain vocational areas varies. For example, for management positions, the average hourly wage is \$35.58, for business and finance it is \$21.16, for natural and applied sciences it is \$31.43, for health occupations it is \$26.58, and for sales it is \$14.54. To calculate the average of these values, calculate the sum of the five hourly rates and divide the total by 5:

$$\sum_{i=1}^{5} x_i = x_1 + x_2 + x_3 + x_4 + x_5$$
$$= 35.58 + 21.16 + 31.43 + 26.58 + 14.54$$
$$= 129.29,$$
$$\bar{x} = \frac{129.29}{5} = 25.86.$$

The results suggest that the average hourly rate of the five vocational types in Ontario is \$25.86 and represents a point estimate of the average hourly wages. Due to concerns such as rounding, underreporting, and failing to include all possible vocational types, the point estimate may be somewhat unreliable.

In later chapters, we discuss how to assess the **reliability** of the sample mean and how to use a measure of reliability to decide whether sample information provides definitive evidence. Also available on *Connect* is an explanation of the geometric mean, which provides a measure of the rate of change exhibited by a variable over time.

Another descriptive measure of the central tendency of a population or a sample of measurements is the **median** (M_d). Intuitively, the median divides a population or sample into two roughly equal parts.[2]

Consider a population or a sample of measurements, and arrange the measurements in increasing order. The **median**, M_d, is found as follows:

1   If the number of measurements is odd, the median is the middle measurement in the ordering.

2   If the number of measurements is even, the median is the average of the two middle measurements in the ordering.

Example 2.6 Personal Expenditures

Statistics Canada (http://www.statcan.gc.ca) compiles data on personal expenditures. Listed below are the average annual amounts people in Canada spent on rent for the years 1997 to 2005 (covering nine years):

6,606   6,806   7,043   7,265   (7,523)   7,873   8,207   8,533   8,856

Because the number of annual rent payment values is odd, the median of this sample is the middle value in the list (note that average annual rent has increased from 1997 to 2005, so the data are already in ascending order). The median is therefore $7,523 (it is circled).

Example 2.7 DVD Recorder Satisfaction

The manufacturer of a DVD recorder randomly selects a sample of 20 purchasers who have owned the recorder for one year. Each purchaser in the sample is asked to rank their satisfaction with the recorder on the following ten-point scale:

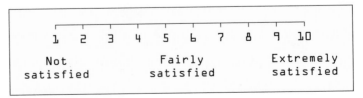

---

[2]To remember the median, recall that it is the same name given to the boundary separating highway lanes, and there is typically an equal number of lanes on either side of the median.

Suppose that the following rankings, arranged in increasing order, are obtained:

1   3   5   5   7   8   8   8   8   ⑧   ⑧   9   9   9   9   9   10   10   10   10

Because the number of satisfaction ratings is even, the median of this sample is the average of the two middle ratings. Both of these ratings are 8—they are circled. Therefore, the median of this sample is 8, and we estimate that the median satisfaction rating of all the DVD recorder owners is 8. This estimated median satisfaction rating seems relatively high. Note, however, that there are four rather low individual satisfaction ratings: 1, 3, 5, and 5. This suggests that some DVD recorders may be of low quality. If the manufacturer wishes to satisfy all of its customers, it must investigate the situation.

BI

A third measure of the central tendency of a population or sample is the **mode**, which is denoted M_o.

The **mode**, M_o, of a population or sample of measurements is the measurement that occurs most frequently.

For example, the mode of the satisfaction ratings given in Example 2.7 is 8. This is because more purchasers (six) gave the DVD recorder a rating of 8 than any other rating. Sometimes the highest frequency occurs at two or more different measurements. When this happens, two or more modes exist. When exactly two modes exist, we say the data are **bimodal**. When more than two modes exist, we say the data are **multimodal**. Finally, when data are presented in classes (such as in a frequency histogram), the class with the highest frequency is called the **modal class**.

Comparing the mean, median, and mode In order to compare the mean, median, and mode, look at Figure 2.16. Part (a) of this figure depicts a population described by a symmetrical relative frequency curve. For such a population, the mean (μ), median (M_d), and mode (M_o) are all equal. Note that in this case all three of these quantities are located under the highest point of the curve. It follows that when the frequency distribution of a sample of measurements is approximately symmetrical (normal or mound-shaped), then the sample mean, median, and mode will be nearly the same. For instance, consider a sample of 49 DVD price points, and note that the stem-and-leaf display of these prices is given in the page margin. Because the number of prices is odd, the median is the middle price, the 25th price. Counting 25 prices from the top of the stem-and-leaf display, we find that the median is 31.6. Furthermore, since the stem-and-leaf display is fairly symmetrical, this sample median is approximately equal to the sample mean, which is 31.55.

DVD Prices

29	8
30	1344
30	5666889
31	001233444
㉛	555⑥6777889
32	0001122344
32	556788
33	3

FIGURE **2.16**   Relationships among the Mean, μ; the Median, M_d; and the Mode, M_o

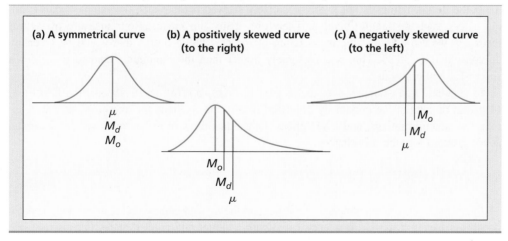

Salaries

```
12 | 7
13 | 2 8
14 | 1 4 6
15 | 2 4
16 | 2
17 | 1 7
18 |
19 | 2
20 |
21 |
22 |
23 |
24 | 1
```

Ratings

```
 1 | 0
 2 |
 3 | 0
 4 |
 5 | 0 0
 6 |
 7 | 0
 8 | 0 0 0 0 0 0
 9 | 0 0 0 0 0
10 | 0 0 0 0
```

Figure 2.16(b) depicts a population that is positively skewed (to the right). Here the population mean is larger than the population median, and the population median is larger than the population mode (the mode is located under the highest point of the relative frequency curve). In this case, the population mean *averages in* the large values in the upper tail of the distribution. Thus, the population mean is more affected by these large values than is the population median. To understand this, note that the stem-and-leaf display of a sample of 13 internists' salaries is given in the page margin and is skewed to the right. Here the mean of the 13 salaries, which is 159.769 (or $159,769), is affected by averaging in the large salaries (192 and 241) in the right-hand tail of the distribution. Thus, this mean is larger than the sample median, $152,000. The median is said to be **resistant** to the large salaries 192 and 241 because the value of the median is affected only by the fact that these salaries are the two largest salaries in the sample. The value of the median is not affected by the **exact sizes** of the salaries 192 and 241. For example, if the largest salary were smaller—say 200—the median would remain the same but the mean would decrease. If the largest salary were larger—say 300—the median would also remain the same but the mean would increase. Therefore, *the median is resistant to extreme values but the mean is not.*

Figure 2.16(c) depicts a population that is negatively skewed (to the left). Here the population mean is smaller than the population median, and the population median is smaller than the population mode. In this case, the population mean averages in the small values in the lower tail of the distribution, and the mean is more affected by these small values than is the median. For instance, the stem-and-leaf display of a sample of purchaser satisfaction ratings is given in the page margin and is skewed to the left. In this case, the mean of these ratings, which equals 7.7, is affected by averaging in the smaller ratings (1, 3, 5, and 5) in the left-hand tail of the distribution. Thus, the mean is smaller than the sample median, 8.

When a population is positively or negatively skewed (to the right or left) with a very long tail, the population mean can be substantially affected by the extreme values in the tail of the distribution. In such a case, the median might be better than the mean as a measure of central tendency. The following case illustrates that the choice of the mean or the median as a measure of central tendency can depend on the purpose of the study being conducted.

When a population is symmetrical or not highly skewed, then the population mean and the population median are either equal or roughly equal, and both provide a good measure of the population central tendency. In this situation, we usually make inferences about the population mean because much of statistical theory is based on the mean rather than the median. We illustrate these ideas in the following case, which also shows that we can obtain the mean and the median by using Excel and MegaStat outputs.

Example 2.8   The Marketing Research Case

The Excel output in Figure 2.17(a) tells us that the mean and the median of the sample of 60 bottle design ratings are 30.35 and 31, respectively. Because the stem-and-leaf display of the bottle design ratings is not highly negatively skewed (to the left), the sample mean is not much less than the sample median. Therefore, using the mean as our measure of central tendency, we estimate that the mean rating of the new bottle design that would be given by all consumers is 30.35. This is considerably higher than the minimum standard of 25 for a successful bottle design.

To conclude this example, note that Figures 2.17(b), 2.17(c), and 2.18 give the Excel and MegaStat outputs of the previously discussed means and medians for internists' salaries, customer satisfaction ratings, and DVD prices. Other quantities in the outputs will be discussed as we proceed through this chapter.

To conclude this section, note that the mean and the median convey useful information about a population having a relative frequency curve with a sufficiently regular shape. For instance, the

FIGURE 2.17 Excel Outputs of Statistics Describing Three Data Sets

(a) Statistics describing the 60 bottle design ratings

STATISTICS	
Mean	30.35
Standard Error	0.401146
Median	31
Mode	32
Standard Deviation	3.107263
Sample Variance	9.655085
Kurtosis	1.423397
Skewness	−1.17688
Range	15
Minimum	20
Maximum	35
Sum	1821
Count	60

(b) Statistics describing 13 internists' salaries

STATISTICS	
Mean	159.7692
Standard Error	8.498985
Median	152
Mode	#N/A
Standard Deviation	30.64353
Sample Variance	939.0256
Kurtosis	3.409669
Skewness	1.695197
Range	114
Minimum	127
Maximum	241
Sum	2077
Count	13

(c) Statistics describing 20 customer satisfaction ratings

STATISTICS	
Mean	7.7
Standard Error	0.543381
Median	8
Mode	8
Standard Deviation	2.430075
Sample Variance	5.905263
Kurtosis	2.128288
Skewness	−1.56682
Range	9
Minimum	1
Maximum	10
Sum	154
Count	20

FIGURE 2.18 MegaStat Output of Statistics Describing the 49 DVD Price Points

Descriptive statistics

	Prices
count	49
mean	31.553
sample variance	0.639
sample standard deviation	0.799
minimum	29.8
maximum	33.3
range	3.5
sum	1,546.100
sum of squares	48,814.850
deviation sum of squares (SS)	30.662
1st quartile	31.000
median	31.600
3rd quartile	32.100
interquartile range	1.100
mode	31.700

empirical rule	
mean − 1s	30.754
mean + 1s	32.352
percent in interval (68.26%)	63.3%
mean − 2s	29.955
mean + 2s	33.152
percent in interval (95.44%)	95.9%
mean − 3s	29.155
mean + 3s	33.951
percent in interval (99.73%)	100.0%

low extremes	0
low outliers	0
high outliers	0
high extremes	0

mean and median would be useful in describing the mound-shaped, or single-peaked, distributions in Figure 2.16 on page 41. However, these measures of central tendency do not adequately describe a double-peaked distribution. For example, the mean and the median of the exam scores in the double-peaked dot plot display of Figure 2.10 (page 33) are 75.225 and 77. Looking at the display, neither the mean nor the median represents a typical exam score. This is because the exam scores really have no central value. In this case, the most important message conveyed by the double-peaked dot plot display is that the exam scores fall into two distinct groups.

Exercises for Section 2.2

CONCEPTS

2.10 Explain the difference between the terms for each of the following:
   a. A population parameter and its point estimate.
   b. A population mean and a corresponding sample mean.

2.11 Explain how the population mean, median, and mode compare when the population's relative frequency curve is
   a. Symmetrical.
   b. Negatively skewed (with a tail to the left).
   c. Positively skewed (with a tail to the right).
   d. Normally distributed.

METHODS AND APPLICATIONS

2.12 Calculate the mean, median, and mode of each population of numbers:
   a. 9, 8, 10, 10, 12, 6, 11, 10, 12, 8
   b. 110, 120, 70, 90, 90, 100, 80, 130, 140

2.13 Calculate the mean, median, and mode of each population of numbers:
   a. 17, 23, 19, 20, 25, 18, 22, 15, 21, 20
   b. 505, 497, 501, 500, 507, 510, 501

FIGURE 2.19   MegaStat Outputs of Statistics Describing Three Data Sets

(a) Satisfaction rating statistics

Descriptive statistics

	Rating
count	65
mean	42.95
median	43.00
sample variance	6.98
sample standard deviation	2.64
minimum	36
maximum	48
range	12
empirical rule	
mean − 1s	40.31
mean + 1s	45.60
percent in interval (68.26%)	63.1%
mean − 2s	37.67
mean + 2s	48.24
percent in interval (95.44%)	98.5%
mean − 3s	35.03
mean + 3s	50.88
percent in interval (99.73%)	100.0%

(b) Waiting time statistics

Descriptive statistics

	WaitTime
count	100
mean	5.460
median	5.250
sample variance	6.128
sample standard deviation	2.475
minimum	0.4
maximum	11.6
range	11.2
empirical rule	
mean − 1s	2.985
mean + 1s	7.935
percent in interval (68.26%)	66.0%
mean − 2s	0.509
mean + 2s	10.411
percent in interval (95.44%)	96.0%
mean − 3s	−1.966
mean + 3s	12.886
percent in interval (99.73%)	100.0%

(c) Breaking strength statistics

Descriptive statistics

	Strength
count	40
mean	22.990
median	23.000
sample variance	0.552
sample standard deviation	0.743
minimum	21.3
maximum	24.5
range	3.2
empirical rule	
mean − 1s	22.247
mean + 1s	23.733
percent in interval (68.26%)	67.5%
mean − 2s	21.504
mean + 2s	24.476
percent in interval (95.44%)	95.0%
mean − 3s	20.762
mean + 3s	25.218
percent in interval (99.73%)	100.0%

2.14   THE VIDEO GAME SATISFACTION RATING CASE

Recall that Table 2.7 (page 35) presents the satisfaction ratings for the XYZ-Box game system that have been given by 65 randomly selected purchasers. Figure 2.19(a) gives the MegaStat output of statistics describing the 65 satisfaction ratings.

a. Does the sample mean $\bar{x} = 42.95$ provide evidence that the mean of the population of all possible customer satisfaction ratings for the XYZ-Box is at least 42? (Recall that a "very satisfied" customer gives a rating that is at least 42.) Explain your answer.

b. Use the stem-and-leaf display in Figure 2.11 (page 35) to verify that the median of the satisfaction ratings is 43. How do the mean and median compare? What does the stem-and-leaf display tell you about why they compare in this way?

2.15   THE BANK CUSTOMER WAITING TIME CASE

Recall that Table 2.8 (page 36) presents the waiting times for teller service during peak business hours of 100 randomly selected bank customers. Figure 2.19(b) gives the MegaStat output of statistics describing the 100 waiting times.

a. Does the sample mean $\bar{x} = 5.460$ provide evidence that the mean of the population of all possible customer waiting times during peak business hours is less than six minutes (as is desired by the bank manager)? Explain your answer.

b. The median of the waiting times is 5.250. How do the mean and median compare? What does the histogram in Figure 2.13 (page 36) tell you about why they compare in this way?

2.16   THE TRASH BAG CASE

Consider the trash bag problem. Suppose that an independent laboratory has tested 130-L trash bags and has found that none of the bags currently on the market

have a mean breaking strength of 23 kg or more. On the basis of these results, the producer of the new, improved trash bag feels sure that its bag will be the strongest such bag on the market if the new trash bag's mean breaking strength can be shown to be at least 23 kg. Recall that Table 2.9 (page 37) presents the breaking strengths of 40 trash bags of the new type that were selected during a 40-hour pilot production run. Figure 2.19(c) gives the MegaStat output of statistics describing the 40 breaking strengths.

a. Does the sample mean $\bar{x} = 22.990$ provide evidence that the mean of the population of all possible trash bag breaking strengths is at least 23 kg? Explain your answer.

b. Use the stem-and-leaf display in Figure 2.15 (page 37) to verify that the median of the breaking strengths is 23.00. How do the mean and median compare? What does the stem-and-leaf display tell you about why they compare in this way?

Exercises 2.17 through 2.21 refer to the information in Table 2.10, which gives data concerning the number of fatalities by different modes of transportation in 2003 for Canada, the United States, and Mexico. In each exercise:

a. Compute the mean and median.

b. Compare the mean and median and explain if there is a case to be made for skewness.

c. Plot the values for the separate countries.

2.17   Analyze the data concerning air fatalities in Table 2.10 as described above.

2.18   Analyze the data concerning passenger cars and light trucks in Table 2.10 as described above.

2.19   Analyze the data concerning pedestrians in Table 2.10 as described above.

2.20   Analyze the data concerning motorcycles in Table 2.10 as described above.

TABLE **2.10** Data Comparing 2003 Transportation Fatalities by Mode for North America ✈

	Canada	USA	Mexico
Air	68	700	49
Air carriers	15	69	0
General aviation	53	631	49
Road	2,766	42,643	10,052
Passenger cars and light trucks	1,990	31,904	3,706
Passenger cars	U	19,460	3,586
Motorcycles	177	3,661	6
Buses	3	40	43
Large trucks	93	723	150
Pedestrians	376	4,749	1,478
Other	127	1,566	19
Pipeline	0	12	U
Rail	79	856	U
Grade crossing	27	329	59
Railroad	52	531	U
Transit, total	N	188	U
Transit rail	N	97	U
Water transport	U	816	28
Passenger vessels	U	U	N
Recreational boats	U	703	N
Commercial passenger vessels	4	U	N
Commercial freight vessels	2	N	U

Source: North American Transportation Statistics Database, available at http://nats.sct.gob.mx/nats/sys/tables.jsp?!=38id=12 as of April 12, 2004.

U = unavailable

N = data are nonexistent

TABLE **2.11** 2003/2004 NHL Payrolls ✈

Team	Payroll	Team	Payroll
Detroit Red Wings	$C85,641,720	Phoenix Coyotes	$C43,174,725
New York Rangers	84,137,588	Montréal Canadiens	42,742,700
Dallas Stars	75,436,774	Calgary Flames	40,042,833
Philadelphia Flyers	74,992,772	Carolina Hurricanes	39,499,612
Colorado Avalanche	69,720,704	San Jose Sharks	37,900,500
Toronto Maple Leafs	68,703,954	Tampa Bay Lightning	37,471,917
St. Louis Blues	67,842,500	Columbus Blue Jackets	37,400,000
Los Angeles Kings	59,217,180	Edmonton Oilers	36,712,500
Anaheim Mighty Ducks	58,626,425	Buffalo Sabres	36,249,675
Washington Capitals	55,985,325	Chicago Blackhawks	33,954,252
New Jersey Devils	53,824,824	Atlanta Thrashers	31,402,250
Boston Bruins	51,225,900	Minnesota Wild	29,920,550
Vancouver Canucks	46,281,950	Florida Panthers	28,740,250
New York Islanders	44,952,050	Pittsburgh Penguins	25,740,000
Ottawa Senators	43,549,000	Nashville Predators	24,125,750

Source: National Hockey League Players' Association.

2.21 Analyze the data concerning total rail fatalities in Table 2.10 as described above. ✈

2.22 In 2004, the NHL's collective bargaining agreement was set to expire. At that time, the owners wanted to adopt a salary cap to help combat escalating players' salaries and to create parity in the league. The players, of course, were against a cap of any kind. The payrolls for all NHL teams in the 2003/2004 season are given in ✈ Table 2.11. A frequency histogram of the data is given in Figure 2.20 on the next page. Using these data, answer the following questions:

a. Calculate the mean and median payrolls and comment on the shape of the distribution.

b. What percentage of Canadian team payrolls exceed the mean salary? exceed the median salary?

FIGURE **2.20** Frequency Histogram of NHL Team Payrolls

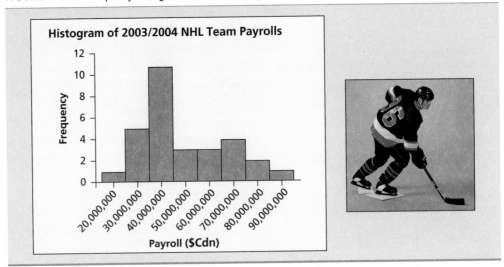

c. In 2005, a salary cap of $C42.9 million was imposed for each team, with each team's payroll to be no lower than $23.15 million. Approximately what percentage of the teams in the NHL were affected immediately by this salary cap?

d. A salary cap is supposed to create parity in the league, to give everyone an equal chance, since all teams are able to spend the same amount of money. Which measure do you feel will be more affected by a salary cap? Would it be the mean salary, the median salary, the modal salary, or perhaps some other measure not involving central tendency? Think about how much the salaries varied before the cap. Would this be the case after the cap?

2.3 MEASURES OF VARIATION

Range, variance, and standard deviation In addition to estimating a population's central tendency, it is important to estimate the **variation** of the population's individual values. For example, Figure 2.21 shows two histograms. Each portrays the distribution of 20 repair times (in days) for personal computers at a major service centre. Because the mean (and median and mode) of each distribution equals four days, the measures of central tendency do not indicate any difference between the Local and National Service Centres. However, the repair times for the Local Service Centre are clustered quite closely together, whereas the repair times for the

FIGURE **2.21** Repair Times for Personal Computers at Two Service Centres

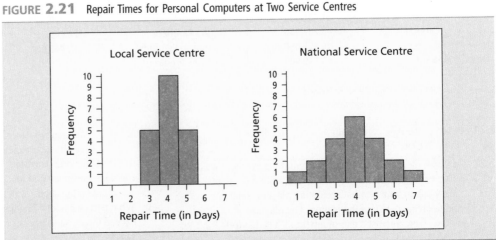

National Service Centre are spread farther apart (the repair time might be as little as one day, but could also be as long as seven days). Therefore, we need measures of variation to express how the two distributions differ.

One way to measure the variation of a set of measurements is to calculate the **range**.

CHAPTER 3

The **range** of the measurements is the largest measurement minus the smallest measurement.

In Figure 2.21, the smallest and largest repair times for the Local Service Centre are three days and five days; therefore, the range is 5 days − 3 days = 2 days. On the other hand, the range for the National Service Centre is 7 days − 1 day = 6 days. The National Service Centre's larger range indicates that this service centre's repair times exhibit more variation.

In general, the range is not the best measure of a data set's variation. One reason is that it is based only on the smallest and largest measurements in the data set and therefore may reflect an extreme measurement that is not entirely representative of the data set's variation. For example, in the marketing research case, the smallest and largest ratings in the sample of 60 bottle design ratings are 20 and 35. However, to simply estimate that most bottle design ratings are between 20 and 35 misses the fact that 57, or 95 percent, of the 60 ratings are at least as large as the minimum rating of 25 for a successful bottle design. In general, to fully describe a population's variation, it is useful to estimate intervals that contain *different percentages* (for example, 70 percent, 95 percent, or almost 100 percent) of the individual population values. To estimate such intervals, we use the **population variance** and the **population standard deviation**.

LO6

The Population Variance and Standard Deviation

The **population variance** σ^2 (*sigma squared*) is the average of the squared deviations of the individual population measurements from the population mean μ.

The **population standard deviation** σ (*sigma*) is the square root of the population variance.

For example, consider again the population of revenues for five of the biggest companies in Canada as reported by *The Globe and Mail* for 2008. These revenues (in billions of dollars) are 38, 37, 36, 34, and 34. To calculate the variance and standard deviation of these revenues, we first calculate the population mean, which is 35.8. Next we calculate the deviations of the individual population measurements from the population mean $\mu = 35.8$ as follows:

$$38 - 35.8 = 2.2, \quad 37 - 35.8 = 1.2, \quad 36 - 35.8 = 0.2, \quad 34 - 35.8 = -1.8,$$
$$34 - 35.8 = -1.8.$$

Then we compute the sum of the squares of these deviations:

$$2.2^2 + 1.2^2 + 0.2^2 + (-1.8)^2 + (-1.8)^2 = 4.84 + 1.44 + 0.04 + 3.24 + 3.24 = 12.8.$$

Finally, we calculate the population variance σ^2, the average of the squared deviations, by dividing the sum of the squared deviations, 12.8, by the number of squared deviations, 5. That is, σ^2 equals 12.8/5 = 2.56. Furthermore, this implies that the population standard deviation σ, the square root of σ^2, is $\sqrt{2.56} = 1.60$.

To see that the variance and standard deviation measure the variation, or spread, of the individual population measurements, suppose that the measurements are spread far apart. Then many measurements will be far from the mean μ, many of the squared deviations from the mean will be large, and the sum of squared deviations will be large. It follows that the average of the squared deviations—the population variance—will be relatively large. On the other hand, if the population measurements are clustered closely together, many measurements will be close to μ, many of the squared deviations from the mean will be small, and the average of the squared deviations—the population variance—will be small. Therefore, the more spread out the population measurements, the larger is the population variance, and the larger is the population standard deviation.

To further understand the population variance and standard deviation, note that one reason we square the deviations of the individual population measurements from the population mean is that the sum of the raw deviations themselves is zero. This is because the negative deviations cancel the positive deviations. For example, in the revenue situation, the raw deviations are 2.2, 1.2, 0.2, −1.8, and −1.8, which sum to zero. Of course, we could make the deviations positive by finding their absolute values. We square the deviations instead because the resulting population variance and standard deviation have many important interpretations that we study throughout this book. Because the population variance is an average of squared deviations of the original population values, the variance is expressed in squared units of the original population values. On the other hand, the population standard deviation—the square root of the population variance—is expressed in the same units as the original population values. Because the population standard deviation is expressed in the same units as the population values, it is more often used to make practical interpretations about the variation of these values.

When a population is too large to measure all the population units, we estimate the population variance and the population standard deviation by the **sample variance** and the **sample standard deviation**. We calculate the sample variance by dividing the sum of the squared deviations of the sample measurements from the sample mean by $n - 1$, the sample size minus one.[3] Although we might intuitively think that we should divide by n rather than by $n - 1$, it can be shown that dividing by n tends to produce an estimate of the population variance that is too small. On the other hand, dividing by $n - 1$ tends to produce a larger estimate that is more appropriate. Therefore, we obtain the following:

The Sample Variance and the Sample Standard Deviation

The **sample variance** s^2 (*s squared*) is defined to be

$$s^2 = \frac{\sum_{i=1}^{n} (x_i - \bar{x})^2}{n - 1} = \frac{(x_1 - \bar{x})^2 + (x_2 - \bar{x})^2 + \cdots + (x_n - \bar{x})^2}{n - 1}$$

and is the **point estimate of the population variance** σ^2.

The **sample standard deviation** $s = \sqrt{s^2}$ is the square root of the sample variance and is the **point estimate of the population standard deviation** σ.

Example 2.9 Canadian Manufacturing Statistics

2008/05	3.88
2008/06	5.23
2008/07	3.64
2008/08	3.91
2008/09	4.37
2008/10	4.52
2008/11	2.01
2008/12	2.45
2009/01	4.18
2009/02	5.24
2009/03	5.86
2009/04	4.50
2009/05	4.00

Statistics Canada compiles data on manufacturing statistics for Canada. Listed in the margin are the monthly numbers of asphalt shingle production (in millions of metric bundles) in Canada from May 2008 to May 2009.

The first step in calculating the sample variance and standard deviation is to compute the mean. For the asphalt production data, the mean is

$$\frac{3.88 + 5.23 + \cdots + 4.50 + 4.00}{13} = 4.14$$

It then follows that

$$\sum_{i=1}^{13} (x_i - \bar{x})^2 = (x_1 - \bar{x})^2 + (x_2 - \bar{x})^2 + (x_3 - \bar{x})^2 + \cdots + (x_{13} - \bar{x})^2$$

$$= (3.88 - 4.14)^2 + (5.23 - 4.14)^2 + (3.64 - 4.14)^2 + \cdots + (4.00 - 4.14)^2 = 13.47.$$

---

[3]Note that this value of one represents a "lost degree of freedom." When dealing with a sample, one data point must remain fixed so that there is a reference point to examine the other data points. As an exercise, find a few friends and try to put yourselves in a line in terms of height from tallest to shortest. To do this, you will need one person to stand still to be a reference point to compare yourself and others to (you will not be able to form a line if everyone keeps moving around). This fixed point (person) is then no longer free to move and is said to be a lost degree (point) of freedom.

Therefore, the variance and the standard deviation of the sample are

$$s^2 = \frac{13.47}{12} = 1.12 \text{ and } s = \sqrt{1.12} = 1.06.$$

Here $s^2 = 1.12$ and $s = 1.06$ are the point estimates of the variance and standard deviation, σ^2 and σ, respectively, of the entire population. The sample standard deviation, s, is expressed in the same units as the sample values. Therefore, we say that $s = 1.06$ million metric bundles.

Before explaining how we can use s^2 and s in a practical way, we present a formula that makes it easier to compute s^2. This formula is useful when we are using a handheld calculator that is not equipped with a statistics mode to compute s^2.

The **sample variance** can be calculated using the computational formula

$$s^2 = \frac{1}{n-1}\left[\sum_{i=1}^{n} x_i^2 - \frac{\left(\sum_{i=1}^{n} x_i\right)^2}{n}\right].$$

A practical interpretation: The empirical rule In the next box, we give a practical interpretation of the population standard deviation. This interpretation is often referred to as the **empirical rule for a normally distributed population**.

The Empirical Rule for a Normally Distributed Population

If a population has mean μ and standard deviation σ and is described by a normal curve, then, as illustrated in Figure 2.22,

1 68.26 percent of the population measurements are within (plus or minus) one standard deviation of the mean and thus lie in the interval $[\mu - \sigma, \mu + \sigma] = [\mu \pm \sigma]$.

2 95.44 percent of the population measurements are within (plus or minus) two standard deviations of the mean and thus lie in the interval $[\mu - 2\sigma, \mu + 2\sigma] = [\mu \pm 2\sigma]$.

3 99.73 percent of the population measurements are within (plus or minus) three standard deviations of the mean and thus lie in the interval $[\mu - 3\sigma, \mu + 3\sigma] = [\mu \pm 3\sigma]$.

FIGURE 2.22 The Empirical Rule

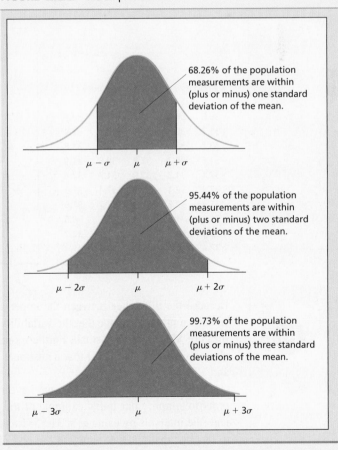

68.26% of the population measurements are within (plus or minus) one standard deviation of the mean.

95.44% of the population measurements are within (plus or minus) two standard deviations of the mean.

99.73% of the population measurements are within (plus or minus) three standard deviations of the mean.

In general, an interval that contains a specified percentage of the individual measurements in a population is called a **tolerance interval**. It follows that the one, two, and three standard deviation intervals around μ are tolerance intervals containing, respectively, 68.26 percent, 95.44 percent, and 99.73 percent of the measurements in a normally distributed population. Often we interpret the **three-sigma interval** $[\mu \pm 3\sigma]$ to be a tolerance interval that contains *almost all* of the measurements in a normally distributed population. Of course, we usually do not know the true values of μ and σ. Therefore, we must estimate the tolerance intervals by replacing μ and σ in these intervals with the mean $\bar{x}$ and standard deviation s of a sample that has been randomly selected from the normally distributed population.

Example 2.10 DVD Price Points

Consider the sample of 49 DVD prices given below. For these data, $\bar{x} = 31.5531$ and $s = 0.7992$ are the point estimates of the mean μ and the standard deviation σ, respectively, of the population of all DVD prices. Furthermore, the histogram of the 49 DVD prices suggests that the population of all DVD prices is normally distributed. To more simply illustrate the empirical rule, we will round $\bar{x}$ to 31.6 and s to 0.8. Using these values, we have the following:

1   Using the interval $[\bar{x} \pm s] = [31.6 \pm 0.8] = [31.6 - 0.8, 31.6 + 0.8] = [30.8, 32.4]$, we estimate that 68.26 percent of all individual DVDs will cost between \$30.80 and \$32.40.

2   Using the interval $[\bar{x} \pm 2s] = [31.6 \pm 2(0.8)] = [31.6 \pm 1.6] = [30.0, 33.2]$, we estimate that 95.44 percent of all individual DVDs will cost between \$30.00 and \$33.20.

3   Using the interval $[\bar{x} \pm 3s] = [31.6 \pm 3(0.8)] = [31.6 \pm 2.4] = [29.2, 34.0]$, we estimate that 99.73 percent of all individual DVDs will cost between \$29.20 and \$34.00.

A sample of 49 DVD price points

30.8	30.9	32.0	32.3	32.6
31.7	30.4	31.4	32.7	31.4
30.1	32.5	30.8	31.2	31.8
31.6	30.3	32.8	30.6	31.9
32.1	31.3	32.0	31.7	32.8
33.3	32.1	31.5	31.4	31.5
31.3	32.5	32.4	32.2	31.6
31.0	31.8	31.0	31.5	30.6
32.0	30.4	29.8	31.7	32.2
32.4	30.5	31.1	30.6	

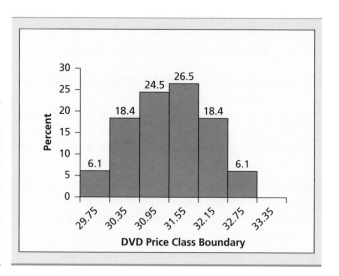

Because the difference between the upper and lower limits of each tolerance interval is fairly small, we might conclude that the variability of the individual DVD prices around the estimated mean of \$31.60 is fairly small. Furthermore, the interval $[\bar{x} \pm 3s] = [29.2, 34.0]$ implies that almost any individual DVD that a customer might purchase this year will cost between \$29.20 and \$34.00.

Before continuing, recall that we have rounded $\bar{x}$ and s to one decimal point accuracy in order to simplify our initial example of the empirical rule. If, instead, we calculate the empirical rule intervals by using $\bar{x} = 31.5531$ and $s = 0.7992$ and then round the interval endpoints to one decimal place accuracy at the end of the calculations, we obtain the same intervals as obtained above. In general, however, rounding intermediate calculated results can lead to inaccurate final results. Because of this, throughout this book we will avoid greatly rounding intermediate results.

We next note that if we actually count the number of the 49 DVD prices that are contained in each of the intervals $[\bar{x} \pm s] = [30.8, 32.4]$, $[\bar{x} \pm 2s] = [30.0, 33.2]$, and $[\bar{x} \pm 3s] = [29.2, 34.0]$, we find that these intervals contain, respectively, 33, 47, and 49 of the 49 DVD prices. The corresponding sample percentages—67.35 percent, 95.92 percent, and 100 percent—are close to the theoretical percentages—68.26 percent, 95.44 percent, and 99.73 percent—that apply to a normally distributed population. This is further evidence that the population of all DVD prices is (approximately) normally distributed and thus that the empirical rule holds for this population.

A quality improvement application: Meeting customer requirements Tolerance intervals are often used to determine whether customer requirements are being met. Customer requirements often specify that a quality characteristic must be inside an acceptable range of values called **specifications**. Specifications are written for **individual measurements**. For example, suppose that marketing research done by the fast-food restaurant of Example 1.3 (page 10) suggests that coffee tastes best if its temperature is between 67°C and 75°C. Therefore, the customer requirements (specifications) would say that the temperature of each individual cup of coffee must be between 67°C and 75°C (this specification would typically be written as 71°C $\pm$ 4°C).

If a process is able to consistently produce output that meets customer requirements (specifications), we say that the process is **capable** (of meeting the requirements). From a practical standpoint, this means that almost all of the individual measurements must be within the specification limits. Furthermore, if the population of all process measurements is approximately normally distributed, it is common practice to conclude that a process that is in statistical control is capable of meeting customer requirements if the three-sigma tolerance interval estimate $[\bar{x} \pm 3s]$ is within the specification limits. We say this because if this interval is within the specification limits, then we estimate that almost all (99.73 percent) of the process measurements are within the specification limits.

For example, recall that the runs plot of the 24 coffee temperatures in Figure 1.3 (page 11) indicates that the fast-food restaurant's coffee-making process is in statistical control. The mean and the standard deviation of these temperatures are $\bar{x} = 71.2083$ and $s = 2.9779$, respectively. It follows that we estimate that the interval

$$[\bar{x} \pm 3s] = [71.2083 \pm 3(2.9779)]$$
$$= [62.27, 80.14]$$

contains 99.73 percent of all coffee temperatures. Because this interval tells us that some coffee temperatures are outside the customer specifications of 67°C to 75°C, the coffee-making process is not capable of meeting customer requirements. Here, although the process is exhibiting a constant amount of variation around a constant level (or mean), the constant amount of variation—as indicated by the standard deviation of $s = 2.9779$—is too large. Suppose that to reduce the standard deviation of the coffee temperatures, the restaurant tests a new coffeemaker. A sample of 24 coffee temperatures is in control and approximately normally distributed with a mean of $\bar{x} = 71.1208$ and a reduced standard deviation of $s = 0.9597$. It follows that we estimate that the interval

$$[\bar{x} \pm 3s] = [71.1208 \pm 3(0.9597)]$$
$$= [68.24, 74.00]$$

contains 99.73 percent of all coffee temperatures. We infer that almost all coffee temperatures produced by the new coffee-making process are within the customer specifications of 65°C to 75°C. Therefore, the improved process is capable of meeting customer requirements.

Skewness and the empirical rule The empirical rule holds for normally distributed populations. In addition, this rule also approximately holds for populations having **mound-shaped** (single-peaked) distributions that are not very positively or negatively skewed (to the right or left).

In some situations, the skewness of a mound-shaped distribution of population measurements can make it tricky to know whether and how to use the empirical rule. For example, we concluded in Example 2.8 that the distribution of 60 bottle design ratings is somewhat but not highly negatively skewed (to the left). The mean and the standard deviation of the 60 bottle design ratings are $\bar{x} = 30.35$ and $s = 3.1073$, respectively. If we actually count the number of ratings contained in each of the intervals $[\bar{x} \pm s] = [27.2, 33.5]$, $[\bar{x} \pm 2s] = [24.1, 36.6]$, and $[\bar{x} \pm 3s] = [21, 39.7]$, we find that these intervals contain, respectively, 44, 57, and 59 of the 60 ratings. The corresponding sample percentages—73.33 percent, 95 percent, and 98.33 percent—are, respectively, greater than, approximately equal to, and less than the theoretical percentages—68.26 percent, 95.44 percent, and 99.73 percent—given by the empirical rule. Therefore, if we consider the population of all consumer ratings of the bottle design, we might estimate that (1) at least 68.26 percent of all ratings will be between 27 and 34, (2) approximately 95.44 percent of the ratings will be between 24 and 35 (a rating cannot exceed 35), and (3) less than 99.73 percent of the ratings will be between 21 and 35. Result (3), and the low ratings of 20 and 22 found, suggests that the bottle design ratings distribution is too negatively skewed (to the left) to use the empirical rule to make conclusions about almost all ratings. However, we are not necessarily concerned about almost all ratings, because the bottle design will be successful if it appeals to a large percentage of consumers. Results (1) and (2), which describe 68.26 percent and 95.44 percent of all consumer ratings, imply that large percentages of consumer ratings will exhibit reasonably small variability around the estimated mean rating of 30.35. This and the fact that 57, or 95 percent, of the 60 ratings are at least as large as the minimum rating of 25 for a successful bottle design suggest that the bottle design will be successful.

BI

Chebyshev's theorem If we fear that the empirical rule does not hold for a particular population, we can consider using **Chebyshev's theorem** to find an interval that contains a specified percentage of the individual measurements in the population.

Chebyshev's Theorem

Consider any population that has mean μ and standard deviation σ. Then for any value of k greater than 1, at least $100(1 - 1/k^2)$ percent of the population measurements lie in the interval $[\mu \pm k\sigma]$.

CHAPTER 3

For example, if we choose k equal to 2, then at least $100(1 - 1/2^2)\% = 100(3/4)\% = 75\%$ of the population measurements lie in the interval $[\mu \pm 2\sigma]$. As another example, if we choose k equal to 3, then at least $100(1 - 1/3^2)\% = 100(8/9)\% = 88.89\%$ of the population measurements lie in the interval $[\mu \pm 3\sigma]$. As yet a third example, suppose that we wish to find an interval containing at least 99.73 percent of all population measurements. Here we would set $100(1 - 1/k^2)$ percent equal to 99.73 percent, which implies that $1 - 1/k^2 = 0.9973$. If we solve for k, we find that $k = 19.25$. This says that at least 99.73 percent of all population measurements lie in the interval $[\mu \pm 19.25\sigma]$. Unless σ is extremely small, this interval will be so long that it will tell us very little about where the population measurements lie. We conclude that Chebyshev's theorem can help us find an interval that contains a reasonably high percentage (such as 75 percent or 88.89 percent) of all population measurements. However, unless σ is extremely small, Chebyshev's theorem will not provide a useful interval that contains almost all (say, 99.73 percent) of the population measurements.

Although Chebyshev's theorem technically applies to any population, it is only of practical use when analyzing a *non-mound-shaped* (for example, a double-peaked) *population that is not extremely positively or negatively skewed (to the right or left)*. Why is this? First, *we would not use Chebyshev's theorem to describe a mound-shaped population that is not very skewed because we can use the empirical rule to do this.* In fact, the empirical rule is better for such a population because it gives us a shorter interval that will contain a given percentage of measurements. For example, if the empirical rule can be used to describe a population, the interval $[\mu \pm 3\sigma]$ will contain 99.73 percent of all measurements. On the other hand, if we use Chebyshev's theorem, the interval $[\mu \pm 19.25\sigma]$ is needed. As another example, the empirical rule tells us that 95.44 percent of all measurements lie in the interval $[\mu \pm 2\sigma]$, whereas Chebyshev's theorem tells us only that at least 75 percent of all measurements lie in this interval.

It is not appropriate to use Chebyshev's theorem—or any other result making use of the population standard deviation σ—to describe a population that is extremely skewed. This is because if a population is extremely skewed, the measurements in the long tail to the left or right will greatly inflate σ. This implies that tolerance intervals calculated using σ will be so long that they are of little use. In this case, it is best to measure variation by using **percentiles**, which are discussed in Section 2.4.

z scores We can determine the relative location of any value in a population or sample by using the mean and standard deviation to compute the value's z score. For any value x in a population or sample, the **z score** corresponding to x is defined as follows:

z score:

$$z = \frac{x - \text{mean}}{\text{standard deviation}}.$$

The z score, which is also called the **standardized value**, is the number of standard deviations that x is from the mean. A positive z score says that x is above (greater than) the mean, while a negative z score says that x is below (less than) the mean. For instance, a z score equal to 2.3 says that x is 2.3 standard deviations above the mean. Similarly, a z score equal to -1.68 says that x is 1.68 standard deviations below the mean. A z score equal to zero says that x equals the mean.

A z score indicates the relative location of a value within a population or sample. For example, below we calculate the z scores for each of the revenues for the five biggest companies in Canada in 2008 as reported by *The Globe and Mail*. Recall that for these companies, the mean revenue is $35.8 billion and the standard deviation is $1.60 billion.

Company	Revenue	x − Mean	z score
Royal Bank of Canada	38	(38 − 35.8) = 2.2	2.2/1.60 = 1.375
Power Corp. of Canada	37	(37 − 35.8) = 1.2	1.2/1.60 = 0.75
Power Financial	36	(36 − 35.8) = 0.2	0.2/1.60 = 0.125
Manulife Financial	34	(34 − 35.8) = −1.8	−1.8/1.60 = −1.125
Great-West Life Company	34	(34 − 35.8) = −1.8	−1.8/1.60 = −1.125

These z scores tell us that Royal Bank of Canada is the farthest above the mean, with revenues 1.375 standard deviations above the mean. If a company was found to have a z score of zero, then the company's revenues would be the same as the mean for the five companies.

Values in two different populations or samples with the same z score are the same number of standard deviations from their respective means and, therefore, have the same relative locations. For example, suppose that the mean score on the midterm exam for students in Section A of a statistics course is 65 and the standard deviation of the scores is 10. Meanwhile, the mean score on the same exam for students in Section B is 80 and the standard deviation is 5. A student in Section A who scores an 85 and a student in Section B who scores a 90 have the same relative locations within their respective sections because their z scores, $(85 - 65)/10 = 2$ and $(90 - 80)/5 = 2$, are equal.

The coefficient of variation Sometimes we need to measure the size of the standard deviation of a population or sample relative to the size of the population or sample mean.

The **coefficient of variation**, which makes this comparison, is defined for a population or sample as follows:

$$\text{Coefficient of variation} = \frac{\text{standard deviation}}{\text{mean}} \times 100.$$

The coefficient of variation compares populations or samples with different means and different standard deviations. For example, many financial Web sites give the mean and standard deviation for fund returns. Suppose Fund X is found to have a mean return of 10.39 percent with a standard deviation of 16.18 percent, while the mean return for Fund Y is 17.7 percent with a standard deviation of 15.81 percent. Then the coefficient of variation for Fund X is $(16.18/10.39) \times 100 = 155.73$, and the coefficient of variation for Fund Y is $(15.81/17.7) \times 100 = 89.32$. This tells us that for Fund X, the standard deviation is 155.73 percent of the value of its mean return. For Fund Y, the standard deviation is 89.32 percent of the value of its mean return.

In the context of situations like the stock fund comparison, the coefficient of variation is often used as a measure of **risk** because it measures the variation of the returns (the standard deviation) relative to the size of the mean return. For instance, although Funds X and Y have comparable standard deviations (16.18 percent versus 15.81 percent), Fund X has a higher coefficient of variation than does Fund Y (155.73 versus 89.32). This says that *relative to the mean return*, the variation in returns for Fund X is higher. That is, we would conclude that investing in Fund X is riskier than investing in Fund Y.

Exercises for Section 2.3

CONCEPTS

2.23 Define the range, variance, and standard deviation for a population.

2.24 Discuss how the variance and the standard deviation measure variation.

2.25 Why are the variance and standard deviation usually considered more effective measures of variation than the range?

2.26 The empirical rule for a normally distributed population and Chebyshev's theorem have the same basic purpose. In your own words, explain what this purpose is.

2.27 When is a process capable, and what are process specification limits? Give an example of a situation in which process capability is important.

METHODS AND APPLICATIONS

2.28 Consider the following population of five numbers: 5, 8, 10, 12, 15. Calculate the range, variance, and standard deviation of this population.

2.29 Table 2.12 lists the number of university degrees, diplomas, and certificates granted in each province in Canada in 2003. These data are available from Statistics Canada (http://www.statcan.gc.ca). Calculate the range, variance, and standard deviation for these educational attainment numbers.

2.30 Table 2.13 lists the aircraft movement statistics from Transport Canada for January 2006 compared to January 2005 at tower-controlled airports (see http://www.tc.gc.ca).
   a. Calculate the population range, variance, and standard deviation of the five percentage change values (note that negative values indicate that there was greater movement in 2005 than in 2006).

TABLE **2.12** University Degrees, Diplomas, and Certificates Granted by Provinces in 2003

Province	
Newfoundland and Labrador	2,975
Prince Edward Island	625
Nova Scotia	8,785
New Brunswick	4,555
Quebec	57,785
Ontario	79,000
Manitoba	5,870
Saskatchewan	5,865
Alberta	17,200
British Columbia	19,015

Source: Adapted from the Statistics Canada CANSIM database http://cansim2.statcan.ca, table number 477-0014, February 2006.

TABLE **2.13** Percentage Change of Movement of Aircraft in Tower-Controlled Airports in Canada

Air Carriers	1.2
Other Commercial	3.2
Private	11.0
Government	
• Civil	5.9
• Military	−1.5

Source: Based on Statistics Canada, International Trade Data; retrieved from their Trade Data Online (TDO) Web site: www.ic.gc.ca (Catalogue 51-007, Volume 1, no. 1, January 2006); and *Aircraft Movement Statistics: NAV CANADA Towers and Flights Service Stations*, Catalogue 51-007, Volume 1, no. 1, January 2008.

b. Using the population of change values, compute and interpret the z score for each type of air transportation movement.

2.31 In order to control costs, a company wishes to study the amount of money its sales force spends entertaining clients. The following is a random sample of six entertainment expenses (lunch costs for four people) from expense reports submitted by members of the sales force.

$157 $132 $109 $145 $125 $139

a. Calculate $\bar{x}$, s^2, and s for the expense data. In addition, show that the two different formulas for calculating s^2 give the same result.

b. Assuming that the distribution of entertainment expenses is approximately normally distributed, calculate estimates of tolerance intervals containing 68.26 percent, 95.44 percent, and 99.73 percent of all entertainment expenses by the sales force.

c. If a member of the sales force submits an entertainment expense (lunch cost for four) of $190, should this expense be considered unusually high (and possibly worthy of investigation by the company)? Explain your answer.

d. Compute and interpret the z score for each of the six entertainment expenses.

2.32   THE TRASH BAG CASE

The mean and the standard deviation of the sample of 40 trash bag breaking strengths are $\bar{x} = 22.990$ and $s = 0.7428$, respectively.

a. What do the stem-and-leaf display and histogram in Figures 2.14 and 2.15 (page 37) say about whether the empirical rule should be used to describe the trash bag breaking strengths?

b. Use the empirical rule to calculate estimates of tolerance intervals containing 68.26 percent, 95.44 percent, and 99.73 percent of all possible trash bag breaking strengths.

c. Does the estimate of a tolerance interval containing 99.73 percent of all breaking strengths provide evidence that almost any bag a customer might purchase will have a breaking strength that exceeds 20 kg? Explain your answer.

d. How do the percentages of the 40 breaking strengths in Table 2.9 (page 37) that actually fall into the intervals $[\bar{x} \pm s]$, $[\bar{x} \pm 2s]$, and $[\bar{x} \pm 3s]$ compare to those given by the empirical rule? Do these comparisons indicate that the statistical inferences you made in parts b and c are reasonably valid?

2.33   THE BANK CUSTOMER WAITING TIME CASE

The mean and the standard deviation of the sample of 100 bank customer waiting times are $\bar{x} = 5.46$ and $s = 2.475$, respectively.

a. What does the histogram in Figure 2.13 (page 36) say about whether the empirical rule should be used to describe the bank customer waiting times?

b. Use the empirical rule to calculate estimates of tolerance intervals containing 68.26 percent, 95.44 percent, and 99.73 percent of all possible bank customer waiting times.

c. Does the estimate of a tolerance interval containing 68.26 percent of all waiting times provide evidence that at least two thirds of all customers will have to wait less than eight minutes for service? Explain your answer.

d. How do the percentages of the 100 waiting times in Table 2.8 (page 36) that actually fall into the intervals $[\bar{x} \pm s]$, $[\bar{x} \pm 2s]$, and $[\bar{x} \pm 3s]$ compare to those given by the empirical rule? Do these comparisons indicate that the statistical inferences you made in parts b and c are reasonably valid?

2.34   THE VIDEO GAME SATISFACTION RATING CASE

The mean and the standard deviation of the sample of 65 customer satisfaction ratings are $\bar{x} = 42.95$ and $s = 2.6424$, respectively.

a. What do the stem-and-leaf display and histogram in Figures 2.11 (page 35) and 2.12 (page 36) say about whether the empirical rule should be used to describe the satisfaction ratings?

b. Use the empirical rule to calculate estimates of tolerance intervals containing 68.26 percent, 95.44 percent, and 99.73 percent of all possible satisfaction ratings.

c. Does the estimate of a tolerance interval containing 99.73 percent of all satisfaction ratings provide evidence that 99.73 percent of all customers will give a satisfaction rating for the XYZ-Box game system that is at least 35 (the minimal rating of a "satisfied" customer)? Explain your answer.

d. How do the percentages of the 65 customer satisfaction ratings in Table 2.7 (page 35) that actually fall into the intervals $[\bar{x} \pm s]$, $[\bar{x} \pm 2s]$, and $[\bar{x} \pm 3s]$ compare to those given by the empirical rule? Do these comparisons indicate that the statistical inferences you made in parts b and c are reasonably valid?

2.35 Consider the 63 automated banking machine (ABM) transaction times in Table 2.14 on the next page.

a. Construct a stem-and-leaf display for the 63 ABM transaction times. Describe the shape of the distribution of transaction times.

b. When we compute the sample mean and sample standard deviation for the transaction times, we find that $\bar{x} = 36.56$ and $s = 4.475$. Compute each of the intervals $[\bar{x} \pm s]$, $[\bar{x} \pm 2s]$, and $[\bar{x} \pm 3s]$. Then count the number and find the percentage of transaction times that actually fall into each interval.

c. How do the percentages of transaction times that fall into the intervals $[\bar{x} \pm s]$, $[\bar{x} \pm 2s]$, and $[\bar{x} \pm 3s]$ compare to those given by the empirical rule? How do the percentages of transaction times that fall into the intervals $[\bar{x} \pm 2s]$ and $[\bar{x} \pm 3s]$ compare to those given by Chebyshev's theorem?

d. Explain why the empirical rule does not describe the transaction times extremely well.

TABLE **2.14**   ABM Transaction Times (in Seconds) for 63 Withdrawals

Transaction	Time	Transaction	Time	Transaction	Time
1	32	22	34	43	37
2	32	23	32	44	32
3	41	24	34	45	33
4	51	25	35	46	33
5	42	26	33	47	40
6	39	27	42	48	35
7	33	28	46	49	33
8	43	29	52	50	39
9	35	30	36	51	34
10	33	31	37	52	34
11	33	32	32	53	33
12	32	33	39	54	38
13	42	34	36	55	41
14	34	35	41	56	34
15	37	36	32	57	35
16	37	37	33	58	35
17	33	38	34	59	37
18	35	39	38	60	39
19	40	40	32	61	44
20	36	41	35	62	40
21	32	42	33	63	39

2.36   Three telecommunications companies reported their mean monthly profit and standard deviations for a year. The results are presented below.

	Company A	Company B	Company C
Mean	$10,930	$13,000	$34,450
Standard deviation	$4,196	$9,360	$4,116

a. For each company, find an interval within which you would expect 95.44 percent of all monthly profit values to fall (assuming that profits are normally distributed).
b. Using the intervals you computed in part a, compare the three companies with respect to mean monthly profits and variability of profits.
c. Calculate the coefficient of variation for each company, and use the results to compare profits. Which company is more variable?

2.37   The data in the next column give 18 measurements of a critical dimension for an automobile part. Here one part has been randomly selected each hour from the previous hour's production, and the measurements are given in time order. Assume that the process producing this part is in statistical control.

Hour	Measurement (cm)	Hour	Measurement (cm)
1	3.005	10	3.005
2	3.020	11	3.015
3	2.980	12	2.995
4	3.015	13	3.020
5	2.995	14	3.000
6	3.010	15	2.990
7	3.000	16	2.985
8	2.985	17	3.020
9	3.025	18	2.985

a. When we compute the sample mean and sample standard deviation of the 18 dimensions, we obtain $\bar{x} = 3.0028$ and $s = 0.01437$, respectively. Assuming the dimensions are mound-shaped, use these values to compute an estimated tolerance interval that you would expect to contain almost all (99.73 percent) of the auto part's dimensions. Based on this interval, can you conclude that the process is capable of meeting specifications of 3.00 ± 0.03— that is, 2.97 to 3.03? Explain your answer.
b. After a research and development program is carried out to improve the manufacturing process that produces the auto part, the following 18 measurements of the dimension are obtained (they are given in time order). Does the process appear to be in statistical control? Justify your answer.

Hour	Measurement (cm)	Hour	Measurement (cm)
1	3.010	10	3.005
2	3.005	11	2.995
3	2.990	12	2.995
4	3.010	13	3.010
5	2.995	14	3.000
6	2.990	15	2.990
7	3.000	16	2.995
8	2.990	17	3.010
9	3.010	18	3.000

c. When we compute the sample mean and sample standard deviation of the 18 observed dimensions from the improved process, we obtain $\bar{x} = 3$ and $s = 0.00786$, respectively. Assuming the measurements are normally distributed, use these results to compute an estimated tolerance interval that you would expect to contain almost all (99.73 percent) of the dimensions produced by the improved process. Based on this interval, can you conclude that the improved process is capable of meeting specifications of 3.00 ± 0.03—that is, 2.97 to 3.03? Explain your answer.

2.4 PERCENTILES, QUARTILES, AND BOX-AND-WHISKERS DISPLAYS

Percentiles, quartiles, and five-number displays In this section, we consider **percentiles** and their applications. We begin by defining the *p*th **percentile**.

For a set of measurements arranged in increasing order, the *p*th **percentile** is a value such that p percent of the measurements fall at or below the value, and $(100 - p)$ percent of the measurements fall at or above the value.

There are various procedures for calculating percentiles. One procedure is as follows: To calculate the *p*th percentile for a set of n measurements, we first arrange the measurements in increasing order (by, for example, constructing a stem-and-leaf display). Then we calculate the index $i = (p/100)n$. If i is not an integer, the next integer greater than i denotes the position of the *p*th percentile in the ordered arrangement. If i is an integer, then the *p*th percentile is the average of the measurements in positions i and $i + 1$ in the ordered arrangement. For example, Figure 2.23(a) on the next page presents the stem-and-leaf display of 65 test scores. In order to calculate the 75th percentile of these 65 scores, we calculate the index $i = (75/100)65 = 48.75$. Because $i = 48.75$ is not an integer, the 75th percentile is the 49th score in the stem-and-leaf display. Counting up to the 49th score in this display, we find that the 75th percentile is 21 (see Figure 2.23(a)). This implies that we estimate that approximately 75 percent of all scores are less than or equal to 21. As another example, Figure 2.23(b) presents the stem-and-leaf display of the 60 bottle design ratings. In order to calculate the fifth percentile of these 60 ratings, we calculate the index $i = (5/100)60 = 3$. Because $i = 3$ is an integer, the fifth percentile is the average of the third and fourth ratings in the stem-and-leaf display. Counting up to these ratings in this display, we find that the fifth percentile is $(24 + 25)/2 = 24.5$ (see Figure 2.23(b)). Since any rating is a whole number, we estimate that approximately 5 percent of all ratings are 24 or less and approximately 95 percent of all ratings are 25 or more.

In general, unless percentiles correspond to very high or very low percentages, they are resistant (like the median) to extreme values. For example, the 75th percentile of the test scores would remain 21 even if the three largest scores—26, 27, and 29—were, instead, 35, 56, and 84. On the other hand, the standard deviation in this situation would increase from 3.9612 to 10.2119. In general, if a population is highly positively or negatively skewed (to the right or left), it can be best to describe the variation of the population by using various percentiles. For example, we might describe the variation of the yearly incomes of all people in Canada by using the 10th, 25th, 50th, 75th, and 90th percentiles of these incomes.

One appealing way to describe the variation of a set of measurements is to divide the data into four parts, each containing approximately 25 percent of the measurements. This can be done by defining the **first**, **second**, and **third quartiles** as follows:

FIGURE **2.23** Using Stem-and-Leaf Displays to Find Percentiles and Five-Number Summaries

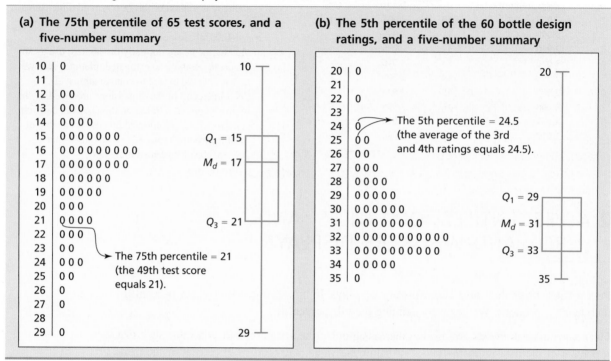

(a) **The 75th percentile of 65 test scores, and a five-number summary**

(b) **The 5th percentile of the 60 bottle design ratings, and a five-number summary**

The **first quartile**, denoted Q_1, is the **25th percentile**.
The **second quartile** (or **median**), denoted M_d, is the **50th percentile**.
The **third quartile**, denoted Q_3, is the **75th percentile**.

Note that the second quartile is simply another name for the median. Furthermore, the procedure we have described here that would be used to find the 50th percentile (second quartile) will always give the same result as the previously described procedure for finding the median. For example, to find the second quartile of the 65 test scores, we find the 50th percentile by calculating $i = (50/100)65 = 32.5$, which says that the second quartile is the 33rd score in the stem-and-leaf display of Figure 2.23(a). Counting up to the 33rd score in the display, we find that the second quartile equals 17, which is the median of the scores.

Because $i = (25/100)65 = 16.25$, the first quartile (25th percentile) of the 65 test scores is the 17th score in the stem-and-leaf display of Figure 2.23(a). Therefore, $Q_1 = 15$. Remembering that the median of the scores is 17, and that the 75th percentile of the scores is 21, the quartiles are $Q_1 = 15$, $M_d = 17$, and $Q_3 = 21$.

We often describe a set of measurements by using a **five-number summary**. The summary consists of (1) the smallest measurement; (2) the first quartile, Q_1; (3) the median, M_d; (4) the third quartile, Q_3; and (5) the largest measurement. It is easy to graphically depict a five-number summary; we have done this for the 65 test scores alongside the stem-and-leaf display of Figure 2.23(a). Notice that we have drawn a vertical line extending from the smallest score to the largest score. In addition, a rectangle is drawn that extends from Q_1 to Q_3, and a horizontal line is drawn to indicate the location of the median. The summary divides the scores into four parts, with the middle 50 percent of the scores depicted by the rectangle. The summary indicates that the largest 25 percent of the scores is more spread out than the smallest 25 percent, and that the second-largest 25 percent of the scores is more spread out than the second-smallest 25 percent. Overall, the summary indicates that the test scores are somewhat positively skewed (to the right).

As another example, for the 60 bottle design ratings, $Q_1 = 29$, $M_d = 31$, and $Q_3 = 33$. The graphical five-number summary of the ratings is shown alongside the stem-and-leaf display of the ratings in Figure 2.23(b). The summary shows that the smallest 25 percent of the ratings is more spread out than any of the other quarters of the ratings, and that the other three quarters are equally spread out. Overall, the summary shows that the bottle design ratings are negatively skewed (to the left).

Using the first and third quartiles, we define the **interquartile range** to be $IQR = Q_3 - Q_1$. This quantity can be interpreted as the length of the interval that contains the *middle 50 percent* of the measurements. For instance, Figure 2.23(a) tells us that the interquartile range of the sample of 65 test scores is $Q_3 - Q_1 = 21 - 15 = 6$. This says that we estimate that the middle 50 percent of all scores fall within a range of six points.

The procedure we have presented for calculating the first and third quartiles is not the only procedure for computing these quantities. In fact, several procedures exist, and, for example, different statistical computer packages use several somewhat different methods for computing the quartiles. One procedure calculates what are called **lower** and **upper hinges** and then defines the first quartile to be the lower hinge and the third quartile to be the upper hinge. In general, the different methods for computing the first and third quartiles sometimes produce somewhat different results. However, no matter what procedure is used to compute the quartiles, the objective is to divide the data into four parts, each containing approximately 25 percent of the measurements.

Box-and-whiskers displays (box plots) A more sophisticated modification of the graphical five-number summary is called a **box-and-whiskers display** (sometimes called a **box plot**). Such a display is constructed by using Q_1, M_d, Q_3, and the interquartile range. As an example, again consider the 20 customer satisfaction ratings:

1   3   5   5   7   8   8   8   8   8   9   9   9   9   9   9   10 10 10 10

It can be shown that $Q_1 = 7.5$, $M_d = 8$, $Q_3 = 9$, and $IQR = Q_3 - Q_1 = 9 - 7.5 = 1.5$ for these ratings. To construct a box-and-whiskers display, we first draw a box that extends from Q_1 to Q_3. As shown in Figure 2.24(a) on the next page, for the satisfaction ratings data this box extends from $Q_1 = 7.5$ to $Q_3 = 9$. The box contains the middle 50 percent of the data set. Next, a vertical line is drawn through the box at the value of the median M_d (sometimes a plus sign ($+$) is plotted at the median instead of a vertical line). This line divides the data set into two roughly equal parts. We next define what we call **inner** and **outer fences**. The **inner fences** are located $1.5 \times IQR$ below Q_1 and $1.5 \times IQR$ above Q_3. For the satisfaction ratings data, the inner fences are

$$Q_1 - 1.5(IQR) = 7.5 - 1.5(1.5) = 5.25 \quad \text{and} \quad Q_3 + 1.5(IQR) = 9 + 1.5(1.5) = 11.25.$$

The **outer fences** are located $3 \times IQR$ below Q_1 and $3 \times IQR$ above Q_3. For the satisfaction ratings data, the outer fences are

$$Q_1 - 3(IQR) = 7.5 - 3(1.5) = 3.0 \quad \text{and} \quad Q_3 + 3(IQR) = 9 + 3(1.5) = 13.5.$$

The inner and outer fences help us to draw the plot's **whiskers**: dashed lines extending below Q_1 and above Q_3 (as in Figure 2.24(a)). One whisker is drawn from Q_1 to the smallest measurement between the inner fences. For the satisfaction ratings data, this whisker extends from $Q_1 = 7.5$ down to 7, because 7 is the smallest rating between the inner fences 5.25 and 11.25. The other whisker is drawn from Q_3 to the largest measurement between the inner fences. For the satisfaction ratings data, this whisker extends from $Q_3 = 9$ up to 10, because 10 is the largest rating between the inner fences 5.25 and 11.25. The inner and outer fences are also used to identify **outliers**. An **outlier** is a measurement that is separated from (that is, different from) most of the other measurements in the data set. Measurements that are located between the inner and outer fences are considered to be **mild outliers**, whereas measurements that are located outside the outer fences are considered to be **extreme outliers**. We indicate the locations of mild outliers by plotting these measurements with the symbol *, and we indicate the locations of extreme outliers by plotting these measurements with the symbol o. For the satisfaction ratings data, the ratings 3 and 5 are mild outliers (*) because these ratings are between the inner fence of 5.25 and the outer fence of 3.0. The rating 1 is an extreme outlier (o) because this rating is outside the outer fence 3.0. These outliers are plotted in Figure 2.24(a). Part (b)

FIGURE **2.24**   A Box-and-Whiskers Display of the Satisfaction Ratings

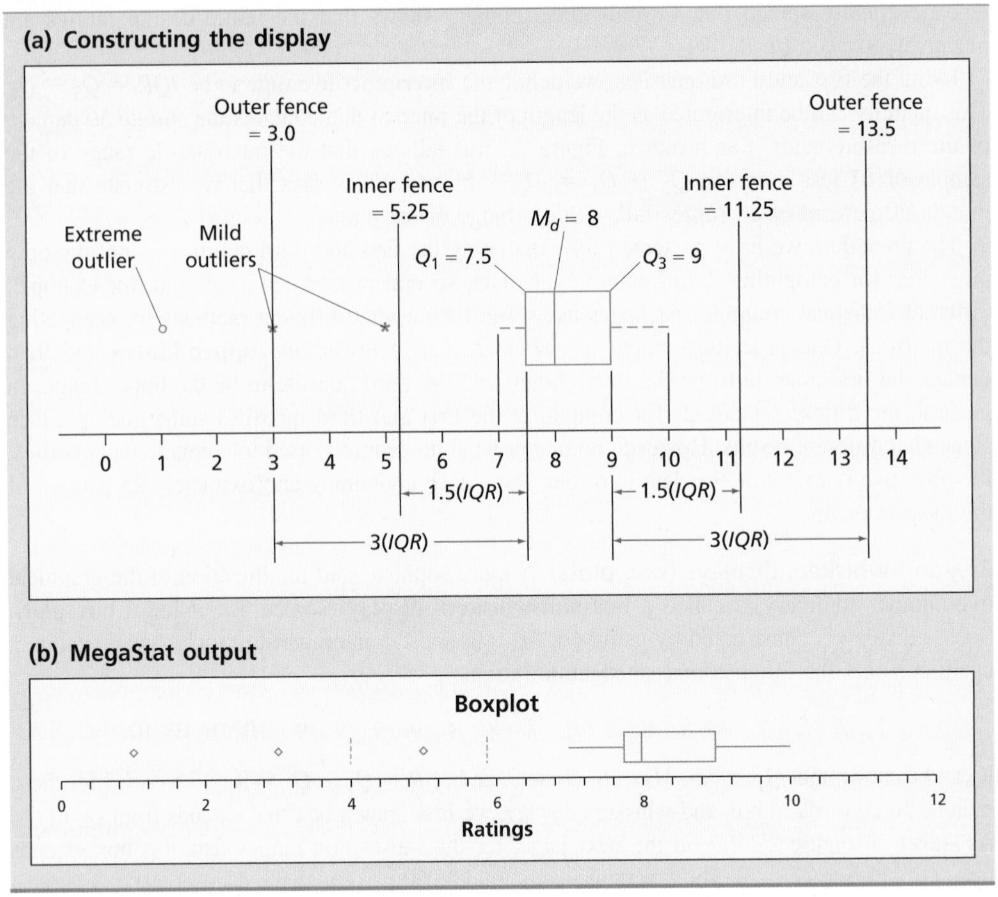

(a) Constructing the display

(b) MegaStat output

of Figure 2.24 gives the MegaStat output of the box-and-whiskers plot. Notice that MegaStat identifies the median by using a vertical line. In addition, MegaStat plots all outliers using the same symbol and marks the inner and outer fences using vertical dashed lines. Note here that MegaStat computes the quartiles Q_1 and Q_3 and the inner and outer fences using methods that differ slightly from the methods we have described. The MegaStat Help menus describe how the calculations are done. We now summarize how to construct a box-and-whiskers display:

Constructing a Box-and-Whiskers Display (Box Plot)

1   Draw a **box** that extends from the first quartile Q_1 to the third quartile Q_3. Also draw a vertical line through the box located at the median M_d.

2   Determine the values of the **inner fences** and **outer fences**. The inner fences are located 1.5 × IQR below Q_1 and 1.5 × IQR above Q_3. That is, the **inner fences** are

$Q_1 - 1.5(IQR)$ and $Q_3 + 1.5(IQR)$.

The outer fences are located 3 × IQR below Q_1 and 3 × IQR above Q_3. That is, the **outer fences** are

$Q_1 - 3(IQR)$ and $Q_3 + 3(IQR)$.

3   Draw **whiskers** as dashed lines that extend below Q_1 and above Q_3. Draw one whisker from Q_1 to the **smallest** measurement that is between the inner fences. Draw the other whisker from Q_3 to the **largest** measurement that is between the inner fences.

4   Measurements that are located between the inner and outer fences are called **mild outliers**. Plot these measurements using the symbol *.

5   Measurements that are located outside the outer fences are called **extreme outliers**. Plot these measurements using the symbol o.

FIGURE 2.25   MegaStat Output of a Stem-and-Leaf Display and Box Plot of Exam Scores

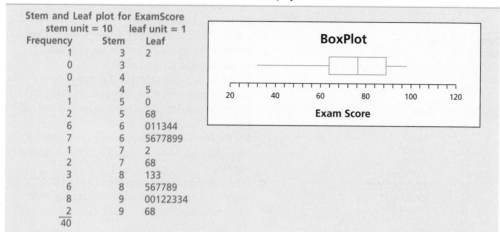

When interpreting a box-and-whiskers display, keep several points in mind. First, the box (between Q_1 and Q_3) contains the middle 50 percent of the data. Second, the median (which is inside the box) divides the data into two roughly equal parts. Third, if one of the whiskers is longer than the other, the data set is probably skewed in the direction of the longer whisker. Last, observations designated as outliers should be investigated. Understanding the causes behind the outlying observations will often provide useful information. For instance, understanding why several of the satisfaction ratings in the box plot of Figure 2.24 are substantially lower than the great majority of the ratings may suggest actions that can improve the DVD recorder manufacturer's product and/or service. Outliers can also be caused by inaccurate measuring, reporting, or plotting of the data. Such possibilities should be investigated, and incorrect data should be adjusted or eliminated.

Generally, a box plot clearly depicts the central tendency, variability, and overall range of a set of measurements. A box plot also portrays whether the measurements are symmetrically distributed. However, the exact shape of the distribution is better portrayed by a stem-and-leaf display and/or a histogram. For instance, Figure 2.25 shows the MegaStat output of the stem-and-leaf display and box plot of scores on a 100-point statistics exam. We see that although the box plot in Figure 2.25 tells us that the exam scores are somewhat negatively skewed with a tail to the left, it does not reveal the double-peaked nature of the exam score distribution. On the other hand, the stem-and-leaf display clearly shows that this distribution is double-peaked. In summary, graphical five-number summaries and box-and-whiskers displays are perhaps best used to compare different sets of measurements, for example, 3-month returns for investment funds of all types versus 12-month returns.

Exercises for Section 2.4

CONCEPTS

2.38 Explain each of the following in your own words: a percentile; the first quartile, Q_1; the third quartile, Q_3; and the interquartile range, IQR.

2.39 Suppose that you are using a box-and-whiskers display to depict a population or sample of measurements. How would you interpret each of the following?
  a. The whisker to the right is much longer than the whisker to the left.
  b. The interquartile range is much longer than either of the whiskers and there are no outliers.
  c. The distance between Q_1 and the median is far less than the distance between the median and Q_3.
  d. The interquartile range is very short.

METHODS AND APPLICATIONS

2.40 Consider the 65 game system satisfaction ratings, the 40 trash bag breaking strengths, and the 100 bank customer waiting times.
  a. Using the stem-and-leaf displays of these data sets on the next page, find for each data set
    (1) The 90th percentile.
    (2) The median.
    (3) The first quartile.
    (4) The third quartile.
    (5) The 10th percentile.
    (6) The interquartile range.
  b. Construct a five-number summary and a box-and-whiskers display for each data set.

MegaStat Stem-and-Leaf Display of the
65 Satisfaction Ratings

Stem and Leaf plot for Rating
stem unit = 1   leaf unit = 0.1

Frequency	Stem	Leaf
1	36	0
0	37	
3	38	000
4	39	0000
5	40	00000
6	41	000000
6	42	000000
8	43	00000000
12	44	000000000000
9	45	000000000
7	46	0000000
3	47	000
1	48	0
65		

MegaStat Stem-and-Leaf Display of the Waiting Times

Stem and Leaf plot for WaitTime
stem unit = 1   leaf unit = 0.1

Frequency	Stem	Leaf
2	0	4 8
6	1	1 3 4 6 8 8
9	2	0 2 3 4 5 7 8 9 9
11	3	1 2 4 5 6 7 7 8 8 9 9
17	4	0 0 1 2 3 3 3 4 4 5 5 5 6 7 7 8 9
15	5	0 1 1 2 2 3 4 4 5 6 6 7 8 8 8
13	6	1 1 2 3 3 3 4 5 5 6 7 7 8
10	7	0 2 2 3 4 4 5 7 8 9
7	8	0 1 3 4 6 6 7
6	9	1 2 3 5 8 9
3	10	2 7 9
1	11	6
100		

MegaStat Stem-and-Leaf Display of the Breaking Strengths

Stem and Leaf plot for Strength
stem unit = 1   leaf unit = 0.1

Frequency	Stem	Leaf
1	21	3
2	21	6 9
6	22	0 0 2 3 4 4
9	22	5 5 5 6 7 7 8 8 9
12	23	0 0 0 1 1 1 2 2 3 3 4 4
6	23	5 6 6 8 9 9
3	24	1 2 3
1	24	5
40		

2.41 Statistics Canada (http://www.statcan.gc.ca) provides data about the average number of days lost per worker by cause for each province. Listed in the next column

are the values of days lost for each province because of "Personal or Family Responsibility" (PorF) and "Illness or Disability" (IorD) for 2004.

a. For the Personal or Family Responsibility values, compute the mean, median, mode, standard deviation, variance, and range.

b. Based on the values computed in part a, describe the shape of the distribution (this exercise might be easier to complete if you create stem-and-leaf and box-and-whisker displays).

c. For the Illness or Disability values, compute the mean, median, mode, standard deviation, variance, and range.

d. Based on the values computed in part c, describe the shape of the distribution (this exercise might be easier to complete if you create stem-and-leaf and box-and-whisker displays).

Average Number of Days Lost per Worker by Cause

Province	PorF	IorD
Newfoundland and Labrador	1.5	8.8
Prince Edward Island	1.6	6.0
Nova Scotia	1.9	9.1
New Brunswick	1.7	8.0
Quebec	1.4	9.4
Ontario	1.9	6.7
Manitoba	1.8	8.0
Saskatchewan	2.2	8.0
Alberta	1.9	5.6
British Columbia	1.5	7.3

Source: Adapted from the Statistics Canada CANSIM database
http://cansim2.statcan.ca, table number 279-0029, February 2006.

2.42 In Section 2.4, we presented a commonly accepted way to compute the first, second, and third quartiles. Some statisticians, however, advocate an alternative method for computing Q_1 and Q_3. This method defines the first quartile, Q_1, as the **lower hinge** and the third quartile, Q_3, as the **upper hinge**. In order to calculate these quantities for a set of n measurements, we first arrange the measurements in increasing order. Then, if n is even, the lower hinge is the median of the smallest $n/2$ measurements, and the upper hinge is the median of the largest $n/2$ measurements. If n is odd, we insert M_d into the data set to obtain a set of $n + 1$ measurements. Then the lower hinge is the median of the smallest $(n + 1)/2$ measurements and the upper hinge is the median of the largest $(n + 1)/2$ measurements.

a. Consider a sample of $n = 20$ customer satisfaction ratings:

1 3 5 5 7 8 8 8 8 8   8 9 9 9 9 9 10 10 10 10

The smallest 10 ratings   The largest 10 ratings

Using the method presented in Section 2.4, find Q_1 and Q_3. Then find the lower hinge and the upper hinge for the satisfaction ratings. How do your results compare?

b. Consider the following sample of $n = 11$ doctors' salaries (in thousands of dollars):

127 132 138 141 146 152 154 171 177 192 241

Using the method presented in Section 2.4, find Q_1 and Q_3. The median of the 11 salaries is $M_d = 152$. If we insert this median into the data set, we obtain the following set of $n + 1 = 12$ salaries:

127 132 138 141 146 152   152 154 171 177 192 241

The smallest 6 salaries   The largest 6 salaries

Find the lower hinge and the upper hinge for the salaries. Compare your values of Q_1 and Q_3 with the lower and upper hinges.

c. For the 11 doctors' salaries, which quantities —Q_1, M_d, and Q_3 as defined in Section 2.4 or the lower hinge, M_d, and the upper hinge—in your opinion best divide the salaries into four parts?

2.5 DESCRIBING QUALITATIVE DATA

Bar charts and pie charts Recall that when we employ a qualitative or categorical variable we simply record into which of several categories a population element falls. For example, for each automobile produced in Canada we might record the manufacturer—Chrysler, Ford, General Motors, or some other manufacturer. We often display such data graphically. For instance, Table 2.15 gives the number of military personnel for each province in Canada in 2008 according to Statistics Canada (http://www.statcan.gc.ca). Figure 2.26 on the next page provides the same information in both a **bar chart** (a) and a **pie chart** (b) format.

In general, bar charts and pie charts are convenient ways to summarize the percentages of population units that are contained in several different categories.

Estimating proportions Suppose that a population unit can fall into one of several categories. We are often interested in a specific category, and, in such cases, we often wish to estimate

$p =$ the proportion of all population elements that are contained in the category of interest.

TABLE **2.15**   Military Personnel and Pay (Personnel)

	2008 Annual average number of employees[1]
Canada and outside Canada	**90,753**
Newfoundland and Labrador	1,287
Prince Edward Island	233
Nova Scotia	10,414
New Brunswick	5,812
Quebec	18,509
Ontario	30,932
Manitoba	4,013
Saskatchewan	1,105
Alberta	9,488
British Columbia	7,137
Yukon	x
Northwest Territories	156
Nunavut	x
Outside Canada	1,659

x: suppressed to meet the confidentiality requirements of the Statistics Act

Notes:
– Employment data are not in full-time equivalent and do not distinguish between full-time and part-time employees.
– As at December 31.

1. Civilian employees are excluded. Reservists are included as of January 1974.

Source: Statistics Canada, CANSIM, table (for free) 183-0004 and Catalogue no 68-213-XIB.
Last modified: 2009-08-27.

FIGURE 2.26 Number of Military Personnel by Province and Territory

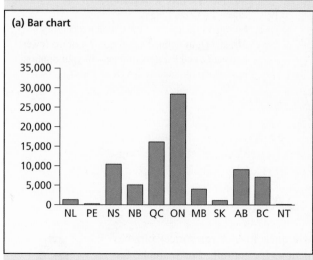

(a) Bar chart

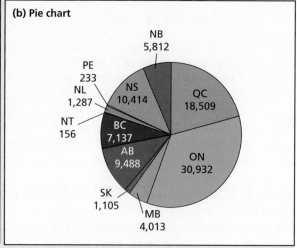

(b) Pie chart

In order to estimate this proportion, we can randomly select a sample from the population. Then the **sample proportion**

$\hat{p}$ = the proportion of the sample elements that are contained in the category of interest

is a reasonable point estimate of the **population proportion p**.

In the following examples, we introduce two new cases that illustrate estimating a population proportion p.

The Marketing Ethics Case: Estimating Marketing Researchers' Disapproval Rates

In the book *Essentials of Marketing Research*, Dillon, Madden, and Firtle discuss a survey of marketing professionals, the results of which were originally published by Akoah and Riordan in the *Journal of Marketing Research*. In the study, marketing researchers were presented with various scenarios involving ethical issues such as confidentiality, conflict of interest, and social acceptability. The marketing researchers were asked to indicate whether they approved or disapproved of the actions described in each scenario. For instance, one scenario that involved the issue of confidentiality was described as follows:

> **Use of ultraviolet ink** A project director went to the marketing research director's office and requested permission to use an ultraviolet ink to precode a questionnaire for a mail survey. The project director pointed out that although the cover letter promised confidentiality, respondent identification was needed to permit adequate cross-tabulations of the data. The marketing research director gave approval.

Of the 205 marketing researchers who participated in the survey, 117 said they disapproved of the actions taken in the scenario.

In this situation, we would like to make an inference about the population of all marketing researchers. Specifically, we wish to estimate the population proportion

p = the proportion of all marketing researchers who disapprove
of the actions taken in the ultraviolet ink scenario.

Because 117 of the 205 surveyed marketing researchers said they disapproved, the sample proportion

$$\hat{p} = \frac{117}{205} = 0.57$$

is the point estimate of p. This point estimate says we estimate that p, the proportion of all marketing researchers who disapprove, is 0.57. That is, we estimate that 57 percent of all marketing researchers disapprove of the actions taken in the ultraviolet ink scenario.

Example 2.12 The Electronic Article Surveillance Case: Estimating Consumer Reaction to False Alarms

In an article titled "Consumer responses to electronic article surveillance alarms" in the *Journal of Retailing*, Dawson studies the unintended effects of false electronic article surveillance (EAS) alarms. EAS, an important weapon used by retailers to combat shoplifting, places a small sensor on an item of merchandise. If a shoplifter attempts to exit the store with the item, an electronic alarm is set off by the sensor. When an item is legitimately purchased, the sales clerk removes the sensor to prevent the alarm from sounding when the customer exits the store. Sometimes, however, the clerk forgets to remove the sensor during the purchase. This results in a false alarm when the customer exits—an embarrassing situation for the customer. Such false alarms occur quite frequently. In fact, according to Dawson's article, "nearly half of all consumers have experienced an accidental EAS alarm."

Dawson conducted a survey to study consumer reaction to such false alarms. Based on a systematic random sample of 250 consumers, 40 of these consumers said that if they were to set off an EAS alarm because store personnel did not deactivate the merchandise, "they would never shop at the store again."

Suppose we wish to estimate p, the population proportion of all consumers who would say they would never shop at the store again if subjected to an EAS false alarm. Since 40 of the 250 sampled consumers said they would never shop at the store again, the sample proportion $\hat{p} = 40/250 = 0.16$ is the point estimate of p. This point estimate says we estimate that 16 percent of all consumers would say they would never shop at the store again if subjected to an EAS false alarm.

Finally, suppose a retailer is considering installing an EAS system. In an attempt to convince the retailer to purchase the system, a company that markets EAS systems claims that no more than 5 percent of consumers would say that they would never shop at a store again if they were subjected to an EAS false alarm. Based on Dawson's survey results, the retailer would have a hard time believing this claim. That is, the sample proportion $\hat{p} = 0.16$ suggests that more than 5 percent of all consumers would say that they would never shop at the store again. But is the evidence here conclusive? We will address this question in later chapters.

The Pareto chart A **Pareto charts** is used to help identify important quality problems and opportunities for process improvement. By using these charts we can prioritize problem-solving activities. The Pareto chart is named for Vilfredo Pareto (1848–1923), an Italian economist. Pareto suggested that in many economies, most of the wealth is held by a small minority of the population. It has been found that the **Pareto principle** often applies to defects. That is, only a few defect types account for most of a product's quality problems.

Here defects can be divided into two categories—the **vital few** and the **trivial many**. The vital few are the small number of defects that account for a large percentage of the total, while the trivial many are the large number of defects that account for the small remaining percentage of the total. If the vital few defects are very costly to an organization, it may wish to work on eliminating their causes before working to solve other problems.

To illustrate the use of Pareto charts, suppose that a jam producer wishes to evaluate the labels being placed on 500-mL jars of raspberry jam. Every day for two weeks, all defective labels found on inspection are classified by type of defect. If a label has more than one defect, we will record the type of defect that is most noticeable. The Excel output

FIGURE 2.27   Excel Frequency Table and Pareto Chart of Labelling Defects

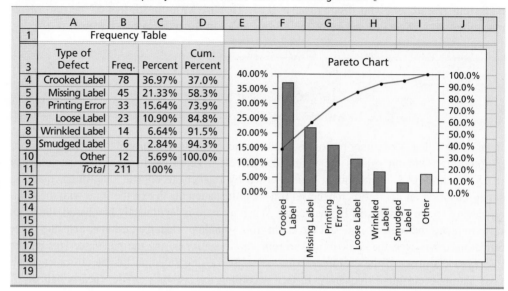

in Figure 2.27 presents the frequencies and percentages of the types of defects observed over the two-week period.

In general, the first step in setting up a Pareto chart summarizing data concerning types of defects (or categories) is to construct a frequency table like the one in Figure 2.27. Defects or categories should be listed at the left of the table in *decreasing order by frequencies*—the defect with the highest frequency will be at the top of the table, the defect with the second-highest frequency below the first, and so forth. If an "other" category is employed, it should be placed at the bottom of the table. The "other" category should make up less than 50 percent of the total of the frequencies, and the frequency for the "other" category should not exceed the frequency for the defect at the top of the table. If the frequency for the "other" category is too high, data should be collected so that the "other" category can be broken down into new categories. Once the frequency and the percentage for each category are determined, a cumulative percentage for each category is computed. As illustrated in Figure 2.27, the cumulative percentage for a particular category is the sum of the percentages corresponding to the particular category and the categories that are above that category in the table.

The Pareto chart is a **bar chart**. Different kinds of defects or problems are listed on the horizontal scale. The heights of the bars on the vertical scale typically represent the frequency of occurrence (or the percentage of occurrence) for each defect or problem. The bars are arranged in decreasing height from left to right. Thus, the most frequent defect will be at the far left, the next most frequent defect to its right, and so forth. If an "other" category is employed, its bar is placed at the far right. The Pareto chart for the labelling defects data is given in Figure 2.27. Here the heights of the bars represent the percentages of occurrences for the different labelling defects, and the vertical scale on the far left corresponds to these percentages. The chart graphically illustrates that crooked labels, missing labels, and printing errors are the most frequent labelling defects.

As is also illustrated in Figure 2.27, a Pareto chart is sometimes augmented by plotting a **cumulative percentage point** for each bar in the Pareto chart. The vertical coordinate of this cumulative percentage point equals the cumulative percentage in the frequency table corresponding to the bar. The cumulative percentage points corresponding to the different bars are connected by line segments, and a vertical scale corresponding to the cumulative percentages is placed on the far right. Examining the cumulative percentage points in Figure 2.27, we see that crooked and missing labels make up 58.3 percent of the labelling defects, and crooked labels, missing labels, and printing errors make up 73.9 percent of the labelling defects.

Exercises for Section 2.5

CONCEPTS

2.43 Find an example of a pie chart or a bar chart in a newspaper or magazine. Copy it, and hand it in with a written analysis of the information conveyed by the chart.

2.44 What is a population proportion? Give an example of a population proportion that might interest you in the profession you intend to enter.

METHODS AND APPLICATIONS

2.45 Statistics Canada reports on exports to other countries on a monthly basis. In Figure 2.28(a) are the export values to our principal trading partners for September 2006. Also presented are Excel bar and pie charts. Using these graphics, write an analysis of which visual presentation is the most informative and why.

2.46 In Figure 2.28(b) are the import values for Canada's principal trading partners for September 2006 as well as Excel bar and pie charts. Using these graphics, write an analysis of which visual presentation is the most informative and why.

2.47 Which chart (bar or pie chart) would you use to compare exports versus imports in Exercises 2.45 and 2.46?

2.48 **THE MARKETING ETHICS CASE: CONFLICT OF INTEREST**

Consider the marketing ethics case described in Example 2.11 on pages 64 and 65. One of the scenarios presented to the 205 marketing researchers is as follows:

> A marketing testing firm to which X company gives most of its business recently went public. The marketing research director of X company had been looking for a good investment and proceeded to buy $20,000 of their stock. The firm continues as X company's leading supplier for testing.

Of the 205 marketing researchers who participated in the ethics survey, 111 said that they disapproved of the actions taken in the scenario. Use this sample result to compute a point estimate of the proportion of all marketing researchers who disapprove of the actions taken in this conflict of interest scenario.

FIGURE 2.28   Export and Import Values for Canada's Principal Trading Partners

(a) Export Values

Country	Export ($ millions)
United States	29,208
Japan	882
United Kingdom	1,043
Other European Countries	1,885
All Others	4,865

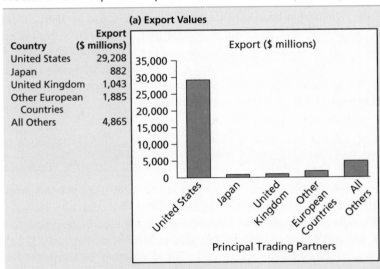
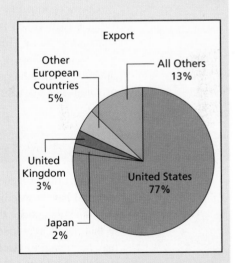

Source: Adapted from Statistics Canada CANSIM database, http://cansim2.statcan.ca, table no. 228-0001, March 2006.

(b) Import Values

Country	Import ($ millions)
United States	21,906
Japan	1,039
United Kingdom	942
Other European Countries	2,763
All Others	7,263

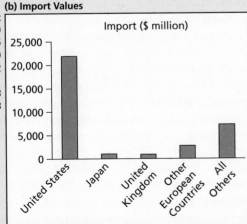
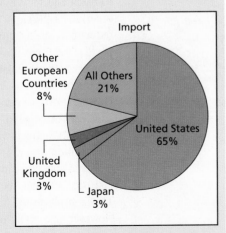

Source: Adapted from Statistics Canada CANSIM database, http://cansim2.statcan.ca, table no 228-0001, March 2006.

2.49 The Web site http://Morningstar.ca lists the Top 10 "Biggest" Canadian Mutual Funds. As of October 27, 2009, the largest fund was AGF Canadian Growth Equity. Morningstar uses pie charts to demonstrate the Asset Weights and Geographic Weights of each fund. To the right are the Asset Weights for AGF Canadian Growth Equity fund. Construct a pie chart of these data.

Category	% of Fund
Cash	0.1
Fixed Income	0.2
Canadian Equity	89.6
U.S. Equity	5.1
International Equity	0.7
Other	4.3

2.6 USING SCATTER PLOTS TO STUDY RELATIONSHIPS BETWEEN VARIABLES

CHAPTER 1

Statistical methods are often used to study and quantify relationships between variables. The purpose of studying such relationships is often to describe, predict, or control a variable of interest called the **dependent variable** (which is denoted y). We accomplish this by relating y to one or more other variables that are called **independent variables**. One way to relate variables is to perform **regression analysis**. This technique allows us to find an equation that relates y to the independent variable(s). Then, for instance, we might use the regression equation to predict y on the basis of the independent variable(s). We explain regression analysis in detail in Chapters 11 and 12. A simpler way to relate variables is to graphically study relationships between the variables. We discuss the graphical approach in this section.

One way to explore the relationship between a dependent variable y and an independent variable (denoted x) is to make a **scatter diagram**, or **scatter plot**, of y versus x. First, data concerning the two variables are observed in pairs. To construct the scatter plot, each value of y is plotted against its corresponding value of x. If y and x are related, the plot shows us the direction of the relationship. That is, y could be positively related to x (y increases as x increases) or y could be negatively related to x (y decreases as x increases).

Example 2.13 Requirements of a Bulk Chemical Product

A manufacturer produces a bulk chemical product. Customer requirements state that this product must have a specified viscosity when melted at a temperature of 150°C (viscosity measures how thick and gooey the product is when melted). Chemical XB-135 is used in the production of this chemical product, and the company's chemists feel that the amount of chemical XB-135 may be related to viscosity. In order to verify and quantify this relationship, 24 batches of the product are produced. The amount (x) of chemical XB-135 (in kilograms) is varied from batch to batch and the viscosity (y) obtained for each batch is measured. Table 2.16 gives (in time order) the values of x and the corresponding values of y obtained for the 24 batches. The Excel output of a scatter plot of y versus x is given in Figure 2.29. The scatter plot indicates a strong positive relationship between y and x—that is, as the amount of chemical XB-135 used is increased, the viscosity of the product increases. We must now be careful. It would be tempting to conclude that increases in the amount of chemical XB-135 *cause* increases in viscosity. However, this is not necessarily the case. Perhaps some other factor could be causing the apparent relationship. For instance, the 24 batches were produced in time order. If some other variable that affects viscosity (such as temperature or pressure in the reaction chamber, or the composition of a raw material) is changing over time, this change could be responsible for the observed increases in viscosity. Assuming that we have held other variables that may affect viscosity constant, the evidence supporting a cause-and-effect relationship may be quite strong. This is because the manufacturer has purposely varied the amount of chemical XB-135 used. However, it is really up to the scientific community to establish and understand any cause-and-effect relationship that may exist.

TABLE **2.16** Viscosity Data for 24 Batches of a Chemical Product Produced on August 1, 2010 🖉

Batch	Kilograms of Chemical XB-135 (x)	Viscosity (y)	Batch	Kilograms of Chemical XB-135 (x)	Viscosity (y)
1	10.0	31.76	13	11.2	32.93
2	10.0	31.91	14	11.2	33.19
3	10.2	32.02	15	11.4	33.35
4	10.2	31.85	16	11.4	32.76
5	10.4	32.17	17	11.6	33.33
6	10.4	32.30	18	11.6	33.19
7	10.6	32.60	19	11.8	33.28
8	10.6	32.15	20	11.8	33.57
9	10.8	32.52	21	12.0	33.60
10	10.8	32.46	22	12.0	33.43
11	11.0	32.41	23	12.2	33.91
12	11.0	32.77	24	12.2	33.76

FIGURE **2.29** Excel Output of a Scatter Plot of Viscosity versus Amount of Chemical XB-135

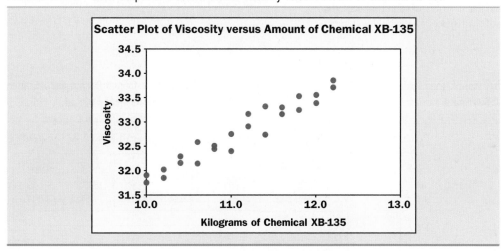

If we are convinced that we can control viscosity by changing the amount of chemical XB-135, we may wish to quantify the relationship between y and x. One way to do this is to calculate the **covariance** and the **correlation coefficient** between y and x. How this is done is discussed in Chapter 11. We would also like to develop an equation relating y to x. This can be done by using regression analysis (see Chapter 11). With such an equation, we can predict y on the basis of x, and we can determine the amount of chemical XB-135 to use in order to achieve a specified viscosity.

Because the plot points in Figure 2.29 seem to fluctuate around a straight line, we say that there is a **straight-line** (or **linear**) **relationship between y and x**. However, not all relationships are linear. For example, demand for a product, y, might increase at an increasing or decreasing rate as advertising expenditure to promote the product, x, increases. In this case, we say that there is a **curved relationship** between y and x. We discuss curved relationships in Chapter 12.

Exercises for Section 2.6

CONCEPTS

2.50 Draw a scatter plot of *y* versus *x* in which *y* increases in a linear (straight-line) fashion as *x* increases.

2.51 Draw a scatter plot of *y* versus *x* in which *y* decreases linearly as *x* increases.

2.52 What is the difference between a scatter plot and a runs plot?

METHODS AND APPLICATIONS

2.53 In the book *Essentials of Marketing Research*, Dillon, Madden, and Firtle present a scatter plot of the number of units sold of 20 varieties of a canned soup versus the amount of shelf space allocated to each variety. The scatter plot is shown in Figure 2.30.

   a. Does there appear to be a relationship between *y* (units sold) and *x* (shelf space)? Does the relationship appear to be straight-line (linear) or curved? How does *y* (units sold) change as *x* (shelf space) increases?

   b. If you were told that a variety of soup is allocated a small amount of shelf space, what would you guess about sales?

   c. Do you think that the amount of shelf space allocated to a variety causes sales to be higher or lower? Give an alternative explanation for the appearance of the scatter plot.

2.54 **THE FAST-FOOD RESTAURANT RATING CASE**

Recently, researchers at The Ohio State University studied U.S. consumer ratings of fast-food restaurants. Each of 406 randomly selected individuals rated the six fast-food restaurants shown in the Excel output of Figure 2.31. Each individual gave each restaurant a rating of 1, 2, 3, 4, 5, or 6 on the basis of taste, convenience, familiarity, and price and then ranked the restaurants from 1 through 6 on the basis of overall preference. In each case, 1 is the best rating and 6 the worst. The mean ratings given by the 406 individuals are given in Figure 2.31 along with a scatter plot of mean preference versus mean taste. Construct scatter plots of mean preference versus each of mean convenience, mean familiarity, and mean price. Then interpret all the scatter plots.

FIGURE **2.30**   A Scatter Plot of Units Sold versus Shelf Space

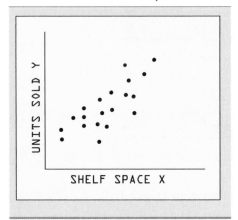

Source: *Essentials of Marketing Research*, by W. R. Dillon, T. J. Madden, and N. H. Firtle (Burr Ridge, IL: Richard D. Irwin, 1993), p. 452. Copyright © 1993. Reprinted by permission of McGraw-Hill Companies, Inc.

FIGURE **2.31**   Excel Output of the Mean Restaurant Ratings and a Scatter Plot of Mean Preference versus Mean Taste

	A	B	C	D	E	F
1	Restaurant	Meantaste	Meanconv	Meanfam	Meanprice	Meanpref
2	Borden Burger	3.5659	2.7005	2.5282	2.9372	4.2552
3	Hardee's	3.329	3.3483	2.7345	2.7513	4.0911
4	Burger King	2.4231	2.7377	2.3368	3.0761	3.0052
5	McDonald's	2.0895	1.938	1.4619	2.4884	2.2429
6	Wendy's	1.9661	2.892	2.3376	4.0814	2.5351
7	White Castle	3.8061	3.7242	2.6515	1.708	4.7812

Source: The Ohio State University.

2.7 MISLEADING GRAPHS AND CHARTS

The statistical analyst's goal should be to present the most accurate and truthful portrayal of a data set that is possible. Such a presentation allows managers using the analysis to make informed decisions. However, it is possible to construct statistical summaries that are misleading. Although we do not advocate using misleading statistics, you should be aware of some of the ways statistical graphs and charts can be manipulated in order to distort the truth. By knowing what to look for, you can avoid being misled by a small number of unscrupulous practitioners.

As an example, suppose that the faculty at a major university will soon vote on a proposal to join a union. Both the union organizers and the university administration plan to distribute recent salary statistics to the entire faculty. Suppose that the mean faculty salary at the university and the mean salary increase at the university (expressed as a percentage) for each of the years 2007 through 2010 are as follows:

Year	Mean Salary (All Ranks)	Mean Salary Increase
2007	$60,000	3.0%
2008	61,600	4.0
2009	63,500	4.5
2010	66,100	6.0

The university administration does not want the faculty to unionize and, therefore, hopes to convince the faculty that substantial progress has been made to increase salaries without a union. On the other hand, the union organizers wish to portray the salary increases as minimal so that the faculty will feel the need to unionize.

Figure 2.32 gives two bar charts of the mean salaries at the university for each year from 2007 to 2010. Notice that in Figure 2.32(a) the administration has started the vertical scale of the bar chart at a salary of $58,000 by using a **scale break** (⌇). Alternatively, the chart could be set up without the scale break by simply starting the vertical scale at $58,000. Starting the vertical scale at a value far above zero makes the salary increases look more dramatic. Notice that when the union organizers present the bar chart in Figure 2.32(b), which has a vertical scale starting at zero, the salary increases look far less impressive.

Figure 2.33 on the next page presents two bar charts of the mean salary increases (in percentages) at the university for each year from 2007 to 2010. In Figure 2.33(a), the administration has made the widths of the bars representing the percentage increases proportional to their heights. This makes the upward movement in the mean salary increases look more dramatic because the observer's eye tends to compare the areas of the bars, while the improvements in the mean salary increases are really only proportional to the heights of the bars. When the union organizers present the bar chart of Figure 2.33(b), the improvements in the mean salary increases look less impressive because each bar has the same width.

Figure 2.34 on the next page gives two runs plots (also called **time series plots**) of the mean salary increases at the university from 2007 to 2010. In Figure 2.34(a), the administration has stretched the vertical axis of the graph. That is, the vertical axis is set up so that the distances between the percentages are large. This makes the upward trend of the mean salary increases

FIGURE **2.32** Two Bar Charts of the Mean Salaries at a Major University from 2007 to 2010

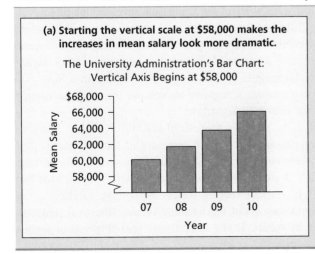
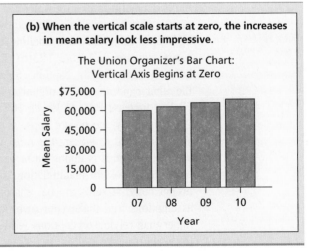

(a) Starting the vertical scale at $58,000 makes the increases in mean salary look more dramatic.

The University Administration's Bar Chart: Vertical Axis Begins at $58,000

(b) When the vertical scale starts at zero, the increases in mean salary look less impressive.

The Union Organizer's Bar Chart: Vertical Axis Begins at Zero

FIGURE 2.33 Two Bar Charts of the Mean Salary Increases at a Major University from 2007 to 2010

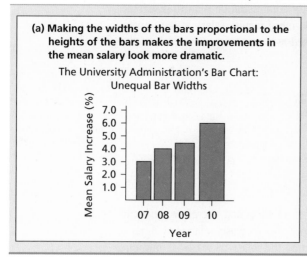

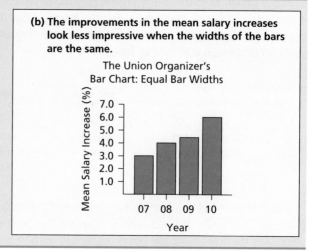

FIGURE 2.34 Two Runs Plots of the Mean Salary Increases at a Major University from 2007 to 2010

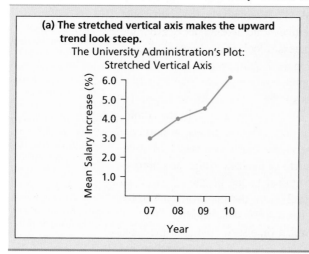

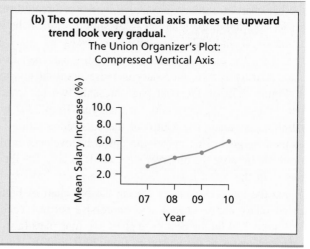

appear to be steep. In Figure 2.34(b), the union organizers have compressed the vertical axis (that is, the distances between the percentages are small). This makes the upward trend of the mean salary increases appear to be gradual. As we will see in the exercises, stretching and compressing the horizontal axis in a runs plot can also greatly affect the impression given by the plot.

It is also possible to create totally different interpretations of the same statistical summary by simply using different labelling or captions. For example, consider the bar chart of mean salary increases in Figure 2.33(b). To create a favourable interpretation, the university administration might use the caption "Salary Increase Is Higher for the Fourth Year in a Row." On the other hand, the union organizers might create a negative impression by using the caption "Salary Increase Fails to Reach 10% for Fourth Straight Year."

In summary, we do not approve of using statistics to mislead and distort reality. Statistics should be used to present the most truthful and informative summary of the data that is possible. However, it is important to carefully study any statistical summary so that you will not be misled. Look for manipulations such as stretched or compressed axes on graphs, axes that do not begin at zero, and bar charts with bars of varying widths. Also think carefully about assumptions, and make your own conclusions about the meaning of any statistical summary rather than relying on captions written by others. Doing these things will help you to see the truth and to make well-informed decisions.

Exercises for Section 2.7

CONCEPTS

2.55 When you construct a bar chart or graph, what is the effect of starting the vertical axis at a value that is far above zero? Explain.

2.56 Find an example of a misleading use of statistics in a newspaper, magazine, corporate annual report, or other source. Then explain why your example is misleading.

METHODS AND APPLICATIONS

2.57 Figure 2.35 gives two more time series plots of the previously discussed salary increases. In Figure 2.35(a), the administration has compressed the horizontal axis. In Figure 2.35(b), the union organizers have stretched the horizontal axis. Discuss the different impressions given by the two time series plots.

2.58 In the article "How to display data badly" in the May 1984 issue of *The American Statistician*, Wainer

presents a stacked bar chart of the number of public and private elementary schools (1929–1970). This bar chart is given in Figure 2.36. Wainer also gives a line graph of the number of private elementary schools (1930–1970). This graph is shown in Figure 2.37.

a. Looking at the bar chart of Figure 2.36, does there appear to be an increasing trend in the number of private elementary schools from 1930 to 1970?

b. Looking at the line graph of Figure 2.37, does there appear to be an increasing trend in the number of private elementary schools from 1930 to 1970?

c. Which portrayal of the data do you think is more appropriate? Explain.

d. Is either portrayal of the data entirely appropriate? Explain.

FIGURE 2.35 Two Runs Plots of the Mean Salary Increases at a Major University from 2007 to 2010

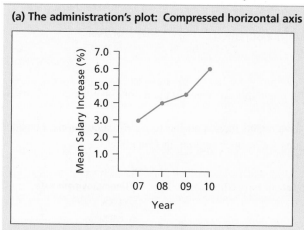 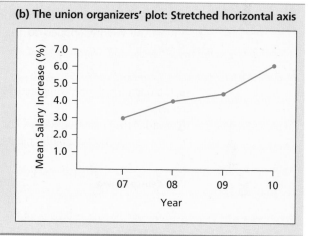

(a) The administration's plot: Compressed horizontal axis

(b) The union organizers' plot: Stretched horizontal axis

FIGURE 2.36 Wainer's Stacked Bar Chart

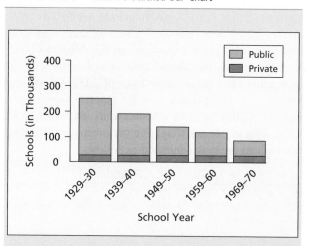

FIGURE 2.37 Wainer's Line Graph

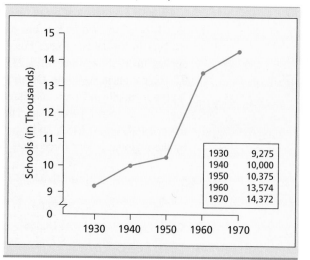

2.8 WEIGHTED MEANS AND GROUPED DATA

Weighted means In Section 2.2, we studied the mean, which is an important measure of central tendency. In order to calculate a mean, we sum the population (or sample) measurements and then divide this sum by the number of measurements in the population (or sample). When we do this, each measurement counts equally. That is, each measurement is given the same importance or weight.

Sometimes it makes sense to give different measurements unequal weights. In such a case, a measurement's weight reflects its importance, and the mean calculated using the unequal weights is called a **weighted mean**.

We calculate a weighted mean by multiplying each measurement by its weight, summing the resulting products, and dividing the resulting sum by the sum of the weights:

> **Weighted Mean**
>
> The weighted mean equals[4]
>
> $$\frac{\sum w_i x_i}{\sum w_i},$$
>
> where
> x_i = the value of the ith measurement,
> w_i = the weight applied to the ith measurement.

Such a quantity can be computed for a population of measurements or for a sample of measurements.

In order to illustrate the need for a weighted mean and the required calculations, consider the September 2009 unemployment rates for various regions in Canada:[5]

Census Region	Civilian Labour Force (Thousands)	Unemployment Rate
Atlantic	1,235	11.2%
Quebec	4,197	8.8%
Ontario	7,182	9.2%
West	5,774	6.1%

If we wish to compute a mean unemployment rate for Canada, we should use a weighted mean. This is because each of the four regional unemployment rates applies to a different number of workers in the labour force. For example, the 11.2 percent unemployed for Atlantic Canada applies to a labour force of 1,235,000 workers and thus should count less heavily than the 9.2 percent unemployed for Ontario, which applies to a larger labour force of 7,182,000 workers.

The unemployment rate measurements are x_1 = 11.2 percent, x_2 = 8.8 percent, x_3 = 9.2 percent, and x_4 = 6.1 percent, and the weights applied to these measurements are w_1 = 1,235, w_2 = 4,197, w_3 = 7,182, and w_4 = 5,774. That is, we are weighting the unemployment rates by the regional labour force sizes. The weighted mean is computed as follows:

$$\mu = \frac{1{,}235(11.2) + 4{,}197(8.8) + 7{,}182(9.2) + 5{,}774(6.1)}{1{,}235 + 4{,}197 + 7{,}182 + 5{,}774}$$
$$= \frac{152{,}061.4}{18{,}388}$$
$$= 8.27\%.$$

---

[4]We often drop the indices when using sigma (Σ) notation when it is clear what we are summing.
[5]Source: Adapted from the Statistics Canada CANSIM database http://cansim2.statcan.ca, table number 282-0087, October 2009.

In this case, the unweighted mean of the four regional unemployment rates is 8.825 percent. Therefore, the unweighted mean overestimates the Canadian unemployment rate by 0.56 percentage points (or overestimates Canadian unemployment by 0.0056(18,387,800) = 102,972 workers).

The weights chosen for calculating a weighted mean will vary depending on the situation. For example, in order to compute the mean percentage return for a portfolio of investments, the percentage returns for various investments might be weighted by the dollar amounts invested in each. Or, in order to compute a mean profit margin for a company consisting of several divisions, the profit margins for the different divisions might be weighted by the sales volumes of the divisions. Again, the idea is to choose weights that represent the relative importance of the measurements in the population or sample.

Descriptive statistics for grouped data We usually calculate measures of central tendency and variability using the individual measurements in a population or sample. However, sometimes the only data available are in the form of a frequency distribution or a histogram. For example, newspapers and magazines often summarize data using frequency distributions and histograms without giving the individual measurements in a data set. Data summarized in frequency distribution or histogram form are often called **grouped data**. In this section, we show how to compute descriptive statistics for such data.

Suppose we are given a frequency distribution summarizing a sample of 65 customer satisfaction ratings for a consumer product.

Satisfaction Rating	Frequency
36–38	4
39–41	15
42–44	25
45–47	19
48–50	2

Because we do not know each of the 65 individual satisfaction ratings, we cannot compute an exact value for the mean satisfaction rating. However, we can calculate an approximation of this mean. In order to do this, we use the midpoint of each class to represent the measurements in the class. When we do this, we are really assuming that the average of the measurements in each class equals the class midpoint. Letting M_i denote the midpoint of class i, and letting f_i denote the frequency of class i, we compute the mean by calculating a weighted mean of the class midpoints using the class frequencies as the weights. The logic here is that if f_i measurements are included in class i, then the midpoint of class i should count f_i times in the weighted mean. In this case, the sum of the weights equals the sum of the class frequencies, which equals the sample size. Therefore, we obtain the following equation for the sample mean of grouped data:

Sample Mean for Grouped Data

$$\bar{x} = \frac{\sum f_i M_i}{\sum f_i} = \frac{\sum f_i M_i}{n},$$

where
   f_i = the frequency for class i,
   M_i = the midpoint for class i,
   $n = \sum f_i$ = the sample size.

TABLE **2.17**   Calculating the Sample Mean of the Satisfaction Rating

Satisfaction Rating	Frequency (f_i)	Class Midpoint (M_i)	f_iM_i
36–38	4	37	$4(37) = 148$
39–41	15	40	$15(40) = 600$
42–44	25	43	$25(43) = 1{,}075$
45–47	19	46	$19(46) = 874$
48–50	2	49	$2(49) = 98$
	$n = 65$		2,795

$$\bar{x} = \frac{\sum f_iM_i}{n} = \frac{2{,}795}{65} = 43$$

Table 2.17 summarizes the calculation of the mean satisfaction rating for the previously given frequency distribution of satisfaction ratings. Note that in this table each midpoint is halfway between its corresponding class limits. For example, for the first class $M_1 = (36 + 38)/2 = 37$. We find that the sample mean satisfaction rating is 43.

We can also compute an approximation of the sample variance for grouped data. Recall that when we compute the sample variance using individual measurements, we compute the squared deviation from the sample mean $(x_i - \bar{x})^2$ for each individual measurement x_i and then sum the squared deviations. For grouped data, we do not know each of the x_i values. Because of this, we again let the class midpoint M_i represent each measurement in class i. It follows that we compute the squared deviation $(M_i - \bar{x})^2$ for each class and then sum these squares, weighting each squared deviation by its corresponding class frequency f_i. That is, we approximate $\sum (x_i - \bar{x})^2$ by using $\sum f_i(M_i - \bar{x})^2$. Finally, we obtain the sample variance for the grouped data by dividing this quantity by the sample size minus 1. We summarize this calculation in the following box:

Sample Variance for Grouped Data

$$s^2 = \frac{\sum f_i(M_i - \bar{x})^2}{n - 1},$$

where $\bar{x}$ is the sample mean for the grouped data.

Table 2.18 illustrates calculating the sample variance of the previously given frequency distribution of satisfaction ratings. We find that the sample variance is $s^2 = 8.15625$ and, therefore, that the sample standard deviation is $s = \sqrt{8.15625} = 2.8559$.

Finally, although we have illustrated calculating the mean and variance for grouped data in the context of a sample, similar calculations can be done for a population of measurements. If we

TABLE **2.18**   Calculating the Sample Variance of the Satisfaction Ratings

Satisfaction Rating	Frequency f_i	Class Midpoint M_i	Deviation $(M_i - \bar{x})$	Squared Deviation $(M_i - \bar{x})^2$	$f_i(M_i - \bar{x})^2$
36–38	4	37	$37 - 43 = -6$	36	$4(36) = 144$
39–41	15	40	$40 - 43 = -3$	9	$15(9) = 135$
42–44	25	43	$43 - 43 = 0$	0	$25(0) = 0$
45–47	19	46	$46 - 43 = 3$	9	$19(9) = 171$
48–50	2	49	$49 - 43 = 6$	36	$2(36) = 72$
	65				$\sum f_i(M_i - \bar{x})^2 = 522$

$$s^2 = \text{sample variance} = \frac{\sum f_i(M_i - \bar{x})^2}{n - 1} = \frac{522}{65 - 1} = 8.15625$$

let N be the size of the population, the grouped data formulas for the population mean and variance are given in the following box:

Population Mean for Grouped Data	**Population Variance for Grouped Data**
$$\mu = \frac{\sum f_i M_i}{N}$$	$$\sigma^2 = \frac{\sum f_i (M_i - \mu)^2}{N}$$

Exercises for Section 2.8

CONCEPTS

2.59 Consider calculating a student's grade point average using a scale where 4.0 represents an A and 0.0 represents an F. Explain why the grade point average is a weighted mean. What are the x_i values? What are the weights?

2.60 When you perform grouped data calculations, you represent the measurements in a class by using the midpoint of the class. Describe the assumption that is being made when you do this.

2.61 When we compute the mean, variance, and standard deviation using grouped data, the results obtained are approximations of the population (or sample) mean, variance, and standard deviation. Explain why this is true.

METHODS AND APPLICATIONS

2.62 The 2010 total return percentages for several popular funds were as follows:

Fund	2010 Total Return %
Fund A	10.7
Fund B	21.7
Fund C	9.9
Fund D	5.8
Fund E	5.5

Suppose that an investor had $100,000 invested in Fund A, $500,000 invested in Fund B, $500,000 invested in Fund C, $200,000 invested in Fund D, and $50,000 invested in Fund E.
  a. Compute a weighted mean that measures the 2010 average total return for the investor's portfolio.
  b. Compare your weighted mean with the unweighted mean of the five total return percentages. Explain why they differ.

2.63 The following are the 2009 unemployment rates and civilian labour force sizes for five provinces in Canada.

Province	Size of Civilian Labour Force (Thousands)	Unemployment Rate (%)
NL	255.9	15.3
PE	78.9	11.8
NS	499.6	9.5
NB	400.1	8.1
QC	4,196.7	8.8

Source: Adapted from the Statistics Canada CANSIM database, http://cansim2.statcan.ca, table number 282-0087, October 2009.

Using a weighted mean, compute an average unemployment rate for the five provinces.

2.64 The following frequency distribution summarizes the masses of 195 fish caught by anglers participating in a professional fishing tournament.

Mass (kg)	Frequency
1–3	53
4–6	118
7–9	21
10–12	3

  a. Calculate the (approximate) sample mean for these data.
  b. Calculate the (approximate) sample variance for these data.

2.65 The following is a frequency distribution summarizing earnings per share (EPS) growth data for 30 firms.

EPS Growth (Percent)	Frequency
0–49	1
50–99	17
100–149	5
150–199	4
200–249	1
250–299	2

Calculate the (approximate) population mean, variance, and standard deviation for these data.

2.66 The Data and Story Library Web site (a Web site devoted to applications of statistics) gives a histogram of the ages of a sample of 60 CEOs taken in 1993. We present the data in the form of a frequency distribution to the right. Calculate the (approximate) sample mean, variance, and standard deviation of these data.

Age (Years)	Frequency
28–32	1
33–37	3
38–42	3
43–47	13
48–52	14
53–57	12
58–62	9
63–67	1
68–72	3
73–77	1

Source: http://lib.stat.cmu.edu/DASL/Stories/ceo.html, April 15, 2005.

CHAPTER SUMMARY

We began this chapter by studying how to depict the shape of the distribution of a data set. We learned that **stem-and-leaf displays** and **histograms** are useful graphics for portraying a data set's distribution. We also learned about some common population shapes. We saw that data sets often have shapes that are **symmetrical**, **positively skewed (with a tail to the right)**, or **negatively skewed (with a tail to the left)**.

Next we presented and compared several measures of **central tendency**. We defined the **population mean** and we saw how to estimate it by using a **sample mean**. We also defined the **median** and **mode**, and we compared the mean, median, and mode for symmetrical distributions and for distributions that are positively or negatively skewed (to the right or left). We then studied measures of **variation** (or **spread**). We defined the **range**, **variance**, and **standard deviation**, and we saw how to estimate a population variance and standard deviation by using a sample. We learned that a good way to interpret the standard deviation when a population is (approximately) normally distributed is to use the **empirical rule**,

and we applied this rule to assess **process capability**. We next studied **Chebyshev's theorem**, which gives us intervals containing reasonably large fractions of the population units no matter what the population's shape might be. We also saw that when a data set is highly skewed, it is best to use **percentiles** and **quartiles** to measure variation, and we learned how to construct a **box-and-whiskers display** by using the quartiles.

After learning how to measure and depict central tendency and variability, we presented several methods for portraying qualitative data. In particular, we used **bar charts** for this purpose. We also discussed using a sample to estimate the proportion of population units that fall into a category of interest.

We studied using **scatter plots** to examine relationships between variables. Next we discussed misleading graphs and statistics, and we explained some of the tactics that are commonly used to try to distort the truth. We concluded with the concept of a **weighted mean** and then explained how to compute descriptive statistics for **grouped data**.

GLOSSARY OF TERMS

bar chart: A graphical display of categorical data (data in categories) made up of vertical or horizontal bars. (page 63)

box-and-whiskers display (box plot): A graphical portrayal of a data set that depicts both the central tendency and the variability of the data. It is constructed using Q_1, M_d, and Q_3. (page 59)

capable process: A process that is able to consistently produce output that meets (or conforms to) specifications (requirements). (page 51)

central tendency: A term referring to the middle of a population or sample of measurements. (page 38)

Chebyshev's theorem: A theorem that (for any population) allows us to find an interval that contains a specified percentage of the individual measurements in the population. (page 52)

coefficient of variation: A quantity that measures the variation of a population or sample relative to its mean. (page 54)

dependent variable (denoted y): A variable that we wish to describe, predict, or control. (page 68)

empirical rule: For a normally distributed population, this rule tells us that 68.26 percent, 95.44 percent, and 99.73 percent of the population measurements are within one, two, and three standard deviations, respectively, of the population mean. (page 49)

extreme outlier (in a box-and-whiskers display): A measurement located outside the outer fences. (page 59)

first quartile (denoted Q_1): A value below which approximately 25 percent of the measurements lie; the 25th percentile. (page 58)

frequency: The count of the number of measurements in a class or the number of measurements with a particular value. (page 27)

frequency distribution: A numerical summary that divides the values of a variable into classes and gives the number of values in each class. (pages 27)

grouped data: Data presented in the form of a frequency distribution or a histogram. (page 75)

histogram: A graphical portrayal of a data set that shows the data set's distribution. It divides the data into classes and gives the

frequency for each class. Histograms are particularly useful for summarizing large data sets. (page 27)

independent variable (denoted x): A predictor variable that can be used to describe, predict, or control a dependent variable. (page 68)

inner fences (in a box-and-whiskers display): Points located $1.5 \times IQR$ below Q_1 and $1.5 \times IQR$ above Q_3. (page 59)

interquartile range (denoted IQR): The difference between the third quartile and the first quartile (that is, $Q_3 - Q_1$). (page 59)

median (denoted M_d): A measure of central tendency that divides a population or sample into two roughly equal parts. (page 40)

mild outlier (in a box-and-whiskers display): A measurement located between the inner and outer fences. (page 59)

mode (denoted M_o): The measurement in a sample or a population that occurs most frequently. (page 41)

mound-shaped: Description of a relative frequency curve that is "piled up in the middle." (page 52)

negatively skewed (to the left): Description of a relative frequency curve with a long tail to the left. (page 31)

normal curve: A bell-shaped, symmetrical relative frequency curve. We will present the exact equation that gives this curve in Chapter 5. (page 31)

outer fences: Points located $3 \times IQR$ below Q_1 and $3 \times IQR$ above Q_3. (page 59)

outlier: An unusually large or small observation that is well separated from the remaining observations. (page 33)

Pareto chart: A bar chart of the frequencies or percentages for various types of defects. These are used to identify opportunities for improvement. (page 65)

percentile: The value such that a specified percentage of the measurements in a population or sample fall at or below it. (page 53)

point estimate: A one-number estimate for the value of a population parameter. (page 39)

population mean (denoted μ): The average of a population of measurements. (page 38)

population parameter: A descriptive measure of a population. It is calculated using the population measurements. (page 38)

population proportion (denoted p): The proportion of population units that are contained in a category of interest. (page 64)

population standard deviation (denoted σ): The square root of the population variance. It is a measure of the variation of the population measurements. (page 47)

population variance (denoted σ^2): The average of the squared deviations of the individual population measurements from the population mean. It is a measure of the variation of the population measurements. (page 47)

positively skewed (to the right): Description of a relative frequency curve with a long tail to the right. (page 31)

range: The difference between the largest and smallest measurements in a population or sample. It is a simple measure of variation. (page 47)

relative frequency: The frequency of a class divided by the total number of measurements. (page 28)

relative frequency histogram: A graphical portrayal of a data set that shows the data set's distribution. It divides the data into classes, gives the relative frequency for each class, and is particularly useful for summarizing large data sets. (page 29)

sample mean (denoted $\bar{x}$): The average of the measurements in a sample. It is the point estimate of the population mean. (page 39)

sample proportion (denoted $\hat{p}$): The proportion of sample elements that are contained in a category of interest. (page 64)

sample size (denoted n): The number of measurements in a sample. (page 39)

sample standard deviation (denoted s): The square root of the sample variance. It is the point estimate of the population standard deviation. (page 48)

sample statistic: A descriptive measure of a sample. It is calculated from the measurements in the sample. (page 39)

sample variance (denoted s^2): A measure of the variation of the sample measurements. It is the point estimate of the population variance. (page 48)

scatter plot: A plot of the values of a dependent variable y versus the values of an independent variable x. (page 68)

stem-and-leaf display: A graphical portrayal of a data set that shows the data set's distribution. It displays the data in the form of stems and leaves. (page 26)

third quartile (denoted Q_3): A value below which approximately 75 percent of the measurements lie; the 75th percentile. (page 58)

tolerance interval: An interval of numbers that contains a specified percentage of the individual measurements in a population. (page 50)

weighted mean: A mean where different measurements are given different weights based on their importance. (page 74)

z score (of a measurement): The number of standard deviations that a measurement is from the mean. This quantity indicates the relative location of a measurement within its distribution. (page 53)

IMPORTANT FORMULAS

The sample mean, $\bar{x}$: page 39

The sample variance, s^2: page 48

The sample standard deviation, s: page 48

Computational formula for s^2: page 49

The empirical rule: page 49

Chebyshev's theorem: page 52

z score: page 53

The coefficient of variation: page 54

The pth percentile: page 57

The weighted mean: page 74

Sample mean for grouped data: page 75

Sample variance for grouped data: page 76

Population mean for grouped data: page 77

Population variance for grouped data: page 77

Mc Graw Hill **connect** ™ Practise and learn online with *Connect*. Questions and tables with online data sets are marked with 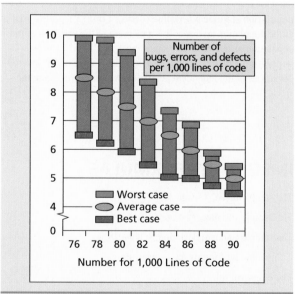.

SUPPLEMENTARY EXERCISES

2.67 In the book *Modern Statistical Quality Control and Improvement*, Farnum presents data concerning the elapsed times from the completion of medical lab tests until the results are recorded on patients' charts. Table 2.19 gives the times it took (in hours) to deliver and chart the results of 84 lab tests over one week.

   a. Construct a frequency histogram and a relative frequency histogram for the lab test waiting time data.

   b. Looking at the histogram, are most of the test results delivered and charted within several hours?

   c. Are there some deliveries with excessively long waiting times? Which deliveries might be investigated in order to discover reasons behind unusually long delays?

2.68 Figure 2.38 depicts data for a study of 80 software projects at NASA's Goddard Space Center. The figure shows the number of bugs per 1,000 lines of code from 1976 to 1990. Write a short paragraph describing how the reliability of the software has improved. Explain how the data indicate improvement.

2.69 It is well known to long-term investors that portfolio diversification is important. The motto "Don't put all your eggs in one basket" rings very true in this case. That is, investors should invest in a variety of investments with differing levels of historical return and risk. This risk is often measured in terms of the volatility of an investment over time. When volatility, sometimes referred to as

standard deviation, increases, so too does the level of return. The opposite is also true.

The answer seems to lie in asset allocation. Investment experts know the importance of asset allocation. In a nutshell, asset allocation is a method of creating a diversified portfolio of investments that minimize historical risk and maximize potential returns to help you meet your retirement goals and needs.

The mean return and standard deviation combinations for the various investment classes are shown in Table 2.20.

Suppose that future returns of each investment class will continue to behave in the future as they have over the past ten years. That is, for each investment class, regard the mean return and standard deviation in Table 2.20 as the population mean and the population standard deviation of all possible future returns. Then do the following:

   a. Assuming that future returns for the various investment classes are mound-shaped, for each investment class compute intervals that will contain approximately 68.26 percent and 99.73 percent of all future returns.

   b. Making no assumptions about the population shapes of future returns, for each investment class, compute the intervals that will contain at least 75 percent and 88.89 percent of all future returns.

   c. Assuming that future returns are mound-shaped, find

      (1) An estimate of the maximum return that might be realized for each investment class.

      (2) An estimate of the minimum return (or maximum loss) that might be realized for each investment class.

TABLE **2.19** Elapsed Time (in Hours) for Completing and Delivering Medical Lab Tests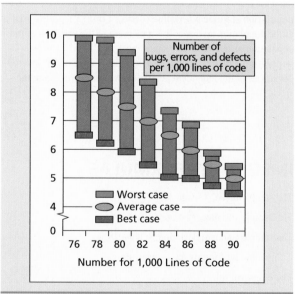

6.1	8.7	1.1	4.0
2.1	3.9	2.2	5.0
2.1	7.1	4.3	8.8
3.5	1.2	3.2	1.3
1.3	9.3	4.2	7.3
5.7	6.5	4.4	16.2
1.3	1.3	3.0	2.7
15.7	4.9	2.0	5.2
3.9	13.9	1.8	2.2
8.4	5.2	11.9	3.0
24.0	24.5	24.8	24.0
1.7	4.4	2.5	16.2
17.8	2.9	4.0	6.7
5.3	8.3	2.8	5.2
17.5	1.1	3.0	8.3
1.2	1.1	4.5	4.4
5.0	2.6	12.7	5.7
4.7	5.1	2.6	1.6
3.4	8.1	2.4	16.7
4.8	1.7	1.9	12.1
9.1	5.6	13.0	6.4

Source: *Modern Statistical Quality Control and Improvement*, by N. R. Farnum (Belmont, CA: Duxbury Press, 1994), p. 55. Reprinted by permission of Brooks/Cole, an imprint of the Wadsworth Group, a division of Thompson Learning. Fax 1-800-730-2215.

FIGURE **2.38** Software Performance at NASA's Goddard Space Center, 1976–1990

Number of bugs, errors, and defects per 1,000 lines of code

Worst case
Average case
Best case

Number for 1,000 Lines of Code

Source: Reprinted from the January 15, 1992, issue of *Business Week* by special permission. Copyright © 1992 by The McGraw-Hill Companies.

TABLE **2.20** Mean Return and Standard Deviation for Seven Investment Classes over a Ten-Year Period

Investment Class	Mean Return	Std. Deviation
Money Market	2.75%	0.08%
Fixed Income	0.8	1.0
Balanced	6.4	1.48
Canadian Equity	19.6	2.75
U.S. Equity	12.4	3.1
Global Equity	22.3	5.1
Sector Funds	33.1	5.9

TABLE **2.21** Personal Expenditure on Food and Nonalcoholic Beverages, Alcoholic Beverages, and Tobacco in Canada (Figures Are Given in Millions of Dollars)

Year	1997	1998	1999	2000	2001	2002	2003	2004	2005
Food and nonalcoholic beverages	12,580	13,039	13,493	14,137	14,946	15,581	16,173	16,851	17,732
Alcoholic beverages bought in stores	2,476	2,620	2,781	2,915	3,105	3,329	3,509	3,645	3,831
Tobacco products	2,185	2,326	2,311	2,338	2,543	3,041	3,388	3,621	3,547

Source: Adapted from Statistics Canada, http://www.statcan.gc.ca, *National Income and Expenditure Accounts, Quarterly Estimates,* Catalogue 13-001-XIB, reference period 1997–2005.

2.70 Table 2.21 presents data on the average annual amount Canadians spent on food and nonalcoholic beverages, alcoholic beverages (bought in stores), and tobacco products for the years 1997 to 2005. Depict the data graphically and summarize what the data suggest in terms of changes in expenditures over time.

2.71 THE INTERNATIONAL BUSINESS TRAVEL EXPENSE CASE

Suppose that a large international corporation wishes to obtain its own benchmark for one-day travel expenses in Moscow. To do this, it records the one-day travel expenses for a random sample of 35 executives visiting Moscow. The mean and the standard deviation of these expenses are calculated to be $\bar{x} = \$538$ and $s = \$41$, respectively. Furthermore, a histogram shows that the expenses are approximately normally distributed.

a. Find an interval that you estimate contains 99.73 percent of all one-day travel expenses in Moscow.

b. If an executive submits an expense of $720 for a one-day stay in Moscow, should this expense be considered unusually high? Why or why not?

2.72 THE U.K. INSURANCE CASE

Figure 2.39 summarizes information concerning insurance expenditures of households in the United Kingdom in 1993.

a. Approximately what percentage of households spent on life insurance?

b. What is the approximate average expenditure (in UK£) per household on life insurance? *Note:* The averages given in Figure 2.39 are for households that spend in the class.

FIGURE **2.39** Insurance Expenditures of Households in the United Kingdom (1993)

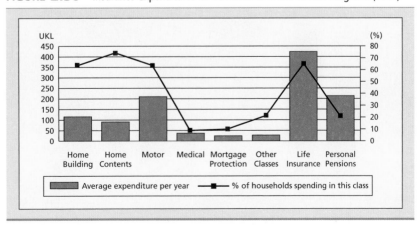

Source: CSO family expenditure survey.

FIGURE **2.40** A Graph Comparing the Resale Values
of Chevy, Dodge, and Ford Trucks

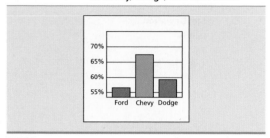

Source: Reprinted courtesy of General Motors Corporation.

69	47	52	68	59
52	79	77	69	78
57	78	85	85	67
46	90	86	88	78
41	94	65	80	55
98	78	87	75	64
51	82	97	53	82
87	98	98	94	66
55	58	44	87	86
95	53	57	84	72

2.73 Figure 2.40 was used in various Chevrolet magazine advertisements in 1997 to compare the overall resale values of Chevrolet, Dodge, and Ford trucks in the years from 1990 to 1997. What is somewhat misleading about this graph?

2.74 The final course grades for 50 students in a statistics course are presented in the table to the right.
  a. Convert each grade into a letter grade and construct a histogram of the grades.
  b. Compute the mean grade for the class.
  c. Compute the standard deviation for the class.
  d. If Samantha obtains a grade of 75 percent and Donald obtains a grade of 55 percent, who is farther away from the class mean?

2.75 **INTERNET EXERCISE**
Statistics Canada (http://www.statcan.gc.ca) reports on their main page the latest indicators for Canada (typically statistics current up to the last month). Explore the Unemployment Rate link and determine whether or not the unemployment graphs provided are or are not histograms.

CHAPTER 3
Probability

LEARNING OBJECTIVES

After reading this chapter, you should be able to

LO1 define a sample space

LO2 explain what is meant by the probability of an event

LO3 understand probability rules (addition, multiplication, and the rule of complements)

LO4 explain what is meant by a conditional probability

LO5 provide a definition of an independent event

LO6 understand Bayes' theorem

CHAPTER OUTLINE

3.1 The Concept of Probability

3.2 Sample Spaces and Events

3.3 Some Elementary Probability Rules

3.4 Conditional Probability and Independence

3.5 Bayes' Theorem

The word "probability" has many interpretations. The most commonly used definition describes probability as a limiting long-run relative frequency. Mathematically speaking, if you repeat an experiment n times and let n approach infinity and, at the same time, count the number of outcomes corresponding to the event of interest, calling this value f, then the value f/n represents the probability of the event occurring. Probability allows us to measure the degree of certainty or uncertainty of an event occurring in the long run. When the probability of an event is 0 (1), it never (always) occurs. Anything between 0 and 1 represents a level of uncertainty.

What is the probability of getting a flush in poker (all five cards are the same suit)? What is the probability of winning Lotto 6/49? If a red number comes up on ten consecutive spins of a roulette wheel, what is the probability of observing a red number on the next spin? What is the probability of passing a ten-question multiple choice exam by simply guessing all the answers (not studying)? To help you answer these and other questions about probability, some basic rules, helpful examples, and a case will be introduced.

The BBM Canada Radio Ratings Case: If you were conducting research to assess how many people listen to a certain radio station, how would you get started? Radio-rating companies survey a selection of people (a sample) from the target area (or population of interest). Data obtained from a survey conducted in London, Ontario, by BBM Canada (http://www.bbm.ca) will be used to demonstrate probability rules.

3.1 THE CONCEPT OF PROBABILITY

The concept of **probability** deals with uncertainty. Intuitively, the probability of an event is a number that measures the chance, or likelihood, that the event will occur. For instance, the probability that your favourite hockey team will win its next game measures the likelihood of a victory. The probability of an event is always a number between 0 and 1. The closer an event's probability is to 1, the greater is the likelihood that the event will occur; the closer the event's probability is to 0, the smaller is the likelihood that the event will occur. For example, if you believe that the probability that your favourite hockey team will win its next game is 0.95, then you are almost sure that your team will win. However, if you believe that the probability of victory is only 0.10, then you have very little confidence that your team will win.

When performing statistical studies, we sometimes collect data by performing a **controlled experiment**. For instance, we might purposely vary the operating conditions of a manufacturing process in order to study the effects of these changes on the process output. Alternatively, we sometimes obtain data by observing **uncontrolled events**. For example, we might observe the closing price of a share of General Motors of Canada's stock every day for 30 trading days.

An **experiment** is any process of observation that has an uncertain outcome. The possible outcomes for an experiment are called **experimental outcomes**.

For example, if the experiment consists of tossing a coin, the experimental outcomes are head and tail. If the experiment consists of rolling a die, the experimental outcomes are 1, 2, 3, 4, 5, and 6. If the experiment consists of subjecting an automobile to a tailpipe emissions test, the experimental outcomes are pass and fail.

We often wish to assign probabilities to experimental outcomes. This can be done using several methods. Regardless of the method used, *probabilities must be assigned to the experimental outcomes so that two conditions are met*:

1 The probability assigned to each experimental outcome must be between 0 and 1. That is, if E represents an experimental outcome and $P(E)$ represents the probability of this outcome, then $0 \leq P(E) \leq 1$.

2 The probabilities of all of the experimental outcomes must sum to 1 for a single experiment.

Sometimes, when all of the experimental outcomes are equally likely, we can use logic to assign probabilities. This method is called the **classical method**. As a simple example, consider the experiment of tossing a fair coin. Here there are *two* equally likely experimental outcomes—head (H) and tail (T). Therefore, logic suggests that the probability of observing a head, denoted $P(H)$, is $1/2 = 0.5$, and the probability of observing a tail, denoted $P(T)$, is also $1/2 = 0.5$. Notice that each probability is between 0 and 1. Furthermore, because H and T are all of the experimental outcomes, $P(H) + P(T) = 1$.

Probability is often interpreted to be a **long-run relative frequency**. As an example, consider repeatedly tossing a coin. If we get six heads in the first ten tosses, then the relative frequency, or fraction, of heads is $6/10 = 0.6$. If we get 47 heads in the first 100 tosses, the relative frequency of heads is $47/100 = 0.47$. If we get 5,067 heads in the first 10,000 tosses, the relative frequency of heads is $5,067/10,000 = 0.5067$.[1] Since the relative frequency of heads is approaching (that is, getting closer to) 0.5, we might estimate that the probability of obtaining a head when tossing the coin is 0.5. When we say this, we mean that if we tossed the coin an indefinitely large number of times (that is, a number of times *approaching infinity*), the relative frequency of heads obtained would approach 0.5. Of course, in actuality it is impossible to toss a coin (or perform any experiment) an indefinitely large number of times. Therefore, a relative frequency interpretation of probability is a mathematical idealization.

---

[1]The English mathematician John Kerrich actually obtained this result when he tossed a coin 10,000 times while imprisoned by the Germans during World War II.

To summarize, suppose that E is an experimental outcome that might occur when a particular experiment is performed. Then the probability that E will occur, $P(E)$, can be interpreted to be the number that would be approached by the relative frequency of E if we performed the experiment an indefinitely large number of times. It follows that we often think of a probability in terms of the percentage of the time the experimental outcome would occur in many repetitions of the experiment. For instance, when we say that the probability of obtaining a head when we toss a coin is 0.5, we are saying that when we repeatedly toss the coin an indefinitely large number of times, we will obtain a head on 50 percent of the repetitions.

Sometimes it is either difficult or impossible to use the classical method to assign probabilities. Since we can often make a relative frequency interpretation of probability, we can estimate a probability by performing the experiment in which an outcome might occur many times. Then we estimate the probability of the experimental outcome to be the proportion of the time that the outcome occurs during the many repetitions of the experiment. For example, to estimate the probability that a randomly selected consumer prefers Coca-Cola to all other soft drinks, we perform an experiment in which we ask a randomly selected consumer for their preference. There are two possible experimental outcomes: "prefers Coca-Cola" and "does not prefer Coca-Cola." However, we have no reason to believe that these experimental outcomes are equally likely, so we cannot use the classical method. We might perform the experiment, say, 1,000 times by surveying 1,000 randomly selected consumers. Then, if 140 of those surveyed said that they prefer Coca-Cola, we would estimate the probability that a randomly selected consumer prefers Coca-Cola to all other soft drinks to be 140/1,000 = 0.14. This is called the **relative frequency method** for assigning probability.

Example 3.1 Estimating a Probability

Willie, a salesperson at a local electronics store, tells a colleague, Kenny, that he believes that there is an 80 percent chance that he will make a sale to any customer. Kenny challenges this claim over the next month by keeping track of Willie's success rate. It turns out that Willie made 1,000 sales in 1,500 attempts. Using this information, Kenny estimates that the probability of Willie making a sale is 1,000/1,500, or 66.67 percent, not the 80 percent that Willie claimed. What happened here? There are a few possibilities here. (1) Willie is wrong, and his success rate is not 80 percent, but lower. (2) It is 80 percent and something strange has occurred. (3) He has not made enough attempts. Remember that probability is a long-run phenomenon. There is also the possibility that the sample is not representative of the population. We will rule that possibility out here.

If we cannot perform the experiment many times, we might estimate the probability by using our previous experience with similar situations, intuition, or special expertise that we may possess. For example, a company president might estimate the probability of success for a one-time business venture to be 0.7. Here, on the basis of knowledge of the success of previous similar ventures, the opinions of company personnel, and other pertinent information, the president believes that there is a 70 percent chance that the venture will be successful.

When we use experience, intuitive judgment, or expertise to assess a probability, we call it a **subjective probability**. Such a probability may or may not have a relative frequency interpretation. For instance, when the company president estimates that the probability of a successful business venture is 0.7, this may mean that if business conditions similar to those that are about to be encountered could be repeated many times, then the business venture would be successful in 70 percent of the repetitions. Or, the president may not be thinking in relative frequency terms but rather may consider the venture a "one-shot" proposition. We will discuss some other subjective probabilities later. However, the interpretations of statistical inferences we will explain in later chapters are based on the relative frequency interpretation of probability. For this reason, we will concentrate on this interpretation.

3.2 SAMPLE SPACES AND EVENTS

In order to calculate probabilities by using the classical method, it is important to understand and use the idea of a **sample space**.

The **sample space** of an experiment is the set of all possible experimental outcomes. The experimental outcomes in the sample space are often called **sample space outcomes**.

Example 3.2　Defining a Sample Space

A company is choosing a new chief executive officer (CEO). It has narrowed the list of candidates to four finalists (identified by last name only)—Adams, Chung, Hill, and Rankin. If we consider our experiment to be making a final choice of the company's CEO, then the experiment's sample space consists of the following four possible experimental outcomes:

$A \equiv$ Adams is chosen as CEO.

$C \equiv$ Chung is chosen as CEO.

$H \equiv$ Hill is chosen as CEO.

$R \equiv$ Rankin is chosen as CEO.

Each of these outcomes is a sample space outcome, and the set of these sample space outcomes is the sample space.

Next, suppose that industry analysts feel (subjectively) that the probabilities that Adams, Chung, Hill, and Rankin will be chosen as CEO are 0.1, 0.2, 0.5, and 0.2, respectively. That is, in probability notation,

$$P(A) = 0.1, \quad P(C) = 0.2, \quad P(H) = 0.5, \quad \text{and} \quad P(R) = 0.2.$$

Notice that each probability assigned to a sample space outcome is between 0 and 1 and that the sum of the probabilities equals 1.

Example 3.3　Rolling a Die—Even or Odd

Consider an experiment in which a student rolls a six-sided fair die three times. The outcome on the die will either be an even number (2, 4, 6) or an odd number (1, 3, 5). We will let E denote rolling an even number and O denote rolling an odd number. Then Figure 3.1 depicts a tree diagram of the sample space outcomes for the experiment. The diagram shows the experiment as a three-step process—rolling an even or an odd number on the first roll (E or O), and doing the same for the second and third rolls. The tree diagram has eight different branches, and the eight sample space outcomes are listed at the ends of the branches. We see that the sample space is

$$EEE \quad EEO \quad EOE \quad EOO$$
$$OEE \quad OEO \quad OOE \quad OOO$$

Because we are rolling a fair die, there is an equally likely chance of rolling an even number or an odd number. That is, there is a 50–50 chance (or probability of 0.5) of rolling an even or an odd number. The probability does not change from roll to roll. Intuitively, it would make sense that each of the eight sample outcomes listed above is equally likely to occur. That is,

$$P(EEE) = P(EEO) = \cdots = P(OOO) = \frac{1}{8}.$$

FIGURE **3.1** A Tree Diagram Illustrating Three Rolls of a Fair Die

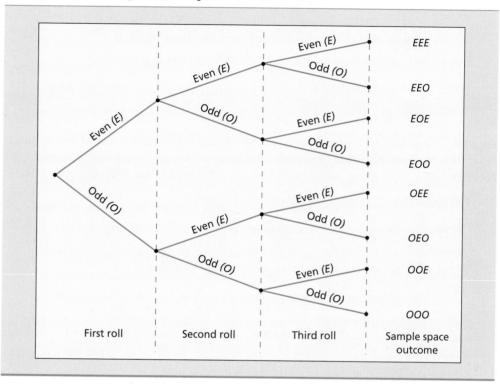

Here, as in Example 3.2, the sum of the probabilities of the sample space outcomes is 1.

Events and finding probabilities by using sample spaces At the beginning of this chapter, we informally talked about events. We now give the formal definition of an event.

An **event** is a set (or collection) of sample space outcomes.

For instance, if we consider the die-rolling situation, the event "the student will roll at least two out of three even numbers" consists of the sample space outcomes *EEE, EEO, EOE,* and *OEE,* while the event "the student will roll three even numbers" consists of the sample space outcome *EEE.* In general, we see that the word description of an event determines the sample space outcomes that correspond to the event.

Suppose that we wish to find the probability that an event will occur. We can find such a probability as follows:

The **probability of an event** is the sum of the probabilities of the sample space outcomes that correspond to the event.

LO2

As an example, in the CEO situation, suppose only Adams and Hill are internal candidates (they already work for the company). Letting *INT* denote the event that "an internal candidate is selected for the CEO position," then *INT* consists of the sample space outcomes *A* and *H* (that is, *INT* will occur if and only if either of the sample space outcomes *A* or *H* occurs). It follows that $P(INT) = P(A) + P(H) = 0.1 + 0.5 = 0.6$. This says that the probability that an internal candidate will be chosen to be CEO is 0.6.

In general, we have seen that the probability of any sample space outcome (experimental outcome) is a number between 0 and 1, and we have also seen that the probabilities of all the sample space outcomes sum to 1. It follows that *the probability of an event* (that is, the probability of a set of sample space outcomes) *is a number between 0 and 1.*

If A is an event, then $0 \leq P(A) \leq 1$.
Moreover:

1   If an event never occurs, then the probability of this event equals 0.
2   If an event is certain to occur, then the probability of this event equals 1.

Example 3.4   Probability Exercises

Recall the die-rolling experiment, where we were interested in the number of even numbers (E) or odd numbers (O) rolled. Remember that in this case, each of the eight sample space outcomes was equally likely, with a probability of 1/8. Consider the following probabilities:

1   The probability that three even numbers will be rolled is

$$P(EEE) = \frac{1}{8}.$$

2   The probability that exactly two even numbers will be rolled is

$$P(EEO) + P(EOE) + P(OEE) = \frac{1}{8} + \frac{1}{8} + \frac{1}{8} = \frac{3}{8},$$

since the outcomes EEO, EOE, and OEE correspond to exactly two even numbers being rolled.

3   The probability that at most one even number will be rolled is

$$P(EOO) + P(OEO) + P(OOE) + P(OOO) = \frac{1}{8} + \frac{1}{8} + \frac{1}{8} + \frac{1}{8} = \frac{1}{2},$$

since the outcomes EOO, OEO, and OOE correspond to exactly one even number being rolled and OOO corresponds to no even numbers being rolled.

4   The probability that at least one even number will be rolled is

$$P(EOO) + P(OEO) + P(OOE) + P(EEO) + P(EOE) + P(OEE) + P(EEE)$$

$$= \frac{1}{8} + \frac{1}{8} + \frac{1}{8} + \frac{1}{8} + \frac{1}{8} + \frac{1}{8} + \frac{1}{8} = \frac{7}{8},$$

since the outcomes EOO, OEO, OOE, EEO, EOE, OEE, and EEE correspond to two or more even numbers being rolled. The only outcome missing from this sample space is OOO. We could have answered this question using this fact. We will discuss this approach in the next section when we discuss complementary events.

Notice that in the die-rolling example we find that, for instance, the probability that exactly two even numbers will be rolled is

$$\frac{\text{the number of sample space outcomes resulting in two even numbers}}{\text{the total number of sample space outcomes}} = \frac{3}{8}.$$

In general, when a sample space is finite, we can use the following method for computing the probability of an event.

If all of the sample space outcomes are equally likely, then the probability that an event will occur is equal to the ratio

$$\frac{\text{the number of sample space outcomes that correspond to the event}}{\text{the total number of sample space outcomes}}.$$

When we use this rule, we are using the classical method for computing probabilities. Furthermore, it is important to emphasize that we can use this rule only when all of the sample space outcomes are equally likely (as they are in the die-rolling example). For example, if we were to use this rule in the CEO situation, we would find that the probability of choosing an internal candidate as CEO is

$$P(INT) = \frac{\text{the number of internal candidates}}{\text{the total number of candidates}} = \frac{2}{4} = 0.5.$$

This result is not equal to the correct value of $P(INT)$, which we previously found to be equal to 0.6. Here, this rule does not give us the correct answer because the sample space outcomes A, C, H, and R are not equally likely—recall that $P(A) = 0.1$, $P(C) = 0.2$, $P(H) = 0.5$, and $P(R) = 0.2$.

Example 3.5 Probability of Subscribing to the *Canadian Chronicle*

Suppose that 650,000 of 1,000,000 households in a Canadian city subscribe to a newspaper called the *Canadian Chronicle*, and consider randomly selecting one of the households in this city. That is, consider selecting one household by giving each and every household in the city the same chance of being selected. Let A be the event that the randomly selected household subscribes to the *Canadian Chronicle*. Then, because the sample space of this experiment consists of 1,000,000 equally likely sample space outcomes (households), it follows that

$$P(A) = \frac{\text{the number of households that subscribe to the \textit{Canadian Chronicle}}}{\text{the total number of households in the city}}$$

$$= \frac{650,000}{1,000,000}$$

$$= 0.65.$$

This says that the probability that the randomly selected household subscribes to the *Canadian Chronicle* is 0.65.

Example 3.6 The BBM Canada Radio Ratings Case

As discussed in the introduction to this chapter, BBM Canada is a radio ratings service. Figure 3.2 on the next page gives portions of a BBM ratings report for the London, Ontario, market for two surveys. Each survey was conducted from September to October, for 2005 and 2006. This report is based on sampling people 12 years of age or older and gives the share, or estimated total hours, as a percentage, of people who tuned into that radio station compared to all hours listening to the radio. As stated by BBM, "Share does not indicate the size of a station's audience—only its relative performance compared to other stations." As shown in Figure 3.2, the station with the largest share for 2006 is CIQM-FM, at 15.7 percent (this station also had the largest share in the 2005 survey, at 14.4 percent). BBM's computation of share is as follows:

$$\text{Share} = \frac{\text{number of people listening to that station}}{\text{total number of people listening to the radio}}.$$

If you add the share percentages, the total is 72.2 percent. What this means is that 27.8 percent of those people surveyed were either listening to a radio station not on the list or not listening at all. To compute the percentage of people who listen to a station for at least 15 minutes in a week, the equation is

$$\text{Percentage listening} = \frac{\text{central (Ctrl) number}}{\text{Ctrl reach total}}.$$

FIGURE 3.2 Top-Line Radio Statistics: London Ctrl S4-2006

Source: BBM Canada
Demographics: A12+
Area: 5369 (London Ctrl)
Timeblock: Monday–Sunday 5 A.M.–1 A.M.

Station	Market	Sep.–Oct. 2006 405,295		Sep.–Oct. 2005 402,314	
Universe		Share	Ctrl Reach	Share	Ctrl Reach
Station	**Market**	**%**	**(000)**	**%**	**(000)**
CFHKFM	London Ctrl	7.5	80.5	7.6	89.6
CFPL	London Ctrl	3.7	37.9	3.9	49.0
CFPLFM	London Ctrl	11.0	85.3	11.6	93.5
CHSTFM	London Ctrl	11.0	78.1	10.9	83.2
CIQMFM	London Ctrl	15.7	100.5	14.4	97.6
CJBK	London Ctrl	3.5	38.8	4.9	41.0
CJBXFM	London Ctrl	13.7	83.3	11.1	66.4
CKDKFM	Woodstock/London Ctrl	4.1	52.7	5.6	57.0
CKSL	London Ctrl	2.0	14.6	2.7	22.1

TERMS
Central (Ctrl) Market Area: A BBM-defined geographical area, usually centred around one urban centre. The definition of a Central Market Area generally corresponds to Statistics Canada Census Metropolitan Areas, Census Agglomeration, Cities, Counties, Census Divisions, or Regional Districts.
Universe: Estimated Population of the Central Market Area.
Share: Within the central market area, the estimated total hours tuned to that station expressed as a percentage of total hours tuned to all radio.
Central (Ctrl) Reach: The estimated number of different people, within the central market area, who tuned to that station for at least one quarter hour during the week.

So the percentage of people in the London market who listen to CFHK-FM for at least 15 minutes in a week is $80.5/(80.5 + 37.9 + \cdots + 52.7 + 14.6) = 80.5/571.7 = 14.08\%$.

To conclude this section, we note that in Appendix B (Part 1), available on *Connect*, we discuss several **counting rules** that can be used to count the number of sample space outcomes in an experiment. These rules are particularly useful when there are many sample space outcomes and thus these outcomes are difficult to list.

Exercises for Sections 3.1 and 3.2

CONCEPTS

3.1   Define the following terms: experiment, event, probability, sample space.

3.2   Explain the properties that must be satisfied by a probability.

METHODS AND APPLICATIONS

3.3   A weather forecaster reports that the probability of precipitation is 70 percent.
   a. What approach was used to determine this probability?
   b. How would you interpret this probability?

3.4   A statistics professor believes that there is less than a 1 percent chance that the Toronto Maple Leafs will win the Stanley Cup this year.
   a. What approach was used to determine this probability?
   b. Interpret this probability.

3.5   In a large statistics class of 500 students, 82.4 percent stated that they preferred multiple choice exams to written question exams.

   a. What approach was used to determine this probability, or proportion?
   b. How would you interpret this probability?

3.6   An economist believes that there is a 75 percent chance that the Canadian economy will recover in late 2011.
   a. What approach was used to determine this probability?
   b. How would you interpret this probability?

3.7   The manager of a local hardware store buys digital clock radios in cartons of 20 radios each. She randomly selects three radios and thoroughly tests them. If all three radios are of acceptable quality, then the carton is accepted. Suppose that in a certain carton, unknown to the manager, only 14 of the 20 are of acceptable quality.
   a. What is the chance that the carton would be accepted using this sampling process?
   b. What is the chance that the carton would be accepted if 10 out of the 20 radios are defective?

3.8 A student is writing a multiple choice quiz consisting of three questions, with each question having four choices (exactly one is the correct answer, of course).
  a. What is the chance that the student will get a perfect score on the quiz by guessing every answer?
  b. What is the chance that the student will get at least one question correct by guessing every answer?

3.9 Two randomly selected grocery store patrons are each asked to take a blind taste test and then to state which of three diet colas (marked as A, B, and C) they prefer.
  a. Draw a tree diagram depicting the sample space outcomes for the test results.
  b. List the sample space outcomes that correspond to each of the following events:
    (1) Both patrons prefer diet cola A.
    (2) The two patrons prefer the same diet cola.
    (3) The two patrons prefer different diet colas.
    (4) Diet cola A is preferred by at least one of the two patrons.
    (5) Neither of the patrons prefers diet cola C.
  c. Assuming that all sample space outcomes are equally likely, find the probability of each of the events in part b.

3.10 Suppose that a couple will have three children. Let B denote a boy and G denote a girl.
  a. Draw a tree diagram depicting the sample space outcomes for this experiment.
  b. List the sample space outcomes that correspond to each of the following events:
    (1) All three children will be the same sex.
    (2) Exactly two of the three children will be girls.
    (3) Exactly one of the three children will be a girl.
    (4) The oldest child is a girl.
  c. Assuming that all sample space outcomes are equally likely, find the probability of each of the events in part b.

3.11 Four people will enter an automobile showroom, and each will either purchase a car (P) or not purchase a car (N).
  a. Draw a tree diagram depicting the sample space of all possible purchase decisions that could potentially be made by the four people.
  b. List the sample space outcomes that correspond to each of the following events:
    (1) Exactly three people will purchase a car.
    (2) Two or fewer people will purchase a car.
    (3) One or more people will purchase a car.
    (4) All four people will make the same purchase decision.
  c. Assuming that all sample space outcomes are equally likely, find the probability of each of the events in part b.

3.12 **The BBM Canada Radio Rating Case**
  a. Using the information given in the BBM Canada report in Figure 3.2 on page 90, estimate each of the following:
    (1) The probability that a randomly selected resident of London would report listening to CFPL for at least 15 minutes in one week in 2005.
    (2) The probability that a randomly selected resident of London would report listening to CFPL for at least 15 minutes in one week in 2006.
  b. How do the values differ (if at all) between 2005 and 2006 for CFPL listeners?
  c. What is the likelihood that someone reports *not* listening to CFPL in 2006?
  d. Which station showed the greatest change in share percentage between 2005 and 2006?

3.13 Let A, B, C, D, and E be sample space outcomes forming a sample space. Suppose that $P(A) = 0.2$, $P(B) = 0.15$, $P(C) = 0.3$, and $P(D) = 0.2$. What is $P(E)$? Explain how you got your answer.

3.3 SOME ELEMENTARY PROBABILITY RULES

We can often calculate probabilities by using formulas called **probability rules**. We will begin by presenting the simplest probability rule: the **rule of complements**. To start, we define the **complement** of an event:

Given an event A, the **complement of A** is the event consisting of all sample space outcomes that are not in A. The complement of A is denoted $\overline{A}$. Furthermore, $P(\overline{A})$ denotes *the probability that A will not occur*.

LO3

FIGURE **3.3** The Complement of an Event (the Shaded Region Is $\overline{A}$, the Complement of A)

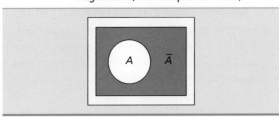

Figure 3.3 is a **Venn diagram** depicting the complement, $\overline{A}$, of an event A. $\overline{A}$ is the set of all sample space outcomes that are not in A. In any probability situation, either an event, A, or its complement, $\overline{A}$, must occur. Therefore, we have

$$P(A) + P(\overline{A}) = 1.$$

The Rule of Complements

Consider an event A. Then the probability that A *will not occur* is

$$P(\overline{A}) = 1 - P(A).$$

Example 3.7 Complementary Probability

Recall from Example 3.5 that the probability that a randomly selected household in a Canadian city subscribes to the *Canadian Chronicle* is 0.65. It follows that the probability of the complement of this event (that is, the probability that a randomly selected household in the Canadian city does not subscribe to the *Canadian Chronicle*) is $1 - 0.65 = 0.35$.

Example 3.8 Using a Complement to Make a Probability Calculation Easier

Suppose that we wish to roll a fair die five times. We want to find P(in at least one of the five rolls, a number other than one comes up). We will define our event as follows:

$$E \equiv \text{in at least one of the five rolls, a number other than one comes up.}$$

We could try drawing a probability tree, but there are $6^5 = 7{,}776$ possible outcomes! Instead, we will try to determine the complement of E. We will define the complement of E as follows:

$$\overline{E} \equiv \text{all five rolls come up as ones.}$$

This outcome only happens once out of the 7,776 possible outcomes, so $P(\overline{E}) = \dfrac{1}{7{,}776}$. Thus, $P(E) = 1 - P(\overline{E}) = 1 - \dfrac{1}{7{,}776} = \dfrac{7{,}775}{7{,}776}$. Using the complementary event approach saves a lot of time. That probability tree would probably take hours (and a very large sheet of paper) to draw!

In order to introduce the idea of union and intersection, we make the following definitions:

The Intersection and Union of Two Events

Given two events A and B,

1   The **intersection of A and B** is the event consisting of the sample space outcomes belonging to both A and B. The intersection is denoted by $A \cap B$. Furthermore, $P(A \cap B)$ denotes the probability that both A and B will simultaneously occur.

2   The **union of A and B** is the event consisting of the sample space outcomes belonging to A or B (or both). The union is denoted $A \cup B$. Furthermore, $P(A \cup B)$ denotes the probability that A or B (or both) will occur. This probability is also equivalent to at least one of A or B occurring.

What if we are not interested in the probability that both A and B will occur? Consider the next example.

Example 3.9 Probability of Exactly One Event Occurring

Suppose that a factory's alarm system will fail 15 percent of the time. The chance that its sprinkler system will fail is 10 percent. They will both fail 5 percent of the time. What is the chance that exactly one of the systems will fail? We will define our events as follows:

$$A \equiv \text{alarm system fails} \quad \Rightarrow \overline{A} \equiv \text{alarm system works.}$$
$$S \equiv \text{sprinkler system fails} \Rightarrow \overline{S} \equiv \text{sprinkler system works.}$$

$P(\text{exactly one system fails}) = P(A \cap \overline{S}) + P(\overline{A} \cap S)$. We will use a Venn diagram to help solve this equation.

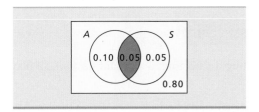

From the Venn diagram, we see that $P(\text{exactly one system fails}) = P(A \cap \overline{S}) + P(\overline{A} \cap S) = 0.10 + 0.05 = 0.15$.

Next, we note that Figure 3.4 on the next page shows Venn diagrams depicting the events A, B, $A \cap B$, and $A \cup B$. This leads to the following general result:

The Addition Rule

Let A and B be events. Then the probability that A or B (or both) will occur is

$$P(A \cup B) = P(A) + P(B) - P(A \cap B).$$

LO3

The reasoning behind this result will be illustrated in Example 3.11 on page 94. Similarly, the Venn diagrams in Figure 3.4 show that when we compute $P(A) + P(B)$, we are counting each of the sample space outcomes in $A \cap B$ twice. We correct for this by subtracting $P(A \cap B)$.

We next define the idea of **mutually exclusive events**:

Mutually Exclusive Events

Two events, A and B, are **mutually exclusive** if they have no sample space outcomes in common. In this case, the events A and B cannot occur simultaneously, and thus

$$P(A \cap B) = 0.$$

Noting that Figure 3.5 on the next page is a Venn diagram depicting two mutually exclusive events, we consider the following example.

FIGURE 3.4   Venn Diagrams Depicting the Events A, B, $A \cap B$, and $A \cup B$

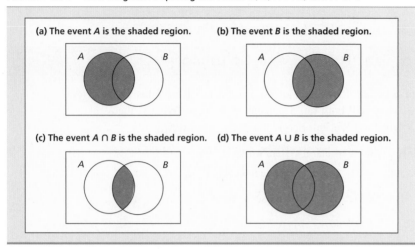

(a) The event A is the shaded region.

(b) The event B is the shaded region.

(c) The event $A \cap B$ is the shaded region.

(d) The event $A \cup B$ is the shaded region.

FIGURE 3.5   Two Mutually Exclusive Events

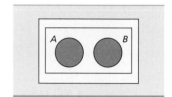

Example 3.10 Mutually Exclusive Events

Consider randomly selecting a card from a standard deck of 52 playing cards. We define the following events:

$J \equiv$ the randomly selected card is a jack.

$Q \equiv$ the randomly selected card is a queen.

$R \equiv$ the randomly selected card is a red card (that is, a diamond or a heart).

Because there is no card that is both a jack and a queen, the events J and Q are mutually exclusive. On the other hand, two cards are both jacks and red cards—the jack of diamonds and the jack of hearts—so the events J and R are not mutually exclusive.

We have seen that for any two events A and B, the probability that A or B (or both) will occur is

$$P(A \cup B) = P(A) + P(B) - P(A \cap B).$$

Therefore, when calculating $P(A \cup B)$, we should always subtract $P(A \cap B)$ from the sum of $P(A)$ and $P(B)$. However, when A and B are mutually exclusive, $P(A \cap B)$ equals 0. Therefore, in this case—and only in this case—we have the following:

LO3

The Addition Rule for Two Mutually Exclusive Events

Let A and B be mutually exclusive events. Then the probability that A or B will occur is

$$P(A \cup B) = P(A) + P(B).$$

Example 3.11 Union of Events

Again consider randomly selecting a card from a standard deck of 52 playing cards, and define the following events:

$J \equiv$ the randomly selected card is a jack.

$Q \equiv$ the randomly selected card is a queen.

$R \equiv$ the randomly selected card is a red card (a diamond or a heart).

Since there are 4 jacks, 4 queens, and 26 red cards, we have $P(J) = \frac{4}{52}$, $P(Q) = \frac{4}{52}$, and $P(R) = \frac{26}{52}$. Furthermore, since there is no card that is both a jack and a queen, the events J and Q are mutually exclusive and thus $P(J \cap Q) = 0$. It follows that the probability that the randomly selected card is a jack or a queen is

$$P(J \cup Q) = P(J) + P(Q)$$
$$= \frac{4}{52} + \frac{4}{52} = \frac{8}{52} = \frac{2}{13}.$$

Since two cards are both jacks and red cards—the jack of diamonds and the jack of hearts—the events J and R are not mutually exclusive. Therefore, the probability that the randomly selected card is a jack or a red card is

$$P(J \cup R) = P(J) + P(R) - P(J \cap R)$$
$$= \frac{4}{52} + \frac{26}{52} - \frac{2}{52} = \frac{28}{52} = \frac{7}{13}.$$

We now consider an arbitrary group of events—$A_1, A_2, \ldots, A_N$. We will denote the probability that A_1 or A_2 or ... or A_N occurs (that is, the probability that at least one of the events occurs) as $P(A_1 \cup A_2 \cup \cdots \cup A_N)$. We can use sample spaces to reason out such a probability. For instance, in the playing card situation of Example 3.11, there are 4 jacks, 4 queens, and 22 red cards that are not jacks or queens (the 26 red cards minus the 2 red jacks and the 2 red queens). Therefore, because there are 30 cards in total corresponding to the event $J \cup Q \cup R$, it follows that

$$P(J \cup Q \cup R) = \frac{30}{52} = \frac{15}{26}.$$

Because some cards are both jacks and red cards, and because some cards are both queens and red cards, we say that the events J, Q, and R are not mutually exclusive. When, however, a group of events is mutually exclusive, there is a simple formula for the probability that at least one of the events will occur:

> **The Addition Rule for N Mutually Exclusive Events**
>
> The events $A_1, A_2, \ldots, A_N$ are mutually exclusive if no two of the events have any sample space outcomes in common. In this case, no two of the events can occur simultaneously, and
>
> $$P(A_1 \cup A_2 \cup \cdots \cup A_N) = P(A_1) + P(A_2) + \cdots + P(A_N).$$

LO3

As an example of using this formula, again consider the playing card situation and the events J and Q. If we define the event

$$K \equiv \text{the randomly selected card is a king,}$$

then the events J, Q, and K are mutually exclusive. Therefore,

$$P(J \cup Q \cup K) = P(J) + P(Q) + P(K)$$
$$= \frac{4}{52} + \frac{4}{52} + \frac{4}{52} = \frac{12}{52} = \frac{3}{13}.$$

Example 3.12 The BBM Canada Radio Ratings Case

Recall that Figure 3.2 on page 90 gives the BBM Canada estimates of the share of each radio station in the London, Ontario, market (based on 2006 data). Because the share percentages provide the relative performance of certain stations, the event that a listener listening to a specific station is mutually exclusive of the same event for all other stations. Therefore, the probability that a randomly selected resident of London listens to at least one of the nine stations listed is the sum of the individual station probabilities

$$P(\text{CFHK-FM}) + P(\text{CFPL}) + \cdots + P(\text{CKSL})$$

or

$$0.075 + 0.037 + \cdots + 0.020 = 0.722.$$

As stated earlier, this total is less than one because some people do not listen to the radio and other people may be listening to a station not in the area.

Exercises for Section 3.3

CONCEPTS

3.14 Explain what it means for two events to be mutually exclusive; for N events.

3.15 If A and B are events, define $\bar{A}, A \cup B, A \cap B$, and $\bar{A} \cap \bar{B}$.

METHODS AND APPLICATIONS

3.16 Consider a standard deck of 52 playing cards, a randomly selected card from the deck, and the following events:

R = red, B = black, A = ace, N = nine,
D = diamond, C = club.

a. Describe the sample space outcomes that correspond to each of these events.

b. For each of the following pairs of events, indicate whether the events are mutually exclusive. In each case, if you think the events are mutually exclusive, explain why the events have no common sample space outcomes. If you think the events are not mutually exclusive, list the sample space outcomes that are common to both events.

  (1) R and A.　　**(3)** A and N.　　**(5)** D and C.
  (2) R and C.　　**(4)** N and C.

3.17 Of 10,000 students at a university, 2,500 have a MasterCard card (M), 4,000 have a Visa card (V), and 1,000 have both.

a. Find the probability that a randomly selected student
  (1) Has a MasterCard card.
  (2) Has a Visa card.
  (3) Has both credit cards.

b. Construct and fill in a two-way table summarizing the credit card data. Employ the following pairs of events: M and $\bar{M}$, V and $\bar{V}$.

c. Use the table from part b to find the probability that a randomly selected student
  (1) Has a MasterCard card or a Visa card.
  (2) Has neither credit card.
  (3) Has exactly one of the two credit cards.

3.18 The card game of Euchre employs a deck that consists of all four of each of the aces, kings, queens, jacks, tens, and nines (one of each suit—clubs, diamonds, spades, and hearts).

a. Find the probability that a randomly selected card from a Euchre deck is
  (1) A jack (J).　　**(3)** A jack or an ace (A).
  (2) A spade (S).　**(4)** A jack or a spade.

b. Are the events J and A mutually exclusive? J and S? Why or why not?

3.19 Each month, a brokerage house studies various companies and rates each company's stock as being either low risk or moderate to high risk. In a recent report, the brokerage house summarized its findings about 15 Internet services companies and 25 financial sector companies in the following table:

Company Type	Low Risk	Moderate to High Risk
Internet Services	6	9
Financial Sector	20	5

If we randomly select one of the total of 40 companies, find

a. The probability that the company is in the financial sector.

b. The probability that the company's stock is low risk.

c. The probability that the company's stock is moderate to high risk.

d. The probability that the company is in the financial sector and has a stock that is low risk.

e. The probability that the company is in Internet services or has a stock that is low risk.

3.20 In the book *Essentials of Marketing Research*, Dillon, Madden, and Firtle present the results of a concept study for a new wine cooler. Three hundred consumers between 21 and 49 years of age were randomly selected. After sampling the new beverage, each was asked to rate the appeal of the following phrase as it relates to the new wine cooler:

Not sweet like wine coolers, not filling like beer, and more refreshing than wine or mixed drinks

The rating was made on a scale from 1 to 5, with 5 representing "extremely appealing" and 1 representing "not at all appealing." The results obtained are given in Table 3.1.

Based on these results, estimate the probability that a randomly selected 21- to 49-year-old consumer

a. Would give the phrase a rating of 5.

b. Would give the phrase a rating of 3 or higher.

c. Is in the 21–24 age group; the 25–34 age group; the 35–49 age group.

TABLE **3.1** Results of a Concept Study for a New Wine Cooler

		Gender		Age Group		
Rating	Total	Male	Female	21–24	25–34	35–49
Extremely appealing (5)	151	68	83	48	66	37
(4)	91	51	40	36	36	19
(3)	36	21	15	9	12	15
(2)	13	7	6	4	6	3
Not at all appealing (1)	9	3	6	4	3	2

Source: *Essentials of Marketing Research*, by W. R. Dillon, T. J. Madden, and N. H. Firtle (Burr Ridge, IL: Richard D. Irwin, 1993), p. 390.

d. Is a male who gives the phrase a rating of 4.

e. Is a 35- to 49-year-old who gives the phrase a rating of 1.

3.21 Students at a Canadian university participate in various sports in the following proportions:

Football 30%   Both football and basketball 10%
Basketball 40%   Both football and soccer 15%
Soccer 30%   Both soccer and basketball 10%
All three sports 10%

If a student is selected at random, what is the chance that they would

a. Play at least one sport?

b. Play football only?

c. Be a basketball player or a soccer player?

d. Play exactly one sport?

3.22 A young salesperson makes ten calls per day. Past history has shown that she has a 25 percent chance of making a sale on any call.

a. What is the chance that she will make no sales on a given day?

b. What is the chance that she will make at least one sale?

c. If she sells for 250 days of the year, on about how many of those days will she make at least one sale?

3.23 **The BBM Canada Radio Rating Case**

Using the information from 2006 in Figure 3.2 on page 90, estimate the probability that a randomly selected London, Ontario, resident (12 years of age or older) would

a. Listen to at least one of the top two radio stations in terms of share percentage (CIQM-FM and CJBX-FM).

b. Not listen to any of the top five radio stations.

c. Not listen to any of the nine stations listed.

d. Listen to at least one of the bottom three stations (CKSL, CJBX, or CFPL).

3.4 CONDITIONAL PROBABILITY AND INDEPENDENCE

Conditional probability In Table 3.2 on the next page, we introduce a **contingency table** summarizing the subscription data for the *Canadian Chronicle* and another local newspaper, *News Matters*. Suppose that we randomly select a household, and that the chosen household reports that it subscribes to *News Matters*. Given this new information, we wish to find the probability that the household subscribes to the *Canadian Chronicle*. This new probability is called a **conditional probability**.

The probability of the event A, given the condition that the event B has occurred, is written as $P(A|B)$—the probability of A given B. We often refer to such a probability as the **conditional probability of A given B**.

LO4

In order to find the conditional probability that a household subscribes to the *Canadian Chronicle*, given that it subscribes to *News Matters*, notice that if we know that the randomly selected household subscribes to *News Matters*, we know that we are considering one of 500,000 households (see Table 3.2). That is, we are now considering what we might call a reduced sample space of 500,000 households. Since 250,000 of these 500,000 *News Matters* subscribers also subscribe to the *Canadian Chronicle*, we have

$$P(A|B) = \frac{250,000}{500,000} = 0.5.$$

This says that the probability that the randomly selected household subscribes to the *Canadian Chronicle*, given that the household subscribes to *News Matters*, is 0.5. That is, 50 percent of the *News Matters* subscribers also subscribe to the *Canadian Chronicle*.

TABLE **3.2**　A Contingency Table Summarizing Subscription Data for the *Canadian Chronicle*
and *News Matters*

Events	Subscribes to News Matters, B	Does Not Subscribe to News Matters, $\bar{B}$	Total
Subscribes to *Canadian Chronicle*, A	250,000	400,000	650,000
Does Not Subscribe to *Canadian Chronicle*, $\bar{A}$	250,000	100,000	350,000
Total	500,000	500,000	1,000,000

Next suppose that we randomly select another household from the community of 1,000,000 households, and suppose that this newly chosen household reports that it subscribes to the *Canadian Chronicle*. We now wish to find the probability that this household subscribes to *News Matters*. We write this new probability as $P(B|A)$. If we know that the randomly selected household subscribes to the *Canadian Chronicle*, we know that we are considering a reduced sample space of 650,000 households (see Table 3.2). Since 250,000 of these 650,000 *Canadian Chronicle* subscribers also subscribe to *News Matters*, we have

$$P(B|A) = \frac{250,000}{650,000} = 0.3846.$$

This says that the probability that the randomly selected household subscribes to *News Matters*, given that the household subscribes to the *Canadian Chronicle*, is 0.3846. That is, 38.46 percent of the *Canadian Chronicle* subscribers also subscribe to *News Matters*.

If we divide both the numerator and the denominator of each of the conditional probabilities $P(A|B)$ and $P(B|A)$ by 1,000,000, we obtain

$$P(A|B) = \frac{250,000}{500,000} = \frac{250,000/1,000,000}{500,000/1,000,000} = \frac{P(A \cap B)}{P(B)},$$

$$P(B|A) = \frac{250,000}{650,000} = \frac{250,000/1,000,000}{650,000/1,000,000} = \frac{P(A \cap B)}{P(A)}.$$

We express these conditional probabilities in terms of $P(A)$, $P(B)$, and $P(A \cap B)$ in order to obtain a more general formula for a conditional probability. We need a more general formula because, although we can use the reduced sample space approach we have demonstrated to find conditional probabilities when all of the sample space outcomes are equally likely, this approach may not give correct results when the sample space outcomes are *not* equally likely. We now give expressions for conditional probability that are valid for any sample space:

Conditional Probability

1 The **conditional probability that *A* will occur given that *B* will occur** is written **$P(A|B)$** and is defined to be

$$P(A|B) = \frac{P(A \cap B)}{P(B)}.$$

Here we assume that $P(B)$ is greater than 0.

2 The **conditional probability that *B* will occur given that *A* will occur** is written **$P(B|A)$** and is defined to be

$$P(B|A) = \frac{P(A \cap B)}{P(A)}.$$

Here we assume that $P(A)$ is greater than 0.

If we multiply both sides of the equation

$$P(A|B) = \frac{P(A \cap B)}{P(B)}$$

by $P(B)$, we obtain the equation

$$P(A \cap B) = P(B)P(A|B).$$

Similarly, if we multiply both sides of the equation

$$P(B|A) = \frac{P(A \cap B)}{P(A)}$$

by $P(A)$, we obtain the equation

$$P(A \cap B) = P(A)P(B|A).$$

In summary, we now have two equations that can be used to calculate $P(A \cap B)$. These equations are often referred to as the **general multiplication rule** for probabilities. These equations are very useful for solving Bayes' theorem questions. We will explore Bayes' theorem in the next section.

The General Multiplication Rule—Two Ways to Calculate $P(A \cap B)$

Given any two events A and B,

$$P(A \cap B) = P(A)P(B|A)$$

$$= P(B)P(A|B).$$

LO3

Example 3.13 Conditional Probability (General Multiplication Rule)

In a soft drink taste test, each of 1,000 consumers chose between two colas—Cola 1 and Cola 2—and stated whether they preferred their cola drinks sweet or very sweet. Unfortunately, some of the survey information was lost. The following information remains:

1   68.3 percent of the consumers (that is, 683 consumers) preferred Cola 1 to Cola 2.

2   62 percent of the consumers (that is, 620 consumers) preferred their cola sweet (rather than very sweet).

3   85 percent of the consumers who said that they liked their cola sweet preferred Cola 1 to Cola 2.

To recover all of the lost survey information, consider randomly selecting one of the 1,000 survey participants, and define the following events:

$C_1 \equiv$ the randomly selected consumer prefers Cola 1.
$C_2 \equiv$ the randomly selected consumer prefers Cola 2.
$S \equiv$ the randomly selected consumer prefers sweet cola drinks.
$V \equiv$ the randomly selected consumer prefers very sweet cola drinks.

From the survey information that remains, (1) says that $P(C_1) = 0.683$, (2) says that $P(S) = 0.62$, and (3) says that $P(C_1|S) = 0.85$.

We will see that we can recover all of the lost survey information if we can find $P(C_1 \cap S)$. The general multiplication rule says that

$$P(C_1 \cap S) = P(C_1)P(S|C_1) = P(S)P(C_1|S).$$

Although we know that $P(C_1) = 0.683$, we do not know $P(S|C_1)$. Therefore, we cannot calculate $P(C_1 \cap S)$ as $P(C_1)P(S|C_1)$. However, because we know that $P(S) = 0.62$ and that $P(C_1|S) = 0.85$, we can calculate

$$P(C_1 \cap S) = P(S)P(C_1|S) = (0.62)(0.85) = 0.527.$$

TABLE 3.3   A Summary of the Number of Consumers Corresponding to the Events C_1, C_2, S, V, and $C_1 \cap S$

Events	S (Sweet)	V (Very Sweet)	Total
C_1 (Cola 1)	527		683
C_2 (Cola 2)			317
Total	620	380	1,000

TABLE 3.4   Subtractions to Obtain the Number of Consumers Corresponding to the Events $C_1 \cap V$, $C_2 \cap S$, and $C_2 \cap V$

Events	S (Sweet)	V (Very Sweet)	Total
C_1 (Cola 1)	527	683 − 527 = 156	683
C_2 (Cola 2)	620 − 527 = 93	380 − 156 = 224	317
Total	620	380	1,000

TABLE 3.5   A Contingency Table Summarizing the Cola Brand and Sweetness Preferences

Events	S (Sweet)	V (Very Sweet)	Total
C_1 (Cola 1)	527	156	683
C_2 (Cola 2)	93	224	317
Total	620	380	1,000

With 1,000 consumers in total, this implies that 527 preferred Cola 1 and preferred their cola sweet. We have summarized the number of consumers corresponding to other events in Tables 3.3 and 3.4. A final contingency table with all the values in place is given in Table 3.5.

In the next example, we will again illustrate how to make use of a contingency table to calculate a conditional probability.

Example 3.14 Conditional Probability from a Contingency Table

A retailer analyzed its most recent sales and determined the relationship between how customers paid for items and the cost of the items. The results are given in the table below:

		Payment Type	
Price Level	Cash	Credit Card	Debit Card
Under $10	0.20	0.05	0.10
$10–$50	0.05	0.20	0.15
Over $50	0.02	0.15	0.08

Suppose that we were interested in the proportion of purchases that were made by credit card. In order to determine this probability, we simply need to add the values in the "Credit Card" column. What we are saying here is that $P(\text{credit card}) = P(\text{credit card} \cap \text{under } \$10) + P(\text{credit card} \cap \$10–\$50) + P(\text{credit card} \cap \text{over } \$50)$. This results in an answer of $0.05 + 0.20 + 0.15 = 0.40$. Therefore, 40 percent of the purchases were made by credit card.

Now suppose that we want to know the proportion of credit card purchases that are between $10 and $50. That is, we want

$$P(\$10–\$50 \mid \text{credit card}) = \frac{P(\$10–\$50 \cap \text{credit card})}{P(\text{credit card})} = \frac{0.20}{0.40} = 0.5.$$

So 50 percent of the credit card purchases are between $10 and $50.

Independence   Recall in Example 3.13 on the previous page that $P(C_1) = 0.683$, while $P(C_1 \mid S) = 0.85$. Because $P(C_1 \mid S)$ is greater than $P(C_1)$, the probability that a randomly selected consumer will prefer Cola 1 is higher if we know that the person prefers sweet cola than it is if we have no knowledge of the person's sweetness preference. Another way to see this is to use Table 3.5 to calculate

LO5

$$P(C_1 \mid V) = \frac{P(C_1 \cap V)}{P(V)} = \frac{156/1,000}{380/1,000} = 0.4105.$$

Since $P(C_1|S) = 0.85$ is greater than $P(C_1|V) = 0.4105$, the probability that a randomly selected consumer will prefer Cola 1 is higher if the consumer prefers sweet colas than it is if the consumer prefers very sweet colas. Since the probability of the event C_1 is influenced by whether the event S occurs, we say that the events C_1 and S are **dependent**. If $P(C_1|S)$ were equal to $P(C_1)$, then the probability of the event C_1 would not be influenced by whether S occurs. In this case, we would say that the events C_1 and S are **independent**. This leads to the following definition of **independence**:

> **Independent Events**
>
> Two events A and B are **independent** if and only if
>
> 1 $P(A|B) = P(A)$ or, equivalently,
>
> 2 $P(B|A) = P(B)$.
>
> Here we assume that $P(A)$ and $P(B)$ are greater than 0.

LO5

When we say that conditions (1) and (2) are equivalent, we mean that condition (1) holds if and only if condition (2) holds. Although we will not prove this, we will demonstrate it in the next example.

Example 3.15 Conditional Probability

In the soft drink taste test of Example 3.13, we saw that $P(C_1|S) = 0.85$ does not equal $P(C_1) = 0.683$. This implies that $P(S|C_1)$ does not equal $P(S)$, which means that S and C_1 are not independent events. To demonstrate this, note from Table 3.5 that

$$P(S|C_1) = \frac{P(C_1 \cap S)}{P(C_1)} = \frac{527/1,000}{683/1,000} = 0.7716.$$

This probability is larger than $P(S) = 620/1,000 = 0.62$. In summary:

1 A comparison of $P(C_1|S) = 0.85$ and $P(C_1) = 0.683$ says that a consumer is more likely to prefer Cola 1 if the consumer prefers sweet colas.

2 A comparison of $P(S|C_1) = 0.7716$ and $P(S) = 0.62$ says that a consumer is more likely to prefer sweet colas if the consumer prefers Cola 1.

This suggests, but does not prove, that one reason Cola 1 is preferred to Cola 2 is that Cola 1 is sweet (as opposed to very sweet).

If the occurrences of the events A and B have nothing to do with each other, then we know that A and B are independent events. This implies that $P(A|B)$ equals $P(A)$ and that $P(B|A)$ equals $P(B)$. Recall that the general multiplication rule tells us that for any two events A and B, we can say that

$$P(A \cap B) = P(A)P(B|A).$$

Therefore, if $P(B|A)$ equals $P(B)$, it follows that

$$P(A \cap B) = P(A)P(B),$$

which is called the **multiplication rule for independent events**. To summarize:

> **The Multiplication Rule for Two Independent Events**
>
> If A and B are independent events, then
>
> $$P(A \cap B) = P(A)P(B).$$

LO3

As a simple example, define the events U and P as follows:

$U \equiv$ your favourite university football team wins its first game next season.

$P \equiv$ your favourite professional football team wins its first game next season.

Suppose you believe that for next season $P(U) = 0.6$ and $P(P) = 0.6$. Then, because the outcomes of a university football game and a professional football game probably have nothing to do with each other, it is reasonable to assume that U and P are independent events. It follows that

$$P(U \cap P) = P(U)P(P) = (0.6)(0.6) = 0.36.$$

This probability might be surprisingly low. That is, since you believe that each of your teams has a 60 percent chance of winning, you might feel reasonably confident that both your university and professional teams will win their first game. Yet the chance of this happening is really only 0.36!

Next consider a group of events $A_1, A_2, \ldots, A_N$. Intuitively, the events $A_1, A_2, \ldots, A_N$ are independent if the occurrences of these events have nothing to do with each other. Denoting the probability that A_1 and A_2 and ... and A_N will simultaneously occur as $P(A_1 \cap A_2 \cap \cdots \cap A_N)$, we have the following:

LO3

> **The Multiplication Rule for N Independent Events**
>
> If $A_1, A_2, \ldots, A_N$ are independent events, then
>
> $$P(A_1 \cap A_2 \cap \cdots \cap A_N) = P(A_1)P(A_2) \cdots P(A_N).$$

This says that the multiplication rule for two independent events can be extended to any number of independent events.

Example 3.16 Multiplication Rule (Independent Events)

This example is based on a real situation encountered by a major producer and marketer of consumer products. The company assessed the service it provides by surveying the attitudes of its customers regarding ten different aspects of customer service—order filled correctly, billing amount on invoice correct, delivery made on time, and so forth. When the survey results were analyzed, the company was dismayed to learn that only 59 percent of the survey participants indicated that they were satisfied with all ten aspects of the company's service. Upon investigation, each of the ten departments responsible for the aspects of service considered in the study insisted that it satisfied its customers 95 percent of the time. That is, each department claimed that its error rate was only 5 percent. Company executives were confused and felt that there was a substantial discrepancy between the survey results and the claims of the departments providing the services. However, a company statistician pointed out that there was no discrepancy. To understand this, consider randomly selecting a customer from among the survey participants, and define ten events (corresponding to the ten aspects of service studied):

$A_1 \equiv$ the customer is satisfied that the order is filled correctly (aspect 1).

$A_2 \equiv$ the customer is satisfied that the billing amount on the invoice is correct (aspect 2).

$\vdots$

$A_{10} \equiv$ the customer is satisfied that the delivery is made on time (aspect 10).

Also, define the event

$S \equiv$ the customer is satisfied with all ten aspects of customer service.

Since ten different departments are responsible for the ten aspects of service being studied, it is reasonable to assume that all ten aspects of service are independent of each other. For instance, billing amounts would be independent of delivery times. Therefore, $A_1, A_2, \ldots, A_{10}$ are independent events, and

$$P(S) = P(A_1 \cap A_2 \cap \cdots \cap A_{10})$$
$$= P(A_1)P(A_2) \cdots P(A_{10}).$$

If, as the departments claim, each department satisfies its customers 95 percent of the time, then the probability that the customer is satisfied with all ten aspects is

$$P(S) = (0.95)(0.95) \cdots (0.95) = 0.95^{10} = 0.5987.$$

This result is very close to the 59 percent satisfaction rate reported by the survey participants.

If the company wants to increase the percentage of its customers who are satisfied with all ten aspects of service, it must improve the quality of service provided by the ten departments. For example, to satisfy 95 percent of its customers with all ten aspects of service, the company must require each department to raise the fraction of the time it satisfies its customers to x, where

$$x^{10} = 0.95.$$

It follows that

$$x = 0.95^{\frac{1}{10}} = 0.9949$$

and that each department must satisfy its customers 99.49 percent of the time (rather than the current 95 percent of the time).

Exercises for Section 3.4

CONCEPTS

3.24 Explain the concept of a conditional probability. Give an example of a conditional probability that would be of interest to a university student; to a business.

3.25 Explain what it means for two events to be independent.

METHODS AND APPLICATIONS

3.26 Of the 10,000 students at a university, 2,500 have a Campus Rewards card, 4,000 have a Super Student Saver card, and 1,000 have both.
   a. What proportion of Campus Rewards card holders have Super Student Saver cards?
   b. What proportion of Super Student Saver cardholders have a Campus Rewards card?
   c. Are the events "having a Campus Rewards card" and "having a Super Student Saver" card independent? Justify your answer.

3.27 Each month a brokerage house studies various companies and rates each company's stock as being either low risk or moderate to high risk. In a recent report, the brokerage house summarized its findings about 15 Internet services companies and 25 financial sector companies in the following table:

Company Type	Low Risk	Moderate to High Risk
Internet Services	6	9
Financial Sector	20	5

Suppose we randomly select one of the total of 40 companies.
   a. Find the probability that the company's stock is moderate to high risk given that the firm is in the financial sector.

   b. Find the probability that the company's stock is moderate to high risk given that the firm is an Internet services company.
   c. Determine if the company type is independent of the level of risk of the firm's stock.

3.28 John and Jane are housemates. The probability that John watches a certain television show is 0.4. The probability that Jane watches the show is 0.5. The probability that John watches the show given that Jane does is 0.7.
   a. Find the probability that both John and Jane watch the show.
   b. Find the probability that Jane watches the show given that John does.
   c. Do John and Jane watch the show independently of each other? Justify your answer.

3.29 In Exercise 3.28, find the probability that either John or Jane watches the show.

3.30 In the July 29, 2001, issue of *The Journal News* (Hamilton, Ohio), Lynn Elber of the Associated Press reported that "while 40 percent of American families own a television set with a V-chip installed to block designated programs with sex and violence, only 17 percent of those parents use the device."[2]
   a. Use the report's results to estimate the probability that a randomly selected American family has used a V-chip to block programs containing sex and violence.
   b. According to the report, more than 50 percent of parents have used the TV rating system (TV-14, etc.) to control their children's TV viewing. How does this compare to the percentage using the V-chip?

---

[2]Source: *The Journal News* (Hamilton, Ohio), July 29, 2001, p. C5.

3.31 According to the Associated Press report in Exercise 3.30, 47 percent of parents who purchased TV sets after V-chips became standard equipment in January 2000 are aware that their sets have V-chips, and of those who are aware of the option, 36 percent have programmed their V-chips. Using these results, estimate the probability that a randomly selected parent who has bought a TV set since January 2000 has programmed the V-chip.

3.32 Fifteen percent of the employees in a company have managerial positions, and 25 percent of the employees in the company have MBA degrees. Also, 60 percent of the managers have MBA degrees.

a. Using the probability formulas,
  (1) Find the proportion of employees who are managers and have MBA degrees.
  (2) Find the proportion of MBAs who are managers.
b. Are the events "being a manager" and "having an MBA" independent? Justify your answer.

3.33 In Exercise 3.32, find the proportion of employees who either have MBAs or are managers.

3.34 A local business classifies its customers in two ways: according to (1) whether or not their account is overdue and (2) whether they are a new or an old customer. An analysis was conducted on the business's records. The findings are given in the following table:

Age	Payment Status	
	Overdue	Not Overdue
New	0.03	0.18
Old	0.58	0.21

An account is randomly selected.
a. What is the probability that the account is new?
b. What is the probability that the account is overdue?
c. If the account is not overdue, what is the probability that it is old?
d. If the account is old, what is the probability that it is not overdue?
e. Is the age of the account independent of the account's payment status? Justify your answer.

3.35 In a survey of 100 insurance claims, 40 are fire claims (*FIRE*), 16 of which are fraudulent (*FRAUD*). There are 40 fraudulent claims in total.
a. Construct a contingency table summarizing the claims data. Use the pairs of events *FIRE* and $\overline{FIRE}$, and *FRAUD* and $\overline{FRAUD}$.
b. What proportion of the fire claims are fraudulent?
c. Are the events "a claim is fraudulent" and "a claim is a fire claim" independent? Use your probability of part b to prove your answer.

3.36 Suppose that two randomly selected customers are each asked to take a blind taste test and then to state which of three energy drinks (marked as *A*, *B*, or *C*) they prefer. Suppose that drink *A*'s distributor claims that 80 percent of all people prefer drink *A* and that only 10 percent prefer each of drinks *B* and *C*.
a. Assuming that the distributor's claim is true and that the two taste test participants make independent drink preference decisions, find the probability of each sample space outcome.
b. Find the probability that neither taste test participant will prefer energy drink *A*.
c. If, when the taste test is carried out, neither participant prefers energy drink *A*, use the probability you computed in part b to decide whether the distributor's claim seems valid. Explain.

3.37 A sprinkler system inside an office building has two types of activation devices, D_1 and D_2, which operate independently. When there is a fire, if either device operates correctly, the sprinkler system is turned on. In case of fire, the probability that D_1 operates correctly is 0.95, and the probability that D_2 operates correctly is 0.92. Find the probability that
a. Both D_1 and D_2 will operate correctly.
b. The sprinkler system will come on.
c. The sprinkler system will fail.

3.38 A product is assembled using ten different components, each of which must meet specifications for five different quality characteristics. Suppose that there is a 0.9973 probability that each individual specification will be met.
a. Assuming that all 50 specifications are met independently, find the probability that the product meets all 50 specifications.
b. Suppose that we wish to have a 99.73 percent chance that all 50 specifications will be met. If each specification will have the same chance of being met, how large must we make the probability of meeting each individual specification?

3.39 In a murder trial in Vancouver, the prosecution claims that the defendant was cut on the left middle finger at the murder scene, but the defendant claims the cut occurred in Winnipeg, the day after the murders had been committed. Because the defendant is a sports celebrity, many people noticed him before he reached Winnipeg. Twenty-two people saw him casually, one person on the plane to Winnipeg carefully studied his hands looking for a championship ring, and another person stood with him as he signed autographs and drove him from the airport to the hotel. None of these 24 people saw a cut on the defendant's finger. If in fact he was not cut at all, it would be extremely unlikely that he left blood at the murder scene.
a. Since a person casually meeting the defendant would not be looking for a cut, assume that the probability is 0.9 that such a person would not have seen the cut, even if it was there. Furthermore, assume that the person who carefully looked at the defendant's hands had a 0.5 probability of not seeing the cut even if it was there and that the person who

drove the defendant from the airport to the hotel had a 0.6 probability of not seeing the cut even if it was there. Given these assumptions, and also assuming that all 24 people looked at the defendant independently of each other, what is the probability that all 24 people would not have seen the cut, even if it was there?

b. What is the probability that at least one of the 24 people would have seen the cut if it was there?

c. Given the result of part b and the fact that none of the 24 people saw a cut, do you think the defendant had a cut on his hand before he reached Winnipeg?

d. How might you estimate what the assumed probabilities in part a would actually be? (*Note:* This would not be easy.)

3.5 BAYES' THEOREM

Sometimes we have an initial or **prior** probability that an event will occur. Then, based on new information, we revise the prior probability to what is called a **posterior** probability. This revision can be done by using a theorem called **Bayes' theorem**.

Example 3.17 Bayes' Theorem—Driver's Education

In a certain area, sixty percent of new drivers enroll in driver's education classes. Records show that during the first year of driving, new drivers without driver's education have an 8 percent chance of having an accident, but those with driver's education have a 5 percent chance. Aidan, a first-year driver, has had no accidents. What is the probability that he has driver's education?

We can define our events:

1   $D \equiv$ driver has driver's education.

2   $A \equiv$ driver has an accident in the first year of driving.

We are given the following prior probabilities:

$$P(D) = 0.60, \text{ so } P(\overline{D}) = 0.40.$$
$$P(A|\overline{D}) = 0.08, \text{ so } P(\overline{A}|\overline{D}) = 0.92.$$
$$P(A|D) = 0.05, \text{ so } P(\overline{A}|D) = 0.95.$$

We want to determine the posterior probability, $P(D|\overline{A})$. By definition,

$$P(D|\overline{A}) = \frac{P(D \cap \overline{A})}{P(\overline{A})} = \frac{P(\overline{A}|D)P(D)}{P(\overline{A} \cap D) + P(\overline{A} \cap \overline{D})} = \frac{P(\overline{A}|D)P(D)}{P(\overline{A}|D)P(D) + P(\overline{A}|\overline{D})P(\overline{D})}.$$

Thus,

$$P(D|\overline{A}) = \frac{(0.95)(0.6)}{(0.95)(0.6) + (0.92)(0.4)} = 0.6077.$$

So, if Aidan has not had any accidents in his first year of driving, then there is a 60.77 percent chance that he has driver's education.

In the preceding example, there were two **states of nature**—D (driver's education) and $\overline{D}$ (no driver's education)—and two outcomes—A (accident) and $\overline{A}$ (no accident). In general, there might be any number of states of nature and any number of experimental outcomes. This leads to a general statement of Bayes' theorem.

LO6

> **Bayes' Theorem**
>
> Let $S_1, S_2, \ldots, S_k$ be k mutually exclusive states of nature, one of which must be true, and suppose that $P(S_1), P(S_2), \ldots, P(S_k)$ are the prior probabilities of these states of nature. Also let E be a particular outcome of an experiment designed to help determine which state of nature is really true. Then the **posterior probability** of a particular state of nature, say S_i, given the experimental outcome E, is
>
> $$P(S_i|E) = \frac{P(S_i \cap E)}{P(E)} = \frac{P(S_i)P(E|S_i)}{P(E)},$$
>
> where
>
> $$P(E) = P(S_1 \cap E) + P(S_2 \cap E) + \cdots + P(S_k \cap E)$$
> $$= P(S_1)P(E|S_1) + P(S_2)P(E|S_2) + \cdots + P(S_k)P(E|S_k).$$

Bayes' theorem is illustrated again in the following case.

Example 3.18 The Oil-Drilling Case

An oil company is attempting to decide whether to drill for oil on a particular site. There are three possible states of nature:

1   No oil (state of nature S_1, which we will denote as *none*).

2   Some oil (state of nature S_2, which we will denote as *some*).

3   Much oil (state of nature S_3, which we will denote as *much*).

Based on experience and knowledge concerning the site's geological characteristics, the oil company feels that the prior probabilities of these states of nature are as follows:

$$P(S_1 \equiv none) = 0.7, \qquad P(S_2 \equiv some) = 0.2, \qquad P(S_3 \equiv much) = 0.1.$$

In order to obtain more information about the potential drilling site, the oil company can perform a seismic experiment that has three readings—low, medium, and high. Moreover, information exists concerning the accuracy of the seismic experiment. The company's historical records tell us the following information:

1   Of 100 past sites that were drilled and produced no oil, 4 sites gave a high reading. Therefore,

$$P(\text{high}|\text{none}) = \frac{4}{100} = 0.04.$$

2   Of 400 past sites that were drilled and produced some oil, 8 sites gave a high reading. Therefore,

$$P(\text{high}|\text{some}) = \frac{8}{400} = 0.02.$$

3   Of 300 past sites that were drilled and produced much oil, 288 sites gave a high reading. Therefore,

$$P(\text{high}|\text{much}) = \frac{288}{300} = 0.96.$$

Intuitively, these conditional probabilities tell us that sites that produce no oil or some oil seldom give a high reading, while sites that produce much oil often give a high reading. Figure 3.6(a) shows a tree diagram that illustrates the prior probabilities of no, some, and much oil and the above conditional probabilities. This figure also gives the conditional probabilities

FIGURE 3.6 A Tree Diagram and Probability Revision Tables for Bayes' Theorem in the Oil-Drilling Example

(a) A tree diagram illustrating the prior and conditional probabilities

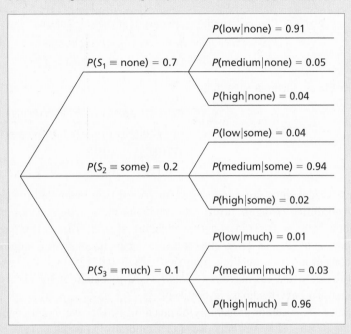

(b) A probability revision table for calculating the probability of a high reading and the posterior probabilities of no oil (S_1), some oil (S_2), and much oil (S_3), given a high reading

S_j	$P(S_j)$	$P(high|S_j)$	$P(S_j \cap high) = P(S_j)P(high|S_j)$	$P(S_j|high) = P(S_j \cap high)/P(high)$
$S_1 \equiv$ none	$P(none) = 0.7$	$P(high|none) = 0.04$	$P(none \cap high) = 0.7(0.04) = 0.028$	$P(none|high) = 0.028/0.128 = 0.21875$
$S_2 \equiv$ some	$P(some) = 0.2$	$P(high|some) = 0.02$	$P(some \cap high) = 0.2(0.02) = 0.004$	$P(some|high) = 0.004/0.128 = 0.03125$
$S_3 \equiv$ much	$P(much) = 0.1$	$P(high|much) = 0.96$	$P(much \cap high) = 0.1(0.96) = 0.096$	$P(much|high) = 0.096/0.128 = 0.75$
Total	1		$P(high) = 0.028 + 0.004 + 0.096 = 0.128$	1

(c) A probability revision table for calculating the probability of a medium reading and the posterior probabilities of no oil (S_1), some oil (S_2), and much oil (S_3), given a medium reading

S_j	$P(S_j)$	$P(medium|S_j)$	$P(S_j \cap medium) = P(S_j)P(medium|S_j)$	$P(S_j|medium) = P(S_j \cap medium)/P(medium)$
$S_1 \equiv$ none	$P(none) = 0.7$	$P(medium|none) = 0.05$	$P(none \cap medium) = 0.7(0.05) = 0.035$	$P(none|medium) = 0.035/0.226 = 0.15487$
$S_2 \equiv$ some	$P(some) = 0.2$	$P(medium|some) = 0.94$	$P(some \cap medium) = 0.2(0.94) = 0.188$	$P(some|medium) = 0.188/0.226 = 0.83186$
$S_3 \equiv$ much	$P(much) = 0.1$	$P(medium|much) = 0.03$	$P(much \cap medium) = 0.1(0.03) = 0.003$	$P(much|medium) = 0.003/0.226 = 0.01327$
Total	1		$P(medium) = 0.035 + 0.188 + 0.003 = 0.226$	1

(d) A probability revision table for calculating the probability of a low reading and the posterior probabilities of no oil (S_1), some oil (S_2), and much oil (S_3), given a low reading

S_j	$P(S_j)$	$P(low|S_j)$	$P(S_j \cap low) = P(S_j)P(low|S_j)$	$P(S_j|low) = P(S_j \cap low)/P(low)$
$S_1 \equiv$ none	$P(none) = 0.7$	$P(low|none) = 0.91$	$P(none \cap low) = 0.7(0.91) = 0.637$	$P(none|low) = 0.637/0.646 = 0.98607$
$S_2 \equiv$ some	$P(some) = 0.2$	$P(low|some) = 0.04$	$P(some \cap low) = 0.2(0.04) = 0.008$	$P(some|low) = 0.008/0.646 = 0.01238$
$S_3 \equiv$ much	$P(much) = 0.1$	$P(low|much) = 0.01$	$P(much \cap low) = 0.1(0.01) = 0.001$	$P(much|low) = 0.001/0.646 = 0.00155$
Total	1		$P(low) = 0.637 + 0.008 + 0.001 = 0.646$	1

for medium and low readings of the seismic experiment given each of the states of nature (none, some, or much).

Now suppose that when the company performs the seismic experiment on the site in question, it obtains a high reading. The previously given conditional probabilities suggest that given this new information, the company might feel that the likelihood of much oil is higher than its prior probability, $P(much) = 0.1$, and that the likelihoods of some oil and no oil are lower than the prior probabilities $P(some) = 0.2$ and $P(none) = 0.7$. To be more specific, we wish to *revise the prior probabilities* of no, some, and much oil to what we call **posterior probabilities**. We can do this by using Bayes' theorem as follows.

If we wish to compute $P(\text{none}|\text{high})$, we first calculate

$$P(\text{high}) = P(\text{none} \cap \text{high}) + P(\text{some} \cap \text{high}) + P(\text{much} \cap \text{high})$$
$$= P(\text{none})P(\text{high}|\text{none}) + P(\text{some})P(\text{high}|\text{some}) + P(\text{much})P(\text{high}|\text{much})$$
$$= (0.7)(0.04) + (0.2)(0.02) + (0.1)(0.96) = 0.128.$$

Then Bayes' theorem says that

$$P(\text{none}|\text{high}) = \frac{P(\text{none} \cap \text{high})}{P(\text{high})} = \frac{P(\text{none})P(\text{high}|\text{none})}{P(\text{high})}$$
$$= \frac{0.7(0.04)}{0.128} = \frac{0.028}{0.128} = 0.21875.$$

These calculations are summarized in part (b) of Figure 3.6. This table, which is called a **probability revision table**, also contains the calculations of the revised probabilities $P(\text{some}|\text{high}) = 0.03125$ and $P(\text{much}|\text{high}) = 0.75$. The revised probabilities in part (b) of Figure 3.6 tell us that given that the seismic experiment gives a high reading, the revised probabilities of no, some, and much oil are 0.21875, 0.03125, and 0.75, respectively. Figures 3.7(c) and (d) show the calculations for the revised probabilities for no, some, and much oil given medium and low readings, respectively.

Since the posterior probability of much oil is 0.75, we might conclude that we should drill on the oil site. However, this decision should also be based on economic considerations.

In this section, we have only introduced Bayes' theorem. There is an entire subject called **Bayesian statistics**, which uses Bayes' theorem to update prior belief about a probability or population parameter to posterior belief. The use of Bayesian statistics is controversial in the case where the prior belief is largely based on subjective considerations, because many statisticians do not believe that we should base decisions on subjective considerations. Realistically, however, we all do this in our daily lives.

Exercises for Section 3.5

CONCEPTS

3.40　What is a prior probability? What is a posterior probability?

3.41　Explain the purpose behind using Bayes' theorem.

METHODS AND APPLICATIONS

3.42　Suppose that A_1, A_2, and B are events; A_1 and A_2 are mutually exclusive; and

$$P(A_1) = 0.8, \qquad P(B|A_1) = 0.1,$$
$$P(A_2) = 0.2, \qquad P(B|A_2) = 0.3.$$

Use this information to find $P(A_1|B)$ and $P(A_2|B)$.

3.43　Suppose that A_1, A_2, A_3, and B are events; A_1, A_2, and A_3 are mutually exclusive; and

$$P(A_1) = 0.2, \qquad P(A_2) = 0.5, \qquad P(A_3) = 0.3,$$
$$P(B|A_1) = 0.02, \qquad P(B|A_2) = 0.05, \qquad P(B|A_3) = 0.04.$$

Use this information to find $P(A_1|B)$, $P(A_2|B)$, and $P(A_3|B)$.

3.44　Consider a screening test for a certain type of cancer. Suppose that it is known that 0.5 percent of the population actually have this type of cancer. The test cannot perfectly screen for the disease, but suppose that it properly detects cancer 95 percent of the time and it improperly detects cancer 2 percent of the time. If the result of the test is positive, what is the chance that the person actually has cancer?

3.45　A department store is considering a new credit policy to try to reduce the number of customers defaulting on payments. A suggestion is made to discontinue credit to any customer who has been one week or more late with their payment at least twice. Past records show 95 percent of defaults were late at least twice. Also, 3 percent of all customers default, and 30 percent of those who have not defaulted have had at least two late payments.

a. Find the probability that a customer with at least two late payments will default.

b. Based on part a, should the policy be adopted? Explain.

3.46 A company administers an aptitude test for managers to aid in selecting new management trainees. Prior experience suggests that 60 percent of all applicants for management trainee positions would be successful if they were hired. Furthermore, past experience with the aptitude test indicates that 85 percent of applicants who turn out to be successful managers pass the test and 90 percent of applicants who turn out not to be successful managers fail the test.

    a. If an applicant passes the aptitude test for managers, what is the probability that the applicant will succeed in a management position?

    b. Based on your answer to part a, do you think that the aptitude test for managers is a valuable way to screen applicants for management trainee positions? Explain.

3.47 Three data entry specialists enter requisitions into a computer. Specialist 1 processes 30 percent of the requisitions, specialist 2 processes 45 percent, and specialist 3 processes 25 percent. The proportions of incorrectly entered requisitions by data entry specialists 1, 2, and 3 are 0.03, 0.05, and 0.02, respectively. Suppose that a random requisition is found to have been incorrectly entered. What is the probability that it was processed by data entry specialist 1? by data entry specialist 2? by data entry specialist 3?

3.48 A truth serum given to a suspect is known to be 90 percent reliable when the person is guilty and 99 percent reliable when the person is innocent. In other words, 10 percent of the guilty are judged innocent by the serum and 1 percent of the innocent are judged guilty. If a person was selected from a group of suspects of which only 5 percent are guilty of having committed a crime, and the serum indicates that the suspect is guilty of having committed a crime, what is the probability that the suspect is innocent?

3.49 A firm designs and builds automatic electronic control devices and installs them in customers' plants. In

shipment, a device has a prior probability of 0.10 of getting out of alignment. Before a control device is installed, test equipment is used to check the device's alignment. The test equipment has two readings, "in" or "out" of alignment. If the control device is in alignment, there is a 0.8 probability that the test equipment will read "in." If the control device is not in alignment, there is a 0.9 probability that the test equipment will read "out."

    a. Draw a tree diagram illustrating the prior and conditional probabilities for this situation.

    b. Construct a probability revision table for calculating the probability that the test equipment reads "in" and for calculating the posterior probabilities of the control device being in alignment and out of alignment given that the test equipment reads "in." What is $P(\text{in} \mid \text{reads "in"})$? What is $P(\text{out} \mid \text{reads "in"})$?

    c. Construct a probability revision table for calculating the probability that the test equipment reads "out" and for calculating the posterior probabilities of the control device being in alignment and out of alignment given that the test equipment reads "out." What is $P(\text{in} \mid \text{reads "out"})$? What is $P(\text{out} \mid \text{reads "out"})$?

3.50 Suppose that a box contains one fair coin and one coin with heads on both sides. One coin is selected from the box at random and tossed once and the result is a head.

    a. What is the chance that the coin is the fair coin?

    b. Now suppose that the same coin is tossed again, and the result is a head again. What is the chance that this coin is the fair coin?

3.51 Two sections of a statistics course are being taught. From what she has heard about the two instructors, Melanie estimates that the chances of passing the course are 0.90 if she gets Professor Chapin and 0.75 if she gets Professor Fulford. The section that she is in is determined by the registrar's office. Suppose that her chances of being in Professor Chapin's section are 40 percent. Melanie does indeed pass the course. What are the chances that she was enrolled in Professor Chapin's section?

CHAPTER SUMMARY

In this chapter, we studied **probability**. We began by defining an **event** to be an experimental outcome that may or may not occur and by defining the **probability of an event** to be a number that measures the likelihood that the event will occur. We learned that a probability is often interpreted as a **long-run relative frequency**, and we saw that probabilities can be found by examining **sample spaces** and by using **probability rules**. We learned several important probability rules—**addition rules**, **multiplication rules**, and the **rule of complements**. We also studied a

special kind of probability called a **conditional probability**, which is the probability that one event will occur given that another event occurs, and we used probabilities to define **independent events**.

We concluded this chapter by discussing **Bayes' theorem**. We learned that this theorem is used to revise **prior probabilities** to **posterior probilities** based on new information. We saw that the **general multiplication rule** for probabilities is very useful when solving **Bayes' theorem** problems.

GLOSSARY OF TERMS

Bayes' theorem: A theorem (formula) that is used to compute posterior probabilities by revising prior probabilities. (pages 105–106)

Bayesian statistics: An area of statistics that uses Bayes' theorem to update prior belief about a probability or population parameter to posterior belief. (page 108)

complement (of an event): If A is an event, the complement of A is the event that A will not occur. (page 91)

conditional probability: The probability that one event will occur given that we know that another event occurs. (page 97)

dependent events: When the probability of one event is influenced by whether another event occurs, the events are said to be dependent. (page 101)

event: A set of sample space outcomes. (page 87)

experiment: A process of observation that has an uncertain outcome. (page 84)

independent events: When the probability of one event is not influenced by whether another event occurs, the events are said to be independent. (page 101)

mutually exclusive events: Events that have no sample space outcomes in common and, therefore, cannot occur simultaneously. (page 93)

posterior probability: A revised probability obtained by updating a prior probability after receiving new information. (page 105)

prior probability: The initial probability that an event will occur. (page 105)

probability (of an event): A number that measures the chance, or likelihood, that an event will occur when an experiment is carried out. (page 87)

sample space: The set of all possible experimental outcomes (sample space outcomes). (page 86)

sample space outcome: A distinct outcome of an experiment (that is, an element in the sample space). (page 86)

subjective probability: A probability assessment that is based on experience, intuitive judgment, or expertise. (page 85)

IMPORTANT FORMULAS

Probabilities when all sample space outcomes are equally likely: page 88

The rule of complements: page 92

The addition rule for two events: page 93

The addition rule for two mutually exclusive events: page 94

The addition rule for N mutually exclusive events: page 95

Conditional probability: page 98

The general multiplication rule: page 99

Independent events: page 101

The multiplication rule for two independent events: page 101

The multiplication rule for N independent events: page 102

Bayes' theorem: page 106

Probability revision table: page 107

Connect ™ Practise and learn online with *Connect*. Questions and tables with online data sets are marked with ✈.

SUPPLEMENTARY EXERCISES

Exercises 3.52 through 3.55 are based on the following situation: An investor holds two stocks, each of which can rise (R), remain unchanged (U), or decline (D) on any particular day.

3.52 Construct a tree diagram showing all possible combined movements for both stocks on a particular day (for instance, RR, RD, and so on, where the first letter denotes the movement of the first stock and the second letter denotes the movement of the second stock).

3.53 If all outcomes are equally likely, find the probability that both stocks rise; that both stocks decline; that exactly one stock declines.

3.54 Find the probabilities you found in Exercise 3.53 by assuming that for each stock $P(R) = 0.6$, $P(U) = 0.1$, and

$P(D) = 0.3$, and assuming that the two stocks move independently.

3.55 Assume that for the first stock (on a particular day)

$$P(R) = 0.4, P(U) = 0.2, P(D) = 0.4,$$

and that for the second stock (on a particular day)

$$P(R) = 0.8, P(U) = 0.1, P(D) = 0.1.$$

Assuming that these stocks move independently, find the probability that both stocks decline; the probability that exactly one stock rises; the probability that exactly one stock is unchanged; the probability that both stocks rise.

Statistics Canada (http://www.statcan.gc.ca) reports various employment statistics. The values of employment (employed or not employed) by sex and age for 2009 are provided below.

(*Note:* Some rounding has been done to ease the calculations; numbers are in thousands.) Using the information contained in the tables, answer Exercises 3.56 through 3.60. ✈

	Women		Men		Both Sexes*	
Employment:	Yes	No	Yes	No	Yes	No
Age						
15–24 years	1,229	173	1,201	265	2,430	438
25–44 years	3,567	243	3,887	355	7,454	598
45–64 years	3,126	185	3,399	278	6,525	464
65 and older	154	6	286	14	440	20

*Numbers may not add due to rounding.
Source: Adapted from the Statistics Canada Web site, http://www40.statcan.gc.ca/l01/cst01/labor20a-eng.htm.

3.56 Find the probability that a randomly selected woman aged 15 to 24 is employed.

3.57 Find the probability that a randomly selected woman aged 45 to 64 is unemployed.

3.58 Find the probability that a randomly selected woman is employed if she is older than 25 years.

3.59 Repeat Exercises 3.56 to 3.58 for a randomly selected male.

3.60 Find the probability that a randomly selected individual (regardless of sex) is employed and is older than 45.

3.61 Suppose that in a survey of 1,000 Ontario residents, 721 residents believed that the amount of violent television programming had increased over the past ten years, 454 residents believed that the overall quality of television programming had decreased over the past ten years, and 362 residents believed both.

  a. What proportion of the 1,000 Ontario residents believed that the amount of violent programming had increased over the past ten years?

  b. What proportion of the 1,000 Ontario residents believed that the overall quality of programming had decreased over the past ten years?

  c. What proportion of the 1,000 Ontario residents believed that both the amount of violent programming had increased and the overall quality of programming had decreased over the past ten years?

  d. What proportion of the 1,000 Ontario residents believed that either the amount of violent programming had increased or the overall quality of programming had decreased over the past ten years?

  e. What proportion of the Ontario residents who believed that the amount of violent programming had increased believed that the overall quality of programming had decreased?

  f. What proportion of the Ontario residents who believed that the overall quality of programming had decreased believed that the amount of violent programming had increased?

  g. What sort of dependence seems to exist between whether Ontario residents believed that the amount of violent programming had increased and whether Ontario residents believed that the overall quality of programming had decreased? Explain your answer.

3.62 Enterprise Industries has been running a television advertisement for Fresh liquid laundry detergent. When a survey was conducted, 21 percent of the individuals surveyed had purchased Fresh, 41 percent of the individuals surveyed had recalled seeing the advertisement, and 13 percent of the individuals surveyed had purchased Fresh and recalled seeing the advertisement.

  a. What proportion of the individuals surveyed who recalled seeing the advertisement had purchased Fresh?

  b. Based on your answer to part a, does the advertisement seem to have been effective? Explain.

3.63 A company employs 400 salespeople. Of these, 83 received a bonus last year, 100 attended a special sales training program at the beginning of last year, and 42 both attended the special sales training program and received a bonus. (*Note:* The bonus was based totally on sales performance.)

  a. What proportion of the 400 salespeople received a bonus last year?

  b. What proportion of the 400 salespeople attended the special sales training program at the beginning of last year?

  c. What proportion of the 400 salespeople both attended the special sales training program and received a bonus?

  d. What proportion of the salespeople who attended the special sales training program received a bonus?

  e. Based on your answers to parts a and d, does the special sales training program seem to have been effective? Explain your answer.

3.64 Suppose that A and B are events and that $P(A)$ and $P(B)$ are both positive.

  a. If A and B are mutually exclusive, what is $P(A \cap B)$?

  b. If A and B are independent events, explain why $P(A \cap B)$ is positive.

  c. Can two mutually exclusive events, each having a positive probability of occurrence, also be independent? Prove your answer using your answers to parts a and b.

3.65 On any given day, suppose that the probability that a beach on Lake Ontario is contaminated by E. coli is 0.10. Each day, a test is conducted to determine whether the beach is contaminated by E. coli. This test has proven correct 80 percent of the time. Suppose that on a particular day the test indicates E. coli contamination. What is the probability that such contamination actually exists?

3.66 A marketing major will interview for an internship with a major consumer products manufacturer/distributor. Before the interview, the marketing major feels that the chances of being offered an internship are 40 percent. Suppose that of the students who have been offered internships with this company, 90 percent had good interviews, and that of the students who have not been offered internships, 50 percent had good interviews. If the marketing major has a good interview, what is the probability that they will be offered an internship?

3.67 Suppose you are at a house party with 34 other people. You have recently taken a statistics course and you wonder how many people in this group of 35 have the same birthday. You get everyone to write their birthday down (just the month and day) on a cocktail napkin.

  a. What is the chance that you will share a birthday with someone else at the party?

  b. What is the chance that there will be at least one matched birthday at this party?

  c. How many need to attend the party in order for there to be about a 50 percent chance that there is at least one matched birthday?

3.68 Suppose that two independent events, A and B, occur with probability 0.4 and 0.3.

  a. What is $P(A \cap B)$?

  b. What is $P(A \mid B)$?

  c. What is $P(A \cup B)$?

  d. What is P(exactly one of A or B occurring), or $P(A$ or B but not both)?

3.69 In the book *Making Hard Decisions: An Introduction to Decision Analysis*, Clemen presents an example in which he discusses the 1982 John Hinckley trial. In describing the case, Clemen says:

> In 1982 John Hinckley was on trial, accused of having attempted to kill President Reagan. During Hinckley's trial, Dr. Daniel R. Weinberger told the court that when individuals diagnosed as schizophrenics were given computerized axial tomography (CAT) scans, the scans showed brain atrophy in 30% of the cases compared with only 2% of the scans done on normal people. Hinckley's defense attorney wanted to introduce as evidence Hinckley's CAT scan, which showed brain atrophy. The defense argued that the presence of atrophy strengthened the case that Hinckley suffered from mental illness.

a. Approximately 1.5 percent of the people in the United States suffer from schizophrenia. If we consider the prior probability of schizophrenia to be 0.015, use the information given to find the probability that a person has schizophrenia given that a person's CAT scan shows brain atrophy.

b. John Hinckley's CAT scan showed brain atrophy. Discuss whether your answer to part a helps or hurts the case that Hinckley suffered from mental illness.

c. It can be argued that 0.015 is not a reasonable prior probability of schizophrenia. This is because 0.015 is the probability that a randomly selected U.S. citizen has schizophrenia. However, John Hinckley is not a randomly selected U.S. citizen. Rather, he was accused of attempting to assassinate the president

of the United States. Therefore, it might be reasonable to assess a higher prior probability of schizophrenia. Suppose you are a juror who believes there is only a 10 percent chance that Hinckley suffers from schizophrenia. Using 0.10 as the prior probability of schizophrenia, find the probability that a person has schizophrenia given that a person's CAT scan shows brain atrophy.

d. If you are a juror with a prior probability of 0.10 that John Hinckley suffers from schizophrenia and given your answer to part c, does the fact that Hinckley's CAT scan showed brain atrophy help the case that Hinckley suffered from mental illness?

e. If you are a juror with a prior probability of 0.25 that Hinckley suffers from schizophrenia, find the probability of schizophrenia given that Hinckley's CAT scan showed brain atrophy. In this situation, how strong is the case that Hinckley suffered from mental illness?

3.70   INTERNET EXERCISE

BBM Canada reports on radio statistics for a variety of cities across the country. Go to http://www.bbm.ca/index.php?lang=english, click on Radio Market Rankings, and select a city. Compare the share aggregates found for the city of your choice to those reported in this chapter for London, Ontario. The London data can be found under Diary Radio Data by clicking the link with the latest year (for example, Spring 2010 Top-line Radio report). How do the aggregates compare? What factor do you feel would make the aggregates differ?

CHAPTER **4**
Discrete Random Variables

LEARNING OBJECTIVES

After reading this chapter, you should be able to

LO1 describe what is meant by a random variable

LO2 explain the difference between a discrete random variable and a continuous random variable

LO3 describe the ways in which the probability distribution of a discrete random variable can be depicted

LO4 calculate the mean (or expected value), variance, and standard deviation of discrete random variables

LO5 distinguish between the binomial distribution and the Poisson distribution

LO6 identify and understand the characteristics of a hypergeometric random variable

LO7 calculate probabilities using the hypergeometric formula

CHAPTER OUTLINE

4.1 Two Types of Random Variables

4.2 Discrete Probability Distributions

4.3 The Binomial Distribution

4.4 The Poisson Distribution

4.5 The Hypergeometric Distribution

People often struggle with the concepts of randomness and variables, but both are around us every day. If there were no randomness in our lives, and if things never varied at all, life would be pretty boring. We would always know what things would occur in our lives and when they would occur. Of course, it would be nice to know if and when some things will occur in our lives, like marriage, children, or winning the lottery. Only a journey through life can tell us whether these things will happen. In this chapter, we will deal specifically with **discrete random variables** and their probability distributions.

In Chapter 1 we introduced the idea of variables. Variables were defined as characteristics that we may be interested in analyzing. For example, we could be talking about hair colour, eye colour, sex, salary, age, or IQ. Of course, the first three characteristics in the list are qualitative (or categorical) in nature and the last three are quantitative (or numerical) in nature. In

this chapter, we will further explore the concept of variables that are numerical in nature. Specifically, we will deal with discrete random variables. Random variables that are discrete in nature will take on a finite number of values, or an infinitely countable number of values. Some examples of discrete random variables are the number of roommates you have, the number of text messages you receive in a day, and the number of questions you get correct on a multiple choice exam.

In this chapter, we will also introduce the concept of a **continuous random variable** to help you better understand discrete random variables. Examples of continuous random variables are the amount of coffee you drink every day (measured in litres), the amount of time you spend on your cell phone each day, and the time between incoming cell phone calls. Continuous random variables will be discussed in greater detail in Chapter 5.

connect Practise and learn online with *Connect*. Throughout this chapter, questions and tables with online data sets are marked with ⚡.

4.1 TWO TYPES OF RANDOM VARIABLES

LO1

A **random variable** is a variable that assumes numerical values that are determined by the outcome of an experiment, where one and only one numerical value is assigned to each experimental outcome.

Before an experiment is carried out, its outcome is uncertain. It follows that since a random variable assigns a number to each experimental outcome, a random variable can be thought of as *representing an uncertain numerical outcome*.

To illustrate the idea of a random variable, suppose that Sound City sells and installs satellite radio systems. One of Sound City's most popular satellite radio systems is the top-of-the-line SatStar system. Consider (the experiment of) selling the SatStar system at the Sound City store during a particular week. If we let x denote the number of systems sold during the week, then x is a random variable. That is, looked at before the week, the number of systems, x, that will be sold is uncertain, and, therefore, x is a random variable.

LO2

VS

CHAPTER 3

Notice that x, the number of SatStar satellite radios sold in a week, might be 0 or 1 or 2 or 3, and so forth. In general, when the possible values of a random variable can be counted or listed, then the random variable is a **discrete random variable**. That is, either a discrete random variable may assume a finite number of possible values or the possible values may take the form of a **countable** sequence or list such as 0, 1, 2, 3, 4, . . . (a **countably infinite** list).

Some other examples of discrete random variables are as follows:

1 The number, out of the next three customers entering a store, who will make a purchase. Here x could be 0, 1, 2, or 3.

2 The number, out of four patients taking a new antibiotic, who experience gastrointestinal distress as a side effect. Here x could be 0, 1, 2, 3, or 4.

3 The number of televisions in a sample of eight five-year-old televisions that have not needed a single repair. Here x could be any of the values 0, 1, 2, 3, 4, 5, 6, 7, and 8.

4 The rating on a 1 through 5 scale given to a song by a listener in a music survey. Here x could be 1, 2, 3, 4, or 5.

5 The number of major fires in a large city during the last two months. Here x could be 0, 1, 2, 3, and so forth (there is no definite maximum number of fires).

The values of the random variables described in (1), (2), (3), and (4) are countable and finite. In contrast, the values of the random variable described in (5) are countable and infinite (or a countably infinite list). For example, in theory there is no limit to the number of major fires that could occur in a city in two months.

Not all random variables have values that are countable. When a random variable may assume any numerical value in one or more intervals on the real number line, then the random variable is a **continuous random variable**.

Example 4.1   Happy Birthday!

Consider your age for a second. How old are you? Most of you will give answers like 19, 20, 21, and so forth, but are you really that age? When someone asks us how old we are, we do not actually tell them our exact age. Instead, we tell them our age as of our last birthday. It is very difficult to keep track of your actual age because it is *continuously changing*. In fact, you have aged a little since you starting reading this example! Your age is an example of a continuous random variable. In theory, your age could be expressed to an infinite number of decimal places. In practice (thankfully), we always round down to the nearest whole number until we are forced to add one to that value every year on our birthday.

Some other examples of continuous random variables are

1   The temperature (in degrees Celsius) of a cup of coffee served at a McDonald's restaurant.
2   The volume (in millilitres) of strawberry jam dispensed by an automatic filling machine into a 500-mL jar.
3   The time (in seconds) that a customer in a store must wait to receive a credit card authorization.
4   The interest rate (in percent) charged for mortgage loans at a bank.

Exercises for Section 4.1

CONCEPTS

4.1   Explain the concept of a random variable.

4.2   Explain how the values of a discrete random variable differ from the values of a continuous random variable.

4.3   Classify each of the following random variables as discrete or continuous:
  a. x = the number of girls born to a couple who will have three children.
  b. x = the number of defects found on an automobile at final inspection.
  c. x = the mass (in grams) of the sandwich meat in a submarine sandwich.
  d. x = the number of incorrect lab procedures conducted at a hospital during a particular week.
  e. x = the number of customers served during a given day at a drive-through window.
  f. x = the time needed by a clerk to complete a task.
  g. x = the temperature of a pizza oven at a particular time.

4.2 DISCRETE PROBABILITY DISTRIBUTIONS

The value assumed by a discrete random variable depends on the outcome of an experiment. Because the outcome of the experiment is uncertain, the value assumed by the random variable is also uncertain. However, it is often useful to know the probabilities that are associated with the different values that the random variable can take on. That is, we often wish to know the random variable's **probability distribution**.

The **probability distribution** of a discrete random variable is a table, graph, or formula that gives the probability associated with each possible value that the random variable can assume.

LO3

We denote the probability distribution of the discrete random variable x as $p(x)$. As will be demonstrated in the following example, we can sometimes use the sample space of an experiment and probability rules to find the probability distribution of a random variable.

Example 4.2   True–False Quiz

Consider a pop quiz consisting of three true–false questions. The sample space when a student takes such a quiz consists of the outcomes

$$CCC \quad CCI \quad CIC \quad ICC$$
$$CII \quad ICI \quad IIC \quad III$$

TABLE **4.1**   Finding the Probability Distribution of x = the Number of Questions Answered Correctly When the Student Studies and Has a 90 Percent Chance of Answering Each Question Correctly

Value of x = the Number of Correct Answers	Sample Space Outcomes Corresponding to Value of x	Probability of Sample Space Outcome	$p(x)$ = Probability of the Value of x
$x = 0$ (no correct answers)	III	$(0.1)(0.1)(0.1) = 0.001$	$p(0) = 0.001$
$x = 1$ (one correct answer)	CII	$(0.9)(0.1)(0.1) = 0.009$	$p(1) = 0.009 + 0.009 + 0.009 = 0.027$
	ICI	$(0.1)(0.9)(0.1) = 0.009$	
	IIC	$(0.1)(0.1)(0.9) = 0.009$	
$x = 2$ (two correct answers)	CCI	$(0.9)(0.9)(0.1) = 0.081$	$p(2) = 0.081 + 0.081 + 0.081 = 0.243$
	CIC	$(0.9)(0.1)(0.9) = 0.081$	
	ICC	$(0.1)(0.9)(0.9) = 0.081$	
$x = 3$ (three correct answers)	CCC	$(0.9)(0.9)(0.9) = 0.729$	$p(3) = 0.729$

where C represents a correct choice and I represents an incorrect choice. We now define the random variable x to be the number of questions that the student answers correctly. Here x can assume the value 0, 1, 2, or 3. That is, the student could answer anywhere between 0 and 3 questions correctly. Here, we will assume that the student studies and has a 0.9 probability of answering each question correctly. Table 4.1 summarizes finding the probabilities associated with each of the values of x (0, 1, 2, and 3). As an example of the calculations, consider finding the probability that x equals 2. Two questions will be answered correctly if and only if we obtain one of the sample space outcomes

$$CCI \qquad CIC \qquad ICC$$

Assuming that the three questions will be answered independently, these sample space outcomes have probabilities

$$P(CCI) = (0.9)(0.9)(0.1) = 0.081,$$
$$P(CIC) = (0.9)(0.1)(0.9) = 0.081,$$
$$P(ICC) = (0.1)(0.9)(0.9) = 0.081.$$

Therefore,

$$P(x = 2) = P(CCI) + P(CIC) + P(ICC)$$
$$= 0.081 + 0.081 + 0.081$$
$$= 0.243.$$

Similarly, we can obtain probabilities associated with $x = 0$, $x = 1$, and $x = 3$. The probability distribution of x is summarized as follows:

x, Number of Questions Answered Correctly	$p(x)$, Probability of x
0	$p(0) = P(x = 0) = 0.001$
1	$p(1) = P(x = 1) = 0.027$
2	$p(2) = P(x = 2) = 0.243$
3	$p(3) = P(x = 3) = 0.729$

Notice that the probabilities in this probability distribution sum to $0.001 + 0.027 + 0.243 + 0.729 = 1$.

To show the advantage of studying, note that the above probability distribution says that if the student has a 0.9 probability of answering each question correctly, then the probability that the student will answer all three questions correctly is 0.729. Furthermore, the probability that the student will answer *at least* two out of three questions correctly is (since the events $x = 2$ and $x = 3$ are mutually exclusive)

$$
\begin{aligned}
P(x \geq 2) &= P(x = 2 \text{ or } x = 3) \\
&= P(x = 2) + P(x = 3) \\
&= 0.243 + 0.729 \\
&= p(2) + p(3) \\
&= 0.972.
\end{aligned}
$$

By contrast, if the student is totally unprepared and has only a 0.5 probability of answering each question correctly, then the probabilities that the student will answer zero, one, two, and three questions correctly are, respectively, 1/8, 3/8, 3/8, and 1/8. Therefore, the probability that the unprepared student will answer all three questions correctly is only $1/8 = 0.125$, and the probability that this student will answer at least two out of three questions correctly is only $3/8 + 1/8 = 0.5$.

In general, a discrete probability distribution $p(x)$ must satisfy two conditions:

> A **discrete probability distribution $p(x)$** must be such that
>
> 1 $p(x) \geq 0$ for each value of x,
>
> 2 $\displaystyle\sum_{\text{All } x} p(x) = 1.$

The first of these conditions says that each probability in a probability distribution must be zero or positive. The second condition says that the probabilities in a probability distribution must sum to 1. Looking at the probability distribution illustrated in Example 4.2, we can see that these properties are satisfied.

It is often not possible to examine the entire sample space of an experiment. In such a case, we sometimes collect data that will allow us to estimate the probabilities in a probability distribution.

Example 4.3   Estimating a Probability Distribution

Sound City sells the SatStar satellite radio system. Define the random variable x to be the number of units sold in a particular week. In order to know the true probabilities of the various values of x, we would have to observe sales during all of the (potentially infinite number of) weeks in which the SatStar satellite radio system could be sold. That is, if we consider an experiment in which we randomly select a week and observe sales of the systems, the sample space would consist of a potentially infinite number of equally likely weeks. Obviously, it is not possible to examine this entire sample space.

Suppose, however, that Sound City has kept historical records of these sales during the last 100 weeks. These records give us the following information:

1   No systems have been sold in 3 (that is, $3/100 = 0.03$) of the weeks.

2   One system has been sold in 20 (that is, 0.20) of the weeks.

3   Two systems have been sold in 50 (that is, 0.50) of the weeks.

4   Three systems have been sold in 20 (that is, 0.20) of the weeks.

5   Four systems have been sold in 5 (that is, 0.05) of the weeks.

6   Five systems have been sold in 2 (that is, 0.02) of the weeks.

7   No more than five systems were sold in any of the past 100 weeks.

TABLE **4.2**   An Estimate (Based on 100 Weeks of Historical Data) of the Probability Distribution of x, the Number of SatStar Satellite Radio Systems Sold at Sound City in a Week

x, Number of Systems Sold	$p(x)$, the Probability of x
0	$p(0) = P(x = 0) = 3/100 = 0.03$
1	$p(1) = P(x = 1) = 20/100 = 0.20$
2	$p(2) = P(x = 2) = 50/100 = 0.50$
3	$p(3) = P(x = 3) = 20/100 = 0.20$
4	$p(4) = P(x = 4) = 5/100 = 0.05$
5	$p(5) = P(x = 5) = 2/100 = 0.02$

FIGURE **4.1**   A Graph of the Probability Distribution of x, the Number of SatStar Satellite Radio Systems Sold at Sound City in a Week

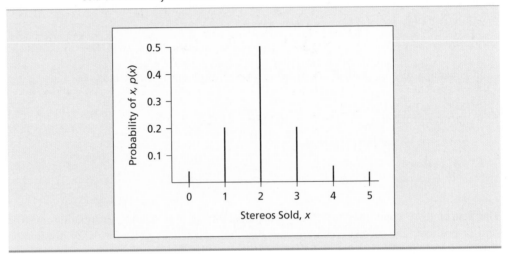

It follows that we might *estimate* that the probability distribution of x, the number of SatStar satellite radio systems sold during a particular week at Sound City, is as shown in Table 4.2. A graph of this distribution is shown in Figure 4.1.

Finally, it is reasonable to use the historical sales data from the past 100 weeks to estimate the true probabilities associated with the various numbers of satellite radio systems sold if the sales process remains stable over time and is not seasonal (that is, if sales are not higher at one time of the year than at others).

Suppose that the experiment described by a random variable x is repeated an indefinitely large number of times. If the values of the random variable x observed on the repetitions are recorded, we will obtain the population of all possible observed values of the random variable x. This population has a mean, which we denote as μ_x and which we sometimes call the **expected value of x**. In order to calculate μ_x, we multiply each value of x by its probability $p(x)$ and then sum the resulting products over all possible values of x.

LO4

The **mean**, or **expected value**, of a discrete random variable x is

$$\mu_x = \sum_{\text{All } x} xp(x).$$

In the next example, we illustrate how to calculate μ_x, and we reason that the calculation really does give the mean of all possible observed values of the random variable x.

Example 4.4   Expected Value

Remember that Table 4.2 gives the probability distribution of x, the number of SatStar satellite radio systems sold in a week at Sound City. Using this distribution, it follows that

$$\mu_x = \sum_{\text{All }x} xp(x)$$
$$= 0p(0) + 1p(1) + 2p(2) + 3p(3) + 4p(4) + 5p(5)$$
$$= 0(0.03) + 1(0.20) + 2(0.50) + 3(0.20) + 4(0.05) + 5(0.02)$$
$$= 2.1.$$

To see that such a calculation gives the mean of all possible observed values of x, recall from Example 4.3 that the probability distribution in Table 4.2 was estimated from historical records of SatStar satellite radio system sales during the last 100 weeks. Also recall that these historical records tell us that during the last 100 weeks Sound City sold

1   Zero systems in 3 of the 100 weeks, for a total of $0(3) = 0$ systems.

2   One system in 20 of the 100 weeks, for a total of $1(20) = 20$ systems.

3   Two systems in 50 of the 100 weeks, for a total of $2(50) = 100$ systems.

4   Three systems in 20 of the 100 weeks, for a total of $3(20) = 60$ systems.

5   Four systems in 5 of the 100 weeks, for a total of $4(5) = 20$ systems.

6   Five systems in 2 of the 100 weeks, for a total of $5(2) = 10$ systems.

In other words, Sound City sold a total of

$$0 + 20 + 100 + 60 + 20 + 10 = 210 \text{ systems}$$

in 100 weeks, or an average of $210/100 = 2.1$ systems per week. Now the average

$$\frac{210}{100} = \frac{0 + 20 + 100 + 60 + 20 + 10}{100}$$

can be written as

$$\frac{0(3) + 1(20) + 2(50) + 3(20) + 4(5) + 5(2)}{100},$$

which can be rewritten as

$$0\left(\frac{3}{100}\right) + 1\left(\frac{20}{100}\right) + 2\left(\frac{50}{100}\right) + 3\left(\frac{20}{100}\right) + 4\left(\frac{5}{100}\right) + 5\left(\frac{2}{100}\right)$$
$$= 0(0.03) + 1(0.20) + 2(0.50) + 3(0.20) + 4(0.05) + 5(0.02),$$

which equals $\mu_x = 2.1$. That is, if observed sales values occur with relative frequencies equal to those specified by the probability distribution in Table 4.2, then the average number of satellite radio systems sold per week is equal to the expected value of x.

Of course, if we observed sales for another 100 weeks, the relative frequencies of the observed sales values would probably not be exactly as specified by the estimated probabilities in Table 4.2. Rather, the observed relative frequencies would differ somewhat, and the average number of systems sold per week would not exactly equal $\mu_x = 2.1$ (although the average would likely be close). However, the point is this: If the probability distribution in Table 4.2 were the true probability distribution of weekly sales, and if we were to observe sales for an indefinitely large number of weeks, then we would observe sales values with relative frequencies that are exactly equal to those specified by the probabilities in Table 4.2. In this case, when we calculate the expected value of x to be $\mu_x = 2.1$, we are saying that *in the long run* (that is, over an indefinitely large number of weeks), Sound City would average selling 2.1 SatStar satellite radio systems per week.

As another example, again consider Example 4.2, and let the random variable x denote the number of the three true–false questions that the student who studies answers correctly. Using the probability distribution shown in Table 4.1, the expected value of x is

$$\mu_x = 0(0.001) + 1(0.027) + 2(0.243) + 3(0.729)$$

$$= 2.7.$$

This expected value says that if a student takes a large number of three-question true–false quizzes and has a 0.9 probability of answering any single question correctly, then the student will average approximately 2.7 correct answers per quiz.

Example 4.5   Expected Profit

An insurance company sells a $20,000 whole life insurance policy for an annual premium of $300. Actuarial tables show that a person who would be sold such a policy with this premium has a 0.001 probability of death during a year. Let x be a random variable representing the insurance company's profit made on one of these policies during a year. The probability distribution of x is as follows:

x, Profit	p(x), Probability of x
$300 (if the policyholder lives)	0.999
$300 − $20,000 = −$19,700	0.001
(a $19,700 loss if the policyholder dies)	

The expected value of x (expected profit per year) is

$$\mu_x = \$300(0.999) + (-\$19,700)(0.001)$$

$$= \$280.$$

This says that if the insurance company sells a very large number of these policies, it will average a profit of $280 per policy per year. Since insurance companies actually do sell large numbers of policies, it is reasonable for these companies to make profitability decisions based on expected values.

Next suppose that we wish to find the premium that the insurance company must charge for a $20,000 policy if the company wishes the average profit per policy per year to be greater than $0. If we let *prem* denote the premium the company will charge, then the probability distribution of the company's yearly profit, x, is as follows:

x, Profit	p(x), Probability of x
prem (if policyholder lives)	0.999
prem − $20,000 (if policyholder dies)	0.001

The expected value of x (expected profit per year) is

$$\mu_x = prem(0.999) + (prem - 20,000)(0.001)$$
$$= prem - 20.$$

In order for this expected profit to be greater than zero, the premium must be greater than $20. If, as previously stated, the company charges $300 for such a policy, the $280 charged in excess of the needed $20 compensates the company for commissions paid to salespeople, administrative costs, dividends paid to investors, and other expenses.

In general, it is reasonable to base decisions on an expected value if we perform the experiment related to the decision (for example, if we sell the life insurance policy) many times. If we do not (for instance, if we perform the experiment only once), then it may not be a good idea to base decisions on the expected value. For example, it might not be wise for you—as an individual—to sell one person a $20,000 life insurance policy for a premium of $300. To see this, again consider the probability distribution of yearly profit:

x, Profit	p(x), Probability of x
$300 (if policyholder lives)	0.999
$300 − $20,000 = −$19,700 (if policyholder dies)	0.001

Then recall that the expected profit per year is $280. However, since you are selling only one policy, you will not receive the $280. You will either gain $300 (with probability 0.999) or you will lose $19,700 (with probability 0.001). Although the decision is personal, and although the chance of losing $19,700 is very small, many people would not risk such a loss when the potential gain is only $300.

Just as the population of all possible observed values of a discrete random variable x has a mean μ_x, this population also has a variance σ_x^2 and a standard deviation σ_x. Recall that the variance of a population is the average of the squared deviations of the different population values from the population mean. To find σ_x^2, we calculate $(x - \mu_x)^2$ for each value of x, multiply $(x - \mu_x)^2$ by the probability $p(x)$, and sum the resulting products over all possible values of x.

The Variance and Standard Deviation of a Discrete Random Variable

The **variance** of a discrete random variable x is

$$\sigma_x^2 = \sum_{\text{All } x} (x - \mu_x)^2 \, p(x).$$

The **standard deviation** of x is the square root of the variance of x. That is,

$$\sigma_x = \sqrt{\sigma_x^2}.$$

Example 4.6 Variance Calculation

Table 4.2 on page 118 gives the probability distribution of x, the number of SatStar satellite radio systems sold in a week at Sound City. Remembering that we have calculated μ_x (in Example 4.4) to be 2.1, it follows that

$$
\begin{aligned}
\sigma_x^2 &= \sum_{\text{All } x} (x - \mu_x)^2 p(x) \\
&= (0 - 2.1)^2 p(0) + (1 - 2.1)^2 p(1) + (2 - 2.1)^2 p(2) + (3 - 2.1)^2 p(3) \\
&\quad + (4 - 2.1)^2 p(4) + (5 - 2.1)^2 p(5) \\
&= (4.41)(0.03) + (1.21)(0.20) + (0.01)(0.50) + (0.81)(0.20) + (3.61)(0.05) \\
&\quad + (8.41)(0.02) \\
&= 0.89
\end{aligned}
$$

and that the standard deviation of x is $\sigma_x = \sqrt{0.89} = 0.9434$.

An application of Chebyshev's theorem The variance, σ_x^2, and the standard deviation, σ_x, measure the spread of the population of all possible observed values of the random variable. To see how to use σ_x, remember that Chebyshev's theorem (see Chapter 2, page 52) tells us

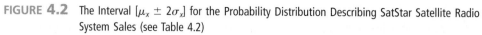

FIGURE 4.2   The Interval $[\mu_x \pm 2\sigma_x]$ for the Probability Distribution Describing SatStar Satellite Radio System Sales (see Table 4.2)

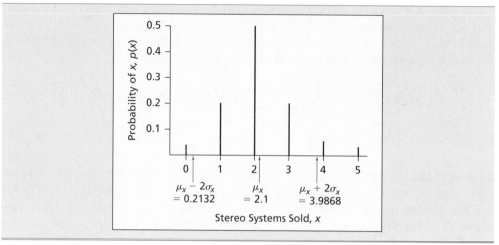

that for any value of k that is greater than 1, at least $100(1 - 1/k^2)$ percent of all possible observed values of the random variable x lie in the interval $[\mu_x \pm k\sigma_x]$. Stated in terms of a probability, we have

$$P(x \text{ falls in the interval } [\mu_x \pm k\sigma_x]) \geq 1 - 1/k^2.$$

For example, consider the probability distribution (in Table 4.2) of x, the number of SatStar satellite radio systems sold in a week at Sound City. If we set k equal to 2, and if we use $\mu_x = 2.1$ and $\sigma_x = 0.9434$ to calculate the interval

$$[\mu_x \pm 2\sigma_x] = [2.1 \pm 2(0.9434)]$$
$$= [0.2132, 3.9868],$$

then Chebyshev's theorem tells us that

$$P(x \text{ falls in the interval } [0.2132, 3.9868]) \geq 1 - 1/2^2 = 3/4.$$

This says that in at least 75 percent of all weeks, Sound City will sell between 0.2132 and 3.9868 SatStar satellite radio systems. As illustrated in Figure 4.2, there are three values of x between 0.2132 and 3.9868—namely, $x = 1$, $x = 2$, and $x = 3$. Therefore, the exact probability that x will be in the interval $[\mu_x \pm 2\sigma_x]$ is

$$p(1) + p(2) + p(3) = 0.20 + 0.50 + 0.20 = 0.90.$$

This illustrates that although Chebyshev's theorem guarantees us that at least $100(1 - 1/k^2)$ percent of all possible observed values of a random variable x fall in the interval $[\mu_x \pm k\sigma_x]$, the percentage is often considerably higher.

In some cases, the graph of the probability distribution of a discrete random variable has the symmetrical, bell-shaped appearance of a normal curve. For example, the graph in Figure 4.2 is roughly bell-shaped and symmetrical. In such a situation—and *under certain additional assumptions*—the probability distribution can sometimes be *approximated* by a normal curve. We will discuss the needed assumptions in Chapter 5. As an example of such assumptions, note that although the graph in Figure 4.2 is roughly bell-shaped and symmetrical, it can be shown that there are not enough values of x, and thus not enough probabilities $p(x)$, for us to approximate the probability distribution by using a normal curve. If, however, the probability distribution of a discrete random variable x can be approximated by a normal curve, then the **empirical rule** for normally distributed populations describes the population of all possible values of x. Specifically, we can say that approximately 68.26 percent, 95.44 percent, and 99.73 percent of all possible observed values of x fall in the intervals $[\mu_x \pm \sigma_x]$, $[\mu_x \pm 2\sigma_x]$, and $[\mu_x \pm 3\sigma_x]$, respectively.

To summarize, the standard deviation, σ_x, of a discrete random variable measures the spread of the population of all possible observed values of x. When the probability distribution of x can be approximated by a normal curve, this spread can be characterized by the empirical rule. When this is not possible, we can use Chebyshev's theorem to characterize the spread of x.

Exercises for Section 4.2

CONCEPTS

4.4 What is a discrete probability distribution? Explain in your own words.

4.5 What conditions must be satisfied by the probabilities in a discrete probability distribution? Explain what these conditions mean.

4.6 Describe how to compute the mean (or expected value) of a discrete random variable, and interpret what this quantity tells us about the observed values of the random variable.

4.7 Describe how to compute the standard deviation of a discrete random variable, and interpret what this quantity tells us about the observed values of the random variable.

METHODS AND APPLICATIONS

4.8 Decide whether each of the following is a valid probability distribution. If the probability distribution is valid, show why. Otherwise, show which condition(s) of a probability distribution are not satisfied.

a.

x	p(x)
−1	0.2
0	0.6
1	0.2

c.

x	p(x)
1/2	−1
3/4	0
1	2

b.

x	p(x)
2	0.25
4	0.35
6	0.3

d.

x	p(x)
0.1	2/7
0.7	4/7
0.9	1/7

4.9 Consider each of the following probability distributions.

a.

x	p(x)
0	0.2
1	0.8

c.

x	p(x)
−2	0.1
0	0.3
2	0.4
5	0.2

b.

x	p(x)
0	0.25
1	0.45
2	0.2
3	0.1

Calculate μ_x and σ_x for each distribution. Then explain, using the probabilities, why μ_x is the mean of all possible observed values of x.

4.10 For each of the following, write out and graph the probability distribution of x. That is, list all the possible values of x as well as the corresponding probabilities. Then graph the distribution.

a. Two randomly selected grocery store patrons are each asked to take a blind taste test and then state which of three diet colas (marked A, B, and C) they prefer. Let x represent the number of patrons who prefer diet cola A. Assume that each cola is equally likely to be preferred.

b. Suppose that a couple will have three children. Let B denote a boy and G denote a girl. Assume that boys and girls are equally likely to be born. Let x represent the number of girls born to the couple.

c. Four people will enter an automobile showroom and each will either purchase a car (P) or not purchase a car (N). Let x represent the number of people who will purchase a car. Assume that P and N are equally likely.

4.11 For each of the following, find μ_x, σ_x^2, and σ_x. Then interpret μ_x, and employ Chebyshev's theorem to find intervals that contain at least 3/4 and 8/9 of the observed values of x.

a. x = the number of patrons who prefer diet cola A as defined in Exercise 4.10a.

b. x = the number of girls born to the couple as defined in Exercise 4.10b.

c. x = the number of people who will purchase a car as defined in Exercise 4.10c.

4.12 Suppose that the probability distribution of a random variable x can be described by the formula

$$p(x) = \frac{x}{15}$$

for each of the values $x = 1, 2, 3, 4,$ and 5. For example, $P(x = 2) = p(2) = 2/15$.

a. Write out the probability distribution of x.

b. Show that the probability distribution of x satisfies the properties of a discrete probability distribution.

c. Calculate the mean of x.

d. Calculate the variance, σ_x^2, and the standard deviation, σ_x.

4.13 The following table summarizes investment outcomes and corresponding probabilities for a particular oil well:

x = the outcome in $	p(x)
−$40,000 (no oil)	0.25
10,000 (some oil)	0.7
70,000 (much oil)	0.05

Find the expected monetary outcome and interpret this value.

TABLE **4.3** Probability Distribution of Outcomes for an Investment

Outcome	Probability of Outcome	Assumptions
$300	0.2	Pessimistic
600	0.6	Moderately successful
900	0.2	Optimistic

Source: *Foundations of Financial Management,* by S. B. Block, G. A. Hirt, and D. Short, 7th Cdn. ed., p. 451. Copyright © 2005. Reprinted by permission of McGraw-Hill Companies, Inc.

4.14 In the book *Foundations of Financial Management* (7th Cdn. ed.), Block, Hirt, and Short discuss risk measurement for investments. Block, Hirt, and Short present an investment with the possible outcomes and associated probabilities given in Table 4.3. The authors state that the probabilities

> are generally based on some combination of past experience, industry ratios and trends, interviews with company executives, and sophisticated simulation techniques. The probability values may be easy to estimate for the introduction of a mechanical stamping process for which the manufacturer has 10 years of past data, but they are difficult to assess for a new product in a foreign market. (p. 451)

a. Use the probability distribution in Table 4.3 to calculate the expected value (mean) and the standard deviation of the investment outcomes. Interpret the expected value.

b. Block, Hirt, and Short interpret the standard deviation of the investment outcomes as follows: "Generally, the larger the standard deviation (or spread of possible outcomes), the greater is the risk" (p. 452). Explain why this makes sense. Use Chebyshev's theorem to illustrate your point.

c. Block, Hirt, and Short compare three investments with the following means and standard deviations of the investment outcomes:

Investment 1	Investment 2	Investment 3
$\mu = \$600$	$\mu = \$600$	$\mu = \$600$
$\sigma = \$20$	$\sigma = \$190$	$\sigma = \$300$

Which of these investments involves the most risk? the least risk? Explain why by using Chebyshev's theorem to compute an interval for each investment that will contain at least 8/9 of the investment outcomes.

d. Block, Hirt, and Short continue by comparing two more investments:

Investment A	Investment B
$\mu = \$6,000$	$\mu = \$600$
$\sigma = \$600$	$\sigma = \$190$

The authors explain that Investment A

> appears to have a high standard deviation, but not when related to the expected value of the distribution. A standard deviation of $600 on an investment with an expected value of $6,000 may indicate less risk than a standard deviation

of $190 on an investment with an expected value of only $600.

> We can eliminate the size difficulty by developing a third measure, the **coefficient of variation** (V), which allows for a comparable scale across different investments. This rather imposing term calls for nothing more difficult than dividing the standard deviation of an investment by the expected value. Generally, the larger the coefficient of variation, the greater is the risk. (p. 453)

Calculate the coefficient of variation for investments A and B:

$$\text{Coefficient of variation } (V) = \frac{\sigma}{\mu}.$$

Which investment carries the greater risk?

e. Calculate the coefficient of variation for investments 1, 2, and 3 in part c. Based on the coefficient of variation, which investment involves the most risk? the least risk? Do you obtain the same results as you did by comparing standard deviations (in part c)? Why?

4.15 An insurance company will insure a $50,000 diamond for its full value against theft at a premium of $400 per year. Suppose that the probability that the diamond will be stolen is 0.005, and let x denote the insurance company's profit.

a. Set up the probability distribution of the random variable x.

b. Calculate the insurance company's expected profit.

c. Find the premium that the insurance company should charge if it wants its expected profit to be $1,000.

4.16 In the book *Foundations of Financial Management* (7th Cdn. ed.), Block, Hirt, and Short discuss a semiconductor firm that is considering two choices: (1) expanding the production of semiconductors for sale to end users and (2) entering the highly competitive home computer market. The cost of each project is $60 million, but the net present value of the cash flows from sales and the risks are different.

Figure 4.3 gives a tree diagram of the project choices. The tree diagram gives a probability distribution of expected sales for each project. It also gives the present value of cash flows from sales and the net present value (NPV = present value of cash flow from sales minus initial cost) corresponding to each sales alternative.

a. For each project choice, calculate the expected net present value.

b. Which project has the higher expected net present value?

FIGURE 4.3   A Tree Diagram of Two Project Choices

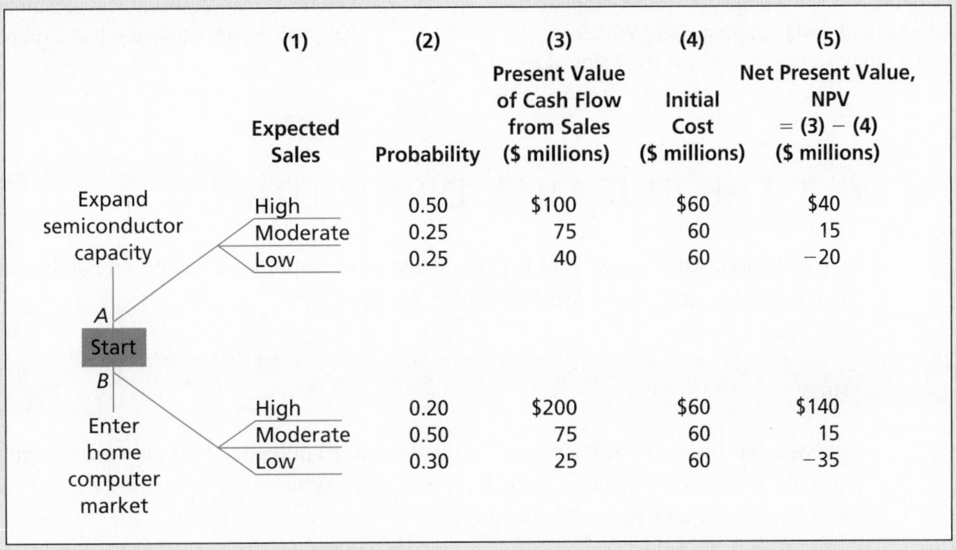

	(1) Expected Sales	(2) Probability	(3) Present Value of Cash Flow from Sales ($ millions)	(4) Initial Cost ($ millions)	(5) Net Present Value, NPV = (3) − (4) ($ millions)
Expand semiconductor capacity	High	0.50	$100	$60	$40
	Moderate	0.25	75	60	15
	Low	0.25	40	60	−20
A Start					
B Enter home computer market	High	0.20	$200	$60	$140
	Moderate	0.50	75	60	15
	Low	0.30	25	60	−35

Source: *Foundations of Financial Management*, by S. B. Block, G. A. Hirt, and D. Short, 7th Cdn. ed., p. 462. Copyright © 2005. Reprinted by permission of McGraw-Hill Companies, Inc.

c. For each project choice, calculate the variance and standard deviation of the net present value.

d. Calculate the coefficient of variation for each project choice. See Exercise 4.14d for a discussion of the coefficient of variation.

e. Which project carries the lesser risk? Explain.

f. In your opinion, which project should be undertaken? Justify your answer.

4.17 Five thousand raffle tickets are to be sold at $10 each to benefit a local community group. The prizes, the number of each prize to be given away, and the dollar value of winnings for each prize are as follows:

Prize	Number to Be Given Away	Dollar Value
Automobile	1	$13,000
Flat panel TV	2	3,000 each
DVR	5	400 each
Gift card	50	20 each

If you buy one ticket, calculate your expected winnings. (Form the probability distribution of $x =$ your dollar winnings, and remember to subtract the cost of your ticket.)

4.18 Company A is considering the acquisition of two separate but large companies, Company B and Company C, with sales and assets equal to its own. Table 4.4 gives the probabilities of returns for each of the three companies under various economic conditions. The table also gives the probabilities of returns for each possible combination: Company A plus Company B, and Company A plus Company C.

a. For each of Companies A, B, and C, find the mean return and the standard deviation of returns.

b. Find the mean return and the standard deviation of returns for the combination of Company A plus Company B.

c. Find the mean return and the standard deviation of returns for the combination of Company A plus Company C.

d. Compare the mean returns for each of the two possible combinations—Company A plus Company B and Company A plus Company C. Is either mean higher? How do they compare to Company A's mean return?

TABLE 4.4   Return Distributions for Companies *A*, *B*, and *C* and for Two Possible Acquisitions

Economic Condition	Probability	Company A Returns	Company B Returns	Company C Returns	Company A + B Returns	Company A + C Returns
1	0.2	17%	19%	13%	18%	15%
2	0.2	15	17	11	16	13
3	0.2	13	15	15	14	14
4	0.2	11	13	17	12	14
5	0.2	9	11	19	10	14

e. Compare the standard deviations of the returns for each of the two possible combinations—Company A plus Company B and Company A plus Company C. Which standard deviation is smaller? Which possible combination involves less risk? How does the risk carried by this combination compare to the risk carried by Company A alone?

f. Which acquisition would you recommend—Company A plus Company B or Company A plus Company C?

CHAPTER 1

4.3 THE BINOMIAL DISTRIBUTION

In this section, we discuss what is perhaps the most important discrete probability distribution—the binomial distribution.[1] We begin with an example.

Example 4.7 To Purchase or Not to Purchase

Suppose that historical sales records indicate that 40 percent of all customers who enter Dollar Bill's discount department store make a purchase. What is the probability that two of the next three customers will make a purchase?

In order to find this probability, we first note that the experiment of observing three customers making a purchase decision has several distinguishing characteristics:

1   The experiment consists of three identical **trials**; each trial consists of a customer making a purchase decision.

2   Two outcomes are possible on each trial: the customer makes a purchase (which we call a **success** and denote as S), or the customer does not make a purchase (which we call a **failure** and denote as F).

3   Since 40 percent of all customers make a purchase, it is reasonable to assume that $P(S)$, the probability that a customer makes a purchase, is 0.4 and is constant for all customers. This implies that $P(F)$, the probability that a customer does not make a purchase, is 0.6 and is constant for all customers.

4   We assume that customers make independent purchase decisions. That is, we assume that the outcomes of the three trials are independent of each other.

It follows that the sample space of the experiment consists of the following eight sample space outcomes:

SSS	FFS
SSF	FSF
SFS	SFF
FSS	FFF

Here the sample space outcome SSS represents all three customers making purchases. The sample space outcome SFS represents the first customer making a purchase, the second customer not making a purchase, and the third customer making a purchase.

Two out of three customers make a purchase if one of the sample space outcomes SSF, SFS, and FSS occurs. Furthermore, since the trials (purchase decisions) are independent, we can simply multiply the probabilities associated with the different trial outcomes (each of which is S or F) to find the probability of a sequence of outcomes:

$$P(SSF) = P(S)P(S)P(F) = (0.4)(0.4)(0.6) = (0.4)^2(0.6),$$
$$P(SFS) = P(S)P(F)P(S) = (0.4)(0.6)(0.4) = (0.4)^2(0.6),$$
$$P(FSS) = P(F)P(S)P(S) = (0.6)(0.4)(0.4) = (0.4)^2(0.6).$$

---

[1]*Study Hint:* Remember that "bi" means two, so that "binomial" means "two numbers" or, generally, two possible options/outcomes.

It follows that the probability that two out of the next three customers will make a purchase is

$$P(SSF) + P(SFS) + P(FSS)$$
$$= (0.4)^2(0.6) + (0.4)^2(0.6) + (0.4)^2(0.6)$$
$$= 3(0.4)^2(0.6) = 0.288.$$

Here we will assume that p is the probability that a customer makes a purchase, $q = 1 - p$ is the probability that a customer does not make a purchase, and purchase decisions (trials) are independent. To generalize the probability that two out of the next three customers make a purchase, which equals

$$3(0.4)^2(0.6),$$

we note the following:

1 The 3 in this expression is the number of sample space outcomes (SSF, SFS, and FSS) that correspond to the event "two out of the next three customers will make a purchase." Note that this number equals the number of ways we can arrange two successes among the three trials.

2 The 0.4 is p, the probability that a customer makes a purchase.

3 The 0.6 is $q = 1 - p$, the probability that a customer does not make a purchase.

Now notice that although each of the sample space outcomes SSF, SFS, and FSS represents a different arrangement of the two successes among the three trials, each of these sample space outcomes consists of two successes and one failure. For this reason, the probability of each of these sample space outcomes equals $(0.4)^2(0.6)^1 = p^2q^1$. It follows that p is raised to a power that equals the number of successes (2) in the three trials, and q is raised to a power that equals the number of failures (1) in the three trials.

Therefore, the probability that two of the next three customers will make a purchase is

$$\left(\begin{array}{c} \text{The number of ways} \\ \text{to arrange 2 successes} \\ \text{among 3 trials} \end{array} \right) p^2q^1.$$

We can now generalize the previous result and find the probability that x of the next n customers will make a purchase. In general, each sample space outcome describing the occurrence of x successes (purchases) in n trials represents a different arrangement of x successes in n trials. However, each outcome consists of x successes and $n - x$ failures. Therefore, the probability of each sample space outcome is p^xq^{n-x}. It follows by analogy that the probability that x of the next n trials are successes (purchases) is

$$\left(\begin{array}{c} \text{The number of ways} \\ \text{to arrange } x \text{ successes} \\ \text{among } n \text{ trials} \end{array} \right) p^xq^{n-x}.$$

We can use the expression we have just arrived at to compute the probability of x successes in the next n trials if we can find a way to calculate the number of ways to arrange x successes among n trials:

The number of ways to arrange x successes among n trials equals

$$\frac{n!}{x!(n - x)!},$$

where $n!$ is pronounced "n factorial" and is calculated as $n! = n(n - 1)(n - 2) \cdots (1)$ and where (by definition) $0! = 1$.

For instance, using this formula, we can see that the number of ways to arrange $x = 2$ successes among $n = 3$ trials equals

$$\frac{n!}{x!(n-x)!} = \frac{3!}{2!(3-2)!} = \frac{3!}{2!1!} = \frac{3 \cdot 2 \cdot 1}{2 \cdot 1 \cdot 1} = 3.$$

Of course we have previously seen that the three ways to arrange $x = 2$ successes among $n = 3$ trials are *SSF*, *SFS*, and *FSS*.

Using the preceding formula, we obtain the following general result:

The Binomial Distribution

A **binomial experiment** has the following characteristics:

1   The experiment consists of n **identical trials**.

2   Each trial results in a **success** or a **failure**.

3   The probability of a success on any trial is p and remains constant from trial to trial. This implies that the probability of failure, q, on any trial is $1 - p$ and remains constant from trial to trial.

4   The trials are **independent** (that is, the results of the trials have nothing to do with each other).

Furthermore, if we define the random variable

x = the total number of successes in n trials of a binomial experiment,

then we call x a **binomial random variable**, and the probability of obtaining x successes in n trials is

$$p(x) = \frac{n!}{x!(n-x)!} p^x q^{n-x}.$$

Noting that we sometimes refer to the formula for $p(x)$ as the **binomial formula**, we illustrate the use of this formula in the following example.

Example 4.8 Binomial Probability Calculation

Consider the discount department store situation discussed in Example 4.7. In order to find the probability that three of the next five customers will make purchases, we calculate

$$
\begin{aligned}
p(3) &= \frac{5!}{3!(5-3)!} (0.4)^3 (0.6)^{5-3} = \frac{5!}{3!2!} (0.4)^3 (0.6)^2 \\
&= \frac{5 \cdot 4 \cdot 3 \cdot 2 \cdot 1}{(3 \cdot 2 \cdot 1)(2 \cdot 1)} (0.4)^3 (0.6)^2 \\
&= 10(0.064)(0.36) \\
&= 0.2304.
\end{aligned}
$$

Here we see that

1   $\frac{5!}{3!(5-3)!} = 10$ is the number of ways to arrange three successes among five trials. For instance, two ways to do this are described by the sample space outcomes *SSSFF* and *SFSSF*. There are eight other ways.

2   $(0.4)^3 (0.6)^2$ is the probability of any sample space outcome consisting of three successes and two failures.

Thus far we have shown how to calculate binomial probabilities. We next give several examples that illustrate some practical applications of the binomial distribution. As we demonstrate in the next two examples, the term "success" does not necessarily refer to a *desirable* experimental outcome. Rather, it refers to an outcome that we wish to investigate.

Example 4.9 Dropped Cell Phone Calls

Suppose that a cell phone service provider claims that only 1 percent of its calls are dropped on average. If we let the random variable x = the number of dropped calls, then in order to determine the probability of having at least one dropped call in the next ten calls received, we calculate

$$P(x \geq 1) = P(x = 1) + P(x = 2) + \cdots + P(x = 10).$$

An easier approach to this problem involves using the complement of this event. That is, $P(x \geq 1) = 1 - P(x = 0)$, or $P(x \geq 1) = 1 - p(0)$, where

$$p(0) = \frac{10!}{0!10!}(0.01)^0(0.99)^{10} = 0.9044.$$

Thus, $p(x \geq 1) = 1 - 0.9044 = 0.0956.$

Consider also this next example, dealing with nausea and the drug Phe-Mycin. You would not consider feeling nauseated a success, just like you would not consider a dropped call a success, but if you are interested in finding out about these things, then they will be considered the successes of the experiment.

Example 4.10 Phe-Mycin and Nausea

Antibiotics occasionally cause nausea as a side effect. A major drug company has developed a new antibiotic called Phe-Mycin. The company claims that, at most, 10 percent of all patients treated with Phe-Mycin would experience nausea as a side effect of taking the drug. Suppose that we randomly select $n = 4$ patients and treat them with Phe-Mycin. Each patient will either experience nausea (which we arbitrarily call a success) or not experience nausea (a failure). We will assume that p, the true probability that a patient will experience nausea as a side effect, is 0.10, the maximum value of p claimed by the drug company. Furthermore, it is reasonable to assume that patients' reactions to the drug would be independent of each other. Let x denote the number of patients among the four who will experience nausea as a side effect. It follows that x is a binomial random variable that can take on any of the potential values 0, 1, 2, 3, and 4. That is, anywhere between none of the patients and all four of the patients could potentially experience nausea as a side effect. Furthermore, we can calculate the probability associated with each possible value of x as shown in Table 4.5 on the next page. For instance, the probability that none of the four randomly selected patients experience nausea is

$$p(0) = P(x = 0) = \frac{4!}{0!(4 - 0)!}(0.1)^0(0.9)^{4-0}$$

$$= \frac{4!}{0!4!}(0.1)^0(0.9)^4$$

$$= \frac{4!}{(1)(4!)}(1)(0.9)^4$$

$$= 0.9^4 = 0.6561.$$

Because Table 4.5 lists each possible value of x and also gives the probability of each value, we say that this table gives the **binomial probability distribution of** x.

TABLE 4.5   The Binomial Probability Distribution of x, the Number of Four Randomly Selected Patients Who Will Experience Nausea as a Side Effect of Being Treated with Phe-Mycin

x (Number Who Experience Nausea)	$p(x) = \dfrac{n!}{x!(n-x)!} p^x (1-p)^{n-x}$
0	$p(0) = P(x = 0) = \dfrac{4!}{0!(4-0)!} (0.1)^0 (0.9)^{4-0} = 0.6561$
1	$p(1) = P(x = 1) = \dfrac{4!}{1!(4-1)!} (0.1)^1 (0.9)^{4-1} = 0.2916$
2	$p(2) = P(x = 2) = \dfrac{4!}{2!(4-2)!} (0.1)^2 (0.9)^{4-2} = 0.0486$
3	$p(3) = P(x = 3) = \dfrac{4!}{3!(4-3)!} (0.1)^3 (0.9)^{4-3} = 0.0036$
4	$p(4) = P(x = 4) = \dfrac{4!}{4!(4-4)!} (0.1)^4 (0.9)^{4-4} = 0.0001$

FIGURE 4.4   The Binomial Probability Distribution with $p = 0.1$ and $n = 4$

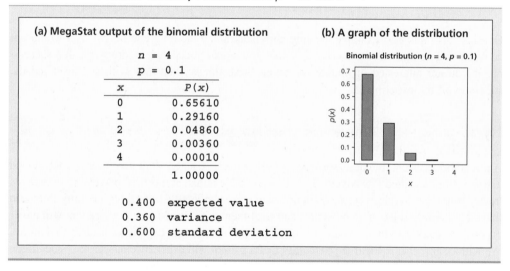

(a) MegaStat output of the binomial distribution

$n = 4$
$p = 0.1$

x	$P(x)$
0	0.65610
1	0.29160
2	0.04860
3	0.00360
4	0.00010
	1.00000

0.400   expected value
0.360   variance
0.600   standard deviation

(b) A graph of the distribution

The binomial probabilities given in Table 4.5 need not be hand-calculated. Excel and MegaStat can be used to calculate binomial probabilities. For instance, Figure 4.4(a) gives the MegaStat output of the binomial probability distribution listed in Table 4.5. Figure 4.4(b) shows a graph of this distribution.

In order to interpret these binomial probabilities, consider administering the antibiotic Phe-Mycin to all possible samples of four randomly selected patients. Then, for example,

$$P(x = 0) = 0.6561$$

says that none of the four sampled patients would experience nausea in 65.61 percent of all possible samples. Furthermore, as another example,

$$P(x = 3) = 0.0036$$

says that three out of the four sampled patients would experience nausea in only 0.36 percent of all possible samples.

TABLE 4.6 A Portion of a Binomial Probability Table

(a) A table for _n_ = 4 trials

	↓	0.05	0.10	0.15	0.20	0.25	0.30	0.35	0.40	0.45	0.50	
						Values of _p_ (0.05 to 0.50)						
	0	0.8145	0.6561	0.5220	0.4096	0.3164	0.2401	0.1785	0.1296	0.0915	0.0625	4
	1	0.1715	0.2916	0.3685	0.4096	0.4219	0.4116	0.3845	0.3456	0.2995	0.2500	3
Number of	2	0.0135	0.0486	0.0975	0.1536	0.2109	0.2646	0.3105	0.3456	0.3675	0.3750	2 Number of
Successes	3	0.0005	0.0036	0.0115	0.0256	0.0469	0.0756	0.1115	0.1536	0.2005	0.2500	1 Successes
	4	0.0000	0.0001	0.0005	0.0016	0.0039	0.0081	0.0150	0.0256	0.0410	0.0625	0
		0.95	0.90	0.85	0.80	0.75	0.70	0.65	0.60	0.55	0.50	↑

Values of _p_ (0.50 to 0.95) ⟶

(b) A table for _n_ = 8 trials

	↓	0.05	0.10	0.15	0.20	0.25	0.30	0.35	0.40	0.45	0.50	
						Values of _p_ (0.05 to 0.50)						
	0	0.6634	0.4305	0.2725	0.1678	0.1001	0.0576	0.0319	0.0168	0.0084	0.0039	8
	1	0.2793	0.3826	0.3847	0.3355	0.2670	0.1977	0.1373	0.0896	0.0548	0.0313	7
	2	0.0515	0.1488	0.2376	0.2936	0.3115	0.2965	0.2587	0.2090	0.1569	0.1094	6
Number of	3	0.0054	0.0331	0.0839	0.1468	0.2076	0.2541	0.2786	0.2787	0.2568	0.2188	5 Number of
Successes	4	0.0004	0.0046	0.0185	0.0459	0.0865	0.1361	0.1875	0.2322	0.2627	0.2734	4 Successes
	5	0.0000	0.0004	0.0026	0.0092	0.0231	0.0467	0.0808	0.1239	0.1719	0.2188	3
	6	0.0000	0.0000	0.0002	0.0011	0.0038	0.0100	0.0217	0.0413	0.0703	0.1094	2
	7	0.0000	0.0000	0.0000	0.0001	0.0004	0.0012	0.0033	0.0079	0.0164	0.0313	1
	8	0.0000	0.0000	0.0000	0.0000	0.0000	0.0001	0.0002	0.0007	0.0017	0.0039	0
		0.95	0.90	0.85	0.80	0.75	0.70	0.65	0.60	0.55	0.50	↑

Values of _p_ (0.50 to 0.95) ⟶

Binomial probability tables (see Appendix A, pages 644 to 648) Another way to avoid hand-calculating binomial probabilities is to use **binomial tables**, which have been constructed to give the probability of x successes in n trials. A table of binomial probabilities is given in Table A.1. A portion of this table is reproduced in Table 4.6(a) and (b). Part (a) of this table gives binomial probabilities corresponding to $n = 4$ trials. Values of p, the probability of success, are listed across the top of the table (ranging from $p = 0.05$ to $p = 0.50$ in steps of 0.05), and more values of p (ranging from $p = 0.50$ to $p = 0.95$ in steps of 0.05) are listed across the bottom of the table. When the value of p being considered is one of those across the top of the table, values of x (the number of successes in four trials) are listed down the left side of the table. For instance, to find the probabilities that we have computed in Table 4.5, we look in part (a) of Table 4.6 ($n = 4$) and read down the column labelled 0.10. Remembering that the values of x are on the left side of the table because $p = 0.10$ is on top of the table, we find the probabilities in Table 4.5 (they are shaded). For example, the probability that none of the four patients experience nausea is $p(0) = 0.6561$, the probability that one of the the four patients experiences nausea is $p(1) = 0.2916$, and so forth. If the value of p is across the bottom of the table, then we read the values of x from the right side of the table. As an example, if p equals 0.60, then the probability of two successes in four trials is $p(2) = 0.3456$ (we have shaded this probability).

Example 4.11 Phe-Mycin Revisited

Suppose that we wish to investigate whether p, the probability that a patient will experience nausea as a side effect of taking Phe-Mycin, is greater than 0.10, the maximum value of p claimed by the drug company. This assessment will be made by assuming that p equals 0.10 and by using sample information to weigh the evidence against this assumption and in favour of the conclusion that p is greater than 0.10. Suppose that when a sample of $n = 4$ randomly selected patients is treated with Phe-Mycin, three of the four patients experience nausea. Since the fraction of patients in the sample that experience nausea is $3/4 = 0.75$, which is far greater than 0.10, we have some evidence contradicting the assumption that p equals 0.10. To evaluate the strength of this evidence, we calculate the probability that at least 3 out of 4 randomly selected patients would experience nausea as a side effect if, in fact, p equals 0.10. Using the binomial probabilities in Table 4.6(a), and realizing that the events $x = 3$ and $x = 4$ are mutually exclusive, we have

$$
\begin{aligned}
P(x \geq 3) &= P(x = 3 \text{ or } x = 4) \\
&= P(x = 3) + P(x = 4) \\
&= 0.0036 + 0.0001 \\
&= 0.0037.
\end{aligned}
$$

This probability says that if p equals 0.10, then in only 0.37 percent of all possible samples of four randomly selected patients would at least three of the four patients experience nausea as a side effect. This implies that if we are to believe that p equals 0.10, then we must believe that we have observed a sample result that is so rare that it can be described as a 37 in 10,000 chance. Because observing such a result is very unlikely, we have very strong evidence that p does not equal 0.10 and is, in fact, greater than 0.10.

Next suppose that we consider what our conclusion would have been if only one of the four randomly selected patients had experienced nausea. Since the sample fraction of patients who experienced nausea is $1/4 = 0.25$, which is greater than 0.10, we would have some evidence to contradict the assumption that p equals 0.10. To evaluate the strength of this evidence, we calculate the probability that at least one out of four randomly selected patients would experience nausea as a side effect of being treated with Phe-Mycin if, in fact, p equals 0.10. Using the binomial probabilities in Table 4.6(a), we have

$$
\begin{aligned}
P(x \geq 1) &= P(x = 1 \text{ or } x = 2 \text{ or } x = 3 \text{ or } x = 4) \\
&= P(x = 1) + P(x = 2) + P(x = 3) + P(x = 4) \\
&= 0.2916 + 0.0486 + 0.0036 + 0.0001 \\
&= 0.3439.
\end{aligned}
$$

This probability says that if p equals 0.10, then in 34.39 percent of all possible samples of four randomly selected patients, at least one of the four patients would experience nausea. Since it is not particularly difficult to believe that a 34.39 percent chance has occurred, we would not have much evidence against the claim that p equals 0.10.

Example 4.11 illustrates what is sometimes called the *rare event approach to making a statistical inference*. The idea of this approach is that if the probability of an observed sample result under a given assumption is *small*, then we have *strong evidence* that the assumption is false. Although there are no strict rules, many statisticians judge the probability of an observed sample result to be small if it is less than 0.05. The logic behind this will be explained more fully in Chapter 8.

Example 4.12   Testing a Warranty Claim

The manufacturer of the TruColour-5000 flat panel television claims that 95 percent of its TVs last at least five years without requiring a single repair. Suppose that we contact $n = 8$ randomly selected TruColour-5000 purchasers five years after they purchased their TVs. Each purchaser's TV will have needed no repairs (a success) or will have been repaired at least once (a failure). We will assume that p, the true probability that a purchaser's TV will require no

TABLE **4.7** The Binomial Distribution of x, the Number of Eight TruColour-5000 Flat Panel Televisions that Have Lasted at Least Five Years Without Needing a Single Repair, When $p = 0.95$ 🖉

	$n = 8$
	$p = 0.95$
x	$p(x)$
0	0.00000
1	0.00000
2	0.00000
3	0.00002
4	0.00036
5	0.00542
6	0.05146
7	0.27933
8	0.66342
	1.00000

7.600 expected value
0.380 variance
0.616 standard deviation

repairs within five years, is 0.95, as claimed by the manufacturer. Furthermore, it is reasonable to believe that the repair records of the purchasers' TVs are independent of each other. Let x denote the number of the $n = 8$ randomly selected TVs that have lasted at least five years without a single repair. Then x is a binomial random variable that can take on any of the potential values 0, 1, 2, 3, 4, 5, 6, 7, and 8. The binomial distribution of x is listed in Table 4.7. Here we have obtained these probabilities from Table 4.6(b). To use the table, we look at the column corresponding to $p = 0.95$. Because $p = 0.95$ is listed at the bottom of the table, we read the values of x and their corresponding probabilities from bottom to top (we have shaded the probabilities). Notice that the values of x are listed on the right side of the table.

Figure 4.5(a) gives the MegaStat output of the binomial distribution with $p = 0.95$ and $n = 8$ (that is, the binomial distribution of Table 4.7). This binomial distribution is graphed in Figure 4.5(b).

FIGURE **4.5** The Binomial Probability Distribution with $p = 0.95$ and $n = 8$

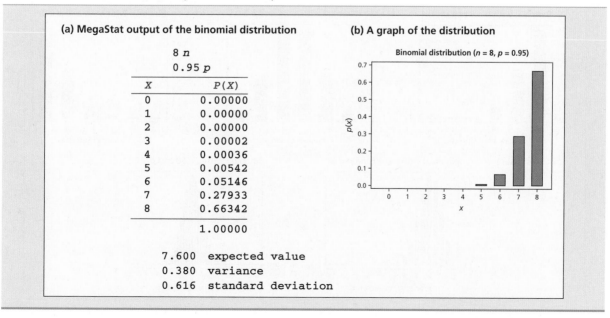

Next suppose that when we actually contact eight randomly selected purchasers, we find that five out of the eight TVs owned by these purchasers have lasted at least five years without a single repair. Since the sample fraction, $5/8 = 0.625$, of TVs needing no repairs is less than 0.95, we have some evidence contradicting the manufacturer's claim that p equals 0.95. To evaluate the strength of this evidence, we will calculate the probability that five or fewer of the eight randomly selected TVs would last at least five years without a single repair if, in fact, p equals 0.95. Using the binomial probabilities in Table 4.7, we have

$$P(x \leq 5) = P(x = 5 \text{ or } x = 4 \text{ or } x = 3 \text{ or } x = 2 \text{ or } x = 1 \text{ or } x = 0)$$
$$= P(x = 5) + P(x = 4) + P(x = 3) + P(x = 2) + P(x = 1) + P(x = 0)$$
$$= 0.0054 + 0.0004 + 0.0000 + 0.0000 + 0.0000 + 0.0000$$
$$= 0.0058.$$

This probability says that if p equals 0.95, then in only 0.58 percent of all possible samples of eight randomly selected TruColour-5000 TVs would five or fewer of the eight TVs last at least five years without a single repair. Therefore, if we are to believe that p equals 0.95, we must believe that a 58 in 10,000 chance has occurred. Since it is difficult to believe that such a small chance has occurred, we have strong evidence that p does not equal 0.95 and is, in fact, less than 0.95.

In Examples 4.10 and 4.12, we have illustrated binomial distributions with different values of n and p. The values of n and p are often called the **parameters** of the binomial distribution. Figure 4.6 shows several different binomial distributions. We see that depending on the parameters, a binomial distribution can be positively skewed (to the right), negatively skewed (to the left), or symmetrical.

We next consider calculating the mean, variance, and standard deviation of a binomial random variable. If we place the binomial probability formula into the expressions (given in Section 4.2) for the mean and variance of a discrete random variable, we can derive formulas that allow us to easily compute μ_x, σ_x^2, and σ_x for a binomial random variable.

FIGURE 4.6 Several Binomial Distributions

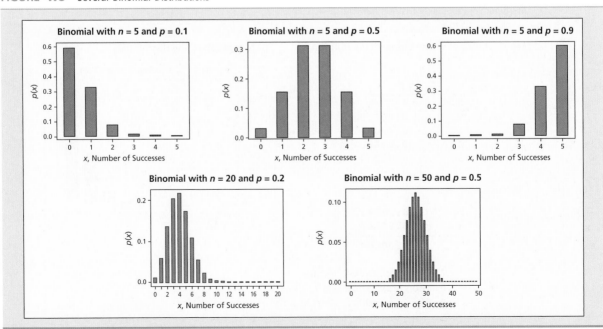

> **The Mean, Variance, and Standard Deviation of a Binomial Random Variable**
>
> If x is a binomial random variable, then
>
> $$\mu_x = np, \quad \sigma_x^2 = npq, \quad \text{and} \quad \sigma_x = \sqrt{npq},$$
>
> where n is the number of trials, p is the probability of success on each trial, and $q = 1 - p$ is the probability of failure on each trial.

As a simple example, again consider the television manufacturer, and recall that x is the number of eight randomly selected TruColour-5000 televisions that last five years without a single repair. If the manufacturer's claim that p equals 0.95 is true (which implies that q equals $1 - p = 1 - 0.95 = 0.05$), it follows that

$$\mu_x = np = 8(0.95) = 7.6,$$
$$\sigma_x^2 = npq = 8(0.95)(0.05) = 0.38,$$
$$\sigma_x = \sqrt{npq} = \sqrt{0.38} = 0.6164.$$

In order to interpret $\mu_x = 7.6$, suppose that we were to randomly select all possible samples of eight TruColour-5000 televisions and record the number of TVs in each sample that last five years without a repair. If we averaged all of our results, we would find that the average number of TVs per sample that last five years without a repair is equal to 7.6.

To conclude this section, note that in Section 4.5 we discuss the **hypergeometric distribution**. This distribution is related to the binomial distribution. The main difference between the two distributions is that in the case of the hypergeometric distribution, the trials are not independent and the probabilities of success and failure change from trial to trial. This occurs when we sample without replacement from a finite population. However, when the finite population is large compared to the sample, the binomial distribution can be used to approximate the hypergeometric distribution. The details are explained in Section 4.5.

Exercises for Section 4.3

CONCEPTS

4.19 List the four characteristics of a binomial experiment.

4.20 Suppose that x is a binomial random variable. Explain what the values of x represent. That is, how are the values of x defined?

4.21 Explain the logic behind the rare event approach to making statistical inferences.

METHODS AND APPLICATIONS

4.22 Suppose that x is a binomial random variable with $n = 5$, $p = 0.3$, and $q = 0.7$.
  a. Write the binomial formula for this situation and list the possible values of x.
  b. For each value of x, calculate $p(x)$, and graph the binomial distribution.
  c. Find $P(x = 3)$.
  d. Find $P(x \le 3)$.
  e. Find $P(x < 3)$.
  f. Find $P(x \ge 4)$.
  g. Find $P(x > 2)$.
  h. Use the probabilities you computed in part b to calculate the mean, μ_x, the variance, σ_x^2, and the

standard deviation, σ_x, of this binomial distribution. Show that the formulas for μ_x, σ_x^2, and σ_x given in this section give the same results.
  i. Calculate the interval $[\mu_x \pm 2\sigma_x]$. Use the probabilities of part b to find the probability that x will be in this interval.

4.23 Thirty percent of all customers who enter a store will make a purchase. Suppose that six customers enter the store and that these customers make independent purchase decisions.
  a. Let $x = $ the number of the six customers who will make a purchase. Write the binomial formula for this situation.
  b. Use the binomial formula to calculate
    (1) The probability that exactly five customers make a purchase.
    (2) The probability that at least three customers make a purchase.
    (3) The probability that two or fewer customers make a purchase.
    (4) The probability that at least one customer makes a purchase.

4.24 The customer service department for a wholesale electronics outlet claims that 90 percent of all customer complaints are resolved to the satisfaction of the customer. In order to test this claim, a random sample of 15 customers who have filed complaints is selected.

a. Let x = the number of sampled customers whose complaints were resolved to the customer's satisfaction. Assuming the claim is true, write the binomial formula for this situation.

b. Use the binomial tables (see Table A.1) to find each of the following if we assume that the claim is true:
  (1) $P(x \leq 13)$.
  (2) $P(x > 10)$.
  (3) $P(x \geq 14)$.
  (4) $P(9 \leq x \leq 12)$.
  (5) $P(x \leq 9)$.

c. Suppose that of the 15 customers selected, 9 have had their complaints resolved satisfactorily. Using part b, do you believe the claim of 90 percent satisfaction? Explain.

4.25 An industry representative claims that 50 percent of all satellite dish owners subscribe to at least one premium movie channel. In an attempt to justify this claim, the representative will poll a randomly selected sample of dish owners.

a. Suppose that the representative's claim is true, and suppose that a sample of four dish owners is randomly selected. Assuming independence, use an appropriate formula to compute
  (1) The probability that none of the dish owners in the sample subscribes to at least one premium movie channel.
  (2) The probability that more than two dish owners in the sample subscribe to at least one premium movie channel.

b. Suppose that the representative's claim is true, and suppose that a sample of 20 dish owners is randomly selected. Assuming independence, what is the probability that
  (1) Nine or fewer dish owners in the sample subscribe to at least one premium movie channel?
  (2) More than 11 dish owners in the sample subscribe to at least one premium movie channel?
  (3) Fewer than five dish owners in the sample subscribe to at least one premium movie channel?

c. Suppose that, when we survey 20 randomly selected dish owners, we find that 4 of the dish owners actually subscribe to at least one premium movie channel. Using a probability you found in this exercise as the basis for your answer, do you believe the industry representative's claim? Explain.

4.26 For each of the following, calculate μ_x, σ_x^2, and σ_x by using the formulas given in this section. Then (1) interpret μ_x and (2) find the probability that x falls in the interval $[\mu_x \pm 2\sigma_x]$.

a. The situation of Exercise 4.23, where x = the number of the six customers who will make a purchase.

b. The situation of Exercise 4.24, where x = the number of 15 sampled customers whose complaints were resolved to the customer's satisfaction.

4.27 The January 1986 mission of the Space Shuttle Challenger was the 25th shuttle mission. It was unsuccessful due to an explosion caused by an O-ring seal failure.

a. According to NASA, the probability of such a failure in a single mission was 1/60,000. Using this value of p and assuming all missions are independent, calculate the probability of no mission failures in 25 attempts. Then calculate the probability of at least one mission failure in 25 attempts.

b. According to a study conducted for the U.S. Air Force, the probability of such a failure in a single mission was 1/35. Recalculate the probability of no mission failures in 25 attempts and the probability of at least one mission failure in 25 attempts.

c. Based on your answers to parts a and b, which value of p seems more likely to be true? Explain.

d. How small must p be made in order to ensure that the probability of no mission failures in 25 attempts is 0.999?

4.28 Suppose that the reliability rate of home security systems is 0.99. If ten homes equipped with this system experience an attempted break-in, what is the chance that
a. Exactly three alarms are triggered?
b. No more than two alarms are triggered?
c. At least one alarm is triggered?

4.29 Suppose that it has been estimated that 20 percent of incoming e-mail messages are considered to be spam. In the next six e-mail messages received (assuming they are all independent, and your spam filter is off), what is the chance that
a. Two or more messages will be spam?
b. No spam messages will be received?
c. More than four message will be spam?

4.30 Suppose that a jar contains five balls: two red and three black. Two balls are randomly selected, one at a time, with replacement. This means that the ball is selected, its colour is recorded, and then it is placed back into the jar. What is the chance that
a. No black balls are selected?
b. One of each colour is selected?
c. Both balls are the same colour?

4.4 THE POISSON DISTRIBUTION

We now discuss a discrete random variable that describes the number of occurrences of an event over a specified interval of time or space. For instance, we might wish to describe (1) the number of customers who arrive at the checkout counters of a grocery store in one hour or (2) the number of major fires in a city during the last two months.

Such a random variable can often be described by a **Poisson distribution**. We describe this distribution and give two assumptions needed for its use in the following box:

LO5

The Poisson Distribution

Consider the number of times an event occurs over an interval of time or space, and assume that

1   The probability of the event's occurrence is the same for any two intervals of equal length.

2   Whether the event occurs in any interval is independent of whether the event occurs in any other nonoverlapping interval.

Then the probability that the event will occur x times in a specified interval is

$$P(x) = \frac{e^{-\mu}\mu^x}{x!}.$$

Here μ is the mean (or expected) number of occurrences of the event in the specified interval, and $e = 2.718281 \ldots$ is the base of the natural logarithm.

In theory, there is no limit to how large x might be. That is, theoretically speaking, the event under consideration could occur an indefinitely large number of times during any specified interval. This says that a **Poisson random variable** might take on any of the values 0, 1, 2, 3, . . . , and so forth. We will now look at an example.

Example 4.13 Air Traffic Controller Error—Probability Calculations

In an article in the August 15, 1998, edition of *The Journal News* (Hamilton, Ohio), the Associated Press reported that the Cleveland Air Route Traffic Control Center, the busiest in the United States for guiding planes on cross-country routes, had experienced an unusually high number of errors since the end of July.[2] An error occurs when controllers direct flights either within five miles (8 km) of each other horizontally, or within 2,000 feet (600 m) vertically at a height of 18,000 feet (5.5 km) or more (the standard is 1,000 feet (300 m) vertically at heights less than 18,000 feet (5.5 km)). The controllers' union blamed the errors on a staff shortage, whereas the U.S. Federal Aviation Administration claimed that the cause was improved error reporting and an unusual number of thunderstorms.

Now suppose that an air traffic control centre in Canada has been averaging 20.8 errors per year and that the centre experiences 3 errors in a week. The Canadian Air Transport Security Authority (CATSA) must decide whether this occurrence is unusual enough to warrant an investigation of the causes of the (possible) increase in errors. To investigate this possibility, we will find the probability distribution of x, the number of errors in a week, when we assume that the centre is still averaging 20.8 errors per year.

Arbitrarily choosing a time unit of one week, the average (or expected) number of errors per week is 20.8/52 = 0.4. Therefore, we can use the Poisson formula (note that the Poisson assumptions given in the shaded box above are probably satisfied) to calculate the probability of no errors in a week to be

$$p(0) = P(x = 0) = \frac{e^{-\mu}\mu^0}{0!} = \frac{e^{-0.4}(0.4)^0}{1} = 0.6703.$$

Similarly, the probability of three errors in a week is

$$p(3) = P(x = 3) = \frac{e^{-0.4}(0.4)^3}{3!} = \frac{e^{-0.4}(0.4)^3}{3 \cdot 2 \cdot 1} = 0.0072.$$

We can easily obtain these probabilities from Table 4.8 on the next page.

---

[2]Source: "Errors on the rise at traffic control center in Ohio," by F. J. Frommer, *The Journal News*, August 15, 1998.

TABLE **4.8** A Portion of a Poisson Probability Table

x, Number of Occurrences	μ, Mean Number of Occurrences									
	0.1	0.2	0.3	0.4	0.5	0.6	0.7	0.8	0.9	1.0
0	0.9048	0.8187	0.7408	0.6703	0.6065	0.5488	0.4966	0.4493	0.4066	0.3679
1	0.0905	0.1637	0.2222	0.2681	0.3033	0.3293	0.3476	0.3595	0.3659	0.3679
2	0.0045	0.0164	0.0333	0.0536	0.0758	0.0988	0.1217	0.1438	0.1647	0.1839
3	0.0002	0.0011	0.0033	0.0072	0.0126	0.0198	0.0284	0.0383	0.0494	0.0613
4	0.0000	0.0001	0.0003	0.0007	0.0016	0.0030	0.0050	0.0077	0.0111	0.0153
5	0.0000	0.0000	0.0000	0.0001	0.0002	0.0004	0.0007	0.0012	0.0020	0.0031
6	0.0000	0.0000	0.0000	0.0000	0.0000	0.0000	0.0001	0.0002	0.0003	0.0005

x, Number of Occurrences	μ, Mean Number of Occurrences									
	1.1	1.2	1.3	1.4	1.5	1.6	1.7	1.8	1.9	2.0
0	0.3329	0.3012	0.2725	0.2466	0.2231	0.2019	0.1827	0.1653	0.1496	0.1353
1	0.3662	0.3614	0.3543	0.3452	0.3347	0.3230	0.3106	0.2975	0.2842	0.2707
2	0.2014	0.2169	0.2303	0.2417	0.2510	0.2584	0.2640	0.2678	0.2700	0.2707
3	0.0738	0.0867	0.0998	0.1128	0.1255	0.1378	0.1496	0.1607	0.1710	0.1804
4	0.0203	0.0260	0.0324	0.0395	0.0471	0.0551	0.0636	0.0723	0.0812	0.0902
5	0.0045	0.0062	0.0084	0.0111	0.0141	0.0176	0.0216	0.0260	0.0309	0.0361
6	0.0008	0.0012	0.0018	0.0026	0.0035	0.0047	0.0061	0.0078	0.0098	0.0120
7	0.0001	0.0002	0.0003	0.0005	0.0008	0.0011	0.0015	0.0020	0.0027	0.0034
8	0.0000	0.0000	0.0001	0.0001	0.0001	0.0002	0.0003	0.0005	0.0006	0.0009

Source: From Brooks/Cole, Copyright © 1991.

Poisson probability tables (see Appendix A, pages 648 to 650) As with the binomial distribution, tables have been constructed that give Poisson probabilities. A table of these probabilities is given in Table A.2. A portion of this table is reproduced in Table 4.8. In this table, values of the mean number of occurrences, μ, are listed across the top of the table, and values of x (the number of occurrences) are listed down the left side of the table. In order to use the table in the traffic control situation, we look at the column in Table 4.8 corresponding to 0.4, and we find the probabilities of 0, 1, 2, 3, 4, 5, and 6 errors (we have shaded these probabilities). For instance, the probability of one error in a week is 0.2681. Also note that the probability of any number of errors greater than six is so small that it is not listed in the table. Table 4.9 summarizes the Poisson distribution of x, the number of errors in a week. This table also shows how the probabilities associated with the different values of x are calculated.

Poisson probabilities can also be calculated by using Excel and MegaStat. For instance, Figure 4.7(a) gives the MegaStat output of the Poisson distribution presented in Table 4.9. This Poisson distribution is graphed in Figure 4.7(b).

Next recall that there have been three errors at the air traffic control centre in the last week. This is considerably more errors than 0.4, the expected number of errors assuming the centre is still averaging 20.8 errors per year. Therefore, we have some evidence to contradict this assumption. To evaluate the strength of this evidence, we calculate the probability that three or more errors will occur in a week if, in fact, μ equals 0.4. Using the Poisson probabilities in Table 4.9 (for $\mu = 0.4$), we obtain

$$P(x \geq 3) = p(3) + p(4) + p(5) + p(6) = 0.0072 + 0.0007 + 0.0001 + 0.0000 = 0.008.$$

This probability says that if the centre is averaging 20.8 errors per year, then there would be three or more errors in a week in only 0.8 percent of all weeks. That is, if we are to believe that the control centre is averaging 20.8 errors per year, then we must believe that an 8 in 1,000 chance has occurred. Since it is very difficult to believe that such a rare event has occurred, we have strong evidence that the average number of errors per week has increased. Therefore, an investigation by CATSA into the reasons for such an increase is probably justified.

TABLE 4.9 The Poisson Distribution of x, the Number of Errors at an Air Traffic Control Centre in a Week, When $\mu = 0.4$

x, the Number of Errors in a Week	$p(x) = \dfrac{e^{-\mu}\mu^x}{x!}$
0	$p(0) = \dfrac{e^{-0.4}(0.4)^0}{0!} = 0.6703$
1	$p(1) = \dfrac{e^{-0.4}(0.4)^1}{1!} = 0.2681$
2	$p(2) = \dfrac{e^{-0.4}(0.4)^2}{2!} = 0.0536$
3	$p(3) = \dfrac{e^{-0.4}(0.4)^3}{3!} = 0.0072$
4	$p(4) = \dfrac{e^{-0.4}(0.4)^4}{4!} = 0.0007$
5	$p(5) = \dfrac{e^{-0.4}(0.4)^5}{5!} = 0.0001$
6	$p(6) = \dfrac{e^{-0.4}(0.4)^6}{6!} = 0.0000$

FIGURE 4.7 The Poisson Probability Distribution with a Mean of 0.4

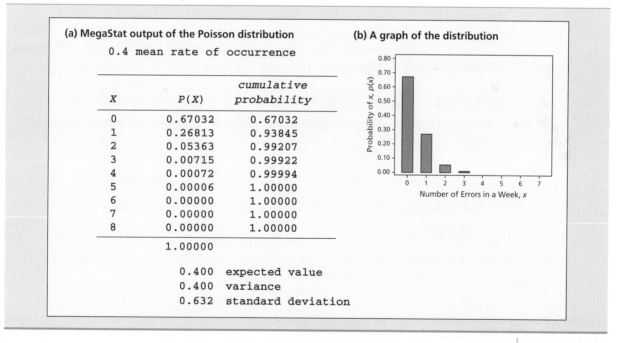

(a) MegaStat output of the Poisson distribution

0.4 mean rate of occurrence

X	P(X)	cumulative probability
0	0.67032	0.67032
1	0.26813	0.93845
2	0.05363	0.99207
3	0.00715	0.99922
4	0.00072	0.99994
5	0.00006	1.00000
6	0.00000	1.00000
7	0.00000	1.00000
8	0.00000	1.00000
	1.00000	

0.400	expected value
0.400	variance
0.632	standard deviation

(b) A graph of the distribution

Example 4.14 Potholes!

Suppose that it has been determined that the number of potholes over a particular stretch of a highway follows a Poisson distribution with an average of three potholes for every 6 km of highway. If a 4-km stretch of highway is selected, what is the chance that there will be exactly two potholes?

Here, we let $x =$ the number of potholes on a 4-km stretch of this highway. It follows that x has a Poisson distribution with $\mu = 2$ since we expect three potholes on average for every

FIGURE **4.8**   Several Poisson Distributions

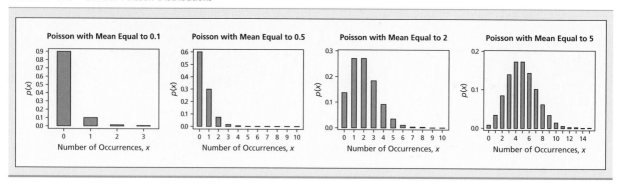

6-km stretch of highway, which translates to 0.5 per kilometre and we are sampling 4 km. Now, we want to determine the probability that there are exactly two potholes, or

$$P(x = 2) = p(2) = \frac{e^{-2}(2^2)}{2!} = 2e^{-2} = 0.2707.$$

The mean, μ, is often called the **parameter** of the Poisson distribution. Figure 4.8 shows several Poisson distributions. We see that depending on its parameter (mean), a Poisson distribution can be very positively skewed (to the right) or quite symmetrical.

Finally, if we place the Poisson probability formula into the general expressions (of Section 4.2) for μ_x, σ_x^2, and σ_x, we can derive formulas for calculating the mean, variance, and standard deviation of a Poisson distribution:

The Mean, Variance, and Standard Deviation of a Poisson Random Variable

Suppose that *x* is a **Poisson random variable**. If μ is the average number of occurrences of an event over the specified interval of time or space of interest, then

$$\mu_x = \mu, \qquad \sigma_x^2 = \mu, \qquad \sigma_x = \sqrt{\mu}.$$

Here we see that both the mean and the variance of a Poisson random variable equal the average number of occurrences, μ, of the event of interest over the specified interval of time or space. For example, in the air traffic control situation, the Poisson distribution of x, the number of errors at the air traffic control centre in a week, has a mean of $\mu_x = 0.4$ and a standard deviation of $\sigma_x = \sqrt{0.4} = 0.6325$.

Exercises for Section 4.4

CONCEPTS

4.31   The values of a Poisson random variable are $x = 0, 1, 2, 3, \ldots$. Explain what these values represent.

4.32   Explain the assumptions that must be satisfied for a Poisson distribution to adequately describe a random variable x.

METHODS AND APPLICATIONS

4.33   Suppose that x has a Poisson distribution with $\mu = 2$.
    a. Write the Poisson formula and describe the possible values of x.

b. Starting with the smallest possible value of x, calculate $p(x)$ for each value of x until $p(x)$ becomes smaller than 0.001.

c. Graph the Poisson distribution using your results of part b.

d. Find $P(x = 2)$.

e. Find $P(x \leq 4)$.

f. Find $P(x < 4)$.

g. Find $P(x \geq 1)$ and $P(x > 2)$.

h. Find $P(1 \leq x \leq 4)$.

i. Find $P(2 < x < 5)$.

j. Find $P(2 \leq x < 6)$.

4.34 Suppose that x has a Poisson distribution with $\mu = 2$.

  a. Use the formulas given in this section to compute the mean, μ_x, variance, σ_x^2, and standard deviation, σ_x.

  b. Calculate the intervals $[\mu_x \pm 2\sigma_x]$ and $[\mu_x \pm 3\sigma_x]$. Then use the probabilities you calculated in Exercise 4.33 to find the probability that x will be inside each of these intervals.

4.35 A coffee-shop manager wishes to provide prompt service for customers at the drive-through window. The coffee shop can currently serve up to ten customers per 15-minute period without significant delay. The average arrival rate is seven customers per 15-minute period. Let x denote the number of customers arriving per 15-minute period. Assume that x has a Poisson distribution.

  a. Find the probability that ten customers will arrive in a particular 15-minute period.

  b. Find the probability that ten or fewer customers will arrive in a particular 15-minute period.

  c. Find the probability that there will be a significant delay at the drive-up window. That is, find the probability that more than ten customers will arrive during a particular 15-minute period.

4.36 A telephone company's goal is to have no more than five monthly line failures on any 100 km of line. The company currently experiences an average of two monthly line failures per 50 km of line. Let x denote the number of monthly line failures per 100 km of line. Assume that x has a Poisson distribution.

  a. Find the probability that the company will meet its goal on a particular 100 km of line.

  b. Find the probability that the company will not meet its goal on a particular 100 km of line.

  c. Find the probability that the company will have no more than five monthly failures on a particular 200 km of line.

  d. Find the probability that the company will have more than 12 monthly failures on a particular 150 km of line.

4.37 A local law enforcement agency claims that the number of times that a patrol car passes through a particular neighbourhood follows a Poisson process with a mean of three times per nightly shift. Let x denote the number of times that a patrol car passes through the neighbourhood during a nightly shift.

  a. Calculate the probability that no patrol cars pass through the neighbourhood during a nightly shift.

  b. Suppose that during a randomly selected nightly shift no patrol cars pass through the neighbourhood. Based on your answer in part a, do you believe the agency's claim? Explain.

  c. Assuming that nightly shifts are independent and assuming that the agency's claim is correct, find the probability that exactly one patrol car will pass through the neighbourhood on each of four consecutive nights.

4.38 When the number of trials, n, is large, binomial probability tables may not be available. Furthermore, if a computer is not available, hand calculations will be tedious. As an alternative, the Poisson distribution can be used to approximate the binomial distribution when n is large and p is small. Here the mean of the Poisson distribution is taken to be $\mu = np$. That is, when n is large and p is small, we can use the Poisson formula with $\mu = np$ to calculate binomial probabilities; we will obtain results close to those we would obtain by using the binomial formula. A common rule is to use this approximation when $n/p \geq 500$.

For example, in the 1978 movie *Coma*, a young female intern at a Boston hospital was very upset when her friend, a young nurse, went into a coma during routine anaesthesia at the hospital. Upon investigation, she found that 10 of the last 30,000 healthy patients at the hospital had gone into comas during routine anaesthesias. When she confronted the hospital administrator with this fact and the fact that the national average was 6 out of 100,000 healthy patients going into comas during routine anaesthesias, the administrator replied that 10 out of 30,000 was still quite small and thus not that unusual.

  a. Use the Poisson distribution to approximate the probability that 10 or more of 30,000 healthy patients would slip into comas during routine anaesthesias, if in fact the true average at the hospital was 6 in 100,000. *Hint:* $\mu = np = 30{,}000(6/100{,}000) = 1.8$.

  b. Given the hospital's record and part a, what conclusion would you draw about the hospital's medical practices regarding anaesthesia?

(*Note:* It turned out that the hospital administrator was part of a conspiracy to sell body parts and was purposely putting healthy adults into comas during routine anaesthesias. If the intern had taken a statistics course, she could have avoided a great deal of danger.)

4.39 Suppose that an automobile parts wholesaler claims that 0.5 percent of the car batteries in a shipment are defective. A random sample of 200 batteries is taken, and four are found to be defective.

  a. Use the Poisson approximation discussed in Exercise 4.38 to find the probability that four or more car batteries in a random sample of 200 such batteries would be found to be defective, if we assume that the wholesaler's claim is true.

  b. Based on your answer to part a, do you believe the claim? Explain.

4.40 Suppose that the number of potholes on a local city's streets follows a Poisson distribution with an average of three potholes per 10 km. If a person drives 3 km down one of the streets, what is the chance that

  a. They will see no potholes?

  b. They will see at least one pothole?

  c. They will see more than three potholes?

4.41 It has been determined that errors in a university essay follow a Poisson distribution and occur at a rate of one error per five pages on average. If a student wrote a ten-page essay, what is the chance that

  a. There would be at least one error?

  b. There would be no more than one error?

  c. There would be more than two errors?

4.42 Suppose that the number of errors per 1,000 lines of computer code is described by a Poisson distribution with an average of four errors for every 1,000 lines of code.
  a. What is the probability of obtaining four errors in 1,000 lines of code?

b. What is the probability of obtaining eight errors in 2,000 lines of code?

c. What is the probability of obtaining five errors in 1,500 lines of code?

4.5 THE HYPERGEOMETRIC DISTRIBUTION

In Section 4.3, we learned that one of the conditions that needed to be satisfied in order to use the binomial probability distribution was that the trials were independent. This ensured that the probability of success and failure would remain constant from trial to trial. If the trials are not independent, then we cannot apply the binomial probability formula to find the probability of x successes in n trials. Instead, we must use the **hypergeometric probability distribution**.

Suppose that a population consists of N items, of which r are labelled as successes and $N - r$ are labelled as failures. If we randomly select a sample of n items *without replacement*, it can be shown that the probability of obtaining exactly x successes in n trials is given by the hypergeometric probability distribution

LO6

$$p(x) = \frac{\binom{r}{x}\binom{N-r}{n-x}}{\binom{N}{n}},$$

where $\binom{r}{x}$ is shorthand for $\frac{r!}{(r-x)!\,x!}$, the number of ways to choose x items from a population of r items.

Example 4.15 High-Risk Stocks

LO7

Consider a small population of $N = 6$ high-risk stocks that gave the following percentage returns last year: -36, -15, 3, 15, 33, and 54. We note that $r = 4$ of the returns are positive, and $N - r = 6 - 4 = 2$ of the returns are negative. Suppose that we randomly selected $n = 3$ of the six stocks to put in an investment portfolio at the beginning of the year. Let x represent the number of stocks that gave positive returns (successes). It follows that the probability that x is at least 2, or $P(x \geq 2)$, is

$$p(2) + p(3) = \frac{\binom{4}{2}\binom{2}{1}}{\binom{6}{3}} + \frac{\binom{4}{3}\binom{2}{0}}{\binom{6}{3}} = \frac{\left(\frac{4!}{2!2!}\right)\left(\frac{2!}{1!1!}\right)}{\frac{6!}{3!3!}} + \frac{\left(\frac{4!}{3!1!}\right)\left(\frac{2!}{0!2!}\right)}{\frac{6!}{3!3!}}$$

$$= \frac{(6)(2)}{20} + \frac{(4)(1)}{20} = 0.8$$

Note that on the first random selection from the population of N items, the probability of a success is r/N. Since we are making selections without replacement, the probability of a success changes as we continue to make selections. However, if the population size, N, is much larger than the sample size, n (say, at least 20 times as large), then making the selections will not substantially change the probability of a success. In this case, we can assume that the probability of a success stays essentially constant from selection to selection, and the different selections are essentially independent of each other. Therefore, we can approximate the hypergeometric distribution by the easier-to-compute binomial distribution

$$p(x) = \frac{n!}{x!(n-x)!}p^x(1-p)^{n-x} = \frac{n!}{x!(n-x)!}\left(\frac{r}{N}\right)^x\left(1 - \frac{r}{N}\right)^{n-x}.$$

Consider the following example.

Example 4.16 Big Screen Televisions

Suppose that you own an electronics store and purchase (randomly select) 15 big screen TVs from a production run of 500. Of the 500 TVs, 450 are destined to last at least five years without needing a single repair. We will find the *exact* probability that at least 14 of the 15 big screen TVs will last at least five years without needing a single repair. If we let x = the number of TVs that will last at least five years without needing a single repair, then x follows a hypergeometric distribution and $P(x \geq 14)$ is given by

$$P(x \geq 14) = P(x = 14) + P(x = 15) = p(14) + p(15).$$

Plugging in the values of $N = 500$, $r = 450$, $N - r = 50$, and $n = 15$, we get

$$p(x) = \frac{\left(\dfrac{450!}{(450 - x)!x}\right)\left(\dfrac{50!}{(50 - 15 + x)!(15 - x)!}\right)}{\dfrac{500!}{485!15!}}.$$

Thus,

$$p(15) = \frac{\left(\dfrac{450!}{435!15!}\right)\left(\dfrac{50!}{50!0!}\right)}{\dfrac{500!}{485!15!}} \quad \text{and} \quad p(14) = \frac{\left(\dfrac{450!}{436!14!}\right)\left(\dfrac{50!}{49!1!}\right)}{\dfrac{500!}{485!15!}}.$$

LO7

A standard calculator may not be able to handle these calculations. Using a computer, we get $P(x \geq 14) = p(14) + p(15) = 0.5469$.

As we can see in this example, the calculations are difficult. We will approximate this probability by using the binomial approximation to the hypergeometric distribution. Here, we will just set $p = 450/500 = 0.9$. Using this approximation, we get $P(x \geq 14) = p(14) + p(15)$, where

$$p(x) = \frac{15!}{(15 - x)!x!}(0.9^x)(0.1^{15-x}).$$

This gives us $P(x \geq 14) = 0.5490$. This is much easier to calculate using a calculator and, as you can see, the approximation is very close to the exact answer (equal to two decimal places).

To further illustrate the similarities (and differences) when comparing the hypergeometric distribution to the binomial distribution, consider the mean and variance of the **hypergeometric random variable**:

$$\mu = n\left(\frac{r}{N}\right) \quad \text{and} \quad \sigma^2 = n\left(\frac{r}{N}\right)\left(\frac{N - r}{N}\right)\left(\frac{N - n}{N - 1}\right).$$

If we let $\frac{r}{N} = p$ and $\frac{N-r}{N} = q$, then you will see that the formula for the mean of a hypergeometric random variable is identical to the formula for the mean of a binomial random variable. This is not the case with the variance formula, however. The different formula here results from the fact that draws are made without replacement.

Exercises for Section 4.5

CONCEPTS

4.43 Suppose that x is a hypergeometric random variable. Explain what the values of x represent, that is, how the values of x are defined.

4.44 What is the difference between a hypergeometric random variable and a binomial random variable?

METHODS AND APPLICATIONS

4.45 Let $N = 10$, $r = 4$, and $n = 2$. Using the hypergeometric probability distribution formula, find
a. $P(x = 2)$.
b. $P(x = 0)$.
c. $P(x \geq 1)$.

4.46 Let $N = 15$, $r = 3$, and $n = 4$. Using the hypergeometric probability distribution formula, find
  a. $P(x = 1)$.
  b. $P(x < 3)$.
  c. $P(x \geq 2)$.

4.47 Let $N = 12$, $r = 5$, and $n = 5$. Using the hypergeometric probability distribution formula, find
  a. $P(x = 0)$.
  b. $P(x \leq 3)$.
  c. $P(x \geq 1)$.

4.48 Let $N = 20$, $r = 6$, and $n = 5$. Using the hypergeometric probability distribution formula, find
  a. $P(x = 5)$.
  b. $P(x < 2)$.
  c. $P(x \geq 2)$.

4.49 A box contains four red balls and six black balls. If two balls are selected from the box without replacement, what is the chance that
  a. Both balls are black?
  b. Both balls are red?
  c. A ball of each colour is drawn?

4.50 A box contains four red balls and six black balls, and another box contains six red balls and two black balls. A box is selected at random and a ball is drawn. What is the chance that
  a. It is a black ball?
  b. It is a red ball?

4.51 Suppose that a committee of five people is to be selected from a group of eight women and seven men.
  a. What is the probability that there will be exactly one man on the committee?
  b. What is the probability that there will be exactly one woman on the committee?
  c. What is the probability that there will be at least one woman on the committee?

4.52 Suppose that a committee of four is to be selected from a group of six women and four men.
  a. What is the probability that there will be no men on the committee?
  b. What is the probability that there will be no women on the committee?
  c. What is the probability that there will be at least one man on the committee if there is exactly one woman on the committee?

4.53 Suppose that you randomly select three flat panel TVs from a small production run of ten TVs, and nine are destined to last at least five years without needing a single repair.
  a. What is the probability that all three of the TVs will last at least five years without requiring a single repair?
  b. What is the probability that one of the TVs will require a single repair?
  c. Can we apply the binomial approximation to the hypergeometric distribution in this question? Explain.

CHAPTER SUMMARY

In this chapter, we began our study of **random variables**. We learned that **a random variable represents an uncertain numerical outcome**. We also learned that a random variable whose values can be listed is called a **discrete random variable**, while the values of a **continuous random variable** correspond to one or more intervals on the real number line. We saw that a **probability distribution** of a discrete random variable is a table, graph, or formula that gives the probability associated with each of the random variable's possible values. We also discussed several descriptive measures of a discrete random variable—its **mean** (or **expected**

value), its **variance**, and its **standard deviation**. We concluded this chapter by studying some important, commonly used discrete probability distributions—the **binomial distribution**, the **Poisson distribution**, and the **hypergeometric distribution**. We demonstrated how to find probabilities associated with each distribution and discussed relationships between the **binomial** and **Poisson** distributions as well as the **binomial** and **hypergeometric distributions**. We also demonstrated how we can use probability distributions to make statistical inferences.

GLOSSARY OF TERMS

binomial distribution: The probability distribution that describes a binomial random variable. (page 128)

binomial experiment: An experiment that consists of n independent, identical trials, each of which results in either a success or a failure and is such that the probability of success on any trial is the same. (page 128)

binomial random variable: A random variable that is defined to be the total number of successes in n trials of a binomial experiment. (page 128)

binomial tables: Tables in which we can look up binomial probabilities. (page 131)

continuous random variable: A random variable whose values correspond to one or more intervals of numbers on the real number line. (page 114)

discrete random variable: A random variable whose values can be counted or listed. (page 114)

expected value (of a random variable): The mean of the population of all possible observed values of a random variable. That is, the long-run average value obtained if values of a random variable are observed a (theoretically) infinite number of times. (page 118)

hypergeometric probability distribution: The probability distribution that describes a hypergeometric random variable. (page 142)

hypergeometric random variable: A discrete random variable that is defined to be the number of successes in n dependent trials due to sampling without replacement. (page 143)

Poisson distribution: The probability distribution that describes a Poisson random variable. (page 137)

Poisson random variable: A discrete random variable that can often be used to describe the number of occurrences of an event over a specified interval of time or space. (page 137)

probability distribution (of a discrete random variable): A table, graph, or formula that gives the probability associated with each of the random variable's values. (page 115)

random variable: A variable that assumes numerical values that are determined by the outcome of an experiment. That is, a variable that represents an uncertain numerical outcome. (page 114)

standard deviation (of a discrete random variable): The standard deviation of the population of all possible observed values of a random variable. It measures the spread of the population of all possible observed values of the random variable. (page 121)

variance (of a discrete random variable): The variance of the population of all possible observed values of a random variable. It measures the spread of the population of all possible observed values of the random variable. (page 121)

IMPORTANT FORMULAS

Properties of a discrete probability distribution: page 117

Mean (expected value) of a discrete random variable: page 118

Variance and standard deviation of a discrete random variable: page 121

Binomial probability formula: page 128

Mean, variance, and standard deviation of a binomial random variable: page 135

Poisson probability formula: page 137

Mean, variance, and standard deviation of a Poisson random variable: page 140

Hypergeometric probability formula: page 142

Mean and variance of a hypergeometric random variable: page 143

Connect Practise and learn online with *Connect.* Questions and tables with online data sets are marked with ✈.

SUPPLEMENTARY EXERCISES

4.54 An investor holds two stocks, each of which can rise (R), remain unchanged (U), or decline (D) on any particular day. Let x equal the number of stocks that rise on a particular day.
  a. Write the probability distribution of x assuming that all outcomes are equally likely.
  b. Write the probability distribution of x assuming that for each stock $P(R) = 0.6$, $P(U) = 0.1$, and $P(D) = 0.3$ and that movements of the two stocks are independent.
  c. Write the probability distribution of x assuming that

$$P(R) = 0.4, P(U) = 0.2, P(D) = 0.4$$

  for the first stock;

$$P(R) = 0.8, P(U) = 0.1, P(D) = 0.1$$

  for the second stock; and movements of the two stocks are independent.

4.55 Repeat Exercise 4.54, letting x equal the number of stocks that decline on that particular day.

4.56 **a.** Consider Exercise 4.54, and let x equal the number of stocks that rise on that particular day. Find μ_x and σ_x for
  (1) The probability distribution of x in Exercise 4.54a.
  (2) The probability distribution of x in Exercise 4.54b.
  (3) The probability distribution of x in Exercise 4.54c.
  b. In which case is μ_x the largest? Interpret this in words.
  c. In which case is σ_x the largest? Interpret this in words.

4.57 Suppose that the probability distribution of a random variable x can be described by the formula

$$p(x) = \frac{(x - 3)^2}{55}$$

  for each of the values $x = -2, -1, 0, 1$, and 2.
  a. Write the probability distribution of x.
  b. Show that the probability distribution of x satisfies the properties of a discrete probability distribution.

  c. Calculate the mean of x.
  d. Calculate the variance and standard deviation of x.

4.58 A rock concert promoter has scheduled an outdoor concert on Canada Day. If it does not rain, the promoter will make $30,000. If it does rain, the promoter will lose $15,000 in guarantees made to the band and other expenses. The probability of rain on Canada Day is 0.4.
  a. What is the promoter's expected profit? Is the expected profit a reasonable decision criterion? Explain.
  b. How much should an insurance company charge to insure the promoter's full losses? Explain your answer.

4.59 The demand (in number of copies per day) for a city newspaper is listed below with corresponding probabilities:

x = Demand	p(x)
50,000	0.1
70,000	0.25
90,000	0.4
110,000	0.2
130,000	0.05

  a. Find the expected demand and interpret this value.
  b. Using Chebyshev's theorem, find the minimum percentage of all possible daily demand values that will fall in the interval $[\mu_x \pm 2\sigma_x]$.
  c. Calculate the interval $[\mu_x \pm 2\sigma_x]$. According to the probability distribution of demand, x, previously given, what percentage of all possible daily demand values fall in the interval $[\mu_x \pm 2\sigma_x]$?

4.60 United Medicine, Inc., claims that a drug, Viro, significantly relieves the symptoms of a certain viral infection for 80 percent of all patients. Suppose that this drug is given to eight randomly selected patients who have been diagnosed with the viral infection.

   a. Let x equal the number of the eight randomly selected patients whose symptoms are significantly relieved. What distribution describes the random variable x? Explain.

   b. Assuming that the company's claim is correct, find $P(x \leq 3)$.

   c. Suppose that of the eight randomly selected patients, three have had their symptoms significantly relieved by Viro. Based on the probability in part b, would you believe the claim of United Medicine, Inc.? Explain.

4.61 A consumer advocate claims that 80 percent of cable television subscribers are not satisfied with their cable service. In an attempt to justify this claim, a randomly selected sample of cable subscribers will be polled on this issue.

   a. Suppose that the advocate's claim is true, and suppose that a random sample of five cable subscribers is selected. Assuming independence, use an appropriate formula to compute the probability that four or more subscribers in the sample are not satisfied with their service.

   b. Suppose that the advocate's claim is true, and suppose that a random sample of 25 cable subscribers is selected. Assuming independence, find

   (1) The probability that 15 or fewer subscribers in the sample are not satisfied with their service.

   (2) The probability that more than 20 subscribers in the sample are not satisfied with their service.

   (3) The probability that between 20 and 24 (inclusive) subscribers in the sample are not satisfied with their service.

   (4) The probability that exactly 24 subscribers in the sample are not satisfied with their service.

   c. Suppose that when we survey 25 randomly selected cable television subscribers, we find that 15 are actually not satisfied with their service. Using a probability you found in this exercise as the basis for your answer, do you believe the consumer advocate's claim? Explain.

4.62 A retail store has implemented procedures aimed at reducing the number of bad cheques cashed by its cashiers. The store's goal is to cash no more than eight bad cheques per week. The average number of bad cheques cashed is three per week. Let x denote the number of bad cheques cashed per week. Assume that x has a Poisson distribution.

   a. Find the probability that the store's cashiers will not cash any bad cheques in a particular week.

   b. Find the probability that the store will meet its goal during a particular week.

   c. Find the probability that the store will not meet its goal during a particular week.

   d. Find the probability that the store's cashiers will cash no more than ten bad cheques per two-week period.

   e. Find the probability that the store's cashiers will cash no more than five bad cheques per three-week period.

4.63 Suppose that the number of accidents occurring in an industrial plant is described by a Poisson process with an average of 1.5 accidents every three months. During the last three months, four accidents occurred.

   a. Find the probability that no accidents will occur during the current three-month period.

   b. Find the probability that fewer accidents will occur during the current three-month period than occurred during the last three-month period.

   c. Find the probability that no more than 12 accidents will occur during a particular year.

   d. Find the probability that no accidents will occur during a particular year.

4.64 A high-security government institution has installed four security systems to detect attempted break-ins. The four security systems operate independently of each other, and each has a 0.85 probability of detecting an attempted break-in. Assume an attempted break-in occurs. Use the binomial distribution to find the probability that at least one of the four security systems will detect it.

4.65 A new stain-removal product claims to completely remove the stains on 90 percent of all stained garments. Assume that the product will be tested on 20 randomly selected stained garments, and let x denote the number of these garments from which the stains will be completely removed. Use the binomial distribution to find $P(x \leq 13)$ if the stain-removal product's claim is correct. If x actually turns out to be 13, what do you think of the claim?

4.66 Consider Exercise 4.65, and find $P(x \leq 17)$ if the stain-removal product's claim is correct. If x actually turns out to be 17, what do you think of the claim?

4.67 A province has averaged one small business failure per week over the past several years. Let x denote the number of small business failures in the next eight weeks. Use the Poisson distribution to find $P(x \geq 17)$ if the mean number of small business failures remains what it has been. If x actually turns out to be 17, what does this imply?

4.68 A candy company claims that its new chocolate almond bar averages ten almonds per bar. Let x denote the number of almonds in the next bar that you buy. Use the Poisson distribution to find $P(x \leq 4)$ if the candy company's claim is correct. If x actually turns out to be 4, what do you think of the claim?

4.69 Consider Exercise 4.68, and find $P(x \leq 8)$ if the candy company's claim is true. If x actually turns out to be 8, what do you think of the claim?

4.70 Suppose that a Canada Revenue Agency auditor is to randomly select three corporations from a list of ten. Of the ten corporations, it is known that four earned profits and six recorded losses during the year for which the returns are being audited. In the random sample of three, what is the chance that

   a. Exactly one will have recorded a loss?

   b. None will have recorded losses?

   c. At least one will have earned a profit?

CHAPTER **5**
Continuous Random Variables

LEARNING OBJECTIVES

After reading this chapter, you should be able to

LO1 describe a continuous probability distribution (probability curve)

LO2 distinguish between the uniform distribution, the normal distribution, and the exponential distribution

LO3 use the normal table to calculate the area under the curve to the left or right of specific points and over intervals

LO4 compute a z value of an observed data point using the mean and the standard deviation

LO5 determine a z value based on a given probability

LO6 read the cumulative normal table to compute areas under the normal curve

CHAPTER OUTLINE

5.1 Continuous Probability Distributions

5.2 The Uniform Distribution

5.3 The Normal Probability Distribution

5.4 The Cumulative Normal Table

5.5 Approximating the Binomial Distribution by Using the Normal Distribution

5.6 The Exponential Distribution

In Chapter 4, we introduced the idea of a random variable and defined discrete and continuous random variables. With discrete random variables, we can assign probabilities to the specific values that the random variable x will take on and then make use of the discrete probability distribution for the random variable x to compute various probabilities associated with x.

In this chapter, we discuss **continuous probability distributions**. When a random variable is said to be continuous, like the time to failure of an electronic component or the height or weight of an individual, it is impossible to assign a specific probability to each individual value that the random variable could take on because an infinite number of values is

possible. Instead we have to generate a continuous probability distribution for the random variable. We will begin the chapter by explaining the general idea behind this type of random variable and its corresponding distribution, and then we will present three important continuous distributions—the **uniform**, the **normal**, and the **exponential distribution**. We will also explore when and how the normal distribution (continuous) can be used to approximate the binomial distribution (discrete). This has already been mentioned in Chapter 4.

In order to illustrate the concepts in this chapter, we continue with the coffee temperature case and also introduce the wine case.

The Wine Case: A wine maker is test-marketing a new bottle for one of its popular brands of Chardonnay. The new bottle will have a screwcap instead of a cork (no more searching for a corkscrew). However, the new corkless bottle will only be used if less than 10 percent of all current customers would no longer buy the wine if the corkless bottle were used. The wine maker

uses sample information and a probability based on the normal approximation to the binomial distribution to provide very strong evidence that less than 10 percent of all current customers would stop purchasing the wine if the new corkless bottles were used. This implies that the wine maker can go ahead with the new bottles without alienating its customers.

connect Practise and learn online with *Connect*. Throughout this chapter, questions and tables with online data sets are marked with ✈.

5.1 CONTINUOUS PROBABILITY DISTRIBUTIONS

CHAPTER 3

L01

Remember (from Section 4.1) that the values of a continuous random variable correspond to one or more intervals on the real-number line. We often wish to compute probabilities about the range of values that a continuous random variable x might attain. We do this by assigning probabilities to intervals of values by using what we call a **continuous probability distribution**. To understand this idea, suppose that $f(x)$ is a continuous function of the numbers on the real line, and consider the continuous curve that results when $f(x)$ is graphed. Such a curve is illustrated in Figure 5.1.

> **Continuous Probability Distributions**
>
> The curve $f(x)$ is the **continuous probability distribution** of the random variable x if the probability that x will be in a specified interval of numbers is the area under the curve $f(x)$ corresponding to the interval. Sometimes we refer to a continuous probability distribution as a **probability curve** or a **probability density function**.

An **area** under a continuous probability distribution (or probability curve) is a **probability**. For instance, consider the range of values on the number line from the number a to the number b—that is, the interval of numbers from a to b. If the continuous random variable x is described by the probability curve $f(x)$, then the area under $f(x)$ corresponding to the interval from a to b is the probability that x will attain a value between a and b. Such a probability is illustrated as the shaded area in Figure 5.1. We write this probability as $P(a \le x \le b)$. Since there is no area under a continuous curve at a single point, the probability that a continuous random variable x attains a single value is always equal to 0. It follows that in Figure 5.1 we have $P(x = a) = 0$ and $P(x = b) = 0$. Therefore, $P(a \le x \le b)$ equals $P(a < x < b)$ because each of the interval endpoints a and b has a probability that is equal to 0.

We know that any probability is 0 or positive, and we also know that the sum of the probabilities assigned to all possible values of x must be 1. It follows that, similar to the conditions required for a discrete probability distribution, a probability curve must satisfy the following properties:

> **Properties of a Continuous Probability Distribution**
>
> The **continuous probability distribution** (or **probability curve**) $f(x)$ of a random variable x must satisfy the following three conditions:
>
> 1 $f(x) \ge 0$ for any value of x.
> 2 $P(a \le x \le b)$ is given by the area under the probability curve between a and b.
> 3 The total area under the curve of $f(x)$ is equal to 1.

FIGURE 5.1   An Example of a Continuous Probability Distribution $f(x)$

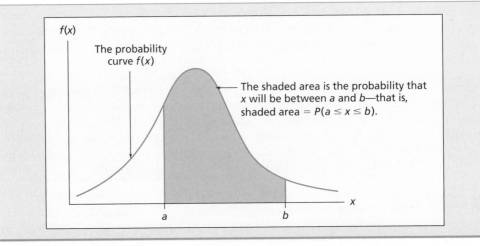

Any continuous curve $f(x)$ that satisfies these conditions is a valid continuous probability distribution. Such probability curves can have a variety of shapes—bell-shaped and symmetrical, positively skewed (to the right), negatively skewed (to the left), or any other shape. In a practical problem, the shape of a probability curve would be estimated by looking at a relative frequency histogram of observed data (as we have done in Chapter 2). Later in this chapter, we study probability curves with several different shapes. For example, in the next section we introduce the **uniform distribution**, which has a rectangular shape.

It is important to point out that *the height of a probability curve $f(x)$ at a particular point is not a probability. In order to calculate a probability concerning a continuous random variable, we must compute an appropriate area under the curve $f(x)$.* In theory, such areas are calculated by calculus methods and/or numerical techniques, and needed areas under commonly used probability curves have been compiled in statistical tables.

Finally, we wish to emphasize that a continuous (or discrete) probability distribution is used to represent a population. That is, if $f(x)$ is a continuous probability distribution for a random variable x, then the area under the curve $f(x)$ between a and b—that is, $P(a \leq x \leq b)$—is *the proportion of values in the population of all possible values of x that are between a and b.*

5.2 THE UNIFORM DISTRIBUTION

Suppose that over a period of several days the manager of a large hotel has recorded the waiting times of 1,000 people waiting for an elevator in the lobby at dinnertime (5:00 P.M. to 7:00 P.M.). The observed waiting times range from zero minutes to four minutes. Furthermore, when the waiting times are arranged into a histogram, the bars making up the histogram have approximately equal heights, giving the histogram a rectangular appearance. This implies that the relative frequencies of all waiting times from zero minutes to four minutes are about the same. Therefore, it is reasonable to use the **uniform distribution** to describe the random variable x, the amount of time a randomly selected hotel patron spends waiting for the elevator. In general, the equation that describes the uniform distribution is given in the following box, and this equation is graphed in Figure 5.2(a) on the next page.

The Uniform Distribution

If a and b are numbers on the real line, the probability curve describing the **uniform distribution** is

$$f(x) = \begin{cases} \dfrac{1}{b - a} & \text{for } a \leq x \leq b, \\ 0 & \text{otherwise.} \end{cases}$$

Furthermore, the mean and the standard deviation of the population of all possible observed values of a random variable x that has a uniform distribution are

$$\mu_x = \frac{a + b}{2} \quad \text{and} \quad \sigma_x = \frac{b - a}{\sqrt{12}}.$$

LO2

Notice that the total area under the uniform distribution is the area of a rectangle with a base equal to $(b - a)$ and a height equal to $1/(b - a)$. Therefore, the probability curve's total area is

$$\text{base} \times \text{height} = (b - a)\left(\frac{1}{b - a}\right) = 1$$

FIGURE **5.2**   The Uniform Distribution

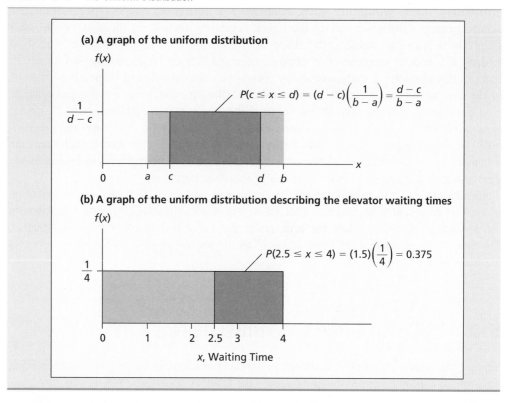

(a) A graph of the uniform distribution

$f(x)$

$\dfrac{1}{d-c}$

$P(c \le x \le d) = (d-c)\left(\dfrac{1}{b-a}\right) = \dfrac{d-c}{b-a}$

$0 \quad a \quad c \qquad d \quad b$

x

(b) A graph of the uniform distribution describing the elevator waiting times

$f(x)$

$\dfrac{1}{4}$

$P(2.5 \le x \le 4) = (1.5)\left(\dfrac{1}{4}\right) = 0.375$

$0 \quad 1 \quad 2 \ \ 2.5 \ \ 3 \qquad 4$

x, Waiting Time

(remember that the total area under any continuous probability curve must equal 1). Furthermore, if c and d are numbers that are as illustrated in Figure 5.2(a), then the probability that x will be between c and d is the area of a rectangle with base $(d-c)$ and height $1/(b-a)$. That is,

$$P(c \le x \le d) = \text{base} \times \text{height}$$

$$= (d-c)\left(\frac{1}{b-a}\right)$$

$$= \frac{d-c}{b-a}.$$

Example 5.1   Waiting for the Elevator

In the introduction to this section, we said that the amount of time, x, that a randomly selected hotel patron spends waiting for the elevator at dinnertime is uniformly distributed between zero minutes and four minutes. In this case, $a = 0$ and $b = 4$. Therefore,

$$f(x) = \begin{cases} \dfrac{1}{b-a} = \dfrac{1}{4-0} = \dfrac{1}{4} & \text{for } 0 \le x \le 4, \\ 0 & \text{otherwise.} \end{cases}$$

Noting that this equation is graphed in Figure 5.2(b), suppose that the hotel manager wishes to find the probability that a randomly selected patron will spend at least 2.5 minutes waiting for the elevator. This probability is the area under the curve $f(x)$ that corresponds to the interval [2.5, 4]. As shown in Figure 5.2(b), this probability is the area of a rectangle with a base equal to $4 - 2.5 = 1.5$ and a height equal to $1/4$. That is,

$$P(x \ge 2.5) = P(2.5 \le x \le 4) = \text{base} \times \text{height} = 1.5 \times \frac{1}{4} = 0.375.$$

Similarly, the probability that a randomly selected patron will spend less than one minute waiting for the elevator is

$$P(x < 1) = P(0 \le x \le 1) = \text{base} \times \text{height} = 1 \times \frac{1}{4} = 0.25.$$

We next note that the mean waiting time for the elevator at dinnertime is

$$\mu_x = \frac{a+b}{2} = \frac{0+4}{2} = 2 \text{ (minutes)}$$

and that the standard deviation of this waiting time is

$$\sigma_x = \frac{b-a}{\sqrt{12}} = \frac{4-0}{\sqrt{12}} = 1.1547 \text{ (minutes)}.$$

Therefore, because

$$\mu_x - \sigma_x = 2 - 1.1547 = 0.8453$$

and

$$\mu_x + \sigma_x = 2 + 1.1547 = 3.1547,$$

the probability that the waiting time of a randomly selected patron will be within (plus or minus) one standard deviation of the mean waiting time is

$$P(0.8453 \le x \le 3.1547) = (3.1547 - 0.8453) \times \frac{1}{4}$$

$$= 0.57735.$$

Exercises for Sections 5.1 and 5.2

CONCEPTS

5.1 A discrete probability distribution assigns probabilities to individual values. To what are probabilities assigned by a continuous probability distribution?

5.2 How do we use the continuous probability distribution (or probability curve) of a random variable x to find probabilities? Explain.

5.3 What three properties must be satisfied by a continuous probability distribution (or probability curve)?

5.4 Explain the meaning of the height of a probability curve over a given point.

5.5 When is it appropriate to use the uniform distribution to describe a random variable x?

METHODS AND APPLICATIONS

5.6 Suppose that the random variable x has a uniform distribution with $a = 2$ and $b = 8$.
   a. Write the formula for the probability curve of x, and write an interval that gives the possible values of x.
   b. Graph the probability curve of x.
   c. Find $P(3 \le x \le 5)$.
   d. Find $P(1.5 \le x \le 6.5)$.
   e. Calculate the mean, μ_x, variance, σ_x^2, and standard deviation, σ_x.

   f. Calculate the interval $[\mu_x \pm 2\sigma_x]$. What is the probability that x will be in this interval?

5.7 Consider the figure given below. Find the value of h that makes the function $f(x)$ a valid continuous probability distribution.

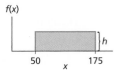

5.8 Assume that the waiting time x for an elevator is uniformly distributed between zero minutes and six minutes.
   a. Write the formula for the probability curve of x.
   b. Graph the probability curve of x.
   c. Find $P(2 \le x \le 4)$.
   d. Find $P(3 \le x \le 6)$.
   e. Find $P(\{0 \le x \le 2\} \text{ or } \{5 \le x \le 6\})$.

5.9 Refer to Exercise 5.8.
   a. Calculate the mean, μ_x, the variance, σ_x^2, and the standard deviation, σ_x.
   b. Find the probability that the waiting time of a randomly selected patron will be within one standard deviation of the mean.

5.10 Consider the figure given below. Find the value of K that makes the function $f(x)$ a valid continuous probability distribution.

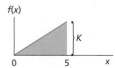

5.11 Suppose that an airline quotes a flight time of 2 hours, 10 minutes between two cities. Furthermore, suppose that historical flight records indicate that the actual flight time between the two cities, x, is uniformly distributed between 2 hours and 2 hours, 20 minutes. Let the time unit be one minute.
  a. Write the formula for the probability curve of x.
  b. Graph the probability curve of x.
  c. Find $P(125 \leq x \leq 135)$.
  d. Find the probability that a randomly selected flight between the two cities will be at least five minutes late.

5.12 Refer to Exercise 5.11.
  a. Calculate the mean flight time and the standard deviation of the flight time.

b. Find the probability that the flight time will be within one standard deviation of the mean.

5.13 Consider the figure given below. Find the value of c that makes the function $f(x)$ a valid continuous probability distribution.

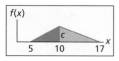

5.14 A weather forecaster predicts that the May rainfall in a local area will be between 3 cm and 6 cm but has no idea where within the interval the amount will be. Let x be the amount of May rainfall in the local area, and assume that x is uniformly distributed in the interval 3 cm to 6 cm.
  a. Write the formula for the probability curve of x.
  b. Graph the probability curve of x.
  c. What is the probability that the May rainfall will be at least 4 cm? at least 5 cm? at most 4.5 cm?

5.15 Refer to Exercise 5.14.
  a. Calculate the expected May rainfall.
  b. What is the probability that the observed May rainfall will fall within two standard deviations of the mean? within one standard deviation of the mean?

CHAPTER 5

LO2

5.3 THE NORMAL PROBABILITY DISTRIBUTION

The normal curve The bell-shaped appearance of the normal probability distribution is illustrated in Figure 5.3. The equation that defines this normal curve is given in the following box:

The Normal Probability Distribution

The **normal probability distribution** is defined by the equation

$$f(x) = \frac{1}{\sigma\sqrt{2\pi}} e^{-\frac{1}{2}\left(\frac{x-\mu}{\sigma}\right)^2} \text{ for all real values of } x.$$

Here μ and σ are the mean and standard deviation of the population of all possible observed values of the random variable x under consideration. Furthermore, $\pi = 3.141592\ldots$, and $e = 2.718281\ldots$ is the base of the natural logarithm.

The normal probability distribution has several important properties:

1 There is an entire family of normal probability distributions; the specific shape of each normal distribution is determined by its mean, μ, and its standard deviation, σ.

2 The highest point on the normal curve is located at the mean, which is also the median and the mode of the distribution.

3 The normal distribution is symmetrical: The curve's shape to the left of the mean is the mirror image of its shape to the right of the mean.

4 The tails of the normal curve extend to infinity in both directions and never touch the horizontal axis. However, the tails get close enough to the horizontal axis quickly enough to ensure that the total area under the normal curve equals 1.

5 Since the normal curve is symmetrical, the area under the normal curve to the right of the mean, μ, equals the area under the normal curve to the left of the mean, and each of these areas equals 0.5 (see Figure 5.3).

Intuitively, the mean μ positions the normal curve on the real line. This is illustrated in Figure 5.4(a). This figure shows two normal curves with different means, μ_1 and μ_2 (where μ_1

FIGURE **5.3** The Normal
                Probability Curve

FIGURE **5.4** How the Mean μ and Standard Deviation σ Affect the Position
                and Shape of a Normal Probability Curve

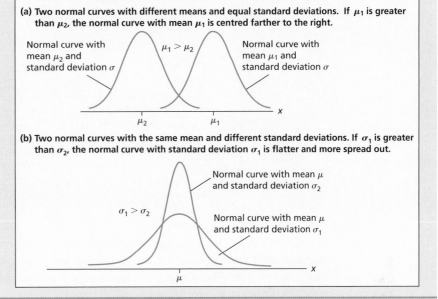

FIGURE **5.5** An Area under a Normal Curve Corresponding to the Interval $[a, b]$

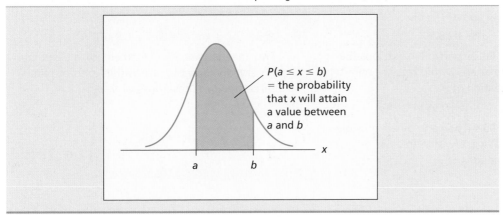

is greater than μ_2), and with equal standard deviations. We see that the normal curve with mean μ_1 is centred farther to the right.

The variance, σ^2 (and the standard deviation, σ), measure the spread of the normal curve. This is illustrated in Figure 5.4(b), which shows two normal curves with the same mean and two different standard deviations, σ_1 and σ_2. Because σ_1 is greater than σ_2, the normal curve with standard deviation σ_1 is more spread out (flatter) than the normal curve with standard deviation σ_2. In general, larger standard deviations result in normal curves that are flatter and more spread out, while smaller standard deviations result in normal curves that have higher peaks and are less spread out.

Suppose that a random variable x is normally distributed with mean μ and standard deviation σ. If a and b are numbers on the real line, we consider the probability that x will attain a value between a and b. That is, we consider

$$P(a \le x \le b),$$

which equals the area under the normal curve with mean μ and standard deviation σ corresponding to the interval $[a, b]$. Such an area is depicted in Figure 5.5 and can be found using

FIGURE **5.6**   Three Important Percentages Concerning a Normally Distributed Random Variable
x with Mean μ and Standard Deviation σ

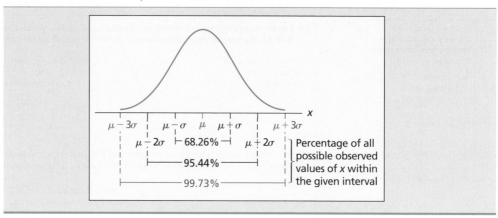

a statistical table called a **normal table**. There are three important areas under a normal curve. These areas form the basis for the **empirical rule** for a normally distributed population (discussed on page 49 in Chapter 2). Specifically, if x is normally distributed with mean μ and standard deviation σ, the following can be shown (using a normal table), as illustrated in Figure 5.6:

Three Important Areas under the Normal Curve

1 $P(\mu - \sigma \leq x \leq \mu + \sigma) = 0.6826.$

This means that 68.26 percent of all possible observed values of x are within (plus or minus) one standard deviation of μ.

2 $P(\mu - 2\sigma \leq x \leq \mu + 2\sigma) = 0.9544.$

This means that 95.44 percent of all possible observed values of x are within (plus or minus) two standard deviations of μ.

3 $P(\mu - 3\sigma \leq x \leq \mu + 3\sigma) = 0.9973.$

This means that 99.73 percent of all possible observed values of x are within (plus or minus) three standard deviations of μ.

Finding normal curve areas   There is a unique normal curve for every combination of μ and σ. Since there are many (theoretically, an unlimited number of) such combinations, we would like to have one table of normal curve areas that applies to all normal curves. There is such a table, and we can use it by thinking in terms of how many standard deviations a value of interest is from the mean. Specifically, consider a random variable x that is normally distributed with mean μ and standard deviation σ. Then the random variable

$$z = \frac{x - \mu}{\sigma}$$

expresses the number of standard deviations that x is from the mean μ. To understand this idea, notice that if x equals μ (that is, x is zero standard deviations from μ), then $z = (\mu - \mu)/\sigma = 0$. However, if x is one standard deviation above the mean (that is, if x equals $\mu + \sigma$), then $x - \mu = \sigma$ and $z = \sigma/\sigma = 1$. Similarly, if x is two standard deviations below the mean (that is, if x equals $\mu - 2\sigma$), then $x - \mu = -2\sigma$ and $z = -2\sigma/\sigma = -2$. Figure 5.7 illustrates that for values of x of, respectively, $\mu - 3\sigma$, $\mu - 2\sigma$, $\mu - \sigma$, μ, $\mu + \sigma$, $\mu + 2\sigma$, and $\mu + 3\sigma$, the corresponding values of z are -3, -2, -1, 0, 1, 2, and 3. This figure also illustrates the following general result:

FIGURE **5.7** If *x* Is Normally Distributed with Mean μ and Standard Deviation σ, Then

$$z = \frac{x - \mu}{\sigma} \text{ Is Normally Distributed with Mean 0 and Standard Deviation 1}$$

FIGURE **5.8**

The Area under the Standard Normal Curve between 0 and 1 Equals 0.3413; That Is, $P(0 \le z \le 1) = 0.3413$

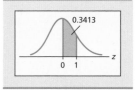

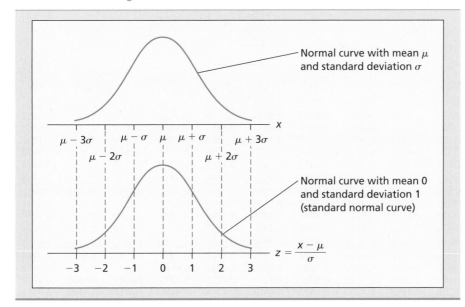

The Standard Normal Distribution

If a random variable *x* (or, equivalently, the population of all possible observed values of *x*) is normally distributed with mean μ and standard deviation σ, then the random variable

$$z = \frac{x - \mu}{\sigma}$$

(or, equivalently, the population of all possible observed values of *z*) is normally distributed with mean 0 and standard deviation 1. A normal distribution (or curve) with mean 0 and standard deviation 1 is called a **standard normal distribution** (or **curve**).

Table A.3 is a table of areas under the standard normal curve. This table is called a **normal table**, and it is reproduced in Table 5.1 on the next page. Specifically,

The normal table gives, for many different values of *z*, the area under the standard normal curve between 0 and *z*.

The values of *z* in the table range from 0.00 to 3.09 in increments of 0.01. As can be seen from Table 5.1, values of *z* accurate to the nearest tenth (0.0, 0.1, 0.2, . . . , 2.9, 3.0) are given in the far left column (headed *z*) of the table. Further graduations to the nearest hundredth (0.00, 0.01, 0.02, . . . , 0.09) are given across the top of the table. The areas under the normal curve are given in the body of the table, accurate to four decimal places.

As a first example, suppose that we wish to find the area under the standard normal curve between 0 and 1. In order to find this area, we must find the area in the normal table corresponding to a *z* value of 1.00. Looking at Table 5.1, we first scan down the far left column of the table (starting at the top) until we find the value 1.0. Having found this value, we now scan across the row in the table corresponding to the *z* value 1.0 until we find the column in the table corresponding to 0.00. The desired area is in the row corresponding to the *z* value 1.0 and in the column headed 0.00. We see that this area equals 0.3413 (we have shaded it), and we illustrate this area in Figure 5.8. The area under the standard normal curve

LO3

TABLE **5.1**   A Table of Areas under the Standard Normal Curve

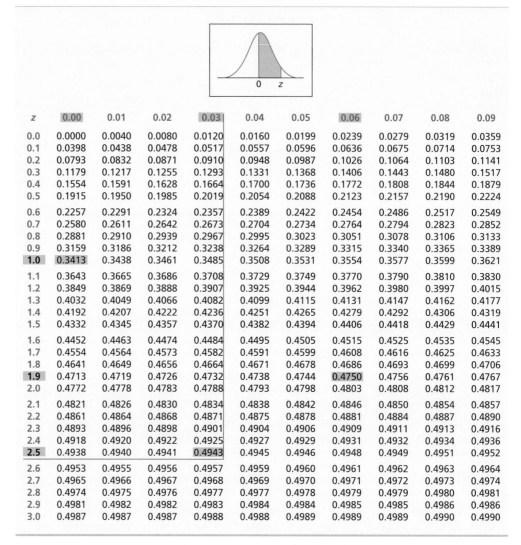

z	0.00	0.01	0.02	0.03	0.04	0.05	0.06	0.07	0.08	0.09
0.0	0.0000	0.0040	0.0080	0.0120	0.0160	0.0199	0.0239	0.0279	0.0319	0.0359
0.1	0.0398	0.0438	0.0478	0.0517	0.0557	0.0596	0.0636	0.0675	0.0714	0.0753
0.2	0.0793	0.0832	0.0871	0.0910	0.0948	0.0987	0.1026	0.1064	0.1103	0.1141
0.3	0.1179	0.1217	0.1255	0.1293	0.1331	0.1368	0.1406	0.1443	0.1480	0.1517
0.4	0.1554	0.1591	0.1628	0.1664	0.1700	0.1736	0.1772	0.1808	0.1844	0.1879
0.5	0.1915	0.1950	0.1985	0.2019	0.2054	0.2088	0.2123	0.2157	0.2190	0.2224
0.6	0.2257	0.2291	0.2324	0.2357	0.2389	0.2422	0.2454	0.2486	0.2517	0.2549
0.7	0.2580	0.2611	0.2642	0.2673	0.2704	0.2734	0.2764	0.2794	0.2823	0.2852
0.8	0.2881	0.2910	0.2939	0.2967	0.2995	0.3023	0.3051	0.3078	0.3106	0.3133
0.9	0.3159	0.3186	0.3212	0.3238	0.3264	0.3289	0.3315	0.3340	0.3365	0.3389
1.0	0.3413	0.3438	0.3461	0.3485	0.3508	0.3531	0.3554	0.3577	0.3599	0.3621
1.1	0.3643	0.3665	0.3686	0.3708	0.3729	0.3749	0.3770	0.3790	0.3810	0.3830
1.2	0.3849	0.3869	0.3888	0.3907	0.3925	0.3944	0.3962	0.3980	0.3997	0.4015
1.3	0.4032	0.4049	0.4066	0.4082	0.4099	0.4115	0.4131	0.4147	0.4162	0.4177
1.4	0.4192	0.4207	0.4222	0.4236	0.4251	0.4265	0.4279	0.4292	0.4306	0.4319
1.5	0.4332	0.4345	0.4357	0.4370	0.4382	0.4394	0.4406	0.4418	0.4429	0.4441
1.6	0.4452	0.4463	0.4474	0.4484	0.4495	0.4505	0.4515	0.4525	0.4535	0.4545
1.7	0.4554	0.4564	0.4573	0.4582	0.4591	0.4599	0.4608	0.4616	0.4625	0.4633
1.8	0.4641	0.4649	0.4656	0.4664	0.4671	0.4678	0.4686	0.4693	0.4699	0.4706
1.9	0.4713	0.4719	0.4726	0.4732	0.4738	0.4744	0.4750	0.4756	0.4761	0.4767
2.0	0.4772	0.4778	0.4783	0.4788	0.4793	0.4798	0.4803	0.4808	0.4812	0.4817
2.1	0.4821	0.4826	0.4830	0.4834	0.4838	0.4842	0.4846	0.4850	0.4854	0.4857
2.2	0.4861	0.4864	0.4868	0.4871	0.4875	0.4878	0.4881	0.4884	0.4887	0.4890
2.3	0.4893	0.4896	0.4898	0.4901	0.4904	0.4906	0.4909	0.4911	0.4913	0.4916
2.4	0.4918	0.4920	0.4922	0.4925	0.4927	0.4929	0.4931	0.4932	0.4934	0.4936
2.5	0.4938	0.4940	0.4941	0.4943	0.4945	0.4946	0.4948	0.4949	0.4951	0.4952
2.6	0.4953	0.4955	0.4956	0.4957	0.4959	0.4960	0.4961	0.4962	0.4963	0.4964
2.7	0.4965	0.4966	0.4967	0.4968	0.4969	0.4970	0.4971	0.4972	0.4973	0.4974
2.8	0.4974	0.4975	0.4976	0.4977	0.4977	0.4978	0.4979	0.4979	0.4980	0.4981
2.9	0.4981	0.4982	0.4982	0.4983	0.4984	0.4984	0.4985	0.4985	0.4986	0.4986
3.0	0.4987	0.4987	0.4987	0.4988	0.4988	0.4989	0.4989	0.4989	0.4990	0.4990

between 0 and 1 is the probability that the random variable z will be between 0 and 1. That is, we have found that

$$P(0 \leq z \leq 1) = 0.3413.$$

Next suppose that a random variable x is normally distributed with mean μ and standard deviation σ, and remember that z is the number of standard deviations σ that x is from μ. It follows that, when we say that $P(0 \leq z \leq 1)$ equals 0.3413, we are saying that 34.13 percent of all possible observed values of x are between the mean μ (where z equals 0) and a point that is one standard deviation above μ (where z equals 1). That is, 34.13 percent of all possible observed values of x are between μ and $\mu + \sigma$. The normal curve in Figure 5.9(a) illustrates that by the symmetry of the normal curve, the area under the standard normal curve between -1 and 0 is equal to the area under this curve between 0 and 1. That is,

$$P(-1 \leq z \leq 0) = P(0 \leq z \leq 1) = 0.3413.$$

This says that 34.13 percent of all possible observed values of x are between $\mu - \sigma$ and μ. If we add the two areas in Figure 5.9(a), we have

$$P(-1 \leq z \leq 1) = 0.3413 + 0.3413 = 0.6826.$$

FIGURE **5.9**   Some Areas under the Standard Normal Curve

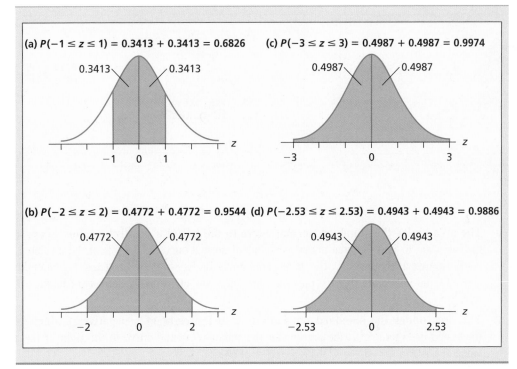

(a) $P(-1 \leq z \leq 1) = 0.3413 + 0.3413 = 0.6826$

0.3413   0.3413

−1   0   1 z

(c) $P(-3 \leq z \leq 3) = 0.4987 + 0.4987 = 0.9974$

0.4987   0.4987

−3   0   3 z

(b) $P(-2 \leq z \leq 2) = 0.4772 + 0.4772 = 0.9544$

0.4772   0.4772

−2   0   2 z

(d) $P(-2.53 \leq z \leq 2.53) = 0.4943 + 0.4943 = 0.9886$

0.4943   0.4943

−2.53   0   2.53 z

That is, 68.26 percent of all possible observed values of x are within (plus or minus) one standard deviation of the mean μ. Similarly, if we look up the z value 2.00 in the normal table, we find that $P(0 \leq z \leq 2) = 0.4772$. This implies, as illustrated in Figure 5.9(b), that $P(-2 \leq z \leq 2) = 0.4772 + 0.4772 = 0.9544$. In other words, 95.44 percent of all possible observed values of x are within (plus or minus) two standard deviations of μ. Furthermore, if we look up the z value 3.00 in the normal table, we find that $P(0 \leq z \leq 3) = 0.4987$. This implies, as illustrated in Figure 5.9(c), that $P(-3 \leq z \leq 3) = 0.4987 + 0.4987 = 0.9974$. Actually, the probability 0.4987 in Table 5.1 is rounded slightly, and a more precise calculation shows that $P(-3 \leq z \leq 3)$ is actually closer to 0.9973. This says that 99.73 percent of all possible observed values of x are within (plus or minus) three standard deviations of the mean μ.

As a final example of this kind of area, consider finding the area under the standard normal curve between 0 and 2.53. There is nothing special about this area, but we want to demonstrate using the normal table when the needed z value does not end in .00. To look up this value, we locate the area in the normal table in the row corresponding to 2.5 and in the column headed by 0.03. This area is 0.4943 (we have shaded it in Table 5.1), which implies that $P(0 \leq z \leq 2.53) = 0.4943$. This implies, as illustrated in Figure 5.9(d), that $P(-2.53 \leq z \leq 2.53) = 0.4943 + 0.4943 = 0.9886$. In other words, 98.86 percent of all possible observed values of x are within (plus or minus) 2.53 standard deviations of the mean μ.

Before continuing, recall that there is no area under a continuous probability curve at a single value of a random variable. Because the standard normal curve is a continuous probability curve, it follows, for example, that $P(-2.53 \leq z \leq 2.53)$ equals $P(-2.53 < z < 2.53)$. Keep this idea in mind as we continue through this section.

Thus far we have shown how to find *the area under the standard normal curve between 0 and a positive z value,* which, by the symmetry of the curve, *equals the area under the curve between 0 and the corresponding negative z value.* We now show how to find some other areas that will be important in later sections.

FIGURE **5.10**   Calculating $P(z \leq 1)$

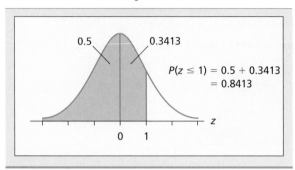

$$P(z \leq 1) = 0.5 + 0.3413$$
$$= 0.8413$$

FIGURE **5.11**   Calculating $P(z \geq -1)$

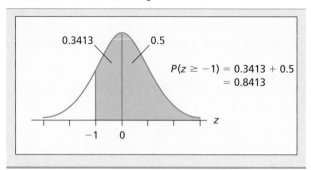

$$P(z \geq -1) = 0.3413 + 0.5$$
$$= 0.8413$$

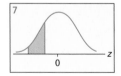

1   **The area under the standard normal curve to the left of a positive z value:** Suppose that we want to find the area under the standard normal curve to the left of the z value 1. As illustrated in Figure 5.10, this is the area under the curve between 0 and 1, which the normal table tells us is 0.3413, plus the area under the curve to the left of 0 (the mean), which is 0.5. Therefore, $P(z \leq 1) = 0.5 + 0.3413 = 0.8413$.

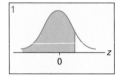

2   **The area under the standard normal curve to the right of a negative z value:** As illustrated in Figure 5.11, the area under the standard normal curve to the right of the z value -1 is $P(z \geq -1) = 0.3413 + 0.5 = 0.8413$.

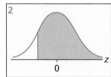

3   **The area under the standard normal curve to the right of a positive z value— a right-hand tail area:** Consider finding the area under the standard normal curve to the right of the z value 1. As illustrated in Figure 5.12, this is the area under the curve to the right of 0, which is 0.5, minus the area under the curve between 0 and 1, which the normal table tells us is 0.3413. Therefore, $P(z \geq 1) = 0.5 - 0.3413 = 0.1587$.

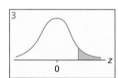

4   **The area under the standard normal curve to the left of a negative z value— a left-hand tail area:** As illustrated in Figure 5.13, the symmetry of the standard normal curve implies that the area under the standard normal curve to the left of the z value -1 equals the area under this curve to the right of the z value 1. That is, $P(z \leq -1)$ equals $P(z \geq 1)$. Therefore, $P(z \leq -1) = 0.5 - 0.3413 = 0.1587$.

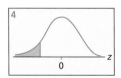

5   **Right-hand tail areas corresponding to z values greater than 3.09, and left-hand tail areas corresponding to z values less than -3.09:** The largest z value in the normal table is 3.09. Because the area under the standard normal curve between 0 and 3.09 is 0.499, the area under this curve to the right of 3.09 is $0.5 - 0.499 = 0.001$ (see Figure 5.14). Therefore, if we wish to find the area under the standard normal curve to the right of any z value greater than 3.09, the most we can say (without using a computer) is that this area is less than 0.001. Similarly, the area under the standard normal curve to the left of any z value less than -3.09 is also less than 0.001.

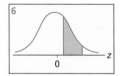

6   **The area under the standard normal curve between two positive z values:** Consider finding the area under the standard normal curve between 1 and 2. As illustrated in Figure 5.15(a), this area equals the area under the curve between 0 and 2, which the normal table tells us is 0.4772, minus the area under the curve between 0 and 1, which the normal table tells us is 0.3413. Therefore, $P(1 \leq z \leq 2) = 0.4772 - 0.3413 = 0.1359$.

7   **The area under the standard normal curve between two negative z values:** As illustrated in Figure 5.15(b), the symmetry of the normal curve implies that the area under the standard normal curve between -2 and -1 equals the area under this curve between 1 and 2. That is, $P(-2 \leq z \leq -1)$ equals $P(1 \leq z \leq 2)$. Therefore, $P(-2 \leq z \leq -1) = 0.4772 - 0.3413 = 0.1359$.

FIGURE **5.12** Calculating $P(z \geq 1)$

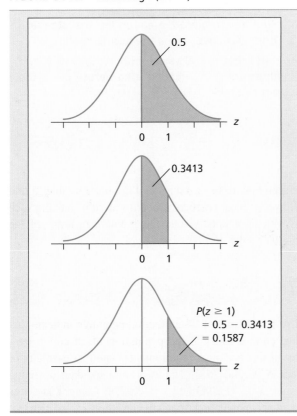

FIGURE **5.13** Calculating $P(z \leq -1)$

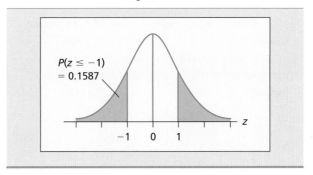

FIGURE **5.14** Calculating $P(z \geq 3.09)$

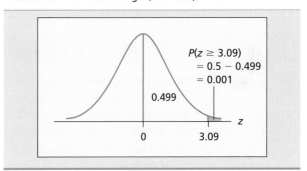

FIGURE **5.15** Calculating $P(1 \leq z \leq 2)$ and $P(-2 \leq z \leq -1)$

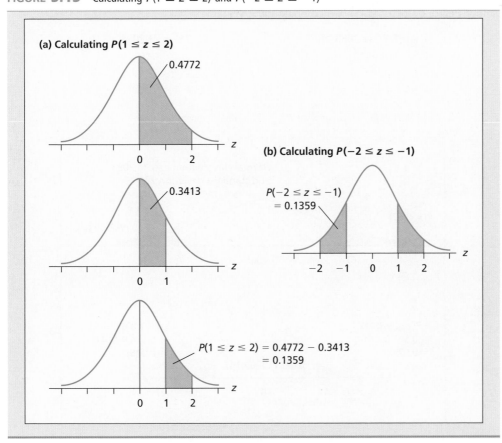

Finding Normal Probabilities

1 Formulate the problem in terms of the random variable x.

2 Calculate relevant z values and restate the problem in terms of the standard normal random variable

$$z = \frac{x - \mu}{\sigma}.$$

3 Find the required area under the standard normal curve by using the normal table.

4 Note that it is always useful to draw a picture illustrating the needed area before using the normal table.

Some practical applications We have seen how to use z values and the normal table to find areas under the standard normal curve. However, most practical problems are not stated in such terms. We now consider an example in which we must restate the problem in terms of the standard normal random variable z before using the normal table.

Example 5.2 The Coffee Temperature Case

LO4

Recall that the runs plot and histogram of the sample of 24 coffee temperatures indicate that the coffee-making process is in statistical control and that the population of all coffee temperatures is normally distributed. Also recall that customer requirements state that each cup of coffee should have a temperature between 67°C and 75°C. The mean and standard deviation of the sample of 24 coffee temperatures are $\bar{x} = 71.2083$ and $s = 2.9779$. Using $\bar{x}$ and s as point estimates of the population mean μ and population standard deviation σ, we want to calculate the probability that x, the temperature of a randomly selected cup of coffee, is outside the requirements (that is, less than 67°C or greater than 75°C). In order to compute the probability $P(x < 67 \text{ or } x > 75)$, we compute the z values

$$z = \frac{67 - 71.2083}{2.9779} = -1.41 \qquad \text{and} \qquad z = \frac{75 - 71.2083}{2.9779} = 1.27.$$

FIGURE 5.16   Finding $P(x < 67 \text{ or } x > 75)$ in the Coffee Temperature Case

Normal curve with mean 71.2083 and standard deviation 2.9779

$P(x < 67)$

$P(x > 75)$

67   71.2083   75 x

LO5

Standard normal curve

$P(z < -1.41)$
$= 0.5 - 0.4207$
$= 0.0793$

$P(z > 1.27)$
$= 0.5 - 0.4147$
$= 0.0853$

0.4207   0.4147

$z = -1.41$ 0 $z = 1.27$ z

Because the events $\{x < 67\}$ and $\{x > 75\}$ are mutually exclusive, we have

$$P(x < 67 \text{ or } x > 75) = P(x < 67) + P(x > 75)$$
$$= P(z < -1.41) + P(z > 1.27)$$
$$= (0.5 - 0.4207) + (0.5 - 0.3980)$$
$$= 0.0793 + 0.102 = 0.1813.$$

This calculation is illustrated in Figure 5.16. The probability of 0.1813 says that 18.13 percent of the coffee temperatures do not meet customer requirements. Therefore, if management believes that meeting this requirement is important, the coffee-making process must be improved.

Finding a point on the horizontal axis under a normal curve In order to use many of the formulas given in later chapters, we must be able to find the value of z so that the tail area to the right of z under the standard normal curve is a particular value. For instance, we might need to find the value of z so that the tail area to the right of z under the standard normal curve is 0.025. This value of z is denoted $z_{0.025}$, and we illustrate $z_{0.025}$ in Figure 5.17(a). We refer to $z_{0.025}$ as *the point on the horizontal axis under the standard normal curve that gives a right-hand tail area equal to 0.025.* It is easy to use a normal table to find such a z point. For instance, in order to find $z_{0.025}$, we note from Figure 5.17(b) that the area under the standard normal curve between 0 and $z_{0.025}$ equals $0.5 - 0.025 = 0.4750$. Remembering that areas under the standard normal curve between 0 and z are the four-digit numbers given in the body of a normal table, we scan the body of the table and find the area 0.4750. We have shaded this area in Table 5.1 (page 156), and we note that the area 0.4750 is in the row corresponding to a z value of 1.9 and the column headed by 0.06. It follows that the z value corresponding to 0.4750 is 1.96, which gives a right-hand tail area equal to 0.025. Therefore, $z_{0.025} = 1.96$.

In general, *we let z_α denote the point on the horizontal axis under the standard normal curve that gives a right-hand tail area equal to α.* With this definition in mind, we consider the following example.

LO5

FIGURE **5.17**   The Point $z_{0.025} = 1.96$

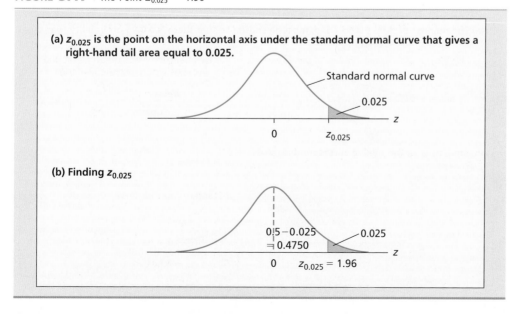

(a) $z_{0.025}$ **is the point on the horizontal axis under the standard normal curve that gives a right-hand tail area equal to 0.025.**

Standard normal curve

0.025

0          $z_{0.025}$ z

(b) **Finding** $z_{0.025}$

0.5 − 0.025 = 0.4750   0.025

0          $z_{0.025} = 1.96$ z

Example 5.3 Stocking Energy Drinks

Weekly demand at a grocery store for a brand of energy drink is approximately normally distributed with a mean of 1,000 cans and a standard deviation of 100. How many cans of the energy drink should the grocery store stock for a given week so that there is only a 5 percent chance that the store will run out of the popular drinks?

Let the random variable x represent the weekly demand for the energy drink. We will let d be the specific number of energy drinks to be stocked. So the value of d must be chosen so that $P(x > d) = 0.05$.

Figure 5.18(a) shows that the number of cans stocked, d, is located under the right-hand tail of the normal curve with mean $\mu = 1,000$ and standard deviation $\sigma = 100$. In order to find d, we need to determine how many standard deviations d must be above the mean in order to give a right-hand tail area that is equal to 0.05.

The z value corresponding to d is

$$z = \frac{d - \mu}{\sigma} = \frac{d - 1,000}{100},$$

and this z value is the number of standard deviations that d is from μ. This z value is illustrated in Figure 5.18(b), and it is the point on the horizontal axis under the standard normal curve that gives a right-hand tail area equal to 0.05. That is, the z value corresponding to d is $z_{0.05}$. Since the area under the standard normal curve between 0 and $z_{0.05}$ is $0.5 - 0.05 = 0.45$—see Figure 5.18(b)—we look for 0.45 in the body of the normal table. In Table 5.1, we see that the areas closest to 0.45 are 0.4495, which has a corresponding z value of 1.64, and 0.4505, which has a corresponding z value of 1.65. Although it would probably be sufficient to use either of these z values, we interpolate halfway between them and assume that $z_{0.05}$ equals 1.645. To find d, we solve the equation

$$\frac{d - 1,000}{100} = 1.645$$

for d. Doing this yields

$$d - 1,000 = 1.645(100)$$

FIGURE **5.18** Finding the Number of Cans of Energy Drinks Stocked, d, so That $P(x > d) = 0.05$ When $\mu = 1,000$ and $\sigma = 100$

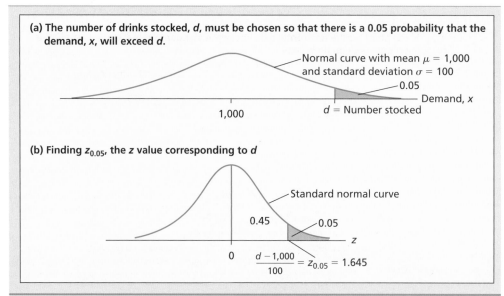

(a) The number of drinks stocked, d, must be chosen so that there is a 0.05 probability that the demand, x, will exceed d.

(b) Finding $z_{0.05}$, the z value corresponding to d

FIGURE **5.19**   The z Value $-z_{0.025} = -1.96$ Gives a Left-Hand Tail Area of 0.025 under the Standard Normal Curve

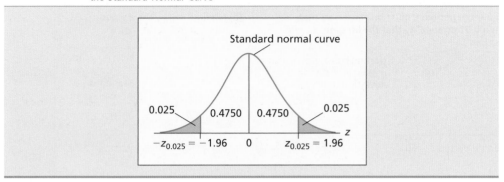

or

$$d = 1,000 + 1.645(100) = 1,164.5.$$

This last equation says that d is 1.645 standard deviations ($\sigma = 100$) above the mean ($\mu = 1,000$). Rounding $d = 1,164.5$ up so that the store's chances of running short of energy drinks will be *no more* than 5 percent, the store should plan to stock 1,165 energy drinks at the beginning of each week.

Sometimes we need to find the point on the horizontal axis under the standard normal curve that gives a particular *left-hand tail area* (say, for instance, an area of 0.025). Looking at Figure 5.19, it is easy to see that if, for instance, we want a left-hand tail area of 0.025, the needed z value is $-z_{0.025}$, where $z_{0.025}$ gives a right-hand tail area equal to 0.025. Therefore, since $z_{0.025} = 1.96$, it follows that $-z_{0.025} = -1.96$ gives a left-hand tail area equal to 0.025. In general, $-z_\alpha$ is the point on the horizontal axis under the standard normal curve that gives a left-hand tail area equal to α.

Example 5.4 How Long Should the Warranty Last?

LO5

Extensive testing indicates that the lifetime of the Everlast automobile battery is normally distributed with a mean of $\mu = 60$ months and a standard deviation of $\sigma = 6$ months. The Everlast's manufacturer has decided to offer a free replacement battery to any purchaser whose Everlast battery does not last at least as long as the minimum lifetime specified in its guarantee. How can the manufacturer establish the guarantee period so that only 1 percent of the batteries will need to be replaced free of charge?

If the battery will be guaranteed to last l months, l must be chosen to allow only a 0.01 probability that the lifetime, x, of an Everlast battery will be less than l. That is, we must choose l so that

$$P(x < l) = 0.01$$

Figure 5.20(a) on the next page shows that the guarantee period, l, is located under the left-hand tail of the normal curve with mean $\mu = 60$ and standard deviation $\sigma = 6$. In order to find l, we need to determine how many standard deviations l must be below the mean in order to give a left-hand tail area that equals 0.01. The z value corresponding to l is

$$z = \frac{l - \mu}{\sigma} = \frac{l - 60}{6},$$

FIGURE **5.20**   Finding the Guarantee Period, l, so That $P(x < l) = 0.01$ When $\mu = 60$ and $\sigma = 6$

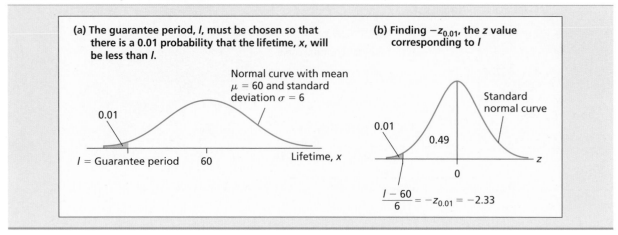

and this z value is the number of standard deviations that l is from μ. This z value is illustrated in Figure 5.20(b), and it is the point on the horizontal axis under the standard normal curve that gives a left-hand tail area equal to 0.01. That is, the z value corresponding to l is $-z_{0.01}$. Since the area under the standard normal curve between 0 and $-z_{0.01}$ is $5 - 0.01 = 0.49$—see Figure 5.20(b)—we look for 0.49 in the body of the normal table. In Table 5.1 (page 156), we see that the area closest to 0.49 is 0.4901, which has a corresponding z value of 2.33. Therefore, $-z_{0.01}$ is (roughly) -2.33. To find l, we solve the equation

$$\frac{l - 60}{6} = -2.33$$

for l. Doing this yields

$$l - 60 = -2.33(6)$$

or

$$l = 60 - 2.33(6) = 46.02.$$

Note that this last equation says that l is 2.33 standard deviations ($\sigma = 6$) below the mean ($\mu = 60$). Rounding $l = 46.02$ down so that *no more* than 1 percent of the batteries will need to be replaced free of charge, it seems reasonable to guarantee the Everlast battery to last 46 months.

In Section 2.3, we saw that the intervals $[\mu \pm \sigma]$, $[\mu \pm 2\sigma]$, and $[\mu \pm 3\sigma]$ are **tolerance intervals** containing, respectively, 68.26 percent, 95.44 percent, and 99.73 percent of the measurements in a normally distributed population having mean μ and standard deviation σ. Now we will demonstrate how to use the normal table to find the value k so that the interval $[\mu \pm k\sigma]$ contains any desired percentage of the measurements in a normally distributed population.

Consider computing a tolerance interval $[\mu \pm k\sigma]$ that contains 99 percent of the measurements in a normally distributed population with mean μ and standard deviation σ. As illustrated in Figure 5.21, we must find the value k so that the area under the normal curve with mean μ and standard deviation σ between $(\mu - k\sigma)$ and $(\mu + k\sigma)$ is 0.99. As also shown in this figure, the area under this normal curve between μ and $(\mu + k\sigma)$ is equal to 0.495. Because the z value corresponding to a value of x tells us how many standard deviations x is from μ, the z value corresponding to $(\mu + k\sigma)$ is obviously k. It follows that k is the point on the horizontal axis under the standard normal curve so that the area under this curve between 0

FIGURE **5.21**   Finding a Tolerance Interval [$\mu \pm k\sigma$] That Contains 99 Percent of the Measurements in a Normally Distributed Population

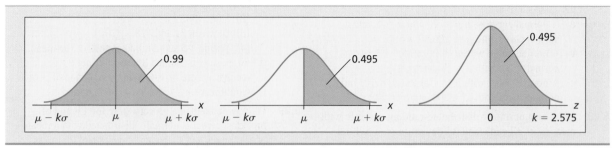

and k is 0.495. Looking up 0.495 in the body of the normal table (Table 5.1 on page 156), we find that the values closest to 0.495 are 0.4949, which has a corresponding z value of 2.57, and 0.4951, which has a corresponding z value of 2.58. Although it would be sufficient to use either of these z values, we interpolate halfway between them and assume that k equals 2.575. It follows that the interval [$\mu \pm 2.575\sigma$] contains 99 percent of the measurements in a normally distributed population with mean μ and standard deviation σ.

Example 5.5 Business Statistics Grades

LO5

Suppose that course grades in a recent business statistics course are normally distributed with mean $\mu = 68$ and standard deviation $\sigma = 10$. We will find a tolerance interval such that 99 percent of the test scores lie in the interval [$\mu \pm k\sigma$].

We just determined that the value of k that corresponds to a 99 percent tolerance interval is 2.575, so the 99 percent tolerance interval is given by [68 − 2.575(10), 68 + 2.575(10)], or [42.25, 93.75]. This tells us that 99 percent of the observations in a normally distributed population with a mean of 68 and a standard deviation of 10 would lie in that interval.

Whenever we use a normal table to find a z value corresponding to a particular normal curve area, we will use the **halfway interpolation** procedure illustrated in Example 5.3 and in the paragraph above Example 5.5 if the area we are looking for is exactly halfway between two areas in the table. Otherwise, as illustrated in Example 5.4, we will use the z value corresponding to the area in the table that is closest to the desired area.

Exercises for Section 5.3

CONCEPTS

5.16 List five important properties of the normal probability curve.

5.17 **a.** Explain what the mean, μ, tells us about a normal curve.
  b. Explain what the standard deviation, σ, tells us about a normal curve.

5.18 If the random variable x is normally distributed, what percentage of all possible observed values of x will be
  a. Within one standard deviation of the mean?
  b. Within two standard deviations of the mean?
  c. Within three standard deviations of the mean?

5.19 Explain how to compute the z value corresponding to a value of a normally distributed random variable. What does the z value tell us about the value of the random variable?

5.20 Explain how x relates to the mean μ if the z value corresponding to x
  a. Equals zero.
  b. Is positive.
  c. Is negative.

5.21 Why do we compute z values when using the normal table?

METHODS AND APPLICATIONS

5.22 In each case, sketch the two specified normal curves on the same set of axes:
   a. A normal curve with $\mu = 20$ and $\sigma = 3$, and a normal curve with $\mu = 20$ and $\sigma = 6$.
   b. A normal curve with $\mu = 20$ and $\sigma = 3$, and a normal curve with $\mu = 30$ and $\sigma = 3$.
   c. A normal curve with $\mu = 100$ and $\sigma = 10$, and a normal curve with $\mu = 200$ and $\sigma = 20$.

5.23 Let x be a normally distributed random variable with mean $\mu = 30$ and standard deviation $\sigma = 5$. Find the z value for each of the following observed values of x:
   a. $x = 25$.   **d.** $x = 40$.
   b. $x = 15$.   **e.** $x = 50$.
   c. $x = 30$.
   In each case, explain what the z value tells us about how the observed value of x compares to the mean, μ.

5.24 If the random variable z has a standard normal distribution, sketch and find each of the following probabilities:
   a. $P(0 \leq z \leq 1.5)$.   **f.** $P(-1 \leq z \leq 1)$.
   b. $P(z \geq 2)$.   **g.** $P(-2.5 \leq z \leq 0.5)$.
   c. $P(z \leq 1.5)$.   **h.** $P(1.5 \leq z \leq 2)$.
   d. $P(z \geq -1)$.   **i.** $P(-2 \leq z \leq -0.5)$.
   e. $P(z \leq -3)$.

5.25 Suppose that the random variable z has a standard normal distribution. Sketch each of the following z_α points, and use the normal table to find each z_α point.
   a. $z_{0.01}$.   **d.** $-z_{0.01}$.
   b. $z_{0.05}$.   **e.** $-z_{0.05}$.
   c. $z_{0.02}$.   **f.** $-z_{0.10}$.

5.26 Suppose that the random variable x is normally distributed with mean $\mu = 1,000$ and standard deviation $\sigma = 100$. Sketch and find each of the following probabilities:
   a. $P(1,000 \leq x \leq 1,200)$.   **e.** $P(x \leq 700)$.
   b. $P(x > 1,257)$.   **f.** $P(812 \leq x \leq 913)$.
   c. $P(x < 1,035)$.   **g.** $P(x > 891)$.
   d. $P(857 \leq x \leq 1,183)$.   **h.** $P(1,050 \leq x \leq 1,250)$.

5.27 Suppose that the random variable x is normally distributed with mean $\mu = 500$ and standard deviation $\sigma = 100$. For each of the following, use the normal table to find the needed value k. In each case, make a sketch.
   a. $P(x \geq k) = 0.025$.   **f.** $P(x > k) = 0.95$.
   b. $P(x \geq k) = 0.05$.   **g.** $P(x \leq k) = 0.975$.
   c. $P(x < k) = 0.025$.   **h.** $P(x \geq k) = 0.0228$.
   d. $P(x \leq k) = 0.015$.   **i.** $P(x > k) = 0.9772$.
   e. $P(x < k) = 0.985$.

5.28 Stanford–Binet IQ Test scores are normally distributed with a mean score of 100 and a standard deviation of 16.
   a. Sketch the distribution of Stanford–Binet IQ test scores.
   b. Write the equation that gives the z value corresponding to a Stanford–Binet IQ test score. Sketch the distribution of such z values.

   c. Find the probability that a randomly selected person has an IQ test score
      (1) Over 140.
      (2) Under 88.
      (3) Between 72 and 128.
      (4) Within 1.5 standard deviations of the mean.
   d. Suppose you take the Stanford–Binet IQ Test and receive a score of 136. What percentage of people would receive a score higher than yours?

5.29 Weekly demand at a grocery store for a brand of breakfast cereal is normally distributed with a mean of 800 boxes and a standard deviation of 75 boxes.
   a. What is the probability that weekly demand is
      (1) 959 boxes or less?
      (2) Greater than 1,004 boxes?
      (3) Less than 650 boxes or greater than 950 boxes?
   b. The store orders cereal from a distributor weekly. How many boxes should the store order for a week to have only a 2.5 percent chance of running short of this brand of cereal during the week?

5.30 The lifetimes of a particular brand of DVD player are normally distributed with a mean of eight years and a standard deviation of six months. Find each of the following probabilities, where x denotes the lifetime in years. In each case, sketch the probability.
   a. $P(7 \leq x \leq 9)$.   **e.** $P(x \leq 7)$.
   b. $P(8.5 \leq x \leq 9.5)$.   **f.** $P(x \geq 7)$.
   c. $P(6.5 \leq x \leq 7.5)$.   **g.** $P(x \leq 10)$.
   d. $P(x \geq 8)$.   **h.** $P(x > 10)$.

5.31 An investment broker reports that the yearly returns on common stocks are approximately normally distributed with a mean return of 12.4 percent and a standard deviation of 20.6 percent. The firm also reports that the yearly returns on tax-free municipal bonds are approximately normally distributed with a mean return of 5.2 percent and a standard deviation of 8.6 percent. Find the probability that a randomly selected
   a. Common stock will give a positive yearly return.
   b. Tax-free municipal bond will give a positive yearly return.
   c. Common stock will give more than a 10 percent return.
   d. Tax-free municipal bond will give more than a 10 percent return.
   e. Common stock will give a loss of at least 10 percent.
   f. Tax-free municipal bond will give a loss of at least 10 percent.

5.32 A tire company has developed a new type of steel-belted radial tire. Extensive testing indicates that the population of lifetimes obtained by all tires of this new type is normally distributed with a mean of 65,000 km and a standard deviation of 6,500 km. The company wishes to offer a guarantee providing a discount on a new set of tires if the original tires purchased do not exceed the lifetime stated in the guarantee. What should the guaranteed lifetime be if the tire company desires that no more than 2 percent of the tires will fail to meet the guaranteed lifetime?

5.33 Recall from Exercise 5.31 that yearly returns on common stocks are normally distributed with a mean of 12.4 percent and a standard deviation of 20.6 percent.

a. What percentage of yearly returns are at or below the 10th percentile of the distribution of yearly returns? What percentage are at or above the 10th percentile? Find the 10th percentile of the distribution of yearly returns.

b. Find the first quartile, Q_1, and the third quartile, Q_3, of the distribution of yearly returns.

5.34 Two students take a personality questionnaire known to have a normal distribution of scores. The students receive raw scores of 63 and 93, which correspond to z values (often called the standardized scores) of -1 and 1.5, respectively. Find the mean and standard deviation of the distribution of raw scores.

5.35 THE TRASH BAG CASE

Suppose that a population of measurements is normally distributed with mean μ and standard deviation σ.

a. Write an expression (involving μ and σ) for a tolerance interval containing 98 percent of all the population measurements.

b. Estimate a tolerance interval containing 98 percent of all the trash bag breaking strengths by using the fact that a random sample of 40 breaking strengths has a mean of $\bar{x} = 22.990$ and a standard deviation of $s = 0.7428$.

5.36 Consider the situation of Exercise 5.31.

a. Use the investment broker's report to estimate the maximum yearly return that might be obtained by investing in tax-free municipal bonds.

b. Find the probability that the yearly return obtained by investing in common stocks will be higher than the maximum yearly return that might be obtained by investing in tax-free municipal bonds.

5.37 Suppose that yearly dental care expenses for a family of four are normally distributed with a mean expense equal to $3,000 and a standard deviation of $500. An insurance company has decided to offer a dental insurance premium reduction if a policyholder's dental care expenses do not exceed a specified dollar amount. What dollar amount should be established if the insurance company wants families with the lowest 33 percent of yearly dental care expenses to be eligible for the premium reduction?

5.38 Suppose that the 33rd percentile of a normal distribution is equal to 656 and that the 97.5th percentile of this normal distribution is 896. Find the mean μ and the standard deviation σ of the normal distribution. Hint: Sketch these percentiles.

5.39 In the book *Advanced Managerial Accounting*, Magee discusses monitoring cost variances. A **cost variance** is the difference between a budgeted cost and an actual cost. Magee describes the following situation:

Michael Bitner has responsibility for control of two manufacturing processes. Every week he receives a cost variance report for each of the two processes, broken down by labor costs, materials costs, and so on. One of the two processes, which we'll call process A, involves a stable, easily controlled production process with little fluctuation in variances. Process B involves more random events: the equipment is more sensitive and prone to breakdown, the raw material prices fluctuate more, and so on.

"It seems like I'm spending more of my time with process B than with process A," says Michael Bitner. "Yet I know that the probability of an inefficiency developing and the expected costs of inefficiencies are the same for the two processes. It's just the magnitude of random fluctuations that differs between the two, as you can see in the information below.

"At present, I investigate variances if they exceed $2,500, regardless of whether it was process A or B. I suspect that such a policy is not the most efficient. I should probably set a higher limit for process B."

The means and standard deviations of the cost variances of processes A and B, when these processes are in control, are as follows:

	Process A	Process B
Mean Cost Variance (in Control)	$ 0	$ 0
Standard Deviation of Cost Variance (in Control)	$5,000	$10,000

Furthermore, the means and standard deviations of the cost variances of processes A and B, when these processes are out of control, are as follows:

	Process A	Process B
Mean Cost Variance (out of Control)	$7,500	$ 7,500
Standard Deviation of Cost Variance (out of Control)	$5,000	$10,000

a. Recall that the current policy is to investigate a cost variance if it exceeds $2,500 for either process. Assume that cost variances are normally distributed and that both process A and process B cost variances are in control. Find the probability that a cost variance for process A will be investigated. Find the probability that a cost variance for process B will be investigated. Which in-control process will be investigated more often?

b. Assume that cost variances are normally distributed and that both process A and process B cost variances are out of control. Find the probability that a cost variance for process A will be investigated. Find the probability that a cost variance for process B will be investigated. Which out-of-control process will be investigated more often?

c. If both processes A and B are almost always in control, which process will be investigated more often?

d. Suppose that we wish to reduce the probability that process B will be investigated (when it is in control) to 0.3085. What cost variance investigation policy should be used? That is, how large a cost variance should trigger an investigation? Using this new policy, what is the probability that an out-of-control cost variance for process B will be investigated?

5.40 Suppose that the masses of all residents who use an elevator in a high-rise condominium are approximately normal with mean $\mu = 80$ kg and standard deviation $\sigma = 20$ kg.

    a. What is the probability that a resident on the elevator will weigh less than 50 kg?

    b. Find a 95 percent tolerance interval for this population of residents.

5.41 Suppose that the grades of students taking an economics course are approximately normal with mean $\mu = 75$ and variance 400.

    a. What is the probability that a student will pass the course if a grade of at least 50 is needed?

b. What proportion of the class received an A, or scored between 80 and 89?

c. What minimum grade is needed to have scored in the 90th percentile of the class?

5.42 It has been determined that the heights of female toddlers at a local day care facility are approximately normal with a mean of 0.75 m and a standard deviation of 0.025 m.

    a. What percentage of toddlers are taller than 1 m?

    b. What percentage of toddlers are between 0.5 m and 1 m tall?

    c. Find a 95 percent tolerance interval for the female toddlers.

5.4 THE CUMULATIVE NORMAL TABLE

The cumulative normal table is a table of cumulative areas under the standard normal curve, and it is reproduced in Table 5.2. Specifically,

> The **cumulative normal table** gives, for many different values of z, the area under the standard normal curve at or below z.

LO6

Two such areas are shown in the figures to the right of Table 5.2—one with a negative z value and one with a positive z value. The values of z in the cumulative normal table range from -3.49 to 3.49 in increments of 0.01. As can be seen from Table 5.2, values of z accurate to the nearest tenth are given in the far left column (headed z) of the table. Further graduations to the nearest hundredth (0.00, 0.01, 0.02, . . . , 0.09) are given across the top of the table. The areas under the normal curve are given in the body of the table, accurate to four decimal places.

As an example, suppose that we wish to find the area under the standard normal curve at or below a z value of 1.00. This area is illustrated in Figure 5.22 on page 170. To find this area, we scan down the far left column of the table (starting at the top) until we find the value 1.0. We now scan across the row in the table corresponding to the z value 1.0 until we find the column corresponding to the heading 0.00. The desired area (which we have shaded red) is in the row corresponding to the z value 1.0 and in the column headed 0.00. This area, which equals 0.8413, is the probability that the random variable z is less than or equal to 1.00. That is, we have found that $P(z \le 1.00) = 0.8413$. As another example, the area under the standard normal curve at or below the z value 2.53 is found in the row corresponding to 2.5 and in the column corresponding to 0.03. We find that this area is 0.9943—that is, $P(z \le 2.53) = 0.9943$.

TABLE **5.2** Cumulative Areas under the Standard Normal Curve

z	0.00	0.01	0.02	0.03	0.04	0.05	0.06	0.07	0.08	0.09
−3.4	0.0003	0.0003	0.0003	0.0003	0.0003	0.0003	0.0003	0.0003	0.0003	0.0002
−3.3	0.0005	0.0005	0.0005	0.0004	0.0004	0.0004	0.0004	0.0004	0.0004	0.0003
−3.2	0.0007	0.0007	0.0006	0.0006	0.0006	0.0006	0.0006	0.0005	0.0005	0.0005
−3.1	0.0010	0.0009	0.0009	0.0009	0.0008	0.0008	0.0008	0.0008	0.0007	0.0007
−3.0	0.0013	0.0013	0.0013	0.0012	0.0012	0.0011	0.0011	0.0011	0.0010	0.0010
−2.9	0.0019	0.0018	0.0018	0.0017	0.0016	0.0016	0.0015	0.0015	0.0014	0.0014
−2.8	0.0026	0.0025	0.0024	0.0023	0.0023	0.0022	0.0021	0.0021	0.0020	0.0019
−2.7	0.0035	0.0034	0.0033	0.0032	0.0031	0.0030	0.0029	0.0028	0.0027	0.0026
−2.6	0.0047	0.0045	0.0044	0.0043	0.0041	0.0040	0.0039	0.0038	0.0037	0.0036
−2.5	0.0062	0.0060	0.0059	0.0057	0.0055	0.0054	0.0052	0.0051	0.0049	0.0048
−2.4	0.0082	0.0080	0.0078	0.0075	0.0073	0.0071	0.0069	0.0068	0.0066	0.0064
−2.3	0.0107	0.0104	0.0102	0.0099	0.0096	0.0094	0.0091	0.0089	0.0087	0.0084
−2.2	0.0139	0.0136	0.0132	0.0129	0.0125	0.0122	0.0119	0.0116	0.0113	0.0110

TABLE **5.2** (*Continued*)

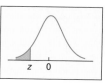

z	0.00	0.01	0.02	0.03	0.04	0.05	0.06	0.07	0.08	0.09
−2.1	0.0179	0.0174	0.0170	0.0166	0.0162	0.0158	0.0154	0.0150	0.0146	0.0143
−2.0	0.0228	0.0222	0.0217	0.0212	0.0207	0.0202	0.0197	0.0192	0.0188	0.0183
−1.9	0.0287	0.0281	0.0274	0.0268	0.0262	0.0256	0.0250	0.0244	0.0239	0.0233
−1.8	0.0359	0.0351	0.0344	0.0336	0.0329	0.0322	0.0314	0.0307	0.0301	0.0294
−1.7	0.0446	0.0436	0.0427	0.0418	0.0409	0.0401	0.0392	0.0384	0.0375	0.0367
−1.6	0.0548	0.0537	0.0526	0.0516	0.0505	0.0495	0.0485	0.0475	0.0465	0.0455
−1.5	0.0668	0.0655	0.0643	0.0630	0.0618	0.0606	0.0594	0.0582	0.0571	0.0559
−1.4	0.0808	0.0793	0.0778	0.0764	0.0749	0.0735	0.0721	0.0708	0.0694	0.0681
−1.3	0.0968	0.0951	0.0934	0.0918	0.0901	0.0885	0.0869	0.0853	0.0838	0.0823
−1.2	0.1151	0.1131	0.1112	0.1093	0.1075	0.1056	0.1038	0.1020	0.1003	0.0985
−1.1	0.1357	0.1335	0.1314	0.1292	0.1271	0.1251	0.1230	0.1210	0.1190	0.1170
−1.0	0.1587	0.1562	0.1539	0.1515	0.1492	0.1469	0.1446	0.1423	0.1401	0.1379
−0.9	0.1841	0.1814	0.1788	0.1762	0.1736	0.1711	0.1685	0.1660	0.1635	0.1611
−0.8	0.2119	0.2090	0.2061	0.2033	0.2005	0.1977	0.1949	0.1922	0.1894	0.1867
−0.7	0.2420	0.2389	0.2358	0.2327	0.2296	0.2266	0.2236	0.2206	0.2177	0.2148
−0.6	0.2743	0.2709	0.2676	0.2643	0.2611	0.2578	0.2546	0.2514	0.2483	0.2451
−0.5	0.3085	0.3050	0.3015	0.2981	0.2946	0.2912	0.2877	0.2843	0.2810	0.2776
−0.4	0.3446	0.3409	0.3372	0.3336	0.3300	0.3264	0.3228	0.3192	0.3156	0.3121
−0.3	0.3821	0.3783	0.3745	0.3707	0.3669	0.3632	0.3594	0.3557	0.3520	0.3483
−0.2	0.4207	0.4168	0.4129	0.4090	0.4052	0.4013	0.3974	0.3936	0.3897	0.3859
−0.1	0.4602	0.4562	0.4522	0.4483	0.4443	0.4404	0.4364	0.4325	0.4286	0.4247
−0.0	0.5000	0.4960	0.4920	0.4880	0.4840	0.4801	0.4761	0.4721	0.4681	0.4641
0.0	0.5000	0.5040	0.5080	0.5120	0.5160	0.5199	0.5239	0.5279	0.5319	0.5359
0.1	0.5398	0.5438	0.5478	0.5517	0.5557	0.5596	0.5636	0.5675	0.5714	0.5753
0.2	0.5793	0.5832	0.5871	0.5910	0.5948	0.5987	0.6026	0.6064	0.6103	0.6141
0.3	0.6179	0.6217	0.6255	0.6293	0.6331	0.6368	0.6406	0.6443	0.6480	0.6517
0.4	0.6554	0.6591	0.6628	0.6664	0.6700	0.6736	0.6772	0.6808	0.6844	0.6879
0.5	0.6915	0.6950	0.6985	0.7019	0.7054	0.7088	0.7123	0.7157	0.7190	0.7224
0.6	0.7257	0.7291	0.7324	0.7357	0.7389	0.7422	0.7454	0.7486	0.7517	0.7549
0.7	0.7580	0.7611	0.7642	0.7673	0.7704	0.7734	0.7764	0.7794	0.7823	0.7852
0.8	0.7881	0.7910	0.7939	0.7967	0.7995	0.8023	0.8051	0.8078	0.8106	0.8133
0.9	0.8159	0.8186	0.8212	0.8238	0.8264	0.8289	0.8315	0.8340	0.8365	0.8389
1.0	0.8413	0.8438	0.8461	0.8485	0.8508	0.8531	0.8554	0.8577	0.8599	0.8621
1.1	0.8643	0.8665	0.8686	0.8708	0.8729	0.8749	0.8770	0.8790	0.8810	0.8830
1.2	0.8849	0.8869	0.8888	0.8907	0.8925	0.8944	0.8962	0.8980	0.8997	0.9015
1.3	0.9032	0.9049	0.9066	0.9082	0.9099	0.9115	0.9131	0.9147	0.9162	0.9177
1.4	0.9192	0.9207	0.9222	0.9236	0.9251	0.9265	0.9279	0.9292	0.9306	0.9319
1.5	0.9332	0.9345	0.9357	0.9370	0.9382	0.9394	0.9406	0.9418	0.9429	0.9441
1.6	0.9452	0.9463	0.9474	0.9484	0.9495	0.9505	0.9515	0.9525	0.9535	0.9545
1.7	0.9554	0.9564	0.9573	0.9582	0.9591	0.9599	0.9608	0.9616	0.9625	0.9633
1.8	0.9641	0.9649	0.9656	0.9664	0.9671	0.9678	0.9686	0.9693	0.9699	0.9706
1.9	0.9713	0.9719	0.9726	0.9732	0.9738	0.9744	0.9750	0.9756	0.9761	0.9767
2.0	0.9772	0.9778	0.9783	0.9788	0.9793	0.9798	0.9803	0.9808	0.9812	0.9817
2.1	0.9821	0.9826	0.9830	0.9834	0.9838	0.9842	0.9846	0.9850	0.9854	0.9857
2.2	0.9861	0.9864	0.9868	0.9871	0.9875	0.9878	0.9881	0.9884	0.9887	0.9890
2.3	0.9893	0.9896	0.9898	0.9901	0.9904	0.9906	0.9909	0.9911	0.9913	0.9916
2.4	0.9918	0.9920	0.9922	0.9925	0.9927	0.9929	0.9931	0.9932	0.9934	0.9936
2.5	0.9938	0.9940	0.9941	0.9943	0.9945	0.9946	0.9948	0.9949	0.9951	0.9952
2.6	0.9953	0.9955	0.9956	0.9957	0.9959	0.9960	0.9961	0.9962	0.9963	0.9964
2.7	0.9965	0.9966	0.9967	0.9968	0.9969	0.9970	0.9971	0.9972	0.9973	0.9974
2.8	0.9974	0.9975	0.9976	0.9977	0.9977	0.9978	0.9979	0.9979	0.9980	0.9981
2.9	0.9981	0.9982	0.9982	0.9983	0.9984	0.9984	0.9985	0.9985	0.9986	0.9986
3.0	0.9987	0.9987	0.9987	0.9988	0.9988	0.9989	0.9989	0.9989	0.9990	0.9990
3.1	0.9990	0.9991	0.9991	0.9991	0.9992	0.9992	0.9992	0.9992	0.9993	0.9993
3.2	0.9993	0.9993	0.9994	0.9994	0.9994	0.9994	0.9994	0.9995	0.9995	0.9995
3.3	0.9995	0.9995	0.9995	0.9996	0.9996	0.9996	0.9996	0.9996	0.9996	0.9997
3.4	0.9997	0.9997	0.9997	0.9997	0.9997	0.9997	0.9997	0.9997	0.9997	0.9998

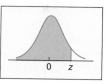

FIGURE **5.22**   Finding $P(z \leq 1)$

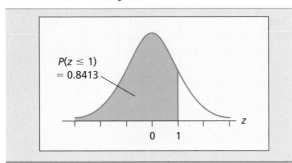

FIGURE **5.23**   Finding $P(z \geq 2)$

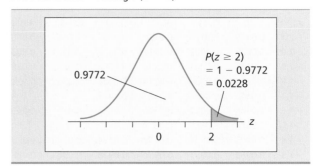

FIGURE **5.24**   Finding $P(z \leq -1)$ or $P(z \geq 1)$

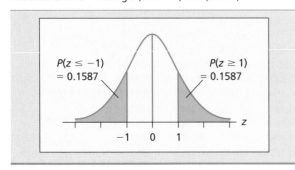

FIGURE **5.25**   Finding $P(-1 \leq z \leq 1)$

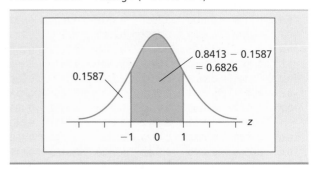

We now show how to use the cumulative normal table to find several other kinds of normal curve areas. First, suppose that we wish to find the area under the standard normal curve at or above a z value of 2—that is, we wish to find $P(z \geq 2)$. This area is illustrated in Figure 5.23 and is called a **right-hand tail area**. Since the total area under the normal curve equals 1, the area under the curve at or above 2 equals 1 minus the area under the curve at or below 2. That is, we find that $P(z \geq 2) = 1 - P(z \leq 2) = 1 - 0.9772 = 0.0228$.

Next suppose that we wish to find the area under the standard normal curve at or below a z value of -1. That is, we wish to find $P(z \leq -1)$. This area is illustrated in Figure 5.24 and is called a **left-hand tail area**. The needed area is found in the row of the cumulative normal table corresponding to -1 and in the column headed by 0.00. We find that $P(z \leq -1) = 0.1587$. Notice that the area under the standard normal curve at or below -1 is equal to the area under this curve at or above 1. This is true because of the symmetry of the normal curve. Therefore, $P(z \geq 1) = 0.1587$.

Finally, suppose that we wish to find the area under the standard normal curve between the z values of -1 and 1. This area is illustrated in Figure 5.25, and we can see that this area equals the area under the curve at or below 1 minus the area under the curve at or below -1. Referring to Table 5.2, we see that $P(-1 \leq z \leq 1) = P(z \leq 1) - P(z \leq -1) = 0.8413 - 0.1587 = 0.6826$.

Example 5.6   The Coffee Temperature Case

We will revisit the coffee temperature case and calculate $P(x < 67)$ or $P(x > 75)$ using the cumulative normal probability table. Recall that the sample mean was 71.2083 and the sample standard deviation was 2.9779. We use these values to estimate μ and σ, respectively. In order to compute the probability $P(x < 67 \text{ or } x > 75)$, we compute the z values

$$z = \frac{67 - 71.2083}{2.9779} = -1.41 \quad \text{and} \quad z = \frac{75 - 71.2083}{2.9779} = 1.27.$$

FIGURE **5.26**   Finding $P(x < 67 \text{ or } x > 75)$ in the Coffee Temperature Case

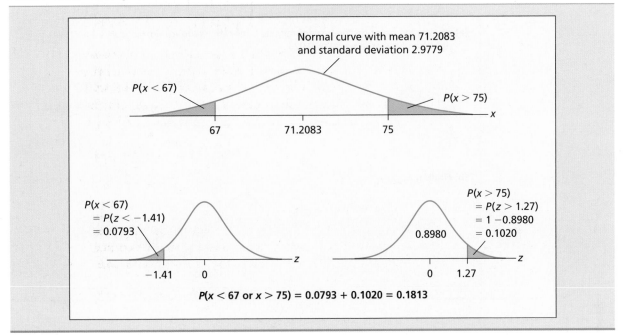

These z values tell us that 67°C is 1.41 standard deviations below the mean and that 75°C is 1.27 standard deviations above the mean. Because the events $\{x < 67\}$ and $\{x > 75\}$ are mutually exclusive, $P(x < 67 \text{ or } x > 75)$ is the sum of $P(x < 67)$ and $P(x > 75)$. As shown in Figure 5.26, $P(x < 67)$ equals $P(z < -1.41)$. We obtain this probability by finding the entry in Table 5.2 corresponding to the z value -1.41, which is 0.0793. As also shown in Figure 5.26, $P(x > 75)$ equals $P(z > 1.27)$. Finding the entry in Table 5.2 corresponding to the z value 1.27, we find that $P(z \leq 1.27) = 0.8980$. It follows that $P(z > 1.27)$ equals $1 - 0.8980 = 0.1020$. Finally, $P(x < 67 \text{ or } x > 75) = 0.0793 + 0.1020 = 0.1813$. This probability says that 18.13 percent of the coffee temperatures do not meet customer requirements. Therefore, if management believes that meeting this requirement is important, the coffee-making process must be improved.

In order to use many of the formulas given in later chapters, we must be able to find the z value so that the tail area to the right of z under the standard normal curve is a particular value. For instance, we might need to find the z value so that the tail area to the right of z under the standard normal curve is 0.025. This z value is denoted $z_{0.025}$, and we illustrate $z_{0.025}$ in Figure 5.27 on the next page. We refer to $z_{0.025}$ as *the point on the horizontal axis under the standard normal curve that gives a right-hand tail area equal to 0.025.* It is easy to use the cumulative normal table to find such a point. For instance, in order to find $z_{0.025}$, we note from Figure 5.27 that the area under the standard normal curve at or below $z_{0.025}$ equals 0.975. Remembering that areas under the standard normal curve at or below z are the four-digit numbers given in the body of Table 5.2, we scan the body of the table and find the area 0.9750. We have shaded this area in Table 5.2, and we note that the area 0.9750 is in the row corresponding to a z of 1.9 and in the column headed by 0.06. It follows that the z value corresponding to 0.9750 is 1.96. Because the z value 1.96 gives an area under the standard normal curve at or below z that equals 0.975, it also gives a right-hand tail area equal to 0.025. Therefore, $z_{0.025} = 1.96$.

FIGURE **5.27**   The Point $z_{0.025} = 1.96$

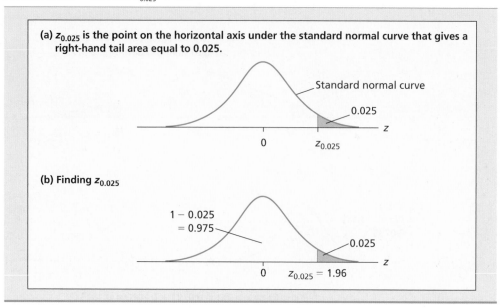

(a) $z_{0.025}$ is the point on the horizontal axis under the standard normal curve that gives a right-hand tail area equal to 0.025.

Standard normal curve

0.025

0   $z_{0.025}$ z

(b) Finding $z_{0.025}$

$1 - 0.025$
$= 0.975$

0.025

0   $z_{0.025} = 1.96$ z

Example 5.7 Finding a Tolerance Interval

Consider computing a tolerance interval $[\mu \pm k\sigma]$ that contains 99 percent of the measurements in a normally distributed population with mean μ and standard deviation σ. As illustrated in Figure 5.28, we must find the value k so that the area under the normal curve with mean μ and standard deviation σ between $(\mu - k\sigma)$ and $(\mu + k\sigma)$ is 0.99. As also shown in this figure, the area under this normal curve between μ and $(\mu + k\sigma)$ is equal to 0.495. Because the z value corresponding to a value of x tells us how many standard deviations x is from μ, the z value corresponding to $(\mu + k\sigma)$ is obviously k. It follows that k is the point on the horizontal axis under the standard normal curve so that the area under this curve at or below k equals 0.995 (see Figure 5.28). Looking for 0.995 in the body of the cumulative normal table (Table 5.2), we find that the values closest to 0.995 are 0.9949, which has a corresponding z value of 2.57, and 0.9951, which has a corresponding z value of 2.58. Although it would be sufficient to use either of these z values, we interpolate halfway between them and assume that k equals 2.575. It follows that the interval $[\mu \pm 2.575\sigma]$ contains 99 percent of the measurements in a normally distributed population with mean μ and standard deviation σ.

FIGURE **5.28**   Finding a Tolerance Interval $[\mu \pm k\sigma]$ That Contains 99 Percent of the Measurements in a Normally Distributed Population

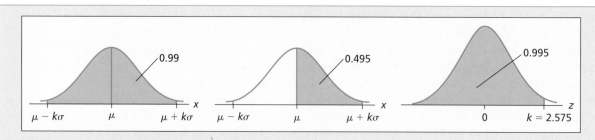

Exercises for Section 5.4

CONCEPTS

5.43 When looking up probabilities using a cumulative normal probability table, what does the probability given for each z value in the table represent?

5.44 When using a cumulative normal probability table, you need to make sure that the probability statement is in "less than" form. What do you need to do if the probability statement is some form of "greater than" statement?

5.45 What is $P(z < -10.7)$ (roughly)? What is $P(z > 16.1)$ (roughly)?

METHODS AND APPLICATIONS

5.46 Let z be a standard normal random variable. Find the following probabilities using the cumulative normal probability table.

  a. $P(0 \leq z \leq 1.5)$.   **f.** $P(-1 \leq z \leq 1)$.
  b. $P(z \geq 2)$.   **g.** $P(-2.5 \leq z \leq 0.5)$.
  c. $P(z \leq 1.5)$.   **h.** $P(1.5 \leq z \leq 2)$.
  d. $P(z \geq -1)$.   **i.** $P(-2 \leq z \leq -0.5)$.
  e. $P(z \geq 3)$.

5.47 Let z be a standard normal random variable. Find the following probabilities using the cumulative normal probability table.

  a. $P(0 \leq z \leq 0.5)$.   **f.** $P(-1.12 \leq z \leq 1)$.
  b. $P(z \geq 1.23)$.   **g.** $P(-2.21 \leq z \leq 0.53)$.
  c. $P(z \leq 1.45)$.   **h.** $P(1.57 \leq z \leq 2.18)$.
  d. $P(z \geq -1.06)$.   **i.** $P(-2.07 \leq z \leq -0.53)$.
  e. $P(z \geq 3.04)$.

5.48 Let x be a normally distributed random variable with a mean of 15 and a variance of 25. Find the following probabilities using the cumulative normal probability table.

  a. $P(15 \leq x \leq 20)$.   **f.** $P(10 \leq x \leq 20)$.
  b. $P(x \geq 20)$.   **g.** $P(20 \leq x \leq 25)$.
  c. $P(x \leq 17)$.   **h.** $P(13 \leq x \leq 20)$.
  d. $P(x \geq 10)$.   **i.** $P(5 \leq x \leq 10)$.
  e. $P(x \geq 30)$.

5.49 Let x be a normally distributed random variable with a mean of 12 and a standard deviation of 3. Find the following probabilities using the cumulative normal probability table.

  a. $P(15 \leq x \leq 20)$.   **f.** $P(10 \leq x \leq 20)$.
  b. $P(x \geq 20)$.   **g.** $P(20 \leq x \leq 25)$.
  c. $P(x \leq 17)$.   **h.** $P(13 \leq x \leq 20)$.
  d. $P(x \geq 10)$.   **i.** $P(5 \leq x \leq 10)$.
  e. $P(x \geq 30)$.

5.50 Suppose that the time to complete all parts of this particular question is approximately normally distributed with a mean of eight minutes and a standard deviation of one minute. Use the cumulative normal probability table to answer the following questions.

  a. What is the probability that a student will finish in less than five minutes?

  b. What is the probability that it will take more than 11 minutes?

  c. What is the probability that it will take between 5 and 11 minutes?

  d. What percentage of students will take more than six minutes but less than eight minutes to finish?

5.51 Let z be a standard normal random variable. What probabilities would you look for in the cumulative normal probability table to find

  a. $z_{0.05}$?   **e.** $-z_{0.05}$?
  b. $z_{0.025}$?   **f.** $-z_{0.025}$?
  c. $z_{0.005}$?   **g.** $-z_{0.005}$?
  d. $z_{0.01}$?

5.5 APPROXIMATING THE BINOMIAL DISTRIBUTION BY USING THE NORMAL DISTRIBUTION

Figure 5.29 on the next page illustrates several binomial distributions. In general, we can see that as n gets larger and as p gets closer to 0.5, the graph of a binomial distribution tends to have the symmetrical, bell-shaped appearance of a normal curve. It follows that under the conditions given in the following box, we can approximate the binomial distribution by using a normal distribution.

The Normal Approximation of the Binomial Distribution

Consider a binomial random variable x, where n is the number of trials performed and p is the probability of success on each trial. If n and p have values so that $np \geq 5$ and $n(1 - p) \geq 5$, then x is approximately normally distributed with mean $\mu = np$ and standard deviation $\sigma = \sqrt{npq}$, where $q = 1 - p$.

FIGURE **5.29**   Several Binomial Distributions

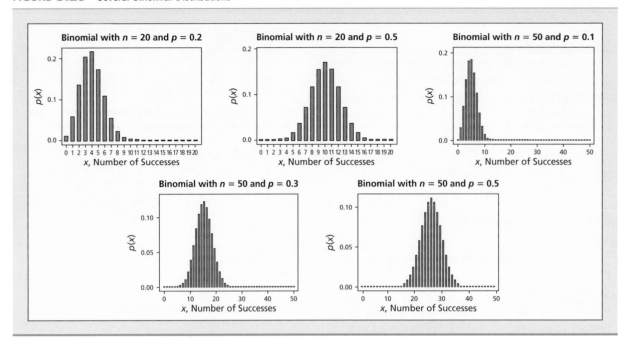

This approximation is often useful because binomial tables for large values of n are often unavailable. The conditions $np \geq 5$ and $n(1 - p) \geq 5$ must be met in order for the approximation to be appropriate. Note that if p is near 0 or near 1, then n must be larger for a good approximation, while if p is near 0.5, then n need not be as large.[1]

When we say that we can approximate the binomial distribution by using a normal distribution, we are saying that we can compute binomial probabilities by finding corresponding areas under a normal curve (rather than by using the binomial formula). One key component to this approximation is the **continuity correction**. In order to use the normal approximation to the binomial, we must apply a continuity correction. We illustrate how to do this in the following example.

V S

CHAPTER 4

Example 5.8   Flipping a Fair Coin

Consider an experiment where we flip a fair coin 50 times. We will let x represent the number of heads obtained in 50 flips of this fair coin. So x is a binomial random variable with $n = 50$ and $p = 0.5$. x has a mean of 25 and a standard deviation of $\sqrt{12.5}$. We will use the normal approximation to the binomial distribution to approximate $P(x = 23)$. We check to see that both np and $n(1 - p)$ are at least 5; they are both 25 in this case, so we can safely use the approximation. We need to apply the continuity correction in order to find the approximate probability. If we do not, our answer will be 0, which is clearly not a good approximation. How do we apply the continuity correction? We need to look at this problem in the discrete world first and try to rewrite the probability statement as a range of values. We can write $P(x = 23)$ as $P(22 < x < 24)$. We would get the same answer if we treated x as a binomial (discrete) random variable. Now that you see this written as $P(22 < x < 24)$, you might be tempted to just use the values 22 and 24 and standardize them to their equivalent z values. This is not right either. What we do is compromise. We meet in the middle on each side. That is, we use 22.5 and 23.5, and we approximate $P(x = 23)$ by calculating the normal probability curve area $P(22.5 < x < 23.5)$. This area is illustrated in Figure 5.30. Calculating the z values

$$z = \frac{22.5 - 25}{3.5355} = -0.71 \qquad \text{and} \qquad z = \frac{23.5 - 25}{3.5355} = -0.42,$$

---

[1]As an alternative to the rule that both np and $n(1 - p)$ must be at least 5, some statisticians suggest using the more conservative rule that both np and $n(1 - p)$ must be at least 10.

FIGURE **5.30** Approximating the Binomial Probability $P(x = 23)$ by Using the Normal Curve When $\mu = np = 25$ and $\sigma = \sqrt{npq} = 3.5355$

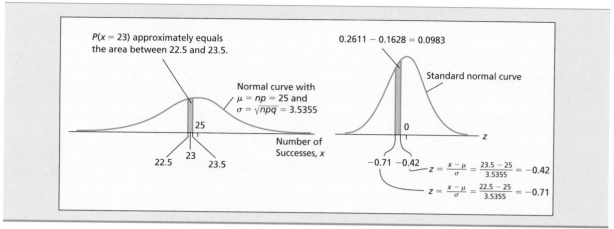

we find that $P(22.5 \leq x \leq 23.5) = P(-0.71 \leq z \leq -0.42) = 0.2611 - 0.1628 = 0.0983$. Therefore, we estimate that the binomial probability $P(x = 23)$ is 0.0983.

Making the proper continuity correction can sometimes be tricky. A good way to approach this is to list the numbers of successes that are included in the event for which the binomial probability is being calculated. Then assign the appropriate area under the normal curve to each number of successes in the list. Putting these areas together gives the normal curve area that must be calculated. For example, again consider the binomial random variable x with $n = 50$ and $p = 0.5$. If we wish to find $P(27 \leq x \leq 29)$, then the event $27 \leq x \leq 29$ includes 27, 28, and 29 successes. Because we assign the areas under the normal curve corresponding to the intervals [26.5, 27.5], [27.5, 28.5], and [28.5, 29.5] to the values 27, 28, and 29, respectively, then the area to be found under the normal curve is $P(26.5 \leq x \leq 29.5)$. Table 5.3 gives several other examples.

Example 5.9 The Wine Case

A wine maker is test-marketing a new bottle for one of its popular brands of Chardonnay. The new bottle will have a screwcap instead of a cork. The consumer will be able to enjoy a glass of Chardonnay and not have to worry about whether or not a corkscrew is handy. The screwcap design will mean that the bottles will have to be redesigned, but corkers will no longer be needed. It turns out that the screwcap will be slightly less expensive than having a cork. However, the new screwcap may alienate some customers. A company study has shown that its introduction

TABLE **5.3** Several Examples of the Continuity Correction ($n = 50$)

Binomial Probability	Numbers of Successes Included in Event	Normal Curve Area (with Continuity Correction)
$P(25 < x \leq 30)$	26, 27, 28, 29, 30	$P(25.5 \leq x \leq 30.5)$
$P(x \leq 27)$	0, 1, 2, ..., 26, 27	$P(x \leq 27.5)$
$P(x > 30)$	31, 32, 33, ..., 50	$P(x \geq 30.5)$
$P(27 < x < 31)$	28, 29, 30	$P(27.5 \leq x \leq 30.5)$

FIGURE **5.31** Approximating the Binomial Probability $P(x \leq 63)$ by Using the Normal Curve When $\mu = np = 100$ and $\sigma = \sqrt{npq} = 9.4868$

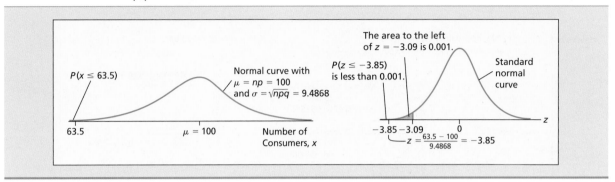

will increase profits if less than 10 percent of the Chardonnay's purchasers are lost. That is, if we let p represent the true proportion of current Chardonnay purchasers who would stop purchasing the wine if the new screwcap were used, profits will increase as long as p is less than 10 percent.

Suppose that (after trying the new bottle) 63 of 1,000 randomly selected purchasers say that they would stop buying the wine if the new bottle were used. To assess whether p is less than 0.10, we will assume for the sake of argument that p equals 0.10, and we will use the sample information to weigh the evidence against this assumption and in favour of the conclusion that p is less than 0.10. Let the random variable x represent the number of the 1,000 purchasers who say they would stop buying the wine. Assuming that p equals 0.10, then x is a binomial random variable with $n = 1,000$ and $p = 0.10$. Since the sample result of 63 is less than $\mu = np = 1,000(0.1) = 100$, the expected value of x when p equals 0.10, we have some evidence to contradict the assumption that p equals 0.10. To evaluate the strength of this evidence, we calculate the probability that *63 or fewer* of the 1,000 randomly selected purchasers would say that they would stop buying the wine if the new bottles were used if, in fact, p equals 0.10.

Since both $np = 1,000(0.10) = 100$ and $n(1 - p) = 1,000(1 - 0.10) = 900$ are at least 5, we can use the normal approximation to the binomial distribution to compute the needed probability. The appropriate normal curve has mean $\mu = np = 1,000(0.10) = 100$ and standard deviation $\sigma = \sqrt{npq} = \sqrt{1,000(0.10)(1 - 0.10)} = 9.4868$. In order to make the continuity correction, we note that the discrete value $x = 63$ is assigned the area under the normal curve corresponding to the interval from 62.5 to 63.5. It follows that the binomial probability $P(x \leq 63)$ is approximated by the normal probability $P(x \leq 63.5)$. This is illustrated in Figure 5.31. Calculating the z value for 63.5 to be

$$z = \frac{63.5 - 100}{9.4868} = -3.85,$$

we find that

$$P(x \leq 63.5) = P(z \leq -3.85).$$

Because 3.85 is larger than 3.09, which is the largest z value in the normal table, the area under the standard normal curve to the left of -3.85 is less than $0.5 - 0.499 = 0.001$. This says that if p equals 0.10, then in fewer than 1 in 1,000 of all possible random samples of 1,000 purchasers would 63 or fewer say they would stop buying the wine if the new bottles were used. Since it is very difficult to believe that such a small chance (a smaller than 1 in 1,000 chance) has occurred, we have very strong evidence that p does not equal 0.10 and is, in fact, less than 0.10. Therefore, it seems that using the new bottles will be profitable.

Exercises for Section 5.5

CONCEPTS

5.52 Explain why it might be convenient to approximate binomial probabilities by using areas under an appropriate normal curve.

5.53 Under what condition may we use the normal approximation to the binomial distribution?

5.54 Explain how we make a continuity correction. Why is a continuity correction needed when we approximate a binomial distribution by a normal distribution?

METHODS AND APPLICATIONS

5.55 Suppose that x has a binomial distribution with $n = 200$ and $p = 0.4$.
  a. Show that the normal approximation to the binomial distribution can appropriately be used to calculate probabilities about x.
  b. Make continuity corrections for each of the following, and then use the normal approximation to the binomial distribution to find each probability:
    (1) $P(x = 80)$.
    (2) $P(x \leq 95)$.
    (3) $P(x < 65)$.
    (4) $P(x \geq 100)$.
    (5) $P(x > 100)$.

5.56 Repeat Exercise 5.55 with $n = 200$ and $p = 0.5$.

5.57 An advertising agency conducted an ad campaign aimed at making consumers in a Western province aware of a new product. Upon completion of the campaign, the agency claimed that 20 percent of consumers in the province had become aware of the product. The product's distributor surveyed 1,000 consumers in the province and found that 150 were aware of the product.
  a. Assuming that the ad agency's claim is true:
    (1) Verify that you may use the normal approximation to the binomial.
    (2) Calculate the mean, μ, and the standard deviation, σ, you should use in the normal approximation.
    (3) Find the probability that 150 or fewer consumers in a random sample of 1,000 consumers would be aware of the product.
  b. Should the distributor believe the ad agency's claim? Explain.

5.58 **THE MARKETING ETHICS CASE**
Recall that in Example 2.11 (page 64) we found that of the 205 randomly selected marketing researchers who participated in the survey, 117 said they disapprove of the actions taken in the ultraviolet ink scenario. Suppose that before the survey was taken, a marketing manager claimed that at least 65 percent of all marketing researchers would disapprove of that scenario.
  a. Assuming that the manager's claim is correct, calculate the probability that 117 or fewer of 205 randomly selected marketing researchers would disapprove of the scenario. Use the normal approximation to the binomial.
  b. Based on your result of part a, do you believe the marketing manager's claim? Explain.

5.59 A department store will place a sale item in a special display for a one-day sale. Previous experience suggests that 20 percent of all customers who pass such a special display will purchase the item. If 2,000 customers will pass the display on the day of the sale, and if a one-item-per-customer limit is placed on the sale item, how many units of the sale item should the store stock in order to have at most a 1 percent chance of running short of the item on the day of the sale? Assume here that customers make independent purchase decisions.

5.60 **THE ELECTRONIC ARTICLE SURVEILLANCE CASE**
Recall that in Example 2.12 (page 65) we found that based on a survey of 250 consumers, 40 said that if they were to set off an EAS alarm because store personnel failed to deactivate merchandise leaving the store, then they would never shop at that store again. A company marketing the alarm system claimed that no more than 5 percent of all consumers would say that they would never shop at that store again if they were subjected to a false alarm.
  a. Assuming that the company's claim is valid, use the normal approximation to the binomial distribution to calculate the probability that at least 40 of the 250 randomly selected consumers would say that they would never shop at that store again if they were subjected to a false alarm.
  b. Do you believe the company's claim based on your answer to part a? Explain.

5.6 THE EXPONENTIAL DISTRIBUTION

Suppose that the number of times that a particular event occurs over an interval of time or space has a Poisson distribution. Furthermore, consider an arbitrary time or space unit (for example, minute, week, centimetre, hectare), and let x denote the number of time or space units between successive occurrences of the event. Then it can be shown that x is described by an **exponential distribution** with parameter λ. Here λ is the mean number of events that occur per time or space unit. Furthermore, the mean value of x can be proven to be $1/\lambda$.

FIGURE **5.32**   A Graph of the Exponential Distribution $f(x) = \lambda e^{-\lambda x}$

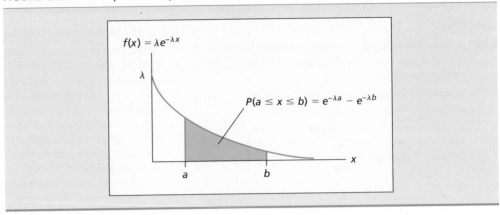

In words, $1/\lambda$ is *the mean number of time or space units between successive occurrences of the event*. In general, we can describe the exponential distribution as follows:

The Exponential Distribution

If λ is a positive number, then the equation describing the exponential distribution is

$$f(x) = \begin{cases} \lambda e^{-\lambda x} & \text{for } x \geq 0, \\ 0 & \text{otherwise.} \end{cases}$$

Using this probability curve, it can be shown that

$$P(a \leq x \leq b) = e^{-\lambda a} - e^{-\lambda b}.$$

In particular, since $e^0 = 1$ and $e^{-\infty} = 0$, this implies that

$$P(x \leq c) = 1 - e^{-\lambda c} \text{ and } P(x \geq c) = e^{-\lambda c}.$$

Furthermore, the mean and the standard deviation of the population of all possible observed values of a random variable x that has an exponential distribution are

$$\mu_x = \frac{1}{\lambda} \quad \text{and} \quad \sigma_x = \frac{1}{\lambda}.$$

The graph of the equation describing the exponential distribution and the probability $P(a \leq x \leq b)$, where x is described by this exponential distribution, is illustrated in Figure 5.32.

We illustrate the use of the exponential distribution in the following examples.

Example 5.10   Cell Phone Batteries

Suppose that the time to failure of one brand of cell phone battery is exponentially distributed with a mean of 40,000 hours. That is, on average, after 40,000 hours of use, the battery can no longer be charged and has to be replaced. The company that manufactures these batteries, which have a 1,000-hour guarantee, has a device that can measure hours of usage. If a customer's battery is deemed unusable before 1,000 hours, then the company will replace the battery free of charge. The equation of the exponential distribution of x is $f(x) = \lambda e^{-\lambda x} = (1/40,000)e^{-x/40,000}$ in this case. This distribution has a mean of 40,000, as noted before. Suppose we wanted to find the proportion of customers who would have their batteries replaced free of charge. We would need to determine $P(x < 1,000)$. In this case,

$$P(x < 1,000) = 1 - e^{-\frac{1,000}{40,000}} = 1 - e^{-\frac{1}{40}} = 0.0247.$$

Example 5.11 Hospital Emergency Room Arrivals

Suppose that the number of people who arrive at a hospital emergency room during a given time period has a Poisson distribution. It follows that the time, x, between successive arrivals of people to the emergency room has an exponential distribution. Furthermore, historical records indicate that the mean time between successive arrivals of people to the emergency room is seven minutes. Therefore, $\mu_x = 1/\lambda = 7$, which implies that $\lambda = 1/7 = 0.14286$. Noting that $\sigma_x = 1/\lambda = 7$, it follows that

$$\mu_x - \sigma_x = 7 - 7 = 0 \quad \text{and} \quad \mu_x + \sigma_x = 7 + 7 = 14.$$

Therefore, the probability that the time between successive arrivals of people to the emergency room will be within (plus or minus) one standard deviation of the mean interarrival time is

$$P(0 \le x \le 14) = e^{-\lambda a} - e^{-\lambda b}$$
$$= e^{-(0.14286)(0)} - e^{-(0.14286)(14)}$$
$$= 1 - 0.1353$$
$$= 0.8647.$$

Example 5.12 Useful Life of an Electronic Component

Suppose that an electronic component in a computer is known to have a useful life represented by an exponential distribution with a rate of 10^{-5} $(1/100,000)$ failures per hour. Given that the component is still functioning properly at 200,000 hours, what is the probability that it will survive to 250,000 hours? We will use the exponential distribution to determine a conditional probability. If we let x represent the time until failure of the electronic component, with a rate parameter $\lambda = 10^{-5}$, then the probability distribution function of x can be written as $f(x) = 10^{-5}e^{-10^{-5}x}$. We want to find $P(x > 250,000 | x > 200,000)$:

$$P(x > 250,000 | x > 200,000) = \frac{P(x > 200,000 \cap x > 250,000)}{P(x > 200,000)}$$

$$= \frac{P(x > 250,000)}{P(x > 200,000)} = \frac{e^{-\frac{250,000}{100,000}}}{e^{-\frac{200,000}{100,000}}} = e^{-\frac{50,000}{100,000}} = 0.6065.$$

It is interesting to note that this is the same as $P(x > 50,000)$ for the random variable x. It is like the component forgot that it had already survived 200,000 hours and just wanted to survive at least 50,000 hours. This example illustrates a property of the exponential distribution referred to as the **memoryless property**.

To conclude this section, we note that the exponential and related Poisson distributions are useful in analyzing waiting lines, or **queues**. In general, **queueing theory** attempts to determine the number of servers (for example, doctors in an emergency room) that strikes an optimal balance between the time customers wait for service and the cost of providing the service. The reader is referred to any textbook on management science or operations research for a discussion of queueing theory.

Exercises for Section 5.6

CONCEPTS

5.61 Give two examples of situations in which the exponential distribution might appropriately be used. In each case, define the random variable that has the exponential distribution.

5.62 State the formula for the exponential probability curve. Define each symbol in the formula.

5.63 Explain the relationship between the Poisson and exponential distributions.

METHODS AND APPLICATIONS

5.64 Suppose that the random variable x has an exponential distribution with $\lambda = 2$.
  a. Write the formula for the exponential probability curve of x. What are the possible values of x?
  b. Sketch the probability curve.
  c. Find $P(x \le 1)$.
  d. Find $P(0.25 \le x \le 1)$.
  e. Find $P(x \ge 2)$.
  f. Calculate the mean, μ_x, the variance, σ_x^2, and the standard deviation, σ_x, of the exponential distribution of x.
  g. Find the probability that x will be in the interval $[\mu_x \pm 2\sigma_x]$.

5.65 Repeat Exercise 5.64 with $\lambda = 3$.

5.66 Recall in Exercise 4.35 (page 141) that the number of customer arrivals at a coffee shop's drive-up window in a 15-minute period is Poisson distributed with a mean of seven customer arrivals per 15-minute period. Define the random variable x to be the time (in minutes) between successive customer arrivals at the drive-up window.
  a. Write the formula for the exponential probability curve of x.
  b. Sketch the probability curve of x.
  c. Find the probability that the time between arrivals is
    (1) Between one and two minutes.
    (2) Less than one minute.
    (3) More than three minutes.
    (4) Between 0.5 and 3.5 minutes.
  d. Calculate μ_x, σ_x^2, and σ_x.
  e. Find the probability that the time between arrivals falls within one standard deviation of the mean; within two standard deviations of the mean.

5.67 The length of a particular telemarketing phone call, x, has an exponential distribution with mean equal to 1.5 minutes.
  a. Write the formula for the exponential probability curve of x.
  b. Sketch the probability curve of x.
  c. Find the probability that the length of a randomly selected call will be
    (1) No more than three minutes.
    (2) Between one and two minutes.
    (3) More than four minutes.
    (4) Less than 30 seconds.

5.68 The maintenance department in a factory claims that the number of breakdowns of a particular machine follows a Poisson distribution with a mean of two breakdowns every 500 hours. Let x denote the time (in hours) between successive breakdowns.
  a. Find λ and μ_x.
  b. Write the formula for the exponential probability curve of x.
  c. Sketch the probability curve.
  d. Assuming that the maintenance department's claim is true, find the probability that the time between successive breakdowns is at most five hours.
  e. Assuming that the maintenance department's claim is true, find the probability that the time between successive breakdowns is between 100 and 300 hours.
  f. Suppose that the machine breaks down five hours after its most recent breakdown. Based on your answer to part d, do you believe the maintenance department's claim? Explain.

5.69 Suppose that the number of accidents occurring in an industrial plant is described by a Poisson distribution with an average of one accident per month. Let x denote the time (in months) between successive accidents.
  a. Find the probability that the time between successive accidents is
    (1) More than two months.
    (2) Between one and two months.
    (3) Less than one week (1/4 of a month).
  b. Suppose that an accident occurs less than one week after the plant's most recent accident. Would you consider this event unusual enough to warrant special investigation? Explain.

CHAPTER SUMMARY

In this chapter, we discussed **continuous probability distributions**. We began by learning that a continuous probability distribution is described by a continuous probability curve and that in this context probabilities are areas under the probability curve. We next studied several important continuous probability distributions—the **uniform distribution**, the **normal distribution**, and the **exponential distribution**. In particular, we concentrated on the normal distribution, which is the most important continuous probability distribution. We learned about the properties of the normal curve, and we saw how to use a **normal table** to find various areas under a normal curve. We also saw that the normal curve can be employed to approximate binomial probabilities, and we demonstrated how we can use a normal curve probability to make a statistical inference.

GLOSSARY OF TERMS

continuous probability distribution (or probability curve): A curve that is defined so that the probability that a random variable will be in a specified interval of numbers is the area under the curve corresponding to the interval. (page 148)

exponential probability distribution: A probability distribution that describes the time or space between successive occurrences of an event when the number of times the event occurs over an interval of time or space is described by a Poisson distribution. (pages 177–178)

normal probability distribution: The most important continuous probability distribution. Its probability curve is the bell-shaped normal curve. (page 152)

normal table: A table in which we can look up areas under the standard normal curve. (pages 154–156, 168–169)

queueing theory: A methodology that attempts to determine the number of servers that strikes an optimal balance between the

time customers wait for service and the cost of providing the service. (page 179)

standard normal distribution (or curve): A normal distribution (or curve) with mean 0 and standard deviation 1. (page 155)

uniform distribution: A continuous probability distribution with a rectangular shape that says that the probability is distributed evenly (or uniformly) over an interval of numbers. (page 149)

z_α point: The point on the horizontal axis under the standard normal curve that gives a right-hand tail area equal to α. (page 161)

$-z_\alpha$ point: The point on the horizontal axis under the standard normal curve that gives a left-hand tail area equal to α. (page 163)

z value: A value that tells us the number of standard deviations that a value x is from the mean of a normal curve. If the z value is positive, then x is above the mean. If the z value is negative, then x is below the mean. (page 154)

IMPORTANT FORMULAS

The uniform probability curve: page 149

Mean and standard deviation of a uniform distribution: page 149

The normal probability curve: page 152

z values: page 154

Normal approximation to the binomial distribution: page 173

The exponential probability curve: page 178

Mean and standard deviation of an exponential distribution: page 178

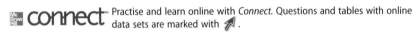 **Connect**™ Practise and learn online with *Connect*. Questions and tables with online data sets are marked with 🡥 .

SUPPLEMENTARY EXERCISES

5.70 In a bottle-filling process, the amount of drink injected into 500-mL bottles is normally distributed with a mean of 500 mL and a standard deviation of 0.625 mL. Bottles containing less than 498.5 mL do not meet the bottler's quality standard. What percentage of filled bottles do not meet the standard?

5.71 A certain school requires an IQ of at least 80 for admittance.
   a. If IQ test scores are normally distributed with mean 100 and standard deviation 16, what percentage of people would qualify for admittance to the school?
   b. If the public school wishes 95 percent of all children to qualify for admittance, what minimum IQ test score should be required for admittance?

5.72 The amount of sales tax paid on a purchase is rounded to the nearest cent. Assume that the round-off error is uniformly distributed in the interval −0.5 cents to 0.5 cents.
   a. Write the formula for the probability curve describing the round-off error.
   b. Graph the probability curve describing the round-off error.
   c. What is the probability that the round-off error exceeds 0.3 cents or is less than −0.3 cents?
   d. What is the probability that the round-off error exceeds 0.1 cents or is less than −0.1 cents?
   e. Find the mean and the standard deviation of the round-off error.
   f. Find the probability that the round-off error will be within one standard deviation of the mean.

5.73 A **consensus forecast** is the average of a large number of individual analysts' forecasts. Suppose the individual forecasts for a particular interest rate are normally distributed with a mean of 5.0 percent and a standard deviation of 1.2 percent. A single analyst is randomly selected. Find the probability that the analyst's forecast is
   a. At least 3.5 percent.
   b. At most 6 percent.
   c. Between 3.5 percent and 6 percent.

5.74 Recall from Exercise 5.73 that individual forecasts of a particular interest rate are normally distributed with a mean of 5 percent and a standard deviation of 1.2 percent.
   a. What percentage of individual forecasts are at or below the 10th percentile of the distribution of forecasts? What percentage are at or above the 10th percentile? Find the 10th percentile of the distribution of individual forecasts.
   b. Find the first quartile, Q_1, and the third quartile, Q_3, of the distribution of individual forecasts.

5.75 The scores on the entrance exam at a well-known, exclusive private school are normally distributed with a mean score of 200 and a standard deviation equal to 50. At what value should the lowest passing score be set if the school wishes only 2.5 percent of those taking the test to pass?

5.76 A machine is used to cut a metal automobile part to its desired length. The machine can be set so that the mean length of the part will be any value that is desired.

The standard deviation of the lengths always runs at 0.02 cm. Where should the mean be set if we want only 0.4 percent of the parts cut by the machine to be shorter than 15 cm long? Assume that the lengths of the parts are normally distributed.

5.77   A motel accepts 325 reservations for 300 rooms on July 1, expecting 10 percent no-shows on average from past records. Use the normal approximation to the binomial to find the probability that all guests who arrive on July 1 will receive a room.

5.78   Suppose a software company finds that the number of errors in its software per 1,000 lines of code is described by a Poisson distribution. Furthermore, it is found that there is an average of four errors per 1,000 lines of code. Let x denote the number of lines of code between successive errors.

    a.   Find the probability that there will be at least 400 lines of code between successive errors in the company's software.

    b.   Find the probability that there will be no more than 100 lines of code between successive errors in the company's software.

5.79   **THE INVESTMENT CASE**

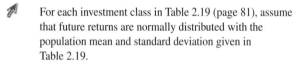

For each investment class in Table 2.19 (page 81), assume that future returns are normally distributed with the population mean and standard deviation given in Table 2.19.

    a.   For each investment class, find the probability of a return that is less than zero (that is, find the probability of a loss). Is your answer reasonable for all investment classes? Explain.

    b.   For each investment class, find the probability of a return that is

        (1)   Greater than 5 percent.

        (2)   Greater than 10 percent.

        (3)   Greater than 20 percent.

        (4)   Greater than 50 percent.

    c.   For which investment classes is the probability of a return greater than 50 percent essentially zero? For which investment classes is the probability of such a return greater than 1 percent? greater than 5 percent?

    d.   For which investment classes is the probability of a loss essentially zero? For which investment classes is the probability of a loss greater than 1 percent? greater than 10 percent? greater than 20 percent?

5.80   The daily water consumption for an Ontario community is normally distributed with a mean consumption of 800,000 L and a standard deviation of 80,000 L. The community water system will experience a noticeable drop in water pressure when the daily water consumption exceeds 984,000 L. What is the probability of experiencing such a drop in water pressure?

5.81   Suppose the times required for a cable company to fix cable problems in its customers' homes are uniformly distributed between 10 minutes and 25 minutes. What is the probability that a randomly selected cable repair visit will take at least 15 minutes?

5.82   Suppose the waiting time to get food after placing an order at a fast-food restaurant is exponentially distributed with a mean of 60 seconds. If a randomly selected customer orders food at the restaurant, what is the probability that the customer will wait at least

    a.   One minute, 30 seconds?

    b.   Two minutes?

5.83   Net interest margin—often referred to as spread—is the difference between the rate banks pay on deposits and the rate they charge for loans. Suppose that the net interest margins for all Canadian banks are normally distributed with a mean of 4.15 percent and a standard deviation of 0.5 percent.

    a.   Find the probability that a randomly selected bank will have a net interest margin that exceeds 5.40 percent.

    b.   Find the probability that a randomly selected bank will have a net interest margin less than 4.40 percent.

    c.   A bank wants its net interest margin to be less than the net interest margins of 95 percent of all Canadian banks. Where should the bank's net interest margin be set?

5.84   In an article in the November 11, 1991, issue of *Advertising Age*, Giges studies global spending patterns. Giges presents data concerning the percentage of adults in various countries who have purchased various consumer items (such as soft drinks, athletic footwear, blue jeans, beer) in the past three months.

    a.   Suppose we wish to justify the claim that less than 50 percent of adults in Germany have purchased blue jeans in the past three months. The survey reported by Giges found that 45 percent of the respondents in Germany had purchased blue jeans in the past three months.[2]

        Assume that a random sample of 400 German adults was selected, and let p be the proportion of all German adults who have purchased blue jeans in the past three months. If we assume that $p = 0.5$, use the normal approximation to the binomial distribution to calculate the probability that 45 percent or fewer of 400 randomly selected German adults would have purchased blue jeans in the past three months. Note: Because 45 percent of 400 is 180, you should calculate the probability that 180 or fewer of 400 randomly selected German adults would have purchased blue jeans in the past three months.

    b.   Based on the probability you computed in part a, would you conclude that p really is less than 0.5? That is, would you conclude that less than 50 percent of adults in Germany have purchased blue jeans in the past three months? Explain.

5.85   Assume that the ages for first marriages are normally distributed with a mean of 26 years and a standard deviation of 4 years. What is the probability that a person getting married for the first time is in their twenties?

---

[2]Source: "Global spending patterns emerge," by N. Giges, *Advertising Age,* November 11, 1991, p. 64.

CHAPTER **6**
Sampling Distributions

You may wonder why sampling is necessary or even practical. A statistician might be hired to find answers to questions concerning populations, such as the spending habits of people aged 18 to 25, the average income level of women aged 25 to 34, the average age of marriage in Canada, and even the potential voting habits of Canadians. Intuitively, if you wanted this information, you would just speak to the entire population. Most times this is not possible due to lack of time or money. Instead, a statistician will often sample from that population and use the information from that sample to make an inference about the population.

Suppose you have a summer job as a beer taster, and the company that you work for wants to know if a new beer they are brewing is appealing or not. A vat of 1,000 L is produced. Suppose you are on a panel of ten independent beer tasters. The panel of tasters can do one of two things. They can each taste a sample of the beer, or they can drink all of it. Some of you may not see a problem with the second option, but it is not necessary. There is no reason not to believe that all of the beer from the same vat is the same. There might be slight variations due to material settling on the bottom or floating to the top, but we will assume that the beer is relatively uniform throughout. A sample from this population (the vat of beer) is all that is needed to get an idea of how the entire batch tastes.

Generally speaking, this is the basis for inferential statistics. Statisticians take random samples from populations of interest in order to make inferences about the populations. Estimates are obtained from the samples. Confidence intervals are constructed and hypotheses are tested based on the sample information. Confidence intervals and hypothesis tests will be discussed a little later on in the text. In order to help explain these sampling distributions, we will revisit the wine case:

6.1 THE SAMPLING DISTRIBUTION OF THE SAMPLE MEAN

LO1

Suppose that we are about to randomly select a sample of n measurements from a population of measurements with mean μ and standard deviation σ. *Before* we actually select the sample, we might potentially obtain many different samples of n measurements. Because different samples generally have different sample means, we might potentially obtain many different sample means. It follows that *before we draw the sample, the sample mean $\bar{x}$ is a random variable.*

LO2

The **sampling distribution of the sample mean $\bar{x}$** is the probability distribution of the population of all possible sample means obtained from samples of size n.

Example 6.1 One Punch or Two?

You have been selected from the audience to play in a game show called the Punch Game. Here is how it works:

1   The game board has holes numbered 1 to 6. Inside each hole is a slip of paper with the number 10, 20, 30, 40, 50, or 60 on it.

2   You have the option of punching just one hole and collecting the prize amount (in $1,000s), or you can punch two holes and collect the average of the values (in $1,000s).

How many holes should you punch? Which option is riskier? To help answer these questions, consider the population of prize amounts. They are given (in $1,000s) in Table 6.1, and a relative frequency histogram describing the population of the six prize amounts is given in Figure 6.1(a). The mean and standard deviation (in $1,000s) of this population are calculated to be 35 and 17.078, respectively. Now, consider randomly selecting a sample of size $n = 2$, without replacement, from this population. Table 6.2(a) lists the 15 distinct samples of size $n = 2$ from this population of six cash prizes, and the sample mean for each sample.

TABLE **6.1**   A Relative Frequency Distribution Describing the Population of Six Individual Cash Prizes (in $1,000s)

Prize	Amount (in $1,000s)	Frequency	Relative Frequency
1	10	1	1/6
2	20	1	1/6
3	30	1	1/6
4	40	1	1/6
5	50	1	1/6
6	60	1	1/6

FIGURE 6.1 A Comparison of Individual Prize Amounts and Sample Means

(a) A relative frequency histogram describing the population of six individual prize amounts

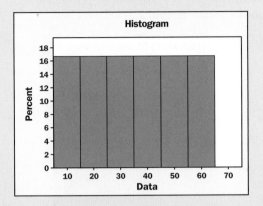

(b) A relative frequency histogram describing the population of 15 sample means

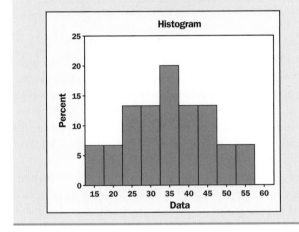

TABLE 6.2 The Population of Sample Means

(a) The population of the 15 samples of $n = 2$ prize amounts and corresponding sample means

Sample	$n = 2$ Returns in Sample		Sample Mean
1	10	20	15
2	10	30	20
3	10	40	25
4	10	50	30
5	10	60	35
6	20	30	25
7	20	40	30
8	20	50	35
9	20	60	40
10	30	40	35
11	30	50	40
12	30	60	45
13	40	50	45
14	40	60	50
15	50	60	55

(b) A relative frequency distribution describing the population of 15 sample mean amounts

Sample Mean	Frequency	Relative Frequency
15	1	1/15
20	1	1/15
25	2	2/15
30	2	2/15
35	3	3/15
40	2	2/15
45	2	2/15
50	1	1/15
55	1	1/15

(Note that each sample is specified according to the two prizes contained in the sample and that the order of selection does not matter.) To get an idea of what the sampling distribution of the sample means looks like, we can plot the relative frequency histogram of the sample means using the information in Table 6.2(b). The histogram is shown in Figure 6.1(b). If we compare Figure 6.1(a) and (b), we notice that they are both centred around a mean of 35, but the histogram of the sample means in Figure 6.1(b) is more *bell-shaped* and *less spread out* than the histogram of the individual prizes in Figure 6.1(a). So, what should you do?

If you punch only one hole, your prize amounts range from $10,000 to $60,000, with each amount being equally likely. If you punch two holes, your prize amounts (the sample means) range from $15,000 to $55,000, but now each payout is not equally likely. By punching two holes instead of one, you are reducing the variability of the prize amounts, thus reducing your risk. You are guaranteed to receive at least $15,000 and have a probability of 13/15 of receiving at least $25,000. If you punch one hole, you are only guaranteed $10,000 and have a 10/15, or 2/3, chance of winning at least $25,000. On the other hand, punching two holes gives you a probability of 2/15 of winning a prize of at least $50,000, and if you only punch one hole, you have a 2/6, or 1/3, chance of obtaining a prize of at least $50,000. So, if you are willing to take the risk, then you should punch only one hole. If you are more conservative (like most of us), then you will elect to punch two holes.

FIGURE **6.2** Monthly Returns of the TSX from 1956 to 2006: A Comparison of Monthly Stock Returns and Sample Mean Returns

(a) The relative frequency histogram describing the population of monthly stock returns from Jan. 1956 to Dec. 2006

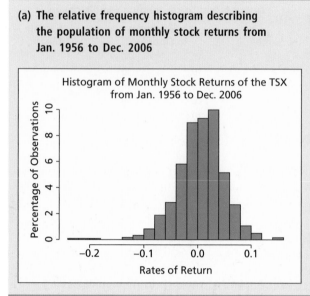

(b) A relative frequency histogram of 1,000,000 samples of size $n = 20$ from the population of monthly stock returns

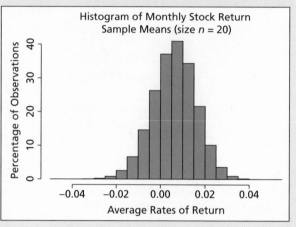

Most of us will never get an opportunity like the one we just described, but it does highlight a very important element in the world of investing. It is important to diversify. Generally speaking, when you diversify your portfolio, you reduce your risk. Some of your stocks will go up when others are going down and some will go up and down faster than others. This is the nature of investing. When you reduce the volatility of your portfolio, you reduce the risk. Let us apply the principles of this example to the monthly returns of the TSX over a 50-year period.

In general, there are several relationships between (1) a population of individual measurements and (2) the population of all possible sample means based on all samples of size n that can be randomly selected from the population of individual measurements. Over this time, as you can imagine, the TSX has experienced some volatility. There were some very good months, a lot of average months, and a few very bad months. Figure 6.2(a) shows the relative frequency histogram of the monthly percentage returns for the 50-year period ended December 2006. The mean and standard deviation of the monthly returns are 0.624 percent and 4.42 percent, respectively.

Thus far we have considered a game show example and a stock return example. Together, these examples illustrate several important facts about randomly selecting a sample of n individual measurements from a population of individual measurements with mean μ and standard deviation σ. Specifically, the following can be shown:

1 **If the population of individual measurements is normally distributed, then the population of all possible sample means is also normally distributed.** This is illustrated in Figure 6.2(a) and (b): Because the population of individual stock returns is (approximately) normally distributed, the population of all possible sample mean returns is also (approximately) normally distributed.

2 **Even if the population of individual measurements is not normally distributed, there are circumstances when the population of all possible sample means is approximately normally distributed.** This result is based on a theorem called the **central limit theorem** (see the next subsection). The result is intuitively illustrated in Figure 6.1(a) and (b). Although the population of six prize amounts does not have a normal distribution (it has a uniform distribution), the population of 15 sample mean prize amounts has a distribution that looks somewhat like a normal distribution.

3   **The mean, $\mu_{\bar{x}}$, of the population of all possible sample means equals μ, the mean of the population of individual measurements.** This is illustrated in both Figures 6.1 and 6.2. That is, in each example, the histogram of prize amounts or monthly stock returns and the histogram of sample means are centred over the same mean μ (note that μ equals 35 in Figure 6.1 and 0.624 percent in Figure 6.2). Furthermore, this implies that although the sample mean for a particular sample of n randomly selected prize amounts or stocks will probably not equal the population mean μ, the mean of the population of all possible sample means (based on all possible samples of n prize amounts or stocks) is equal to μ.

LO3

4   **The standard deviation, $\sigma_{\bar{x}}$, of the population of all possible sample means is less than σ, the standard deviation of the population of individual measurements.**[1] This is also illustrated in both Figures 6.1 and 6.2. That is, in each example, the histogram of all possible sample means is less spread out than the histogram of individual prize amounts or stock returns. Intuitively, $\sigma_{\bar{x}}$ is smaller than σ because each possible sample mean is an average of n measurements (prize amounts or stock returns). *Thus, each sample mean averages out high and low sample measurements (prize amounts or stock returns) and can be expected to be closer to the population mean μ than many of the individual population measurements (prize amounts or stock returns) would be.* It follows that the different possible sample means are more closely clustered around μ than are the individual population measurements. In the stock market example, a sample of n stocks is a portfolio of n stocks, and the sample mean return is the percentage return that an investor would realize if they invested equal amounts in the stocks in the portfolio. Therefore, Figure 6.2 illustrates that the variation among portfolio returns is considerably less than the variation among individual stock returns. Of course, unlike in the game show example, one would probably not invest in the stock market by randomly selecting stocks. However, we have nevertheless illustrated an important investment principle— diversification reduces risk.

LO4

There is a formula that tells us the exact relationship between $\sigma_{\bar{x}}$ and σ. This formula says that if certain conditions are satisfied, $\sigma_{\bar{x}}$ equals σ divided by the square root of the sample size, n. That is,

$$\sigma_{\bar{x}} = \frac{\sigma}{\sqrt{n}}.$$

It follows that $\sigma_{\bar{x}}$ is less than σ if the sample size n is greater than 1. Furthermore, this formula is valid if the sampled population is infinite and is approximately valid if the sampled population is finite and much larger than (say, at least 20 times) the size of the sample. For example, consider randomly selecting $n = 20$ monthly stock returns from the TSX data. The population size of 600 monthly returns is more than 20 times the sample size of 20 ($20 \times 20 = 400$). The population standard deviation of the monthly stock returns is 4.42 percent over the 50-year period, so it follows that

$$\sigma_{\bar{x}} = \frac{\sigma}{\sqrt{n}} = \frac{4.42}{\sqrt{20}} = 0.988\%.$$

Figure 6.2(a) and (b) illustrates the fact that the spread of the distribution of average monthly returns (0.988 percent) is indeed smaller than the spread of the distribution of monthly returns (4.42 percent).

We now summarize what we have learned about the sampling distribution of $\bar{x}$.

---

[1] This is true if the sample size is greater than 1.

The Sampling Distribution of $\bar{x}$

Assume that the population from which we will randomly select a sample of n measurements has mean μ and standard deviation σ. Then the population of all possible sample means

1 Has a normal distribution if the sampled population has a normal distribution.

2 Has mean $\mu_{\bar{x}} = \mu$.

3 Has variance $\sigma_{\bar{x}}^2 = \dfrac{\sigma^2}{n}$ and standard deviation

$$\sigma_{\bar{x}} = \frac{\sigma}{\sqrt{n}}.$$

The formulas for $\sigma_{\bar{x}}^2$ and $\sigma_{\bar{x}}$ in (3) hold exactly if the sampled population is infinite and approximately if the sampled population is finite and much larger than (say, at least 20 times) the size of the sample.

Stated equivalently, the sampling distribution of $\bar{x}$ has mean $\mu_{\bar{x}} = \mu$ and standard deviation $\sigma_{\bar{x}} = \sigma/\sqrt{n}$ (under the conditions described above), and is a normal distribution (if the sampled population has a normal distribution).

In the game show example, we know the values of the mean μ and the standard deviation σ of the sampled population of the winnings. In most situations, however, we randomly select a sample from a population in order to estimate the unknown mean μ and the unknown standard deviation σ of the population. We have seen that the sample mean $\bar{x}$ is the point estimate of μ and the sample standard deviation s is the point estimate of σ. Furthermore, a larger sample is more likely to give a more accurate point estimate $\bar{x}$ of μ and a more accurate point estimate s of σ. Furthermore, we can use the formula $\sigma_{\bar{x}} = \sigma/\sqrt{n}$ to demonstrate why a larger sample is more likely to give a more accurate point estimate $\bar{x}$ of μ. Notice that the sample size n is in the denominator of the formula $\sigma_{\bar{x}} = \sigma/\sqrt{n}$. This implies that the larger the sample size n is, the smaller is $\sigma_{\bar{x}}$. This is logical because the larger the sample size is, the better is the chance that the high and low measurements in the sample will cancel each other out to give a sample mean near μ (because more measurements are being averaged). Therefore, when the sample size is large, the possible sample means will be more closely clustered around μ than when the sample size is smaller. This implies that the sample mean calculated from the actual sample that we select is more likely to be near μ. In the following example, we illustrate this idea and also show how the sampling distribution of $\bar{x}$ can help us to make a statistically based conclusion about a population mean μ.

Example 6.2 Fuel Efficiency

Cars are becoming more and more fuel efficient, which is good for the environment and your wallet. Suppose that the government is providing tax credits for those auto makers that produce more fuel-efficient vehicles for a certain midsize model type. Define the population as the population of all fuel economies (measured in litres per 100 km) that could potentially be produced. The auto maker could always produce one more vehicle, so we will consider this population infinite. Assume also that the population is normally distributed with mean $\mu = 7.6$ and standard deviation $\sigma = 0.2$ (see Figure 6.3(a)). A random sample of n cars will be selected and tested in accordance with government specifications. The distribution of all possible sample means will also be normally distributed with a mean equal to μ and a standard deviation equal to $\sigma/\sqrt{n}$. We illustrate in Figure 6.3(b) and (c) that a larger sample is more likely to give a more accurate point estimate, $\bar{x}$, of μ by using samples of size $n = 5$ and $n = 50$, respectively, in these figures.

We know that the distribution of fuel economies is normal. Suppose that a sample of 50 produced a sample mean of $\bar{x} = 7.51$ L/100 km. Now we wish to determine whether or not the sample information provides strong statistical evidence that the population mean, μ, is less

FIGURE **6.3** A Comparison of (1) the Population of All Fuel Economies, (2) the Sampling Distribution of the Sample Mean $\bar{x}$ When $n = 5$, and (3) the Sampling Distribution of the Sample Mean $\bar{x}$ When $n = 50$

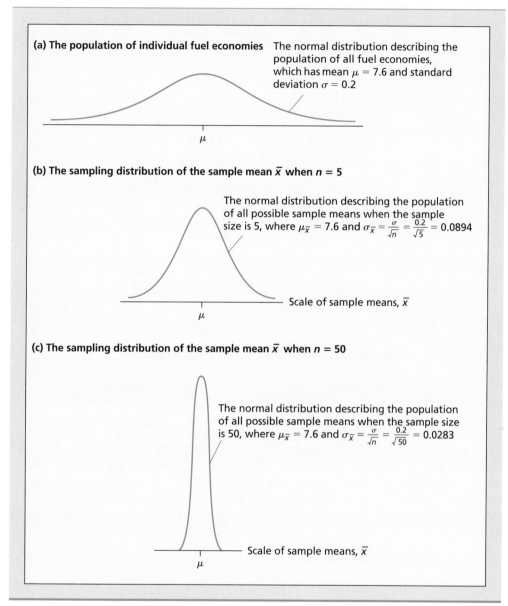

(a) The population of individual fuel economies The normal distribution describing the population of all fuel economies, which has mean $\mu = 7.6$ and standard deviation $\sigma = 0.2$

μ

(b) The sampling distribution of the sample mean $\bar{x}$ when $n = 5$

The normal distribution describing the population of all possible sample means when the sample size is 5, where $\mu_{\bar{x}} = 7.6$ and $\sigma_{\bar{x}} = \frac{\sigma}{\sqrt{n}} = \frac{0.2}{\sqrt{5}} = 0.0894$

Scale of sample means, $\bar{x}$

μ

(c) The sampling distribution of the sample mean $\bar{x}$ when $n = 50$

The normal distribution describing the population of all possible sample means when the sample size is 50, where $\mu_{\bar{x}} = 7.6$ and $\sigma_{\bar{x}} = \frac{\sigma}{\sqrt{n}} = \frac{0.2}{\sqrt{50}} = 0.0283$

Scale of sample means, $\bar{x}$

μ

LO6

than 7.6 L/100 km. If this were the case, then the auto maker would qualify for the tax credits under the current government program.

In order to determine whether or not the mean fuel economy is less than 7.6 L/100 km, we will assume for now that $\mu = 7.6$ L/100 km and use the sample information to determine whether or not we should reject this assumption ($\mu = 7.6$ L/100 km) in favour of the alternative claim that the mean fuel economy might actually be lower.

We assumed that the population of fuel economies was normally distributed and the population standard deviation was known to be 0.2, as given above. Our sample of $n = 50$ produced a sample mean of 7.51 L/100 km. Now we need to determine

$$P(\bar{x} < 7.51 \text{ given that } \mu = 7.6) = P\left(\frac{\bar{x} - \mu_{\bar{x}}}{\sigma_{\bar{x}}} < \frac{7.51 - 7.6}{0.2/\sqrt{50}}\right) = P(z < -3.18) = 0.0007.$$

FIGURE **6.4**   The Probability That $\bar{x} < 7.51$ L/100 km Given that $\mu = 7.6$ L/100 km in Example 6.2

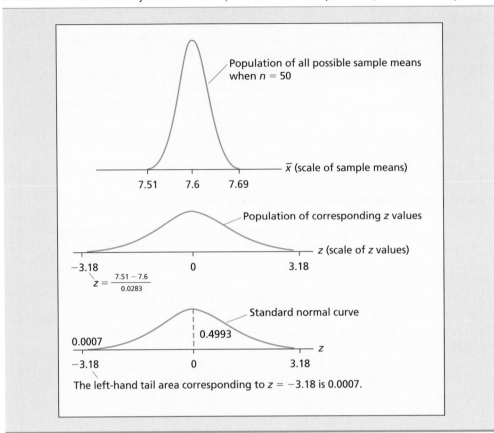

This says that if $\mu = 7.6$ L/100 km, then about 7 in 10,000 of all possible sample means are at most as large as $\bar{x} = 7.51$ L/100 km. (see Figure 6.4). This suggests that it is very unlikely that $\mu = 7.6$ L/100 km. There is very little support for that claim and, in fact, it appears as though μ is actually lower than 7.6. This evidence would probably convince the government that the average fuel economy of this midsize model is less than 7.6 L/100 km, so this model deserves the tax credit.

In the preceding example, the population standard deviation σ was known to be 0.2. Of course, in almost all real-world situations, the value of σ is unknown. If we do not know μ, why would we know σ? For now, though, we will assume, through extensive experience with the population or production process under consideration, that we know the true value of σ.

Sampling a nonnormally distributed population: The central limit theorem We now consider what can be said about the sampling distribution of $\bar{x}$ when the sampled population is not normally distributed. First, as previously stated, the fact that $\mu_{\bar{x}} = \mu$ is still true. Second, as also previously stated, the formula $\sigma_{\bar{x}} = \sigma/\sqrt{n}$ is exactly correct if the sampled population is infinite and is approximately correct if the sampled population is finite and much larger than (say, at least 20 times as large as) the sample size. Third, an extremely important result called the **central limit theorem** tells us that *if the sample size n is large, the sampling distribution of $\bar{x}$ is approximately normal, even if the sampled population is not normally distributed.*

The Central Limit Theorem

If the sample size n is sufficiently large, then the population of all possible sample means is approximately normally distributed (with mean $\mu_{\bar{x}} = \mu$ and standard deviation $\sigma_{\bar{x}} = \sigma/\sqrt{n}$), no matter what probability distribution describes the sampled population. Furthermore, the larger the sample size n is, the more nearly normally distributed is the population of all possible sample means.

LO7

The central limit theorem is illustrated in Figure 6.5 for several population shapes. Notice that as the sample size increases (from 2 to 6 to 30), the populations of all possible sample means become more nearly normally distributed. This figure also illustrates that as the sample size increases, the spread of the distribution of all possible sample means decreases (remember that this spread is measured by $\sigma_{\bar{x}}$, which decreases as the sample size increases).

How large must the sample size be for the sampling distribution of $\bar{x}$ to be approximately normal? In general, the more skewed the probability distribution of the sampled population, the larger the sample size must be for the population of all possible sample means to be approximately normally distributed. For some sampled populations, particularly those described by symmetric distributions, the population of all possible sample means is approximately normally distributed for a fairly small sample size. In addition, studies indicate that *if the sample size is at least 30, for most sampled populations, the population of all possible sample means is approximately normally distributed.* For the subsequent cases, whenever the sample size n is at least 30, we will assume that the sampling distribution of $\bar{x}$ is approximately a normal distribution.

FIGURE 6.5   The Central Limit Theorem Says That the Larger the Sample Size Is, the More Nearly Normally Distributed Is the Population of All Possible Sample Means

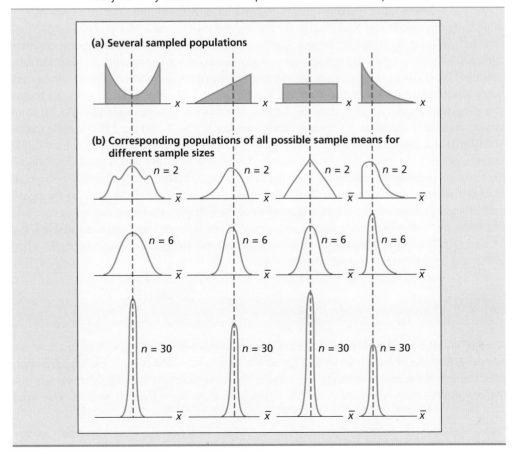

FIGURE **6.6**   Simulating the Sampling Distribution of the Sample Mean When Sampling from an Exponential Distribution

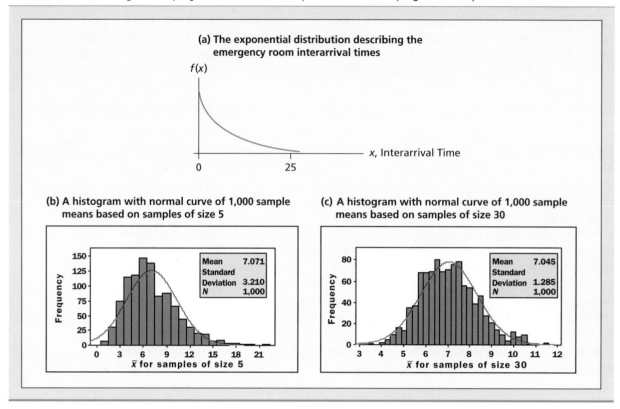

We can see the shapes of sampling distributions such as those illustrated in Figure 6.5 by using computer simulation. Specifically, for a population with a particular probability distribution, we can have the computer draw a given number of samples of n observations, compute the mean of each sample, and arrange the sample means into a histogram.[2] To illustrate this, consider Figure 6.6(a), which shows the exponential distribution describing the hospital emergency room interarrival times discussed in Chapter 5 (page 179). Figure 6.6(b) gives the results of a simulation in which 1,000 samples of five interarrival times were randomly selected from this exponential distribution, the mean of each sample calculated, and the 1,000 sample means arranged into a histogram. Figure 6.6(c) gives the results of a simulation in which 1,000 samples of 30 interarrival times were randomly selected from the exponential distribution, the mean of each sample calculated, and the 1,000 sample means arranged into a histogram. Note that whereas the histogram in Figure 6.6(b) is somewhat positively skewed (to the right), the histogram in Figure 6.6(c) appears approximately bell-shaped. Therefore, we might conclude that when we randomly select a sample of n observations from an exponential distribution, the sampling distribution of the sample mean is somewhat positively skewed (to the right) when $n = 5$ and approximately normal when $n = 30$.

Example 6.3 The Payment Time Case

A management consulting firm has installed a new computer-based billing system in a trucking company. Because of the advantages of the new billing system, and because the trucking company's clients are receptive to using this system, the management consulting firm believes that the new system will reduce the mean bill payment time by more than 50 percent. The mean

---

[2]The use of a computer to simulate sampling from a population is called a Monte Carlo study or simulation. These simulations are very useful in verifying that $\bar{x}$ is a reliable estimate of μ.

payment time using the old billing system was approximately equal to, but no less than, 39 days. Therefore, if μ denotes the new mean payment time, the consulting firm believes that μ will be less than 19.5 days. To assess whether μ is less than 19.5, we will assume that μ equals 19.5 and use a sample of $n = 65$ payment times to weigh the evidence against this assumption and in favour of the conclusion that μ is less than 19.5. The consulting firm finds that the mean of the 65 payment times is $\bar{x} = 18.1077$, and because this sample mean is less than 19.5, we have some evidence supporting the assumption that μ is less than or equal to 19.5. To evaluate the strength of this evidence, we calculate the probability of observing a sample mean that is less than or equal to 18.1077 if, in fact, μ equals 19.5. The management consulting firm plotted the 65 payment times in a stem-and-leaf display, which indicated that the population of all payment times is positively skewed (with a tail to the right). However, the central limit theorem tells us that because the sample size $n = 65$ is large, the sampling distribution of $\bar{x}$ is approximately a normal distribution with mean $\mu_{\bar{x}} = \mu$ and standard deviation $\sigma_{\bar{x}} = \sigma/\sqrt{n}$. Assuming that the population standard deviation σ is known to be 4.2 days, $\sigma_{\bar{x}}$ equals $4.2/\sqrt{65} = 0.5209$. It follows that

$$P(\bar{x} \leq 18.1077 \text{ given that } \mu = 19.5) = P\left(z \leq \frac{18.1077 - 19.5}{0.5209}\right)$$
$$= P(z \leq -2.67).$$

The normal table tells us that the area under the standard normal curve from -2.67 to 0 is 0.4962. It follows that the tail area under this curve to the left of -2.67 is $0.5 - 0.4962 = 0.0038$. Therefore,

$$P(\bar{x} \leq 18.1077 \text{ given that } \mu = 19.5) = 0.0038.$$

This probability says that if μ equals 19.5, then only 0.0038 of all possible sample means are at least as small as the sample mean $\bar{x} = 18.1077$ that we have actually observed. If we are to believe that μ equals 19.5, then we must believe that we have observed a sample mean that can be described as a 38 in 10,000 chance. It is very difficult to believe that such a small chance would occur, so we have very strong evidence that μ does not equal 19.5 and is, in fact, less than 19.5. We conclude that it appears as though the new billing system has reduced the mean bill payment time by more than 50 percent.

Unbiasedness and minimum-variance estimates Recall that a sample statistic is any descriptive measure of the sample measurements. For instance, the sample mean $\bar{x}$ is a statistic, and so are the sample median, the sample variance s^2, and the sample standard deviation s. Not only do different samples give different values of $\bar{x}$, different samples also give different values of the median, s^2, s, or any other statistic. It follows that *before we draw the sample, any sample statistic is a random variable*, and we have the following:

The **sampling distribution** of a sample statistic is the probability distribution of the population of all possible values of the sample statistic.

For example, Figure 6.7(a) on the next page gives the population of the 20 samples of $n = 3$ stock returns that can be randomly selected from the population of six stock returns -36, -15, 3, 15, 33, and 54. This figure also gives the mean, median, and standard deviation of each sample, and Figure 6.7(b) and (c) shows the relative frequency histograms describing the populations of the 20 sample means, 20 sample medians, and 20 sample standard deviations. In general, we wish to estimate a population parameter by using a sample statistic that we call an **unbiased point estimate** of the parameter.

A sample statistic is an **unbiased point estimate** of a population parameter if the mean of the population of all possible values of the sample statistic equals the population parameter.

LO8

We use the sample mean $\bar{x}$ as the point estimate of the population mean μ because $\bar{x}$ *is an unbiased point estimate of* μ. That is, $\mu_{\bar{x}} = \mu$, or the average of all of the different possible sample means (that we could obtain from all of the different possible samples) equals μ. For example, consider the summary of sample means and medians given at the bottom of Figure 6.7(a). We see that (1) the mean of the population of 20 sample means and (2) the mean of the population of 20 sample medians are both equal to 9, which is the mean of the sampled population of the six stock returns $(-36, -15, 3, 15, 33,$ and $54)$. Thus, in this situation both the sample mean and the sample median are unbiased estimates of the population mean. In general, the sample mean is always an unbiased estimate of the population mean. However, the sample median is *not* always an unbiased estimate of the population mean.

Although we want a sample statistic to be an unbiased point estimate of the population parameter of interest, we also want the possible values of the sample statistic to be closely clustered around the population parameter. If this is the case, when we actually randomly select one sample and compute the sample statistic, its value is likely to be close to the value of the population parameter. For example, note from the bottom of Figure 6.7(a) that although both the sample mean and the sample median are unbiased estimates of the population mean in this situation, the standard deviation of the population of 20 sample means, which is 13.26, is less than the standard deviation of the population of 20 sample medians, which is 15.88. This says, as is illustrated in Figure 6.7(b), that the 20 sample means are more closely clustered around the population mean than are the 20 sample medians. Therefore, the sample mean is the

---

FIGURE 6.7   Populations of Sample Means, Medians, and Standard Deviations

(a) The population of the 20 samples of $n = 3$ returns and corresponding populations of sample means, medians, and standard deviations

Sample	$n = 3$ Returns in Sample			Mean	Median	Std. Dev.
1	−36	−15	3	−16.00	−15.00	19.52
2	−36	−15	15	−12.00	−15.00	25.63
3	−36	−15	33	−6.00	−15.00	35.37
4	−36	−15	54	1.00	−15.00	47.09
5	−36	3	15	−6.00	3.00	26.66
6	−36	3	33	0.00	3.00	34.60
7	−36	3	54	7.00	3.00	45.13
8	−36	15	33	4.00	15.00	35.79
9	−36	15	54	11.00	15.00	45.13
10	−36	33	54	17.00	33.00	47.09
11	−15	3	15	1.00	3.00	15.10
12	−15	3	33	7.00	3.00	24.25
13	−15	3	54	14.00	3.00	35.79
14	−15	15	33	11.00	15.00	24.25
15	−15	15	54	18.00	15.00	34.60
16	−15	33	54	24.00	33.00	35.37
17	3	15	33	17.00	15.00	15.10
18	3	15	54	24.00	15.00	26.66
19	3	33	54	30.00	33.00	25.63
20	15	33	54	34.00	33.00	19.52

Summary of sample means and medians

Mean of the 20 sample means = 9

Mean of the 20 sample medians = 9

Standard deviation of the 20 sample means = 13.26

Standard deviation of the 20 sample medians = 15.88

(b) The relative frequency histograms describing the populations of sample means and medians

(c) The relative frequency histogram describing the population of sample standard deviations

preferred point estimate of the population mean. Furthermore, although the sampled population of six stock returns is not normally distributed, some general results apply to estimating the mean μ of a normally distributed population. In this situation, it can be shown that both the sample mean and the sample median are unbiased point estimates of μ. In fact, there are many unbiased point estimates of μ. However, it can be shown that the variance of the population of all possible sample means is smaller than the variance of the population of all possible values of any other unbiased point estimate of μ. For this reason, *we call the sample mean a* **minimum-variance unbiased point estimate of μ.** When we use the sample mean as the point estimate of μ, we are more likely to obtain a point estimate close to μ than if we used any other unbiased sample statistic as the point estimate of μ. This is one reason why we use the sample mean as the point estimate of the population mean.

Technical Note: If we randomly select a sample of size n without replacement from a finite population of size N, then it can be shown that $\sigma_{\bar{x}} = (\sigma/\sqrt{n})\sqrt{(N-n)/(N-1)}$, where the quantity $\sqrt{(N-n)/(N-1)}$ is called the **finite population multiplier.** If the size of the sampled population is at least 20 times the size of the sample (that is, if $N \geq 20n$), then the finite population multiplier is approximately equal to one, and $\sigma_{\bar{x}}$ approximately equals $\sigma/\sqrt{n}$. However, if the population size N is smaller than 20 times the size of the sample, then the finite population multiplier is substantially less than one, and we must include this multiplier in the calculation of $\sigma_{\bar{x}}$. For instance, in our game show example on pages 184–187 (where $N = 6$ is only three times $n = 2$), we have

$$\sigma_{\bar{x}} = \frac{\sigma}{\sqrt{n}}\sqrt{\frac{N-n}{N-1}} = \left(\frac{17.078}{\sqrt{2}}\right)\sqrt{\frac{6-2}{6-1}} = 12.076(0.8944) = 10.8.$$

This finite population multiplier needs to be applied only when $N < 20n$.

Exercises for Section 6.1

CONCEPTS

6.1 Suppose that you randomly select a sample of four measurements from a larger population of measurements. The sampling distribution of the sample mean $\bar{x}$ is the probability distribution of a population. In your own words, describe the units in this population.

6.2 Suppose that you randomly select a sample of n measurements from a normally distributed population of measurements with mean μ and standard deviation σ. Consider the sampling distribution of $\bar{x}$ (that is, consider the population of all possible sample means).
   a. Describe the shape of the population of all possible sample means.
   b. Write formulas that express the central tendency and the variability of the population of all possible sample means. Explain what these formulas say in your own words.

6.3 Explain how the expected value of the population of all possible sample means compares to the expected value of the individual measurements in the population from which the sample is taken.

6.4 Explain how the variability of the population of all possible sample means compares to the variability of the individual measurements in the population from which the sample will be taken. Assume here that the sample size is greater than 1. Intuitively explain why this is true.

6.5 What does the central limit theorem tell us about the sampling distribution of the sample mean?

6.6 In your own words, explain what is meant by an unbiased point estimate.

METHODS AND APPLICATIONS

6.7 Suppose that you take a random sample of size n from an infinite population with mean μ and standard deviation σ. For each of the following situations, find the mean, variance, and standard deviation of the sampling distribution of the sample mean $\bar{x}$:
   a. $\mu = 10, \sigma = 2, n = 25$.
   b. $\mu = 500, \sigma = 0.5, n = 100$.
   c. $\mu = 3, \sigma = 0.1, n = 4$.
   d. $\mu = 100, \sigma = 1, n = 1,600$.

6.8 For each situation in Exercise 6.7, find an interval that contains (approximately or exactly) 99.73 percent of all the possible sample means. In which cases must you assume that the population is normally distributed? Why?

6.9 Suppose that you randomly select a sample of 64 measurements from a population with a mean equal to 20 and a standard deviation equal to 4.
   a. Describe the shape of the sampling distribution of the sample mean $\bar{x}$. Do you need to make any assumptions about the shape of the population? Why or why not?

b. Find the mean and the standard deviation of the sampling distribution of the sample mean $\bar{x}$.

c. Calculate the probability of obtaining a sample mean greater than 21; that is, calculate $P(\bar{x} > 21)$. *Hint:* Find the z value corresponding to 21 by using $\mu_{\bar{x}}$ and $\sigma_{\bar{x}}$ because you need to calculate a probability about $\bar{x}$. Then sketch the sampling distribution and the probability.

d. Calculate the probability of obtaining a sample mean less than 19.385; that is, calculate $P(\bar{x} < 19.385)$.

6.10 Suppose that the percentage returns for a given year for all stocks listed on the TSX are approximately normally distributed with a mean of 12.4 percent and a standard deviation of 20.6 percent. Consider drawing a random sample of $n = 5$ stocks from the population of all stocks and calculating the mean return, $\bar{x}$, of the sampled stocks. Find the mean and the standard deviation of the sampling distribution of $\bar{x}$, and find an interval containing 95.44 percent of all possible sample mean returns.

6.11 THE BANK CUSTOMER WAITING TIME CASE

Recall from Exercise 1.9 on pages 8 and 9 that the bank manager wants to show that the new system reduces typical customer waiting times to less than six minutes. One way to do this is to demonstrate that the mean of the population of all customer waiting times is less than 6. Letting this mean be μ, in this exercise you will investigate whether the sample of 100 waiting times provides evidence to support the claim that μ is less than 6.

Begin by assuming that μ equals 6, and then attempt to use the sample to contradict this assumption in favour of the conclusion that μ is less than 6. Recall that the mean of the sample of 100 waiting times is $\bar{x} = 5.46$ and assume that σ, the standard deviation of the population of all customer waiting times, is known to be 2.47.

a. Consider the population of all possible sample means obtained from random samples of 100 waiting times. What is the shape of this population of sample means? That is, what is the shape of the sampling distribution of $\bar{x}$? Why is this true?

b. Find the mean and standard deviation of the population of all possible sample means, assuming that μ equals 6.

c. The observed sample mean is actually $\bar{x} = 5.46$. Assuming that μ equals 6, find the probability of observing a sample mean that is less than or equal to $\bar{x} = 5.46$.

d. If μ equals 6, what percentage of all possible sample means are less than or equal to 5.46? Since the observed sample mean is actually $\bar{x} = 5.46$, is it more reasonable to believe that (1) μ equals 6 and you have observed one of the sample means that is less than or equal to 5.46 when μ equals 6 or (2) you have observed a sample mean less than or equal to 5.46 because μ is less than 6? Explain. What do you conclude about whether the new system has reduced the typical customer waiting time to less than six minutes?

6.12 THE VIDEO GAME SATISFACTION RATING CASE

Recall (see Chapter 1, Exercise 1.8) that a customer is considered to be very satisfied with their XYZ-Box video game system if the customer's composite score on the survey is at least 42. One way to show that customers are typically very satisfied is to show that the mean of the population of all satisfaction ratings is at least 42. Letting this mean be μ, in this exercise you will investigate whether the sample of 65 satisfaction ratings provides evidence to support the claim that μ exceeds 42 (and, therefore, is at least 42).

Begin by assuming that μ equals 42, and then attempt to use the sample to contradict this assumption in favour of the conclusion that μ exceeds 42. Recall that the mean of the sample of 65 satisfaction ratings is $\bar{x} = 42.95$, and assume that σ, the standard deviation of the population of all satisfaction ratings, is known to be 2.64.

a. Consider the sampling distribution of $\bar{x}$ for random samples of 65 customer satisfaction ratings. Use the properties of this sampling distribution to find the probability of observing a sample mean greater than or equal to 42.95, assuming that μ equals 42.

b. If μ equals 42, what percentage of all possible sample means are greater than or equal to 42.95? Since the observed sample mean is actually $\bar{x} = 42.95$, is it more reasonable to believe that (1) μ equals 42 and you have observed a sample mean that is greater than or equal to 42.95 when μ equals 42 or (2) you have observed a sample mean that is greater than or equal to 42.95 because μ is greater than 42? Explain. What do you conclude about whether customers are typically very satisfied with the XYZ-Box video game system?

6.13 In an article in the *Journal of Management*, Martocchio studied and estimated the costs of employee absences. Based on a sample of 176 blue-collar workers, Martocchio estimated that the mean amount of paid time lost during a three-month period was 1.4 days per employee, with a standard deviation of 1.3 days. Martocchio also estimated that the mean amount of unpaid time lost during a three-month period was 1.0 day per employee, with a standard deviation of 1.8 days.

a. Suppose you randomly select a sample of 100 blue-collar workers. Based on Martocchio's estimates,

   (1) What is the probability that the average amount of paid time lost during a three-month period for the 100 blue-collar workers will exceed 1.5 days?

   (2) What is the probability that the average amount of unpaid time lost during a three-month period for the 100 blue-collar workers will exceed 1.5 days?

b. Suppose you randomly select a sample of 100 blue-collar workers, and suppose the sample mean amount of unpaid time lost during a three-month period actually exceeds 1.5 days. Would it be reasonable to conclude that the mean amount of unpaid time lost has increased above the previously estimated 1.0 days? Explain.

6.14 When a pizza restaurant's delivery process is operating effectively, pizzas are delivered on average within 45 minutes with a standard deviation of 6 minutes. To monitor its delivery process, the restaurant randomly selects five pizzas each night and records their delivery times.

    a. Assume that the population of all delivery times on a given evening is normally distributed and that the delivery process is operating effectively.

        (1) Describe the shape of the population of all possible sample means. How do you know what the shape is?

        (2) Find the mean of the population of all possible sample means.

        (3) Find the standard deviation of the population of all possible sample means.

        (4) Calculate an interval containing 99.73 percent of all possible sample means.

    b. Suppose that the mean of the five sampled delivery times on a particular evening is $\bar{x} = 55$ minutes. Using the interval that you calculated in a(4), what would you conclude about whether the restaurant's delivery process is operating effectively? Why?

6.15 Suppose that faculty members at a Canadian university with a rank of professor earn an average of $78,425 with a standard deviation of $8,000. In an attempt to verify this, a random sample of 40 professors was selected from a human resources database at that university.

    a. Describe the sampling distribution of $\bar{x}$ by giving its mean, variance, and shape. Did you have to make any assumptions?

    b. Suppose that the mean of the sample of 40 professors is $82,537. Does this sample information provide evidence to suggest that the average is correct as stated, or is it likely that the average salary is in fact greater than $78,425?

6.16 It was reported that test scores in a business statistics course were approximately normal with a mean of 70 and a standard deviation of 10. Suppose that a random sample of ten students is selected from the class.

    a. Describe the sampling distribution of $\bar{x}$ by giving its mean, variance, and shape. Did you have to make any assumptions?

    b. Suppose that the mean of the sample of ten students was 67. Does this sample information provide evidence to suggest that the average is correct as stated, or is it likely that the average is in fact less than 70?

6.17 Suppose that the masses of large eggs are approximately normal with a mean of 100 g and a standard deviation of 3 g. Suppose that a carton of eggs contains 12 randomly selected large eggs.

    a. What is the probability that the total mass of the eggs in carton will be more than 1,240 g?

    b. A carton of these eggs is purchased and the eggs are removed from the carton and weighed. The total mass of the eggs in the carton turns out to be 1,150 g. Is there sample evidence to suggest that the eggs in the carton are too light?

6.2 THE SAMPLING DISTRIBUTION OF THE SAMPLE PROPORTION

Let's revisit the wine case. A wine maker wishes to sell its Chardonnay in a new corkless bottle. The screwcap works extremely well and is popular with most consumers, and it is less expensive to produce. While the new, cheaper bottle may alienate some purchasers, a company study shows that its introduction will increase profits if less than 10 percent of the wine's current purchasers are lost. That is, if we let p be the true proportion of all current purchasers who would stop buying the wine if the new bottle were used, profits will increase as long as p is less than 0.10.

Suppose that (after trying the new bottle) 63 of 1,000 randomly selected purchasers say that they would stop buying the wine if the new bottle were used. The point estimate of the population proportion p is the sample proportion $\hat{p} = 63/1,000 = 0.063$. This sample proportion says that we estimate that 6.3 percent of all current purchasers would stop buying the wine if the new bottle were used. Since $\hat{p}$ equals 0.063, we have some evidence that the population proportion p is less than 0.10. In order to determine the strength of this evidence, we need to consider the sampling distribution of $\hat{p}$. In general, assume that we will randomly select a sample of n units from a population, and assume that a proportion p of all the units in the population fall into a particular category (for instance, the category of consumers who would stop buying the wine). Before we actually select the sample, we might potentially obtain many different samples of n units. The number of units that fall into the category in question will vary from sample to sample, so the sample proportion of units falling into the category will also vary from sample to sample. Therefore, we might potentially obtain many different sample proportions. It follows that before we draw the sample, the sample proportion $\hat{p}$ is a random variable. In the following box, we give the properties of the probability distribution of this random variable, which is called **the sampling distribution of the sample proportion $\hat{p}$:**

The Sampling Distribution of the Sample Proportion $\hat{p}$

The population of all possible sample proportions

LO5
LO6

1 Has an approximately normal distribution if the sample size n is large, that is, if $np \geq 5$ and $n(1 - p) \geq 5$.

2 Has mean $\mu_{\hat{p}} = p$.

3 Has variance $\sigma_{\hat{p}}^2 = \dfrac{p(1 - p)}{n}$ and standard deviation $\sigma_{\hat{p}} = \sqrt{\dfrac{p(1 - p)}{n}}$.

Property 1 in the box says that if n is large, the population of all possible sample proportions has an approximately normal distribution. Here it can be shown that n *should be considered large if both np and $n(1 - p)$ are at least 5*.[3] Property 2, which says that $\mu_{\hat{p}} = p$, is valid for any sample size and tells us that $\hat{p}$ is an unbiased estimate of p. That is, although the sample proportion $\hat{p}$ that we calculate probably does not equal p, the average of all the different sample proportions that we could have calculated (from all the different possible samples) is equal to p. Property 3, which says that

$$\sigma_{\hat{p}}^2 = \frac{p(1 - p)}{n} \quad \text{and} \quad \sigma_{\hat{p}} = \sqrt{\frac{p(1 - p)}{n}},$$

is exactly correct if the sampled population is infinite and approximately correct if the sampled population is finite and much larger than (say, at least 20 times as large as) the sample size. Property 3 tells us that the variance and the standard deviation of the population of all possible sample proportions decrease as the sample size increases. That is, the larger n is, the more closely clustered are all the different sample proportions around the true population proportion.

Example 6.4 The Wine Case

In the wine situation, the wine maker must decide whether p, the proportion of all current purchasers who would stop buying the wine if the new bottle were used, is less than 0.10. In order to do this, we assume that p equals 0.10. Then we use the sample information to weigh the evidence against this assumption and in favour of the conclusion that p is less than 0.10. Remember that when 1,000 purchasers of the wine are randomly selected, 63 of these purchasers say they would stop buying it if the new corkless bottle were used. Because the sample proportion $\hat{p} = 0.063$ is less than 0.10, we have some evidence contradicting the assumption that p equals 0.10. To evaluate the strength of this evidence, we calculate the probability of observing a sample proportion that is less than or equal to 0.063 if, in fact, p equals 0.10.

If p equals 0.10, we can assume that the sampling distribution of $\hat{p}$ is approximately a normal distribution because both $np = 1,000(0.10) = 100$ and $n(1 - p) = 1,000(1 - 0.10) = 900$ are at least 5. Furthermore, the mean and standard deviation of the sampling distribution of $\hat{p}$ are $\mu_{\hat{p}} = p = 0.10$ and

$$\sigma_{\hat{p}} = \sqrt{\frac{p(1 - p)}{n}} = \sqrt{\frac{(0.10)(0.90)}{1,000}} = 0.0094868.$$

---

[3]Some statisticians suggest using the more conservative rule that both np and $n(1 - p)$ must be at least ten.

Therefore,

$$P(\hat{p} \leq 0.063 \text{ given that } p = 0.10) = P\left(z \leq \frac{0.063 - \mu_{\hat{p}}}{\sigma_{\hat{p}}}\right) = P\left(z \leq \frac{0.063 - 0.10}{0.0094868}\right)$$

$$= P(z \leq -3.90).$$

Because the tail area under the normal curve to the left of −3.90 is smaller than the tail area to the left of −3.09, this probability is less than 0.001. It says that if p equals 0.10, fewer than 1 in 1,000 of all possible sample proportions are at least as small as the sample proportion $\hat{p} = 0.063$ that we have actually observed. If we are to believe that p equals 0.10, then we must believe that we have observed a sample proportion that can be described as less than a 1 in 1,000 chance. Therefore, we have extremely strong evidence that p does not equal 0.10 and is, in fact, less than 0.10. That is, we conclude that we have extremely strong evidence that less than 10 percent of current purchasers would stop buying the wine if the new bottle were used. Therefore, we have extremely strong evidence that introducing the new corkless bottle will be profitable.

Exercises for Section 6.2

CONCEPTS

6.18   What population is described by the sampling distribution of $\hat{p}$?

6.19   Suppose that you randomly select a sample of n units from a population and that you compute the sample proportion $\hat{p}$ of these units that fall into a category of interest. Consider the sampling distribution of $\hat{p}$.
  a. If the sample size n is large, the sampling distribution of $\hat{p}$ is approximately a normal distribution. What condition must be satisfied to guarantee that n is large enough to say that $\hat{p}$ is normally distributed?
  b. Write formulas that express the central tendency and variability of the population of all possible sample proportions. Explain what each of these formulas means in your own words.

6.20   Describe the effect of increasing the sample size on the population of all possible sample proportions.

METHODS AND APPLICATIONS

6.21   In each of the following cases, find the mean, variance, and standard deviation of the sampling distribution of the sample proportion $\hat{p}$:
  a. $p = 0.5, n = 250.$ **c.** $p = 0.8, n = 400.$
  b. $p = 0.1, n = 100.$ **d.** $p = 0.98, n = 1,000.$

6.22   In each of the following cases, determine whether the sample size n is large enough to say that the sampling distribution of $\hat{p}$ is a normal distribution:
  a. $p = 0.4, n = 100.$ **d.** $p = 0.8, n = 400.$
  b. $p = 0.1, n = 10.$ **e.** $p = 0.98, n = 1,000.$
  c. $p = 0.1, n = 50.$ **f.** $p = 0.99, n = 400.$

6.23   Consider an experiment where a fair coin is flipped 25 times and the number of heads observed is recorded.

Find an interval that contains 68.26 percent of all the possible sample proportions.

6.24   For each situation in Exercise 6.21, find an interval that contains approximately 95.44 percent of all the possible sample proportions.

6.25   Suppose that you randomly select a sample of $n = 100$ units from a population and that you compute the sample proportion $\hat{p}$ of these units that fall into a category of interest. Suppose the true population proportion p equals 0.9.
  a. Describe the shape of the sampling distribution of $\hat{p}$. Why can you validly describe the shape?
  b. Find the mean and the standard deviation of the sampling distribution of $\hat{p}$.
  c. Calculate the following probabilities about the sample proportion $\hat{p}$. In each case, sketch the sampling distribution and the probability.
    (1) $P(\hat{p} \geq 0.96).$
    (2) $P(0.855 \leq \hat{p} \leq 0.945).$
    (3) $P(\hat{p} \leq 0.915).$

6.26   Suppose that a study was conducted regarding parents' use of blocking software for controlling their children's Internet browsing. The study asked parents who own computers with blocking software installed whether they use the devices to block Web sites with objectionable content.
  a. Suppose that you wish to use the study results to justify the claim that less than 20 percent of parents who own computers with blocking software installed use the software. The study actually found that 17 percent of the parents polled used the software. If the poll surveyed 1,000 parents, and if you assume that 20 percent of parents who have blocking software installed actually use it (that is, $p = 0.2$), calculate the probability of observing a sample

proportion of 0.17 or less. That is, calculate $P(\hat{p} \leq 0.17)$.

b. Based on the probability that you computed in part a, would you conclude that less than 20 percent of parents who own computers with blocking software installed actually use it? Explain.

6.27 On May 16, 2007, Ipsos Reid released the results of a poll concerning Canadian attitudes toward spring cleaning. The poll results were based on online interviews of a randomly selected sample of 1,317 adult Canadians from May 1 to 4, 2007.

a. The poll's results state that 39 percent of Canadians would rather clean out their basements or their garages than look at their taxes or finances.[4] Suppose you want to use these results to test a claim. Assume that one third of Canadian adults would rather clean out their basements or garages than look at their taxes or finances (that is, $p = 1/3$). Calculate the probability of observing a sample proportion of 0.39 or higher. That is, calculate $P(\hat{p} \geq 0.39)$.

b. Based on the probability that you calculated in part a, does it seem very likely that more than one third of Canadians would rather clean out their basements or garages than look at their taxes or finances?

6.28 A bank published a report on improvements in customer satisfaction and loyalty. A key measure of customer satisfaction is the response (on a scale from 1 to 10) to the question, "Considering all the business you do with the bank, what is your overall satisfaction?" Here a response of 9 or 10 represents "customer delight."

a. Historically, the percentage of bank customers expressing customer delight has been 48 percent. Suppose that you wish to use the results of a survey of 350 bank customers to justify the claim that more than 48 percent of all current bank customers would express customer delight. The survey finds that 189 of 350 randomly selected bank customers express customer delight. Assuming that the proportion of customer delight is $p = 0.48$, calculate the probability of observing a sample proportion greater than or equal to $189/350 = 0.54$. That is, calculate $P(\hat{p} \geq 0.54)$.

b. Based on the probability that you computed in part a, would you conclude that more than 48 percent of current bank customers express customer delight? Explain.

6.29 Again consider the survey of 350 bank customers discussed in Exercise 6.28.

a. Assume that 48 percent of bank customers would currently express customer delight. That is, assume $p = 0.48$.

(1) Find the probability that the sample proportion obtained from the sample of 350 customers would be within three percentage points of the population proportion. That is, find $P(0.45 \leq \hat{p} \leq 0.51)$.

(2) Find the probability that the sample proportion obtained from the sample of 350 customers would

be within six percentage points of the population proportion. That is, find $P(0.42 \leq \hat{p} \leq 0.54)$.

b. Based on your results in part a, would it be reasonable to state that the survey's margin of error is ± 3 percentage points? ± 6 percentage points? Explain.

6.30 **THE MARKETING ETHICS CASE: CONFLICT OF INTEREST**

a. Consider the Marketing Ethics Case from Chapter 2 and remember that 111 of 205 randomly selected marketing researchers disapproved of the actions taken in the conflict of interest scenario. Suppose that you wish to justify the claim that a majority (more than 50 percent) of all marketing researchers disapprove of these actions. Assuming that p, the proportion of all marketing researchers who disapprove of the actions taken, equals 0.5, calculate a probability that expresses the amount of doubt cast by the sample result on the assumption that p equals 0.5.

b. Based on the probability that you computed in part a, would you conclude that p really is greater than 0.5? That is, would you conclude that a majority of marketing researchers disapprove of the actions taken in the conflict of interest scenario? Explain.

6.31 A special advertising section in the July 20, 1998, issue of *Fortune* magazine discusses outsourcing. According to the article, outsourcing is "the assignment of critical, but noncore, business functions to outside specialists." This allows a company to immediately bring operations up to best-in-world standards while avoiding huge capital investments. The article includes the results of a poll of business executives addressing the benefits of outsourcing.

a. Suppose you wish to use the poll's results to justify the claim that less than 26 percent of business executives feel that the benefits of outsourcing are either "less or much less than expected." The poll actually found that 15 percent of the respondents felt that the benefits of outsourcing were either "less or much less than expected."[5] If 1,000 randomly selected business executives were polled, and if for the sake of argument you assume that 20 percent of all business executives feel that the benefits of outsourcing are either less or much less than expected (that is, $p = 0.20$), calculate the probability of observing a sample proportion of 0.15 or less. That is, calculate $P(\hat{p} \leq 0.15)$.

b. Based on the probability that you computed in part a, would you conclude that less than 20 percent of business executives feel that the benefits of outsourcing are either "less or much less than expected"? Explain.

6.32 On April 16, 2007, Ipsos Reid released the results of a poll concerning Canadian teens' attitudes toward the environment. The poll results were based on an online poll between March 22 and April 22 via an online sample of 1,996 Canadian teens aged 13 to 19.

a. The poll's results state that 19 percent of Canadian teens consider themselves to be "green fiends"—

---

[4]Source: http://www.ipsos-na.com/news-polls/pressrelease.aspx?id=3492, "Canadians would rather clean the garage than do financial spring cleaning!" May 16, 2007.

[5]Source: "Outsourcing 98," by M. R. Ozanne and M. F. Corbette, *Fortune* (July 20, 1998), p. 510.

people who recycle everything, conserve energy, and encourage others to do the same.[6] Assume that one-sixth of Canadian teens fall into this category (that is, $p = 1/6$). Calculate the probability of observing a sample proportion of 0.19 or higher. That is, calculate $P(\hat{p} \geq 0.19)$.

b. Based on the probability that you calculated in part a, does it seem very likely that more than one sixth of Canadian teens recycle everything, conserve energy, and encourage others to do so? Explain.

6.33 A coin that is believed to be fair is flipped $n = 50$ times and 22 heads are observed. Based on this sample evidence, is there any reason to believe that p, the probability of heads, is less than 0.5?

6.34 Tony's Pizza has a 30-minute guarantee that states, "If your pizza is not delivered within 30 minutes of your order being taken, then your order will be free." Tony believes that he has a success rate better than 95 percent. Records are kept for every order taken. A random sample of $n = 200$ orders is collected and it is determined that eight people did not receive their order within the 30-minute guarantee period. Based on this information, is there any evidence to suggest that Tony's claim is true?

6.35 Suppose that a random sample of $n = 1,000$ Canadians was taken and they were asked whether or not they believe that the economic outlook will be better next year than it is currently. Five hundred fifty-eight people agreed that the outlook would be better next year. What is the probability that the sample proportion would accurately reflect the population proportion to within 3 percent (either way)?

6.36 A fair die is rolled $n = 54$ times and four sixes are observed.

a. Describe the sampling distribution of $\hat{p}$ by stating its mean, variance, and shape. Did you have to make any assumptions?

b. Based on the sample information, is there statistical evidence to suggest that the die is not fair, that in fact p is less than $1/6$ for the sixes?

6.37 Dial-up access to the Internet appears to be a thing of the past in Canada. Suppose that it is believed that 66 percent of those who have access to the Internet use some form of high-speed connection. To challenge this claim, a random sample of $n = 700$ Canadians who have access to the Internet was obtained. Out of the 700, 440 said they used high-speed Internet. Is there evidence to suggest that the value of 66 percent is too high?

CHAPTER SUMMARY

A **sampling distribution** is the probability distribution that describes the population of all possible values of a sample statistic. In this chapter, we studied the properties of two important sampling distributions—the sampling distribution of the sample mean, $\bar{x}$, and the sampling distribution of the sample proportion, $\hat{p}$.

Because different samples that can be randomly selected from a population give different sample means, there is a population of sample means corresponding to a particular sample size. The probability distribution describing the population of all possible sample means is called the **sampling distribution of the sample mean, $\bar{x}$**. We studied the properties of this sampling distribution when the sampled population is and is not normally distributed. We found that when the sampled population has a normal distribution, then the sampling distribution of the sample mean is a normal distribution. Furthermore, the **central limit theorem** tells us that if the sampled population is not normally distributed, then the sampling distribution of the sample mean is approximately a normal distribution when the sample size is large (at least 30). We also saw that

the mean of the sampling distribution of $\bar{x}$ always equals the mean of the sampled population, and we presented formulas for the variance and the standard deviation of this sampling distribution. Finally, we explained that the sample mean is a **minimum-variance unbiased point estimate** of the mean of a normally distributed population.

We also studied the properties of the **sampling distribution of the sample proportion $\hat{p}$**. We found that if the sample size is large, then this sampling distribution is approximately a normal distribution, and we gave a rule for determining whether the sample size is large. We found that the mean of the sampling distribution of $\hat{p}$ is the population proportion p, and we gave formulas for the variance and the standard deviation of this sampling distribution.

Finally, we demonstrated that knowing the properties of sampling distributions can help us make statistical inferences about population parameters. In fact, we will see that the properties of various sampling distributions provide the foundation for most of the techniques to be discussed in future chapters.

GLOSSARY OF TERMS

central limit theorem: A theorem telling us that when the sample size n is sufficiently large, then the population of all possible sample means is approximately normally distributed no matter what probability distribution describes the sampled population. (pages 190–191)

minimum-variance unbiased point estimate: An unbiased point estimate of a population parameter with a variance that is smaller than the variance of any other unbiased point estimate of the parameter. (page 195)

sampling distribution of a sample statistic: The probability distribution of the population of all possible values of the sample statistic. (page 193)

sampling distribution of the sample mean $\bar{x}$: The probability distribution of the population of all possible sample means obtained from samples of a particular size n. (page 184)

when a population is normally distributed (page 188)

central limit theorem (page 191)

---

[6]Source: http://www.ipsos-na.com/news-polls/pressrelease.aspx?id=3441, "Teens talk the talk but don't walk the walk," April 16, 2007.

sampling distribution of the sample proportion $\hat{p}$: The probability distribution of the population of all possible sample proportions obtained from samples of a particular size n. (page 198)

unbiased point estimate: A sample statistic is an unbiased point estimate of a population parameter if the mean of the population of all possible values of the sample statistic equals the population parameter. (page 193)

IMPORTANT FORMULAS

The sampling distribution of the sample mean: pages 188 and 191

The sampling distribution of the sample proportion: page 198

connect™   Practise and learn online with *Connect*. Questions and tables with online data sets are marked with ⬈.

SUPPLEMENTARY EXERCISES

6.38 An energy drink maker claims that its cans contain 500 mL of the drink. A student who recently took a statistics course believes that the company may be slightly underfilling the cans. She takes a random sample of $n = 40$ cans and carefully measures the volume of the drink in each. The sample of 40 reveals a mean of 495.4 mL and a standard deviation of 9.5 mL. Based on the sample information, is there reason to believe that the company is underfilling the cans?

6.39 A chain of audio/video equipment discount stores employs 36 salespeople. Daily dollar sales for individual sellers employed by the chain have a mound-shaped distribution with a mean of $2,000 and a standard deviation of $300.

  a. Suppose that the chain's management decides to implement an incentive program that awards a daily bonus to any salesperson who achieves daily sales over $2,150. Calculate the probability that an individual salesperson will earn the bonus on any particular day.

  b. Suppose that (as an alternative) the chain's management decides to award a daily bonus to the entire sales force if all 36 achieve an *average* daily sales figure that exceeds $2,150. Calculate the probability that average daily sales for the entire sales force will exceed $2,150 on any particular day.

  c. Intuitively, do you think it would be more difficult for an individual salesperson to achieve a daily sales figure that exceeds $2,150 or for the entire sales force of 36 to achieve an average sales figure that exceeds $2,150? Are the probabilities you computed in parts a and b consistent with your intuition? Explain.

  d. Sketch the distribution of individual daily sales figures and the probability you computed in part a. Place values that are three standard deviations above and below the mean in the tails of the distribution. Also sketch the distribution of all possible sample means (the sampling distribution of $\bar{x}$) and the probability you computed in part b. Place values that are three standard deviations of $\bar{x}$ above and below the mean in the tails of the sampling distribution. Compare the sketches. Do you see why the results in parts a and b turned out the way they did? Explain why.

6.40 In the book *Essentials of Marketing Research*, Dillon, Madden, and Firtle discuss an advertising study for a new suntan lotion. In this study, each respondent is assigned to a group whose members will evaluate an ad for the new lotion. Each respondent is asked to rate the ad on six items:

high quality/low quality	persuasive/nonpersuasive
informative/uninformative	artful/artless
good/bad	refined/vulgar

The rating for each item is made using a seven-point scale, where, for example, a rating of 1 on the informative/uninformative dimension indicates that the ad is extremely uninformative, and a rating of 7 says that the ad is extremely informative.

Rating	Probability
1	0
2	0.05
3	0.05
4	0.10
5	0.20
6	0.40
7	0.20

Suppose experience shows that a "very informative" ad is typically rated by a large group of respondents according to the probability distribution given in the table above.

  a. Calculate the mean, variance, and standard deviation of the ratings for a typical "very informative" ad.

  b. Suppose that a group of 36 randomly selected respondents rates a typical "very informative" ad, and consider the sample mean $\bar{x}$ of the 36 ratings. Find the mean and standard deviation of the population of all possible sample means. What is the shape of the population of all possible sample means? How do you know?

  c. Sketch the sampling distribution of the sample mean $\bar{x}$ and compare it to a sketch of the distribution of individual ratings.

  d. Suppose that a randomly selected group of 36 respondents rates a typical "very informative" ad. Find the probability that the respondents give the ad a sample mean rating less than 5.

  e. Suppose that 36 randomly selected respondents are exposed to a new ad in order to determine whether the ad is "very informative," and suppose that the sample mean rating is less than 5. In light of the probability you computed in part d, what would you conclude about whether the new ad is "very informative"? Explain.

6.41 On December 18, 2006, Ipsos Reid released the results of a poll concerning the top priorities for Canadians when it comes to planning for retirement, financially speaking. The poll results were based on a representative randomly selected sample of 1,201 adult Canadians interviewed by telephone from October 12 to 26, 2006.

    a. The poll's results state that 61 percent of Canadians feel that home ownership is the top priority when it comes to planning for retirement, financially speaking.[7] Suppose you want to use these results to test a claim. Assume that two thirds of Canadian adults believe this to be true (that is, $p = 2/3$). Calculate the probability of observing a sample proportion of 0.61 or lower. That is, calculate $P(\hat{p} \le 0.61)$.

    b. Based on the probability that you calculated in part a, does it seem very likely that less than two thirds of Canadian adults feel that home ownership is the top priority when it comes to planning for retirement, financially speaking? Explain.

6.42 Suppose that you randomly select a sample of size 100.

    a. What is the probability of obtaining a sample mean greater than 50.2 when the sampled population has mean 50 and standard deviation 1? Must you assume that the population is normally distributed in order to answer this question? Why or why not?

    b. Rework part a of this exercise with a sample size of 225. Compare your answer here with that of part a. Why are they different?

6.43 Each day, a manufacturing plant receives a large shipment of drums of Chemical ZX-900. These drums are supposed to have a mean fill of 200 L, while the fills have a standard deviation known to be 100 L.

    a. Suppose that the mean fill for the shipment is actually 200 L. If you draw a random sample of 100 drums from the shipment, what is the probability that the average fill for the 100 drums is between 188 L and 189 L?

    b. The plant manager is worried that the drums of Chemical ZX-900 are underfilled. Because of this, the manager decides to draw a sample of 100 drums from each daily shipment and will reject the shipment (send it back to the supplier) if the average fill for the 100 drums is less than 189 L. Suppose that a shipment that actually has a mean fill of 200 L is received. What is the probability that this shipment will be rejected and sent back to the supplier?

6.44 A recent poll was conducted to investigate the stock market's appeal in light of the "market meltdown" that began in the fall of 2008. A poll of 1,250 Canadian investors was conducted. Assume that 50 percent of all Canadian investors currently find the market less attractive than they did in 2008 before the meltdown (that is, $p = 0.5$)

    a. Find the probability that the sample proportion obtained from the sample of 1,250 investors would be

        (1) Within 4 percentage points of the population proportion—that is, find $P(0.46 \le \hat{p} \le 0.54)$.

        (2) Within 2 percentage points of the population proportion.

        (3) Within 1 percentage point of the population proportion.

    b. Based on these probabilities, would it be reasonable to claim a ± 2 percentage point margin of error? a ± 1 percentage point margin of error? Explain.

6.45 Again consider the stock market poll discussed in Exercise 6.44.

    a. Suppose you wish to use the poll's results to justify the claim that less than 50 percent of Canadian investors find the stock market less attractive than in 2008. The poll actually found that 41 percent of the respondents said the stock market is less attractive than in 2008. Assuming that $p = 0.5$, calculate the probability of observing a sample proportion of 0.41 or less. That is, calculate $P(\hat{p} \le 0.41)$.

    b. Based on the probability that you computed in part a, would you conclude that less than 50 percent of Canadian investors find the stock market to be less attractive than in 2008? Explain.

6.46 Canco Heating and Cooling, Inc., advertises that any customer buying an air conditioner during the first 16 days of July will receive a 25 percent discount if the average high temperature for this 16-day period is more than five degrees above normal.

    a. If daily high temperatures in July are normally distributed with a mean of 29°C and a standard deviation of 13°C, what is the probability that Canco Heating and Cooling will have to give its customers the 25 percent discount?

    b. Based on the probability you computed in part a, do you think that Canco's promotion is ethical? Write a paragraph justifying your opinion.

6.47 **THE TRASH BAG CASE**

Recall that the trash bag manufacturer has concluded that its new 130-L bag will be the strongest such bag on the market if its mean breaking strength is at least 23 kg. In order to provide statistical evidence that the mean breaking strength of the new bag is at least 23 kg, the manufacturer randomly selects a sample of n bags and calculates the mean $\bar{x}$ of the breaking strengths of these bags. If the sample mean so obtained is at least 23 kg, this provides some evidence that the mean breaking strength of all new bags is at least 23 kg.

    Suppose that (unknown to the manufacturer) the breaking strengths of the new 130-L bag are normally distributed with a mean of $\mu = 22.9$ kg and a standard deviation of $\sigma = 0.7$ kg.

    a. Find an interval containing 95.44 percent of all possible sample means if the sample size is $n = 5$.

    b. Find an interval containing 95.44 percent of all possible sample means if the sample size is $n = 40$.

    c. If the trash bag manufacturer hopes to obtain a sample mean that is at least 23 kg (so that it can provide evidence that the population mean breaking strength of the new bags is at least 23 kg), which sample size ($n = 5$ or $n = 40$) would be best? Explain.

6.48 A computer supply house receives a large shipment of CD-ROMs each week. Past experience has shown that the number of flaws per CD can be described by the following probability distribution:

Number of Flaws per CD	Probability
0	0.65
1	0.2
2	0.1
3	0.05

a. Calculate the mean and standard deviation of the number of flaws per CD.

b. Suppose that you randomly select a sample of 100 CDs. Describe the shape of the sampling distribution of the sample mean $\bar{x}$. Then compute the mean and the standard deviation of the sampling distribution of $\bar{x}$.

c. Sketch the sampling distribution of the sample mean $\bar{x}$ and compare it to the distribution describing the number of flaws on a single CD.

d. The supply house's managers are worried that the CDs being received have an excessive number of flaws. Because of this, a random sample of 100 disks is drawn from each shipment and the shipment is rejected (sent back to the supplier) if the average number of flaws per disk for the 100 sample disks is greater than 0.75. Suppose that the mean number of flaws per disk for this week's entire shipment is actually 0.55. What is the probability that this shipment will be rejected and sent back to the supplier?

6.49   Most Canadian parents would consider themselves to be positive role models for their children when it comes to finances. However, it appears as though parents need to spend more time talking about the management of finances with their children. On August 31, 2006, Ipsos Reid released the results of a poll concerning this topic. The poll results were based on an online survey of 1,338 Canadian households from August 8 to 14, 2006. The results state that 46 percent of Canadian teenagers would like to learn more about budgeting, while only 13 percent say that their parents have planned a back-to-school budget with them.[8]

a. Suppose you want to use these results to test a claim. Assume that half of Canadian teens would like to learn more about budgeting (that is, $p = 0.5$). Calculate the probability of observing a sample proportion of 0.46 or lower. That is, calculate $P(\hat{p} \leq 0.46)$.

b. Based on the probability that you calculated in part a, does it seem very likely that less than half of Canadian teens would like to learn more about budgeting? Explain.

6.50   On January 7, 2000, the Gallup Organization released the results of a poll comparing lifestyles of today with those of yesteryear. The poll results were based on telephone interviews with a randomly selected national sample of 1,031 adults, 18 years and older, conducted December 20 to 21, 1999. One question asked if the respondent had vacationed for six days or longer within the last 12 months.

a. Suppose that you will attempt to use the poll's results to justify the claim that more than 40 percent of U.S. adults have vacationed for six days or longer within the last 12 months. The poll actually found that 42 percent of the respondents had done so.[9] Assuming that 40 percent of U.S. adults have vacationed for six days or longer within

the last 12 months (that is, $p = 0.4$), calculate the probability of observing a sample proportion of 0.42 or more; that is, calculate $P(\hat{p} \geq 0.42)$.

b. Based on the probability that you computed in part a, would you conclude that more than 40 percent of U.S. adults have vacationed for six days or longer within the last 12 months? Explain.

6.51   **THE INTERNATIONAL BUSINESS TRAVEL EXPENSE CASE**

Suppose that a large international corporation wants to assess whether the mean, μ, of all one-day travel expenses in Moscow exceeds $500. Recall that the mean of a random sample of 35 one-day travel expenses is $\bar{x} = \$538$ (Chapter 2, Exercise 2.71, page 81), and assume that σ is known to equal $40.

a. Assuming that μ equals $500 and the sample size is 35, what is the probability of observing a sample mean that is greater than or equal to $538?

b. Based on your answer in part a, do you think that the mean of all one-day travel expenses in Moscow exceeds $500? Explain.

6.52   **THE U.K. INSURANCE CASE**

Suppose that you wish to assess whether more than 60 percent of all U.K. households spent on life insurance in 1993. That is, you wish to assess whether the proportion, p, of all U.K. households that spent on life insurance in 1993 exceeds 0.60. Assume here that the U.K. insurance survey is based on 1,000 randomly selected households and that 640 of these households spent on life insurance in 1993.

a. Assuming that p equals 0.60 and the sample size is 1,000, what is the probability of observing a sample proportion that is at least 0.64?

b. Based on your answer in part a, do you think more than 60 percent of all U.K. households spent on life insurance in 1993? Explain.

6.53   **INTERNET EXERCISE**

The best way to observe, first-hand, the concepts of sampling distributions is to conduct sampling experiments with real data. However, sampling experiments can be prohibitively time-consuming and tedious. An excellent alternative is to conduct computer-assisted sampling experiments or simulations. *Visual Statistics* by Doane, Mathieson, and Tracy (McGraw-Hill/Irwin) includes a simulation module to illustrate sampling distributions and the central limit theorem. In this exercise, you will download and install the central limit theorem demonstration module from *Visual Statistics* and use the software to demonstrate the central limit theorem.

From the Irwin/McGraw-Hill Business Statistics Centre (http://www.mhhe.com/business/opsci/bstat/), select in turn "Visual Statistics and Other Data Visualization Tools," "Visual Statistics by Doane," and "Free Stuff," and download both the CLT module and the Worktext. When the download is complete, install the CLT module by double-clicking the installation file (vs_setup.exe). Study the overview and orientation sections of the Worktext and work through the first four learning exercises on the Width of Car Hood example.

---

[8]Source: http://www.ipsos-na.com/news-polls/pressrelease.aspx?id=3173, "Canadian parents consider themselves positive financial role models for their children," August 31, 2006.

[9]Source: http://www.gallup.com/poll/3352/Trends-Show-Bathing-Exercise-Up-Watching-Down.aspx. The Gallup Organization, January 7, 2000.

CHAPTER **7**
Confidence Intervals

LEARNING OBJECTIVES

After reading this chapter, you should be able to

LO1 understand the concept of a confidence interval

LO2 construct a confidence interval for a population mean when the population standard deviation (σ) is both known and unknown

LO3 define what is meant by the "margin of error"

LO4 explain when a *z* value should be used and when a *t* value should be used to construct a confidence interval for μ

LO5 determine the sample size for a confidence interval for μ when σ is both known and unknown

LO6 construct a confidence interval for a population proportion

LO7 determine the sample size for a confidence interval for *p* (with and without prior information)

LO8 calculate a confidence interval for a difference in population means when the population standard deviation (σ) is both known and not known

LO9 understand the difference between independent and dependent (paired) samples and be able to calculate a confidence interval for a population of paired differences

LO10 calculate a confidence interval for a difference in population proportions when large, independent samples are used

CHAPTER OUTLINE

7.1 *z*-Based Confidence Intervals for a Population Mean: σ Known

7.2 *t*-Based Confidence Intervals for a Population Mean: σ Unknown

7.3 Sample Size Determination

7.4 Confidence Intervals for a Population Proportion

7.5 Comparing Two Population Means by Using Independent Samples: Variances Known

7.6 Comparing Two Population Means by Using Independent Samples: Variances Unknown

7.7 Comparing Two Population Means by Using Paired Differences

7.8 Comparing Two Population Proportions by Using Large, Independent Samples

In Chapter 6, we discussed the idea of sampling from a population in order to make inferences about that population. We used point estimates to estimate these population parameters. We learned in Chapter 6 that in the long run the expected value of these point estimates will equal the population parameter of interest. This illustrated the concept of an unbiased estimator. These individual estimates on their own are not very useful for making inferences. Instead, we will construct intervals using these point estimates. These intervals will be used to make inferences about the underlying population of interest. We will use the statistical theory from Chapter 6 to learn how to construct these intervals.

As an election draws near, you are very likely to hear or read about results from a poll. These polls are excellent

examples of the concepts discussed in Chapter 6. We are sampling from the population in order to find out information about that population. We know that these polls are never completely accurate. We would have to speak to the entire population in order to achieve greater accuracy, and even then there would be no guarantees. People change their minds all the time, and the data collector and data entry person could make mistakes quite easily with so much information to sift through. When the results from these polls are announced, you usually hear or read something like, "This poll is said to be accurate to within plus or minus 3 percentage points, 19 times out of 20." You may have ignored that part of the poll, but that is statistics at work. By the end of the chapter, you should be able to understand exactly what that sentence means.

Suppose a local university offers two sections of an Introductory Business Statistics course, one in the morning and one in the afternoon. Both sections are taught by the same professor. The average course grade for each section is calculated. Students may be interested in the historical difference in averages. This could affect which section they enroll in. Could it be that the average in the morning class is higher than that in the afternoon class, or is it the other way around?

We conclude this chapter by using confidence intervals to *compare two populations*. Specifically, we compare two population means and two population proportions. We make these comparisons by studying their *differences*. For instance, to compare two population means, say μ_1 and μ_2, we consider the difference between these means, $\mu_1 - \mu_2$. If we use a confidence interval and conclude that $\mu_1 - \mu_2$ is a positive number, then we conclude that μ_1 is greater than μ_2. On the other hand, if a confidence interval reveals that $\mu_1 - \mu_2$ is a negative number, then we conclude that μ_1 is less than μ_2.

We explain many of this chapter's methods in the context of five cases. The last three are new:

The Payment Time Case: We use a confidence interval to more completely assess the reduction in mean payment time that was achieved by the new billing system.

The Wine Case: We use a confidence interval to provide strong evidence that less than 10 percent of all current purchasers will stop buying the wine if the new screwcap is used and, therefore, that it is reasonable to use the screwcap.

The Coffee Cup Case: The production supervisor of a plant that produces coffee cups uses confidence intervals for the difference between two population means to determine which production process yields higher average hourly output, measured in kilograms of coffee cups. By maximizing average

hourly output, the plant can increase productivity and improve its profitability.

The Repair Cost Comparison Case: In order to reduce the costs of automobile accident claims, an insurance company uses confidence intervals for the difference between two population means to compare repair cost estimates for damaged cars at two different garages.

The Advertising Media Case: An advertising agency is test marketing a new product by using one advertising campaign in Toronto and another in Vancouver. The agency uses confidence intervals for the difference between two population proportions to compare the effectiveness of the two advertising campaigns.

Mc Graw Hill CONNECT Practise and learn online with *Connect*. Throughout this chapter, questions and tables with online data sets are marked with ⤴.

7.1 z-BASED CONFIDENCE INTERVALS FOR A POPULATION MEAN: σ KNOWN

LO1

An example of calculating and interpreting a confidence interval for μ We have seen that we use the sample mean as the point estimate of the population mean. A **confidence interval** for the population mean is an interval constructed around the sample mean so that we are reasonably sure, or confident, that this interval contains the population mean. For example, suppose that the makers of the new SlimPhone claim that their phone is lightweight. In fact, they claim that the phone has a mass of 70 g. Due to variations in the mass of the material used in the phones, it is easy to see that each phone would not have a mass of *exactly* 70 g. In order to check the phone maker's claim, we collect a random sample of these phones. We weigh the sample of phones and construct a confidence interval for μ, the population mean mass of all the phones. Suppose that we are able to obtain three separate random samples, each of size $n = 5$. From each sample, we obtain a sample mean and construct a confidence interval. We assume that the mass of the phones is approximately normal and that the population standard deviation, σ, is known to be 0.6 g. In Chapter 6, we learned that the sampling distribution of $\bar{x}$ was also approximately normal with mean $\mu_{\bar{x}} = \mu$ and standard deviation $\sigma_{\bar{x}} = \sigma/\sqrt{n}$. To obtain a confidence interval for μ, we use $\bar{x}$ and $\sigma_{\bar{x}}$ to calculate the interval using the following formula:

LO2

$$\left[\bar{x} \pm 2\sigma_{\bar{x}}\right] = \left[\bar{x} \pm 2\left(\frac{\sigma}{\sqrt{n}}\right)\right]$$

$$= \left[\bar{x} - 2\left(\frac{\sigma}{\sqrt{5}}\right), \bar{x} + 2\left(\frac{\sigma}{\sqrt{5}}\right)\right].$$

TABLE **7.1**   The Sample Mean $\bar{x}$ and the Interval $[\bar{x} \pm 0.537]$ Given by Each of Three Samples

Sample 1	Sample 2	Sample 3
$x_1 = 70.654$	$x_1 = 70.467$	$x_1 = 70.974$
$x_2 = 70.018$	$x_2 = 70.519$	$x_2 = 69.815$
$x_3 = 70.405$	$x_3 = 70.697$	$x_3 = 69.516$
$x_4 = 70.412$	$x_4 = 71.735$	$x_4 = 70.212$
$x_5 = 70.193$	$x_5 = 69.784$	$x_5 = 69.793$
$\bar{x} = 70.336$	$\bar{x} = 70.640$	$\bar{x} = 70.062$
$\mu = [\bar{x} \pm 0.537]$	$\mu = [\bar{x} \pm 0.537]$	$\mu = [\bar{x} \pm 0.537]$
$= [70.336 \pm 0.537]$	$= [70.640 \pm 0.537]$	$= [70.062 \pm 0.537]$
$= [69.799, 70.873]$	$= [70.103, 71.177]$	$= [69.525, 70.599]$

Note: This formula should make more sense later in the chapter when we discuss its origin in more detail. For now, we use the formula to construct confidence intervals.

Recall that we know the true population standard deviation, $\sigma = 0.6$ g. We do not usually know the value of σ, but assume that we know it for now. Later on in this chapter, we show how to calculate a confidence interval without knowing σ. Assuming, for now, that $\sigma = 0.6$ g, we will calculate the interval

$$\left[\bar{x} \pm 2\left(\frac{0.6}{\sqrt{5}}\right)\right] = [\bar{x} \pm 0.537].$$

It is easy to see that each confidence interval of size $n = 5$ that we construct depends on the value of $\bar{x}$. Each confidence interval is unique, because each $\bar{x}$ we obtain is different. This relates to the fact that we view the sample mean $\bar{x}$ as a random variable. The sample mean varies from sample to sample. Some of the confidence intervals will contain the value of μ, and some will not. In our case, as long as the sample mean is within 0.537 g of the value of μ, then the interval will contain μ. Suppose for now that the true value of μ (which is also unknown) is $\mu = 70$ g. We then see in Table 7.1 that two of the three intervals contain this true value of μ.

We now discuss the interpretation of a confidence interval. In the formula above, we see that the interval is given by $[\bar{x} \pm 2(0.6/\sqrt{5})]$ or $[\bar{x} \pm 2\sigma_{\bar{x}}]$ in general. Where does the 2 come from? We are making use of the **empirical rule**. This should all make sense a little later. To try to understand confidence intervals in general, consider the following:

1   The empirical rule for a normally distributed population implies that the probability is 0.9544 that $\bar{x}$ is within plus or minus

$$2\sigma_{\bar{x}} = 2\left(\frac{\sigma}{\sqrt{n}}\right) = 2\left(\frac{0.6}{\sqrt{5}}\right) = 0.537$$

of μ. This is illustrated in Figure 7.1 on the next page.

2   In this case, if we repeatedly took samples of $n = 5$ from this population, each interval would have the form

$$\bar{x} \pm 0.537.$$

Some intervals would contain the true value of μ and some would not, but what proportion of the intervals would contain μ?

3   Combining (1) and (2), we come up with the concept of a confidence interval. That is, if we repeatedly sampled from this population, then we would expect that 95.44 percent of the intervals would contain the true value of μ and 4.56 percent of the intervals would not contain the true value of μ. In practice, we will never know if our interval contains μ or not. If we did know this, then we would not need a confidence interval. The three cases illustrated in Table 7.1 are all examples of 95.44 percent confidence intervals. Later on, we will see that 95 percent is the value that is used most of the time.

FIGURE **7.1**　Three 95.44 Percent Confidence Intervals for μ

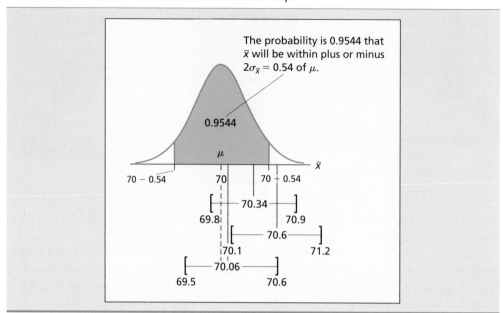

A general confidence interval formula A little later in this section, we will see how to make practical use of confidence intervals. First, however, we present a general formula for finding a confidence interval using the empirical rule:

$$\left[\bar{x} \pm 2\sigma_{\bar{x}}\right] = \left[\bar{x} \pm 2\left(\frac{\sigma}{\sqrt{n}}\right)\right].$$

We make use of the two-standard-deviation part of the empirical rule, and this makes the above interval a 95.44 percent confidence interval. In general, the level of confidence in the interval is expressed as $100(1 - \alpha)$ percent. We refer to the value $1 - \alpha$ as the **confidence coefficient**. The complement of this confidence coefficient is, of course, α. For now, we will not need to know what α specifically represents. At this point, we will say that α represents the probability of an error. This error is discussed in Chapter 8 (Hypothesis Testing).

The following box summarizes the formula used in calculating a $100(1 - \alpha)$ percent confidence interval for a population mean μ:

A Confidence Interval for a Population Mean μ: σ Known

Suppose that the sampled population is normally distributed. Then a **$100(1 - \alpha)$ percent confidence interval for μ** is

This interval is also approximately correct for nonnormal populations if the sample size is large (at least 30).

LO2　$\left[\bar{x} \pm z_{\alpha/2}\left(\frac{\sigma}{\sqrt{n}}\right)\right] = \left[\bar{x} - z_{\alpha/2}\left(\frac{\sigma}{\sqrt{n}}\right), \bar{x} + z_{\alpha/2}\left(\frac{\sigma}{\sqrt{n}}\right)\right].$

To find a general formula for a confidence interval for a population mean μ, we assume that the sampled population is normally distributed, or the sample size n is large. Under these conditions, the sampling distribution of the sample mean $\bar{x}$ is exactly (or approximately, by the central limit theorem) a normal distribution with mean $\mu_{\bar{x}} = \mu$ and standard deviation $\sigma_{\bar{x}} = \sigma/\sqrt{n}$. Then, in order to obtain a confidence interval that has a $1 - \alpha$ probability of containing μ, we find the point $z_{\alpha/2}$ that gives a right-hand tail area under the standard normal

FIGURE 7.2 The Point $z_{\alpha/2}$

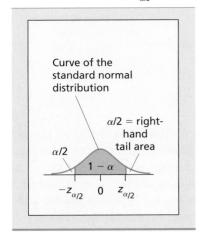

FIGURE 7.3 The Point $z_{0.025}$

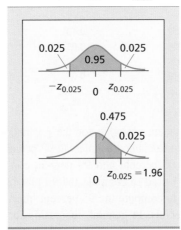

FIGURE 7.4 The Point $z_{0.005}$

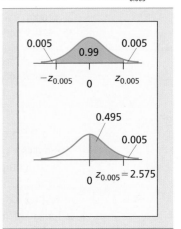

curve equal to $\alpha/2$, and we find the point $-z_{\alpha/2}$ that gives a left-hand tail area under this curve equal to $\alpha/2$ (see Figure 7.2). Noting from Figure 7.2 that the area under the standard normal curve between $-z_{\alpha/2}$ and $z_{\alpha/2}$ is $1 - \alpha$, it can be shown that the probability is $1 - \alpha$ that the sample mean $\bar{x}$ will be within plus or minus $z_{\alpha/2}\sigma_{\bar{x}}$ units of the population mean μ. The quantity $z_{\alpha/2}\sigma_{\bar{x}}$ is called the **margin of error** when estimating μ by $\bar{x}$. If this margin of error is added to and subtracted from $\bar{x}$ to form the interval

LO3

$$\left[\bar{x} \pm z_{\alpha/2}\sigma_{\bar{x}}\right] = \left[\bar{x} \pm z_{\alpha/2}\frac{\sigma}{\sqrt{n}}\right],$$

then the level of confidence that this interval will contain the population mean is $1 - \alpha$. In other words, this interval is a confidence interval for μ based on a confidence coefficient of $1 - \alpha$, and hence we call this interval a **100(1 − α) percent confidence interval for the population mean**. Here **100(1 − α) percent** is called the **confidence level** associated with the confidence interval.

For example, suppose we wish to find a 95 percent confidence interval for the population mean. Since the confidence level is 95 percent, we have $100(1 - \alpha) = 95$. This implies that the confidence coefficient is $1 - \alpha = 0.95$, which implies that $\alpha = 0.05$ and $\alpha/2 = 0.025$. Therefore, we need to find the point $z_{0.025}$. As shown in Figure 7.3, the area under the standard normal curve between $-z_{0.025}$ and $z_{0.025}$ is 0.95, and the area under this curve between 0 and $z_{0.025}$ is 0.475. Looking up the area 0.475 in Table A.3, we find that $z_{0.025} = 1.96$. It follows that the interval

$$\left[\bar{x} \pm z_{0.025}\sigma_{\bar{x}}\right] = \left[\bar{x} \pm 1.96\left(\frac{\sigma}{\sqrt{n}}\right)\right]$$

is a 95 percent confidence interval for the population mean μ. This means that if all possible samples were used to calculate this interval, 95 percent of the resulting intervals would contain μ.

As another example, consider a 99 percent confidence interval for the population mean. Because the confidence level is 99 percent, we have $100(1 - \alpha) = 99$, and the confidence coefficient is $1 - \alpha = 0.99$. This implies that $\alpha = 0.01$ and $\alpha/2 = 0.005$. Therefore, we need to find the point $z_{0.005}$. As shown in Figure 7.4, the area under the standard normal curve between $-z_{0.005}$ and $z_{0.005}$ is 0.99, and the area under this curve between 0 and $z_{0.005}$ is 0.495. Looking up the area 0.495 in Table A.3, we find that $z_{0.005} = 2.575$. It follows that the interval

$$\left[\bar{x} \pm z_{0.005}\sigma_{\bar{x}}\right] = \left[\bar{x} \pm 2.575\left(\frac{\sigma}{\sqrt{n}}\right)\right]$$

TABLE **7.2**   The Point $z_{\alpha/2}$ for Various Levels of Confidence

100(1 − α) percent	**α**	**$\alpha/2$**	**Normal Point $z_{\alpha/2}$**
90% = 100(1 − 0.10)%	0.10	0.05	$z_{0.05}$ = 1.645
95% = 100(1 − 0.05)%	0.05	0.025	$z_{0.025}$ = 1.96
98% = 100(1 − 0.02)%	0.02	0.01	$z_{0.01}$ = 2.33
99% = 100(1 − 0.01)%	0.01	0.005	$z_{0.005}$ = 2.575

is a 99 percent confidence interval for the population mean μ. This means that if all possible samples were used to calculate this interval, 99 percent of the resulting intervals would contain μ.

To compare the 95 percent and 99 percent confidence intervals, notice that the margin of error $2.575(\sigma/\sqrt{n})$ used to compute the 99 percent interval is larger than the margin of error $1.96(\sigma/\sqrt{n})$ used to compute the 95 percent interval. Therefore, the 99 percent interval is the longer of these intervals. In general, increasing the confidence level (1) has the advantage of making us more confident that μ is contained in the confidence interval, but (2) has the disadvantage of increasing the margin of error and thus providing a less precise estimate of the true value of μ. We frequently use 95 percent confidence intervals to make conclusions. If conclusions based on stronger evidence are desired, we sometimes use 99 percent intervals.

Table 7.2 shows the confidence levels 95 percent and 99 percent, as well as two other confidence levels—90 percent and 98 percent—that are sometimes used to calculate confidence intervals. In addition, this table gives the values of α, $\alpha/2$, and $z_{\alpha/2}$ that correspond to these confidence levels.

A confidence interval for μ is based on the normal distribution and requires that the true value of the population standard deviation σ be known. Of course in almost all real-world situations this value is not known. However, the concepts and calculations related to confidence intervals are most easily illustrated using the normal distribution. Therefore, in this section we will assume that through extensive experience with the population or process under consideration, we know σ. When σ is unknown, we will construct a confidence interval for μ by using the t distribution. In Section 7.2, we study t-based confidence intervals for μ, and we will revisit the examples of this section assuming that σ is unknown.

Example 7.1 **The SlimPhone (z-based Confidence Interval for μ with σ Known)**

We will construct a 95 percent confidence interval for the true mean mass of the SlimPhone. The population standard deviation is assumed to be known and equal to 0.6 g. Suppose that another random sample of size $n = 5$ yields a sample mean of $\bar{x} = 70.12$ g. As illustrated in Figure 7.3 on the previous page, we will use the normal point $z_{\alpha/2} = z_{0.025} = 1.96$ to construct a 95 percent confidence interval for μ. Thus, the 95 percent confidence interval for μ is

$$\left[\bar{x} \pm z_{0.025}\left(\frac{\sigma}{\sqrt{n}}\right)\right] = \left[70.12 \pm 1.96\left(\frac{0.6}{\sqrt{5}}\right)\right]$$
$$= [70.12 \pm 0.526]$$
$$= [69.594, 70.646].$$

So we are 95 percent confident that the true population mean mass of the SlimPhone is between 69.594 g and 70.646 g.

Suppose that we wanted to be more confident, say, 99 percent confident. We could construct a 99 percent confidence interval for μ. As illustrated in Figure 7.4 on the previous page, we would use the normal point $z_{\alpha/2} = z_{0.005} = 2.575$. This yields the interval

$$\left[\bar{x} \pm z_{0.005}\left(\frac{\sigma}{\sqrt{n}}\right)\right] = \left[70.12 \pm 2.575\left(\frac{0.6}{\sqrt{5}}\right)\right]$$
$$= [70.12 \pm 0.691]$$
$$= [69.429, 70.811].$$

So we are 99 percent confident that the true population mean mass of the SlimPhone is between 69.429 g and 70.811 g. Note that when the level of confidence is increased, everything else being equal, the confidence interval becomes wider. There is a price to pay with the increased confidence. Precision or accuracy is lost as the level of confidence increases.

Example 7.2 The Payment Time Case (z-Based Confidence Interval for μ with σ Known)

Recall from Example 6.3 on pages 192–193 that a management consulting firm has installed a new computerized billing system in a trucking company. The mean payment time using the trucking company's old billing system was approximately equal to, but no less than, 39 days. In order to assess whether the mean payment time, μ, using the new billing system is substantially less than 39 days, the consulting firm will use a sample of $n = 65$ payment times to find a 95 percent confidence interval for μ. The mean of the 65 payment times is $\bar{x} = 18.1077$. Using the point $z_{\alpha/2} = z_{0.025} = 1.96$, and assuming that σ is known to equal 4.2, it follows that the 95 percent confidence interval for μ is

$$\left[\bar{x} \pm z_{0.025}\left(\frac{\sigma}{\sqrt{n}}\right)\right] = \left[18.1077 \pm 1.96\left(\frac{4.2}{\sqrt{65}}\right)\right]$$
$$= [18.1077 \pm 1.021]$$
$$= [17.1, 19.1].$$

Recalling that the mean payment time using the old billing system is 39 days, the point estimate $\bar{x} = 18.1$ says we estimate that the new billing system reduces the mean payment time by 20.9 days. Because the interval says that we are 95 percent confident that the mean payment time using the new billing system is between 17.1 days and 19.1 days, we are 95 percent confident that the new billing system reduces the mean payment time by at most 21.9 days and by at least 19.9 days.

Example 7.3 Coffee Fills (z-Based Confidence Interval for μ with σ Known)

Suppose that data were collected on medium coffee served at Phil Moore's coffee shop. A medium coffee should contain about 312.5 mL. Suppose that it is known that the standard deviation of medium coffee fills at Phil Moore's is $\sigma = 1$ mL. A random sample of 30 medium cups of coffee is obtained from this location and it is found that the sample mean is $\bar{x} = 312$. Constructing a 95 percent confidence interval for μ, the average volume of coffee served in the medium cups, we have

$$\left[\bar{x} \pm z_{0.025}\left(\frac{\sigma}{\sqrt{n}}\right)\right] = \left[312 \pm 1.96\left(\frac{1}{\sqrt{30}}\right)\right]$$
$$= [312 \pm 0.3578]$$
$$= [311.6422, 312.3578].$$

With 95 percent confidence, we say that the average volume of coffee in a medium coffee at Phil Moore's is somewhere between 311.6422 mL and 312.3578 mL. So, if we repeatedly sampled from this population (store), say, 1,000 samples of size $n = 30$, then we would *expect* that 95 percent of the intervals, or 950 intervals, would contain the true average volume and 50 intervals would not contain this true average. We may find that 947 intervals contain μ, and 53 do not. Remember, we *expect* 95 percent of the intervals to contain μ in the long run. In the next chapter, we will use hypothesis testing to determine whether or not $\mu = 312.5$ mL.

FIGURE **7.5** A Probability for Deriving a Confidence Interval for the Population Mean

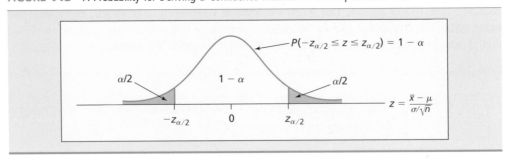

The derivation of the confidence interval formula To show why the interval

$$\left[\bar{x} \pm z_{\alpha/2} \left(\frac{\sigma}{\sqrt{n}} \right) \right]$$

is a $100(1 - \alpha)$ percent confidence interval for μ, recall that if the sampled population is normally distributed or the sample size n is large, then the sampling distribution of $\bar{x}$ is (exactly or approximately) a normal distribution with mean $\mu_{\bar{x}} = \mu$ and standard deviation $\sigma_{\bar{x}} = \sigma/\sqrt{n}$. It follows that the sampling distribution of

$$z = \frac{\bar{x} - \mu}{\sigma/\sqrt{n}}$$

is (exactly or approximately) a standard normal distribution. Therefore, the probability that we will obtain a sample mean $\bar{x}$ such that z is between $-z_{\alpha/2}$ and $z_{\alpha/2}$ is $1 - \alpha$ (see Figure 7.5). That is, we can say that the probability that

$$-z_{\alpha/2} \leq \frac{\bar{x} - \mu}{\sigma/\sqrt{n}} \leq z_{\alpha/2}$$

is equal to $1 - \alpha$. Using some algebraic manipulations, we can show that this is equivalent to saying that the probability that

$$\bar{x} - z_{\alpha/2} \left(\frac{\alpha}{\sqrt{n}} \right) \leq \mu \leq \bar{x} + z_{\alpha/2} \left(\frac{\sigma}{\sqrt{n}} \right)$$

is equal to $1 - \alpha$. This probability statement says that the probability is $1 - \alpha$ (for example, 0.95) that we will obtain a sample mean $\bar{x}$ such that the interval

$$\left[\bar{x} \pm z_{\alpha/2} \frac{\sigma}{\sqrt{n}} \right]$$

contains μ. In other words, this interval is a $100(1 - \alpha)$ percent confidence interval for μ.

Exercises for Section 7.1

CONCEPTS

7.1   Explain why it is important to calculate a confidence interval in addition to calculating a point estimate of a population parameter.

7.2   Write a paragraph explaining exactly what the term "95 percent confidence" means in the context of calculating a 95 percent confidence interval for a population mean.

7.3   For each of the following changes, indicate whether a confidence interval for μ will have a larger or a smaller margin of error:
  a. An increase in the level of confidence.
  b. An increase in the sample size.
  c. A decrease in the level of confidence.
  d. A decrease in the sample size.

METHODS AND APPLICATIONS

7.4 For each of the following confidence levels of $100(1 - \alpha)$ percent, find the $z_{\alpha/2}$ point needed to compute a confidence interval for μ:

    a. 95 percent.   **c.** 99.73 percent.   **e.** 97 percent.
    b. 99 percent.   **d.** 80 percent.   **f.** 92 percent.

7.5 Suppose that for a sample of size $n = 100$ measurements, you find that $\bar{x} = 50$. Assuming that σ equals 2, calculate confidence intervals for the population mean μ with the following confidence levels:

    a. 95 percent.   **c.** 97 percent.   **e.** 99.73 percent.
    b. 99 percent.   **d.** 80 percent.

7.6 THE TRASH BAG CASE

Consider the trash bag case. Suppose that an independent laboratory has tested trash bags and has found that no 130-L bags that are currently on the market have a mean breaking strength of 23 kg or more. On the basis of these results, the producer of the new, improved trash bag feels sure that its 130-L bag will be the strongest such bag on the market if the new trash bag's mean breaking strength can be shown to be at least 23 kg. The mean of the sample of 40 trash bag breaking strengths is $\bar{x} = 22.9$ kg. Let μ denote the mean of the breaking strengths of all possible trash bags of the new type and assume that σ equals 0.7.

    a. Calculate 95 percent and 99 percent confidence intervals for μ.
    b. Using the 95 percent confidence interval, can you be 95 percent confident that μ is at least 23 kg? Explain.
    c. Using the 99 percent confidence interval, can you be 99 percent confident that μ is at least 23 kg? Explain.
    d. Based on your answers to parts b and c, how convinced are you that the new 130-L trash bag is the strongest such bag on the market?

7.7 THE BANK CUSTOMER WAITING TIME CASE

Recall from Exercise 1.9 on pages 8–9 that a bank manager has developed a new system to reduce the time customers spend waiting to be served by tellers during peak business hours. The mean waiting time during peak business hours under the current system is roughly nine to ten minutes. The bank manager hopes that the new system will have a mean waiting time that is less than six minutes. The mean of the sample of 100 bank customer waiting times is $\bar{x} = 5.46$. Let μ denote the mean of all possible bank customer waiting times using the new system and assume that σ equals 2.47.

    a. Calculate 95 percent and 99 percent confidence intervals for μ.
    b. Using the 95 percent confidence interval, can the bank manager be 95 percent confident that μ is less than six minutes? Explain.
    c. Using the 99 percent confidence interval, can the bank manager be 99 percent confident that μ is less than six minutes? Explain.

    d. Based on your answers to parts b and c, how convinced are you that the new mean waiting time is less than six minutes?

7.8 The average cost of a sample of $n = 50$ cell phone calling plans per month from the Payless cell phone company is $\bar{x} = \$48$. Let μ denote the mean cost of calling plans used by all customers who use the Payless calling plans and suppose that $\sigma = \$5$.

    a. Calculate 95 and 99 percent confidence intervals for μ.
    b. Using the 95 percent confidence interval, does it seem plausible that μ is $50?
    c. Using the 99 percent confidence interval, does it seem plausible that μ is $50?
    d. Based on your answers to parts b and c, how confident are you that μ is $50?

7.9 In an article in the *Journal of Management*, Morris, Avila, and Allen studied innovation by surveying firms to find (among other things) the number of new products introduced by the firms. Suppose a random sample of 100 firms is selected and each firm is asked to report the number of new products it has introduced during the last year. The sample mean is found to be $\bar{x} = 5.68$. Assume that σ equals 8.70.

    a. Calculate a 98 percent confidence interval for the population mean number of new products introduced in the last year.
    b. Based on your confidence interval, find a reasonable estimate for the smallest value that the mean number of new products might be. Explain.

7.10 In an article in *Marketing Science*, Silk and Berndt investigate the output of advertising agencies. They describe ad agency output by finding the shares of dollar billing volume coming from various media categories, such as network television, spot television, newspapers, and radio.

    a. Suppose that a random sample of 400 world advertising agencies gives an average percentage share of billing volume from network television equal to 7.46 percent, and assume that σ equals 1.42 percent. Calculate a 95 percent confidence interval for the mean percentage share of billing volume from network television for the population of all world advertising agencies.
    b. Suppose that a random sample of 400 world advertising agencies gives an average percentage share of billing volume from spot television commercials equal to 12.44 percent, and assume that σ equals 1.55 percent. Calculate a 95 percent confidence interval for the mean percentage share of billing volume from spot television commercials for the population of all world advertising agencies.
    c. Compare the confidence intervals in parts a and b. Does it appear that the mean percentage share of billing volume from spot television commercials for world advertising agencies is greater than the mean percentage share of billing volume from network television? Explain.

7.11 A random sample of $n = 20$ prices of detached two-storey houses was taken in Vancouver in December 2006. The sample mean is $\bar{x} = \$581{,}393$. Suppose it is known that $\sigma = \$75{,}000$.

    a. Calculate a 95 percent confidence interval for the population mean price of a detached two-storey house in Vancouver.

    b. Calculate a 99 percent confidence interval for the population mean price of a detached two-storey house in Vancouver.

    c. Based on your answers in parts a and b, how confident are you that the average price of a detached two-storey house in Vancouver is at least $620,000?

7.12 A random sample of $n = 60$ prices of detached two-storey houses was taken in Toronto in December 2006. The sample mean is $\bar{x} = \$425{,}196$. Suppose it is known that $\sigma = \$55{,}000$. A random sample of $n = 40$ prices of detached two-storey houses was taken in Calgary in December 2006. The sample mean is $\bar{x} = \$398{,}459$. Suppose it is known that $\sigma = \$55{,}000$.

    a. Calculate a 99 percent confidence interval for the population mean price of a detached two-storey house in Toronto.

    b. Calculate a 99 percent confidence interval for the population mean price of a detached two-storey house in Calgary.

7.13 To determine the average age of its customers, a large men's clothing manufacturer took a random sample of 40 customers and found $\bar{x} = 38$. Suppose you know that $\sigma = 10$.

    a. Find a 95 percent confidence interval for the mean age, μ, of all the company's customers.

    b. Suppose that you want to narrow the length of the confidence interval to four years. How large a sample is required to achieve this?

7.14 Suppose that you take a random sample of 100 accounts in a large department store chain and find that the mean balance due is $250. From past experience, you also know that $\sigma = \$80$.

    a. Find a 95 percent confidence interval for the mean balance due.

    b. Find a 99 percent confidence interval for the mean balance due.

7.2 *t*-BASED CONFIDENCE INTERVALS FOR A POPULATION MEAN: σ UNKNOWN

CHAPTER 5

LO4

If we do not know σ (which is usually the case), we can use the sample standard deviation s to help construct a confidence interval for μ. The interval is based on the sampling distribution of

$$ t = \frac{\bar{x} - \mu}{s/\sqrt{n}}. $$

If the sampled population is normally distributed, then for any sample size n, this sampling distribution is what is called a **t distribution**. The t distribution was named after William Gossett. While he was doing research at the Guinness brewery in Dublin, Ireland, Gossett used his statistical knowledge to help the brewery select the best-yielding varieties of barley. Another researcher at the brewery had previously published a paper containing some of the brewery's trade secrets, so Guinness prohibited its employees from publishing any papers. Gossett was then unable to publish any works under his name, so he used the pseudonym Student for his publications. This explains why this distribution is referred to as the Student t distribution. It may otherwise have been called the Gossett t distribution.

The curve of the t distribution has a shape similar to that of the standard normal curve. Two t curves and a standard normal curve are illustrated in Figure 7.6. A t curve is symmetrical about zero, which is the mean of any t distribution. However, the t distribution is more spread out, or variable, than the standard normal distribution. Since the above t statistic is a function of two random variables, $\bar{x}$ and s, it is logical that the sampling distribution of this statistic is more variable than the sampling distribution of the z statistic, which is a function of only one random variable, $\bar{x}$. The exact spread, or standard deviation, of the t distribution depends on a parameter called the **number of degrees of freedom** (denoted df). The degrees of freedom df varies depending on the problem. In this situation, the sampling distribution of t has a number of degrees of freedom that equals the sample size minus 1. We say that this sampling distribution is a **t distribution with $n - 1$ degrees of freedom**. As the sample size n (and thus the number of degrees of freedom) increases, the spread of the t distribution decreases (see Figure 7.6). Furthermore, as the number of degrees of freedom approaches infinity, the curve of the t distribution approaches (that is, becomes shaped more and more like) the curve

FIGURE **7.6**   As the Number of Degrees of Freedom Increases, the Spread of the *t* Distribution Decreases and the *t* Curve Approaches the Standard Normal Curve

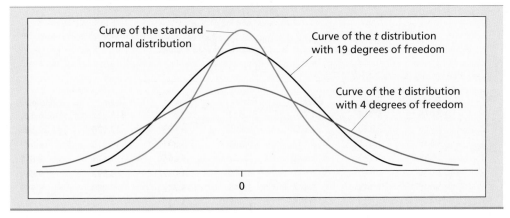

FIGURE **7.7**   An Example of a *t* Point Giving a Specified Right-Hand Tail Area (This *t* Point Gives a Right-Hand Tail Area Equal to α)

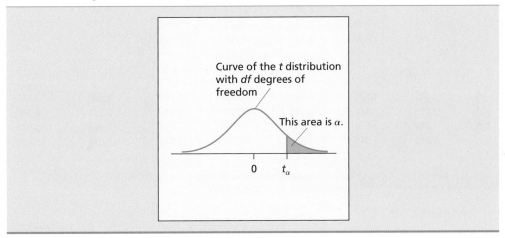

of the standard normal distribution. In fact, when the sample size *n* is at least 30 and thus the number of degrees of freedom $n - 1$ is at least 29, the curve of the *t* distribution is very similar to the standard normal curve. However, the *t* table should be used for *df* values up to and including 100 (Table A.5).

In order to use the *t* distribution, we employ a *t point that is denoted* t_α. As illustrated in Figure 7.7, t_α *is the point on the horizontal axis under the curve of the t distribution that gives a right-hand tail area equal to* α. The value of t_α in a particular situation depends upon the right-hand tail area α and the number of degrees of freedom of the *t* distribution. Values of t_α are tabulated in a *t* **table**. Such a table is given in Table A.5 of Appendix A, and a portion of Table A.5 is reproduced in Table 7.3 on the next page. In this *t* table, the rows correspond to the different numbers of degrees of freedom (denoted *df*). The values of *df* are listed down the left side of the table, while the columns designate the right-hand tail area α. For example, suppose we wish to find the *t* point that gives a right-hand tail area of 0.025 under a *t* curve with *df* = 14 degrees of freedom. To do this, we look in Table 7.3 at the row labelled 14 and the column labelled $t_{0.025}$. We find that this $t_{0.025}$ point is 2.145 (also see Figure 7.8 on the next page). Similarly, when there are *df* = 14 degrees of freedom, we find that $t_{0.005} = 2.977$ (see Table 7.3 and Figure 7.9 on the next page).

TABLE **7.3**   A *t* Table

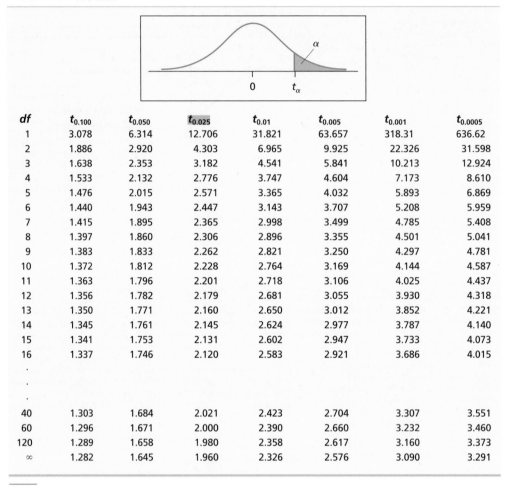

df	$t_{0.100}$	$t_{0.050}$	$t_{0.025}$	$t_{0.01}$	$t_{0.005}$	$t_{0.001}$	$t_{0.0005}$
1	3.078	6.314	12.706	31.821	63.657	318.31	636.62
2	1.886	2.920	4.303	6.965	9.925	22.326	31.598
3	1.638	2.353	3.182	4.541	5.841	10.213	12.924
4	1.533	2.132	2.776	3.747	4.604	7.173	8.610
5	1.476	2.015	2.571	3.365	4.032	5.893	6.869
6	1.440	1.943	2.447	3.143	3.707	5.208	5.959
7	1.415	1.895	2.365	2.998	3.499	4.785	5.408
8	1.397	1.860	2.306	2.896	3.355	4.501	5.041
9	1.383	1.833	2.262	2.821	3.250	4.297	4.781
10	1.372	1.812	2.228	2.764	3.169	4.144	4.587
11	1.363	1.796	2.201	2.718	3.106	4.025	4.437
12	1.356	1.782	2.179	2.681	3.055	3.930	4.318
13	1.350	1.771	2.160	2.650	3.012	3.852	4.221
14	1.345	1.761	2.145	2.624	2.977	3.787	4.140
15	1.341	1.753	2.131	2.602	2.947	3.733	4.073
16	1.337	1.746	2.120	2.583	2.921	3.686	4.015
.							
.							
.							
40	1.303	1.684	2.021	2.423	2.704	3.307	3.551
60	1.296	1.671	2.000	2.390	2.660	3.232	3.460
120	1.289	1.658	1.980	2.358	2.617	3.160	3.373
∞	1.282	1.645	1.960	2.326	2.576	3.090	3.291

FIGURE **7.8**   The *t* Point Giving a Right-Hand Tail Area of 0.025 under the *t* Curve with 14 Degrees of Freedom: $t_{0.025} = 2.145$

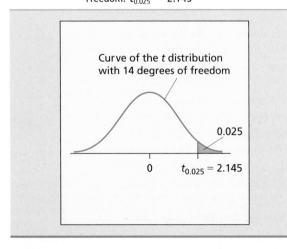

FIGURE **7.9**   The *t* Point Giving a Right-Hand Tail Area of 0.005 under the *t* Curve with 14 Degrees of Freedom: $t_{0.005} = 2.977$

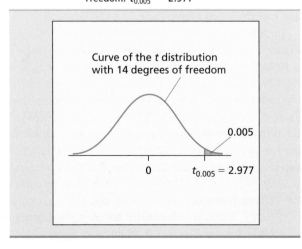

Table 7.3 gives *t* points for degrees of freedom *df* from 1 to 16. The table also gives *t* points for 40, 60, 120, and an infinite number of degrees of freedom. Looking at this table, it is useful to realize that the normal points (*z* values) giving the various right-hand tail areas are listed in the row of the *t* table corresponding to an infinite (∞) number of degrees of freedom. Looking at the row corresponding to ∞, we see that, for example, $z_{0.025} = 1.96$ and $z_{0.005} = 2.576$. Therefore, we can use this row in the *t* table as an alternative to using the normal table when we need to find normal points (*z* values) (such as $z_{\alpha/2}$ in Section 7.1).

Table A.5 of Appendix A gives *t* points for selected values of *df* ranging from 1 to infinity. We can use a computer to find *t* points based on values of *df* greater than 100. Alternatively, because a *t* curve based on more than 100 degrees of freedom is approximately the shape of the standard normal curve, *t* points based on values of *df* greater than 100 can be approximated by their corresponding *z* points. That is, when performing hand calculations, it is reasonable to approximate values of t_α by z_α when *df* is greater than 100.

We now present the formula for a $100(1 - \alpha)$ percent confidence interval for a population mean μ based on the *t* distribution:

A *t*-Based $100(1 - \alpha)$ Percent Confidence Interval for a Population Mean μ: σ Unknown

If the sampled population is normally distributed with mean μ, then a **$100(1 - \alpha)$ percent confidence interval for μ** is

$$\left[\bar{x} \pm t_{\alpha/2}\left(\frac{s}{\sqrt{n}}\right)\right].$$

Here s is the sample standard deviation, $t_{\alpha/2}$ is the *t* point giving a right-hand tail area of $\alpha/2$ under the *t* curve with $n - 1$ degrees of freedom, and n is the sample size. **LO2**

Before presenting an example, we need to make a few comments. First, it has been shown that this confidence interval is approximately valid for many populations that are not exactly normally distributed. In particular, this interval is approximately valid for a mound-shaped, or single-peaked, population, even if the population is somewhat skewed to the right or left. Second, this interval employs the point $t_{\alpha/2}$, which, as shown in Figure 7.10, gives a right-hand tail area equal to $\alpha/2$ under the *t* curve with $n - 1$ degrees of freedom. Here $\alpha/2$ is determined from the desired confidence level, $100(1 - \alpha)$ percent.

CHAPTER 9

FIGURE **7.10**   The Point $t_{\alpha/2}$ with $n - 1$ Degrees of Freedom

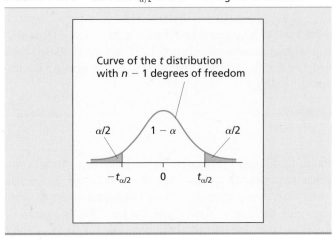

Example 7.4 *t*-Based Confidence Interval for μ

One measure of a company's financial health is its *debt-to-equity ratio*. This quantity is defined to be the ratio of the company's corporate debt to the company's equity. If this ratio is too high, it is one indication of financial instability. For obvious reasons, banks often monitor the financial health of companies to which they have extended commercial loans. Suppose that in order to reduce risk, a large bank has decided to initiate a policy limiting the mean debt-to-equity ratio for its portfolio of commercial loans to 1.5. In order to estimate the mean debt-to-equity ratio of its loan portfolio, the bank randomly selects a sample of 15 of its commercial loan accounts. Audits of these companies result in the following debt-to-equity ratios:

1.31	1.05	1.45	1.21	1.19
1.78	1.37	1.41	1.22	1.11
1.46	1.33	1.29	1.32	1.65

```
1.0 | 5
1.1 | 1 9
1.2 | 1 2 9
1.3 | 1 2 3 7
1.4 | 1 5 6
1.5 |
1.6 | 5
1.7 | 8
```

A stem-and-leaf display of these ratios is given in the page margin, and a box plot of the ratios is given below. The stem-and-leaf display looks reasonably mound-shaped, and both the stem-and-leaf display and the box plot look reasonably symmetrical. Furthermore, the sample mean and standard deviation of the ratios can be calculated to be $\bar{x} = 1.343$ and $s = 0.192$.

Suppose the bank wishes to calculate a 95 percent confidence interval for the loan portfolio's mean debt-to-equity ratio, μ. Because the bank has taken a sample of size $n = 15$, we have $n - 1 = 15 - 1 = 14$ degrees of freedom, and the level of confidence $100(1 - \alpha)\% = 95\%$ implies that $\alpha = 0.05$. Therefore, we use the t point $t_{\alpha/2} = t_{0.05/2} = t_{0.025} = 2.145$ (see Table 7.3). It follows that the 95 percent confidence interval for μ is

$$\left[\bar{x} \pm t_{0.025}\left(\frac{s}{\sqrt{n}} \right) \right] = \left[1.343 \pm 2.145\left(\frac{0.192}{\sqrt{15}} \right) \right]$$
$$= \left[1.343 \pm 0.106 \right]$$
$$= \left[1.237, 1.449 \right].$$

This interval says the bank is 95 percent confident that the mean debt-to-equity ratio for its portfolio of commercial loan accounts is between 1.237 and 1.449. Based on this interval, the bank has strong evidence that the portfolio's mean ratio is less than 1.5 (or that the bank is in compliance with its new policy).

Recall that in the cases discussed in Section 7.1 we calculated z-based confidence intervals for μ by assuming that the population standard deviation σ is known. If σ is actually not known (which is usually true), we should compute t-based confidence intervals. Furthermore, recall that in each of these cases the sample size is large (at least 30). In general, it can be shown that if the sample size is large, the t-based confidence interval for μ is approximately valid even if the sampled population is not normally distributed (or mound-shaped). Therefore, consider the sample of 65 payment times, which has mean $\bar{x} = 18.1077$ and standard deviation $s = 3.9612$. The 95 percent *t*-based confidence interval for the population mean payment time μ is $[18.1077 \pm 1.998(3.9612/\sqrt{65})] = [17.1, 19.1]$, where $t_{0.025} = 1.998$ is based on $n - 1 = 65 - 1 = 64$ degrees of freedom—see Table A.5. This interval is (within rounding) the same as the 95 percent *z*-based interval computed earlier in this chapter. As a third example, the sample of 60 bottle design ratings (see Chapter 1) has mean $\bar{x} = 30.35$ and standard deviation $s = 3.1073$. The 95 percent *t*-based confidence interval for the population mean bottle design rating μ is $[30.35 \pm 2.001(3.1073/\sqrt{60})] = [29.5, 31.2]$, where $t_{0.025} = 2.001$ is based on $n - 1 = 60 - 1 = 59$ degrees of freedom—see Table A.5. This interval is very close to the 95 percent *z*-based interval [29.6, 31.1].

In summary, the *t*-based 95 percent confidence intervals computed using $\bar{x}$ and s for the samples of payment times and bottle design ratings do not differ by much from the *z*-based intervals computed in Section 7.1. Therefore, the practical conclusions reached in Section 7.1 using *z*-based intervals would also be reached using the *t*-based intervals discussed here.

Confidence intervals for μ can be computed using Excel and MegaStat. For example, Figure 7.11 gives the MegaStat output of the sample mean and the half-width (margin of error) for the *t*-based 95 percent confidence interval for μ computed using the sample of $n = 15$ debt-to-equity ratios in Example 7.4.

FIGURE **7.11** MegaStat Outputs for the Debt-to-Equity Ratio Example

Descriptive statistics

	Debt to Equity
count	15
mean	1.3433
sample variance	0.0369
sample standard deviation	0.1921
minimum	1.05
maximum	1.78
range	0.73
sum	20.1500
confidence interval 95% lower	1.2370
confidence interval 95% upper	1.4497
half-width	0.1064
skewness	0.8050
kurtosis	0.8334
coefficient of variation (CV)	14.30%
lst quartile	1.2150
median	1.3200
3rd quartile	1.4300
interquartile range	0.2150
mode	#N/A
low extremes	0
low outliers	0
high outliers	1
high extremes	0

Confidence interval - mean

95%	confidence level
1.3433	mean
0.1921	std. dev.
15	n
2.145	t (df = 14)
0.1064	half-width
1.4497	upper confidence limit
1.2369	lower confidence limit

To conclude this section, we note that if the sample size n is small and the sampled population is not mound-shaped or is highly skewed, the t-based confidence interval for the population mean might not be valid. In this case, we can use a *nonparametric method*—a method that makes no assumption about the shape of the sampled population and is valid for any sample size—to find a confidence interval for the *population median*. Nonparametric methods will be discussed in Chapter 13.

Exercises for Section 7.2

CONCEPTS

7.15 Explain the effect on each of the following as the number of degrees of freedom describing a t curve increases:
  a. The standard deviation of the t curve.
  b. The points t_α and $t_{\alpha/2}$.

7.16 Discuss when it is appropriate to use the t-based confidence interval for μ.

METHODS AND APPLICATIONS

7.17 Using Table 7.3 on page 216, find $t_{0.10}$, $t_{0.025}$, and $t_{0.001}$ based on 11 degrees of freedom. Also, find these t points based on six degrees of freedom.

7.18 Suppose that for a sample of $n = 11$ measurements, you find that $\bar{x} = 72$ and $s = 5$. Assuming normality, compute confidence intervals for the population mean μ with the following levels of confidence:
  a. 95 percent.   **c.** 80 percent.   **e.** 98 percent.
  b. 99 percent.   **d.** 90 percent.   **f.** 99.8 percent.

7.19 The *bad debt ratio* for a financial institution is defined to be the dollar value of loans defaulted divided by the total dollar value of all loans made. Suppose a random sample of seven Ontario banks is selected and that the bad debt ratios (written as percentages) for these banks are 7 percent, 4 percent, 6 percent, 7 percent, 5 percent, 4 percent, and 9 percent. Assuming that the bad debt ratios are approximately normally distributed, the MegaStat output of a 95 percent confidence interval for the mean bad debt ratio of all banks in Ontario is as follows:

	Descriptive statistics
	bad debt
count	7
mean	6.00000
sample standard deviation	1.82574
standard error of the mean	0.69007
confidence interval 95.% lower	4.31147
confidence interval 95.% upper	7.68853

  a. Using the $\bar{x}$ and s on the MegaStat output, verify the calculation of the 95 percent confidence interval, and calculate a 99 percent confidence interval for the mean bad debt ratio.
  b. Banking officials claim that the mean bad debt ratio for all banks in Canada is 3.5 percent and that the mean bad debt ratio for banks in Ontario is higher.

Using the 95 percent confidence interval, can you be 95 percent confident that this claim is true? Using the 99 percent confidence interval, can you be 99 percent confident that this claim is true?

7.20 Suppose that a random sample of $n = 15$ gas stations in Edmonton was sampled during the week of March 8, 2010. The following prices (in cents) for a litre of regular unleaded gasoline were observed: 91.0, 93.7, 94.1, 92.7, 90.9, 90.6, 92.4, 93.7, 95.1, 90.2, 94.5, 91.4, 96.2, 91.3, 90.5. Assume that the prices are approximately normally distributed.
  a. Calculate a 95 percent confidence interval for the average price of a litre of gasoline in Edmonton during the week of March 8, 2010.
  b. Calculate a 99 percent confidence interval for the average price of a litre of gasoline in Edmonton during the week of March 8, 2010.

7.21 A federal agency wishes to assess the effectiveness of a new air traffic control display panel. The mean time required for air traffic controllers to stabilize an air traffic emergency in which two aircraft have been assigned to the same air space is known to be roughly equal to, but no less than, 17 seconds when the current display panel is used. In order to test the new display panel, 20 air traffic controllers are randomly selected and each is trained to use the new panel. When each randomly selected controller uses the new display panel to stabilize a simulated emergency in which two aircraft have been assigned to the same air space, the mean and standard deviation of the 20 stabilization times so obtained are $\bar{x} = 13.8$ seconds and $s = 1.57$ seconds.

  a. Assuming that stabilization times are approximately normally distributed, find a 95 percent confidence interval for the true mean time required to stabilize the emergency situation using the new display panel.
  b. Are you 95 percent confident that the mean stabilization time using the new display panel is less than the 17 seconds for the current display panel? Explain.

FIGURE 7.12 Excel Output for Exercise 7.23

STATISTICS	
Mean	811
Standard Error	8.786353
Median	814
Mode	#N/A
Standard Deviation	19.64688
Sample Variance	386
Kurtosis	−0.12472
Skewness	−0.23636
Range	52
Minimum	784
Maximum	836
Sum	4055
Count	5
Confidence Level (95.0%)	24.39488

FIGURE 7.13 Excel Output for Exercise 7.24

STATISTICS	
Mean	50.575
Standard Error	0.2599
Median	50.65
Mode	50.9
Standard Deviation	1.643753
Sample Variance	2.701923
Kurtosis	−0.2151
Skewness	−0.05493
Range	7.2
Minimum	46.8
Maximum	54
Sum	2023
Count	40
Confidence Level (95.0%)	0.525697

7.22 Whole Foods is an all-natural grocery chain that has 50,000-square-foot (4,600-m^2) stores, more than the industry average of 34,000 square feet (3,200 m^2). Sales per square foot of supermarkets average just under $400 per square foot, as reported by *USA Today* in an article called "A whole new ballgame in grocery shopping." Suppose that sales per square foot in the most recent fiscal year are recorded for a random sample of 10 Whole Foods supermarkets. The data (sales dollars per square foot) are as follows: 854, 858, 801, 892, 849, 807, 894, 863, 829, 815. Using the fact that $\bar{x} = 846.2$ and $s = 32.866$, find a 95 percent confidence interval for the true mean sales dollars per square foot for all Whole Foods supermarkets during the most recent fiscal year. Are you 95 percent confident that this mean is greater than $800, the historical average for Whole Foods?

7.23 A production supervisor at a major chemical company wishes to determine whether a new catalyst, catalyst XA-100, increases the mean hourly yield of a chemical process beyond the current mean hourly yield, which is known to be roughly equal to, but no more than, 750 g per hour. To test the new catalyst, five trial runs using catalyst XA-100 are made. The resulting yields for the trial runs (in grams per hour) are 801, 814, 784, 836, and 820. Assuming that all factors affecting yields of the process have been held as constant as possible during the test runs, it is reasonable to regard the five yields obtained using the new catalyst as a random sample from the population of all possible yields that would be obtained by using the new catalyst. Furthermore, assume that this population is approximately normally distributed.
a. Using the Excel output in Figure 7.12, find a 95 percent confidence interval for the mean of all possible yields obtained using catalyst XA-100.
b. Based on the confidence interval, can you be 95 percent confident that the mean yield using catalyst XA-100 exceeds 750 g per hour? Explain.

7.24 The mean and the standard deviation of a sample of 40 coffee-maker price points are $\bar{x} = 50.575$ and $s = 1.6438$. Calculate a *t*-based 95 percent confidence interval for μ, the mean of the prices of all possible coffee-makers. Also find this interval using the Excel output in Figure 7.13. Are you 95 percent confident that μ is at least $50?

7.25 THE BANK CUSTOMER WAITING TIME CASE

The mean and the standard deviation of the sample of 100 bank customer waiting times (see Chapter 1, Exercise 1.9) are $\bar{x} = 5.46$ and $s = 2.475$. Calculate a *t*-based 95 percent confidence interval for μ, the mean of all possible bank customer waiting times using the new system. Are you 95 percent confident that μ is less than six minutes?

7.26 THE VIDEO GAME SATISFACTION RATING CASE

The mean and the standard deviation of the sample of $n = 65$ customer satisfaction ratings (see Chapter 1, Exercise 1.8) are $\bar{x} = 42.95$ and $s = 2.6424$. Calculate a *t*-based 95 percent confidence interval for μ, the mean of all possible customer satisfaction ratings for the XYZ-Box video game system. Are you 95 percent confident that μ is at least 42, the minimal rating given by a very satisfied customer?

7.27 From a large statistics class at a Canadian university, a random sample of five exam grades was taken: 67, 64, 73, 70, 66.
a. Find a 95 percent confidence interval for the class mean.
b. Find a 99 percent confidence interval for the class mean.
c. What assumption did you make in parts a and b in order to be able to use the *t* distribution to construct the confidence intervals?

7.28 A real estate agency in Canada wants to estimate the average selling price of houses in a suburb of Toronto. It randomly samples 25 recent sales and calculates the average price $\bar{x} = \$425{,}000$ with a sample standard deviation of $s = \$80{,}000$.
   a. Find a 95 percent confidence interval for the mean of all the selling prices.
   b. Find a 99 percent confidence interval for the mean of all the selling prices.
   c. What assumption did you make in parts a and b in order to be able to use the t distribution to construct the confidence intervals?
   d. You recently heard that a friend paid $\$550{,}000$ for a house in the same suburb. Is that plausible, or could there have been a reporting error?

7.29 On a major Canadian highway, a random sample of 20 cars were clocked as they passed by a checkpoint, and their speeds were as follows (in kilometres per hour):

105, 112, 117, 109, 124, 128, 112, 102, 135, 129,

122, 113, 106, 114, 105, 110, 107, 111, 129, 130

   a. Construct a 95 percent confidence interval for the average speed of the cars passing by the checkpoint.
   b. Construct a 99 percent confidence interval for the average speed of the cars passing by the checkpoint.
   c. What assumption did you make in parts a and b in order to be able to use the t distribution to construct the confidence intervals?
   d. The posted speed limit on this highway is 100 km/h. Do you have evidence to suggest that the average speed travelled by the motorists that use this highway is different from the posted speed limit?

7.30 The meat department of a local supermarket chain packages its ground beef using meat trays of two sizes: one designed to hold 500 g of beef and the other to hold 1 kg of beef. A random sample of 35 of the larger meat trays produced measurements with a mean of 1.01 kg and a standard deviation of 0.18 kg. Assume that the masses are normally distributed.
   a. Construct a 99 percent confidence interval for the mean mass of all packages sold in the larger meat trays by the supermarket chain.
   b. The quality control department intends that the mean amount of ground beef in the larger trays be 1 kg. Should the confidence interval in part a concern the quality control department?

7.3 SAMPLE SIZE DETERMINATION

We will now explain how to find the size of the sample that will be needed to make the margin of error in a confidence interval for μ as small as we wish. In order to develop a formula for the needed sample size, we will initially assume that we know σ. Then, if the population is normally distributed or the sample size is large, the z-based $100(1 - \alpha)$ percent confidence interval for μ is

$$\left[\bar{x} \pm z_{\alpha/2}\left(\frac{\sigma}{\sqrt{n}} \right) \right].$$

To find the needed sample size, we set $z_{\alpha/2}(\sigma/\sqrt{n})$ equal to the desired margin of error and solve for n. Letting E denote the desired margin of error, we obtain

$$z_{\alpha/2}\left(\frac{\sigma}{\sqrt{n}} \right) = E.$$

Multiplying both sides of this equation by $\sqrt{n}$ and dividing both sides by E, we obtain

$$\sqrt{n} = \frac{z_{\alpha/2}\sigma}{E}.$$

Squaring both sides of this result gives us the formula for n:

Determining the Sample Size for a Confidence Interval for μ: σ Known

LO5

A sample of size

$$n = \left(\frac{z_{\alpha/2}\sigma}{E} \right)^2$$

makes the margin of error in a $100(1 - \alpha)$ percent confidence interval for μ equal to E. That is, this

sample size makes us $100(1 - \alpha)$ percent confident that $\bar{x}$ is within E units of μ. If the calculated value of n is not a whole number, round this value up to the next whole number (so that the margin of error is at least as small as desired).

If we consider the formula for the sample size n, it intuitively follows that the value E is the farthest that the user is willing to allow $\bar{x}$ to be from μ at a given level of confidence. The value $z_{\alpha/2}$ follows directly from the given level of confidence. Furthermore, because the population standard deviation σ is in the numerator of the formula for n, it follows that the more variable the individual population measurements are, the larger is the sample size needed to estimate μ with a specified accuracy.

In order to use this formula for n, either we must know σ (which is unlikely) or we must compute an estimate of σ. Often we estimate σ by using a **preliminary sample**. In this case, we modify the above formula for n by replacing σ with the standard deviation s of the preliminary sample and by replacing $z_{\alpha/2}$ with $t_{\alpha/2}$. Thus, we obtain

$$n = \left(\frac{t_{\alpha/2}\, s}{E}\right)^2,$$

LO5

where the number of degrees of freedom for the $t_{\alpha/2}$ point is the size of the preliminary sample minus 1. Intuitively, using $t_{\alpha/2}$ compensates for the fact that the preliminary sample's value of s might underestimate σ.

Example 7.5 Sample Size Determination (with σ Known)

A manufacturer of pharmaceutical products analyzes a specimen from each batch of a product to verify the concentration of the active ingredient. It has been determined that the results of repeated measurements follow a normal distribution quite closely. The standard deviation σ is known to be 0.0068 g/L. Suppose that management asks the laboratory to produce results accurate to within ± 0.005 with 95 percent confidence. We can calculate how many measurements must be averaged to comply with this request:

$$n = \left(\frac{z_{0.025}\sigma}{E}\right)^2 = \left(\frac{1.96(0.0068)}{0.005}\right)^2 = 7.11.$$

Rounding this value up to the next integer, we see that a sample size of at least 8 is needed here. A larger sample would also do, but the point of this exercise is to find the smallest sample size that will achieve the desired accuracy.

When the value of σ is not known (which is usually the case), it is very difficult to determine the exact sample size needed in order to be within a desired margin of error. Why is this? When σ is unknown, we substitute s in its place, and we use $t_{\alpha/2}$ instead of $z_{\alpha/2}$. But in order to find the value of $t_{\alpha/2}$, we need to know the number of degrees of freedom, which of course depends on the size of the preliminary sample.

In the next example, we will illustrate how we can make use of preliminary sample information to determine a sample size.

Example 7.6 Sample Size Determination (with σ Unknown)

Consider the following random sample of men's masses from a local health club (in kilograms): 102, 95, 101, 102, 103, 101, 100, 104. The sample mean is 101 kg with a standard deviation of 2.726 kg. The 95 percent confidence interval is [98.721, 103.279]. The interval has a length of 4.558, or a margin of error of 2.279. Now we ask: What is the minimum sample size needed to obtain a confidence interval with a length of no more than 3.6 with 95 percent confidence? You can see that this example is a little different from those using known population standard deviations. We have to do some estimation here. We will make use of the preliminary sample information above to help us. We see that with a sample size of 8, the confidence interval has a length of 4.558, so it appears as though we will need more than 8 observations to reduce the length to 3.6. We can take $t_{0.025} = 2.365$ (based on $df = 8 - 1 = 7$) as the maximum value for $t_{0.025}$ since we expect to take a sample size larger than 8 (and the t value will decrease as we increase the sample size n). We will also assume that the new sample will have the same standard deviation as the original sample of $n = 8$ (2.276):

$$n = \left(\frac{t_{0.025}s}{1.8}\right)^2 = \left(\frac{2.365(2.726)}{1.8}\right)^2 = 12.83$$

So, using this method, we would need $n = 13$ observations to achieve the desired precision.

Sometimes, when we have sample information, as a rough approximation, we may want to use the corresponding value of $z_{\alpha/2}$ along with s.

In general, the purpose behind replacing $z_{\alpha/2}$ with $t_{\alpha/2}$ when we are using a preliminary sample to obtain an estimate of σ is to be *conservative*, so that we compute a sample size that is *at least as large as needed*. Because of this, we often obtain a margin of error that is even smaller than we have requested.

Finally, sometimes we do not have a preliminary sample that can be used to estimate σ. In this case, we have two alternatives. First, we might estimate σ by using our knowledge about a similar population or process. For instance, an auto maker might believe that the standard deviation of the fuel efficiency values for this year's midsize model is about the same as the standard deviation of the fuel efficiency values for last year's model. Thus, it might be reasonable to use the best available estimate of σ for last year's model as a preliminary estimate of σ for this year's model. Second, it can be shown that if we can make a reasonable guess of the range of the population being studied, a conservatively large estimate of σ is this estimated range divided by 4. For example, if the auto maker's design engineers feel that almost all of its midsize cars should get fuel efficiency values within a range of 1.1 L/100 km, then a conservatively large estimate of σ is 1.1/4 L/100 km = 0.275 L/100 km. When employing such an estimate of σ, it is sufficient to use the z-based sample size formula $n = (z_{\alpha/2}\sigma/E)^2$, because a conservatively large estimate of σ will give us a conservatively large sample size.

Exercises for Section 7.3

CONCEPTS

7.31 Explain what is meant by the margin of error for a confidence interval. What error are we talking about in the context of an interval for μ?

7.32 Explain exactly what we mean when we say that a sample of size n makes us 99 percent confident that $\bar{x}$ is within E units of μ.

7.33 Why do you usually need to take a preliminary sample when determining the size of the sample needed to make the margin of error of a confidence interval equal to E?

METHODS AND APPLICATIONS

7.34 Consider a population with a standard deviation equal to 10. You wish to estimate the mean of this population.
   a. How large a random sample is needed to construct a 95.44 percent confidence interval for the mean of this population with a margin of error equal to 1?

b. Suppose that you now take a random sample of the size you determined in part a. If you obtain a sample mean equal to 295, calculate the 95.44 percent confidence interval for the population mean. What is the interval's margin of error?

7.35 Consider a random sample of $n = 20$ prices of detached two-storey houses in Vancouver for which the sample standard deviation is $s = \$72,500$.
   a. How large a random sample of house prices is needed to make you 95 percent confident that $\bar{x}$, the sample mean price of a two-storey house, is within a margin of error of \$25,000 of μ, the true mean price of a two-storey house in Vancouver?
   b. Suppose that you now take a random sample of the size you determined in part a. If you obtain a sample mean equal to \$580,000 and a sample standard deviation of $s = \$75,000$, calculate the 95 percent confidence interval for the population mean. What is the interval's margin of error?

7.36 Consider a random sample of $n = 20$ prices of detached two-storey houses in Calgary for which the sample standard deviation is $s = \$72,500$. How large a random sample of house prices is needed to make you

    a. 95 percent confident that $\bar{x}$, the sample mean price of a two-storey house, is within a margin of error of $\$29,000$ of μ, the true mean price of a two-storey house in Calgary?

    b. 99 percent confident that $\bar{x}$, the sample mean price of a two-storey detached house, is within a margin of error of $\$29,000$ of μ, the true mean price of a two-storey detached house in Calgary?

7.37 Referring to Exercise 7.21 on page 220, regard the sample of 20 stabilization times for which $s = 1.57$ as a preliminary sample. Determine the sample size needed to make you 95 percent confident that $\bar{x}$, the sample mean time required to stabilize the emergency situation, is within a margin of error of 0.5 seconds of μ, the true mean time required to stabilize the emergency situation using the new display panel.

7.38 Referring to Exercise 7.22 on pages 220–221, regard the sample of ten sales figures for which $s = 32.866$ as a preliminary sample. How large a sample of sales figures is needed to make you 95 percent confident that $\bar{x}$, the sample mean sales dollars per square foot, is within a margin of error of $\$10$ of μ, the true mean sales dollars per square foot for all Whole Foods supermarkets?

7.39 Referring to Exercise 7.23 on page 221, regard the sample of five trial runs for which $s = 19.65$ (see Figure 7.12) as a preliminary sample. Determine the number of trial runs of the chemical process needed to make you

    a. 95 percent confident that $\bar{x}$, the sample mean hourly yield, is within a margin of error of 8 g of the true mean hourly yield μ when catalyst XA-100 is used.

    b. 99 percent confident that $\bar{x}$ is within a margin of error of 5 g of μ.

7.4 CONFIDENCE INTERVALS FOR A POPULATION PROPORTION

In Chapter 6, the wine maker decided to replace its current corked bottles with the new corkless bottle if p, the true proportion of all current purchasers who would stop buying the wine if the new corkless bottle were used, is less than 0.10. Suppose that when 1,000 current purchasers are randomly selected and are asked to try the new bottle, 63 say they would stop buying the wine if the new bottle were used. The point estimate of the population proportion p is the sample proportion $\hat{p} = 63/1,000 = 0.063$. This sample proportion says we estimate that 6.3 percent of all current purchasers would stop buying the wine if the new bottle were used. Since $\hat{p}$ equals 0.063, we have some evidence that p is less than 0.10.

In order to see if there is strong evidence that p is less than 0.10, we can calculate a confidence interval for p. As explained in Chapter 6, if the sample size n is large, then the sampling distribution of the sample proportion $\hat{p}$ is approximately a normal distribution with mean $\mu_{\hat{p}} = p$ and standard deviation $\sigma_{\hat{p}} = \sqrt{p(1-p)/n}$. Using the same logic we used in developing confidence intervals for μ, it follows that a $100(1-\alpha)$ percent confidence interval for p is

$$\left[\hat{p} \pm z_{\alpha/2}\sqrt{\frac{p(1-p)}{n}}\right].$$

LO6

Estimating $p(1-p)$ by $\hat{p}(1-\hat{p})$, it follows that a $100(1-\alpha)$ percent confidence interval for p can be calculated as summarized below:

A Large-Sample $100(1-\alpha)$ Percent Confidence Interval for a Population Proportion p

If the sample size n is large, a $100(1-\alpha)$ percent confidence interval for the population proportion p is

$$\left[\hat{p} \pm z_{\alpha/2}\sqrt{\frac{\hat{p}(1-\hat{p})}{n}}\right].$$

Here n should be considered large if both $n\hat{p}$ and $n(1-\hat{p})$ are at least 5.[1]

---

[1]Some statisticians suggest using the more conservative rule that both $n\hat{p}$ and $n(1-\hat{p})$ must be at least 10. Furthermore, because $\hat{p}(1-\hat{p})/(n-1)$ is an unbiased point estimate of $p(1-p)/n$, a more correct $100(1-\alpha)$ percent confidence interval for p is $[\hat{p} \pm z_{\alpha/2}\sqrt{\hat{p}(1-\hat{p})/(n-1)}]$. However, because n is large, there is little difference between intervals obtained by using this formula and those obtained by using the formula in the above box.

Example 7.7　The Wine Case (z-Based Confidence Interval for p)

In the wine case, consider calculating a confidence interval for p, the population proportion of purchasers who would stop buying the wine if the new bottle were used. In order to see whether the sample size $n = 1{,}000$ is large enough to enable us to use the confidence interval formula just given, recall that the point estimate of p is $\hat{p} = 63/1{,}000 = 0.063$. Therefore, because $n\hat{p} = 1{,}000(0.063) = 63$ and $n(1 - \hat{p}) = 1{,}000(0.937) = 937$ are both greater than 5, we can use the confidence interval formula. For example, a 95 percent confidence interval for p is

$$\left[\hat{p} \pm z_{0.025}\sqrt{\frac{\hat{p}(1 - \hat{p})}{n}}\right] = \left[0.063 \pm 1.96\sqrt{\frac{(0.063)(0.937)}{1{,}000}}\right]$$

$$= [0.063 \pm 0.0151]$$

$$= [0.0479, 0.0781].$$

This interval says that we are 95 percent confident that between 4.79 percent and 7.81 percent of all current purchasers would stop buying the wine if the new bottle were used. Below we give the MegaStat output of this interval.

Confidence interval - proportion

1,000 n	95% confidence level	0.078 upper confidence limit
1.960 z	0.063 proportion	0.048 lower confidence limit

A 99 percent confidence interval for p is

$$\left[\hat{p} \pm z_{0.005}\sqrt{\frac{\hat{p}(1 - \hat{p})}{n}}\right] = \left[0.063 \pm 2.575\sqrt{\frac{(0.063)(0.937)}{1{,}000}}\right]$$

$$= [0.063 \pm 0.0198]$$

$$= [0.0432, 0.0828].$$

The upper limits of both the 95 percent and 99 percent intervals are less than 0.10. Therefore, we have very strong evidence that the true proportion p of all current purchasers who would stop buying the wine is less than 0.10. Based on this result, it seems reasonable to use the new bottles.

In the wine example, a sample of 1,000 purchasers gives us a 95 percent confidence interval for p—$[0.063 \pm 0.0151]$—with a reasonably small margin of error of 0.0151. Generally speaking, quite a large sample is needed in order to make the margin of error in a confidence interval for p reasonably small. The next two examples demonstrate that a sample size of 200, which most people would consider quite large, does not necessarily give a 95 percent confidence interval for p with a small margin of error.

Example 7.8　Phe-Mycin (z-Based Confidence Interval for p)

Antibiotics occasionally cause nausea as a side effect. Scientists working for a major drug company have developed a new antibiotic called Phe-Mycin. The company wishes to estimate p, the proportion of all patients who would experience nausea as a side effect when being treated with Phe-Mycin. Suppose that a sample of 200 patients is randomly selected. When these patients are treated with Phe-Mycin, 35 experience nausea. The point estimate of the population proportion p is the sample proportion $\hat{p} = 35/200 = 0.175$. This sample proportion says that we estimate that 17.5 percent of all patients would experience nausea as a side effect of taking Phe-Mycin. Furthermore, because $n\hat{p} = 200(0.175) = 35$ and $n(1 - \hat{p}) = 200(0.825) = 165$

are both at least 5, we can use the previously given formula to calculate a confidence interval for p. Doing this, we find that a 95 percent confidence interval for p is

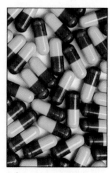

$$\left[\hat{p} \pm z_{0.025}\sqrt{\frac{\hat{p}(1-\hat{p})}{n}}\right] = \left[0.175 \pm 1.96\sqrt{\frac{(0.175)(0.825)}{200}}\right]$$
$$= [0.175 \pm 0.053]$$
$$= [0.122, 0.228].$$

This interval says we are 95 percent confident that between 12.2 percent and 22.8 percent of all patients would experience nausea as a side effect of taking Phe-Mycin. Notice that the margin of error (0.053) in this interval is rather large. Therefore, this interval is fairly long, and it does not provide a very precise estimate of p.

Example 7.9 Got Your Canadian Passport Yet?

According to an Ipsos Reid poll conducted from November 7 to 9, 2006, nearly half (49.05 percent) of Canadians did not have a passport at that time.[2] One thousand one Canadians were surveyed in this poll. The point estimate of p is the sample proportion $\hat{p} = 0.4905$. Because $n\hat{p} = 491$ and $n(1 - \hat{p}) = 511$ are both at least 5, it follows that a 95 percent confidence interval is

$$\left[\hat{p} \pm z_{0.025}\sqrt{\frac{\hat{p}(1-\hat{p})}{n}}\right] = \left[0.4905 \pm 1.96\sqrt{\frac{(0.4905)(0.5095)}{1,001}}\right]$$
$$= [0.4905 \pm 0.0310]$$
$$= [0.4595, 0.5215].$$

This interval says that we are 95 percent confident that between 45.95 percent and 52.15 percent of Canadians did not have a valid Canadian passport at that time.

In order to find the size of the sample needed to estimate a population proportion, we consider the theoretically correct interval

$$\left[\hat{p} \pm z_{\alpha/2}\sqrt{\frac{p(1-p)}{n}}\right].$$

To obtain the sample size needed to make the margin of error in this interval equal to E, we set

$$z_{\alpha/2}\sqrt{\frac{p(1-p)}{n}} = E$$

and solve for n. When we do this, we get the following result:

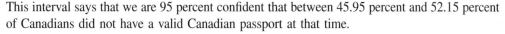

Determining the Sample Size for a Confidence Interval for p

LO7

A sample of size

$$n = p(1-p)\left(\frac{z_{\alpha/2}}{E}\right)^2$$

makes the margin of error in a $100(1 - \alpha)$ percent confidence interval for p equal to E. That is, this sample size makes us $100(1 - \alpha)$ percent confident that $\hat{p}$ is within E units of p. If the calculated value of n is not a whole number, round this value up to the next whole number.

Looking at this formula, we see that the larger $p(1 - p)$ is, the larger n will be. To make sure n is large enough, consider Figure 7.14 on the next page, which is a graph of $p(1 - p)$ versus p.

[2]Source: http://www.ipsos-na.com/news-polls/pressrelease.aspx?id=3285, "The Annual Expedia Winter Survey," November 28, 2007.

FIGURE **7.14**   The Graph of $p(1 - p)$ versus p

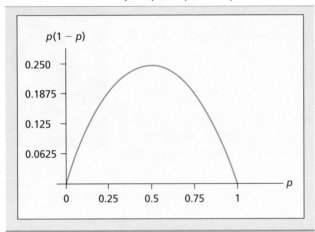

FIGURE **7.15**   MegaStat Output of a
Sample Size Calculation

Sample size - proportion
   0.02 E, error tolerance
      0.5 estimated population proportion
      95% confidence level
      1.960 z
2,400.905 sample size
   2,401 rounded up

This figure shows that $p(1 - p)$ equals 0.25 when p equals 0.5. Furthermore, $p(1 - p)$ is never larger than 0.25. Therefore, if the true value of p could be near 0.5, we should set $p(1 - p)$ equal to 0.25. This will ensure that n is as large as needed to make the margin of error as small as desired. For example, suppose we wish to estimate the proportion p of all registered Canadian voters who currently favour a particular candidate for prime minister of Canada. If this candidate is the leader of a major political party, or if the candidate enjoys broad popularity for some other reason, then p could be near 0.5. Furthermore, suppose we wish to make the margin of error in a 95 percent confidence interval for p equal to 0.02. If the sample to be taken is random, it should consist of

LO7

$$n = p(1 - p)\left(\frac{z_{\alpha/2}}{E}\right)^2 = 0.25\left(\frac{1.96}{0.02}\right)^2 = 2,401$$

registered voters. The MegaStat output of the results of this calculation is shown in Figure 7.15. In reality, a list of all registered voters in Canada may not be available to polling organizations. Therefore, it may not be feasible to take a (technically correct) random sample of registered voters in this country. For this reason, Canadian polling organizations actually employ other (more complicated) kinds of samples. We have explained some of the basic ideas behind these more complex samples in Section 1.6. For now, we consider the samples taken by these polling organizations to be approximately random. Suppose, then, that when the sample of voters is actually taken, the proportion $\hat{p}$ of sampled voters who favour the candidate turns out to be greater than 0.52. It follows, because the sample is large enough to make the margin of error in a 95 percent confidence interval for p equal to 0.02, that the lower limit of such an interval is greater than 0.50. This says we have strong evidence that a majority of all registered voters favour the candidate. For instance, if the sample proportion $\hat{p}$ equals 0.53, we are 95 percent confident that the proportion of all registered voters who favour the candidate is between 0.51 and 0.55.

Major polling organizations conduct public opinion polls concerning many kinds of issues. Whereas making the margin of error in a 95 percent confidence interval for p equal to 0.02 requires a sample size of 2,401, making the margin of error in such an interval equal to 0.03 requires a sample size of only

$$n = p(1 - p)\left(\frac{z_{\alpha/2}}{E}\right)^2 = 0.25\left(\frac{1.96}{0.03}\right)^2 = 1,067.1,$$

or 1,068 (rounding up). Of course, these calculations assume that the proportion p being estimated could be near 0.5. However, for any value of p, increasing the margin of error from 0.02 to 0.03 substantially decreases the needed sample size and thus saves considerable time and money. For this reason, although the most accurate public opinion polls use a margin of error of 0.02, the vast majority of public opinion polls use a margin of error of 0.03 or larger.

When the news media report the results of a public opinion poll, they express the margin of error in a 95 percent confidence interval for p in percentage points. For instance, if the margin of error is 0.03, the media would say the poll's margin of error is 3 percentage points.

The media seldom report the level of confidence, but almost all polling results are based on 95 percent confidence. Sometimes the media make a vague reference to the level of confidence. For instance, if the margin of error is 3 percentage points, the media might say that "the sample result will be within 3 percentage points of the population value in 19 out of 20 samples." Here the "19 out of 20 samples" is a reference to the level of confidence, which is $100(19/20) = 100(0.95) = 95$ percent.

As an example, suppose a news report says a recent poll finds that 34 percent of the public favours military intervention in an international crisis, and suppose the poll's margin of error is reported to be 3 percentage points. This means the sample taken is large enough to make us 95 percent confident that the sample proportion $\hat{p} = 0.34$ is within 0.03 (that is, 3 percentage points) of the true proportion p of the entire public that favours military intervention. That is, we are 95 percent confident that p is between 0.31 and 0.37.

If the population proportion we are estimating is substantially different from 0.5, setting p equal to 0.5 will give a sample size that is much larger than is needed. In this case, we should use our intuition or previous sample information—along with Figure 7.14—to determine the largest reasonable value for $p(1 - p)$. Figure 7.14 implies that for any range of reasonable values of p that does not contain 0.5, the quantity $p(1 - p)$ is maximized by the reasonable value of p that is closest to 0.5. Therefore, *when we are estimating a proportion that is substantially different from 0.5, we use the reasonable value of p that is closest to 0.5 to calculate the sample size needed to obtain a specified margin of error.*

Example 7.10 Sample Size Determination (with Unknown *p*)

Again consider estimating the proportion of all patients who would experience nausea as a side effect of taking the new antibiotic Phe-Mycin. Suppose the drug company wishes to find the size of the random sample that is needed in order to obtain a 2 percent margin of error with 95 percent confidence. In Example 7.8, we employed a sample of 200 patients to compute a 95 percent confidence interval for p. This interval, which is [0.122, 0.228], makes us very confident that p is between 0.122 and 0.228. As shown in Figure 7.16, because 0.228 is the reasonable value of p that is closest to 0.5, the largest reasonable value of $p(1 - p)$ is $0.228(1 - 0.228) = 0.1760$, and thus the drug company should take a sample of

$$ n = p(1 - p)\left(\frac{z_{\alpha/2}}{E}\right)^2 = 0.1760\left(\frac{1.96}{0.02}\right)^2 = 1{,}691 \text{ (rounded up)} $$

LO7

patients.

FIGURE **7.16** The Largest Reasonable Value for $p(1 - p)$ in the Antibiotic Example Is
$(0.228)(1 - 0.228) = 0.1760$

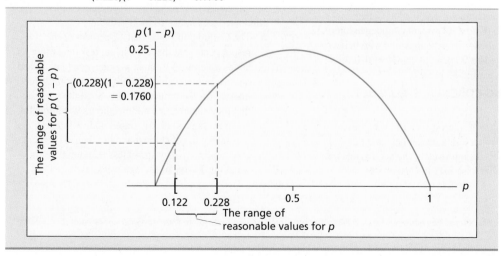

Finally, as a last example of choosing p for sample size calculations, suppose that experience indicates that a population proportion p is at least 0.75. Then 0.75 is the reasonable value of p that is closest to 0.5, and we would use the largest reasonable value of $p(1 - p)$, which is $0.75(1 - 0.75) = 0.1875$.

Exercises for Section 7.4

CONCEPTS

7.40 **a.** What does a population proportion tell you about the population?
b. Explain the difference between p and $\hat{p}$.
c. What is meant when a public opinion poll's margin of error is 0.03?

7.41 Suppose you are using the sample size formula in the box on page 227 to find the sample size needed to make the margin of error in a confidence interval for p equal to E. In each of the following situations, which value of p would be used in the formula for finding n? Explain.
a. You have no idea what value p is—it could be any value between 0 and 1.
b. Past experience tells you that p is no more than 0.3.
c. Past experience tells you that p is at least 0.8.

METHODS AND APPLICATIONS

7.42 In each of the following cases, determine whether the sample size n is large enough to use the large-sample formula presented in the box on page 225 to compute a confidence interval for p.
a. $\hat{p} = 0.1, n = 30.$ **d.** $\hat{p} = 0.8, n = 400.$
b. $\hat{p} = 0.1, n = 100.$ **e.** $\hat{p} = 0.9, n = 30.$
c. $\hat{p} = 0.5, n = 50.$ **f.** $\hat{p} = 0.99, n = 200.$

7.43 In each of the following cases, compute 95 percent, 98 percent, and 99 percent confidence intervals for the population proportion p.
a. $\hat{p} = 0.4, n = 100.$ **c.** $\hat{p} = 0.9, n = 100.$
b. $\hat{p} = 0.1, n = 300.$ **d.** $\hat{p} = 0.6, n = 50.$

7.44 On May 10, 2007, Ipsos Reid reported that 74 percent of Canadian consumers say that good customer service is the best way for companies to express appreciation for their patronage.[3] Suppose that these results are based on an online sample of 1,000 adult Canadians (aged 18 or older). Find a 95 percent confidence interval for the true proportion of Canadian adults who believe this to be true. Are you 95 percent confident that this proportion would exceed 80 percent?

7.45 **THE MARKETING ETHICS CASE: CONFLICT OF INTEREST**

Recall that a conflict of interest scenario was presented to a sample of 205 marketing researchers and that 111 of these researchers disapproved of the actions taken in the scenario (see Exercise 2.48 in Chapter 2).

a. Assuming that the sample of 205 marketing researchers was randomly selected, use this sample information to show that the 95 percent confidence interval for the proportion of all marketing researchers who disapprove of the actions taken in the conflict of interest scenario is as given in the MegaStat output below. Interpret this interval.

Confidence interval - proportion		
205 n	95% confidence level	0.610 upper confidence limit
1.960 z	0.541 proportion	0.473 lower confidence limit

b. On the basis of this interval, is there convincing evidence that a majority of all marketing researchers disapprove of the actions taken in the conflict of interest scenario? Explain.

7.46 Consider a two-way election race between Willie Win and Betty Wont to elect a new student council president at a Canadian university. Suppose that 500 students were randomly selected from the population of students. Suppose that 237 students said they would vote for Betty.
a. Find a point estimate of and a 95 percent confidence interval for p, the proportion of all students who will vote for Betty.
b. Based on your interval, can you be 95 percent confident that Betty will win the election?

7.47 On January 7, 2000, the Gallup Organization released the results of a poll comparing the lifestyles of today with those of yesteryear. The survey results were based on telephone interviews with a randomly selected sample of 1,031 U.S. adults, 18 years and older, conducted December 20 to 21, 1999.[4]
a. The Gallup poll found that 42 percent of the respondents said that they spend less than three hours watching TV on an average weekday. Based on this finding, calculate a 99 percent confidence interval for the proportion of U.S. adults who say that they spend less than three hours watching TV on an average weekday. Based on this interval, is it reasonable to conclude that more than 40 percent of U.S. adults say they spend less than three hours watching TV on an average weekday?

---

[3]Source: http://www.ipsos-na.com/news-polls/pressrelease.aspx?id53482, "Good customer service best way to show customer appreciation," May 10, 2007.

[4]Source: http://www.gallup.com/poll/3352/Trends-Show-Bathing-Exercise-Up-Watching-Down.aspx/, The Gallup Organization, January 7, 2000.

b. The Gallup poll found that 60 percent of the respondents said they took part in some form of daily activity (outside of work, including housework) to keep physically fit. Based on this finding, find a 95 percent confidence interval for the proportion of U.S. adults who say they take part in some form of daily activity to keep physically fit. Based on this interval, is it reasonable to conclude that more than 50 percent of U.S. adults say they take part in some form of daily activity to keep physically fit?

c. In explaining its survey methods, Gallup states the following: "For results based on this sample, one can say with 95 percent confidence that the maximum error attributable to sampling and other random effects is plus or minus 3 percentage points." Explain how your calculations for part b verify that this statement is true.

7.48 In an article in the *Journal of Advertising*, Weinberger and Spotts compare the use of humour in television ads in the United States and the United Kingdom. They found that a substantially greater percentage of U.K. ads use humour.

a. Suppose that a random sample of 400 television ads in the United Kingdom reveals that 142 of these ads use humour. Show that the point estimate of and the 95 percent confidence interval for the proportion of all U.K. television ads that use humour are as given in the MegaStat output below.

Confidence interval - proportion

400 n	95%	confidence level	0.402 upper confidence limit
1.960 z	0.355	proportion	0.308 lower confidence limit

b. Suppose a random sample of 500 television ads in the United States reveals that 122 of these ads use humour. Find a point estimate of and a 95 percent confidence interval for the proportion of all U.S. television ads that use humour.

c. Do the confidence intervals you computed in parts a and b suggest that a greater percentage of U.K. ads use humour? Explain. How might an ad agency use this information?

7.49 In an article in *CA Magazine*, Fitzgerald surveyed Scottish business customers concerning their satisfaction with aspects of their banking relationships. Fitzgerald reports that in 418 telephone interviews conducted by George Street Research, 67 percent of the respondents gave their banks a high rating for overall satisfaction.

a. Assuming that the sample is randomly selected, calculate a 99 percent confidence interval for the proportion of Scottish business customers who give their banks a high rating for overall satisfaction.

b. Based on this interval, can you be 99 percent confident that more than 60 percent of Scottish business customers give their banks a high rating for overall satisfaction?

7.50 In the March 16, 1998, issue of *Fortune* magazine, the results of a survey of 2,221 MBA students from across the United States conducted by the Stockholm-based academic consulting firm Universum showed that only 20 percent of MBA students expect to stay at their first job five years or more.[5] Assuming that a random sample was employed, find a 95 percent confidence interval for the proportion of all U.S. MBA students who expect to stay at their first job five years or more. Based on this interval, is there strong evidence that less than one fourth of all U.S. MBA students expect to stay?

7.51 *Consumer Reports* (January 2005) indicates that profit margins on extended warranties are much greater than on the purchase of most products.[6] In this exercise, you will consider a major electronics retailer that wishes to increase the proportion of customers who buy extended warranties on digital cameras. Historically, 20 percent of digital camera customers have purchased the retailer's extended warranty. To increase this percentage, the retailer has decided to offer a new warranty that is less expensive and more comprehensive. Suppose that three months after starting to offer the new warranty, a random sample of 500 customer sales invoices shows that 152 out of 500 digital camera customers purchased the new warranty. Find a 95 percent confidence interval for the proportion of all digital camera customers who have purchased the new warranty. Are you 95 percent confident that this proportion exceeds 0.20?

7.52 The manufacturer of the ColourSmart-5000 flat panel television claims that 95 percent of its televisions last at least five years without needing a single repair. In order to test this claim, a consumer group randomly selects 400 consumers who have owned a ColourSmart-5000 television for five years. Of these 400 consumers, 316 say their ColourSmart-5000 televisions did not need a repair, whereas 84 say their ColourSmart-5000 televisions did need at least one repair.

a. Find a 99 percent confidence interval for the proportion of all ColourSmart-5000 televisions that have lasted at least five years without needing a single repair.

b. Does this confidence interval provide strong evidence that the percentage of ColourSmart-5000 televisions that last at least five years without a single repair is less than the 95 percent claimed by the manufacturer? Explain.

7.53 In the book *Cases in Finance*, Nunnally and Plath present a case in which the estimated percentage of uncollectible accounts varies with the age of the account. Here the age of an unpaid account is the number of days elapsed since the invoice date.

[5]Source: Shelly Branch, "MBAs: What do they really want?" *Fortune* (March 16, 1998), p. 167.
[6]Source: *Consumer Reports*, January 2005, page 51.

Suppose an accountant believes the percentage of accounts that will be uncollectible increases as the ages of the accounts increase. To test this theory, the accountant randomly selects 500 accounts with ages between 31 and 60 days from the accounts receivable ledger dated one year ago. The accountant also randomly selects 500 accounts with ages between 61 and 90 days from the accounts receivable ledger dated one year ago.

a. If 10 of the 500 accounts with ages between 31 and 60 days were eventually classified as uncollectible, find a point estimate of and a 95 percent confidence interval for the proportion of all accounts with ages between 31 and 60 days that will be uncollectible.

b. If 27 of the 500 accounts with ages between 61 and 90 days were eventually classified as uncollectible, find a point estimate of and a 95 percent confidence interval for the proportion of all accounts with ages between 61 and 90 days that will be uncollectible.

c. Based on these intervals, is there strong evidence that the percentage of accounts aged between 61 and 90 days that will be uncollectible is higher than the percentage of accounts aged between 31 and 60 days that will be uncollectible? Explain.

7.54 Consider Exercise 7.47b and suppose you wish to find the sample size n needed in order to be 95 percent confident that $\hat{p}$, the sample proportion of respondents

who said they took part in some sort of daily activity to keep physically fit, is within a margin of error of 0.02 of p, the true proportion of all U.S. adults who say that they take part in such activity. In order to find an appropriate value for $p(1 - p)$, note that the 95 percent confidence interval for p that you calculated in Exercise 7.47b was [0.57, 0.63]. This indicates that the reasonable value for p that is closest to 0.5 is 0.57, and thus the largest reasonable value for $p(1 - p)$ is $0.57(1 - 0.57) = 0.2451$. Calculate the required sample size n.

7.55 Referring to Exercise 7.52, determine the sample size needed in order to be 99 percent confident that $\hat{p}$, the sample proportion of ColourSmart-5000 televisions that last at least five years without a single repair, is within a margin of error of 0.03 of p, the true proportion of televisions that last at least five years without a single repair.

7.56 Suppose you conduct a poll to estimate the proportion of voters who favour a particular political party. Assuming that 50 percent of the electorate could be in favour of the party, determine the sample size needed so that you are 95 percent confident that $\hat{p}$, the sample proportion of voters who favour the party, is within a margin of error of 0.01 of p, the true proportion of all voters who are in favour of the party.

7.5 COMPARING TWO POPULATION MEANS BY USING INDEPENDENT SAMPLES: VARIANCES KNOWN

A bank manager has developed a new system to reduce the time customers spend waiting to be served by tellers during peak business hours. We let μ_1 denote the mean customer waiting time during peak business hours under the current system. To estimate μ_1, the manager randomly selects $n_1 = 100$ customers and records the length of time each customer spends waiting for service. The manager finds that the sample mean waiting time for these 100 customers is $\bar{x}_1 = 8.79$ minutes. We let μ_2 denote the mean customer waiting time during peak business hours for the new system. During a trial run, the manager finds that the mean waiting time for a random sample of $n_2 = 100$ customers is $\bar{x}_2 = 5.14$ minutes.

In order to compare μ_1 and μ_2, the manager estimates $\mu_1 - \mu_2$, the difference between μ_1 and μ_2. Intuitively, a logical point estimate of $\mu_1 - \mu_2$ is the difference between the sample means:

$$\bar{x}_1 - \bar{x}_2 = 8.79 \text{ minutes} - 5.14 \text{ minutes} = 3.65 \text{ minutes}.$$

This says we estimate that the current mean waiting time is 3.65 minutes longer than the mean waiting time under the new system. That is, we estimate that the new system reduces the mean waiting time by 3.65 minutes.

To compute a confidence interval for $\mu_1 - \mu_2$ (or to test a hypothesis about $\mu_1 - \mu_2$), we need to know the properties of the sampling distribution of $\bar{x}_1 - \bar{x}_2$. To understand this sampling distribution, consider randomly selecting a sample[7] of n_1 measurements from a population with mean μ_1 and variance σ_1^2. Let $\bar{x}_1$ be the mean of this sample. Also consider randomly selecting a sample of n_2 measurements from another population with mean μ_2 and variance σ_2^2. Let $\bar{x}_2$ be the mean of this sample. Different samples from the first population would give

---

[7]Each sample in this chapter is a *random* sample. As has been our practice throughout this book, for brevity we sometimes refer to "random samples" as "samples."

FIGURE 7.17 The Sampling Distribution of $\bar{x}_1 - \bar{x}_2$ Has Mean $\mu_1 - \mu_2$ and Standard Deviation $\sigma_{\bar{x}_1 - \bar{x}_2}$

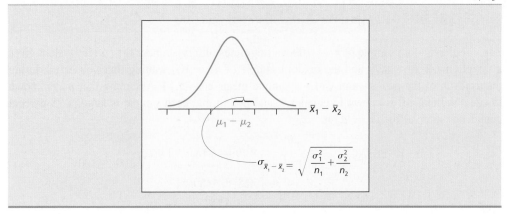

different values of $\bar{x}_1$, and different samples from the second population would give different values of $\bar{x}_2$—so different pairs of samples from the two populations would give different values of $\bar{x}_1 - \bar{x}_2$. In the following box, we describe the sampling distribution of $\bar{x}_1 - \bar{x}_2$, which is the probability distribution of all possible values of $\bar{x}_1 - \bar{x}_2$:

CHAPTER 10

The Sampling Distribution of $\bar{x}_1 - \bar{x}_2$

If the randomly selected samples are **independent** of each other,[8] then the population of all possible values of $\bar{x}_1 - \bar{x}_2$

1 Is normally distributed if each sampled population has a normal distribution, or has approximately a normal distribution if the sampled

populations are not normally distributed and each of the sample sizes n_1 and n_2 is large.

2 Has mean $\mu_{\bar{x}_1 - \bar{x}_2} = \mu_1 - \mu_2$.

3 Has standard deviation $\sigma_{\bar{x}_1 - \bar{x}_2} = \sqrt{\dfrac{\sigma_1^2}{n_1} + \dfrac{\sigma_2^2}{n_2}}$.

Figure 7.17 illustrates the sampling distribution of $\bar{x}_1 - \bar{x}_2$. Using this sampling distribution, we can find a confidence interval for and test a hypothesis about $\mu_1 - \mu_2$. Although the interval and test assume that the true values of the population variances σ_1^2 and σ_2^2 are known, we believe that they are worth presenting because they provide a simple introduction to the basic idea of comparing two population means. Readers who wish to proceed more quickly to the more practical *t*-based procedures of the next section may skip the rest of this section without loss of continuity.

A *z*-Based Confidence Interval for $\mu_1 - \mu_2$, the Difference between Two Population Means, when σ_1 and σ_2 Are Known

Let $\bar{x}_1$ be the mean of a sample of size n_1 that has been randomly selected from a population with mean μ_1 and standard deviation σ_1 and $\bar{x}_2$ be the mean of a sample of size n_2 that has been randomly selected from a population with mean μ_2 and standard deviation σ_2. Furthermore, suppose that each sampled population is normally distributed, or

that each of the sample sizes n_1 and n_2 is large. **LO8** Then, if the samples are independent of each other, a **100(1 − α) percent confidence interval for $\mu_1 - \mu_2$** is

$$\left[\bar{x}_1 - \bar{x}_2 \pm z_{\alpha/2} \sqrt{\frac{\sigma_1^2}{n_1} + \frac{\sigma_2^2}{n_2}} \right].$$

---

[8]This means that there is no relationship between the measurements in one sample and the measurements in the other sample.

Example 7.11   The Bank Customer Waiting Time Case (*z*-Based Confidence Interval for $\mu_1 - \mu_2$ with σ Known)

Suppose the random sample of $n_1 = 100$ waiting times observed under the current system gives a sample mean $\bar{x}_1 = 8.79$ and the random sample of $n_2 = 100$ waiting times observed during the trial run of the new system yields a sample mean $\bar{x}_2 = 5.14$. Assuming that σ_1^2 is known to equal 4.7 and σ_2^2 is known to equal 1.9, and noting that each sample is large, a 95 percent confidence interval for $\mu_1 - \mu_2$ is

$$\left[\bar{x}_1 - \bar{x}_2 \pm z_{0.025} \sqrt{\frac{\sigma_1^2}{n_1} + \frac{\sigma_2^2}{n_2}} \right] = \left[8.79 - 5.14 \pm 1.96 \sqrt{\frac{4.7}{100} + \frac{1.9}{100}} \right]$$

$$= [3.65 \pm 0.5035]$$

$$= [3.15, 4.15].$$

With 95 percent confidence, we believe that the true difference in mean waiting times between the old system and the new system is somewhere between 3.15 minutes and 4.15 minutes. In this case, we have strong evidence that the new system has reduced the mean waiting time.

Exercises for Section 7.5

CONCEPTS

7.57 Suppose you are comparing two population means, μ_1 and μ_2, and consider the difference $\mu_1 - \mu_2$. In each case, indicate how μ_1 relates to μ_2 (that is, is μ_1 greater than, less than, equal to, or not equal to μ_2?).

a. $\mu_1 - \mu_2 < 0$. **d.** $\mu_1 - \mu_2 > 0$.
b. $\mu_1 - \mu_2 = 0$. **e.** $\mu_1 - \mu_2 > 20$.
c. $\mu_1 - \mu_2 < -10$. **f.** $\mu_1 - \mu_2 \neq 0$.

7.58 Suppose you compute a 95 percent confidence interval for $\mu_1 - \mu_2$. If the interval is

a. [3, 5], can you be 95 percent confident that μ_1 is greater than μ_2? Why or why not?
b. [3, 5], can you be 95 percent confident that μ_1 is not equal to μ_2? Why or why not?
c. [−20, −10], can you be 95 percent confident that μ_1 is not equal to μ_2? Why or why not?
d. [−20, −10], can you be 95 percent confident that μ_1 is greater than μ_2? Why or why not?
e. [−3, 2], can you be 95 percent confident that μ_1 is not equal to μ_2? Why or why not?
f. [−10, 10], can you be 95 percent confident that μ_1 is less than μ_2? Why or why not?
g. [−10, 10], can you be 95 percent confident that μ_1 is greater than μ_2? Why or why not?

7.59 Suppose that you calculate a 95 percent confidence interval for $\mu_1 - \mu_2$ to be [1, 15]. Answer each of the following statements with "true," "false," or "cannot say for sure."

a. The difference in sample means is 8.
b. The difference in population means is 8.
c. The difference in population means is somewhere between 1 and 15.
d. Sampling again from the same population, the difference in sample means lies in the interval [1, 15].

e. Changing the confidence level to 90 percent causes the confidence interval to become wider.
f. Everything else being equal, decreasing the sample sizes causes the confidence interval to become narrower.

7.60 In order to employ the formulas of this section, the samples that have been randomly selected from the populations being compared must be independent of each other. In such a case, we say that we are performing an *independent-samples experiment*. In your own words, explain what it means when we say that samples are independent of each other.

7.61 Describe the assumptions that must be met in order to validly use the methods of Section 7.5.

METHODS AND APPLICATIONS

7.62 Suppose you randomly select two independent samples from populations with means μ_1 and μ_2. If $\bar{x}_1 = 25$, $\bar{x}_2 = 20$, $\sigma_1 = 3$, $\sigma_2 = 4$, $n_1 = 100$, and $n_2 = 100$, calculate a 95 percent confidence interval for $\mu_1 - \mu_2$. Can you be 95 percent confident that μ_1 is greater than μ_2? Explain.

7.63 Suppose you select two independent random samples from populations with means μ_1 and μ_2. If $\bar{x}_1 = 151$, $\bar{x}_2 = 162$, $\sigma_1 = 6$, $\sigma_2 = 8$, $n_1 = 625$, and $n_2 = 625$, calculate a 95 percent confidence interval for $\mu_1 - \mu_2$. Can you be 95 percent confident that μ_2 is greater than μ_1? By how much? Explain.

7.64 Some grocery stores have self-serve checkouts. Most people who use the self-serve checkouts do not have a large number of items. You will compare the service times of the express checkout with the service times of the self-serve checkout and see if there is a difference in average service times. Let μ_1 be the average service time for the express checkout and μ_2 be the average service time for the self-serve checkout. Suppose that a random sample of 100 service times in the express checkout gave an average time of 3.7 minutes and a random sample of 100 service times in the self-serve checkout gave an average time of 4.2 minutes. Assuming that the samples are independent and that $\sigma_1 = 0.9$ minutes and $\sigma_2 = 1.6$ minutes, calculate a 95 percent confidence interval for the difference in mean service times between the two checkout methods. Based on this interval, can you be 95 percent confident that the mean service time for those who use the express checkout is less than the mean service time for those who use the self-serve checkout? If so, by how much?

7.65 Who drinks more coffee on average, second-year students at the University of Western Ontario or second-year students at the University of Alberta? Let μ_1 be the average number of cups of coffee drunk per day by University of Western Ontario students and μ_2 be the average number of cups of coffee drunk per day by University of Alberta students. To determine the answer to this question, a random sample of 50 second-year students was taken from each university and the average number of cups of coffee drunk per day was recorded. The results are as follows:

University of Western Ontario	University of Alberta
$\bar{x}_1 = 2.1$	$\bar{x}_2 = 2.9$
$\sigma_1 = 1.0$	$\sigma_2 = 0.8$
$n_1 = 50$	$n_2 = 50$

Calculate a 95 percent confidence interval for the mean difference in cups of coffee drunk by the second-year students at these universities. Based on this interval, can you be 95 percent confident that the mean number of cups of coffee drunk by second-year students at the University of Alberta is higher than the mean number drunk at the University of Western Ontario?

7.66 An Ontario university wishes to demonstrate that car ownership is detrimental to academic achievement.

A random sample of 100 students who do not own cars have a mean grade point average (GPA) of 2.68, while a random sample of 100 students who own cars have a mean GPA of 2.55.

a. Assuming that the independence assumption holds, and letting μ_1 be the mean GPA for all students who do not own cars and μ_2 be the mean GPA for all students who own cars, use the above data to compute a 95 percent confidence interval for $\mu_1 - \mu_2$. Assume that $\sigma_1 = 0.7$ and $\sigma_2 = 0.6$.

b. On the basis of the interval calculated in part a, can the university statistically justify that car ownership harms academic achievement? That is, can the university justify that μ_1 is greater than μ_2? Explain.

7.67 In the *Journal of Marketing*, Bayus studied differences between "early replacement buyers" and "late replacement buyers."[9] Suppose that a random sample of 800 early replacement buyers yields a mean number of automobile dealers visited of $\bar{x}_1 = 3.3$ and a random sample of 500 late replacement buyers yields a mean number of dealers visited of $\bar{x}_2 = 4.5$. Assuming that these samples are independent, let μ_1 be the mean number of dealers visited by early replacement buyers, and let μ_2 be the mean number of dealers visited by late replacement buyers. Calculate a 95 percent confidence interval for $\mu_2 - \mu_1$. Assume that $\sigma_1 = 0.71$ and $\sigma_2 = 0.66$. Based on this interval, can you be 95 percent confident that on average late replacement buyers visit more dealers than do early replacement buyers?

7.68 Students in a large statistics course at a British Columbia university were concerned that the average test scores were much lower on their second term test than on their first term test. Suppose that it was known that the standard deviations for the first and second term tests were $\sigma_1 = 8$ and $\sigma_1 = 10$, respectively. Independent random samples of 45 test scores were taken from the first and second tests and the means were 72 and 65, respectively.

Let μ_1 be the mean score from the first test and μ_2 be the mean score from the second test. Construct a 95 percent confidence interval for $\mu_1 - \mu_2$. Based on this interval, can you be 95 percent confident that the test scores were lower on the second test?

7.6 COMPARING TWO POPULATION MEANS BY USING INDEPENDENT SAMPLES: VARIANCES UNKNOWN

Suppose that (as is usually the case) the true values of the population variances σ_1^2 and σ_2^2 are not known. We then estimate σ_1^2 and σ_2^2 by using s_1^2 and s_2^2, the variances of the samples randomly selected from the populations being compared. There are two approaches to doing this.

CHAPTER 10

---

[9]Early replacement buyers are consumers who replace a product during the early part of its lifetime, while late replacement buyers make replacement purchases late in the product's lifetime. In particular, Bayus studied automobile replacement purchases. Consumers who traded in cars with ages of zero to three years and mileages of no more than 35,000 miles (57,000 km) were classified as early replacement buyers. Consumers who traded in cars with ages of seven or more years and mileages of more than 73,000 miles (120,000 km) were classified as late replacement buyers.

The first approach assumes that the population variances σ_1^2 and σ_2^2 are equal. Denoting the common value of these variances as σ^2, it follows that

$$\sigma_{\bar{x}_1 - \bar{x}_2} = \sqrt{\frac{\sigma_1^2}{n_1} + \frac{\sigma_2^2}{n_2}} = \sqrt{\frac{\sigma^2}{n_1} + \frac{\sigma^2}{n_2}} = \sqrt{\sigma^2\left(\frac{1}{n_1} + \frac{1}{n_2}\right)}.$$

Because we are assuming that $\sigma_1^2 = \sigma_2^2 = \sigma^2$, we do not need separate estimates of σ_1^2 and σ_2^2. Instead, we combine the results of the two independent random samples to compute a single **estimate** of σ^2. This estimate is called the **pooled estimate** of σ^2, and it is a weighted average of the two sample variances s_1^2 and s_2^2. Denoting the pooled estimate as s_p^2, we compute it using the formula

$$s_p^2 = \frac{(n_1 - 1)s_1^2 + (n_2 - 1)s_2^2}{n_1 + n_2 - 2}.$$

Using s_p^2, the estimate of $\sigma_{\bar{x}_1 - \bar{x}_2}$ is

$$\sqrt{s_p^2\left(\frac{1}{n_1} + \frac{1}{n_2}\right)},$$

and we form the statistic

$$\frac{(\bar{x}_1 - \bar{x}_2) - (\mu_1 - \mu_2)}{\sqrt{s_p^2\left(\frac{1}{n_1} + \frac{1}{n_2}\right)}}.$$

It can be shown that if we have randomly selected independent samples from two normally distributed populations with equal variances, the sampling distribution of this statistic is a t distribution with $n_1 + n_2 - 2$ degrees of freedom. Therefore, we can obtain the following confidence interval for $\mu_1 - \mu_2$:

A t-Based Confidence Interval for $\mu_1 - \mu_2$, the Difference between Two Population Means, When $\sigma_1^2 = \sigma_2^2$

LO8 Suppose we have randomly selected independent samples from two normally distributed populations with equal variances. Then a **100(1 − α) percent confidence interval for $\mu_1 - \mu_2$** is

$$\left[\bar{x}_1 - \bar{x}_2 \pm t_{\alpha/2}\sqrt{s_p^2\left(\frac{1}{n_1} + \frac{1}{n_2}\right)}\right],$$

where

$$s_p^2 = \frac{(n_1 - 1)s_1^2 + (n_2 - 1)s_2^2}{n_1 + n_2 - 2}$$

and $t_{\alpha/2}$ is based on $n_1 + n_2 - 2$ degrees of freedom.

Example 7.12   The Coffee Cup Case (t-Based Confidence Interval for $\mu_1 - \mu_2$ with σ_1 and σ_2 Unknown and Equal)

A production supervisor at a coffee cup production plant must determine which of two production processes, Java and Joe, maximizes the hourly yield for coffee cup production. In order to compare the mean hourly yields obtained by using the two processes, the supervisor runs the process using each method for five one-hour periods. The resulting yields (in kilograms of cups per hour) for each method, along with the means, variances, and box plots of the yields,[10] are given in Table 7.4. Assuming that all other factors affecting the production of the cups have been held as constant as possible during the test runs, it seems reasonable to regard the five observed yields for each production process as a random sample from the population of all

[10]All of the box plots presented in this chapter and in Chapter 10 have been obtained using MegaStat.

TABLE 7.4   Coffee Cup Production Using Two Methods 🖋

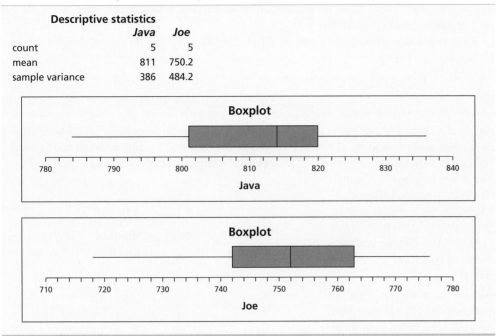

Descriptive statistics

	Java	Joe
count	5	5
mean	811	750.2
sample variance	386	484.2

possible hourly yields for the cups. Furthermore, since the sample variances $s_1^2 = 386$ and $s_2^2 = 484.2$ do not differ substantially (notice that $s_1 = 19.65$ and $s_2 = 22.00$ differ by even less), it might be reasonable to conclude that the population variances are approximately equal.[11] It follows that the pooled estimate

$$s_p^2 = \frac{(n_1 - 1)s_1^2 + (n_2 - 1)s_2^2}{n_1 + n_2 - 2}$$

$$= \frac{(5 - 1)(386) + (5 - 1)(484.2)}{5 + 5 - 2} = 435.1$$

is a point estimate of the common variance σ^2.

We define μ_1 as the mean hourly yield obtained by using the Java process and μ_2 as the mean hourly yield obtained by using the Joe process. If the populations of all possible hourly yields for the production methods are normally distributed, then a 95 percent confidence interval for $\mu_1 - \mu_2$ is

$$\left[\bar{x}_1 - \bar{x}_2 \pm t_{0.025} \sqrt{s_p^2 \left(\frac{1}{n_1} + \frac{1}{n_2} \right)} \right]$$

$$= \left[811 - 750.2 \pm 2.306 \sqrt{435.1 \left(\frac{1}{5} + \frac{1}{5} \right)} \right]$$

$$= [60.8 \pm 30.4217]$$

$$= [30.38, 91.22].$$

Here $t_{0.025} = 2.306$ is based on $n_1 + n_2 - 2 = 5 + 5 - 2 = 8$ degrees of freedom. This interval tells us that we are 95 percent confident that the mean hourly yield obtained by using the Java process is between 30.38 kg and 91.22 kg higher than the mean hourly yield obtained by using the Joe process.

---

[11]We describe how to test the equality of two variances in Chapter 9 (although, as we will explain, this test has drawbacks).

Now we will consider the case where the underlying population variances are not known and are also not equal. Unless we know that the underlying variances are equal, we must use the unequal-variances procedures.

If the population variances σ_1^2 and σ_2^2 differ, the following can be shown:

t-Based Confidence Intervals for $\mu_1 - \mu_2$

LO8 1   When the sampled populations are normally distributed and the sample sizes n_1 and n_2 are equal, the equal-variances *t*-based confidence interval given in the preceding box is approximately valid even if the population variances σ_1^2 and σ_2^2 differ substantially. As a rough rule of thumb, if the larger sample variance is not more than three times the smaller sample variance when the sample sizes are equal, we can use the equal-variances interval.

2   Suppose that the sample sizes are not equal or that the sample variances differ substantially (that is, the larger sample variance is more than three times the smaller sample variance). Then we can use an approximate procedure that is sometimes called an unequal-variances procedure. This procedure says that an **approximate 100 (1 − α) percent confidence interval for $\mu_1 - \mu_2$** is

$$\left[\bar{x}_1 - \bar{x}_2 \pm t_{\alpha/2} \sqrt{\frac{s_1^2}{n_1} + \frac{s_2^2}{n_2}} \right].$$

For the above confidence interval, the degrees of freedom are equal to

$$df = \frac{(s_1^2/n_1 + s_2^2/n_2)^2}{\dfrac{(s_1^2/n_1)^2}{n_1 - 1} + \dfrac{(s_2^2/n_2)^2}{n_2 - 1}}.$$

Here, if *df* is not a whole number, we can round *df* down to the next smallest whole number.

In general, both the equal-variances and the unequal-variances procedures have been shown to be approximately valid when the sampled populations are only approximately normally distributed (say, if they are mound-shaped). Furthermore, although the above summary box might seem to imply that we should use the unequal-variances procedure only if we cannot use the equal-variances procedure, this is not necessarily true. In fact, since the unequal-variances procedure can be shown to be a very accurate approximation whether or not the population variances are equal and for most sample sizes (here, both n_1 and n_2 should be at least 5), *many statisticians believe that it is best to use the unequal-variances procedure in almost every situation.* If each of n_1 and n_2 is large (at least 30), both the equal-variances procedure and the unequal-variances procedure are approximately valid, no matter what probability distributions describe the sampled populations.

To illustrate the unequal-variances procedure, consider the bank customer waiting time situation, and recall that $\mu_1 - \mu_2$ is the difference between the mean customer waiting time under the current system and the mean customer waiting time under the new system. Because of cost considerations, the bank manager wants to implement the new system only if it reduces the mean waiting time by more than three minutes.

To find a 95 percent confidence interval for $\mu_1 - \mu_2$, note that we can use a computer to find that $t_{0.025}$ based on 163 degrees of freedom is 1.97. It follows that the 95 percent confidence interval for $\mu_1 - \mu_2$ is

$$\left[\bar{x}_1 - \bar{x}_2 \pm t_{0.025} \sqrt{\frac{s_1^2}{n_1} + \frac{s_2^2}{n_2}} \right] = \left[8.79 - 5.14 \pm 1.97 \sqrt{\frac{4.8237}{100} + \frac{1.7927}{100}} \right]$$

$$= [3.65 \pm 0.50792]$$

$$= [3.14, 4.16].$$

This interval says that we are 95 percent confident that the new system reduces the mean customer waiting time by between 3.14 minutes and 4.16 minutes. Because the entire 95 percent confidence interval contains values greater than 3, we are 95 percent confident that the new system reduces waiting time by more than three minutes.

FIGURE 7.18 Two-Sample Confidence Interval: Independent Groups (t Test, Unequal Variances)

	Java	Joe	
	811.00	750.20	mean
	19.65	22.00	std. dev.
	5	5	n
		7	df
		60.800	difference (Java - Joe)
		13.192	standard error of difference
		0	hypothesized difference
		29.605	confidence interval 95.% lower
		91.995	confidence interval 95.% upper
		31.195	margin of error

Using the degrees of freedom formula given previously, we would actually obtain a value of 163.657. Notice that in the previous example, $df = 163$ was used. When using that degrees of freedom formula, we should always round the answer down, ignoring the decimal part. Smaller values for df lead to slightly larger values of t. This will give slightly larger confidence intervals. Thus, rounding down will give a slightly more conservative answer.

In general, the degrees of freedom for the unequal-variances procedure will always be less than or equal to $n_1 + n_2 - 2$, the degrees of freedom for the equal-variances procedure. For example, if we use the unequal-variances procedure to analyze the coffee cup data in Table 7.4 on page 237, we can calculate df to be 7.9. This is slightly less than $n_1 + n_2 - 2 = 5 + 5 - 2 = 8$, the degrees of freedom for the equal-variances procedure. Figure 7.18 gives the MegaStat output of the unequal-variances analysis of the coffee cup comparison data. Note that MegaStat rounds df down to 7 and finds that a 95 percent confidence interval for $\mu_1 - \mu_2$ is [29.605, 91.995].

To conclude this section, it is important to point out that if the sample sizes n_1 and n_2 are not large (less than 30), and if we fear that the sampled populations might be far from normally distributed, we can use a **nonparametric method**. One nonparametric method for comparing populations when using independent samples is the **Wilcoxon rank sum test**. This test is discussed in Section 13.2 (pages 487–492).

Exercises for Section 7.6

CONCEPTS

List the assumptions that must be satisfied in order to validly use the formulas in Exercises 7.69 and 7.70.

7.69 The confidence interval formula in the formula box on page 236.

7.70 The confidence interval formula in the formula box on page 238.

METHODS AND APPLICATIONS

Suppose you have taken independent, random samples of sizes $n_1 = 7$ and $n_2 = 7$ from two normally distributed populations with means μ_1 and μ_2, and suppose you obtain $\bar{x}_1 = 240$, $\bar{x}_2 = 210$, $s_1 = 5$, and $s_2 = 6$. Complete Exercises 7.71 and 7.72.

7.71 Using the equal-variances procedure, calculate a 95 percent confidence interval for $\mu_1 - \mu_2$. Can you be 95 percent confident that $\mu_1 - \mu_2$ is not equal to 20? Explain why you can use the equal-variances procedure here.

7.72 Now calculate a 95 percent confidence interval using the unequal-variances procedure. Compare your results to those obtained using the equal-variances procedure.

7.73 The October 7, 1991, issue of *Fortune* magazine reported on the rapid rise of fees and expenses charged by mutual funds. Assuming that stock fund expenses and municipal bond fund expenses are each approximately normally distributed, suppose a random sample of 12 stock funds gives a mean annual expense of 1.63 percent with a standard deviation of 0.31 percent, and an independent random sample of 12 municipal bond funds gives a mean annual expense of 0.89 percent with a standard deviation of 0.23 percent. Let μ_1 be the mean annual expense for stock funds and μ_2 be the mean annual expense for municipal bond funds. Answer the following question first using the equal-variances procedure and then using the unequal-variances procedure. Compare the two confidence intervals.

Calculate a 95 percent confidence interval for the difference between the mean annual expenses for stock funds and municipal bond funds. Can you be 95 percent confident that the mean annual expense for stock funds exceeds that for municipal bond funds by more than 0.5 percentage points? Explain.

7.74 A manager at a local electronics store wishes to compare the effectiveness of two methods for training new salespeople. The experiment is described as follows:

The company selects 22 sales trainees who are randomly divided into two experimental groups of equal size—one receives type *A* and the other type *B* training. The trainees are then assigned and managed without regard to the training they have received. At the year's end, the manager reviews the performances of trainees in these groups and finds the following results:

	A Group	B Group
Average Weekly Sales	$\bar{x}_1 = \$1,500$	$\bar{x}_2 = \$1,300$
Standard Deviation	$s_1 = 225$	$s_2 = 251$

Use the equal-variances procedure to calculate a 95 percent confidence interval for the difference between the mean weekly sales obtained when type *A* training is used and the mean weekly sales obtained when type *B* training is used. Interpret this interval.

7.75 A large discount chain compares the performance of its credit managers in Alberta and Ontario by comparing the mean dollar amounts owed by customers with delinquent charge accounts in these two provinces. Here a small mean dollar amount owed is desirable because it indicates that bad credit risks are not being extended large amounts of credit. Two independent, random samples of delinquent accounts are selected from the populations of delinquent accounts in Alberta and Ontario. The first sample, which consists of 10 randomly selected delinquent accounts in Alberta, gives a mean dollar amount of $524 with a standard deviation of $68. The second sample, which consists of 20 randomly selected delinquent accounts in Ontario, gives a mean dollar amount of $473 with a standard deviation of $22.

Assuming that the normality assumption holds, calculate a 95 percent confidence interval for the difference between the mean dollar amounts owed in Alberta and Ontario. Based on this interval, do you think that these mean dollar amounts differ in a practically important way?

7.76 A loan officer compares the interest rates for 48-month fixed-rate auto loans and 48-month variable-rate auto loans. Two independent, random samples of auto loan rates are selected. A sample of eight 48-month fixed-rate auto loans had the following loan rates:

10.29%	9.75%	9.50%	9.99%
9.75%	9.99%	11.40%	10.00%

A sample of five 48-month variable-rate auto loans had loan rates as follows:

9.59%	8.75%	8.99%	8.50%	9.00%

Calculate a 95 percent confidence interval for the difference between the mean rates for fixed- and variable-rate 48-month auto loans. Can you be 95 percent confident that the difference between these means is 0.4 percentage points or more? Explain.

7.7 COMPARING TWO POPULATION MEANS BY USING PAIRED DIFFERENCES

Example 7.13 The Repair Cost Comparison Case (Paired Differences)

Forest City Casualty, specializing in automobile insurance, wishes to compare the repair costs of moderately damaged cars (repair costs between $700 and $1,400) at two garages. One way to study these costs would be to take two independent samples (here we arbitrarily assume that each sample is of size $n = 7$). First we would randomly select seven moderately damaged cars that have recently been in accidents. Each of these cars would be taken to the first garage (garage 1), and repair cost estimates would be obtained. Then we would randomly select seven *different* moderately damaged cars, and repair cost estimates for these cars would be obtained at the second garage (garage 2). This sampling procedure would give us independent samples because the cars taken to garage 1 differ from those taken to garage 2. However, because the repair costs for moderately damaged cars can range from $700 to $1,400, there can be substantial differences in damages to moderately damaged cars. These differences might tend to conceal any real differences between repair costs at the two garages. For example, suppose the repair cost estimates for the cars taken to garage 1 are higher than those for the cars taken to garage 2. This difference might exist because garage 1 charges customers more for repair work than does garage 2. However, the difference

TABLE 7.5 A Sample of $n = 7$ Paired Differences of the Repair Cost Estimates at Garages 1 and 2 (Cost Estimates in Hundreds of Dollars) ✒

Sample of $n = 7$ Damaged Cars	Repair Cost Estimates at Garage 1	Repair Cost Estimates at Garage 2	Sample of $n = 7$ Paired Differences
Car 1	$ 7.1	$ 7.9	$d_1 = -0.8$
Car 2	9.0	10.1	$d_2 = -1.1$
Car 3	11.0	12.2	$d_3 = -1.2$
Car 4	8.9	8.8	$d_4 = 0.1$
Car 5	9.9	10.4	$d_5 = -0.5$
Car 6	9.1	9.8	$d_6 = -0.7$
Car 7	10.3	11.7	$d_7 = -1.4$
	$\bar{x}_1 = 9.329$	$\bar{x}_2 = 10.129$	$\bar{d} = -0.8 = \bar{x}_1 \cdot \bar{x}_2$
			$s_d^2 = 0.2533$
			$s_d^1 = 0.5033$

could also arise because the cars taken to garage 1 are more severely damaged than the cars taken to garage 2.

LO9

To overcome this difficulty, we can perform a **paired-differences experiment**. Here we could randomly select one sample of $n = 7$ moderately damaged cars. The cars in this sample would be taken to both garages, and a repair cost estimate for each car would be obtained at each garage. The advantage of the paired-differences experiment is that the repair cost estimates at the two garages are obtained for the same cars. Thus, any true differences in the repair cost estimates would not be concealed by possible differences in the severity of damages to the cars.

Suppose that when we perform the paired-differences experiment, we obtain the repair cost estimates in Table 7.5 (these estimates are given in units of $100). To analyze these data, we calculate the difference between the repair cost estimates at the two garages for each car. The resulting **paired differences** are given in the last column of Table 7.5. The mean of the sample of $n = 7$ paired differences is

$$\bar{d} = \frac{-0.8 + (-1.1) + (-1.2) + \cdots + (-1.4)}{7} = -0.8,$$

which equals the difference between the sample means of the repair cost estimates at the two garages:

$$\bar{x}_1 - \bar{x}_2 = 9.329 - 10.129 = -0.8.$$

Furthermore, $\bar{d} = -0.8$ (that is, $-\$80$) is the point estimate of

$$\mu_d = \mu_1 - \mu_2,$$

the mean of the population of all possible paired differences of the repair cost estimates (for all possible moderately damaged cars) at garages 1 and 2—which is equivalent to μ_1, the mean of all possible repair cost estimates at garage 1, minus μ_2, the mean of all possible repair cost estimates at garage 2. This says we estimate that the mean of all possible repair cost estimates at garage 1 is $80 less than the mean of all possible repair cost estimates at garage 2.

In addition, the variance and standard deviation of the sample of $n = 7$ paired differences,

$$s_d^2 = \frac{\sum_{i=1}^{7}(d_i - \bar{d})^2}{7 - 1} = 0.2533$$

and

$$s_d = \sqrt{0.2533} = 0.5033,$$

are the point estimates of σ_d^2 and σ_d, the variance and standard deviation of the population of all possible paired differences.

In general, suppose we wish to compare two population means, μ_1 and μ_2. Also suppose that we have obtained two different measurements (for example, repair cost estimates) on the same n units (for example, cars), and suppose we have calculated the n paired differences between these measurements. Let $\bar{d}$ and s_d be the mean and the standard deviation of these n paired differences. If it is reasonable to assume that the paired differences have been randomly selected from a normally distributed (or at least mound-shaped) population of paired differences with mean μ_d and standard deviation σ_d, then the sampling distribution of

$$\frac{\bar{d} - \mu_d}{s_d/\sqrt{n}}$$

is a t distribution with $n - 1$ degrees of freedom. This implies that we have the following confidence interval for μ_d:

A Confidence Interval for the Mean, μ_d, of a Population of Paired Differences

LO9 Let μ_d be the mean of a *normally distributed population of paired differences*, and let $\bar{d}$ and s_d be the mean and standard deviation of a sample of n paired differences that have been randomly selected from the population. Then a **100(1 − α)**

percent confidence interval for $\mu_d = \mu_1 - \mu_2$ is

$$\left[\bar{d} \pm t_{\alpha/2}\left(\frac{s_d}{\sqrt{n}} \right) \right].$$

Here $t_{\alpha/2}$ is based on $n - 1$ degrees of freedom.

Example 7.14 The Repair Cost Comparison Case (*t*-Based Confidence Interval for μ_d)

Using the data in Table 7.5 on the previous page, and assuming that the population of paired repair cost differences is normally distributed, a 95 percent confidence interval for $\mu_d = \mu_1 - \mu_2$ is

$$\left[\bar{d} \pm t_{0.025}\left(\frac{s_d}{\sqrt{n}} \right) \right] = \left[-0.8 \pm 2.447\left(\frac{0.5033}{\sqrt{7}} \right) \right]$$
$$= [-0.8 \pm 0.4654]$$
$$= [-1.2654, -0.3346].$$

Here $t_{0.025} = 2.447$ is based on $n - 1 = 7 - 1 = 6$ degrees of freedom. This interval says that Forest City Casualty can be 95 percent confident that μ_d, the mean of all possible paired differences of the repair cost estimates at garages 1 and 2, is between −\$126.54 and −\$33.46. That is, we are 95 percent confident that μ_1, the mean of all possible repair cost estimates at garage 1, is between \$126.54 and \$33.46 less than μ_2, the mean of all possible repair cost estimates at garage 2.

In general, an experiment in which we have obtained two different measurements on the same n units is called a **paired-differences experiment**. The idea of this type of experiment is to remove the variability due to the variable (for example, the amount of damage to a car) on which the observations are paired. In many situations, a paired-differences experiment will provide more information than an independent-samples experiment.

The formulas we have given for analyzing a paired-differences experiment are based on the t distribution. These formulas assume that the population of all possible paired differences is normally distributed (or at least mound-shaped). If the sample size is large (say, at least 30), the t-based interval of this section is approximately valid no matter what the shape of the population of all possible paired differences. If the sample size is small, and if we fear that the population of all paired differences might be far from normally distributed, we can use a nonparametric method. One nonparametric method for comparing two populations when using a paired-differences experiment is the **Wilcoxon signed ranks test**, discussed in Section 13.3.

Exercises for Section 7.7

CONCEPTS

7.77 Explain how a paired-differences experiment differs from an independent-samples experiment in terms of how the data for these experiments are collected.

7.78 Why is a paired-differences experiment sometimes more informative than an independent-samples experiment? Give an example of a situation in which a paired-differences experiment might be advantageous.

7.79 What assumptions must be satisfied to appropriately carry out a paired-differences experiment? When can you carry out a paired-differences experiment no matter what the shape of the population of all paired differences might be?

7.80 Suppose a company wishes to compare the hourly output of its employees before and after vacations. Explain how you would collect data for a paired-differences experiment to make this comparison.

METHODS AND APPLICATIONS

7.81 Suppose a sample of 11 paired differences that has been randomly selected from a normally distributed population of paired differences yields a sample mean of $\bar{d} = 103.5$ and a sample standard deviation of $s_d = 5$. Calculate 95 percent and 99 percent confidence intervals for $\mu_d = \mu_1 - \mu_2$. Can you be 95 percent confident that the difference between μ_1 and μ_2 is different from 100? Can you be 99 percent confident?

7.82 Suppose a sample of 49 paired differences that have been randomly selected from a normally distributed population of paired differences yields a sample mean of $\bar{d} = 5$ and a sample standard deviation of $s_d = 7$. Calculate a 95 percent confidence interval for $\mu_d = \mu_1 - \mu_2$. Can you be 95 percent confident that the difference between μ_1 and μ_2 is not 0?

7.83 In the book *Essentials of Marketing Research*, Dillon, Madden, and Firtle present preexposure and postexposure attitude scores from an advertising study involving ten respondents. The data for the experiment are given in Table 7.6. Assuming that the differences between pairs of postexposure and preexposure scores are normally distributed, provide a good estimate for the minimum difference between the mean postexposure attitude score and the mean preexposure attitude score. Justify your answer.

7.84 Ten runners were asked to run a 5-km race in each of two consecutive weeks. The runners wore one brand of shoe

TABLE **7.6** Preexposure and Postexposure Attitude Scores for Exercise 7.83

Subject	Preexposure Attitudes (A_1)	Postexposure Attitudes (A_2)	Attitude Change (d_i)
1	50	53	3
2	25	27	2
3	30	38	8
4	50	55	5
5	60	61	1
6	80	85	5
7	45	45	0
8	30	31	1
9	65	72	7
10	70	78	8

Source: *Essentials of Marketing Research*, by W. R. Dillon, T. J. Madden, and N. H. Firtle (Burr Ridge, IL: Richard D. Irwin, 1993), p. 435. Copyright © 1993. Reprinted by permission of McGraw-Hill Companies, Inc.

in one race and a second brand in the other race. The brand worn in each race is randomly determined. The runners were timed and asked to do their best during each race. The results, in minutes, are given below:

Runner	Brand *A*	Brand *B*
1	15.74	15.99
2	14.98	14.87
3	16.11	15.87
4	15.44	15.93
5	15.37	15.79
6	14.83	14.66
7	15.15	15.49
8	16.02	16.36
9	15.29	15.12
10	14.76	15.01

Assume that the differences between pairs of race times are normally distributed.

a. Calculate a 95 percent confidence interval for the mean difference in race times for the two types of running shoes.

b. Can you be 95 percent confident that there is a difference in mean race times between shoe brands? Justify your answer.

TABLE **7.7**   Weekly Study Time Data for Students Who Perform Well on the Midterm ✈

Student	1	2	3	4	5	6	7	8
Before	15	14	17	17	19	14	13	16
After	9	9	11	10	19	10	14	10

7.85 To compare the fuel efficiency of two types of gasoline, five cars were randomly selected, the type of gasoline used was randomly determined, and the fuel efficiency obtained using each brand was recorded below (in litres per 100 km) for each car:

Car	Type *A*	Type *B*
1	8.4	7.9
2	7.8	7.1
3	11.3	10.9
4	8.1	7.3
5	6.6	5.7

Assume that the differences between pairs of fuel efficiencies are normally distributed.
a. Calculate a 95 percent confidence interval for the mean difference in fuel efficiency for the two types of gasoline.
b. Can you be 95 percent confident that there is a difference in mean fuel efficiency between the different gasoline types? Justify your answer.

7.86 Do students reduce study time in classes where they achieve a higher midterm score? In a *Journal of Economic Education* article (Winter 2005), Krohn and O'Connor studied student effort and performance in a class over a semester. In an intermediate macroeconomics course, they found that "students respond to higher midterm scores by reducing the number of hours they subsequently allocate to studying for the course."[12] Suppose that a random sample of $n = 8$ students who performed well on the midterm exam was taken and weekly study times before and after the exam were compared. The resulting data are given in Table 7.7. Assume that the population of all possible paired differences is normally distributed.
a. Calculate a 95 percent confidence interval for the mean difference in study times before and after the midterm exam. Estimate the minimum reduction in the mean study time from before to after the exams.
b. Can you be 95 percent confident that average study times are reduced after a student does well on a midterm exam?

7.8 COMPARING TWO POPULATION PROPORTIONS BY USING LARGE, INDEPENDENT SAMPLES

Example 7.15 The Advertising Media Case (Difference of Proportions—Large Samples)

Suppose a new product was test marketed in the Toronto and Vancouver metropolitan areas. Equal amounts of money were spent on advertising in the two areas. However, different advertising media were employed in the two areas. Advertising in the Toronto area was done entirely on television, while advertising in the Vancouver area consisted of a mixture of television, radio, newspaper, and magazine ads. Two months after the advertising campaigns commenced, surveys were taken to estimate consumer awareness of the product. In the Toronto area, 631 out of 1,000 randomly selected consumers were aware of the product, whereas in the Vancouver area, 798 out of 1,000 randomly selected consumers were aware of the product. We define p_1 to be the true proportion of consumers in the Toronto area who are aware of the product and p_2 to be the true proportion of consumers in the Vancouver area who are aware of the product. It follows that since the sample proportions of consumers who are aware of the product in the Toronto and Vancouver areas are

$$\hat{p}_1 = \frac{631}{1,000} = 0.631$$

[12]Source: "Student effort and performance over the semester," by Gregory Krohn and Catherine O'Connor, *Journal of Economic Education*, Winter 2005, pages 3–28.

and

$$\hat{p}_2 = \frac{798}{1,000} = 0.798,$$

a point estimate of $p_1 - p_2$ is

$$\hat{p}_1 - \hat{p}_2 = 0.631 - 0.798 = -0.167.$$

This says we estimate that p_1 is 0.167 less than p_2. That is, we estimate that the percentage of consumers who are aware of the product in the Vancouver area is 16.7 percentage points higher than the percentage in the Toronto area.

In order to find a confidence interval for and to carry out a hypothesis test about $p_1 - p_2$, we need to know the properties of the sampling distribution of $\hat{p}_1 - \hat{p}_2$. In general, therefore, consider randomly selecting n_1 units from a population, and assume that a proportion p_1 of all the units in the population fall into a particular category. Let $\hat{p}_1$ denote the proportion of units in the sample that fall into the category. Also consider randomly selecting a sample of n_2 units from a second population, and assume that a proportion p_2 of all the units in this population fall into the particular category. Let $\hat{p}_2$ denote the proportion of units in the second sample that fall into the category.

The Sampling Distribution of $\hat{p}_1 - \hat{p}_2$

If the randomly selected samples are independent of each other, then the population of all possible values of $\hat{p}_1 - \hat{p}_2$

1   Is approximately normal if each of the sample sizes n_1 and n_2 is large. Here n_1 and n_2 are large enough if $n_1 p_1$, $n_1(1 - p_1)$, $n_2 p_2$, and $n_2(1 - p_2)$ are all at least 5.

2   Has mean $\mu_{\hat{p}_1 - \hat{p}_2} = p_1 - p_2$.

3   Has standard deviation

$$\sigma_{\hat{p}_1 - \hat{p}_2} = \sqrt{\frac{p_1(1 - p_1)}{n_1} + \frac{p_2(1 - p_2)}{n_2}}.$$

If we estimate p_1 by $\hat{p}_1$ and p_2 by $\hat{p}_2$ in the expression for $\sigma_{\hat{p}_1 - \hat{p}_2}$, then the sampling distribution of $\hat{p}_1 - \hat{p}_2$ implies the following $100(1 - \alpha)$ percent confidence interval for $p_1 - p_2$:

A Large-Sample Confidence Interval for $p_1 - p_2$, the Difference between Two Population Proportions[13]

Suppose we randomly select a sample of size n_1 from a population, and let $\hat{p}_1$ denote the proportion of units in this sample that fall into a category of interest. Also suppose we randomly select a sample of size n_2 from another population, and let $\hat{p}_2$ denote the proportion of units in this second sample that fall into the category of interest. Then, if each of the sample sizes n_1 and n_2 is large, $(n_1\hat{p}_1, n_1(1 - \hat{p}_1), n_2\hat{p}_2,$ and $n_2(1 - \hat{p}_1)$ must all be at least 5), and if the random samples are independent of each other, a $100(1 - \alpha)$ percent confidence interval for $p_1 - p_2$ is **LO10**

$$\left[\hat{p}_1 - \hat{p}_2 \pm z_{\alpha/2}\sqrt{\frac{\hat{p}_1(1 - \hat{p}_1)}{n_1} + \frac{\hat{p}_2(1 - \hat{p}_2)}{n_2}}\right].$$

---

[13]More correctly, because $\hat{p}_1(1 - \hat{p}_1)/(n_1 - 1)$ and $\hat{p}_2(1 - \hat{p}_2)/(n_2 - 1)$ are unbiased point estimates of $p_1(1 - p_1)/n_1$ and $p_2(1 - p_2)/n_2$, a point estimate of $\sigma_{\hat{p}_1 - \hat{p}_2}$ is

$$s_{\hat{p}_1 - \hat{p}_2} = \sqrt{\frac{\hat{p}_1(1 - \hat{p}_1)}{n_1 - 1} + \frac{\hat{p}_2(1 - \hat{p}_2)}{n_2 - 1}},$$

and a $100(1 - \alpha)$ percent confidence interval for $p_1 - p_2$ is $[\hat{p}_1 - \hat{p}_2 \pm z_{\alpha/2}s_{\hat{p}_1 - \hat{p}_2}]$. Because both n_1 and n_2 are large, there is little difference between the interval obtained by using this formula and that obtained by using the formula in the box above.

Example 7.16 The Advertising Media Case (z-Based Confidence Interval for $p_1 - p_2$)

Recall that in the advertising media situation described at the beginning of this section, 631 of 1,000 randomly selected consumers in Toronto were aware of the new product, while 798 of 1,000 randomly selected consumers in Vancouver were aware of the new product. Also recall that

$$\hat{p}_1 = \frac{631}{1,000} = 0.631$$

and

$$\hat{p}_2 = \frac{798}{1,000} = 0.798.$$

Because $n_1\hat{p}_1 = 1,000(0.631) = 631$, $n_1(1 - \hat{p}_1) = 1,000(1 - 0.631) = 369$, $n_2\hat{p}_2 = 1,000(0.798) = 798$, and $n_2(1 - \hat{p}_2) = 1,000(1 - 0.798) = 202$ are all at least 5, both n_1 and n_2 can be considered large. It follows that a 95 percent confidence interval for $p_1 - p_2$ is

$$\left[\hat{p}_1 - \hat{p}_2 \pm z_{0.025}\sqrt{\frac{\hat{p}_1(1 - \hat{p}_1)}{n_1} + \frac{\hat{p}_2(1 - \hat{p}_2)}{n_2}} \right]$$

$$= \left[0.631 - 0.798 \pm 1.96\sqrt{\frac{(0.631)(0.369)}{1,000} + \frac{(0.798)(0.202)}{1,000}} \right]$$

$$= [-0.167 \pm 0.0389]$$

$$= [-0.2059, -0.1281].$$

This interval says we are 95 percent confident that p_1, the proportion of all consumers in the Toronto area who are aware of the product, is between 0.2059 and 0.1281 less than p_2, the proportion of all consumers in the Vancouver area who are aware of the product. Thus, we have substantial evidence that advertising the new product by using a mixture of television, radio, newspaper, and magazine ads (as in Vancouver) is more effective than spending an equal amount of money on television commercials only.

Let us take note of a few things before we conclude this chapter. We need to make note of the similarities and differences between confidence intervals when the population standard deviation is known and when it is unknown (i.e., using z versus t in the formula). It is important to know which formula to use for each situation. When using t-based confidence intervals, it is important to know how to calculate the degrees of freedom. We finished this part of the chapter by looking at confidence intervals for differences between proportions. The nice thing about this section is that we only deal with large samples, so note that any confidence interval formulas will involve only a z value.

Exercises for Section 7.8

CONCEPTS

7.87 Explain what population is described by the sampling distribution of $\hat{p}_1 - \hat{p}_2$.

7.88 What assumptions must be satisfied in order to use the methods presented in this section?

METHODS AND APPLICATIONS

7.89 Suppose that you have selected two independent random samples from populations with proportions

p_1 and p_2 and that $\hat{p}_1 = 800/1,000 = 0.8$ and $\hat{p}_2 = 950/1,000 = 0.95$. Calculate a 95 percent confidence interval for $p_1 - p_2$. Interpret this interval. Can you be 95 percent confident that $p_1 - p_2$ is less than 0? That is, can you be 95 percent confident that p_1 is less than p_2? Explain.

7.90 The newspaper at a large Canadian university conducted a survey of faculty and students on campus to determine whether or not the parking is adequate. A random sample of 200 faculty members and a random sample of 500 students were selected. One hundred twenty-six of the faculty members and 277 of the students said that parking on campus is inadequate.

Calculate a 95 percent confidence interval for the difference between the proportion of faculty members and the proportion of students who believe that parking on campus is inadequate. On the basis of this interval, can you be 95 percent confident that these proportions differ? Explain.

7.91 Have the attitudes of young Canadian adults about smoking changed in recent years? In 1999, a random sample of 1,000 young adults aged 18 to 24 was taken and 576 of them said that they were smokers. In 2006, a random sample of 900 young adults aged 18 to 24 was taken and 459 of them said they were smokers.

Calculate a 95 percent confidence interval for the difference between the proportion of young adults who smoked in 1999 versus 2006. On the basis of this interval, can you be 95 percent confident that a smaller percentage of young adults were smoking in 2006 compared to those of the same age group in 1999? Explain.

7.92 The digital music players produced by a large Canadian manufacturer during the first two months of 2010 were of poor quality. A random sample of 100 players was obtained during this time and the players were tested. It was determined that 21 of them were defective. Quality control standards were then tightened. A random sample of 100 players was taken during the next two months. It was determined that 12 were defective.

Calculate a 95 percent confidence interval for the difference between the proportions of defective digital music players produced during the first two months and the second two months of 2010. On the basis of this interval, can you be 95 percent confident that the stricter quality control standards made a difference? Explain.

7.93 On January 7, 2000, the Gallup Organization released the results of a poll comparing the lifestyles of today with those of yesteryear. The survey results were based on telephone interviews with a randomly selected national sample of 1,031 adults, 18 years and older, conducted December 20 to 21, 1999. The poll asked several questions and compared the 1999 responses with the responses given in polls taken in previous years. In Figure 7.19, we summarize some of the poll's results.[14] Assume that each poll was based on a randomly selected national sample of 1,031 adults and that the samples in different years are independent.

a. Let p_1 be the December 1999 population proportion of U.S. adults who had taken a vacation lasting six days or more within the last 12 months and p_2 be the December 1968 population proportion who had taken such a vacation. Calculate a 99 percent confidence interval for the difference between p_1 and p_2. Interpret what this interval says about how these population proportions differ.

b. Let p_1 be the December 1999 population proportion of U.S. adults who drove a car or truck to work and p_2 be the April 1971 population proportion who did the same. Calculate a 95 percent confidence interval for the difference between p_1 and p_2. On the basis of this interval, can you conclude that the 1999 and 1971 population proportions differ?

7.94 In a local municipal election to elect a mayor for the city of Melville, only two candidates are running for the position of mayor, Willie Gettin and Betty Wont. In an attempt to see how the voters are voting by age group, a poll is conducted. One thousand citizens of the city aged 18 to 40 are randomly selected and are asked whom they would vote for, and 1,000 residents aged 41 and older are asked the same question. All 2,000 people sampled offered a response. Let $\hat{p}_1$ represent the proportion of voters aged 18 to 40 who said they would vote for Willie and $\hat{p}_2$ represent the proportion of voters aged 41 and older who said that they would vote for Willie. The results are $\hat{p}_1 = 510/1{,}000$ and $\hat{p}_2 = 550/1{,}000$.

Calculate a 95 percent confidence interval for $\hat{p}_1 - \hat{p}_2$ and decide whether or not age makes a difference. That is, is there a difference in the support level for Willie between the two age groups?

FIGURE 7.19 Result of Gallup Survey for Exercise 7.93

	Percentage of respondents	
1 Had taken a vacation lasting six days or more within the last 12 months:	December 1999 42%	December 1968 62%
2 Took part in some sort of daily activity to keep physically fit:	December 1999 60%	September 1977 48%
3 Watched TV more than four hours on an average weekday:	December 1999 28%	April 1981 25%
4 Drove a car or truck to work:	December 1999 87%	April 1971 81%

[14]Source: http://www.galluppoll.com/poll/3352/Trends-Show-Bathing-Exercise-Up-Watching-Down.aspx. The Gallup Poll, January 7, 2000.

CHAPTER SUMMARY

In the first part of this chapter, we discussed **confidence intervals** for population **means** and **proportions**. We began by assuming that the population is either infinite or much larger than (say, at least 20 times as large as) the sample. First, we studied how to compute a confidence interval for a **population mean**. We saw that when the population standard deviation σ is known, we can use the **normal distribution** to compute a confidence interval for a population mean. When σ is not known, if the population is normally distributed (or at least mound-shaped) or if the sample size n is large, we use the **t distribution** to compute this interval. We also studied how to find the size of the sample needed if we wish to compute a confidence interval for a mean with a prespecified **confidence level** and a prespecified **margin of error**. Figure 7.20 is a flowchart summarizing our discussions concerning how to compute an appropriate confidence interval for a population mean.

Next we saw that we are often interested in estimating the proportion of population units falling into a category of interest. We showed how to compute a large-sample confidence interval for a **population proportion**, and we saw how to find the sample size needed to estimate a population proportion with a prespecified **confidence level** and a prespecified **margin of error**.

Next, we explained how to compare two populations by using one-tailed and two-tailed confidence intervals. We discussed how to compare **two population means** by using **independent samples**. Here the measurements in one sample are not related to the measurements in the other sample. We saw that in the unlikely event that the population variances are known, a **z-based** confidence interval can be constructed. When these variances are unknown, **t-based** intervals are appropriate if the underlying populations are at least symmetric in nature. Both **equal-variances** and **unequal-variances t-based confidence intervals** were discussed. We learned that because it can be difficult to compare the population variances, many statisticians believe that it is almost always best to use the unequal-variances procedure, unless of course you have prior knowledge that the underlying variances are indeed equal.

Sometimes samples are not independent. We learned that one such case is what is called a **paired-differences experiment**. In these types of experiments, we would obtain two different measurements on the same sample units, and we learned that we can compare two population means by using a confidence interval using the differences between the pairs of measurements.

FIGURE **7.20**　Computing an Appropriate Confidence Interval for a Population Mean (Single Sample)

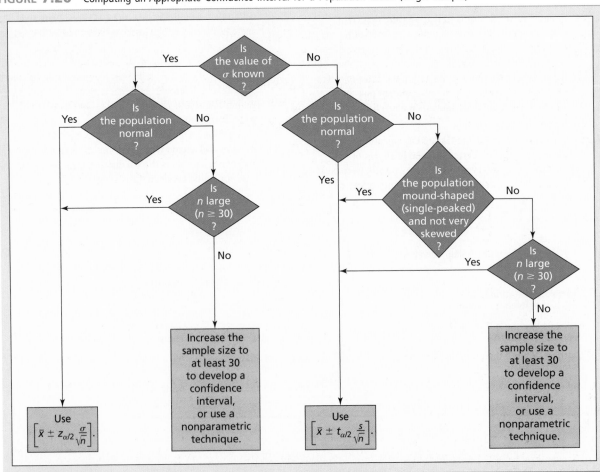

GLOSSARY OF TERMS

confidence coefficient: The (before-sampling) probability that a confidence interval for a population parameter will contain the population parameter. (page 208)

confidence interval: An interval of numbers computed so that we can be very confident (say, 95 percent confident) that a population parameter is contained in the interval. (page 206)

confidence level: The percentage of time that a confidence interval would contain a population parameter if all possible samples were used to calculate the interval. (page 209)

degrees of freedom (for a *t* curve): A parameter that describes the exact spread of the curve of a *t* distribution. (page 214)

independent-samples experiment: An experiment in which there is no relationship between the measurements in the different samples. (page 233)

margin of error: The quantity that is added to and subtracted from a point estimate of a population parameter to obtain a confidence interval for the parameter. It gives the maximum distance between the population parameter of interest and its point estimate when we assume the parameter is inside the confidence interval. (page 209)

paired-differences experiment: An experiment in which two different measurements are taken on the same units and

inferences are made using the differences between the pairs of measurements. (pages 241–243)

sampling distribution of $\hat{p}_1 - \hat{p}_2$: The probability distribution that describes the population of all possible values of $\hat{p}_1 - \hat{p}_2$, where $\hat{p}_1$ is the sample proportion for a random sample taken from one population and $\hat{p}_2$ is the sample proportion for a random sample taken from a second population. (page 245)

sampling distribution of $\bar{x}_1 - \bar{x}_2$: The probability distribution that describes the population of all possible values of $\bar{x}_1 - \bar{x}_2$, where $\bar{x}_1$ is the sample mean of a random sample taken from one population and $\bar{x}_2$ is the sample mean of a random sample taken from a second population. (page 233)

***t* distribution:** A commonly used continuous probability distribution that is described by a distribution curve similar to a normal curve. The *t* curve is symmetrical about zero and is more spread out than a standard normal curve. (page 214)

***t* point, t_α:** The point on the horizontal axis under a *t* curve that gives a right-hand tail area equal to α. (page 215)

***t* table:** A table of *t* values listed according to the area in the tail of the *t* curve and according to values of the degrees of freedom. (page 216)

IMPORTANT FORMULAS

A *z*-based confidence interval for a population mean μ with σ known: page 208

A *t*-based confidence interval for a population mean μ with σ unknown: page 217

Sample size when estimating μ: page 222

A large-sample confidence interval for a population proportion p: page 225

Sample size when estimating p: page 227

Sampling distribution of $\bar{x}_1 - \bar{x}_2$ (independent random samples): page 233

z-based confidence interval for $\mu_1 - \mu_2$: page 233

t-based confidence interval for $\mu_1 - \mu_2$ when $\sigma_1^2 = \sigma_2^2$: page 236

t-based confidence intervals for $\mu_1 - \mu_2$: page 238

Confidence interval for μ_d: page 242

Sampling distribution of $\hat{p}_1 - \hat{p}_2$ (independent random samples): page 245

Large-sample confidence interval for $p_1 - p_2$: page 245

connect™ Practise and learn online with *Connect*. Questions and tables with online data sets are marked with ⫽.

SUPPLEMENTARY EXERCISES

7.95   In an article in the *Journal of Accounting Research*, Ashton, Willingham, and Elliott studied audit delay (the length of time from a company's fiscal year-end to the date of the auditor's report) for industrial and financial companies. In the study, a random sample of 250 industrial companies yielded a mean audit delay of 68.04 days with a standard deviation of 35.72 days, while a random sample of 238 financial companies yielded a mean audit delay of 56.74 days with a standard deviation of 34.87 days. Use these sample results to do the following:

a. Calculate a 95 percent confidence interval for the mean audit delay for all industrial companies. *Note:* $t_{0.025} = 1.97$ when $df = 249$.

b. Calculate a 95 percent confidence interval for the mean audit delay for all financial companies. *Note:* $t_{0.025} = 1.97$ when $df = 237$.

c. Compare the 95 percent confidence intervals you calculated in parts a and b. Is there strong evidence that the mean audit delay for financial companies is shorter than the mean audit delay for industrial companies? Explain.

7.96 In an article in *Accounting and Business Research*, Beattie and Jones investigate the use and abuse of graphic presentations in the annual reports of U.K. firms. The authors found that 65 percent of the sampled companies graph at least one key financial variable, but that 30 percent of the graphics are materially distorted (nonzero vertical axis, exaggerated trend, or the like).

    a. Suppose that in a random sample of 465 graphics from the annual reports of U.K. firms, 142 of the graphics are found to be distorted. Find a point estimate of and a 95 percent confidence interval for the proportion of U.K. annual report graphics that are distorted.

    b. Based on this interval, can you be 95 percent confident that more than 25 percent of all graphics appearing in the annual reports of U.K. firms are distorted? Explain. Does this suggest that auditors should understand proper graphing methods?

    c. Determine the sample size needed in order to be 95 percent confident that $\hat{p}$, the sample proportion of U.K. annual report graphics that are distorted, is within a margin of error of 0.03 of p, the true proportion of U.K. annual report graphics that are distorted.

7.97 On November 3, 2006, Ipsos Reid conducted a survey on behalf of LG Electronics Canada to ask Canadians about their cell phone attitudes. Apparently size does matter! The study found that 82 percent indicated that size was an extremely important attribute for a cell phone. For this particular poll, 1,428 Canadians aged 18 or older who owned or were considering purchasing a cell phone in the next six months were surveyed.[15]

    a. Based on these findings, calculate a 95 percent confidence interval for the proportion of all Canadians aged 18 or older who own or are considering purchasing a cell phone in the next six months who believe that size is important.

    b. In explaining the survey methods, Ipsos Reid stated the following: "For results based on a sample of this size, the results are considered to be accurate to within ±2.6 percentage points." Explain how your calculations in part a verify that this statement is true.

7.98 The manager of a chain of discount department stores wishes to estimate the total number of erroneous discounts allowed by sales clerks during the last month. A random sample of 200 of the chain's 57,532 transactions for the last month reveals that erroneous discounts were allowed on eight of the transactions. Use this sample information to find a point estimate of and a 95 percent confidence interval for the total number of erroneous discounts allowed during the last month.

7.99 Canadian Motor Products has equipped the ZX-900 with a new disc brake system. Define the stopping distance for a ZX-900 to be the distance (in metres) required to bring the automobile to a complete stop from a speed of 50 km/h under normal driving conditions using this new braking system. In addition, define μ to be the mean stopping distance of all ZX-900s. One of the ZX-900's major

competitors is advertised to achieve a mean stopping distance of 18 m. Canadian Motor Products would like to claim in a new advertising campaign that the ZX-900 achieves a shorter mean stopping distance.

    Suppose that Canadian Motor Products randomly selects a sample of $n = 81$ ZX-900s. The company records the stopping distance of each automobile and calculates the mean and standard deviation of the sample of $n = 81$ stopping distances to be $\bar{x} = 17.6$ m and $s = 1.83$ m.

    a. Calculate a 95 percent confidence interval for μ. Can Canadian Motor Products be 95 percent confident that μ is less than 18 m? Explain.

    b. Using the sample of $n = 81$ stopping distances as a preliminary sample, find the sample size necessary to make Canadian Motor Products 95 percent confident that $\bar{x}$ is within a margin of error of 0.3 m of μ.

7.100 A large construction contractor is building 257 homes, which are in various stages of completion. For tax purposes, the contractor needs to estimate the total dollar value of its inventory due to construction in progress. The contractor randomly selects (without replacement) a sample of 40 of the 257 houses and determines the accumulated costs (the amount of money tied up in inventory) for each sampled house. The contractor finds that the sample mean accumulated cost is $\bar{x} = \$75,162.70$ and the sample standard deviation is $s = \$28,865.04$.

    a. Find a point estimate of and a 99 percent confidence interval for the total accumulated costs (total amount of money tied up in inventory) for all 257 houses that are under construction.

    b. Using the confidence interval as the basis for your answer, find a reasonable estimate of the largest possible total dollar value of the contractor's inventory due to construction in progress.

7.101 In an article in the *Journal of Retailing*, Blodgett, Granbois, and Walters investigated negative word-of-mouth consumer behaviour. In a random sample of 201 consumers, 150 reported that they engaged in negative word-of-mouth behaviour (for instance, they vowed never to patronize a retailer again). In addition, the 150 respondents who engaged in such behaviour, on average, told 4.88 people about their dissatisfying experience (with a standard deviation equal to 6.11).

    a. Use these sample results to compute a 95 percent confidence interval for the proportion of all consumers who engage in negative word-of-mouth behaviour. On the basis of this interval, would it be reasonable to claim that more than 70 percent of all consumers engage in such behaviour? Explain.

    b. Use the sample results to compute a 95 percent confidence interval for the mean number of people who are told about a dissatisfying experience by consumers who engage in negative word-of-mouth behaviour. On the basis of this interval, would it be reasonable to claim that these dissatisfied consumers tell, on average, at least three people about their bad experience? Explain. *Note:* $t_{0.025} = 1.98$ when $df = 149$.

---

[15]Source: http://www.ipsos-na.com/news-polls/pressrelease.aspx?id53248, "When it comes to cell phones size does matter," November 3, 2006.

7.102 A random sample of 50 perceived age estimates for a model in a liquor advertisement in a particular country showed that $\bar{x} = 26.22$ years and $s = 3.7432$ years.

a. Use this sample to calculate a 95 percent confidence interval for the population mean age estimate for all viewers of the ad.

b. The liquor industry in this country requires that models appear at least 25 years old. Does the confidence interval make you 95 percent confident that the mean perceived age estimate is at least 25? Is the mean perceived age estimate much more than 25? Explain.

7.103 In an article in the *Journal of Management Information Systems*, Mahmood and Mann investigate how information technology (IT) investment relates to company performance. In particular, Mahmood and Mann obtain sample data concerning IT investment for companies that effectively use information systems. Among the variables studied are the company's IT budget as a percentage of company revenue, percentages of the IT budget spent on staff and training, and number of PCs and terminals as a percentage of total employees.

a. Suppose a random sample of 15 companies considered to effectively use information systems yields a sample mean IT budget as a percentage of company revenue of $\bar{x} = 2.73$ with a standard deviation of $s = 1.64$. Assuming that IT budget percentages are approximately normally distributed, calculate a 99 percent confidence interval for the mean IT budget as a percentage of company revenue for all firms that effectively use information systems. Does this interval provide evidence that a firm can successfully use information systems with an IT budget that is less than 5 percent of company revenue? Explain.

b. Suppose a random sample of 15 companies considered to effectively use information systems yields a sample mean number of PCs and terminals as a percentage of total employees of $\bar{x} = 34.76$ with a standard deviation of $s = 25.37$. Assuming approximate normality, calculate a 99 percent confidence interval for the mean number of PCs and terminals as a percentage of total employees for all firms that effectively use information systems. Why is this interval so wide? What can you do to obtain a narrower (more useful) confidence interval?

7.104 THE INVESTMENT CASE

Suppose that random samples of 50 returns for each of the following investment classes give the indicated sample mean and sample standard deviation:

Fixed annuities: $\bar{x} = 7.83\%$, $s = 0.51\%$

Domestic large cap stocks: $\bar{x} = 13.42\%$, $s = 15.17\%$

Domestic midcap stocks: $\bar{x} = 15.03\%$, $s = 18.44\%$

Domestic small cap stocks: $\bar{x} = 22.51\%$, $s = 21.75\%$

For each investment class, compute a 95 percent confidence interval for the population mean return.

7.105 THE INTERNATIONAL BUSINESS TRAVEL EXPENSE CASE

Recall (see Exercise 2.71 on page 81) that the mean and the standard deviation of a random sample of 35 one-day travel expenses in Moscow are $\bar{x} = \$538$ and $s = \$41$. Find a 95 percent confidence interval for the mean, μ, of all one-day travel expenses in Moscow.

7.106 THE U.K. INSURANCE CASE

Assume that the U.K. insurance survey is based on 1,000 randomly selected U.K. households and that 640 of these households spent on life insurance in 1993. Find a 95 percent confidence interval for the proportion, p, of all U.K. households that spent on life insurance in 1993.

7.107 A local factory bags and ships 1-kg bags of sugar. A random sample of sixteen 1-kg bags of sugar is obtained and the actual masses of the bags are measured. The sample mean is 1.051 kg with a sample standard deviation of $s = 0.06$ kg. The masses are approximately normally distributed. Calculate a 99 percent confidence interval for the average mass of all bags of sugar produced at this factory. Is it plausible that the true average mass of all bags produced at this factory is actually 1.02 kg and not 1 kg? Explain.

7.108 In Chapter 2, Exercise 2.8, we briefly described a series of international quality standards called ISO 9000. In the results of a Quality Systems Update/Deloitte & Touche survey of ISO 9000 registered companies published by CEEM Information Systems, 515 of 620 companies surveyed reported that they are encouraging their suppliers to pursue ISO 9000 registration.[16]

a. Using these survey results, compute a 95.44 percent confidence interval for the proportion of all ISO 9000 registered companies that encourage their suppliers to pursue ISO 9000 registration. Assume that the survey participants were randomly selected.

b. Based on this interval, is there conclusive evidence that more than 75 percent of all ISO 9000 registered companies encourage their suppliers to pursue ISO 9000 registration?

7.109 In its February 2, 1998, issue, *Fortune* magazine published the results of a Yankelovich Partners survey of 600 adults that investigated their ideas about marriage, divorce, and the contributions of the corporate wife. The survey results are shown in Figure 7.21 on the next page. For each statement in the figure, the proportions of men and women who agreed with the statement are given. Assume that the survey results were obtained from independent random samples of 300 men and 300 women. For each statement, calculate a 95 percent confidence interval for the difference between the population proportion of men who agree with the statement and the population proportion of women who agree with the statement. Use the interval to help assess whether you feel that the difference between population proportions has practical significance.

[16]Source: *Is ISO 9000 for You?* (Fairfax, VA: CEEM Information Services).

FIGURE **7.21**   The Results of a Yankelovich Partners Survey of 600 Adults on Marriage, Divorce, and the Contributions of the Corporate Wife (All Respondents with Income $50,000 or More)

People were magnanimous on the general proposition:
- In a divorce in a long-term marriage where the husband works outside the home and the wife is not employed for pay, the wife should be entitled to half the assets accumulated during the marriage.
  93% of women agree
  85% of men agree

But when we got to the goodies, a gender gap began to appear . . .
- The pension accumulated during the marriage should be split evenly.
  80% of women agree
  68% of men agree
- Stock options granted during the marriage should be split evenly.
  77% of women agree
  62% of men agree

. . . and turned into a chasm over the issue of how important a stay-at-home wife is to a husband's success.
- Managing the household and child rearing are extremely important to a husband's success.
  57% of women agree
  41% of men agree
- A corporate wife who also must travel, entertain, and act as a sounding board is extremely important to the success of a high-level business executive.
  51% of women agree
  28% of men agree
- The lifestyle of a corporate wife is more of a job than a luxury.
  73% of women agree
  57% of men agree

Source: Reprinted from the February 2, 1998, issue of *Fortune*. Copyright © 1998 Time, Inc. Reprinted by permission.

Exercises 7.110 and 7.111 deal with the following situation:

In an article in the *Journal of Retailing*, Kumar, Kerwin, and Pereira study factors affecting merger and acquisition activity in retailing by comparing "target firms" and "bidder firms" with respect to several financial and marketing-related variables. Consider two of the financial variables included in the study, and suppose a random sample of 36 target firms gives a mean earnings per share of $1.52 with a standard deviation of $0.92, and that this sample gives a mean debt-to-equity ratio of 1.66 with a standard deviation of 0.82. Furthermore, an independent random sample of 36 bidder firms gives a mean earnings per share of $1.20 with a standard deviation of $0.84, and this sample gives a mean debt-to-equity ratio of 1.58 with a standard deviation of 0.81.

7.110 Calculate a 95 percent confidence interval for the difference between the mean earnings per share for target firms and bidder firms. Interpret the interval.

7.111 Calculate a 95 percent confidence interval for the difference between the mean debt-to-equity ratios for target firms and bidder firms. Interpret the interval.

7.112 INTERNET EXERCISE

Statistics Canada uses what it refers to as "Seasonal Adjustments" when determining the unemployment rates in Canada as a whole and for the provinces. Go to the Statistics Canada Web site (http://www.statcan.gc.ca).
a. Determine what is meant by "seasonal adjustment."
b. Compare and contrast the employment rates in Alberta and Manitoba. What are the differences, and why do you think they exist?
c. Compare and contrast the unemployment rates in your province and the national average. What are the differences, and why do you think they exist?

CHAPTER 8

Hypothesis Testing

LEARNING OBJECTIVES

After reading this chapter, you should be able to

LO1 define and contrast the null hypothesis (H_0) and the research (or alternative; H_a) hypothesis

LO2 explain the difference between and define Type I (α) and Type II (β) errors

LO3 understand which error type is the one most researchers are concerned about

LO4 describe the steps involved in conducting a hypothesis test using a rejection point

LO5 explain what is meant by the term "statistical significance"

LO6 conduct hypothesis tests and take appropriate action or make appropriate decisions based on the results

LO7 describe a situation in which a finding may be statistically significant but not practically significant

LO8 understand the meaning of a p value

LO9 know how to calculate a p value

LO10 know how to make decisions using a p value

CHAPTER OUTLINE

8.1 The Null and Alternative Hypotheses and Errors in Hypothesis Testing

8.2 Type I and Type II Errors and Their Probabilities

8.3 z Tests about a Population Mean (σ Known): One-Sided Alternatives

8.4 z Tests about a Population Mean (σ Known): Two-Sided Alternatives

8.5 t Tests about a Population Mean (σ Unknown)

8.6 z Tests about a Population Proportion

Imagine that you are walking down railway tracks and listening to a digital music player with your headphones on. You hear a noise, and you are not sure what it is. It might be a train, but it might not be. You have two choices to make. You could ignore the sound, and keep walking on the tracks, or you could jump away from the tracks and look behind you. You have, in effect, just conducted your own hypothesis test. In this test, there are

two errors to consider. One of these errors is harmless (jumping off when no train is coming) and one could be fatal (ignoring the noise of a train coming). In this chapter, we discuss testing hypotheses about population means, proportions, and variances.

In order to illustrate how hypothesis testing works, we revisit several cases introduced in previous chapters.

The Payment Time Case: The consulting firm uses hypothesis testing to provide strong evidence that the new electronic billing system has reduced the mean payment time by more than 50 percent.

The Wine Case: The wine maker uses hypothesis testing to supply extremely strong evidence that less than 10 percent of all current purchasers would stop buying the wine if the new bottles were used.

The Electronic Article Surveillance Case: A company that sells and installs electronic article surveillance (EAS) systems claims that no more than 5 percent of all consumers would say they would never shop in a store again if the store subjected them to a false EAS alarm. A store considering the purchase of such a system uses hypothesis testing to provide extremely strong evidence that this claim is not true.

In addition, we introduce two new cases that illustrate how to test a hypothesis:

The Beer Case: A beer drinker uses hypothesis testing to support a claim that the mean volume of beer in the bottle is less than 341 mL. As a result, the consumer will file a complaint with the brewery (and maybe get some free beer).

The Camshaft Case: An automobile manufacturer uses hypothesis testing to study an important quality characteristic affecting V6 engine camshafts. It finds that the mean hardness depth differs from its desired target value and that this problem is one reason why some of the hardness depths fail to meet specifications.

 connect™ Practise and learn online with *Connect*. Throughout this chapter, questions and tables with online data sets are marked with 🛫 .

8.1 THE NULL AND ALTERNATIVE HYPOTHESES AND ERRORS IN HYPOTHESIS TESTING

VS

CHAPTER 9

One of the responsibilities of a major television network's standards and practices division is to reduce the chances that advertisers will make false claims in commercials run on the network. To test claims, the network uses a statistical methodology called **hypothesis testing**.

To see how this might be done, suppose that a company wishes to advertise a claim, and suppose that the network has reason to doubt that this claim is true. The network assumes that *the claim is not valid*. This assumption is called the **null hypothesis** (denoted H_0). The statement that *the claim is valid* is called the **alternative**, or **research**, **hypothesis** (denoted H_a). The network will run the commercial only if the company making the claim provides *sufficient sample evidence* to reject the null hypothesis that the claim is not valid in favour of the alternative hypothesis that the claim is valid.

The Null Hypothesis and the Alternative Hypothesis

LO1

In hypothesis testing:

1   The **null hypothesis**, denoted H_0, is the statement being tested. Usually this statement represents the status quo and is not rejected unless there is convincing sample evidence that it is false.

2   The **alternative**, or **research**, **hypothesis**, denoted H_a, is a statement that will be accepted only if there is convincing sample evidence that H_0 is not true.

Setting up the null and alternative hypotheses in a practical situation can be tricky. In some situations, there is a condition for which we need to attempt to find supportive evidence. We then formulate (1) the alternative hypothesis to be the statement that this condition exists and (2) the null hypothesis to be the statement that this condition does not exist. To illustrate this, we consider the following case study.

Example 8.1 The Payment Time Case

Recall (see Example 6.3 on pages 192–193) that a management consulting firm has installed a computerized billing system in a trucking company. Because of the system's advantages, and because the trucking company's clients are receptive to using this system, the management consulting firm believes that the new system will reduce the mean bill payment time by more than 50 percent. The mean payment time using the old billing system was approximately equal to, but no less than, 39 days. Therefore, if μ denotes the mean payment time using the new system, the consulting firm believes that μ will be less than 19.5 days. Because it is hoped that the new billing system *reduces* mean payment time, we formulate the alternative hypothesis as H_a: $\mu < 19.5$ and the null hypothesis as H_0: $\mu \geq 19.5$. The consulting firm will randomly select a sample of n invoices and determine how much evidence their payment times provide to reject H_0 in favour of H_a. The firm will use the results of the hypothesis test to demonstrate the benefits of the new billing system both to the company and to other trucking companies that are considering using such a system. Note, however, that a potential user will decide whether to install the new system by considering factors beyond the results of the hypothesis test. For example, the cost of the new billing system and the receptiveness of the company's clients to using the new system must also be considered. In complex business and industrial situations such as this, hypothesis testing is used to accumulate knowledge about and understand the problem at hand. The ultimate decision (such as whether to adopt the new billing system) is made on the basis of nonstatistical considerations, intuition, and the results of one or more hypothesis tests.

Example 8.2 The Camshaft Case

On March 8, 1999, Coltec Industries of Charlotte, North Carolina, made an alarming discovery. A Coltec quality control study revealed that the company had supplied the Consolidated Edison–Indian Point 2 nuclear power plant with inadequately hardened engine camshafts. The suspect camshafts were a significant safety hazard because they could cause FM-ALCO 251 engines, which the power plant used to run emergency standby power generators, to fail. Although Coltec was not aware of any engine failures in nuclear power plants, such failures had occurred in commercial applications after approximately 200 hours of operation. Coltec immediately reported its conclusions to the U.S. Nuclear Regulatory Commission, and a crisis was averted at the Consolidated Edison plant. Coltec also substantially improved its camshaft inspection process so that the problem would not occur again.[1]

In general, an engine camshaft is an important part in a variety of commercial and industrial engines. For example, the camshaft of a V6 automobile engine is illustrated in Figure 8.1. Positioned on this (or any) camshaft are metal disks called *eccentrics*. As the camshaft turns, these eccentrics repeatedly make contact with *engine lifters* and thus must have the appropriate hardness to wear properly. To harden the eccentrics, the camshaft is heat treated, and a hardened layer is produced on the surface of the camshaft. The depth of this layer is called the *hardness depth* of the camshaft. If the hardness depth of a camshaft is within given specifications, the camshaft will wear properly, resulting in long engine life.

To illustrate how we might use a hypothesis test to study camshaft hardness, we consider an automobile manufacturer that is having problems properly hardening the camshaft of a V6 automobile engine. The *optimal*, or *target*, hardness depth of this camshaft is 4.5 mm, and specifications state that in order for the camshaft to wear properly, the hardness depth must be between 3.0 mm and 6.0 mm. Unfortunately, however, the hardening process has been

FIGURE **8.1** A Camshaft and Related Parts

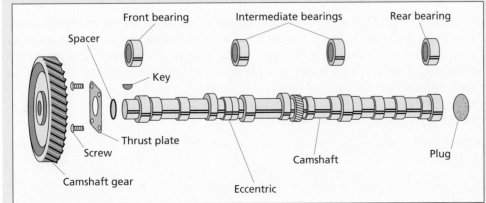

[1]Source: http://www.nrc.gov/reading-rm/doc-collections/event-status/part21/1999/1999161.html.

producing too many out-of-specification camshafts. To investigate why this is so, a quality control analyst randomly selects n camshafts from the population of all camshafts produced on a particular day and measures the hardness depth of each sampled camshaft. Then, letting μ denote the population mean hardness depth of all camshafts produced that day, the analyst will evaluate whether μ differs from the target value of 4.5 mm by testing the null hypothesis H_0: $\mu = 4.5$ versus the alternative hypothesis H_a: $\mu \neq 4.5$. Of course, μ differing from 4.5 is not the only reason the hardness depths of the camshafts produced on the particular day might be out of specification. Another reason might be that the variation of the hardness depths is too large.

We next summarize the sets of null and alternative hypotheses that we have thus far considered.

$$H_0: \mu \geq 19.5 \qquad H_0: \mu = 4.5$$
$$\text{versus} \qquad \text{versus}$$
$$H_a: \mu < 19.5 \qquad H_a: \mu \neq 4.5$$

In general, H_a: $\mu > x$ is called a **one-sided, greater than** alternative hypothesis; H_a: $\mu < x$ is called a **one-sided, less than** alternative hypothesis; and H_a: $\mu \neq x$ is called a **two-sided, not equal to** alternative hypothesis. Many of the alternative hypotheses we consider in this book are one of these three types. Also note that each null hypothesis we have considered involves an *equality*. For example, the null hypothesis H_0: $\mu \geq 19.5$ says that μ is either greater than or *equal to* 19.5. We will see that, in general, the approach we use to test a null hypothesis versus an alternative hypothesis requires that the null hypothesis involve an equality.

The idea of a test statistic Suppose that in the electronic billing case the consultant randomly selects a sample of $n = 40$ new invoices. The sample mean $\bar{x}$ of the 40 payment times is calculated. In order to test H_0: $\mu \geq 19.5$ versus H_a: $\mu < 19.5$, we utilize the **test statistic**

$$z = \frac{\bar{x} - 19.5}{\sigma_{\bar{x}}} = \frac{\bar{x} - 19.5}{\sigma/\sqrt{n}}.$$

The test statistic z measures the distance between $\bar{x}$ and 19.5. The division by $\sigma_{\bar{x}}$ says that this distance is measured in units of the standard deviation of all possible sample means. For example, a value of z equal to, say, 2.4 would tell us that $\bar{x}$ is 2.4 standard deviations above 19.5. In general, the value of the test statistic is less than or equal to zero when $\bar{x}$ is less than or equal to μ, and the value of the test statistic is greater than zero when $\bar{x}$ is greater than μ. Furthermore, the farther the value of the test statistic is from 0 (the farther $\bar{x}$ is away from μ), the stronger is the evidence to support rejecting H_0 in favour of H_a.

Example 8.3 The Beer Case

Suppose that we believe that our favourite beer supplier is underfilling its 341-mL bottles of beer. We want to use hypothesis testing to provide strong evidence that this is true. In order to test this hypothesis, we randomly sample $n = 30$ bottles of beer. Suppose that it is known that the standard deviation of the volume of beer in each bottle is $\sigma = 2$ mL. We determine that $\bar{x} = 340.1$ mL for our sample. We will use the appropriate test to determine if our belief is valid.

We will test H_0: $\mu = 341$ mL versus H_a: $\mu < 341$ mL.

We will first calculate the value of the test statistic:

$$z = \frac{\bar{x} - 341}{\sigma/\sqrt{n}}$$
$$= \frac{340.1 - 341}{2/\sqrt{30}}$$
$$= -2.46.$$

Since we are 2.46 standard deviations to the left of the mean, this provides evidence that we can reject H_0. Later in the chapter, we will learn how to calculate a p value based on this test statistic, and this p value will allow us to make our decision based on a predetermined value of α.

For now, we will say that our data suggest that there is little evidence to support H_0. Therefore, we reject H_0.

8.2 TYPE I AND TYPE II ERRORS AND THEIR PROBABILITIES

To determine exactly how much statistical evidence is required to reject H_0, we consider the errors and the correct decisions that can be made in hypothesis testing. These errors and correct decisions are summarized in Table 8.1. Across the top of the table are listed the two possible **states of nature**. Either H_0 is true or H_0 is false. Down the left side of each table are listed the two possible decisions we can make in the hypothesis test. Using the sample data, we will either reject H_0 or not reject H_0.

TABLE **8.1** Type I and Type II Errors

Decision	State of Nature	
	H_0 **True**	H_0 **False**
Reject H_0	Type I error	Correct decision
Do not reject H_0	Correct decision	Type II error

LO2

In general, the two types of errors that can be made in hypothesis testing are defined here:

Type I and Type II Errors

If we reject H_0 when it is true, this is a **Type I error**.
If we do not reject H_0 when it is false, this is a **Type II error**.

As can be seen in Table 8.1, if we commit a Type I error, we will make a false claim. If we commit a Type II error, we will fail to make a true claim.

We now let the symbol α (alpha) *denote the probability of a Type I error*, and we let β (beta) *denote the probability of a Type II error*. Obviously, we would like both α and β to be small. A common (but not the only) procedure is to base a hypothesis test on taking a sample of a fixed size (for example, $n = 40$ surveys) and setting α equal to a small prespecified value. Setting α low means there is only a small chance of rejecting H_0 when it is true. This implies that we require strong evidence against H_0 before we reject it.

We sometimes choose α as high as 0.10, but we usually choose α between 0.01 and 0.05. A frequent choice for α is 0.05. Since a Type I error is deciding that H_a is valid when it is not, the policy of setting α equal to 0.05 says that, in the long run, only 5 percent of all claims made will be false.

One might wonder why researchers do not set α lower—say at 0.01. One reason is that *it can be shown that for a fixed sample size, the lower we set α, the higher is β, and the higher we set α, the lower is β*. Setting α at 0.05 means that β, the probability of failing to make a true claim (a Type II error), will be smaller than it would be if α were set at 0.01. As long as (1) the claim is plausible and (2) the consequences of making the claim even if it is false are not terribly serious, then it is reasonable to set α equal to 0.05. However, if either (1) or (2) is not true, then we might set α lower than 0.05. For example, suppose a pharmaceutical company wishes to advertise that it has developed an effective treatment for a disease that has formerly been very resistant to treatment (this claim represents H_a). Such a claim may be difficult to believe. Moreover, if the claim is false, patients suffering from the disease would be subjected to false hope and possibly needless expense. In such a case, it might be reasonable for the company to set α at 0.01 because this would lower the chance of advertising the claim if it is false. We usually do not set α lower than 0.01 because doing so often leads to an unacceptably large value of β. However, β can be difficult or impossible to calculate in many situations, and we must often rely on our intuition when deciding how to set α.

One additional point to be made about Type II (β) errors is that they are typically theoretical in nature. Knowing β suggests that we know what the "real world" (the population) is actually like, and if we really knew this, then we would probably not be taking a sample (because samples are taken to estimate what is happening in the population). A Type I (α) error, on the other hand, is a greater issue. Making a claim that there is an effect or rejecting the null hypothesis (the status quo) is a bigger deal than playing it safe and saying there is no effect or failing to reject H_0. Because of this, the Type I (α) error is a more applied issue (as opposed to the more theoretical Type II error).

LO3

Exercises for Sections 8.1 and 8.2

CONCEPTS

8.1 Which hypothesis (the null hypothesis, H_0, or the alternative hypothesis, H_a) is the status quo hypothesis (that is, the hypothesis that states that things remain as is)? Which hypothesis is the hypothesis that says that a hoped-for or suspected condition exists?

8.2 Which hypothesis (H_0 or H_a) is not rejected unless there is convincing sample evidence that it is false? Which hypothesis (H_0 or H_a) will be accepted only if there is convincing sample evidence that it is true?

8.3 Define each of the following:
  a. Type I error.   **c.** α.
  b. Type II error.   **d.** β.

8.4 For each of the following situations, indicate whether an error has occurred and, if so, indicate what kind of error (Type I or Type II) has occurred and state each probability. Try not to refer to Table 8.1.
  a. You do not reject H_0 and H_0 is true.
  b. You reject H_0 and H_0 is true.
  c. You do not reject H_0 and H_0 is false.
  d. You reject H_0 and H_0 is false.

8.5 If you reject H_0, what is the only type of error that you could be making? Explain.

8.6 If you do not reject H_0, what is the only type of error that you could be making? Explain.

8.7 When testing a hypothesis, why do you not set the probability of a Type I error to be extremely small? Explain.

METHODS AND APPLICATIONS

8.8 **THE VIDEO GAME SATISFACTION RATING CASE**

Recall from Exercise 1.8 on page 8 that "very satisfied" customers give the XYZ-Box video game system a rating that is at least 42. Suppose that the manufacturer

of the XYZ-Box wishes to use the 65 satisfaction ratings to provide evidence supporting the claim that the mean composite satisfaction rating for the XYZ-Box exceeds 42.
  a. Letting μ represent the mean composite satisfaction rating for the XYZ-Box, set up the null and alternative hypotheses needed if you wish to attempt to provide evidence supporting the claim that μ exceeds 42.
  b. In the context of this situation, interpret making a Type I error; interpret making a Type II error.

8.9 **THE BANK CUSTOMER WAITING TIME CASE**

Recall from Exercise 1.9 on pages 8–9 that a bank manager has developed a new system to reduce the time customers spend waiting for teller service during peak hours. The manager hopes the new system will reduce waiting times from the current nine to ten minutes to less than six minutes.

Suppose the manager wishes to use the 100 waiting times to support the claim that the mean waiting time under the new system is shorter than six minutes.
  a. Letting μ represent the mean waiting time under the new system, set up the null and alternative hypotheses needed if you wish to attempt to provide evidence supporting the claim that μ is shorter than six minutes.
  b. In the context of this situation, interpret making a Type I error; interpret making a Type II error.

8.10 An automobile parts supplier owns a machine that produces a cylindrical engine part. This part is supposed to have an outside diameter of 3 cm. Parts with diameters that are too small or too large do not meet customer requirements and must be rejected. Lately, the company has experienced problems meeting customer requirements. The technical staff feels that the mean diameter produced by the machine is off target. In order to verify this, a special study will randomly sample 100 parts produced by the machine. The 100 sampled parts will be measured, and if the results obtained cast a substantial amount of doubt on the hypothesis that the mean diameter equals the target value of 3 cm, the company will assign a problem-solving team to intensively search for the causes of the problem.

a. The parts supplier wishes to set up a hypothesis test so that the problem-solving team will be assigned when the null hypothesis is rejected. Set up the null and alternative hypotheses for this situation.

b. In the context of this situation, interpret making a Type I error; interpret making a Type II error.

c. Suppose it costs the company $3,000 a day to assign the problem-solving team to a project. Is this $3,000 figure the daily cost of a Type I error or a Type II error? Explain.

8.11 The Classic Bottling Company has just installed a new bottling process that will fill 355-mL cans of its Classic Cola soft drink. Both overfilling and underfilling cans are undesirable: Underfilling leads to customer complaints, and overfilling costs the company considerable money. In order to verify that the filler is set up correctly, the company wishes to see whether the mean fill, μ, is close to the target fill of 355 mL. To this end, a random sample of 36 filled cans is selected from the output of a test filler run. If the sample results cast a substantial amount of doubt on the hypothesis that the mean fill is the desired 355 mL, then the filler's initial setup will be adjusted.

a. The bottling company wants to set up a hypothesis test so that the filler will be adjusted if the null hypothesis is rejected. Set up the null and alternative hypotheses for this hypothesis test.

b. In the context of this situation, interpret making a Type I error; interpret making a Type II error.

8.12 A large electric power utility has just built a nuclear power plant. This plant discharges waste water that is allowed to flow into a lake. The Ministry of the Environment has ordered that the waste water not be excessively warm so that thermal pollution of the marine environment near the plant can be avoided. Because of this order, the waste water is allowed to cool in specially constructed ponds before being released into the lake. This cooling system works properly if the mean temperature of waste water discharged is 15°C or less. The utility is required to monitor the temperature of the waste water. A sample of 100 temperature readings will be obtained each day, and if the sample results cast a substantial amount of doubt on the hypothesis that the cooling system is working properly (the mean temperature of waste water discharged is 15°C or less), then the plant must be shut down and appropriate actions taken to correct the problem.

a. The utility wishes to set up a hypothesis test so that the power plant will be shut down when the null hypothesis is rejected. Set up the null and alternative hypotheses that should be used.

b. In the context of this situation, interpret making a Type I error; interpret making a Type II error.

c. The ministry periodically conducts spot checks to determine whether the waste water being discharged is too warm. Suppose the ministry has the power to impose very severe penalties (for example, very heavy fines) when the waste water is excessively warm. Other things being equal, should the utility set the probability of a Type I error equal to $\alpha = 0.01$ or $\alpha = 0.05$? Explain.

d. Suppose the utility has been experiencing technical problems with the cooling system. Because the system has been unreliable, the company feels it must take precautions to avoid failing to shut down the plant when its waste water is too warm. Other things being equal, should the utility set the probability of a Type I error equal to $\alpha = 0.01$ or $\alpha = 0.05$? Explain.

8.13 THE DISC BRAKE CASE

Canadian Motor Products has equipped the ZX-900 with a new disc brake system. We define the stopping distance for a ZX-900 as the distance (in metres) required to bring the automobile to a complete stop from a speed of 50 km/h under normal driving conditions using this new braking system. In addition, we define μ to be the mean stopping distance of all ZX-900s. One of the ZX-900's major competitors is advertised to achieve a mean stopping distance of 18 m. Canadian Motor Products would like to claim in a new television commercial that the ZX-900 achieves a shorter mean stopping distance. The standards and practices division of a major television network will permit Canadian Motor Products to run the commercial if $H_0: \mu \geq 18$ can be rejected in favour of $H_a: \mu < 18$ by setting $\alpha = 0.05$. Interpret what it means to set α at 0.05.

8.3 *z* TESTS ABOUT A POPULATION MEAN (σ KNOWN): ONE-SIDED ALTERNATIVES

In this (and the next) section, we discuss hypothesis tests about a population mean that are *based on the normal distribution*. These tests are called *z* **tests**, and they require that the *true value of the population standard deviation* σ be known. Of course in almost all real-world situations the true value of σ is not known. However, the concepts and calculations of hypothesis testing are most easily illustrated using the normal distribution.

CHAPTER 9

Therefore, in this (and the next) section, we will assume that, through extensive experience with the population or process under consideration, we know σ. When σ is unknown, we test hypotheses about a population mean by using the **t distribution**. In Section 8.5, we study **t tests**, and we will revisit the examples of this (and the next) section assuming that σ is unknown.

Testing a greater than alternative hypothesis by using a rejection point rule   In Sections 8.1 and 8.2, we explained how to set up appropriate null and alternative hypotheses. We also discussed how to specify a value for α, the probability of a Type I error (also called the **level of significance**) of the hypothesis test, and we introduced the idea of a test statistic. We can use these concepts to begin developing a seven-step hypothesis-testing procedure. We will introduce these steps in the context of monthly cable TV subscriptions costs and testing a greater than alternative hypothesis.

A marketing company has suggested that the cost of monthly cable TV subscriptions has risen dramatically, which is causing more people to use illegal satellite dishes. Cable TV companies claim that their full cable package subscriptions cost on average $50 a month. The marketing company wants to demonstrate that the cost is significantly greater than $50 and randomly selects 40 cable TV subscribers and determines the price they pay for their monthly cable.

Step 1: State the null hypothesis H_0 and the alternative hypothesis H_a. In this case, we will test H_0: $\mu \leq 50$ versus H_a: $\mu > 50$. Here μ is the mean subscription cost.

Step 2: Specify the level of significance α. The marketing company will be able to support its claim that cable subscription costs have risen if we can reject H_0: $\mu \leq 50$ in favour of H_a: $\mu > 50$ by setting α equal to 0.05.

Step 3: Select the test statistic. In order to test H_0: $\mu \leq 50$ versus H_a: $\mu > 50$, we will test the modified null hypothesis H_0: $\mu = 50$ versus H_a: $\mu > 50$. The idea here is that if there is sufficient evidence to reject the hypothesis that μ equals 50 in favour of $\mu > 50$, then there is certainly also sufficient evidence to reject the hypothesis that μ is less than or equal to 50. In order to test H_0: $\mu = 50$ versus H_a: $\mu > 50$, we randomly select a sample of $n = 40$ subscribers and calculate the mean $\bar{x}$ of the monthly costs. We will then utilize the test statistic

$$z = \frac{\bar{x} - 50}{\sigma_{\bar{x}}} = \frac{\bar{x} - 50}{\sigma/\sqrt{n}}.$$

A positive value of this test statistic results from an $\bar{x}$ that is greater than 50 and thus provides evidence against H_0: $\mu = 50$ and in favour of H_a: $\mu > 50$.

Step 4: Determine the rejection point rule for deciding whether to reject H_0. To decide how large the test statistic must be to reject H_0 in favour of H_a by setting the probability of a Type I error equal to α, we do the following:

- Place the probability of a Type I error, α, in the right-hand tail of the standard normal curve and use the normal table (see Table A.3) to find the normal point z_α. Here z_α, which we call a **rejection point** (or **critical point**), is the point on the horizontal axis under the standard normal curve that gives a right-hand tail area equal to α.

- **Reject H_0: $\mu = 50$ in favour of H_a: $\mu > 50$ if and only if the test statistic z is greater than the rejection point z_α.** This is the **rejection point rule**.

Figure 8.2 illustrates that since we have set α equal to 0.05, we should use the rejection point $z_\alpha = z_{0.05} = 1.645$ (see Table A.3). This says that we should reject H_0 if $z > 1.645$ and we should not reject H_0 if $z \leq 1.645$.

To more fully explain what it means to set α equal to 0.05 and to use the rejection point rule, we consider the sampling distribution of the test statistic z. Because the sample size $n = 40$ is moderately large, the central limit theorem tells us that the sampling distribution of $(\bar{x} - \mu)/\sigma_{\bar{x}}$ is (approximately) a standard normal distribution. It follows that if the null hypothesis H_0: $\mu = 50$ is true, then the sampling distribution of the test statistic $z = (\bar{x} - 50)/\sigma_{\bar{x}}$ is (approximately) a standard normal distribution. Therefore, examining

FIGURE **8.2**   The Rejection Point for Testing $H_0: \mu = 50$ versus $H_a: \mu > 50$ by Setting $\alpha = 0.05$

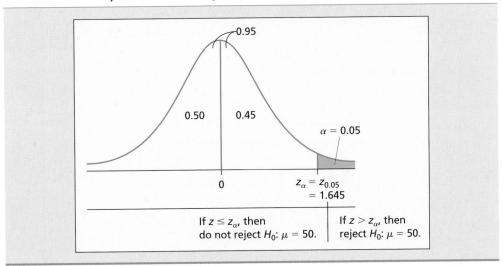

the standard normal curve in Figure 8.2, we can see that the areas under this curve imply the following:

- If $H_0: \mu = 50$ is true, 95 percent of all possible values of the test statistic z are less than or equal to $z_{0.05} = 1.645$ and thus would tell us not to reject $H_0: \mu = 50$—a correct decision.
- If $H_0: \mu = 50$ is true, 5 percent of all possible values of the test statistic z are greater than $z_{0.05} = 1.645$ and thus would tell us to reject $H_0: \mu = 50$: a Type I error.

These two statements explain what it means to set α equal to 0.05 and to use the rejection point rule.

Step 5: Collect the sample data and compute the value of the test statistic. When the sample of $n = 40$ subscriptions is randomly selected, the mean of the cable costs is calculated to be $\bar{x} = 50.575$. Assuming that σ is known to equal 1.65, the value of the test statistic is

$$z = \frac{\bar{x} - 50}{\sigma/\sqrt{n}} = \frac{50.575 - 50}{1.65/\sqrt{40}} = 2.20.$$

Step 6: Decide whether to reject H_0 by using the test statistic value and the rejection point rule. Since the test statistic value $z = 2.20$ is greater than the rejection point $z_{0.05} = 1.645$, we can reject $H_0: \mu = 50$ in favour of $H_a: \mu > 50$ by setting α equal to 0.05. Furthermore, we can be intuitively confident that $H_0: \mu = 50$ is false and $H_a: \mu > 50$ is true. This is because, since we have rejected H_0 by setting α equal to 0.05, we have rejected H_0 by using a test that allows only a 5 percent chance of wrongly rejecting H_0. In general, if we can reject a null hypothesis in favour of an alternative hypothesis by setting the probability of a Type I error equal to α, we say that we have **statistical significance at the α level**.

LO5

Step 7: Interpret the statistical results in managerial (real-world) terms and assess their practical importance. Since we have rejected $H_0: \mu = 50$ in favour of $H_a: \mu > 50$ by setting α equal to 0.05, we conclude (at an α of 0.05) that the average monthly cable subscription cost exceeds \$50. Note, however, that the point estimate of μ, $\bar{x} = 50.575$, indicates that μ is not much larger than 50. Therefore, the marketing company can claim only that cable subscription costs are slightly higher than is claimed by cable companies. This difference between what cable companies claim are the average monthly subscription costs and the sample mean value may or may not be of importance to cable subscribers. Some subscribers may find that any subscription cost greater than \$50 a month is too high and will then look for alternative sources for their television programs. Other subscribers may feel that the difference of \$0.575 (or 58 cents) is trivial and will stick with their cable TV subscriptions. This illustrates that, in general, a finding

LO6

BI

FIGURE 8.3   The Rejection Points for Testing the Average Cable Subscription Cost H_0: $\mu = 50$ versus H_a: $\mu > 50$ by Setting $\alpha = 0.05$ and $\alpha = 0.01$

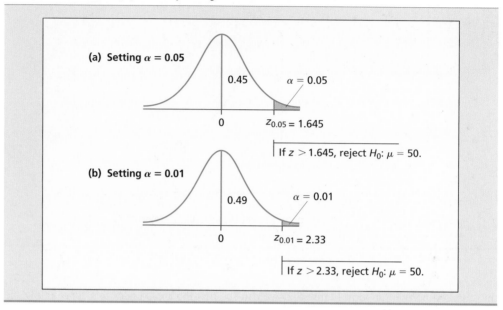

of statistical significance (that is, concluding that the alternative hypothesis is true) can be practically important to some people but not to others. Notice that the point estimate of the parameter involved in a hypothesis test can help us to assess practical importance. We can also use confidence intervals to help assess practical importance, as will be illustrated in Section 8.4.

Considerations in setting α   We have reasoned above that the marketing company has set α equal to 0.05 rather than 0.01 because doing so means that β, the probability of failing to make a true claim (a Type II error), will be smaller than it would be if α were set at 0.01. It is informative, however, to see what would have happened if the company had set α equal to 0.01. Figure 8.3 illustrates that as we decrease α from 0.05 to 0.01, the rejection point z_α increases from $z_{0.05} = 1.645$ to $z_{0.01} = 2.33$. Because the test statistic value $z = 2.20$ is less than $z_{0.01} = 2.33$, we cannot reject H_0: $\mu = 50$ in favour of H_a: $\mu > 50$ by setting α equal to 0.01. This illustrates the point that the smaller we set α, the larger is the rejection point, and thus the stronger is the statistical evidence that we are requiring to reject the null hypothesis H_0. Some statisticians have concluded (somewhat subjectively) that (1) *if we set α equal to 0.05, then we are requiring* **strong** *evidence to reject H_0,* and (2) *if we set α equal to 0.01, then we are requiring* **very strong** *evidence to reject H_0.*

A p value for testing a greater than alternative hypothesis   To decide whether to reject the null hypothesis H_0 at level of significance α, steps 4, 5, and 6 of the seven-step hypothesis-testing procedure compare the test statistic value with a rejection point. Another way to make this decision is to calculate a *p value*, which measures the likelihood of the sample results if the null hypothesis H_0 is true. Sample results that are not likely if H_0 is true are evidence that H_0 is not true. To test H_0 by using a p value, we use the following steps 4, 5, and 6:

Step 4: Collect the sample data and compute the value of the test statistic. In the cable subscription example, we have computed the value of the test statistic to be $z = 2.20$.

Step 5: Calculate the p value by using the test statistic value. The p value for testing H_0: $\mu = 50$ versus H_a: $\mu > 50$ is the area under the standard normal curve to the right of the test statistic value $z = 2.20$. As illustrated in Figure 8.4(b), this area is $0.5 - 0.4861 = 0.0139$. The p value is the probability, computed assuming that H_0: $\mu = 50$ is true, of observing a value of the test statistic that is greater than or equal to the value $z = 2.20$ that we have actually computed from the sample data. The p value of 0.0139 says that if H_0: $\mu = 50$ is true, only

LO7

LO8

LO9

FIGURE 8.4 Testing H_0: $\mu = 50$ versus H_a: $\mu > 50$ by Using Rejection Points and the *p* Value

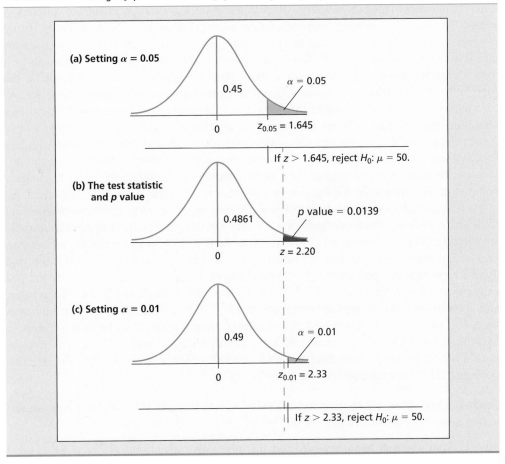

139 in 10,000 of all possible test statistic values are at least as large, or extreme, as the value $z = 2.20$. That is, if we are to believe that H_0 is true, we must believe that we have observed a test statistic value that can be described as a 139 in 10,000 chance. Because it is difficult to believe that we have observed a 139 in 10,000 chance, we intuitively have strong evidence that H_0: $\mu = 50$ is false and H_a: $\mu > 50$ is true.

Step 6: Reject H_0 if the *p* value is less than *α*. Recall that the marketing company has set *α* equal to 0.05. *The p value of 0.0139 is less than the α of 0.05.* Comparing the two normal curves in Figure 8.4(a) and (b), we see that this implies that the test statistic value $z = 2.20$ is greater than the rejection point $z_{0.05} = 1.645$. Therefore, *we can reject H_0 by setting α equal to 0.05.* As another example, suppose that the marketing company had set *α* equal to 0.01. *The p value of 0.0139 is greater than the α of 0.01.* Comparing the two normal curves in Figure 8.4(b) and (c), we see that this implies that the test statistic value $z = 2.20$ is less than the rejection point $z_{0.01} = 2.33$. Therefore, *we cannot reject H_0 by setting α equal to 0.01.* Generalizing these examples, we conclude that the value of the test statistic z will be greater than the rejection point z_α if and only if the *p* value is less than *α*. That is, we can reject H_0 in favour of H_a at level of significance *α* if and only if the *p* value is less than *α*.

LO10

Comparing the rejection point and *p* value methods Thus far we have considered two methods for testing H_0: $\mu = 50$ versus H_a: $\mu > 50$ at the 0.05 and 0.01 values of *α*. Using the first method, we determine whether the test statistic value $z = 2.20$ is greater than the rejection points $z_{0.05} = 1.645$ and $z_{0.01} = 2.33$. Using the second method, we determine whether the *p* value of 0.0139 is less than 0.05 and 0.01. Whereas the rejection point method requires that we look up a different rejection point for each different *α* value, the *p* value method requires only that we calculate a single *p* value and compare it directly with the different

α values. It follows that the p value method is the most efficient way to test a hypothesis at different α values. This can be useful when different decision makers might use different α values. For example, marketing companies do not always evaluate advertising claims by setting α equal to 0.05. The reason is that the consequences of a Type I error (advertising a false claim) are more serious for some claims than for others. For example, the consequences of a Type I error would be fairly serious for a claim about the effectiveness of a drug or for the superiority of one product over another. However, these consequences might not be as serious for a noncomparative claim about an inexpensive and safe product, such as a pencil. Companies sometimes use α values between 0.01 and 0.04 for claims with more serious Type I error consequences, and they sometimes use α values between 0.06 and 0.10 for claims with less serious Type I error consequences. Furthermore, one company's policies for setting α can differ somewhat from those of another. As a result, reporting a claim's p value to each company is the most efficient way to tell the company whether to allow the claim to be advertised.

Because a single p value can help different decision makers to make their own independent decisions, statistical software packages use p values to report the results of hypothesis tests (as we will begin to see in Section 8.5). However, the rejection point approach also has advantages. One is that understanding rejection points helps us to better understand the probability of a Type I error (and the probability of a Type II error). Furthermore, in some situations (for example, in Section 8.5), statistical tables are not complete enough to calculate the p value, and a computer software package or an electronic calculator with statistical capabilities is needed. If these tools are not immediately available, rejection points can be used to carry out hypothesis tests, because statistical tables are almost always complete enough to give the needed rejection points. Throughout this book, we will continue to present both the rejection point and the p value approaches to hypothesis testing.

Testing a less than alternative hypothesis We next consider the payment time case and testing a less than alternative hypothesis:

Step 1: State the null hypothesis H_0 and the alternative hypothesis H_a. In order to study whether the new electronic billing system reduces the mean bill payment time by more than 50 percent, the management consulting firm will test H_0: $\mu \geq 19.5$ versus H_a: $\mu < 19.5$.
Step 2: Specify the level of significance α. The management consulting firm wants to be very sure that it truthfully describes the benefits of the new system both to the company in which it has been installed and to other companies that are considering installing such a system. Therefore, the firm will require very strong evidence to conclude that μ is less than 19.5, which implies that it will test H_0: $\mu \geq 19.5$ versus H_a: $\mu < 19.5$ by setting α equal to 0.01.
Step 3: Select the test statistic. In order to test H_0: $\mu \geq 19.5$ versus H_a: $\mu < 19.5$, we will test the modified null hypothesis H_0: $\mu = 19.5$ versus H_a: $\mu < 19.5$. The idea here is that if there is sufficient evidence to reject the hypothesis that μ equals 19.5 in favour of $\mu < 19.5$, then there is certainly also sufficient evidence to reject the hypothesis that μ is greater than or equal to 19.5. In order to test H_0: $\mu = 19.5$ versus H_a: $\mu < 19.5$, we will randomly select a sample of $n = 65$ invoices paid using the billing system and calculate the mean $\bar{x}$ of the payment times of these invoices. Since the sample size is large, the central limit theorem applies, and we will utilize the test statistic

$$z = \frac{\bar{x} - 19.5}{\sigma / \sqrt{n}}.$$

A value of the test statistic z that is less than zero results when $\bar{x}$ is less than 19.5. This provides evidence to support rejecting H_0 in favour of H_a because the point estimate $\bar{x}$ indicates that μ might be less than 19.5.
Step 4: Determine a rejection point rule for deciding whether to reject H_0. To decide how much less than zero the test statistic must be to reject H_0 in favour of H_a by setting the probability of a Type I error equal to α, we do the following:

- Place the probability of a Type I error, α, in the left-hand tail of the standard normal curve and use the normal table to find the rejection point $-z_\alpha$. Here $-z_\alpha$ is the negative of the

FIGURE **8.5** Testing H_0: $\mu = 19.5$ versus H_a: $\mu < 19.5$ by Using Rejection Points and the p Value

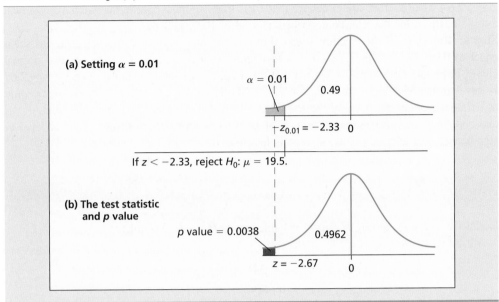

(a) Setting $\alpha = 0.01$

$\alpha = 0.01$

0.49

$-z_{0.01} = -2.33$ 0

If $z < -2.33$, reject H_0: $\mu = 19.5$.

(b) The test statistic and p value

p value = 0.0038

0.4962

$z = -2.67$ 0

normal point z_α. That is, $-z_\alpha$ is the point on the horizontal axis under the standard normal curve that gives a left-hand tail area equal to α.

- **Reject H_0: $\mu = 19.5$ in favour of H_a: $\mu < 19.5$ if and only if the test statistic z is less than the rejection point $-z_\alpha$.** Because α equals 0.01, the rejection point $-z_\alpha$ is $-z_{0.01} = -2.33$ (see Figure 8.5(a)).

Step 5: Collect the sample data and compute the value of the test statistic. When the sample of $n = 65$ invoices is randomly selected, the mean of the payment times of these invoices is calculated to be $\bar{x} = 18.1077$. Assuming that σ is known to equal 4.2, the value of the test statistic is

$$z = \frac{\bar{x} - 19.5}{\sigma/\sqrt{n}} = \frac{18.1077 - 19.5}{4.2/\sqrt{65}} = -2.67.$$

Step 6: Decide whether to reject H_0 by using the test statistic value and the rejection point rule. Since the test statistic value $z = -2.67$ is less than the rejection point $-z_{0.01} = -2.33$, we can reject H_0: $\mu = 19.5$ in favour of H_a: $\mu < 19.5$ by setting α equal to 0.01.

Step 7: Interpret the statistical results in managerial (real-world) terms and assess their practical importance. We conclude (at an α of 0.01) that the mean payment time for the new electronic billing system is less than 19.5 days. This, along with the fact that the sample mean $\bar{x} = 18.1077$ is slightly less than 19.5, implies that it is reasonable for the management consulting firm to conclude that the new electronic billing system has reduced the mean payment time by slightly more than 50 percent (a substantial improvement over the old system).

A p value for testing a less than alternative hypothesis To test H_0: $\mu = 19.5$ versus H_a: $\mu < 19.5$ in the payment time case by using a p value, we use the following steps 4, 5, and 6:

Step 4: Collect the sample data and compute the value of the test statistic. We have computed the value of the test statistic in the payment time case to be $z = -2.67$.

Step 5: Calculate the p value by using the test statistic value. The p value for testing H_0: $\mu = 19.5$ versus H_a: $\mu < 19.5$ is the area under the standard normal curve to the left of the test statistic value $z = -2.67$. As illustrated in Figure 8.5(b), this area is $0.5 - 0.4962 = 0.0038$. The p value is the probability, computed assuming that H_0: $\mu = 19.5$ is true, of observing a value of the test statistic that is less than or equal to the value $z = -2.67$ that we have actually computed from the sample data. The p value of 0.0038 says that if H_0: $\mu = 19.5$ is true, only

38 in 10,000 of all possible test statistic values are at least as negative, or extreme, as the value $z = -2.67$. That is, if we are to believe that H_0 is true, we must believe that we have observed a test statistic value that can be described as a 38 in 10,000 chance.

Step 6: Reject H_0 if the p value is less than α. The management consulting firm has set α equal to 0.01. *The p value of 0.0038 is less than the α of 0.01.* Comparing the two normal curves in Figure 8.5(a) and (b), we see that this implies that the test statistic value $z = -2.67$ is less than the rejection point $-z_{0.01} = -2.33$. Therefore, *we can reject H_0 by setting α equal to 0.01*. In general, the value of the test statistic z will be less than the rejection point $-z_\alpha$ if and only if the p value is less than α. That is, we can reject H_0 in favour of H_a at level of significance α if and only if the p value is less than α.

Example 8.4 The Beer Case (One-Sided z Test)

Recall that we were testing H_0: $\mu = 341$ mL versus H_a: $\mu < 341$ mL.

We found the test statistic

$$z = \frac{\bar{x} - 341}{\sigma/\sqrt{n}} = -2.46.$$

Thus, our p value is $P(z < -2.46) = 0.0069$.

This means that there is very little support for H_0, so we are very likely to reject H_0. If $\alpha = 0.05$, we reject H_0 since our p value is less than 0.05.

Using a rejection point, we need to reject H_0 at $\alpha = 0.05$ if $z < -1.645$. Since $z = -2.46$, we indeed reject H_0 at $\alpha = 0.05$.

A summary of testing a one-sided alternative hypothesis As illustrated in the previous examples, we can test two types of one-sided alternative hypotheses. First, we sometimes test hypotheses of the form H_0: $\mu = \mu_0$ versus H_a: $\mu > \mu_0$, where μ_0 is a specific number that depends on the problem. In this case, if we can reject H_0, we have evidence that $\mu > \mu_0$ and that μ is not less than or equal to μ_0. Second, we sometimes test H_0: $\mu = \mu_0$ versus H_a: $\mu < \mu_0$. In this case, if we can reject H_0, we have evidence that $\mu < \mu_0$ and that μ is not greater than or equal to μ_0. To summarize, we may think of testing a one-sided alternative hypothesis about a population mean as testing H_0: $\mu = \mu_0$ versus H_a: $\mu > \mu_0$ or as testing H_0: $\mu = \mu_0$ versus H_a: $\mu < \mu_0$. In addition, as illustrated in the previous examples, a rejection point rule and a p value tell us whether we can reject H_0: $\mu = \mu_0$ in favour of a particular one-sided alternative hypothesis *at level of significance α*. We summarize the rejection point rules and the p values in the following box:

A Hypothesis Test about a Population Mean: Testing H_0: $\mu = \mu_0$ versus a One-Sided Alternative Hypothesis When σ Is Known

Define the test statistic

$$z = \frac{\bar{x} - \mu_0}{\sigma/\sqrt{n}}$$

and assume that the population sampled is normally distributed, or that the sample size n is large. We can test H_0: $\mu = \mu_0$ versus a particular alternative hypothesis at level of significance α by using the appropriate rejection point rule or, equivalently, the corresponding p value.

Alternative Hypothesis	Rejection Point Rule: Reject H_0 if	p Value (Reject H_0 if p Value $< \alpha$)
H_a: $\mu > \mu_0$	$z > z_\alpha$	The area under the standard normal curve to the right of z
H_a: $\mu < \mu_0$	$z < -z_\alpha$	The area under the standard normal curve to the left of z

When using this summary box, it is vital to understand that the *alternative hypothesis* being tested *determines the rejection point rule and the p value* that should be used to perform the hypothesis test. For example, consider the cable subscription cost example and testing H_0: $\mu = 50$ versus H_a: $\mu > 50$ at level of significance α. Since the alternative hypothesis H_a: $\mu > 50$ is of the form H_a: $\mu > \mu_0$ (that is, it is a greater than alternative hypothesis), the summary box tells us that (1) we should reject H_0 if $z > z_\alpha$ and (2) the *p* value is the area under the standard normal curve to the right of *z*. When we tested H_0: $\mu = 50$ versus H_a: $\mu > 50$, we illustrated using this rejection point rule and this *p* value. As another example, consider the payment time case and testing H_0: $\mu = 19.5$ versus H_a: $\mu < 19.5$ at level of significance α. Since the alternative hypothesis H_a: $\mu < 19.5$ is of the form H_a: $\mu < \mu_0$ (that is, it is a less than alternative hypothesis), the summary box tells us that (1) we should reject H_0 if $z < -z_\alpha$ and (2) the *p* value is the area under the standard normal curve to the left of *z*. When we tested H_0: $\mu = 19.5$ versus H_a: $\mu < 19.5$, we illustrated the results using this rejection point rule and this *p* value. For most future hypothesis tests, we will present hypothesis-testing summary boxes. Therefore, we now present the seven-step hypothesis-testing procedure in a way that emphasizes using a summary box to determine an appropriate rejection point rule and an appropriate *p* value.

The Seven Steps of Hypothesis Testing

1   State the null hypothesis H_0 and the alternative hypothesis H_a.
2   Specify the level of significance α.
3   Select the test statistic.

Using a rejection point rule:

4   Use the summary box to find the rejection point rule corresponding to the alternative hypothesis. Use the specified value of α to find the rejection point given in the rejection point rule.
5   Collect the sample data and compute the value of the test statistic.
6   Decide whether to reject H_0 by using the test statistic value and the rejection point rule.

Using a *p* value:

4   Collect the sample data and compute the value of the test statistic.
5   Use the summary box to find the *p* value corresponding to the alternative hypothesis. Calculate the *p* value by using the test statistic value.
6   Reject H_0 at level of significance α if the *p* value is less than α.

7   Interpret your statistical results in managerial (real-world) terms and assess their practical importance.

Measuring the weight of evidence against the null hypothesis In general, the decision to take an action is sometimes based solely on whether there is sufficient sample evidence to reject a null hypothesis (H_0: $\mu = 50$) by setting α equal to a single, prespecified value (0.05). In such situations, it is often also useful to know all of the information—called the **weight of evidence**—that the hypothesis test provides against the null hypothesis and in favour of the alternative hypothesis. For example, a drug manufacturer would almost certainly wish to know *how much* evidence there is that its new medication is more effective than its former medication. Furthermore, although we tested a hypothesis in the payment time case by setting α equal to a single, prespecified value, the hypothesis test did not immediately lead to a decision as to whether to take an action. In a situation such as this, when hypothesis testing is used more as a way to achieve evolving understanding of an industrial or scientific process, it is particularly important to know the weight of evidence against the null hypothesis and in favour of the alternative hypothesis.

The most informative way to measure the weight of evidence is to use the p value. For every hypothesis test considered in this book, we can interpret the p value to be the *probability, computed assuming that the null hypothesis H_0 is true, of observing a value of the test statistic that is at least as extreme, in the direction of H_a, as the value actually computed from the sample data. The smaller the p value is, the less likely are the sample results if the null hypothesis H_0 is true* and therefore the stronger is the evidence that H_0 is false and that the alternative hypothesis H_a is true. We can use the p value to test H_0 versus H_a at level of significance α as follows:

We reject H_0 in favour of H_a at level of significance α if and only if the p value is less than α.

Experience with hypothesis testing has resulted in statisticians making the following (somewhat subjective) conclusions:

Interpreting the Weight of Evidence against the Null Hypothesis

If the p value for testing H_0 is less than

- 0.10, we have **some evidence** that H_0 is false.
- 0.05, we have **strong evidence** that H_0 is false.

- 0.01, we have **very strong evidence** that H_0 is false.
- 0.001, we have **extremely strong evidence** that H_0 is false.

For example, recall that the p value for testing H_0: $\mu = 50$ versus H_a: $\mu > 50$ in the cable subscription cost example is 0.0139. This p value is less than 0.05 but not less than 0.01. Therefore, we have strong evidence, but not very strong evidence, that H_0: $\mu = 50$ is false and H_a: $\mu > 50$ is true. That is, we have strong evidence that the mean monthly subscription costs exceed \$50. As another example, the p value for testing H_0: $\mu = 19.5$ versus H_a: $\mu < 19.5$ in the payment time case is 0.0038. This p value is less than 0.01 but not less than 0.001. Therefore, we have very strong evidence, but not extremely strong evidence, that H_0: $\mu = 19.5$ is false and H_a: $\mu < 19.5$ is true. That is, we have very strong evidence that the new billing system has reduced the mean payment time to less than 19.5 days.

To conclude this section, we note that while many statisticians believe in assessing the weight of evidence, other statisticians do not. Those who do not might be called **decision theorists**. They contend that measuring the weight of evidence lets the results of a single sample bias our view too much as to the relative validity of H_0 and H_a. Decision theorists state that even in establishing your own personal belief, you should make a choice between H_0 and H_a by setting α equal to a single value that is specified before the sample is taken. Even for decision theorists, however, the p value has the advantage of being the most efficient way to report the results of a hypothesis test to different decision makers who might use different prespecified values of α. In this book, we will continue to assess the weight of evidence, and the decision theorist can regard the p value as simply an efficient way to report the results of a hypothesis test.

Exercises for Section 8.3

CONCEPTS

8.14   Explain what a rejection point is, and explain how it is used to test a hypothesis.

8.15   Explain what a p value is, and explain how it is used to test a hypothesis.

METHODS AND APPLICATIONS

In Exercises 8.16 through 8.22, consider using a random sample of 100 measurements to test H_0: $\mu = 80$ versus H_a: $\mu > 80$.

8.16   If $\bar{x} = 85$ and $\sigma = 20$, calculate the value of the test statistic z.

8.17   Use a rejection point to test H_0 versus H_a by setting α equal to 0.10.

8.18   Use a rejection point to test H_0 versus H_a by setting α equal to 0.05.

8.19   Use a rejection point to test H_0 versus H_a by setting α equal to 0.01.

FIGURE 8.6 MegaStat Output Used to Test H_0: $\mu = 6$ versus H_0: $\mu < 6$ in the
Bank Customer Waiting Time Case

Hypothesis Test: Mean with Sigma Known to Be 2.47

6.0000	hypothesized value
5.4600	mean label
2.4700	std. dev.
0.2470	std. error
100	n
−2.19	z
0.0144	p-value (one-tailed, lower)
4.9759	confidence interval 95.% lower
5.9441	confidence interval 95.% upper
0.4841	margin of error
0.4852	margin of error

8.20 Use a rejection point to test H_0 versus H_a by setting α equal to 0.001.

8.21 Calculate the *p* value and use it to test H_0 versus H_a at each of $\alpha = 0.10, 0.05, 0.01,$ and 0.001.

8.22 How much evidence is there that H_0: $\mu = 80$ is false and H_a: $\mu > 80$ is true?

In Exercises 8.23 through 8.29, consider using a random sample of 49 measurements to test H_0: $\mu = 20$ versus H_a: $\mu < 20$.

8.23 If $\bar{x} = 18$ and $\sigma = 7$, calculate the value of the test statistic *z*.

8.24 Use a rejection point to test H_0 versus H_a by setting α equal to 0.10.

8.25 Use a rejection point to test H_0 versus H_a by setting α equal to 0.05.

8.26 Use a rejection point to test H_0 versus H_a by setting α equal to 0.01.

8.27 Use a rejection point to test H_0 versus H_a by setting α equal to 0.001.

8.28 Calculate the *p* value and use it to test H_0 versus H_a at each of $\alpha = 0.10, 0.05, 0.01,$ and 0.001.

8.29 How much evidence is there that H_0: $\mu = 20$ is false and H_a: $\mu < 20$ is true?

8.30 **THE VIDEO GAME SATISFACTION RATING CASE**

Recall (see Exercise 8.8) that "very satisfied" customers give the XYZ-Box video game system a rating that is at least 42. Letting μ be the mean composite satisfaction rating for the XYZ-Box, you found in Exercise 8.8 that you should test H_0: $\mu \leq 42$ versus H_a: $\mu > 42$ in order to attempt to provide evidence supporting the claim that μ exceeds 42. The random sample of 65 satisfaction ratings yields a sample mean of $\bar{x} = 42.954$. Assume that σ equals 2.64.

a. Use rejection points to test H_0 versus H_a at each of $\alpha = 0.10, 0.05, 0.01,$ and 0.001.

b. Calculate the *p* value and use it to test H_0 versus H_a at each of $\alpha = 0.10, 0.05, 0.01,$ and 0.001.

c. How much evidence is there that the mean composite satisfaction rating exceeds 42?

8.31 **THE BANK CUSTOMER WAITING TIME CASE**

Letting μ be the mean waiting time under the new system, you found in Exercise 8.9 that you should test H_0: $\mu \geq 6$ versus H_a: $\mu < 6$ in order to attempt to provide evidence that μ is less than six minutes. The random sample of 100 waiting times yields a sample mean of $\bar{x} = 5.46$ minutes. Moreover, Figure 8.6 gives the MegaStat output obtained when the waiting time data are used to test H_0: $\mu = 6$ versus H_a: $\mu < 6$. On this output, the label "std. error," which stands for "the standard error of the mean," denotes the quantity $\sigma / \sqrt{n}$, and the label "z" denotes the calculated test statistic. Assume that σ equals 2.47.

a. Use rejection points to test H_0 versus H_a at each of $\alpha = 0.10, 0.05, 0.01,$ and 0.001.

b. Calculate the *p* value and verify that it equals 0.0144, as shown on the MegaStat output. Use the *p* value to test H_0 versus H_a at each of $\alpha = 0.10, 0.05, 0.01,$ and 0.001.

c. How much evidence is there that the new system has reduced the mean waiting time to below six minutes?

8.32 A secret shopper was sent to a local fast food restaurant to determine whether or not the drive-through service standards at that store were being met. It is currently believed that the store is not meeting the required service time standards. In order to meet the current standards, the store's drive-through service time must be 30 seconds or less. This store has two service windows. The time at the second window was recorded. A random sample of 100 service times was recorded at various times of the day during one week. This random sample yielded a sample mean of 29.17 seconds. Assume that it is known that $\sigma = 4$ seconds. Formulate the null hypothesis H_0 and the alternative hypothesis H_a that would be used to determine how much evidence there is that the mean service time at this store is indeed less than 30 seconds. Calculate a *p* value for this test and draw any conclusions at $\alpha = 0.05$.

8.33   Consider the electric power utility waste water situation in Exercise 8.12 and recall that the power plant will be shut down and corrective action will be taken on the cooling system if the null hypothesis H_0: $\mu \leq 15°C$ is rejected in favour of H_a: $\mu > 15°C$. Suppose the utility decides to use a level of significance of $\alpha = 0.05$, and suppose a random sample of 100 temperature readings is obtained. For each of the following sample results, determine whether the power plant should be shut down and the cooling system repaired. In each case, assume that $\sigma = 2$.
a. $\bar{x} = 15.482$.   **b.** $\bar{x} = 15.262$.   **c.** $\bar{x} = 15.618$.

8.34   **THE DISC BRAKE CASE**

Recall that the television network will permit Canadian Motor Products to claim that the ZX-900 achieves a shorter mean stopping distance than a competitor if H_0: $\mu \geq 18$ m can be rejected in favour of H_a: $\mu < 18$ m by setting α equal to 0.05 (see Exercise 8.13). If the stopping distances of a random sample of $n = 81$ ZX-900s have a mean of $\bar{x} = 17.6$ m, will Canadian Motor Products be allowed to run the commercial? Assume that $\sigma = 1.83$ m. Calculate a 95 percent confidence interval for μ. Do the point estimate of μ and confidence interval for μ indicate that μ might be far enough below 18 m to suggest that you have a practically important result?

8.4 z TESTS ABOUT A POPULATION MEAN (σ KNOWN): TWO-SIDED ALTERNATIVES

Testing a not equal to alternative hypothesis We next consider the camshaft case and testing a not equal to alternative hypothesis:

Step 1: State the null hypothesis H_0 and the alternative hypothesis H_a. The quality control analyst will test H_0: $\mu = 4.5$ versus H_a: $\mu \neq 4.5$. Here μ is the mean of the population of the hardness depths of all camshafts produced on a particular day.

Step 2: Specify the level of significance α. The quality control analyst will set α equal to 0.05. To understand this choice of α, recall that the camshaft-hardening process has not been meeting specifications. For this reason, the analyst has decided that it is very important to avoid committing a Type II error. That is, it is very important to avoid failing to reject H_0: $\mu = 4.5$ if μ for the day's production does differ from 4.5 mm. Setting α equal to 0.05 rather than 0.01 makes the probability of this Type II error smaller than it would be if α were set at 0.01.

Step 3: Select the test statistic. The quality control analyst will randomly select $n = 35$ camshafts from the day's production of camshafts and calculate the mean $\bar{x}$ of the hardness depths of these camshafts. Since the sample size is large, the central limit theorem applies, and we will utilize the test statistic

$$z = \frac{\bar{x} - 4.5}{\sigma / \sqrt{n}}.$$

A value of the test statistic that is greater than 0 results when $\bar{x}$ is greater than 4.5. This provides evidence to support rejecting H_0 in favour of H_a because the point estimate $\bar{x}$ indicates that μ might be greater than 4.5. Similarly, a value of the test statistic that is less than 0 results when $\bar{x}$ is less than 4.5. This also provides evidence to support rejecting H_0 in favour of H_a because the point estimate $\bar{x}$ indicates that μ might be less than 4.5.

Step 4: Determine a rejection point rule for deciding whether to reject H_0. To decide how different from zero (positive or negative) the test statistic must be in order to reject H_0 in favour of H_a by setting the probability of a Type I error equal to α, we do the following:

- Divide the probability of a Type I error, α, into two equal parts, and place the area $\alpha/2$ in the right-hand tail of the standard normal curve and the area $\alpha/2$ in the left-hand tail of the standard normal curve. Then use the normal table to find the rejection points $z_{\alpha/2}$ and $-z_{\alpha/2}$. Here $z_{\alpha/2}$ is the point on the horizontal axis under the standard normal curve that gives a right-hand tail area equal to $\alpha/2$, and $-z_{\alpha/2}$ is the point giving a left-hand tail area equal to $\alpha/2$.

FIGURE 8.7   Testing H_0: $\mu = 4.5$ versus H_a: $\mu \neq 4.5$ by Using Rejection Points and the *p* Value

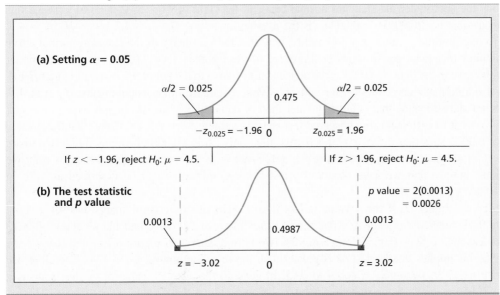

- **Reject H_0: $\mu = 4.5$ in favour of H_a: $\mu \neq 4.5$ if and only if the test statistic z is greater than the rejection point $z_{\alpha/2}$ or less than the rejection point $-z_{\alpha/2}$.** Note that this is equivalent to saying that we should *reject H_0 if and only if the absolute value of the test statistic, $|z|$, is greater than the rejection point $z_{\alpha/2}$.* Because α equals 0.05, the rejection points are (see Figure 8.7(a))

$$z_{\alpha/2} = z_{0.05/2} = z_{0.025} = 1.96 \quad \text{and} \quad -z_{\alpha/2} = -z_{0.025} = -1.96.$$

Step 5: Collect the sample data and compute the value of the test statistic. When the sample of $n = 35$ camshafts is randomly selected, the mean of the hardness depths of these camshafts is calculated to be $\bar{x} = 4.26$. Assuming that σ is known to equal 0.47, the value of the test statistic is

$$z = \frac{\bar{x} - 4.5}{\sigma/\sqrt{n}} = \frac{4.26 - 4.5}{0.47/\sqrt{35}} = -3.02.$$

Step 6: Decide whether to reject H_0 by using the test statistic value and the rejection point rule. Since the test statistic value $z = -3.02$ is less than $-z_{0.025} = -1.96$ (or, equivalently, since $|z| = 3.02$ is greater than $z_{0.025} = 1.96$), we can reject H_0: $\mu = 4.5$ in favour of H_a: $\mu \neq 4.5$ by setting α equal to 0.05.

Step 7: Interpret the statistical results in managerial (real-world) terms and assess their practical importance. We conclude (at an α of 0.05) that the mean camshaft hardness depth μ differs from 4.5 mm. To help determine whether the difference between μ and 4.5 mm is practically important, recall that specifications state that each individual camshaft hardness depth should be between 3 mm and 6 mm. Using $\bar{x} = 4.26$ and $\sigma = 0.47$, we estimate that 99.73 percent of all individual camshaft hardness depths are in the interval $[\bar{x} \pm 3\sigma] = [4.26 \pm 3(0.47)] = [2.85, 5.67]$. This estimated tolerance interval says that, because of a somewhat small $\bar{x}$ of 4.26, we estimate that we are producing some hardness depths that are below the lower specification limit of 3 mm. This is a practically important result. Clearly, the automobile manufacturer must modify the camshaft heat treatment process so that it produces hardness depths with an average value nearer the 4.5-mm target.

A *p* value for testing a not equal to alternative hypothesis   To test H_0: $\mu = 4.5$ versus H_a: $\mu \neq 4.5$ in the camshaft case by using a *p* value, we use the following steps 4, 5, and 6:

Step 4: Collect the sample data and compute the value of the test statistic. We have computed the value of the test statistic in the camshaft case to be $z = -3.02$.

Step 5: Calculate the p value by using the test statistic value. Note from Figure 8.7(b) that the area under the standard normal curve to the right of $|z| = 3.02$ is 0.0013. Twice this area—that is, $2(0.0013) = 0.0026$—is the p value for testing H_0: $\mu = 4.5$ versus H_a: $\mu \neq 4.5$. To interpret the p value as a probability, note that the symmetry of the standard normal curve implies that twice the area under the curve to the right of $|z| = 3.02$ equals the area under this curve to the right of 3.02 plus the area under the curve to the left of -3.02 (see Figure 8.7(b)). Also note that since both positive and negative test statistic values count against H_0: $\mu = 4.5$, a test statistic value that is either greater than or equal to 3.02 or less than or equal to -3.02 is at least as extreme as the observed test statistic value $z = -3.02$. It follows that the p value of 0.0026 says that if H_0: $\mu = 4.5$ is true, then only 26 in 10,000 of all possible test statistic values are at least as extreme as $z = -3.02$. That is, if we are to believe that H_0 is true, we must believe that we have observed a test statistic value that can be described as a 26 in 10,000 chance.

Step 6: Reject H_0 if the p value is less than α. The quality control analyst has set α equal to 0.05. Since *the p value of 0.0026 is less than the α of 0.05*, one half the p value = 0.0013 is less than $\alpha/2 = 0.025$. Comparing the two normal curves in Figure 8.7(a) and (b), we see that this implies that $|z| = 3.02$ is greater than the rejection point $z_{0.025} = 1.96$. Therefore, *we can reject H_0 by setting α equal to 0.05*. In general, the absolute value of the test statistic z will be greater than the rejection point $z_{\alpha/2}$ if and only if the p value is less than α. That is, we can reject H_0 in favour of H_a at level of significance α if and only if the p value is less than α. For example, the p value of 0.0026 is less than an α of 0.01 but not less than an α of 0.001. It follows that we have very strong evidence, but not extremely strong evidence, that H_0: $\mu = 4.5$ is false and H_a: $\mu \neq 4.5$ is true. That is, we have very strong evidence that the mean camshaft hardness depth differs from 4.5 mm.

A summary of testing H_0: $\mu = \mu_0$ In the rest of this chapter and in Chapter 9, we present most of the hypothesis-testing examples using the seven steps and hypothesis-testing summary boxes. However, to be more concise, we do not formally label each step. Rather, for each of the first six steps, we set out in italic font key phrases that indicate that the step is being carried out. After Chapter 9, we continue to use hypothesis-testing summary boxes, and we more informally use the seven steps. In the following box, we summarize how to test H_0: $\mu = \mu_0$ versus H_a: $\mu > \mu_0$, H_a: $\mu < \mu_0$, or H_a: $\mu \neq \mu_0$:

Testing a Hypothesis about a Population Mean: Testing H_0: $\mu = \mu_0$ When σ Is Known

Define the test statistic

$$z = \frac{\overline{x} - \mu_0}{\sigma/\sqrt{n}}$$

and assume that the population sampled is normally distributed or that the sample size n is large. We can test H_0: $\mu = \mu_0$ versus a particular alternative hypothesis at level of significance α by using the appropriate rejection point rule or, equivalently, the corresponding p value.

Alternative Hypothesis	Rejection Point Rule: Reject H_0 if	p Value (Reject H_0 if p Value $< \alpha$)
H_a: $\mu > \mu_0$	$z > z_\alpha$	The area under the standard normal curve to the right of z
H_a: $\mu < \mu_0$	$z < -z_\alpha$	The area under the standard normal curve to the left of z
H_a: $\mu \neq \mu_0$	$|z| > z_{\alpha/2}$—that is, $z > z_{\alpha/2}$ or $z < -z_{\alpha/2}$	Twice the area under the standard normal curve to the right of $|z|$

In many future examples, we will first use a rejection point rule to test the hypotheses under consideration at a fixed value of α, and we will then use a *p* value to assess the weight of evidence against the null hypothesis. For example, suppose that airline flights between Toronto and Vancouver have routinely experienced delays for the last several years. Last year, these delayed flights were an average of 35 minutes late. A consumer advocacy group wishes to assess whether this average has changed. To do this, the consumer group tests a hypothesis about the mean delay time, μ, of flights that were delayed over the last two months. **The null hypothesis to be tested is H_0: $\mu = 35$, and the alternative hypothesis is H_a: $\mu \neq 35$.** If H_0 can be rejected in favour of H_a at the **0.05 level of significance**, the consumer group must conclude that it appears as though the mean delay time over the last two months differs from last year's 35-minute mean delay time. To perform the hypothesis test, we will randomly select $n = 36$ flights that were delayed over the last two months and use their delay times to calculate the value of the **test statistic z in the summary box**. Then, since H_a: $\mu \neq 35$ is of the form H_a: $\mu \neq \mu_0$, we will **reject H_0: $\mu = 35$ if the absolute value of z is greater than $z_{\alpha/2} = z_{0.025} = 1.96$.** Suppose that when the sample is randomly selected, the mean of the delay times of the $n = 36$ flights is calculated to be $\bar{x} = 33$ minutes. Assuming that σ is known to equal 12, the **value of the test statistic** is

$$z = \frac{\bar{x} - 35}{\sigma/\sqrt{n}} = \frac{33 - 35}{12/\sqrt{36}} = -1.$$

Since $|z| = 1$ is less than $z_{0.025} = 1.96$, we cannot reject H_0: $\mu = 35$ in favour of H_a: $\mu \neq 35$. That is, we cannot conclude (at an α of 0.05) that the mean delay time over the last two months differs from last year's 35-minute mean delay time. The *p* value for testing H_0: $\mu = 35$ versus H_a: $\mu \neq 35$ is twice the area under the standard normal curve to the right of $|z| = 1$. Using Table A.3, we find that this *p* value equals $2(0.5 - 0.3413) = 2(0.1587) = 0.3174$. Since the *p* value of 0.3174 is greater than any reasonable value of α, we have little evidence against H_0: $\mu = 35$. That is, we have little evidence that the mean delay time over the last two months differs from last year's 35-minute mean delay time.

Using confidence intervals to test hypotheses   Confidence intervals can be used to test hypotheses. Specifically, we can reject H_0: $\mu = \mu_0$ in favour of H_a: $\mu \neq \mu_0$ by setting the probability of a Type I error equal to α if and only if the $100(1 - \alpha)$ percent confidence interval for μ does not contain μ_0. For example, consider the camshaft case and testing H_0: $\mu = 4.5$ versus H_a: $\mu \neq 4.5$ by setting α equal to 0.05. To do this, we use the mean $\bar{x} = 4.26$ of the sample of $n = 35$ camshafts to calculate the 95 percent confidence interval for μ to be

$$\left[\bar{x} \pm z_{\alpha/2}\left(\frac{\sigma}{\sqrt{n}}\right)\right] = \left[4.26 \pm 1.96\left(\frac{0.47}{\sqrt{35}}\right)\right] = [4.10, 4.42].$$

Because this interval does not contain 4.5, we can reject H_0: $\mu = 4.5$ in favour of H_a: $\mu \neq 4.5$ by setting α equal to 0.05.

Whereas we can use the *two-sided* confidence intervals of this book to test not equal to alternative hypotheses, we must use *one-sided* confidence intervals to test greater than or less than alternative hypotheses. However, it should be emphasized that we do not need to use confidence intervals (one-sided or two-sided) to test hypotheses. We can test hypotheses by using test statistics and rejection points or *p* values. Furthermore, confidence intervals can help us to evaluate practical importance after we have established statistical significance by using a hypothesis test. This is illustrated in the next section.

The effect of sample size   If we can reject a null hypothesis by setting the probability of a Type I error equal to α, we say that we have **statistical significance at the α level**. Whether we have statistical significance at a given level often depends greatly on the size of the sample we have selected. To see this, recall that the marketing company wishes to test H_0: $\mu \leq 50$ versus H_a: $\mu > 50$ and has obtained the sample mean $\bar{x} = 50.575$ based on a sample of $n = 40$ cable TV subscriptions. Assuming that σ is known to equal 1.65, the p value associated with

$$z = \frac{\bar{x} - 50}{\sigma/\sqrt{n}} = \frac{50.575 - 50}{1.65/\sqrt{40}} = \frac{0.575}{0.26089} = 2.20$$

is 0.0139. It follows that we have statistical significance at the 0.05 level but not at the 0.01 level. However, suppose that the manufacturer had obtained the same $\bar{x}$ based on a larger sample of $n = 100$ subscriptions. The test statistic value is then

$$z = \frac{\bar{x} - 50}{\sigma/\sqrt{n}} = \frac{50.575 - 50}{1.65/\sqrt{100}} = \frac{0.575}{0.165} = 3.48,$$

and the p value is the area under the standard normal curve to the right of $z = 3.48$. Looking at the normal table (see Table A.3), we see that the area to the right of 3.09 is $0.5 - 0.4990 = 0.001$. Therefore, because 3.48 is greater than 3.09, the p value is less than 0.001, and we have statistical significance at the 0.001 level. What has happened here is that the numerator of the test statistic has remained the same, while the larger sample size makes the denominator of the test statistic smaller. This results in a larger and more statistically significant value of the test statistic. Understand, however, that the highly statistically significant test statistic value means only that we have extremely strong evidence that μ is greater than 50. It does not necessarily mean that the difference between μ and 50 is large enough to be practically important to cable TV subscribers. In fact, the sample mean $\bar{x} = 50.575$ indicates that μ is not much larger than 50. A difference of about 58 cents would not represent a large increase in cost to potential subscribers.

Exercises for Section 8.4

CONCEPTS

8.35 Suppose you are carrying out a two-sided hypothesis test about a population mean.
  a. Give the rejection point rule for rejecting H_0: $\mu = \mu_0$.
  b. Explain how the p value and α tell you whether H_0: $\mu = \mu_0$ should be rejected.

8.36 Discuss how to assess the practical importance of a statistically significant result.

METHODS AND APPLICATIONS

In Exercises 8.37 through 8.43, consider using a random sample of $n = 81$ measurements to test H_0: $\mu = 40$ versus H_a: $\mu \neq 40$. Suppose that $\bar{x} = 34$ and $\sigma = 18$.

8.37 Calculate the value of the test statistic z.

8.38 Use rejection points to test H_0 versus H_a by setting α equal to 0.10.

8.39 Use rejection points to test H_0 versus H_a by setting α equal to 0.05.

8.40 Use rejection points to test H_0 versus H_a by setting α equal to 0.01.

8.41 Use rejection points to test H_0 versus H_a by setting α equal to 0.001.
  Hint: $z_{0.0005}$ can be shown to equal 3.29.

8.42 Calculate the p value and use it to test H_0 versus H_a at each of $\alpha = 0.10, 0.05, 0.01$, and 0.001.

8.43 How much evidence is there that H_0: $\mu = 40$ is false and H_a: $\mu \neq 40$ is true?

8.44 Consider the automobile parts supplier in Exercise 8.10. Suppose that a problem-solving team will be assigned to rectify the process producing cylindrical engine parts if the null hypothesis H_0: $\mu = 3$ can be rejected in favour of H_a: $\mu \neq 3$ by setting α equal to 0.05.
  a. A sample of 40 parts yields a sample mean diameter of $\bar{x} = 3.006$ cm. Assuming σ equals 0.016, use rejection points and a p value to test H_0 versus H_a by setting α equal to 0.05. Should the problem-solving team be assigned?
  b. Suppose that product specifications state that each and every part must have a diameter between 2.95 cm and 3.05 cm—that is, the specifications are 3 cm $\pm$ 0.05 cm. Use the sample information given in part a to estimate an interval that contains almost all (99.73 percent) of the diameters. Compare this estimated interval with the specification limits. Are the specification limits being met, or are some diameters outside the specification limits? Explain.

8.45 Consider the Classic Bottling Company fill process in Exercise 8.11. Recall that the initial setup of the filler will be adjusted if the null hypothesis H_0: $\mu = 355$ mL is rejected in favour of H_a: $\mu \neq 355$ mL. Suppose that Classic Bottling Company decides to use a level of significance of $\alpha = 0.01$, and suppose a random sample of 36 fills is obtained from a test run of the filler. For each of the following sample results, determine whether the filler's initial setup should be adjusted. In each case,

use a rejection point and a *p* value, and assume that σ equals 0.1.
    a. $\bar{x} = 355.05$.   **b.** $\bar{x} = 354.96$.   **c.** $\bar{x} = 355.02$.

8.46 Use the sample information in part a of Exercise 8.45 and a confidence interval to test H_0: $\mu = 355$ mL versus H_a: $\mu \neq 355$ mL by setting α equal to 0.05. What considerations would help you to decide whether the result has practical importance?

8.47 In an article in the *Journal of Marketing*, Bayus studied the mean numbers of auto dealers visited by two types of buyers.
    a. Letting μ be the mean number of dealers visited by the first type of buyer, suppose that you wish to test

H_0: $\mu = 4$ versus H_a: $\mu \neq 4$. A random sample of 800 of these buyers yields a mean number of dealers visited of $\bar{x} = 3.3$. Assuming σ equals 0.71, calculate the *p* value and test H_0 versus H_a. Do you estimate that μ is less than 4 or greater than 4?
    b. Letting μ be the mean number of dealers visited by the second type of buyer, suppose that you wish to test H_0: $\mu = 4$ versus H_a: $\mu \neq 4$. A random sample of 500 of these buyers yields a mean number of dealers visited of $\bar{x} = 4.3$. Assuming σ equals 0.66, calculate the *p* value and test H_0 versus H_a. Do you estimate that μ is less than 4 or greater than 4?

8.5 *t* TESTS ABOUT A POPULATION MEAN (σ UNKNOWN)

If we do not know σ (which is usually the case), we can base a hypothesis test about μ on the sampling distribution of

$$\frac{\bar{x} - \mu}{s/\sqrt{n}}.$$

If the sampled population is normally distributed, then this sampling distribution is a *t* **distribution with** $n - 1$ **degrees of freedom**. This leads to the following results:

A *t* Test about a Population Mean: Testing H_0: $\mu = \mu_0$ When σ Is Unknown

Define the test statistic

$$t = \frac{\bar{x} - \mu_0}{\sigma/\sqrt{n}}$$

and assume that the population sampled is normally distributed. We can test H_0: $\mu = \mu_0$ versus a particular alternative hypothesis at level of significance α by using the appropriate rejection point rule or, equivalently, the corresponding *p* value.

Alternative Hypothesis	Rejection Point Rule: Reject H_0 if	*p* Value (Reject H_0 if *p* Value $< \alpha$)
H_a: $\mu > \mu_0$	$t > t_\alpha$	The area under the *t* distribution curve to the right of *t*
H_a: $\mu < \mu_0$	$t < -t_\alpha$	The area under the *t* distribution curve to the left of *t*
H_a: $\mu \neq \mu_0$	$\lvert t \rvert > t_{\alpha/2}$—that is, $t > t_{\alpha/2}$ or $t < -t_{\alpha/2}$	Twice the area under the *t* distribution curve to the right of $\lvert t \rvert$

Here t_α, $t_{\alpha/2}$, and the *p* values are based on $n - 1$ degrees of freedom.

Example 8.5 *t* Test about μ

In 2001, the average interest rate charged by Canadian credit card issuers was 18.8 percent. Since that time, there has been a proliferation of new credit cards affiliated with retail stores, oil companies, alumni associations, and so on. A financial officer wishes to study whether the increased competition in the credit card business has reduced interest rates. To do this, the officer

FIGURE **8.8**   MegaStat Stem-and-Leaf Plot and Box Plot of the Interest Rates

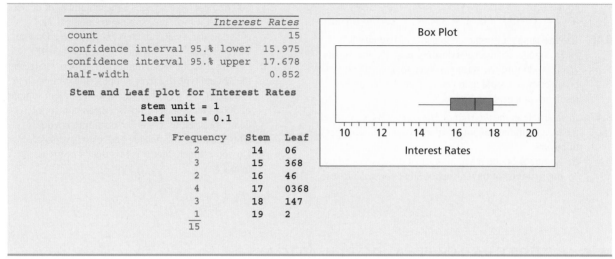

will test a hypothesis about the current mean interest rate, μ, charged by Canadian credit card issuers. **The null hypothesis to be tested is H_0: $\mu = 18.8\%$, and the alternative hypothesis is H_a: $\mu < 18.8\%$.** If H_0 can be rejected in favour of H_a at the **0.05 level of significance**, the officer will conclude that the current mean interest rate is less than the 18.8 percent mean interest rate charged in 2001. To perform the hypothesis test, suppose that we randomly select $n = 15$ credit cards and determine their current interest rates. The interest rates for the 15 sampled cards are given in Table 8.2. A MegaStat stem-and-leaf display and box plot are given in Figure 8.8. The stem-and-leaf display looks reasonably mound-shaped, and both the stem-and-leaf display and the box plot look reasonably symmetrical. It follows that it is appropriate to calculate the value of the **test statistic t in the summary box**. Furthermore, since H_a: $\mu < 18.8\%$ is of the form H_a: $\mu < \mu_0$, we should **reject H_0: $\mu = 18.8\%$ if the value of t is less than the rejection point $-t_\alpha = -t_{0.05} = -1.761$.** Here $-t_{0.05} = -1.761$ is based on $n - 1 = 15 - 1 = 14$ degrees of freedom, and this rejection point is illustrated in Figure 8.9(a). The mean and the standard deviation of the $n = 15$ interest rates in Table 8.2 are $\bar{x} = 16.827$ and $s = 1.538$. This implies that the **value of the test statistic** is

$$t = \frac{\bar{x} - 18.8}{s/\sqrt{n}} = \frac{16.827 - 18.8}{1.538/\sqrt{15}} = -4.97.$$

Since $t = -4.97$ is less than $-t_{0.05} = -1.761$, we reject H_0: $\mu = 18.8\%$ in favour of H_a: $\mu < 18.8\%$. That is, we conclude (at an α of 0.05) that the current mean credit card interest rate is lower than 18.8 percent, the mean interest rate in 2001. Furthermore, the sample mean $\bar{x} = 16.827$ says that we estimate that the mean interest rate is $18.8\% - 16.827\% = 1.973\%$ lower than it was in 2001.

The p value for testing H_0: $\mu = 18.8\%$ versus H_a: $\mu < 18.8\%$ is the area under the curve of the t distribution with 14 degrees of freedom to the left of $t = -4.97$. Tables of t points (such as Table A.5) are not complete enough to give such areas for most t statistic values, so

TABLE **8.2**   Interest Rates Charged by 15 Randomly Selected Credit Cards

15.6%	15.3%	19.2%
17.8	16.4	15.8
14.6	18.4	18.1
17.3	17.6	16.6
18.7	14.0	17.0

FIGURE **8.9**   Testing H_0: $\mu = 18.8\%$ versus H_a: $\mu < 18.8\%$ by Using a Rejection Point and a *p* Value

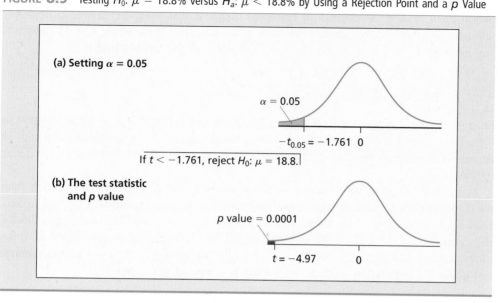

(a) Setting $\alpha = 0.05$

$\alpha = 0.05$

$-t_{0.05} = -1.761$ 0

If $t < -1.761$, reject H_0: $\mu = 18.8$.

(b) The test statistic and *p* value

p value = 0.0001

$t = -4.97$ 0

FIGURE **8.10**   The Excel and MegaStat Outputs for Testing H_0: $\mu = 18.8\%$ versus H_a: $\mu < 18.8\%$

(a) The Excel output

t-statistic
−4.97
p-value
0.000103

(b) The MegaStat output
Hypothesis Test: Mean vs. Hypothesized Value

18.8000 hypothesized value	1.5378 std. dev.	15 n	−4.97 t
16.8267 mean Rate	0.3971 std. error	14 df	0.0001 p-value (one-tailed, lower)
= Significant at 0.05 level			= Significant at 0.01 level

we use computer software packages to calculate *p* values that are based on the *t* distribution. For example, the Excel output in Figure 8.10(a) and the MegaStat output in Figure 8.10(b) tell us that the *p* value for testing H_0: $\mu = 18.8\%$ versus H_a: $\mu < 18.8\%$ is 0.0001. This is also noted in Figure 8.9(b). Notice that the Excel output in Figure 8.10(a) gives a slightly more accurate value of 0.000103 for the *p* value. Because this *p* value is less than 0.05, 0.01, and 0.001, we can reject H_0 at the 0.05, 0.01, and 0.001 levels of significance. As a probability, the *p* value of 0.0001 says that if we are to believe that H_0: $\mu = 18.8\%$ is true, we must believe that we have observed a *t* statistic value ($t = -4.97$) that can be described as a 1 in 10,000 chance. In summary, we have extremely strong evidence that H_0: $\mu = 18.8\%$ is false and H_a: $\mu < 18.8\%$ is true. That is, we have extremely strong evidence that the current mean credit card interest rate is less than 18.8 percent.

Recall that in three cases discussed in Sections 8.3 and 8.4, we tested hypotheses by assuming that the population standard deviation σ is known and by using *z* tests. If σ is actually not known in these cases (which would probably be true), we should test the hypotheses under consideration by using *t* tests. Furthermore, recall that in each case the sample size is large (at least 30). In general, it can be shown that if the sample size is large, the *t* test is approximately valid even if the sampled population is not normally distributed (or mound-shaped). Therefore, consider the camshaft case and testing **H_0: $\mu = 4.5$ versus H_a: $\mu \neq 4.5$** at the **0.05 level of significance**. To perform the hypothesis test, assume that we will randomly select $n = 35$ camshafts and use their hardness depths to calculate the value of the **test statistic *t* in the summary box**. Then, since the alternative hypothesis H_a: $\mu \neq 4.5$ is of the form H_a: $\mu \neq \mu_0$, we will **reject H_0: $\mu = 4.5$ if the absolute value of t is greater than $t_{\alpha/2} = t_{0.025} = 2.032$** (based on $n - 1 = 34$ degrees of freedom). Suppose that when the sample is randomly selected, the mean and the standard deviation of the hardness depths of the $n = 35$ camshafts are calculated to be $\bar{x} = 4.26$ and $s = 0.49$. The **value of the test statistic** is

$$t = \frac{\bar{x} - 4.5}{s/\sqrt{n}} = \frac{4.26 - 4.5}{0.49/\sqrt{35}} = -2.8977.$$

Since $|t| = 2.8977$ is greater than $t_{0.025} = 2.032$, we can reject H_0: $\mu = 4.5$ at α equal to 0.05. The p value for the hypothesis test is twice the area under the t distribution curve with 34 degrees of freedom to the right of $|t| = 2.8977$. Using a computer, we find that this p value is 0.0066.

In summary, the p values obtained for the cases using t tests do not differ by much from the corresponding p values using z tests. Therefore, the practical conclusions reached in Sections 8.3 and 8.4 using z tests would also be reached using the t tests discussed here. Finally, if the sample size is small (< 30) and the sampled population is not mound-shaped, or if the sampled population is highly skewed, then it might be appropriate to use a **nonparametric test about the population median**. Such a test is discussed in Chapter 13.

Exercises for Section 8.5

CONCEPTS

8.48 What assumptions must be met in order to carry out the test about a population mean based on the t distribution?

8.49 How do you decide whether to use a z test or a t test when testing a hypothesis about a population mean?

METHODS AND APPLICATIONS

8.50 Suppose that a random sample of 16 measurements from a normally distributed population gives a sample mean of $\bar{x} = 13.5$ and a sample standard deviation of $s = 6$. Use rejection points to test H_0: $\mu \leq 10$ versus H_a: $\mu > 10$ using levels of significance $\alpha = 0.10$, $\alpha = 0.05$, $\alpha = 0.01$, and $\alpha = 0.001$. What do you conclude at each value of α?

8.51 Suppose that a random sample of nine measurements from a normally distributed population gives a sample mean of $\bar{x} = 2.57$ and a sample standard deviation of $s = 0.3$. Use rejection points to test H_0: $\mu = 3$ versus H_a: $\mu \neq 3$ using levels of significance $\alpha = 0.10$, $\alpha = 0.05$, $\alpha = 0.01$, and $\alpha = 0.001$. What do you conclude at each value of α?

8.52 The *bad debt ratio* for a financial institution is defined to be the dollar value of loans defaulted divided by the total dollar value of all loans made. Suppose that a random sample of seven Ontario banks is selected and that the bad debt ratios (written as percentages) for these banks are 7 percent, 4 percent, 6 percent, 7 percent, 5 percent, 4 percent, and 9 percent.
  a. Banking officials claim that the mean bad debt ratio for all Canadian banks is 3.5 percent and that the mean bad debt ratio for Ontario banks is higher. Set up the null and alternative hypotheses needed to attempt to provide evidence supporting the claim that the mean bad debt ratio for Ontario banks exceeds 3.5 percent.

  b. Assuming that bad debt ratios for Ontario banks are approximately normally distributed, use rejection points and the given sample information to test the hypotheses you set up in part a by setting α equal to 0.10, 0.05, 0.01, and 0.001. How much evidence is there that the mean bad debt ratio for Ontario banks exceeds 3.5 percent? What does this say about the banking official's claim?

8.53 Consider Exercise 8.52. In Figure 8.11(a), we give the MegaStat output of the test statistic and p value for testing H_0: $\mu = 3.5$ versus H_a: $\mu > 3.5$.
  a. Use the p value to test H_0 versus H_a by setting α equal to 0.10, 0.05, 0.01, and 0.001. What do you conclude at each value of α?

  b. How much evidence is there that the mean bad debt ratio for Ontario banks exceeds 3.5 percent?

8.54 In the book *Business Research Methods*, Cooper and Emory discuss using hypothesis testing to study receivables outstanding. To quote Cooper and Emory:

  . . . the controller of a large retail chain may be concerned about a possible slowdown in payments by the company's customers. She measures the rate of payment in terms of the average number of days receivables outstanding. Generally, the company has maintained an average of about 50 days with a standard deviation of 10 days. Since it would be too expensive to analyze all of a company's receivables frequently, we normally resort to sampling.

  a. Set up the null and alternative hypotheses needed to attempt to show that there has been a slowdown in payments by the company's customers (there has been a slowdown if the average days outstanding exceeds 50).

  b. Assume approximate normality and suppose that a random sample of 25 accounts gives an average days outstanding of $\bar{x} = 54$ with a standard

FIGURE 8.11   MegaStat Output for Exercises 8.53, 8.55, and 8.57

(a)   MegaStat output for Exercise 8.53

0.03500	hypothesized value
0.06000	mean Bad Debt Ratio (Percentage)
0.01826	std. dev.
0.00690	std. error
7	n
6	df
3.62	t
0.0055	p value (one-tailed, upper)

(b)   MegaStat output of the test statistic and p value for Exercise 8.55

Hypothesis Test: Mean versus Hypothesized Value

750.000	hypothesized value
811.000	mean Hourly Yield
19.647	std. dev.
8.786	std. error
5	n
4	df
6.94	t
0.0023	p value (two-tailed)

(c)   MegaStat output for Exercise 8.57

Hypothesis Test: Mean versus Hypothesized Value

800.000	hypothesized value
846.200	mean Sales per sq. ft.
32.866	std. dev.
10.393	std. error
10	n
9	df
4.45	t
0.0008	p value (one-tailed, upper)

deviation of $s = 8$. Use rejection points to test the hypotheses you set up in part a at levels of significance $\alpha = 0.10$, $\alpha = 0.05$, $\alpha = 0.01$, and $\alpha = 0.001$. How much evidence is there of a slowdown in payments?

c. Are you qualified to decide whether this result has practical importance? Who would be?

8.55 Consider a chemical company that wishes to determine whether a new catalyst, catalyst XA-100, changes the mean hourly yield of its chemical process from the historical process mean of 750 g per hour. When five trial runs are made using the new catalyst, the following yields (in grams per hour) are recorded: 801, 814, 784, 836, and 820.

a. Let μ be the mean of all possible yields using the new catalyst. Assuming that chemical yields are approximately normally distributed, the MegaStat output of the test statistic and *p* value for testing H_0: $\mu = 750$ versus H_a: $\mu \neq 750$ are as in Figure 8.11(b). Use the sample data to verify that the values of $\bar{x}$, s, and *t* given on the output are correct.

b. Use the test statistic and rejection points to test H_0 versus H_a by setting α equal to 0.10, 0.05, 0.01, and 0.001.

8.56 Consider Exercise 8.55. Use the *p* value to test H_0: $\mu = 750$ versus H_a: $\mu \neq 750$ by setting α equal

to 0.10, 0.05, 0.01, and 0.001. How much evidence is there that the new catalyst changes the mean hourly yield?

8.57 Whole Foods is an all-natural grocery chain that has 50,000-square-foot (4,600-m²) stores, more than the industry average of 34,000 square feet (3,200 m²). Sales per square foot of supermarkets average just under $400 per square foot, as reported by *USA Today* in an article called "A whole new ballgame in grocery shopping." Suppose that sales per square foot in the most recent fiscal year are recorded for a random sample of ten Whole Foods supermarkets. The data (sales dollars per square foot) are as follows: 854, 858, 801, 892, 849, 807, 894, 863, 829, 815. Let μ denote the mean sales dollars per square foot for all Whole Foods supermarkets during the most recent fiscal year, and note that the historical mean sales dollars per square foot for Whole Foods supermarkets in previous years has been $800. In Figure 8.11(c), we present the MegaStat output obtained by using the sample data to test H_0: $\mu = 800$ versus H_a: $\mu > 800$.

a. Use the *p* value to test H_0 versus H_a by setting α equal to 0.10, 0.05, 0.01, and 0.001.

b. How much evidence is there that μ exceeds $800?

8.58 Consider Exercise 8.57. Do you think that the difference between the sample mean of $846.20 and the historical average of $800 has practical importance?

8.59   **THE VIDEO GAME SATISFACTION RATING CASE**

The mean and the standard deviation of the sample of $n = 65$ customer satisfaction ratings in Chapter 1 are $\bar{x} = 42.95$ and $s = 2.6424$. Let μ denote the mean of all possible customer satisfaction ratings for the XYZ-Box video game system, and consider testing $H_0: \mu = 42$ versus $H_a: \mu > 42$. Perform a t test of these hypotheses by setting α equal to 0.05 and using a rejection point. Also interpret the p value of 0.0026 for the hypothesis test.

8.60   **THE BANK CUSTOMER WAITING TIME CASE**

The mean and the standard deviation of the sample of 100 bank customer waiting times in Chapter 1, Exercise 1.9, are $\bar{x} = 5.46$ and $s = 2.475$. Let μ denote the mean of all possible bank customer waiting times using the new system and consider testing $H_0: \mu = 6$ versus $H_a: \mu < 6$. Perform a t test of these hypotheses by setting α equal to 0.05 and using a rejection point. Also, interpret the p value of 0.0157 for the hypothesis test.

8.6 z TESTS ABOUT A POPULATION PROPORTION

In this section, we study a large-sample hypothesis test about a population proportion (that is, about the fraction of population units that possess some qualitative characteristic). We begin with an example.

Example 8.6 The Wine Case

Recall that the wine producer has decided that replacing the current corked bottles with the new corkless bottles is profitable only if p, the true proportion of all current purchasers who would stop buying the wine if the new bottles were used, is less than 0.10. The producer feels that it is unwise to change the bottle design unless it has very strong evidence that p is less than 0.10. Therefore, the bottle design will be changed if and only if the null hypothesis $H_0: p = 0.10$ can be rejected in favour of the alternative hypothesis $H_a: p < 0.10$ at the 0.01 level of significance.

In order to see how to test this kind of hypothesis, remember that when n is large, the sampling distribution of

$$\frac{\hat{p} - p}{\sqrt{\dfrac{p(1 - p)}{n}}}$$

is approximately a standard normal distribution. Let p_0 denote a specified value between 0 and 1 (its exact value will depend on the problem), and consider testing the null hypothesis $H_0: p = p_0$. We then have the following result:

A Large-Sample Test about a Population Proportion: Testing $H_0: p = p_0$

Define the test statistic

$$z = \frac{\hat{p} - p_0}{\sqrt{\dfrac{p_0(1 - p_0)}{n}}}.$$

If the sample size n is large, we can test $H_0: p = p_0$ versus a particular alternative hypothesis at level of significance α by using the appropriate rejection point rule or, equivalently, the corresponding p value.

Alternative Hypothesis	Rejection Point Rule: Reject H_0 if	p Value (Reject H_0 if p Value $< \alpha$)
$H_a: p > p_0$	$z > z_\alpha$	The area under the standard normal curve to the right of z
$H_a: p < p_0$	$z < -z_\alpha$	The area under the standard normal curve to the left of z
$H_a: p \neq p_0$	$\lvert z \rvert > z_{\alpha/2}$—that is, $z > z_{\alpha/2}$ or $z < -z_{\alpha/2}$	Twice the area under the standard normal curve to the right of $\lvert z \rvert$

Here n should be considered large if both np_0 and $n(1 - p_0)$ are at least 5.[2]

---

[2]Some statisticians suggest using the more conservative rule that both np_0 and $n(1 - p_0)$ must be at least 10.

Example 8.7 The Wine Case (z Test about p)

We have seen that the wine producer wishes to test H_0: $p = 0.10$ versus H_a: $p < 0.10$, where p is the proportion of all current purchasers who would stop buying the wine if the new bottles were used. The producer will use the new design if H_0 can be rejected in favour of H_a at the **0.01 level of significance**. To perform the hypothesis test, we randomly select $n = 1,000$ current purchasers of the wine, find the proportion $\hat{p}$ of these purchasers who would stop buying the wine if the new bottles were used, and calculate the value of the **test statistic z in the summary box**. Then, since the alternative hypothesis H_a: $p < 0.10$ is of the form H_a: $p < p_0$, we will **reject H_0: $p = 0.10$ if the value of z is less than $-z_\alpha = -z_{0.01} = -2.33$**. (Note that using this procedure is valid because $np_0 = 1,000(0.10) = 100$ and $n(1 - p_0) = 1,000(1 - 0.10) = 900$ are both at least 5.) Suppose that when the sample is randomly selected, we find that 63 of the 1,000 current purchasers say they would stop buying the wine if the new bottles were used. Since $\hat{p} = 63/1,000 = 0.063$, the **value of the test statistic** is

$$z = \frac{\hat{p} - p_0}{\sqrt{\dfrac{p_0(1 - p_0)}{n}}} = \frac{0.063 - 0.10}{\sqrt{\dfrac{0.10(1 - 0.10)}{1,000}}} = -3.90.$$

Because $z = -3.90$ is less than $-z_{0.01} = -2.33$, we reject H_0: $p = 0.10$ in favour of H_a: $p < 0.10$. That is, we conclude (at an α of 0.01) that the proportion of current purchasers who would stop buying the wine if the new bottles were used is less than 0.10. It follows that the company will use the new design. Furthermore, the point estimate $\hat{p} = 0.063$ says we estimate that 6.3 percent of all current customers would stop buying the wine if the new design were used.

Although the wine producer has made its decision by setting α equal to a single, pre-chosen value of 0.01, it would probably also wish to know the weight of evidence against H_0 and in favour of H_a. The p value is the area under the standard normal curve to the left of $z = -3.90$. Since Table A.3 tells us that the area to the left of -3.09 is 0.001, and since -3.90 is less than -3.09, the p value is less than 0.001. Therefore, we have extremely strong evidence that H_a: $p < 0.10$ is true. That is, we have extremely strong evidence that less than 10 percent of current purchasers would stop buying the wine if the new bottles were used.

Example 8.8 Drug Development z Test about p

Recent medical research has sought to develop drugs that lessen the severity and duration of viral infections. Virol, a relatively new drug, has been shown to provide relief for 70 percent of all patients suffering from viral upper respiratory infections. A major drug company is developing a competing drug called Phantol. The drug company wishes to investigate whether Phantol is more effective than Virol. To do this, the drug company will test a hypothesis about the true proportion, p, of all patients whose symptoms would be relieved by Phantol. **The null hypothesis to be tested is H_0: $p = 0.70$, and the alternative hypothesis is H_a: $p > 0.70$.** If H_0 can be rejected in favour of H_a at the **0.05 level of significance**, the drug company will conclude that Phantol helps more than the 70 percent of patients helped by Virol. To perform the hypothesis test, we will randomly select $n = 300$ patients with viral upper respiratory infections, find the proportion $\hat{p}$ of these patients whose symptoms are relieved by Phantol, and calculate the value of the **test statistic z in the summary box**. Then, since the alternative hypothesis H_a: $p > 0.70$ is of the form H_a: $p > p_0$, we will **reject H_0: $p = 0.70$ if the value of z is greater than $z_\alpha = z_{0.05} = 1.645$**. (Note that using this procedure is valid because $np_0 = 300(0.70) = 210$ and $n(1 - p_0) = 300(1 - 0.70) = 90$ are both at least 5.) Suppose that when the sample is randomly selected, we find that Phantol

provides relief for 231 of the 300 patients. Since $\hat{p} = 231/300 = 0.77$, the **value of the test statistic** is

$$z = \frac{\hat{p} - p_0}{\sqrt{\dfrac{p_0(1 - p_0)}{n}}} = \frac{0.77 - 0.70}{\sqrt{\dfrac{(0.70)(1 - 0.70)}{300}}} = 2.65.$$

Because $z = 2.65$ is greater than $z_{0.05} = 1.645$, we reject H_0: $p = 0.70$ in favour of H_a: $p > 0.70$. That is, we conclude (at an α of 0.05) that Phantol will provide relief for more than 70 percent of all patients suffering from viral upper respiratory infections. More specifically, the point estimate $\hat{p} = 0.77$ of p says that we estimate that Phantol will provide relief for 77 percent of all such patients. Comparing this estimate to the 70 percent of patients whose symptoms are relieved by Virol, we conclude that Phantol is somewhat more effective.

The p value for testing H_0: $p = 0.70$ versus H_a: $p > 0.70$ is the area under the standard normal curve to the right of $z = 2.65$. This p value is $0.5 - 0.4960 = 0.004$ (see Table A.3), and it provides very strong evidence against H_0: $p = 0.70$ and in favour of H_a: $p > 0.70$. That is, we have very strong evidence that Phantol will provide relief for more than 70 percent of all patients suffering from viral upper respiratory infections.

Example 8.9   The Electronic Article Surveillance Case (z Test about p)

Suppose that a company selling electronic article surveillance (EAS) devices claims that the proportion, p, of all consumers who would say they would never shop in a store again if the store subjected them to a false alarm is no more than 0.05. A store considering installing such a device is concerned that p is greater than 0.05 and wishes to test **H_0: $p = 0.05$ versus H_a: $p > 0.05$.** To perform the hypothesis test, the store will calculate a p value and use it to measure the **weight of evidence** against H_0 and in favour of H_a. Recall from Example 2.12 on page 65 that 40 out of 250 consumers in a systematic sample said they would never shop in a store again if the store subjected them to a false alarm. Therefore, the sample proportion of lost consumers is $\hat{p} = 40/250 = 0.16$. Since $np_0 = 250(0.05) = 12.5$ and $n(1 - p_0) = 250(1 - 0.05) = 237.5$ are both at least 5, we can use the **test statistic z in the summary box**. The **value of the test statistic** is

$$z = \frac{\hat{p} - p_0}{\sqrt{\dfrac{p_0(1 - p_0)}{n}}} = \frac{0.16 - 0.05}{\sqrt{\dfrac{(0.05)(0.95)}{250}}} = 7.98.$$

Noting that H_a: $p > 0.05$ is of the form H_a: $p > p_0$, **the p value is the area under the standard normal curve to the right of $z = 7.98$. The normal table tells us that the area under the standard normal curve to the right of 3.09 is 0.001. Therefore, the p value is less than 0.001 and provides extremely strong evidence against H_0: $p = 0.05$ and in favour of H_a: $p > 0.05$.** That is, we have extremely strong evidence that the proportion of all consumers who say they would never shop in a store again if the store subjected them to a false alarm is greater than 0.05. Furthermore, the point estimate $\hat{p} = 0.16$ says we estimate that the percentage of such consumers is 11 percentage points more than the 5 percent maximum claimed by the company selling the EAS devices. We will further investigate the results by looking at a 95 percent confidence interval for p:

$$\left[\hat{p} \pm z_{0.025} \sqrt{\frac{\hat{p}(1 - \hat{p})}{n}} \right] = \left[0.16 \pm 1.96 \sqrt{\frac{(0.16)(0.84)}{250}} \right]$$
$$= [0.1146, 0.2054].$$

This interval says we are 95 percent confident that the percentage of consumers who would say they would never shop in a store again if the store subjected them to a false alarm is between 6.46 and 15.54 percentage points more than the 5 percent maximum claimed by the

FIGURE **8.12**   The MegaStat Output for Testing $H_0: p = 0.05$ versus $H_a: p > 0.05$

Hypothesis test for proportion versus hypothesized value

Observed	Hypothesized		
0.16	0.05 p (as decimal)	0.0138 std. error	0.1146 confidence interval 95.% lower
40/250	13/250 p (as fraction)	7.98 z	0.2054 confidence interval 95.% upper
40.	12.5 X	**7.77E-16** p-value	0.0454 half-width
250	250 n	(one-tailed upper)	

company selling the EAS devices. The rather large increases over the claimed 5 percent maximum implied by the point estimate and the confidence interval would mean substantially more lost consumers and thus are practically important. Figure 8.12 gives the MegaStat output for testing $H_0: p = 0.05$ versus $H_a: p > 0.05$. Note that this output includes a 95 percent confidence interval for p. Also notice that MegaStat expresses the p value for this test in scientific notation. In general, when a p value is less than 0.0001, MegaStat and Excel express the p value in scientific notation. Here the p value of 7.77 E−16 says that we must move the decimal point 16 places to the left to obtain the decimal equivalent. That is, the p value is 0.000000000000000777.

Exercises for Section 8.6

CONCEPTS

8.61 If you test a hypothesis to provide evidence supporting the claim that a majority of voters prefer a political party, explain the difference between p and $\hat{p}$.

8.62 If you test a hypothesis to provide evidence supporting the claim that more than 30 percent of all consumers prefer a particular brand of beer, explain the difference between p and $\hat{p}$.

8.63 If you test a hypothesis to provide evidence supporting the claim that less than 5 percent of the units produced by a process are defective, explain the difference between p and $\hat{p}$.

8.64 What condition must be satisfied in order to appropriately use the methods of this section?

METHODS AND APPLICATIONS

8.65 For each of the following sample sizes and hypothesized values of the population proportion p, determine whether the sample size is large enough to use the large-sample test about p given in this section:
  a. $n = 400$ and $p_0 = 0.5$.
  b. $n = 100$ and $p_0 = 0.01$.
  c. $n = 10,000$ and $p_0 = 0.01$.
  d. $n = 100$ and $p_0 = 0.2$.
  e. $n = 256$ and $p_0 = 0.7$.
  f. $n = 200$ and $p_0 = 0.98$.
  g. $n = 1,000$ and $p_0 = 0.98$.
  h. $n = 25$ and $p_0 = 0.4$.

8.66 Suppose you wish to test $H_0: p \leq 0.8$ versus $H_a: p > 0.8$ and that a random sample of $n = 400$ gives a sample proportion $\hat{p} = 0.86$.
  a. Test H_0 versus H_a at the 0.05 level of significance by using a rejection point. What do you conclude?
  b. Find the p value for this test.

  c. Use the p value to test H_0 versus H_a by setting α equal to 0.10, 0.05, 0.01, and 0.001. What do you conclude at each value of α?

8.67 Suppose you test $H_0: p = 0.3$ versus $H_a: p \neq 0.3$ and that a random sample of $n = 100$ gives a sample proportion $\hat{p} = 0.20$.
  a. Test H_0 versus H_a at the 0.01 level of significance by using a rejection point. What do you conclude?
  b. Find the p value for this test.
  c. Use the p value to test H_0 versus H_a by setting α equal to 0.10, 0.05, 0.01, and 0.001. What do you conclude at each value of α?

8.68 Suppose you are testing $H_0: p \leq 0.5$ versus $H_a: p > 0.5$, where p is the proportion of all beer drinkers who have tried at least one brand of beer from a craft brewery. If a random sample of 500 beer drinkers has been taken and if $\hat{p}$ equals 0.57, how many beer drinkers in the sample have tried at least one brand of beer from a craft brewery?

8.69   THE MARKETING ETHICS CASE: CONFLICT OF INTEREST

Recall that a conflict of interest scenario was presented to a sample of 205 marketing researchers and that 111 of these researchers disapproved of the actions taken (see Exercise 2.48 on page 67).
  a. Let p be the proportion of all marketing researchers who disapprove of the actions taken in the conflict of interest scenario. Set up the null and alternative hypotheses needed to attempt to provide evidence supporting the claim that a majority (more than 50 percent) of all marketing researchers disapprove of the actions taken.
  b. Assuming that the sample of 205 marketing researchers has been randomly selected, use

FIGURE **8.13**   MegaStat Output for Exercise 8.70

Hypothesis test for proportion versus hypothesized value

Observed	Hypothesized	
0.365	0.25	p (as decimal)
146/400	100/400	p (as fraction)
146.	100.	X
400	400	n
	0.0217	std. error
	5.31	z
	5.43E-08	p-value (one-tailed, upper)

rejection points and the previously given sample information to test the hypotheses you set up in part a at the 0.10, 0.05, 0.01, and 0.001 levels of significance. How much evidence is there that a majority of all marketing researchers disapprove of the actions taken?

c. Suppose a random sample of 1,000 marketing researchers reveals that 540 of the researchers disapprove of the actions taken in the conflict of interest scenario. Use rejection points to determine how much evidence there is that a majority of all marketing researchers disapprove of the actions taken.

d. Note that in parts b and c the sample proportion $\hat{p}$ is (essentially) the same. Explain why the results of the hypothesis tests in parts b and c differ.

8.70 Last year, television station CXYZ's share of the 11 P.M. news audience was approximately equal to, but no greater than, 25 percent. The station's management believes that the current audience share is higher than last year's 25 percent share. In an attempt to substantiate this belief, the station surveyed a random sample of 400 11 P.M. news viewers and found that 146 watched CXYZ.

a. Let p be the current proportion of all 11 P.M. news viewers who watch CXYZ. Set up the null and alternative hypotheses needed to attempt to provide evidence supporting the claim that the current audience share for CXYZ is higher than last year's 25 percent share.

b. Use rejection points and the MegaStat output in Figure 8.13 to test the hypotheses you set up in part a at the 0.10, 0.05, 0.01, and 0.001 levels of significance. How much evidence is there that the current audience share is higher than last year's 25 percent share?

c. Calculate the p value for the hypothesis test in part b. Use the p value to carry out the test by setting α equal to 0.10, 0.05, 0.01, and 0.001. Interpret your results.

d. Do you think that the result of the station's survey has practical importance? Why or why not?

8.71 In the book *Essentials of Marketing Research*, Dillon, Madden, and Firtle discuss a marketing research proposal to study day-after recall for a brand of mouthwash. To quote the authors:

The ad agency has developed a TV ad for the introduction of the mouthwash. The objective of the

ad is to create awareness of the brand. The objective of this research is to evaluate the awareness generated by the ad measured by aided- and unaided-recall scores.

A minimum of 200 respondents who claim to have watched the TV show in which the ad was aired the night before will be contacted by telephone in 20 cities.

The study will provide information on the incidence of unaided and aided recall.

Suppose a random sample of 200 respondents shows that 46 of the people interviewed were able to recall the commercial without any prompting (unaided recall).

a. In order for the ad to be considered successful, the percentage of unaided recall must be above the category norm for a TV commercial for the product class. If this norm is 18 percent, set up the null and alternative hypotheses needed to attempt to provide evidence that the ad is successful.

b. Use the previously given sample information to compute the p value for the hypothesis test you set up in part a. Use the p value to carry out the test by setting α equal to 0.10, 0.05, 0.01, and 0.001. How much evidence is there that the TV commercial is successful?

c. Do you think the result of the ad agency's survey has practical importance? Explain your opinion.

8.72 *Quality Progress*, February 2005, reports on the results achieved by Bank of America in improving customer satisfaction and customer loyalty by listening to the "voice of the customer." A key measure of customer satisfaction is the response on a scale from 1 to 10 to the question, "Considering all the business you do with Bank of America, what is your overall satisfaction with Bank of America?"[3] Suppose that a random sample of 350 current customers results in 195 customers giving a response of 9 or 10 representing "customer delight."

a. Let p denote the true proportion of all current Bank of America customers who would respond with a 9 or a 10, and note that the historical proportion of customer delight for Bank of America has been 0.48. Calculate the p value for testing $H_0: p = 0.48$ versus $H_a: p > 0.48$. How much evidence is there that p exceeds 0.48?

b. Bank of America has a base of nearly 30 million customers. Do you think that the sample results have practical importance? Explain your opinion.

8.73 The manufacturer of the ColourSmart-5000 flat panel television claims that 95 percent of its televisions last at least five years without needing a single repair. In order to test this claim, a consumer group randomly selects 400 consumers who have owned a ColourSmart-5000 television for five years. Of these 400 consumers, 316 say that their ColourSmart-5000 televisions did not need repair, while 84 say that their ColourSmart-5000 televisions did need at least one repair.

a. Letting p be the proportion of ColourSmart-5000 televisions that last five years without a single repair, set up the null and alternative hypotheses that the consumer group should use to attempt to show that the manufacturer's claim is false.

b. Use rejection points and the previously given sample information to test the hypotheses you set up in part a by setting α equal to 0.10, 0.05, 0.01,

and 0.001. How much evidence is there that the manufacturer's claim is false?

c. Do you think the results of the consumer group's survey have practical importance? Explain your opinion.

CHAPTER SUMMARY

We began this chapter by learning about the two hypotheses that make up the structure of a hypothesis test. The **null hypothesis** is the statement being tested. Usually it represents the status quo and is not rejected unless there is convincing sample evidence that it is false. The **alternative**, or **research**, **hypothesis** is a statement that is accepted only if there is convincing sample evidence that it is true and that the null hypothesis is false. In some situations, the alternative hypothesis is a condition for which we need to attempt to find supportive evidence. We also learned that two types of errors can be made in a hypothesis test. A **Type I error** occurs when we reject a true null hypothesis, and a **Type II error** occurs when we do not reject a false null hypothesis.

We studied two commonly used ways to conduct a hypothesis test. The first involves comparing the value of a test statistic with what is called a **rejection point**, and the second employs what is called a *p* **value**. The *p* value measures the weight of evidence against the null hypothesis. The smaller the *p* value is, the more we doubt the

null hypothesis. We learned that if we can reject the null hypothesis with the probability of a Type I error equal to α, then we say that the test result has **statistical significance at the α level**. However, we also learned that even if the result of a hypothesis test tells us that statistical significance exists, we must carefully assess whether the result is practically important. One good way to do this is to use a point estimate and confidence interval for the parameter of interest.

The specific hypothesis tests we covered in this chapter all dealt with a hypothesis about one population parameter. First, we studied a test about a **population mean** that is based on the assumption that the population standard deviation σ *is known*. This test employs the **normal distribution**. Second, we studied a test about a population mean that assumes that σ *is unknown*. We learned that this test is based on the *t* **distribution**. Figure 8.14 presents a flowchart summarizing how to select an appropriate test statistic to test a hypothesis about a population mean. Finally, we presented a test about a **population proportion** that is based on the **normal distribution**.

FIGURE 8.14   Selecting an Appropriate Test Statistic to Test a Hypothesis about a Population Mean

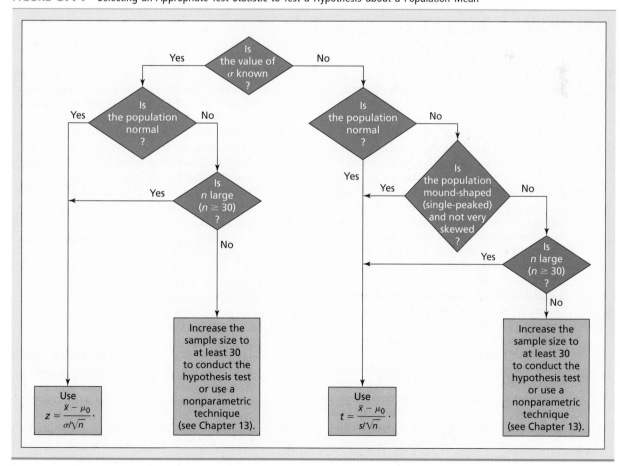

GLOSSARY OF TERMS

alternative (research) hypothesis: A statement that will be accepted only if there is convincing sample evidence that it is true. Sometimes it is a condition for which we need to attempt to find supportive evidence. (page 254)

greater than alternative: An alternative hypothesis that is stated as a greater than ($>$) inequality. (page 256)

less than alternative: An alternative hypothesis that is stated as a less than ($<$) inequality. (page 256)

not equal to alternative: An alternative hypothesis that is stated as a not equal to ($\neq$) inequality. (page 256)

null hypothesis: The statement being tested in a hypothesis test. It usually represents the status quo, and it is not rejected unless there is convincing sample evidence that it is false. (page 254)

one-sided alternative hypothesis: An alternative hypothesis that is stated as either a greater than ($>$) or a less than ($<$) inequality. (page 256)

p value (probability value): The probability, computed assuming that the null hypothesis is true, of observing a value of the test statistic that is at least as extreme as the value actually computed from the sample data. The p value measures how much doubt is cast on the null hypothesis by the sample data. The smaller the p value is, the more we doubt the null hypothesis. (pages 262, 265, 267, 271)

rejection point (or critical point): The value of the test statistic is compared with a rejection point in order to decide whether the null hypothesis can be rejected. (pages 260, 264, 271)

statistical significance at the α level: When we can reject the null hypothesis by setting the probability of a Type I error equal to α. (pages 261, 273)

test statistic: A statistic computed from sample data in a hypothesis test. It is either compared with a rejection point or used to compute a p value. (page 256)

two-sided alternative hypothesis: An alternative hypothesis that is stated as a not equal to ($\neq$) inequality. (page 256)

Type I error: Rejecting a true null hypothesis. (page 257)

Type II error: Failing to reject a false null hypothesis. (page 257)

IMPORTANT FORMULAS AND TESTS

Hypothesis-testing steps: page 267

A hypothesis test about a population mean (σ known): page 272

A hypothesis test about a population mean (σ unknown): page 275

A large-sample hypothesis test about a population proportion: page 280

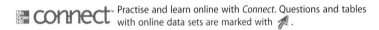 Practise and learn online with *Connect*. Questions and tables with online data sets are marked with ✦.

SUPPLEMENTARY EXERCISES

8.74 The auditor for a large corporation routinely monitors cash disbursements. As part of this process, the auditor examines cheque request forms to determine whether they have been properly approved. Improper approval can occur in several ways. For instance, the cheque may have no approval, the cheque request might be missing, the approval might be written by an unauthorized person, or the dollar limit of the authorizing person might be exceeded.

    a. Last year, the corporation experienced a 5 percent improper cheque request approval rate. Since this was considered unacceptable, efforts were made to reduce the rate of improper approvals. Letting p be the proportion of all cheques that are now improperly approved, set up the null and alternative hypotheses needed to attempt to demonstrate that the current rate of improper approvals is lower than last year's rate of 5 percent.

    b. Suppose that the auditor selects a random sample of 625 cheques that have been approved in the last month. The auditor finds that 18 of these 625 cheques have been improperly approved. Use rejection points and this sample information to test the hypotheses you set up in part a at the 0.10, 0.05, 0.01, and 0.001 levels of significance. How much evidence is there that the rate of improper approvals has been reduced below last year's 5 percent rate?

    c. Find the p value for the test of part b. Use the p value to carry out the test by setting α equal to 0.10, 0.05, 0.01, and 0.001. Interpret your results.

    d. Suppose the corporation incurs a $10 cost to detect and correct an improperly approved cheque. If the corporation disburses at least 2 million cheques per year, does the observed reduction of the rate of improper approvals seem to have practical importance? Explain your opinion.

8.75 In an article in the *Journal of Retailing*, Kumar, Kerwin, and Pereira study factors affecting merger and acquisition activity in retailing. As part of the study, the authors compare the characteristics of target firms (firms targeted for acquisition) and bidder firms (firms attempting to make acquisitions). Among the variables studied in the comparison were earnings per share, debt-to-equity ratio, growth rate of sales, market share, and extent of diversification.

    a. Let μ be the mean growth rate of sales for all target firms (firms that have been targeted for acquisition in the last five years and that have not bid on other firms), and assume growth rates are approximately normally distributed. Furthermore, suppose a random sample of 25 target firms yields a sample mean sales growth rate of $\bar{x} = 0.16$ with a standard deviation of $s = 0.12$. Use rejection points and this sample information to test $H_0: \mu \le 0.10$ versus $H_a: \mu > 0.10$ by setting α equal to 0.10, 0.05, 0.01, and 0.001. How much evidence is there that the mean growth rate of sales for target firms exceeds 0.10 (that is, exceeds 10 percent)?

b. Now let μ be the mean growth rate of sales for all firms that are bidders (firms that have bid to acquire at least one other firm in the last five years), and again assume growth rates are approximately normally distributed. Furthermore, suppose a random sample of 25 bidders yields a sample mean sales growth rate of $\bar{x} = 0.12$ with a standard deviation of $s = 0.09$. Use rejection points and this sample information to test $H_0: \mu \le 0.10$ versus $H_a: \mu > 0.10$ by setting α equal to 0.10, 0.05, 0.01, and 0.001. How much evidence is there that the mean growth rate of sales for bidders exceeds 0.10 (that is, exceeds 10 percent)?

8.76 A consumer electronics firm has developed a new type of remote control button that is designed to operate for a longer time before becoming intermittent. A random sample of 35 of the new buttons is selected and each is tested in continuous operation until it becomes intermittent. The resulting lifetimes are found to have a sample mean of $\bar{x} = 1{,}241.2$ hours and a sample standard deviation of $s = 110.8$ hours.

a. Independent tests reveal that the mean lifetime (in continuous operation) of the best remote control button on the market is 1,200 hours. Letting μ be the mean lifetime of the population of all new remote control buttons that will or could potentially be produced, set up the null and alternative hypotheses needed to attempt to provide evidence that the new button's mean lifetime exceeds the mean lifetime of the best remote control button currently on the market.

b. Using the previously given sample results, use rejection points to test the hypotheses you set up in part a by setting α equal to 0.10, 0.05, 0.01, and 0.001. What do you conclude for each value of α?

c. Suppose that $\bar{x} = 1{,}241.2$ and $s = 110.8$ had been obtained by testing a sample of 100 buttons. Use rejection points to test the hypotheses you set up in part a by setting α equal to 0.10, 0.05, 0.01, and 0.001. Which sample (the sample of 35 or the sample of 100) gives a more statistically significant result? That is, which sample provides stronger evidence that H_a is true?

d. If we define practical importance to mean that μ exceeds 1,200 by an amount that would be clearly noticeable to most consumers, do you think that the result has practical importance? Explain why the samples of 35 and 100 both indicate the same degree of practical importance.

e. Suppose that further research and development effort improves the new remote control button and that a random sample of 35 buttons gives $\bar{x} = 1{,}524.6$ hours and $s = 102.8$ hours. Test your hypotheses of part a by setting α equal to 0.10, 0.05, 0.01, and 0.001.
  (1) Is the result highly statistically significant? Explain.
  (2) Do you think the result is practically important? Explain.

8.77 Again consider the remote control button lifetime situation discussed in Exercise 8.76. Using the sample

information given in the introduction to Exercise 8.76, the p value for testing H_0 versus H_a can be calculated to be 0.0174.

a. Determine whether H_0 would be rejected at each of $\alpha = 0.10$, $\alpha = 0.05$, $\alpha = 0.01$, and $\alpha = 0.001$.

b. Describe how much evidence there is that the new button's mean lifetime exceeds the mean lifetime of the best remote control button currently on the market.

8.78 Calculate and use an appropriate 95 percent confidence interval to help evaluate practical importance as it relates to the hypothesis test in each of the following situations discussed in previous supplementary exercises. Explain what you think each confidence interval says about practical importance.

a. The cheque approval situation of Exercise 8.74.

b. The remote control button situation of Exercise 8.76a, c, and e.

8.79 Several industries located along a river discharge a toxic substance called carbon tetrachloride into the river. The provincial environment ministry monitors the amount of carbon tetrachloride pollution in the river. Specifically, the ministry requires that the carbon tetrachloride contamination average no more than ten parts per million. In order to monitor the carbon tetrachloride contamination in the river, the ministry takes a daily sample of 100 pollution readings at a certain location. If the mean carbon tetrachloride reading for this sample casts substantial doubt on the hypothesis that the average amount of carbon tetrachloride contamination in the river is at most ten parts per million, the ministry must issue a shutdown order. In the event of such a shutdown order, industrial plants along the river must be closed until the carbon tetrachloride contamination is reduced to a more acceptable level. Assume that the ministry decides to issue a shutdown order if a sample of 100 pollution readings implies that $H_0: \mu \le 10$ can be rejected in favour of $H_a: \mu > 10$ by setting $\alpha = 0.01$. If σ equals 2, and a sample mean of 10.37 was recorded, calculate the p value and determine whether or not a shutdown order should be given.

8.80 THE INVESTMENT CASE

Suppose that random samples of 50 returns for each of the following investment classes give the indicated sample mean and sample standard deviation:

Fixed annuities: $\bar{x} = 7.83\%$, $s = 0.51\%$
Domestic large-cap stocks: $\bar{x} = 13.42\%$, $s = 15.17\%$
Domestic midcap stocks: $\bar{x} = 15.03\%$, $s = 18.44\%$
Domestic small-cap stocks: $\bar{x} = 22.51\%$, $s = 21.75\%$

a. For each investment class, set up the null and alternative hypotheses needed to test whether the current mean return differs from the historical (1970 to 1994) mean return given in the data set on *Connect*.

b. Test each hypothesis you set up in part a at the 0.05 level of significance. What do you conclude? For which investment classes does the current mean return differ from the historical mean?

8.81 THE U.K. INSURANCE CASE

Assume that the U.K. insurance survey (see Exercise 6.52 on page 204) is based on 1,000 randomly selected U.K. households and that 640 of these households spent on life insurance in 1993.

a. If p denotes the proportion of all U.K. households that spent on life insurance in 1993, set up the null and alternative hypotheses needed to attempt to justify the claim that more than 60 percent of U.K. households spent on life insurance in 1993.

b. Test the hypotheses you set up in part a by setting $\alpha = 0.10, 0.05, 0.01,$ and 0.001. How much evidence is there that more than 60 percent of U.K. households spent on life insurance in 1993?

8.82 A local factory bags and ships 1-kg bags of sugar. A production manager suspects that the bags are being overfilled. In order to test the claim, a random sample of sixteen 1-kg bags of sugar is obtained and the actual masses of the bags are measured. The sample mean is 1.051 kg with a sample standard deviation of $s = 0.06$ kg. Suppose it is also known that the masses of the bags of sugar have an approximately normal distribution. Use this information to test $H_0: \mu = 1$ kg versus $H_a: \mu > 1$ kg at $\alpha = 0.01$. Is there evidence to support the production manager's claim at the 0.01 level of significance?

8.83 *Consumer Reports* (January 2005) indicates that profit margins on extended warranties are much greater than on the purchase of most products.[4] In this exercise, you will consider a major electronics retailer that wishes to increase the proportion of customers who buy extended warranties on digital cameras. Historically, 20 percent of digital camera customers have purchased the retailer's extended warranty. To increase this percentage, the retailer has decided to offer a new warranty that is less expensive and more comprehensive. Suppose that three months after the company starts to offer the new warranty, a random sample of 500 customer sales invoices shows that 152 out of 500 digital camera customers purchased the new warranty. Letting p denote the proportion of all digital camera customers who have purchased the new warranty, calculate the p value for testing $H_0: p = 0.20$ versus $H_a: p > 0.20$. How much evidence is there that p exceeds 0.20? Does the difference between $\hat{p}$ and 0.2 seem to be practically important? Explain your opinion.

8.84 Business magazines periodically report on the rise of fees and expenses charged by stock funds.

a. Suppose that ten years ago the average annual expense for stock funds was 1.19 percent. Let μ be the current mean annual expense for all stock funds, and assume that stock fund annual expenses are approximately normally distributed. If a random sample of 12 stock funds gives a sample mean annual expense of $\bar{x} = 1.63\%$ with a standard deviation of $s = 0.31\%$, use rejection points and this sample information to test $H_0: \mu \leq 1.19\%$ versus $H_a: \mu > 1.19\%$ by setting α equal to 0.10, 0.05, 0.01, and 0.001. How much evidence is there that the current mean annual expense for stock funds exceeds the average of ten years ago?

b. Do you think that the result in part a has practical importance? Explain your opinion.

8.85 INTERNET EXERCISE

a. Are Canadian consumers comfortable using their credit cards to make purchases over the Internet? Suppose that a noted authority suggests that credit cards will be firmly established on the Internet once the 80 percent barrier is broken, that is, as soon as more than 80 percent of those who make purchases over the Internet are willing to use a credit card to pay for their transactions. Suppose that a recent poll was conducted in which $n = 504$ Internet purchasers were surveyed and it was found that 386 have paid for Internet purchases using a credit card in the past year. According to these results, is there sufficient evidence to suggest that the proportion of Internet purchasers willing to use a credit card now exceeds 80 percent? Set up the appropriate null and alternative hypotheses, and test at the 0.05 and 0.01 levels of significance using a p value.

b. Go to the Ipsos Reid Web site (http://www.ipsos-na.com/news) and find the index of recent poll results (http://www.ipsos-na.com/news-polls). Select an interesting current poll and prepare a brief written summary of the poll or some aspect thereof. Include a statistical test for the significance of a proportion (you may have to make up your own value for the hypothesized proportion p_0) as part of your report. For example, you might select a political poll and test whether a particular party is preferred by a majority of voters ($p > 0.50$).

CHAPTER 9
Statistical Inferences Based on Two Samples

LEARNING OBJECTIVES

After reading this chapter, you should be able to

LO1 determine the difference between a one-tailed test and a two-tailed test

LO2 identify the appropriate formula to use to test your hypothesis (equal variances, unequal variances, variances known, variances unknown) about a difference in population means and proportions

LO3 conduct a hypothesis test for differences in population means using a rejection/critical point and a p value

LO4 conduct a hypothesis test for differences in population proportions using a rejection/critical point and a p value

LO5 understand the difference between the z test and the t test, and when you should use each

LO6 conduct an F test and use it to compare population variances

CHAPTER OUTLINE

9.1 z Tests about a Difference in Population Means: One-Tailed Alternative

9.2 z Tests about a Difference in Population Means: Two-Tailed Alternative

9.3 t Tests about a Difference in Population Means: One-Tailed Alternative

9.4 t Tests about a Difference in Population Means: Two-Tailed Alternative

9.5 z Tests about a Difference in Population Proportions

9.6 F Tests about a Difference in Population Variances

Suppose that you want to compare the average prices for a litre of gasoline in two neighbouring cities in southwestern Ontario. Residents of the smaller city are often heard claiming that gasoline is cheaper on average there than it is in the larger city. Knowing whether or not that statement is true, statistically speaking, could change where you buy gasoline. Maybe it would be worth the drive to the cheaper city once in a while.

In this chapter, we discuss how to conduct hypothesis tests to **compare two populations**. Specifically, we compare two population means, two population variances, and two population proportions. We make these comparisons by studying **differences** and **ratios**. For instance, to compare two

population means, say μ_1 and μ_2, we consider the difference between these means, $\mu_1 - \mu_2$. If, for example, we use a hypothesis test to conclude that $\mu_1 - \mu_2$ is a positive number, then we conclude that μ_1 is greater than μ_2. On the other hand, if a hypothesis test shows that $\mu_1 - \mu_2$ is a negative number, then we conclude that μ_1 is less than μ_2. As another example, if we compare two population variances, say σ_1^2 and σ_2^2, we might consider the ratio σ_1^2/σ_2^2. If this ratio exceeds 1, then we can conclude that σ_1^2 is greater than σ_2^2.

We explain many of this chapter's methods in the context of the three cases listed below:

The Coffee Cup Case: The production supervisor of a plant that produces coffee cups uses hypothesis tests for the difference between two population means to determine which production process yields higher average hourly output, measured in kilograms of coffee cups. By maximizing average hourly output, the plant can increase productivity and improve its profitability.

The Repair Cost Comparison Case: In order to reduce the costs of automobile accident claims, an insurance company uses hypothesis tests for the difference between two population means to compare repair cost estimates for damaged cars at two different garages.

The Advertising Media Case: An advertising agency is test marketing a new product by using one advertising campaign in Toronto and another in Vancouver. The agency conducts a hy- pothesis test for the difference between two population pro- portions to compare the effectiveness of the two advertising campaigns.

 Practise and learn online with *Connect*. Throughout this chapter, questions and tables with online data sets are marked with 🖊 .

9.1 z TESTS ABOUT A DIFFERENCE IN POPULATION MEANS: ONE-TAILED ALTERNATIVE

Consider the bank customer waiting time example. Recall that μ_1 represents the mean waiting time during peak business hours under the current system and μ_2 denotes the mean waiting time for customers under the new system. Random samples of $n_1 = n_2 = 100$ are drawn, and the sample means for the first and second samples are 8.79 minutes and 5.14 minutes, respectively. This yields a difference of 3.65 minutes. Because we know the properties of the sampling distribution of $\bar{X}_1 - \bar{X}_2$, we can easily test a hypothesis about the difference between the mean waiting times.

Now suppose we wish to conduct a one-sided hypothesis test about $\mu_1 - \mu_2$. In the follow- ing box, we describe how we test the null hypothesis H_0: $\mu_1 - \mu_2 = D_0$ versus the two one- sided scenarios H_a: $\mu_1 - \mu_2 > D_0$ and H_a: $\mu_1 - \mu_2 < D_0$. The value of D_0 varies depending on the situation.

LO1 **A One-Tailed z Test about the Difference between Two Population Means: Testing H_0: $\mu_1 - \mu_2 = d_0$ when σ_1 and σ_2 Are Known**

Define the test statistic

$$z = \frac{\bar{x}_1 - \bar{x}_2 - d_0}{\sqrt{\dfrac{\sigma_1^2}{n_1} + \dfrac{\sigma_2^2}{n_2}}}.$$

LO5 Assume that each sampled population is normally dis- tributed, or that each of the sample sizes n_1 and n_2 is

large (n_1, $n_2 > 40$ is more than sufficient). Then, if the samples are independent of each other, we can test H_0: $\mu_1 - \mu_2 = d_0$ versus a particular alternative hypoth- esis at level of significance α by using the appropriate rejection point rule or, equivalently, the correspond- ing p value.

Alternative Hypothesis	Rejection Point Rule: Reject H_0 if	p Value (Reject H_0 if p Value $< \alpha$)
H_a: $\mu_1 - \mu_2 > d_0$	$z > z_\alpha$	The area under the standard normal curve to the right of z
H_a: $\mu_1 - \mu_2 < d_0$	$z < -z_\alpha$	The area under the standard normal curve to the left of z

Often d_0 will be the number 0. In such a case, the null hypothesis H_0: $\mu_1 - \mu_2 = 0$ says there is **no difference** between the population means μ_1 and μ_2. For example, in the bank customer waiting time situation, the null hypothesis H_0: $\mu_1 - \mu_2 = 0$ says there is no difference between the mean customer waiting times under the current and new systems. When d_0 is 0, each alterna- tive hypothesis in the box implies that the population means μ_1 and μ_2 differ. For instance, in the bank customer waiting time situation, the alternative hypothesis H_a: $\mu_1 - \mu_2 > 0$ says that the current mean customer waiting time is longer than the new mean customer waiting time. That is, this alternative hypothesis says that the new system reduces the mean customer waiting time.

Example 9.1 The Bank Customer Waiting Time Case (One-Tailed Alternative)

To attempt to provide evidence supporting the claim that the new system reduces the mean bank customer waiting time, we will test H_0: $\mu_1 - \mu_2 = 0$ versus H_a: $\mu_1 - \mu_2 > 0$ at the *0.05 level of significance*. To perform the hypothesis test, we will use the sample information in Example 7.11 in Chapter 7 to calculate the value of the *test statistic z in the summary box*. Then, since H_a: $\mu_1 - \mu_2 > 0$ is of the form H_a: $\mu_1 - \mu_2 > d_0$, we will *reject H_0*: $\mu_1 - \mu_2 = 0$ *if the value of z is greater than $z_\alpha = z_{0.05} = 1.645$*. Assuming that $\sigma_1^2 = 4.7$ and $\sigma_2^2 = 1.9$, the *value of the test statistic is*

$$z = \frac{\bar{x}_1 - \bar{x}_2 - d_0}{\sqrt{\dfrac{\sigma_1^2}{n_1} + \dfrac{\sigma_2^2}{n_2}}} = \frac{8.79 - 5.14 - 0}{\sqrt{\dfrac{4.7}{100} + \dfrac{1.9}{100}}} = \frac{3.65}{0.2569} = 14.21.$$

LO2

Because z = 14.21 is greater than $z_{0.05} = 1.645$, we reject H_0: $\mu_1 - \mu_2 = 0$ in favour of H_a: $\mu_1 - \mu_2 > 0$. We conclude (at an α of 0.05) that $\mu_1 - \mu_2$ is greater than 0 and, therefore, that the new system reduces the mean customer waiting time. The *p* value for the test is the area under the standard normal curve to the right of $z = 14.21$. Since this *p* value is less than 0.001, we have extremely strong evidence that $\mu_1 - \mu_2$ is greater than 0 and, therefore, that the new system reduces the mean customer waiting time.

BI

Next suppose that because of cost considerations the bank manager wants to implement the new system only if it reduces mean waiting time by more than three minutes. In order to demonstrate that $\mu_1 - \mu_2$ is greater than 3, the manager (setting d_0 equal to 3) will attempt to reject the null hypothesis H_0: $\mu_1 - \mu_2 = 3$ in favour of the alternative hypothesis H_a: $\mu_1 - \mu_2 > 3$ at the 0.05 level of significance. To perform the hypothesis test, we compute

$$z = \frac{\bar{x}_1 - \bar{x}_2 - d_0}{\sqrt{\dfrac{\sigma_1^2}{n_1} + \dfrac{\sigma_2^2}{n_2}}} = \frac{8.79 - 5.14 - 3}{\sqrt{\dfrac{4.7}{100} + \dfrac{1.9}{100}}} = \frac{0.65}{0.2569} = 2.53.$$

Because $z = 2.53$ is greater than $z_{0.05} = 1.645$, we can reject H_0: $\mu_1 - \mu_2 = 3$ in favour of H_a: $\mu_1 - \mu_2 > 3$. The *p* value for the test is the area under the standard normal curve to the right of $z = 2.53$. Table A.3 tells us that this area is $0.5 - 0.4943 = 0.0057$. Therefore, we have very strong evidence against H_0: $\mu_1 - \mu_2 = 3$. In other words, we have very strong evidence that the new system reduces mean waiting time by more than three minutes.

LO3

A 95 percent confidence interval for $\mu_1 - \mu_2$ is

$$\left[\bar{x}_1 - \bar{x}_2 \pm z_{0.025}\sqrt{\frac{\sigma_1^2}{n_1} + \frac{\sigma_2^2}{n_2}} \right] = \left[8.79 - 5.14 \pm 1.96\sqrt{\frac{4.7}{100} + \frac{1.9}{100}} \right]$$

$$= [3.65 \pm 0.5035]$$

$$= [3.15, 4.15].$$

With 95 percent confidence, we believe that the true mean difference in mean waiting times between the old system and the new system is somewhere between 3.15 minutes and 4.15 minutes. In this case, we have strong evidence that the new system has reduced the mean waiting time.

Exercises for Section 9.1

CONCEPTS

9.1 Suppose we want to compare two means, μ_1 and μ_2, using a one-sided hypothesis test. Consider each situation and decide whether or not H_0 would be rejected at $\alpha = 0.05$:
  a. H_a: $\mu_1 - \mu_2 < 0$; $z = -1.79$.
  b. H_a: $\mu_1 - \mu_2 > 0$; $z = 1.79$.
  c. H_a: $\mu_1 - \mu_2 > 4$; $z = -2.01$.
  d. H_a: $\mu_1 - \mu_2 > 0$; $z = 2.17$.
  e. H_a: $\mu_1 - \mu_2 < 0$; $z = -1.24$.
  f. H_a: $\mu_1 - \mu_2 < 4$; $z = -1.15$.

9.2 Determine the significance level, α, of the one-sided hypothesis test for H_0: $\mu_1 - \mu_2 = d_0$ given the following information:
  a. H_a: $\mu_1 - \mu_2 < 1$; $z_\alpha = -1.75$.
  b. H_a: $\mu_1 - \mu_2 > 5$; $z_\alpha = 1.75$.
  c. H_a: $\mu_1 - \mu_2 < 0$; $z_\alpha = -2.05$.
  d. H_a: $\mu_1 - \mu_2 > 10$; $z_\alpha = 2.33$.
  e. H_a: $\mu_1 - \mu_2 > 0$; $z_\alpha = 1.96$.
  f. H_a: $\mu_1 - \mu_2 > 31$; $z_\alpha = 1.88$.

METHODS AND APPLICATIONS

9.3 Suppose we randomly select two independent samples from populations with means μ_1 and μ_2. Suppose $\bar{x}_1 = 25$, $\bar{x}_2 = 20$, $\sigma_1 = 3$, $\sigma_2 = 4$, $n_1 = 100$, and $n_2 = 100$.

  a. Test the null hypothesis $H_0: \mu_1 - \mu_2 = 0$ versus $H_a: \mu_1 - \mu_2 > 0$ by setting $\alpha = 0.05$. What do you conclude about how μ_1 compares to μ_2?

  b. Find the p value for testing $H_0: \mu_1 - \mu_2 = 4$ versus $H_a: \mu_1 - \mu_2 > 4$. Use the p value to test these hypotheses by setting α equal to 0.10, 0.05, 0.01, and 0.001.

9.4 Suppose we select two independent random samples from populations with means μ_1 and μ_2, and suppose that $\bar{x}_1 = 151$, $\bar{x}_2 = 162$, $\sigma_1 = 6$, $\sigma_2 = 8$, $n_1 = 625$, and $n_2 = 625$.

  a. Test the null hypothesis $H_0: \mu_1 - \mu_2 = -10$ versus $H_a: \mu_1 - \mu_2 < -10$ by setting $\alpha = 0.05$. What do you conclude?

  b. Test the null hypothesis $H_0: \mu_1 - \mu_2 = -10$ versus $H_a: \mu_1 - \mu_2 < -10$ by setting α equal to 0.01. What do you conclude?

  c. Find the p value for testing $H_0: \mu_1 - \mu_2 = -10$ versus $H_a: \mu_1 - \mu_2 < -10$. Use the p value to test these hypotheses by setting α equal to 0.10, 0.05, 0.01, and 0.001.

9.5 Some grocery stores have self-serve checkouts. Most people who use the self-serve checkouts do not have a large number of items. We will compare the service times of the express checkout with the service times of the self-serve checkout and see if there is a difference in average service times. Let μ_1 be the average service time for the express checkout and μ_2 be the average service time for the self-serve checkout. Suppose that a random sample of 100 service times in the express checkout gave an average time of 3.7 minutes and a random sample of 100 service times in the self-serve checkout gave an average time of 4.2 minutes. Assume that the samples are independent and that $\sigma_1 = 0.9$ minutes and $\sigma_2 = 1.6$ minutes.

  a. Let μ_1 be the true average service time in the express checkout and μ_2 be the true average service time in the self-serve checkout. Consider testing the null hypothesis $H_0: \mu_1 - \mu_2 = 0$ versus $H_a: \mu_1 - \mu_2 < 0$. Interpret (in practical terms) each of H_0 and H_a.

  b. Use a rejection point to test H_0 at the 0.05 level of significance. Based on this test, what do you conclude about how μ_1 and μ_2 compare? Write your conclusion in practical terms.

  c. Use a p value to test H_0 by setting $\alpha = 0.10, 0.05, 0.01,$ and 0.001. How much evidence is there that μ_1 is less than μ_2?

  d. Calculate a 95 percent confidence interval for the difference in mean service times between the two checkout methods. Based on this interval, can you be 95 percent confident that the mean service time for those who use the express checkout is less than the mean service time for those who use the self-serve checkout? If so, by how much?

9.6 Who drinks more coffee on average, second-year students at the University of Western Ontario or second-year

students at the University of Alberta? Let μ_1 be the average number of cups of coffee drunk per day by University of Western Ontario students and μ_2 be the average number of cups of coffee drunk per day by University of Alberta students. To determine the answer to this question, a random sample of 50 second-year students was taken from each university and the average number of cups of coffee drunk per day was recorded. The results are as follows:

University of Western Ontario	University of Alberta
$\bar{x}_1 = 2.1$	$\bar{x}_2 = 2.9$
$\sigma_1 = 1.0$	$\sigma_2 = 0.8$
$n_1 = 50$	$n_2 = 50$

  a. Set up the null and alternative hypotheses needed to try to establish that the mean number of cups of coffee drunk by second-year students at the University of Alberta is greater than the mean number drunk by second-year students at the University of Western Ontario.

  b. Use rejection points to test the hypotheses you set up in part a by setting α equal to 0.10, 0.05, 0.01, and 0.001. How much evidence is there that second-year students at the University of Alberta drink more coffee on average than their counterparts at the University of Western Ontario?

  c. Calculate a 95 percent confidence interval for the mean difference in cups of coffee drunk by the second-year students at these universities. Based on this interval, can we be 95 percent confident that the mean number of cups of coffee drunk by second-year students at the University of Alberta is higher than the mean number of cups drunk at the University of Western Ontario?

9.7 An Ontario university wishes to demonstrate that car ownership is detrimental to academic achievement. A random sample of 100 students who do not own cars had a mean grade point average (GPA) of 2.68, while a random sample of 100 students who own cars had a mean GPA of 2.55.

  a. Set up the null and alternative hypotheses that should be used to attempt to justify that the mean GPA for students who do not own cars is higher than the mean GPA for car owners.

  b. Test the hypotheses that you set up in part a with $\alpha = 0.05$. Assume that $\sigma_1 = 0.7$ and $\sigma_2 = 0.6$. Interpret the results of this test. That is, what do your results say about whether the university can statistically justify that car ownership hurts academic achievement?

9.8 In the *Journal of Marketing*, Bayus studied differences between "early replacement buyers" and "late replacement buyers." Suppose that a random sample of 800 early replacement buyers yields a mean number of automobile dealers visited of $\bar{x}_1 = 3.3$, and that a random sample of 500 late replacement buyers yields a mean number of dealers visited of $\bar{x}_2 = 4.5$. Assume that these samples are independent and that $\sigma_1 = 0.71$ and $\sigma_2 = 0.66$.

a. Set up the null and alternative hypotheses needed to attempt to show that the mean number of dealers visited by late replacement buyers exceeds the mean number of dealers visited by early replacement buyers by more than 1.

b. Test the hypotheses you set up in part a by using rejection points and by setting α equal to 0.10, 0.05, 0.01, and 0.001. How much evidence is there that H_0 should be rejected?

c. Find the p value for testing the hypotheses you set up in part a. Use the p value to test these hypotheses with α equal to 0.10, 0.05, 0.01, and 0.001. How much evidence is there that H_0 should be rejected? Explain your conclusion in practical terms.

d. Do you think that the results of the hypothesis tests in parts b and c have practical significance? Explain and justify your answer.

9.9   Students in a large statistics course at a British Columbia university were concerned that the average test scores were much lower on their second term test than on their first term test. Suppose that it was known that the standard

deviations for the first and second term tests were $\sigma_1 = 8$ and $\sigma_1 = 10$, respectively. Independent random samples of 45 test scores were taken from the first and second tests and the means were 72 and 65, respectively.

Let μ_1 be the mean score from the first test and μ_2 be the mean score from the second test.

a. Set up the null and alternative hypotheses needed to try to establish whether or not the average on the second term test was lower than the average on the first term test.

b. Use a rejection point to test the hypotheses you set up in part a by setting α equal to 0.01. How much evidence is there that the average on the second term test was lower than the average on the first term test?

c. Use a p value to test H_0 by setting $\alpha = 0.10$, 0.05, 0.01, and 0.001. How much evidence is there that the mean score from test two is lower than the mean score from test one?

d. Let μ_1 be the mean score from the first test and μ_2 be the mean score from the second test. Construct a 95 percent confidence interval for $\mu_1 - \mu_2$. Based on this interval, can you be 95 percent confident that the test scores were lower on the second test?

9.2 z TESTS ABOUT A DIFFERENCE IN POPULATION MEANS: TWO-TAILED ALTERNATIVE

Suppose we wish to conduct a two-sided hypothesis test about $\mu_1 - \mu_2$. In the following box, we describe how this can be done. Here we test the null hypothesis $H_0: \mu_1 - \mu_2 = D_0$, where D_0 is a number whose value varies depending on the situation.

A Two-Tailed z Test about the Difference between Two Population Means: Testing $H_0: \mu_1 - \mu_2 = d_0$ when σ_1 and σ_2 Are Known   LO1

Define the test statistic

$$z = \frac{\bar{x}_1 - \bar{x}_2 - d_0}{\sqrt{\dfrac{\sigma_1^2}{n_1} + \dfrac{\sigma_2^2}{n_2}}}.$$

Assume that each sampled population is normally distributed, or that each of the sample sizes n_1 and n_2 is

large. Then, if the samples are independent of each other, we can test $H_0: \mu_1 - \mu_2 = d_0$ versus a particular alternative hypothesis at level of significance α by using the appropriate rejection point rule or, equivalently, the corresponding p value.

Alternative Hypothesis	Rejection Point Rule: Reject H_0 if	p Value (Reject H_0 if p Value $< \alpha$)
$H_a: \mu_1 - \mu_2 \neq d_0$	$|z| > z_{\alpha/2}$—that is, $z > z_{\alpha/2}$ or $z < -z_{\alpha/2}$	Twice the area under the standard normal curve to the right of $|z|$

It is often the case that d_0 will be 0. In such a case, the null hypothesis $H_0: \mu_1 - \mu_2 = 0$ says there is *no difference* between the underlying population means. For example, in the bank customer waiting time case, the alternative hypothesis $H_a: \mu_1 - \mu_2 \neq 0$ says that the mean waiting times are *different* from one another. Notice that this time we are not specifying that the difference is greater than or less than zero specifically. Now we are just saying that the mean waiting times are *different*. Now the alternative hypothesis says that the new system results in a different mean customer waiting time than the old system.

Example 9.2 The Bank Customer Waiting Time Case (Two-Tailed Alternative)

To attempt to provide evidence supporting the claim that the new system produces a different mean bank customer waiting time, we will test $H_0: \mu_1 - \mu_2 = 0$ versus $H_a: \mu_1 - \mu_2 \neq 0$ at the **0.05 level of significance**. To perform the hypothesis test, we will use the sample information in Example 7.11 in Chapter 7 to calculate the value of the **test statistic z in the summary box**. Then, since $H_a: \mu_1 - \mu_2 \neq 0$ is of the form $H_a: \mu_1 - \mu_2 \neq D_0$, we will **reject $H_0: \mu_1 - \mu_2 = 0$ if the value of $|z|$ is greater than $z_{\alpha/2} = z_{0.025} = 1.96$**. Assuming that $\sigma_1^2 = 4.7$ and $\sigma_2^2 = 1.9$, the **value of the test statistic is**

$$z = \frac{\bar{x}_1 - \bar{x}_2 - d_0}{\sqrt{\dfrac{\sigma_1^2}{n_1} + \dfrac{\sigma_2^2}{n_2}}} = \frac{8.79 - 5.14 - 0}{\sqrt{\dfrac{4.7}{100} + \dfrac{1.9}{100}}} = \frac{3.65}{0.2569} = 14.21.$$

LO3

BI

Because $z = 14.21$ is greater than $z_{0.025} = 1.96$, we reject $H_0: \mu_1 - \mu_2 = 0$ in favour of $H_a: \mu_1 - \mu_2 \neq 0$. We conclude (at an α of 0.05) that $\mu_1 - \mu_2$ is not equal to 0 and, therefore, that there is a difference in the mean customer waiting times.

Exercises for Section 9.2

METHODS AND APPLICATIONS

9.10 Suppose we select two independent random samples from populations with means μ_1 and μ_2, and suppose that $\bar{x}_1 = 151$, $\bar{x}_2 = 162$, $\sigma_1 = 6$, $\sigma_2 = 8$, $n_1 = 625$, and $n_2 = 625$. Find the p value for testing $H_0: \mu_1 - \mu_2 = -10$ versus $H_a: \mu_1 - \mu_2 \neq -10$. Use the p value to test these hypotheses by setting α equal to 0.10, 0.05, 0.01, and 0.001.

9.11 In an article in the *Journal of Management*, Wright and Bonett study the relationship between voluntary organizational turnover and such factors as work performance, work satisfaction, and company tenure. As part of the study, the authors compare work performance ratings for "stayers" (employees who stay in their organization) and "leavers" (employees who voluntarily quit their jobs). Suppose that a random sample of 175 stayers has a mean performance rating (on a 20-point scale) of $\bar{x}_1 = 12.8$ and that a random sample of 140 leavers has a mean performance rating of $\bar{x}_2 = 14.7$. Assume that these random samples are independent and that $\sigma_1 = 3.7$ and $\sigma_2 = 4.5$.
   a. Set up the null and alternative hypotheses needed to try to establish that the mean performance rating for leavers is different from the mean performance rating for stayers.
   b. Use rejection points to test the hypotheses you set up in part a by setting α equal to 0.10, 0.05, 0.01, and 0.001. How much evidence is there that leavers have a different mean performance rating than do stayers?

9.12 In the book *Essentials of Marketing Research*, Dillon, Madden, and Firtle discuss a corporate image study designed to find out whether perceptions of technical support services vary depending on the position of the respondent in the organization. The management of a

company that supplies telephone cable to telephone companies commissioned a media campaign primarily designed to

(1) increase awareness of the company and
(2) create favourable perceptions of the company's technical support. The campaign was targeted to purchasing managers and technical managers at independent telephone companies with greater than 10,000 trunk lines.

Perceptual ratings were measured using a nine-point agree–disagree scale. Suppose the results of a telephone survey of 175 technical managers and 125 purchasing managers reveal that the mean perception score for technical managers is 7.3 and the mean perception score for purchasing managers is 8.2.
   a. Let μ_1 be the mean perception score for all purchasing managers, and let μ_2 be the mean perception score for all technical managers. Set up the null and alternative hypotheses needed to establish whether the mean perception scores for purchasing managers and technical managers differ. *Hint:* If μ_1 and μ_2 do not differ, what does $\mu_1 - \mu_2$ equal?
   b. Assuming that the samples of 175 technical managers and 125 purchasing managers are independent random samples, test the hypotheses you set up in part a by using a rejection point with $\alpha = 0.05$. Assume here that $\sigma_1 = 1.6$ and $\sigma_2 = 1.4$. What do you conclude about whether the mean perception scores for purchasing managers and technical managers differ?
   c. Find the p value for testing the hypotheses you set up in part a. Use the p value to test these hypotheses by setting α equal to 0.10, 0.05, 0.01, and 0.001. How much evidence is there that the mean perception scores for purchasing managers and technical managers differ?

9.3 *t* TESTS ABOUT A DIFFERENCE IN POPULATION MEANS: ONE-TAILED ALTERNATIVE

In Section 7.5, we learned how to calculate a confidence interval for $\mu_1 - \mu_2$ when the population variances were not known but were assumed to be equal. Now suppose we wish to test a hypothesis about $\mu_1 - \mu_2$ under these same circumstances. In the following box, we describe how this can be done using a one-tailed test.

Here we test the null hypothesis H_0: $\mu_1 - \mu_2 = D_0$, where D_0 is a number whose value varies depending on the situation. Often D_0 will be the number 0. In such a case, the null hypothesis H_0: $\mu_1 - \mu_2 = 0$ says there is *no difference* between the population means μ_1 and μ_2. In this case, each alternative hypothesis in the box implies that the population means μ_1 and μ_2 differ in a particular way.

A One-Tailed *t* Test about the Difference between Two Population Means: Testing H_0: $\mu_1 - \mu_2 = d_0$ when $\sigma_1^2 = \sigma_2^2$ **LO1**

Define the test statistic

$$t = \frac{\bar{x}_1 - \bar{x}_2 - d_0}{\sqrt{s_p^2\left(\dfrac{1}{n_1} + \dfrac{1}{n_2}\right)}},$$

where

$$s_p^2 = \frac{(n_1 - 1)s_1^2 + (n_2 - 1)s_2^2}{n_1 + n_2 - 1}$$

and assume that the sampled populations are normally distributed with equal variances. Then, if the samples are independent of each other, we can test H_0: $\mu_1 - \mu_2 = d_0$ versus a particular alternative hypothesis at level of significance α by using the appropriate rejection point rule or, equivalently, the corresponding *p* value.   **LO5**

Alternative Hypothesis	Rejection Point Rule: Reject H_0 if	*p* Value (Reject H_0 if *p* Value $< \alpha$)
H_a: $\mu_1 - \mu_2 > d_0$	$t > t_\alpha$	The area under the *t* distribution curve to the right of *t*
H_a: $\mu_1 - \mu_2 < d_0$	$t < -t_\alpha$	The area under the *t* distribution curve to the left of *t*

Here t_α and the *p* values are based on $n_1 + n_2 - 2$ degrees of freedom.

Example 9.3   The Coffee Cup Case (One-Tailed *t* Test)

In order to compare the mean hourly yields obtained by using the Java and Joe production methods, we will test H_0: $\mu_1 - \mu_2 = 0$ versus H_a: $\mu_1 - \mu_2 > 0$ at the **0.05 level of significance**. To perform the hypothesis test, we will use the sample information in Figure 9.1 on the next page to calculate the value of the **test statistic *t* in the summary box**. Then, since H_a: $\mu_1 - \mu_2 > 0$ is of the form H_a: $\mu_1 - \mu_2 > d_0$, we will **reject H_0: $\mu_1 - \mu_2 = 0$ if *t* is greater than $t_\alpha = t_{0.05} =$ 1.860**. Here the t_α point is based on $n_1 + n_2 - 2 = 5 + 5 - 2 = 8$ degrees of freedom. Using the data in Figure 9.1, the **value of the test statistic** is

$$t = \frac{\bar{x}_1 - \bar{x}_2 - d_0}{\sqrt{s_p^2\left(\dfrac{1}{n_1} + \dfrac{1}{n_2}\right)}} = \frac{811 - 750.2 - 0}{\sqrt{435.1\left(\dfrac{1}{5} + \dfrac{1}{5}\right)}} = 4.6087.$$ **LO2**

Because $t = 4.6087$ is greater than $t_{0.05} = 1.860$, we can reject H_0: $\mu_1 - \mu_2 = 0$ in favour of H_a: $\mu_1 - \mu_2 > 0$. We conclude (at an α of 0.05) that the mean hourly yields obtained by using the two production methods differ.   **BI LO3**

Figure 9.1(a) and (b) gives the MegaStat and Excel outputs for testing H_0 versus H_a. The outputs tell us that $t = 4.61$ and that the associated *p* value is 0.001736 (rounded to 0.0017 on the MegaStat output). The very small *p* value tells us that we have very strong

FIGURE 9.1   MegaStat and Excel Outputs for Testing the Equality of Means in the Coffee Cup Comparison Case Assuming Equal Variances

(a) The MegaStat output

Hypothesis Test: Independent Groups
(t-test, pooled variance)

Java	Joe			
811.00	750.20	mean	4.61 t	
19.65	22.00	std. dev.	0.0017 p-value (two-tailed)	
5	5	n	30.378 confidence interval 95% lower	
			91.222 confidence interval 95% upper	

8 df
60.800 difference (Java - Joe)
435.100 pooled variance
20.859 pooled std. dev.
13.192 standard error of difference
0 hypothesized difference

F-test for equality of variance

484.20 variance: Joe
386.00 variance: Java
1.25 F
0.8314 p-value

(b) The Excel output

t-Test: Two-Sample Assuming Equal Variances

	Java	Joe
Mean	811	750.2
Variance	386	484.2
Observations	5	5
Pooled Variance	435.1	
Hypothesized Mean Diff	0	
df	8	
t Stat	4.608706	
P(T<=t) one-tail	0.000868	
t Critical one-tail	1.859548	
P(T<=t) two-tail	0.001736	
t Critical two-tail	2.306004	

evidence against H_0: $\mu_1 - \mu_2 = 0$ and in favour of H_a: $\mu_1 - \mu_2 > 0$. In other words, we have very strong evidence that the mean hourly yields obtained by using the two production methods differ. Finally, notice that the MegaStat output gives the 95 percent confidence interval for $\mu_1 - \mu_2$, which is [30.378, 91.222].

When the sampled populations are normally distributed and the population variances σ_1^2 and σ_2^2 differ, the following can be shown:

A One-Tailed t Test of H_0: $\mu_1 = \mu_2 = D_0$ when $\sigma_1^2 \neq \sigma_2^2$

1   When the sample sizes n_1 and n_2 are equal, the equal-variances hypothesis test given in the preceding box is approximately valid even if the population variances σ_1^2 and σ_2^2 differ substantially. As a rough rule of thumb, if the larger sample variance is not more than three times the smaller sample variance when the sample sizes are equal, we can use the equal-variances test. We will learn more formal testing procedures for variances later in the chapter.

2   Suppose that the larger sample variance is more than three times the smaller sample variance when the sample sizes are equal, or suppose that both the sample sizes and the sample variances differ substantially. Then we can use the approximate unequal-variances procedure.

We can test H_0: $\mu_1 - \mu_2 = d_0$ by using the test statistic

$$t = \frac{\bar{x}_1 - \bar{x}_2 - d_0}{\sqrt{\dfrac{s_1^2}{n_1} + \dfrac{s_2^2}{n_2}}}$$

and by using the previously given rejection point and p value conditions.

For the test, the degrees of freedom are equal to

$$df = \frac{(s_1^2/n_1 + s_2^2/n_2)^2}{\dfrac{(s_1^2/n_1)^2}{n_1 - 1} + \dfrac{(s_2^2/n_2)^2}{n_2 - 1}}.$$

Here, if df is not a whole number, we will always round it down to the next smallest whole number.

To illustrate the unequal-variances procedure, consider the bank customer waiting time situation. Recall that the bank manager wants to implement the new system only if it reduces the mean waiting time by more than three minutes. Therefore, the manager will test the **null hypothesis H_0: $\mu_1 - \mu_2 = 3$ versus the alternative hypothesis H_a: $\mu_1 - \mu_2 > 3$.** If H_0 can be rejected in favour of H_a at the **0.05 level of significance**, the manager will implement the new system. Suppose that a random sample of $n_1 = 100$ waiting times observed under the current system gives a sample mean of $\bar{x}_1 = 8.79$ and a sample variance of $s_1^2 = 4.8237$. Further, suppose a random sample of $n_2 = 100$ waiting times observed during the trial run of the new system yields a sample mean of $\bar{x}_2 = 5.14$ and a sample variance of $s_2^2 = 1.7927$. Since each sample is large, we can use the **unequal-variances test statistic t in the summary box**. The degrees of freedom for this statistic are

$$df = \frac{(s_1^2/n_1 + s_2^2/n_2)^2}{\dfrac{(s_1^2/n_1)^2}{n_1 - 1} + \dfrac{(s_2^2/n_2)^2}{n_2 - 1}}$$

$$= \frac{[4.8237/100 + 1.7927/100]^2}{\dfrac{(4.8237/100)^2}{99} + \dfrac{(1.7927/100)^2}{99}}$$

$$= 163.657,$$

which we will round down to 163. Therefore, since H_a: $\mu_1 - \mu_2 > 3$ is of the form H_a: $\mu_1 - \mu_2 > d_0$, we will **reject H_0: $\mu_1 - \mu_2 = 3$ if the value of the test statistic t is greater than $t_\alpha = t_{0.05} = 1.65$** (which is based on 163 degrees of freedom and was found using a computer). Using the sample data, the **value of the test statistic** is

$$t = \frac{\bar{x}_1 - \bar{x}_2 - 3}{\sqrt{\dfrac{s_1^2}{n_1} + \dfrac{s_2^2}{n_2}}} = \frac{8.79 - 5.14 - 3}{\sqrt{\dfrac{4.8237}{100} + \dfrac{1.7927}{100}}} = \frac{0.65}{0.25722} = 2.53.$$

LO2

Because $t = 2.53$ is greater than $t_{0.05} = 1.65$, we reject H_0: $\mu_1 - \mu_2 = 3$ in favour of H_a: $\mu_1 - \mu_2 > 3$. We conclude (at an α of 0.05) that $\mu_1 - \mu_2$ is greater than 3 and, therefore, that the new system reduces the mean customer waiting time by more than three minutes. Therefore, the bank manager will implement the new system.

LO3

BI

Figure 9.2 gives the MegaStat output of using the unequal-variances procedure to test H_0: $\mu_1 - \mu_2 = 3$ versus H_a: $\mu_1 - \mu_2 > 3$. The output tells us that $t = 2.53$ and that the associated p value is 0.0062. The very small p value tells us that we have very strong evidence against H_0: $\mu_1 - \mu_2 = 3$. That is, we have very strong evidence that $\mu_1 - \mu_2$ is greater than 3 and, therefore, that the new system reduces the mean customer waiting time by more than three minutes.

Next, we will consider a hypothesis about μ_d, the mean of a population of paired differences. We show how to test the null hypothesis

$$H_0: \mu_d = d_0$$

in the box at the top of the next page. Here the value of the constant d_0 depends on the particular problem. Often d_0 equals 0, and the null hypothesis H_0: $\mu_d = 0$ says that μ_1 and μ_2 do not differ.

FIGURE 9.2 MegaStat Output of the Unequal-Variances Procedure for the Bank Customer Waiting Time Situation

Hypothesis Test: Independent Groups (t-test, unequal variance)				
Current	New		163	df
8.79	5.14	**mean**	3.65000	difference (Current - New)
2.1963	1.3389	**std. dev.**	0.25722	standard error of difference
100	100	**n**	3	hypothesized difference
			2.53	t
F-test for equality of variance			0.0062	p-value (one-tailed, upper)
2.69	F		3.14208	confidence interval 95.% lower
1.46E-06	p-value		4.15792	confidence interval 95.% upper
			0.50792	half-width

LO1 **A One-Tailed Hypothesis Test about the Mean, μ_d, of a Population of Paired Differences: Testing H_0: $\mu_d = d_0$**

Assume that the population of paired differences is normally distributed, and consider testing

$$H_0: \mu_d = d_0$$

LO5 by using the test statistic

$$t = \frac{\bar{d} - d_0}{s_d/\sqrt{n}}.$$

We can test H_0: $\mu_d = d_0$ versus a particular alternative hypothesis at level of significance α by using the appropriate rejection point rule or, equivalently, the corresponding p value.

Alternative Hypothesis	Rejection Point Rule: Reject H_0 if	p Value (Reject H_0 if p Value $< \alpha$)
H_a: $\mu_d > d_0$	$t > t_\alpha$	The area under the t distribution curve to the right of t
H_a: $\mu_d < d_0$	$t < -t_\alpha$	The area under the t distribution curve to the left of t

Here t_α and the p values are based on $n - 1$ degrees of freedom.

Example 9.4 The Repair Cost Comparison Case (One-Tailed t Test)

LO2

BI

LO3

Forest City Casualty currently contracts to have moderately damaged cars repaired at garage 2. However, a local insurance agent suggests that garage 1 provides less expensive repair service that is of equal quality. Because it has done business with garage 2 for years, Forest City has decided to give some of its repair business to garage 1 only if it has very strong evidence that μ_1, the mean repair cost estimate at garage 1, is smaller than μ_2, the mean repair cost estimate at garage 2— that is, if $\mu_d = \mu_1 - \mu_2$ is less than zero. Therefore, we will test H_0: $\mu_d = 0$ or, equivalently, H_0: $\mu_1 - \mu_2 = 0$, versus H_a: $\mu_d < 0$ or, equivalently, H_a: $\mu_1 - \mu_2 < 0$, at the 0.01 level of significance. To perform the hypothesis test, we will use the sample data in Table 9.1 to calculate the value of the test statistic t in the summary box. Since H_a: $\mu_d < 0$ is of the form H_a: $\mu_d < D_0$, we will reject H_0: $\mu_d = 0$ if the value of t is less than $-t_\alpha = -t_{0.01} = -3.143$. Here the t_α point is based on $n - 1 = 7 - 1 = 6$ degrees of freedom. Using the data in Table 9.1, the value of the test statistic is

$$t = \frac{\bar{d} - d_0}{s_d/\sqrt{n}} = \frac{-0.8 - 0}{0.5033/\sqrt{7}} = -4.2053.$$

Because $t = -4.2053$ is less than $-t_{0.01} = -3.143$, we can reject H_0: $\mu_d = 0$ in favour of H_a: $\mu_d < 0$. We conclude (at an α of 0.01) that μ_1, the mean repair cost estimate at garage 1, is less than μ_2, the mean repair cost estimate at garage 2. As a result, Forest City will give some of its repair business to garage 1. Furthermore, Figure 9.3(a), which gives the Excel output of this hypothesis test, shows us that the p value for the test is 0.003. Since this p value is very small, we have very strong evidence that H_0 should be rejected and that μ_1 is less than μ_2.

To demonstrate testing a not equal to alternative hypothesis, Figure 9.3(b) gives the MegaStat output of testing H_0: $\mu_d = 0$ versus H_a: $\mu_d \neq 0$. The output shows that the p value for this two-tailed test is 0.0057.

A 95 percent confidence interval for $\mu_d = \mu_1 - \mu_2$ is

$$\left[\bar{d} \pm t_{0.025}\left(\frac{s_d}{\sqrt{n}} \right) \right] = \left[-0.8 \pm 2.447\left(\frac{0.5033}{\sqrt{7}} \right) \right]$$
$$= [-0.8 \pm 0.4654]$$
$$= [-1.2654, -0.3346].$$

This interval says that Forest City Casualty can by 95 percent confident that μ_d, the mean of all possible paired differences of the repair cost estimates at garages 1 and 2, is between

TABLE 9.1   A Sample of $n = 7$ Paired Differences of the Repair Cost Estimates at Garages 1 and 2 (Cost Estimates in Hundreds of Dollars)

Sample of $n = 7$ Damaged Cars	Repair Cost Estimates at Garage 1	Repair Cost Estimates at Garage 2	Sample of $n = 7$ Paired Differences
Car 1	$ 7.1	$ 7.9	$d_1 = -0.8$
Car 2	9.0	10.1	$d_2 = -1.1$
Car 3	11.0	12.2	$d_3 = -1.2$
Car 4	8.9	8.8	$d_4 = 0.1$
Car 5	9.9	10.4	$d_5 = -0.5$
Car 6	9.1	9.8	$d_6 = -0.7$
Car 7	10.3	11.7	$d_7 = -1.4$
	$\bar{x}_1 = 9.329$	$\bar{x}_2 = 10.129$	$\bar{d} = -0.8 = \bar{x}_1 - \bar{x}_2$
			$s_d^2 = 0.2533$
			$s_d = 0.5033$

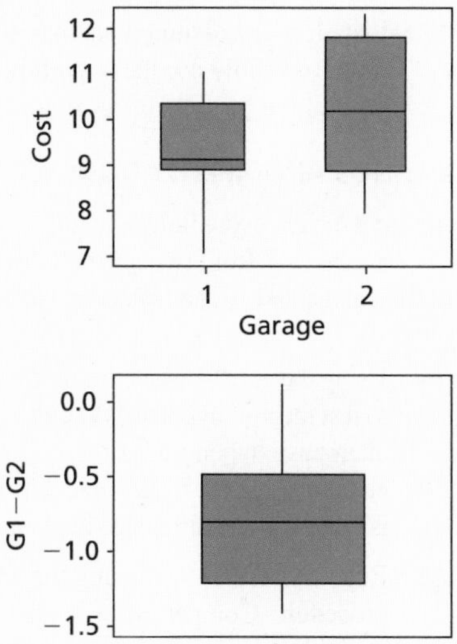

FIGURE 9.3   Excel and MegaStat Outputs of Testing H_0: $\mu_d = 0$

(a) Excel output of testing H_0: $\mu_d = 0$ versus H_a: $\mu_d < 0$

Paired t-Test: Garage1 — Garage2

	Garage 1	Garage 2
Mean	9.328571	10.12857
Variance	1.562381	2.279048
Observations	7	7
Pearson Correlation	0.950744	
Hypothesized Mean Difference	0	
df	6	
t Stat	-4.20526	
P(T<=t) one-tail	0.002826	
t Critical one-tail	1.94318	
P(T<=t) two-tail	0.005653	
t Critical two-tail	2.446912	

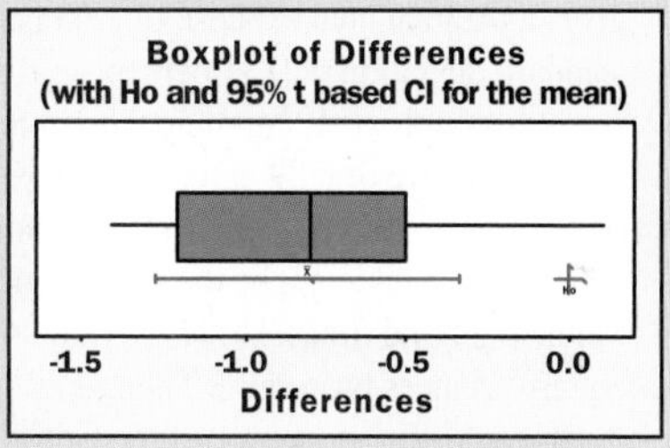

Boxplot of Differences
(with Ho and 95% t based CI for the mean)

(b) MegaStat output of testing H_0: $\mu_d = 0$ versus H_a: $\mu_d \neq 0$

Hypothesis Test: Paired Observations

0.0000	hypothesized value
9.3286	mean Garage1
10.1286	mean Garage2
-0.8000	mean difference (Garage1 - Garage2)
0.5033	std. dev.
0.1902	std. error
7	n
6	df
-4.21	t
0.0057	p-value (two-tailed)

−$126.54 and −$33.46. That is, we are 95 percent confident that μ_1, the mean of all possible repair cost estimates at garage 1, is between $33.46 and $126.54 lower than μ_2, the mean of all possible repair cost estimates at garage 2.

Exercises for Section 9.3

CONCEPTS

9.13 List all of the assumptions that must be satisfied in order to validly use the hypothesis test described in each of the formula boxes in this section.

METHODS AND APPLICATIONS

Suppose we have taken independent, random samples of sizes $n_1 = 7$ and $n_2 = 7$ from two normally distributed populations with means μ_1 and μ_2, and suppose we obtain $\bar{x}_1 = 240$, $\bar{x}_2 = 210$, $s_1 = 5$, and $s_2 = 6$.

9.14 Using the equal-variances procedure, use rejection points to test the null hypothesis $H_0: \mu_1 - \mu_2 \leq 20$ versus the alternative hypothesis $H_a: \mu_1 - \mu_2 > 20$ by setting α equal to 0.10, 0.05, 0.01, and 0.001. How much evidence is there that the difference between μ_1 and μ_2 exceeds 20?

9.15 Repeat Exercise 9.14 using the unequal-variances procedure. Compare your results to those obtained using the equal-variances procedure.

9.16 The October 7, 1991, issue of *Fortune* magazine reported on the rapid rise of fees and expenses charged by mutual funds. Assuming that stock fund expenses and municipal bond fund expenses are each approximately normally distributed, suppose a random sample of 12 stock funds gives a mean annual expense of 1.63 percent with a standard deviation of 0.31 percent, and an independent random sample of 12 municipal bond funds gives a mean annual expense of 0.89 percent with a standard deviation of 0.23 percent. Let μ_1 be the mean annual expense for stock funds, and let μ_2 be the mean annual expense for municipal bond funds. Do parts a and b by using the equal-variances procedure. Then repeat parts a and b using the unequal-variances procedure. Compare your results.

    a. Set up the null and alternative hypotheses needed to attempt to establish that the mean annual expense for stock funds is larger than the mean annual expense for municipal bond funds. Test these hypotheses at the 0.05 level of significance. What do you conclude?

    b. Set up the null and alternative hypotheses needed to attempt to establish that the mean annual expense for stock funds exceeds the mean annual expense for municipal bond funds by more than 0.5 percentage points. Test these hypotheses at the 0.05 level of significance. What do you conclude?

9.17 A real estate agent employs two appraisers to estimate the value of houses for sale, and wonders whether one appraiser (A) is better than the other (B). As a test, he has each of them appraise the same five randomly selected houses. The results are given below:

House	Appraised Value (in $1000s)	
	A	*B*
1	194	181
2	160	155
3	239	232
4	216	206
5	236	221

    a. Set up the null and alternative hypotheses needed to attempt to establish that the appraised values by appraiser *A* are less than the appraised values by appraiser *B*, on average.

    b. Test H_0 at the 0.05 level of significance using the appropriate *p* value. What can you conclude at the 0.05 significance level?

9.18 A loan officer compares the interest rates for 48-month fixed-rate auto loans and 48-month variable-rate auto loans. Two independent, random samples of auto loan rates are selected. A sample of eight 48-month fixed-rate auto loans had the following loan rates:

| 10.29% | 9.75% | 9.50% | 9.99% |
| 9.75% | 9.99% | 11.40% | 10.00% |

A sample of five 48-month variable-rate auto loans had loan rates as follows:

    9.59%   8.75%   8.99%   8.50%   9.00%

    a. Set up the null and alternative hypotheses needed to determine whether the mean rates for 48-month fixed-rate and variable-rate auto loans differ by more than 0.4 percentage points.

    b. Use a hypothesis test to establish that the difference between the mean rates for fixed- and variable-rate 48-month auto loans exceeds 0.4 percentage points. Use α equal to 0.05.

9.19 Suppose a sample of 11 paired differences that has been randomly selected from a normally distributed population of paired differences yields a sample mean of $\bar{d} = 103.5$ and a sample standard deviation of $s_d = 5$.

    a. Test the null hypothesis $H_0: \mu_d \leq 100$ versus $H_a: \mu_d > 100$ by setting α equal to 0.05 and 0.01. How much evidence is there that $\mu_d = \mu_1 - \mu_2$ exceeds 100?

    b. Test the null hypothesis $H_0: \mu_d \geq 110$ versus $H_a: \mu_d < 110$ by setting α equal to 0.05 and 0.01. How much evidence is there that $\mu_d = \mu_1 - \mu_2$ is less than 110?

9.20 Suppose a sample of 49 paired differences that have been randomly selected from a normally distributed population of paired differences yields a sample mean of $\bar{d} = 5$ and a sample standard deviation of $s_d = 7$. Find the *p* value for testing $H_0: \mu_d \leq 3$ versus $H_a: \mu_d > 3$. Use the *p* value to test these hypotheses with α equal to 0.10, 0.05, 0.01, and 0.001. How much evidence is there that μ_d exceeds 3? What does this say about the size of the difference between μ_1 and μ_2?

9.21 Ten runners were asked to run a 5-km race in each of two consecutive weeks. The runners wore one brand of shoe in one race and a second brand in the other race. The brand worn in each race is randomly determined. The runners were timed and asked to do their best during each race. The results, in minutes, are given on the next page:

Runner	Brand *A*	Brand *B*
1	15.74	15.99
2	14.98	14.87
3	16.11	15.87
4	15.44	15.93
5	15.37	15.79
6	14.83	14.66
7	15.15	15.49
8	16.02	16.36
9	15.29	15.12
10	14.76	15.01

Assume that the differences between pairs of race times are normally distributed.

a. Set up the null and alternative hypotheses needed to attempt to establish that brand *A* shoes yield lower times than brand *B* shoes.

b. Use a *p* value to test the hypotheses you set up in part a at the 0.10, 0.05, 0.01, and 0.001 levels of significance. How much evidence is there that brand *A* shoes yield lower times than brand *B* shoes?

9.22 To compare the fuel efficiency of two types of gasoline, five cars were randomly selected, the type of gasoline used was randomly determined, and the fuel efficiency obtained using each type was recorded below (in litres per 100 km) for each car:

Car	Type *A*	Type *B*
1	8.4	7.9
2	7.8	7.1
3	11.3	10.9
4	8.1	7.3
5	6.6	5.7

Assume that the differences between pairs of fuel efficiencies are normally distributed.

a. Set up the null and alternative hypotheses needed to attempt to establish that type *B* gasoline provides better average fuel efficiency than type *A* gasoline.

b. Use a *p* value to test the hypotheses you set up in part a at the 0.10, 0.05, 0.01, and 0.001 levels of significance. How much evidence is there that type *B* gasoline yields better fuel efficiency, on average, than type *A* gasoline?

c. Calculate a 95 percent confidence interval for the mean difference in fuel efficiency for the two types of gasoline.

d. Can you be 95 percent confident that there is a difference in mean fuel efficiency between the different gasoline types? Justify your answer.

9.4 *t* TESTS ABOUT A DIFFERENCE IN POPULATION MEANS: TWO-TAILED ALTERNATIVE

In the last section, we learned how to conduct a one-sided *t* test for $\mu_1 - \mu_2$ when the population variances were unknown and equal and unknown and not equal. In the following box, we describe how this can be done using a two-tailed test:

A Two-Tailed *t* Test about the Difference between Two Population Means: Testing H_0: $\mu_1 - \mu_2 = d_0$ when $\sigma_1^2 = \sigma_2^2$ **LO1**

Define the test statistic

$$t = \frac{\bar{x}_1 - \bar{x}_2 - d_0}{\sqrt{s_p^2\left(\frac{1}{n_1} + \frac{1}{n_2}\right)}}$$

and assume that the sampled populations are normally distributed with equal variances. Then, if the samples

are independent of each other, we can test H_0: $\mu_1 - \mu_2 = d_0$ versus a particular alternative hypothesis at level of significance α by using the appropriate rejection point rule or, equivalently, the corresponding *p* value.

Alternative Hypothesis	Rejection Point Rule: Reject H_0 if	*p* Value (Reject H_0 if *p* Value $< \alpha$)
H_a: $\mu_1 - \mu_2 \neq d_0$	$\|t\| > t_{\alpha/2}$—that is, $t > t_{\alpha/2}$ or $t < -t_{\alpha/2}$	Twice the area under the *t* distribution curve to the right of $\|t\|$

Here $t_{\alpha/2}$ and the *p* values are based on $n_1 + n_2 - 2$ degrees of freedom.

Example 9.5 The Coffee Cup Case (Two-Tailed t Test)

In order to compare the mean hourly yields obtained by using the Java and Joe methods, we will test H_0: $\mu_1 - \mu_2 = 0$ versus H_a: $\mu_1 - \mu_2 \neq 0$ at the *0.05 level of significance.* To perform the hypothesis test, we will use the sample information in Figure 9.1 on page 296 to calculate the value of the *test statistic t in the summary box.* Then, since H_a: $\mu_1 - \mu_2 \neq 0$ is of the form H_a: $\mu_1 - \mu_2 \neq d_0$, we will *reject H_0: $\mu_1 - \mu_2 = 0$ if the absolute value of t is greater than* $t_{\alpha/2} = t_{0.025} = 2.306$. Here the $t_{\alpha/2}$ point is based on $n_1 + n_2 - 2 = 5 + 5 - 2 = 8$ degrees of freedom. The *value of the test statistic* is

$$t = \frac{\bar{x}_1 - \bar{x}_2 - d_0}{\sqrt{s_p^2 \left(\frac{1}{n_1} + \frac{1}{n_2} \right)}} = \frac{811 - 750.2 - 0}{\sqrt{435.1 \left(\frac{1}{5} + \frac{1}{5} \right)}} = 4.6087.$$

LO3

BI

Because $|t| = 4.6087$ *is greater than* $t_{0.025} = 2.306$, *we can reject H_0: $\mu_1 - \mu_2 = 0$ in favour of H_a: $\mu_1 - \mu_2 \neq 0$.* We conclude (at an α of 0.05) that the mean hourly yields obtained by using the two production methods differ.

Figure 9.4(a) and (b) gives the MegaStat and Excel outputs for testing H_0 versus H_a. The outputs tell us that $t = 4.61$ and that the associated p value is 0.001736 (rounded to 0.0017 on the MegaStat output). The very small p value tells us that we have very strong evidence against H_0: $\mu_1 - \mu_2 = 0$. That is, we have very strong evidence that the mean hourly yields obtained by using the two production methods differ.

FIGURE 9.4   MegaStat and Excel Outputs for Testing the Equality of Means in the Coffee Cup Case Assuming Equal Variances

(a) The MegaStat output

Hypothesis Test: Independent Groups

(t-test, pooled variance)

Java	Joe			
811.00	750.20	mean	4.61	t
19.65	22.00	std. dev.	0.0017	p-value (two-tailed)
5	5	n	30.378	confidence interval 95% lower
			91.222	confidence interval 95% upper

8	df
60.800	difference (Java - Joe)
435.100	pooled variance
20.859	pooled std. dev.
13.192	standard error of difference
0	hypothesized difference

F-test for equality of variance

484.20	variance: Joe
386.00	variance: Java
1.25	F
0.8314	p-value

(b) The Excel output

t-Test: Two-Sample Assuming Equal Variances

	Java	Joe
Mean	811	750.2
Variance	386	484.2
Observations	5	5
Pooled Variance	435.1	
Hypothesized Mean Diff	0	
df	8	
t Stat	4.608706	
P(T<=t) one-tail	0.000868	
t Critical one-tail	1.859548	
P(T<=t) two-tail	0.001736	
t Critical two-tail	2.306004	

When the sampled populations are normally distributed and the population variances σ_1^2 and σ_2^2 differ, the following can be shown:

LO1 A Two-Tailed t Test of H_0: $\mu_1 - \mu_2 = d_0$ when $\sigma_1^2 \neq \sigma_2^2$

1   When the sample sizes n_1 and n_2 are equal, the equal-variances t-based hypothesis test given in the preceding box is approximately valid even if the population variances σ_1^2 and σ_2^2 differ substantially. As a rough rule of thumb, if the larger sample variance is not more than three times the smaller sample variance when the sample sizes are equal, we can use the equal-variances interval test.

Furthermore, we can test H_0: $\mu_1 - \mu_2 = d_0$ by using the test statistic

$$t = \frac{\bar{x}_1 - \bar{x}_2 - d_0}{\sqrt{\dfrac{s_1^2}{n_1} + \dfrac{s_2^2}{n_2}}}$$

and by using the previously given rejection point and p value conditions.

2   Suppose that the larger sample variance is more than three times the smaller sample variance when the sample sizes are equal, or suppose that both the sample sizes and the sample variances differ substantially. Then we can use an unequal-variances procedure.

The degrees of freedom are equal to

$$df = \frac{(s_1^2/n_1 + s_2^2/n_2)^2}{\dfrac{(s_1^2/n_1)^2}{n_1 - 1} + \dfrac{(s_2^2/n_2)^2}{n_2 - 1}}.$$

Here, if *df* is not a whole number, we will always round it down to the next smallest whole number.

Next, we will consider a two-tailed hypothesis test about μ_d, the mean of a population of paired differences. We will show how to test the null hypothesis

$$H_0: \mu_d = d_0$$

in the following box. Here the value of the constant d_0 depends on the particular problem. Often d_0 equals 0, and the null hypothesis $H_0: \mu_d = 0$ says that μ_1 and μ_2 do not differ.

A Two-Tailed Hypothesis Test about the Mean, μ_d, of a Population of Paired Differences: Testing $H_0: \mu_d = d_0$ LO1

Assume that the population of paired differences is normally distributed, and consider testing

$$H_0: \mu_d = d_0$$

by using the test statistic

$$t = \frac{\bar{d} - d_0}{s_d/\sqrt{n}}.$$

We can test $H_0: \mu_d = D_0$ versus a particular alternative hypothesis at level of significance α by using the appropriate rejection point rule or, equivalently, the corresponding *p* value.

Alternative Hypothesis	Rejection Point Rule: Reject H_0 if	*p* Value (Reject H_0 if *p* Value $< \alpha$)
$H_a: \mu_d \neq d_0$	$\lvert t \rvert > t_{\alpha/2}$—that is, $t > t_{\alpha/2}$ or $t < -t_{\alpha/2}$	Twice the area under the *t* distribution curve to the right of $\lvert t \rvert$

Here $t_{\alpha/2}$ and the *p* values are based on $n - 1$ degrees of freedom.

Exercises for Section 9.4

CONCEPTS

9.23   List all of the assumptions that must be satisfied in order to validly use the hypothesis test described in each of the formula boxes on pages 301 to 303.

METHODS AND APPLICATIONS

Suppose we have taken independent, random samples of sizes $n_1 = 7$ and $n_2 = 7$ from two normally distributed populations with means μ_1 and μ_2, and suppose we obtain $\bar{x}_1 = 240$, $\bar{x}_2 = 210$, $s_1 = 5$, and $s_2 = 6$.

9.24   Using the equal-variances procedure, use rejection points to test the null hypothesis $H_0: \mu_1 - \mu_2 = 20$ versus the alternative hypothesis $H_a: \mu_1 - \mu_2 \neq 20$ by setting α equal to 0.10, 0.05, 0.01, and 0.001. How much evidence is there that the difference between μ_1 and μ_2 is not equal to 20?

9.25   Repeat Exercise 9.24 using the unequal-variances procedure. Compare your results to those obtained using the equal-variances procedure.

9.26   A marketing research firm wishes to compare the prices charged by two supermarket chains—Miller's and Albert's. The research firm, using a standardized one-week shopping list, makes identical purchases at ten of each chain's stores. The stores for each chain are randomly selected, and all purchases are made during a single week.

The shopping expenses obtained at the two chains, along with box plots of the expenses, are as in Figure 9.5 on the next page.

Because the stores in each sample are different stores in different chains, it is reasonable to assume that the samples are independent, and we assume that weekly expenses at each chain are normally distributed.

FIGURE **9.5** Shopping Expenses at Miller's and Albert's for Exercise 9.26

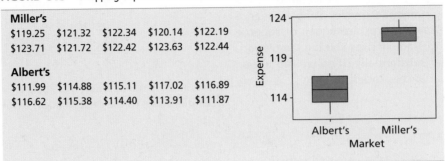

Miller's

| $119.25 | $121.32 | $122.34 | $120.14 | $122.19 |
| $123.71 | $121.72 | $122.42 | $123.63 | $122.44 |

Albert's

| $111.99 | $114.88 | $115.11 | $117.02 | $116.89 |
| $116.62 | $115.38 | $114.40 | $113.91 | $111.87 |

a. Let μ_M be the mean weekly expense for the mean shopping list at Miller's, and let μ_A be the mean weekly expense for the shopping list at Albert's. Test $H_0: \mu_M - \mu_A = 0$ (no difference between μ_M and μ_A) versus $H_a: \mu_M - \mu_A \neq 0$ (μ_M and μ_A differ) by using the summary data $\bar{x}_M = 121.92$, $s_M = 1.40$, $\bar{x}_A = 114.81$, and $s_A = 1.84$. Use rejection points by setting $\alpha = 0.10, 0.05, 0.01,$ and 0.001. How much evidence is there that the mean weekly expenses at Miller's and Albert's differ?

b. Give the p value for testing $H_0: \mu_M - \mu_A = 0$ versus $H_a: \mu_M - \mu_A \neq 0$ and use it to test H_0 versus H_a by setting α equal to 0.10, 0.05, 0.01, and 0.001. How much evidence is there that the mean weekly expenses at Miller's and Albert's differ?

c. Set up the null and alternative hypotheses needed to attempt to establish that the mean weekly expense at Miller's exceeds the mean weekly expense at Albert's by more than $5. Test the hypotheses at the 0.10, 0.05, 0.01, and 0.001 levels of significance. How much evidence is there that the mean weekly expense at Miller's exceeds that at Albert's by more than $5?

9.27 A large discount chain compares the performance of its credit managers in Alberta and Ontario by comparing the mean dollar amounts owed by customers with delinquent charge accounts in these two provinces. Here a small mean dollar amount owed is desirable because it indicates that bad credit risks are not being extended large amounts of credit. Two independent, random samples of delinquent accounts are selected from the populations of delinquent accounts in Alberta and Ontario, respectively. The first sample, which consists of ten randomly selected delinquent accounts in Alberta, gives a mean dollar amount of $524 with a standard deviation of $68. The second sample, which consists of 20 randomly selected delinquent accounts in Ontario, gives a mean dollar amount of $473 with a standard deviation of $22.

a. Set up the null and alternative hypotheses needed to test whether there is a difference between the population mean dollar amounts owed by customers with delinquent charge accounts in Alberta and Ontario.

b. Figure 9.6 gives the MegaStat output of using the unequal-variances procedure to test the equality

of mean dollar amounts owed by customers with delinquent charge accounts in Alberta and Ontario. Assuming that the normality assumption holds, test the hypotheses you set up in part a by setting α equal to 0.10, 0.05, 0.01, and 0.001. How much evidence is there that the mean dollar amounts owed in Alberta and Ontario differ?

9.28 A loan officer compares the interest rates for 48-month fixed-rate auto loans and 48-month variable-rate auto loans. Two independent, random samples of auto loan rates are selected. A sample of eight 48-month fixed-rate auto loans had the following loan rates:

| 10.29% | 9.75% | 9.50% | 9.99% |
| 9.75% | 9.99% | 11.40% | 10.00% |

A sample of five 48-month variable-rate auto loans had loan rates as follows:

| 9.59% | 8.75% | 8.99% | 8.50% | 9.00% |

a. Set up the null and alternative hypotheses needed to determine whether the mean rates for 48-month fixed-rate and variable-rate auto loans differ.

b. Figure 9.7 gives the MegaStat output of using the equal-variances procedure to test the hypotheses you set up in part a. Assuming that the normality and equal-variances assumptions hold, use the MegaStat output and rejection points to test these hypotheses by setting α equal to 0.10, 0.05, 0.01, and 0.001. How much evidence is there that the mean rates for 48-month fixed- and variable-rate auto loans differ?

c. Figure 9.7 gives the p value for testing the hypotheses you set up in part a. Use the p value to test these hypotheses by setting α equal to 0.10, 0.05, 0.01, and 0.001. How much evidence is there that the mean rates for 48-month fixed- and variable-rate auto loans differ?

9.29 Suppose a sample of 49 paired differences that have been randomly selected from a normally distributed population of paired differences yields a sample mean of $\bar{d} = 5$ and a sample standard deviation of $s_d = 7$.

a. Test the null hypothesis $H_0: \mu_d = 0$ versus the alternative hypothesis $H_a: \mu_d \neq 0$ by setting α equal to 0.10, 0.05, 0.01, and 0.001. How much evidence is there that μ_d differs from 0? What does this say about how μ_1 and μ_2 compare?

FIGURE **9.6** MegaStat Output of Testing the Equality of Mean Dollar Amounts Owed for Alberta and Ontario

Hypothesis Test: Independent Groups (t-test, unequal variance)

Alberta	Ontario	
524	473	mean
68	22	std. dev.
10	20	n

9 df
51.000 difference (Alberta - Ontario)
22.059 standard error of difference
0 hypothesized difference
2.31 t
0.0461 p-value (two-tailed)

FIGURE **9.7** MegaStat Output of Testing the Equality of Mean Loan Rates for Fixed and Variable 48-Month Auto Loans

Hypothesis Test: Independent Groups (t-test, pooled variance)

Fixed	Variable		11 df
10.0838	8.9660	mean	1.11775 difference (Fixed - Variable)
0.5810	0.4046	std. dev.	0.27437 pooled variance
8	5	n	0.52381 pooled std. dev.

F-test for equality of variance   0.29862 standard error of difference
0.3376 variance: Fixed   0 hypothesized difference
0.1637 variance: Variable   3.74 t
2.06 F   0.0032 p-value (two-tailed)
0.5052 p-value

TABLE **9.2** Mortgage Loan Interest Rates for Nine Randomly Selected Lending Institutions

	Annual Percentage Rate		
Lending Institution	**25-Year**	**15-Year**	**Difference**
ABC Bank	6.715	6.599	0.116
Home Mortgage	6.648	6.367	0.281
Commercial Bank	6.740	6.550	0.190
Community Bank	6.597	6.362	0.235
Centreville Mortgage	6.425	6.162	0.263
Valley Credit Union	6.880	6.583	0.297
Mortgage Brokers	6.900	6.800	0.100
Best Mortgage	6.675	6.394	0.281
Friendship Mortgage	6.790	6.540	0.250

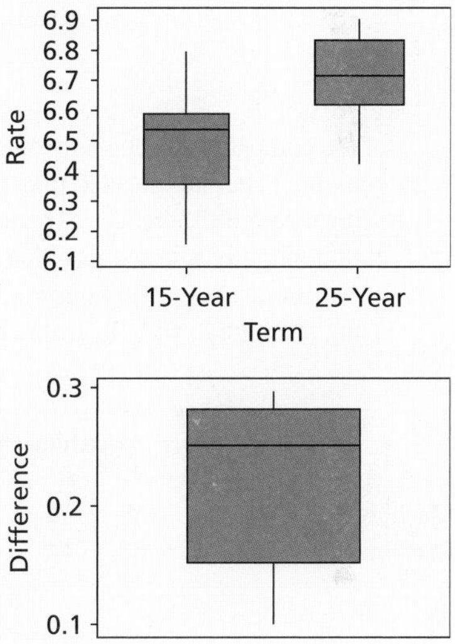

b. Find the *p* value for testing H_0: $\mu_d = 3$ versus H_a: $\mu_d \neq 3$. Use the *p* value to test these hypotheses with α equal to 0.10, 0.05, 0.01, and 0.001. How much evidence is there that μ_d is different from 3?

9.30 A newspaper reported mortgage loan interest rates for 25-year and 15-year fixed-rate mortgage loans for a number of local lending institutions. Of interest is whether there is any systematic difference between 25-year rates and 15-year rates (expressed as annual percentage rate or APR) and, if there is, what the size of that difference is. Table 9.2 displays mortgage loan rates and the difference between 25-year and 15-year rates for nine randomly selected lending institutions. Assume that the population of paired differences is normally distributed.

a. Set up the null and alternative hypotheses needed to determine whether there is a difference between mean 25-year rates and mean 15-year rates.

b. Figure 9.8 on the next page gives the Excel output for testing the hypotheses that you set up in part a. Use the output and rejection points to test these hypotheses by setting α equal to 0.10, 0.05, 0.01, and 0.001. How much evidence is there that mean mortgage loan rates for 25-year and 15-year terms differ?

c. Figure 9.8 gives the *p* value for testing the hypotheses that you set up in part a. Use the *p* value to test these hypotheses by setting α equal to 0.10, 0.05, 0.01, and 0.001. How much evidence is there that mean mortgage loan rates for 25-year and 15-year terms differ?

9.31 National Paper Company must purchase a new machine for producing cardboard boxes. The company must choose between two machines. The machines produce boxes of equal quality, so the company will choose the machine that produces (on average) the most boxes. It is known that there are substantial differences in the abilities

FIGURE **9.8**   Excel Paired-Differences *t* Test of the Mortgage Loan Rate Data for Exercise 9.30

Paired t-Test: 25-Year - 15-Year		
	25-Year	**15-Year**
Mean	6.707777778	6.484111111
Variance	0.021417944	0.033841361
Observations	9	9
Pearson Correlation	0.92798036	
Hypothesized Mean Difference	0	
df	8	
t Stat	9.223422158	
P(T<=t) one-tail	7.73442E-06	
t Critical one-tail	1.859548033	
P(T<=t) two-tail	1.54688E-05	
t Critical two-tail	2.306004133	

TABLE **9.3**   Weekly Study Time Data for Students Who Perform Well on the MidTerm

Student	1	2	3	4	5	6	7	8
Before	15	14	17	17	19	14	13	16
After	9	9	11	10	19	10	14	10

of the company's machine operators. Therefore, National Paper has decided to compare the machines using a paired-differences experiment. Suppose that eight randomly selected machine operators produce boxes for one hour using machine 1 and for one hour using machine 2, with the following results:

	Machine Operator							
	1	2	3	4	5	6	7	8
Machine 1	53	60	58	48	46	54	62	49
Machine 2	50	55	56	44	45	50	57	47

Assuming normality, perform a hypothesis test to determine whether there is a difference between the mean hourly outputs of the two machines. Use $\alpha = 0.05$.

9.32   Do students reduce study time in classes where they achieve a higher midterm score? In a *Journal of Economic Education* article (Winter 2005), Krohn and O'Connor studied student effort and performance in a class over a semester. In an intermediate macroeconomics course, they found that "students respond to higher midterm scores by reducing the number of hours they subsequently allocate to studying for the course."[1] Suppose that a random sample of $n = 8$ students who performed well on the midterm exam was taken and weekly study times before and after the exam were compared. The resulting data are given in Table 9.3. Assume that the population of all possible paired differences is normally distributed.

FIGURE **9.9**   Excel Output for Exercise 9.32

Paired t-Test: Study Time Before - Study Time After		
	Study Time Before	**Study Time After**
Mean	15.625	11.5
Variance	3.982142857	11.71428571
Observations	8	8
Pearson Correlation	0.491533925	
Hypothesized Mean Difference	0	
df	7	
t Stat	3.892951269	
P(T<=t) one-tail	0.00297635	
t Critical one-tail	1.894578604	
P(T<=t) two-tail	0.005952699	
t Critical two-tail	2.364624251	

---

[1]Source: "Student effort and performance over the semester," by Gregory Krohn and Catherine O'Connor, *Journal of Economic Education*, Winter 2005, pages 3–28.

a. Set up the null and alternative hypotheses to test whether there is a difference in the true mean study times before and after the midterm exam.

b. In Figure 9.9, we present the Excel output for the paired-differences test. Use the output and rejection points to test the hypotheses at the 0.10, 0.05, and

0.01 levels of significance. Has the true mean study time changed?

c. Use the *p* value to test the hypotheses at the 0.10, 0.05, and 0.01 levels of significance. How much evidence is there against the null hypothesis?

9.5 *z* TESTS ABOUT A DIFFERENCE IN POPULATION PROPORTIONS

In this section, we wish to conduct a hypothesis test about the difference between two population proportions. In this text, we will only consider cases where n_1 and n_2 are large. This allows us to use a *z* test when conducting our hypothesis tests.

To test the null hypothesis H_0: $p_1 - p_2 = d_0$, we use the test statistic

$$z = \frac{\hat{p}_1 - \hat{p}_2 - d_0}{\sigma_{\hat{p}_1 - \hat{p}_2}}.$$

L05

A commonly employed special case of this hypothesis test is obtained by setting d_0 equal to 0. In this case, the null hypothesis H_0: $p_1 - p_2 = 0$ says there is *no difference* between the population proportions p_1 and p_2. When $D_0 = 0$, *the best estimate of the common population proportion $p = p_1 = p_2$ is obtained by computing*

$$\hat{p} = \frac{\text{the total number of units in the two samples that fall into the category of interest}}{\text{the total number of units in the two samples}}.$$

Therefore, the point estimate of $\sigma_{\hat{p}_1 - \hat{p}_2}$ is

$$s_{\hat{p}_1 - \hat{p}_2} = \sqrt{\frac{\hat{p}(1 - \hat{p})}{n_1} + \frac{\hat{p}(1 - \hat{p})}{n_2}}$$

$$= \sqrt{\hat{p}(1 - \hat{p})\left(\frac{1}{n_1} + \frac{1}{n_2}\right)}.$$

For the case where $d_0 \neq 0$, the point estimate of $\sigma_{\hat{p}_1 - \hat{p}_2}$ is obtained by estimating p_1 by $\hat{p}_1$ and p_2 by $\hat{p}_2$. With these facts in mind, we present the following procedure for testing H_0: $p_1 - p_2 = d_0$:

A Hypothesis Test about the Difference between Two Population Proportions: Testing H_0: $p_1 - p_2 = d_0$

Let $\hat{p}$ be as just defined. Furthermore, define the test statistic

$$z = \frac{\hat{p}_1 - \hat{p}_2 - d_0}{\sigma_{\hat{p}_1 - \hat{p}_2}}$$

and assume that each of the sample sizes n_1 and n_2 is large. Then, if the samples are independent of each

other, we can test H_0: $p_1 - p_2 = d_0$ versus a particular alternative hypothesis at level of significance α by using the appropriate rejection point rule or, equivalently, the corresponding *p* value.

Alternative Hypothesis	Rejection Point Rule: Reject H_0 if	*p* Value (Reject H_0 if *p* Value $< \alpha$)
H_a: $p_1 - p_2 > d_0$	$z > z_\alpha$	The area under the standard normal curve to the right of *z*
H_a: $p_1 - p_2 < d_0$	$z < -z_\alpha$	The area under the standard normal curve to the left of *z*
H_a: $p_1 - p_2 \neq d_0$	$\lvert z \rvert > z_{\alpha/2}$—that is, $z > z_{\alpha/2}$ or $z < -z_{\alpha/2}$	Twice the area under the standard normal curve to the right of $\lvert z \rvert$

L01

Note:

1   If $d_0 = 0$, we estimate $\sigma_{\hat{p}_1 - \hat{p}_2}$ by

$$s_{\hat{p}_1 - \hat{p}_2} = \sqrt{\hat{p}(1 - \hat{p})\left(\frac{1}{n_1} + \frac{1}{n_2}\right)}.$$

2   If $d_0 \neq 0$, we estimate $\sigma_{\hat{p}_1 - \hat{p}_2}$ by

$$s_{\hat{p}_1 - \hat{p}_2} = \sqrt{\frac{\hat{p}_1(1 - \hat{p}_1)}{n_1} + \frac{\hat{p}_2(1 - \hat{p}_2)}{n_2}}.$$

Example 9.6 The Advertising Media Case (z Test about Proportions)

LO2

Recall from Example 7.15 on pages 244 to 245 that p_1 is the proportion of all consumers in the Toronto area who are aware of the new product and that p_2 is the proportion of all consumers in the Vancouver area who are aware of the new product. To test for the equality of these proportions, we will test H_0: $p_1 - p_2 = 0$ versus H_a: $p_1 - p_2 \neq 0$ at the 0.05 level of significance. Because both of the Toronto and Vancouver samples are large (both $n\hat{p}$ and $n(1 - \hat{p}) \geq 5$), we will calculate the value of the *test statistic z in the summary box* (where $d_0 = 0$). Since H_a: $p_1 - p_2 \neq 0$ is of the form H_a: $p_1 - p_2 \neq D_0$, we will *reject H_0: $p_1 - p_2 = 0$ if the absolute value of z is greater than* $z_{\alpha/2} = z_{0.05/2} = z_{0.025} = 1.96$. Because 631 out of 1,000 randomly selected Toronto residents were aware of the product and 798 out of 1,000 randomly selected Vancouver residents were aware of the product, the estimate of $p = p_1 = p_2$ is

$$\hat{p} = \frac{631 + 798}{1,000 + 1,000} = \frac{1,429}{2,000} = 0.7145,$$

and the *value of the test statistic is*

$$z = \frac{\hat{p}_1 - \hat{p}_2 - d_0}{\sqrt{\hat{p}(1 - \hat{p})\left(\frac{1}{n_1} + \frac{1}{n_2}\right)}} = \frac{0.631 - 0.798 - 0}{\sqrt{(0.7145)(0.2855)\left(\frac{1}{1,000} + \frac{1}{1,000}\right)}} = \frac{-0.167}{0.0202} = -8.2673.$$

BI

LO4

Because $|z| - 8.2673$ is greater than 1.96, we reject H_0: $p_1 - p_2 = 0$ in favour of H_a: $p_1 - p_2 \neq 0$. We conclude (at an α of 0.05) that the proportions of consumers who are aware of the product in Toronto and Vancouver differ. We estimate that the percentage of consumers who are aware of the product in Vancouver is 16.7 percentage points higher than the percentage of consumers who are aware of the product in Toronto. The p value for this test is twice the area under the standard normal curve to the right of $|z| = 8.2673$. Since the area under the standard normal curve to the right of 3.29 is 0.0005, the p value for testing H_0 is less than $2(0.0005) = 0.001$. It follows that we have extremely strong evidence that H_0: $p_1 - p_2 = 0$ should be rejected. This small p value provides extremely strong evidence that p_1 and p_2 differ. Figure 9.10 presents the MegaStat output of the hypothesis test of H_0: $p_1 - p_2 = 0$ versus H_a: $p_1 - p_2 \neq 0$.

FIGURE 9.10   MegaStat Output of Statistical Inference in the Advertising Media Case

Testing H_0: $p_1 - p_2 = 0$ versus H_a: $p_1 - p_2 \neq 0$

Hypothesis test for two independent proportions

p1	p2	pc		
0.631	0.798	0.7145	−0.167	difference
631/1,000	798/1,000	1,429/2000	0.	hypothesized difference
631.	798.	1,429. X	0.0202	std. error
1,000	1,000	2,000 n	−8.27	z
			0.00E+00	p-value (two-tailed)

In addition, the 95 percent confidence interval for $\hat{p}_1 - \hat{p}_2$ is

$$\left[\hat{p}_1 - \hat{p}_2 \pm z_{0.025} \sqrt{\frac{\hat{p}_1(1 - \hat{p}_1)}{n_1} + \frac{\hat{p}_2(1 - \hat{p}_2)}{n_2}} \right]$$

$$= \left[0.631 - 0.798 \pm 1.96 \sqrt{\frac{(0.631)(0.369)}{1,000} + \frac{(0.798)(0.202)}{1,000}} \right]$$

$$= [-0.167 \pm 0.0389]$$

$$= [-0.2059, -0.1281].$$

Before we move on to tests for equality of variance, we will summarize what we have learned so far.

In this chapter, we have learned how to conduct hypothesis tests using a *z* test statistic and a *t* test statistic. Why do we switch between using *z* and *t*? Think back to confidence intervals. Remember that *z* values were used in the confidence interval formulas when the values of σ_1 and σ_2 were known, or when the sample sizes were very large. The same is true when conducting hypothesis tests. We will use a *z* test statistic to conduct a hypothesis test when the σ's are known or when the sample sizes are large. We will use a *t* test statistic when the data are approximately normal, the sample sizes are small, and the values of σ are not known. The test statistic will take on the following form, in general:

LO5

$$\text{test statistic} = \frac{\text{estimated difference} - \text{difference under } H_0}{\text{standard error of the estimated difference}}.$$

Note that this form will not hold true in the next section of the text when we test for equality of variances.

Exercises for Section 9.5

CONCEPTS

9.33 What assumptions must be satisfied in order to use the methods presented in this section?

METHODS AND APPLICATIONS

In Exercises 9.34 and 9.35, we assume that we have selected two independent random samples from populations with proportions p_1 and p_2 and that $\hat{p}_1 = 800/1,000 = 0.8$ and $\hat{p}_2 = 950/1,000 = 0.95$.

9.34 Test $H_0: p_1 - p_2 = 0$ versus $H_a: p_1 - p_2 \neq 0$ by using rejection points and by setting α equal to 0.10, 0.05, 0.01, and 0.001. How much evidence is there that p_1 and p_2 differ? Explain. *Hint:* $z_{0.0005} = 3.29$.

9.35 Test $H_0: p_1 - p_2 \geq -0.12$ versus $H_a: p_1 - p_2 < -0.12$ by using a *p* value and by setting α equal to 0.10, 0.05, 0.01, and 0.001. How much evidence is there that p_2 exceeds p_1 by more than 0.12? Explain.

9.36 A newspaper at a large Canadian university conducted a survey of faculty and students on campus to determine whether or not the parking is adequate. A random sample of 200 faculty members and a random sample of 500 students were selected. One hundred twenty-six of the faculty members and 277 of the students said that parking on campus is inadequate.

a. Set up the null and alternative hypotheses needed to determine whether the proportion of faculty members who believe that parking is inadequate is different from the proportion of students who believe that parking is inadequate.

b. Test the hypotheses you set up in part a by using rejection points and by setting α equal to 0.10, 0.05, 0.01, and 0.001. How much evidence is there that the proportions are different?

c. Set up the null and alternative hypotheses needed to determine whether the difference between the proportion of faculty members and the proportion of students who believe that parking is inadequate is more than 0.05 (five percentage points). Test these hypotheses by using a *p* value and by setting α equal to 0.10, 0.05, 0.01, and 0.001. How much evidence is there that the difference between the proportions exceeds 0.05?

d. Construct a 95 percent confidence interval for the difference between the proportion of faculty members and the proportion of students who believe that parking on campus is inadequate. On the basis of this interval, can you be 95 percent confident that these proportions differ? Explain.

FIGURE **9.11** Results of Gallup Survey for Exercise 9.39

	Percentage of respondents	
1 Had taken a vacation lasting six days or more within the last 12 months:	December 1999 42%	December 1968 62%
2 Took part in some sort of daily activity to keep physically fit:	December 1999 60%	September 1977 48%
3 Watched TV more than four hours on an average weekday:	December 1999 28%	April 1981 25%
4 Drove a car or truck to work:	December 1999 87%	April 1971 81%

9.37 Have the attitudes of young Canadian adults about smoking changed in recent years? In 1999, a random sample of 1,000 young adults aged 18 to 24 was taken and 576 of them said that they were smokers. In 2006, a random sample of 900 young adults aged 18 to 24 was taken and 459 of them said they were smokers.

a. Let p_1 be the proportion of young adults who smoked in 1999 and p_2 be the proportion of young adults who smoked in 2006. Set up the null and alternative hypotheses needed to determine whether the proportion of young adults who smoked in 1999 differs from the proportion who smoked in 2006.

b. Find the test statistic z and the p value for testing the hypotheses you set up in part a. Use the p value to test the hypotheses at the 0.10, 0.05, 0.01, and 0.001 levels of significance. How much evidence is there that the proportion of young adults who smoked in 1999 differs from the proportion who smoked in 2006?

9.38 The digital music players produced by a large Canadian manufacturer during the first two months of 2010 were of poor quality. A random sample of 100 players was obtained during this time and the players were tested. It was determined that 21 of them were defective. Quality control standards were then tightened. A random sample of 100 players was taken during the next two months. It was determined that 12 were defective.

a. Let p_1 be the proportion of defective digital music players during the first two months of 2010 and p_2 be the proportion of defective digital music players during the next two months. Set up the null and alternative hypotheses needed to determine whether the proportion of defective digital music players declined after the quality control standards were tightened.

b. Find the test statistic z and the p value for testing the hypotheses you set up in part a. Use the p value to test the hypotheses at the 0.10, 0.05, 0.01, and 0.001 levels of significance. How much evidence is there that the proportion of defective digital music players declined after the quality control standards were tightened?

9.39 On January 7, 2000, the Gallup Organization released the results of a poll comparing the lifestyles of today with those of yesteryear. The survey results were based on telephone interviews with a randomly selected national sample of 1,031 U.S. adults, 18 years and older, conducted December 20 to 21, 1999. The poll asked several questions and compared the 1999 responses with the responses given in polls taken in previous years. In Figure 9.11, we summarize some of the poll's results.[2] Assume that each poll was based on a randomly selected U.S. sample of 1,031 adults and that the samples in different years are independent.

a. Let p_1 be the December 1999 population proportion of U.S. adults who took part in some sort of daily activity to keep physically fit, and let p_2 be the September 1977 population proportion who did the same. Carry out a hypothesis test to attempt to justify that the proportion who took part in such daily activity increased from September 1977 to December 1999. Use $\alpha = 0.05$ and explain your result.

b. Let p_1 be the December 1999 population proportion of U.S. adults who watched TV for more than four hours on an average weekday, and let p_2 be the April 1981 population proportion who did the same. Carry out a hypothesis test to determine whether these population proportions differ. Use $\alpha = 0.05$ and interpret the result of your test.

[2]Source: http://www.Gallup.com/Poll/33528/Trends-Show-Bathing-Exercise-Up-Watching-Down.aspx. The Gallup Poll, December 30, 1999.

9.6 F TESTS ABOUT A DIFFERENCE IN POPULATION VARIANCES

Earlier in the chapter, we saw that we often wish to compare two population means. In addition, it is often useful to compare two population variances. For example, in the bank customer waiting time situation, we might compare the variance of the waiting times experienced under the current and new systems. Or, as another example, we might wish to compare the variance of the coffee cup production obtained when using the Java method with that obtained when using the Joe method. Here the method that produces yields with the smaller variance gives more consistent (or predictable) results.

If σ_1^2 and σ_2^2 are the population variances that we wish to compare, one approach is to test the null hypothesis

$$H_0: \sigma_1^2 = \sigma_2^2.$$

We might test H_0 versus an alternative hypothesis of, for instance,

$$H_a: \sigma_1^2 > \sigma_2^2.$$

Dividing by σ_2^2, we see that testing these hypotheses is equivalent to testing

$$H_0: \frac{\sigma_1^2}{\sigma_2^2} = 1 \qquad \text{versus} \qquad H_a: \frac{\sigma_1^2}{\sigma_2^2} > 1.$$

When conducting a hypothesis test about population variances, we must rely on sample variances, which, because of sampling variability, are random variables. This makes the ratio of sample variances a random variable. It is a random variable with a sampling distribution that is very well known, as we will see. The ratio of sample variances will be used to test hypotheses regarding the equality of population variances.

Intuitively, we would reject H_0 in favour of H_a if s_1^2/s_2^2 is significantly larger than 1. Here s_1^2 is the variance of a random sample of n_1 observations from the population with variance σ_1^2, and s_2^2 is the variance of a random sample of n_2 observations from the population with variance σ_2^2. To decide exactly how large s_1^2/s_2^2 must be in order to reject H_0, we need to consider the sampling distribution of s_1^2/s_2^2.[3]

It can be shown that if the null hypothesis $H_0: \sigma_1^2/\sigma_2^2 = 1$ is true, then the population of all possible values of s_1^2/s_2^2 is described by what is called an **F distribution**. In general, as illustrated in Figure 9.12 on the next page, the curve of the F distribution is skewed to the right. Moreover, the exact shape of this curve depends on two parameters that are called the **numerator degrees of freedom (denoted df_1)** and the **denominator degrees of freedom (denoted df_2)**. The values of df_1 and df_2 that describe the sampling distribution of s_1^2/s_2^2 are given in the following box:

The Sampling Distribution of s_1^2/s_2^2

Suppose we randomly select independent samples from two normally distributed populations with variances σ_1^2 and σ_2^2. Then, if the null hypothesis $H_0: \sigma_1^2/\sigma_2^2 = 1$ is true, the population of all possible values of s_1^2/s_2^2 has an **F distribution** with $df_1 = (n_1 - 1)$ numerator degrees of freedom and $df_2 = (n_2 - 1)$ denominator degrees of freedom.

Note: The F tests we will conduct in this chapter are also referred to as Hartley F-max tests.

In order to use the F distribution, we employ an **F point**, which is denoted F_α. As illustrated in Figure 9.12(a), *F_α is the point on the horizontal axis under the curve of the F distribution that gives a right-hand tail area equal to α.* The value of F_α in a particular situation depends on the

---

[3] Note that we divide by σ_2^2 to form a null hypothesis of the form $H_0: \sigma_1^2/\sigma_2^2 = 1$ rather than subtracting σ_2^2 to form a null hypothesis of the form $H_0: \sigma_1^2 - \sigma_2^2 = 0$. This is because the population of all possible values of $s_1^2 - s_2^2$ has no known sampling distribution.

FIGURE 9.12   *F* Distribution Curves and *F* Points

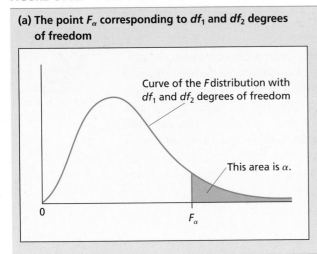

(a) The point F_α corresponding to df_1 and df_2 degrees of freedom

Curve of the *F* distribution with df_1 and df_2 degrees of freedom

This area is α.

0   F_α

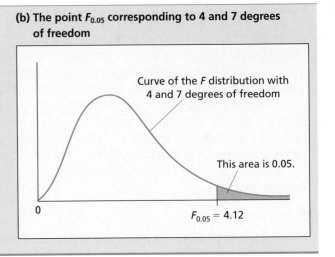

(b) The point $F_{0.05}$ corresponding to 4 and 7 degrees of freedom

Curve of the *F* distribution with 4 and 7 degrees of freedom

This area is 0.05.

0    $F_{0.05} = 4.12$

TABLE 9.4   A Portion of an *F* Table: Values of $F_{0.05}$

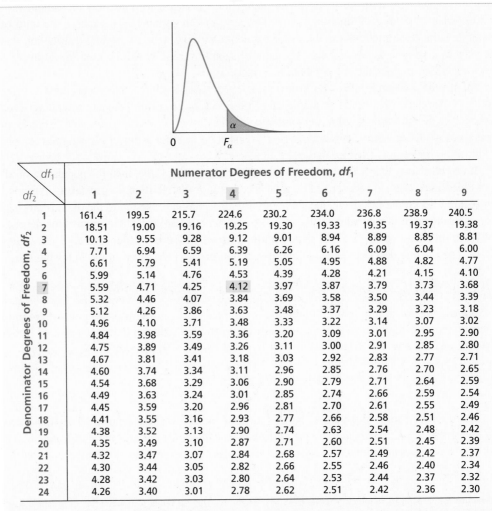

df_1			Numerator Degrees of Freedom, df_1					
df_2	1	2	3	4	5	6	7	8	9
1	161.4	199.5	215.7	224.6	230.2	234.0	236.8	238.9	240.5
2	18.51	19.00	19.16	19.25	19.30	19.33	19.35	19.37	19.38
3	10.13	9.55	9.28	9.12	9.01	8.94	8.89	8.85	8.81
4	7.71	6.94	6.59	6.39	6.26	6.16	6.09	6.04	6.00
5	6.61	5.79	5.41	5.19	5.05	4.95	4.88	4.82	4.77
6	5.99	5.14	4.76	4.53	4.39	4.28	4.21	4.15	4.10
7	5.59	4.71	4.25	4.12	3.97	3.87	3.79	3.73	3.68
8	5.32	4.46	4.07	3.84	3.69	3.58	3.50	3.44	3.39
9	5.12	4.26	3.86	3.63	3.48	3.37	3.29	3.23	3.18
10	4.96	4.10	3.71	3.48	3.33	3.22	3.14	3.07	3.02
11	4.84	3.98	3.59	3.36	3.20	3.09	3.01	2.95	2.90
12	4.75	3.89	3.49	3.26	3.11	3.00	2.91	2.85	2.80
13	4.67	3.81	3.41	3.18	3.03	2.92	2.83	2.77	2.71
14	4.60	3.74	3.34	3.11	2.96	2.85	2.76	2.70	2.65
15	4.54	3.68	3.29	3.06	2.90	2.79	2.71	2.64	2.59
16	4.49	3.63	3.24	3.01	2.85	2.74	2.66	2.59	2.54
17	4.45	3.59	3.20	2.96	2.81	2.70	2.61	2.55	2.49
18	4.41	3.55	3.16	2.93	2.77	2.66	2.58	2.51	2.46
19	4.38	3.52	3.13	2.90	2.74	2.63	2.54	2.48	2.42
20	4.35	3.49	3.10	2.87	2.71	2.60	2.51	2.45	2.39
21	4.32	3.47	3.07	2.84	2.68	2.57	2.49	2.42	2.37
22	4.30	3.44	3.05	2.82	2.66	2.55	2.46	2.40	2.34
23	4.28	3.42	3.03	2.80	2.64	2.53	2.44	2.37	2.32
24	4.26	3.40	3.01	2.78	2.62	2.51	2.42	2.36	2.30

Denominator Degrees of Freedom, df_2

Source: "Tables of percentage points of the inverted beta (*F*) distribution," by M. Merrington and C. M. Thompson, *Biometrika*, Vol. 33 (1943), pp. 73–88. Reproduced by permission of Oxford University Press and *Biometrika* trustees.

size of the right-hand tail area (the size of α) and on the numerator degrees of freedom (df_1) and the denominator degrees of freedom (df_2). Values of F_α are given in an **F table**. Tables A.6, A.7, A.8, and A.9 give values of $F_{0.10}$, $F_{0.05}$, $F_{0.025}$, and $F_{0.01}$, respectively. Each table tabulates values of F_α according to the appropriate numerator degrees of freedom (values listed across the top of the table) and the appropriate denominator degrees of freedom (values listed down the left side of the table). A portion of Table A.7, which gives values of $F_{0.05}$, is reproduced in Table 9.4 on the previous page. For instance, suppose we wish to find the F point that gives a right-hand tail area of 0.05 under the curve of the F distribution with 4 numerator and 7 denominator degrees of freedom. To do this, we scan across the top of Table 9.4 until we find the column corresponding to 4 numerator degrees of freedom, and we scan down the left side of the table until we find the row corresponding to 7 denominator degrees of freedom. The table entry in this column and row is the desired F point. We find that the $F_{0.05}$ point is 4.12 (see Figure 9.12(b)).

We now present the procedure for testing the equality of two population variances when the alternative hypothesis is one-tailed:

Testing the Equality of Population Variances: Testing $H_0: \sigma_1^2 = \sigma_2^2$ versus a One-Tailed Alternative Hypothesis   LO1

Suppose we randomly select independent samples from two normally distributed populations—populations 1 and 2. Let s_1^2 be the variance of the random sample of n_1 observations from population 1, and let s_2^2 be the variance of the random sample of n_2 observations from population 2.

1   In order to test $H_0: \sigma_1^2 = \sigma_2^2$ versus $H_a: \sigma_1^2 > \sigma_2^2$, define the test statistic

$$F = \frac{s_1^2}{s_2^2}$$

and define the corresponding p value to be the area to the right of F under the curve of the F distribution with $df_1 = n_1 - 1$ numerator degrees of freedom and $df_2 = n_2 - 1$ denominator degrees of freedom. We can reject H_0 at level of significance α if and only if

a. $F > F_\alpha$ or, equivalently,
b. p value $< \alpha$.

Here F_α is based on $df_1 = n_1 - 1$ and $df_2 = n_2 - 1$ degrees of freedom.

2   In order to test $H_0: \sigma_1^2 = \sigma_2^2$ versus $H_a: \sigma_1^2 < \sigma_2^2$, define the test statistic

$$F = \frac{s_2^2}{s_1^2}$$

and define the corresponding p value to be the area to the right of F under the curve of the F distribution with $df_1 = n_2 - 1$ numerator degrees of freedom and $df_2 = n_1 - 1$ denominator degrees of freedom. We can reject H_0 at level of significance α if and only if

a. $F > F_\alpha$ or, equivalently,
b. p value $< \alpha$.

Here F_α is based on $df_1 = n_2 - 1$ and $df_2 = n_1 - 1$ degrees of freedom.

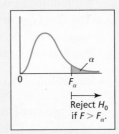

Note that in the tests described in this box, the larger sample variance is in the numerator and the smaller sample variance is in the denominator.

Example 9.7   The Coffee Cup Case (One-Tailed Alternative)

Again consider the production comparison situation of Example 9.3, and suppose the production supervisor wishes to use Figure 9.13 on the next page to determine whether σ_1^2, the variance of the average production yields obtained by using the Java method, is smaller than σ_2^2, the variance of the yields obtained by using the Joe method. To do this, the supervisor will test the null hypothesis

$$H_0: \sigma_1^2 = \sigma_2^2,$$

FIGURE 9.13 Excel Output for Testing $H_0: S_1^2 = S_2^2$ in the Coffee Cup Case

F-Test Two-Sample for Variances		
	Joe	Java
Mean	750.2	811
Variance	484.2	386
Observations	5	5
df	4	4
F	1.254404	
P(F<=f) one-tail	0.415724	
F Critical one-tail	6.388234	

which says the methods produce yields with the same amount of variability, versus the alternative hypothesis

LO6

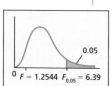

$$H_a: \sigma_1^2 < \sigma_2^2 \quad \text{or, equivalently,} \quad H_a: \sigma_2^2 > \sigma_1^2,$$

which says Java produces yields that are less variable (that is, more consistent) than the yields produced by Joe. Figure 9.13 says that $n_1 = n_2 = 5$, $s_1^2 = 386$, and $s_2^2 = 484.2$. In order to test H_0 versus H_a, we compute the test statistic

$$F = \frac{s_2^2}{s_1^2} = \frac{484.2}{386} = 1.2544,$$

and we compare this value with F_α based on $df_1 = n_2 - 1 = 5 - 1 = 4$ numerator degrees of freedom and $df_2 = n_1 - 1 = 5 - 1 = 4$ denominator degrees of freedom. If we test H_0 versus H_a at the 0.05 level of significance, then Figure 9.13 tells us that when $df_1 = 4$ and $df_2 = 4$, we have $F_{0.05} = 6.39$. Because $F = 1.2544$ is not greater than $F_{0.05} = 6.39$, we cannot reject H_0 at the 0.05 level of significance. That is, at the 0.05 level of significance we cannot conclude that σ_1^2 is less than σ_2^2.

The p value for testing H_0 versus H_a is the area to the right of $F = 1.2544$ under the curve of the F distribution with 4 numerator degrees of freedom and 4 denominator degrees of freedom. The Excel output in Figure 9.13 tells us that this p value equals 0.415724. Since this p value is large, we have little evidence to support rejecting H_0 in favour of H_a. That is, there is little evidence that Java produces yields that are more consistent than the yields produced by Joe.

Again considering the coffee cup comparison case, suppose we wish to test

$$H_0: \sigma_1^2 = \sigma_2^2 \quad \text{versus} \quad H_a: \sigma_1^2 \neq \sigma_2^2.$$

Although we can calculate the left-hand tail rejection point for this hypothesis test, it is common practice to compute the test statistic F so that its value is always greater than 1. This means that we will always compare F with the right-hand tail rejection point when carrying out the test. This can be done by always calculating F to be the larger of s_1^2 and s_2^2 divided by the smaller of s_1^2 and s_2^2. We obtain the following result:

LO1 **Testing the Equality of Population Variances: Testing $H_0: \sigma_1^2 = \sigma_2^2$ versus $H_a: \sigma_1^2 \neq \sigma_2^2$**

Suppose we randomly select independent samples from two normally distributed populations and define all notation as in the previous box. Then, in order to test $H_0: \sigma_1^2 = \sigma_2^2$ versus $H_a: \sigma_1^2 \neq \sigma_2^2$, define the test statistic

$$F = \frac{\text{the larger of } s_1^2 \text{ and } s_2^2}{\text{the smaller of } s_1^2 \text{ and } s_2^2}$$

and let

$df_1 =$ (the size of the sample with the largest variance) $- 1$,

$df_2 =$ (the size of the sample with the smallest variance) $- 1$.

Also define the corresponding *p* value to be twice the area to the right of *F* under the curve of the *F* distribution with df_1 numerator degrees of freedom and df_2 denominator degrees of freedom. We can reject H_0 at level of significance α if and only if

1 $F > F_{\alpha/2}$ or, equivalently,

2 *p* value $< \alpha$.

Here $F_{\alpha/2}$ is based on df_1 and df_2 degrees of freedom.

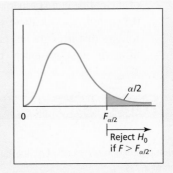

Example 9.8 The Coffee Cup Case (Two-Tailed Alternative)

In the coffee cup comparison situation, we can reject $H_0: \sigma_1^2 = \sigma_2^2$ in favour of $H_a: \sigma_1^2 \neq \sigma_2^2$ at the 0.05 level of significance if

$$F = \frac{\text{the larger of } s_1^2 \text{ and } s_2^2}{\text{the smaller of } s_1^2 \text{ and } s_2^2} = \frac{484.2}{386} = 1.2544$$

L06

is greater than $F_{\alpha/2} = F_{0.05/2} = F_{0.025}$. Here the degrees of freedom are

$$df_1 = (\text{the size of the sample with the largest variance}) - 1$$
$$= n_2 - 1 = 5 - 1 = 4$$

and

$$df_2 = (\text{the size of the sample with the smallest variance}) - 1$$
$$= n_1 - 1 = 5 - 1 = 4.$$

Table A.8 tells us that the appropriate $F_{0.025}$ point equals 9.60. Because $F = 1.2544$ is not greater than 9.60, we cannot reject H_0 at the 0.05 level of significance and thus we have little evidence that the consistencies of the yields produced by Java and Joe differ.

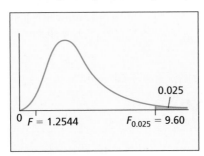

It has been suggested that the *F* test of $H_0: \sigma_1^2 = \sigma_2^2$ be used to choose between the equal-variances and unequal-variances *t*-based procedures when comparing two means. Certainly the *F* test is one approach to making this choice. However, studies have shown that the validity of the *F* test is very sensitive to violations of the normality assumption—much more sensitive, in fact, than the equal-variances procedure is to violations of the equal-variances assumption. While opinions vary, some statisticians believe that this is a serious problem and that the *F* test should never be used to choose between the equal-variances and unequal-variances procedures. Others feel that performing the test for this purpose is reasonable if the test's limitations are kept in mind.

As an example for those who believe that using the *F* test is reasonable, we found in Example 9.8 that we do not reject $H_0: \sigma_1^2 = \sigma_2^2$ at the 0.05 level of significance in the context of the coffee cup comparison situation. Further, the p value related to the F test, which equals 0.831, tells us that there is little evidence to suggest that the population variances differ. It follows that it might be reasonable to compare the mean yields of the production methods by using the equal-variances procedure.

Exercises for Section 9.6

CONCEPTS

9.40 Explain what population is described by the sampling distribution of s_1^2/s_2^2.

9.41 Intuitively explain why a value of s_1^2/s_2^2 that is substantially greater than 1 provides evidence that σ_1^2 is not equal to σ_2^2.

METHODS AND APPLICATIONS

9.42 Use Table 9.4 on page 312 to find the $F_{0.05}$ point for each of the following:
  a. $df_1 = 3$ numerator degrees of freedom and $df_2 = 14$ denominator degrees of freedom.
  b. $df_1 = 6$ and $df_2 = 10$.
  c. $df_1 = 2$ and $df_2 = 22$.
  d. $df_1 = 7$ and $df_2 = 5$.

9.43 Use Tables A.6, A.7, A.8, and A.9 to find the following F_α points:
  a. $F_{0.10}$ with $df_1 = 4$ numerator degrees of freedom and $df_2 = 7$ denominator degrees of freedom.
  b. $F_{0.01}$ with $df_1 = 3$ and $df_2 = 25$.
  c. $F_{0.025}$ with $df_1 = 7$ and $df_2 = 17$.
  d. $F_{0.05}$ with $df_1 = 9$ and $df_2 = 3$.

9.44 Suppose two independent random samples of sizes $n_1 = 9$ and $n_2 = 7$ that have been taken from two normally distributed populations with variances σ_1^2 and σ_2^2 give sample variances of $s_1^2 = 100$ and $s_2^2 = 20$.
  a. Test $H_0: \sigma_1^2 = \sigma_2^2$ versus $H_a: \sigma_1^2 \neq \sigma_2^2$ with $\alpha = 0.05$. What do you conclude?

  b. Test $H_0: \sigma_1^2 \leq \sigma_2^2$ versus $H_a: \sigma_1^2 > \sigma_2^2$ with $\alpha = 0.05$. What do you conclude?

9.45 Suppose two independent random samples of sizes $n_1 = 5$ and $n_2 = 16$ that have been taken from two normally distributed populations with variances σ_1^2 and σ_2^2 give sample standard deviations of $s_1 = 5$ and $s_2 = 9$.
  a. Test $H_0: \sigma_1^2 = s_2^2$ versus $H_a: \sigma_1^2 \neq \sigma_2^2$ with $\alpha = 0.05$. What do you conclude?
  b. Test $H_0: \sigma_1^2 \geq \sigma_2^2$ versus $H_a: \sigma_1^2 < \sigma_2^2$ with $\alpha = 0.01$. What do you conclude?

9.46 A large discount chain compares the performance of its credit managers in Alberta and Ontario by comparing the mean dollar amounts owed by customers with delinquent charge accounts in these two provinces. Here a small mean dollar amount owed is desirable because it indicates that bad credit risks are not being extended large amounts of credit. Two independent, random samples of delinquent accounts are selected from the populations of delinquent accounts in Alberta and Ontario. The first sample, which consists of ten randomly selected delinquent accounts in Alberta, gives a mean dollar amount of $524 with a standard deviation of $68. The second sample, which consists of 20 randomly selected delinquent accounts in Ontario, gives a mean dollar amount of $473 with a standard deviation of $22. Use the information to test $H_0: \sigma_1^2 = s_2^2$ versus $H_a: \sigma_1^2 \neq \sigma_2^2$ with $\alpha = 0.05$. Based on this test, does it make sense to believe that the unequal-variances procedure is appropriate? Explain.

CHAPTER SUMMARY

Sometimes samples are not independent. We learned that one such case is the paired-differences experiment. In these types of experiments, we obtain two different measurements on the same sample units, and we first learned that we can compare two population means by using a confidence interval using the differences between the pairs of measurements. We next explained how to compare **two population proportions** from **large, independent samples** using a confidence interval.

    This chapter was devoted to hypothesis testing. We discussed how to conduct hypothesis tests under many scenarios using various *t* tests and *z* tests. We concluded the chapter by discussing how to compare **two population variances** by using independent samples, and we learned that this comparison is done by using a test based on the *F* distribution (Hartley *F*-max test).

GLOSSARY OF TERMS

***F* distribution:** A continuous probability curve with a shape that depends on two parameters—the numerator degrees of freedom, df_1, and the denominator degrees of freedom, df_2. (page 311)
sampling distribution of s_1^2/s_2^2: The probability distribution that describes the population of all possible values of s_1^2/s_2^2,

where s_1^2 is the sample variance of a random sample taken from one population and s_2^2 is the sample variance of a random sample taken from a second population. (page 311)

IMPORTANT FORMULAS AND TESTS

z test about $\mu_1 - \mu_2$: pages 290, 293

t test about $\mu_1 - \mu_2$ when $\sigma_1^2 = \sigma_2^2$: pages 295, 301

t test about $\mu_1 - \mu_2$ when $\sigma_1^2 \neq \sigma_2^2$: pages 296, 302–303

A hypothesis test about μ_d: pages 298, 303

Large-sample hypothesis test about $p_1 - p_2$: pages 307–308

Sampling distribution of s_1^2/s_2^2 (independent random samples): page 311

A hypothesis test about the equality of σ_1^2 and σ_2^2: pages 313, 314–315

connect Practise and learn online with *Connect*. Questions and tables with online data sets are marked with ✈.

SUPPLEMENTARY EXERCISES

9.47 In its February 2, 1998, issue, *Fortune* magazine published the results of a Yankelovich Partners survey of 600 adults that investigated their ideas about marriage, divorce, and the contributions of the corporate wife. The survey results are shown in Figure 9.14. For each statement in the figure, the proportions of men and women who agreed with the statement are given. Assume that the survey results were obtained from independent random samples of 300 men and 300 women.

For each statement, carry out a hypothesis test that tests the equality of the population proportions of men and women who agree with the statement. Use α equal to 0.10, 0.05, 0.01, and 0.001. How much evidence is there that the population proportions of men and women who agree with each statement differ?

Exercises 9.48 and 9.49 on the next page deal with the following situation:

In an article in the *Journal of Retailing*, Kumar, Kerwin, and Pereira study factors affecting merger and acquisition activity in retailing by comparing target firms and bidder firms with respect to several financial and marketing-related variables. If we consider two of the financial variables included in the study, suppose a random sample of 36 target firms gives a mean earnings per share of $1.52 with a standard deviation of $0.92, and that this sample gives a mean debt-to-equity ratio of 1.66 with a standard deviation of 0.82. Furthermore, an independent random sample of 36 bidder firms gives a mean earnings per share of $1.20 with a standard deviation of $0.84, and this sample gives a mean debt-to-equity ratio of 1.58 with a standard deviation of 0.81.

FIGURE **9.14** The Results of a Yankelovich Partners Survey of 600 Adults on Marriage, Divorce, and the Contributions of the Corporate Wife (All Respondents with Income $50,000 or More)

People were magnanimous on the general proposition:
- In a divorce in a long-term marriage where the husband works outside the home and the wife is not employed for pay, the wife should be entitled to half the assets accumulated during the marriage.
  93% of women agree
  85% of men agree

But when we got to the goodies, a gender gap began to appear . . .
- The pension accumulated during the marriage should be split evenly.
  80% of women agree
  68% of men agree
- Stock options granted during the marriage should be split evenly.
  77% of women agree
  62% of men agree

. . . and turned into a chasm over the issue of how important a stay-at-home wife is to a husband's success.
- Managing the household and child rearing are extremely important to a husband's success.
  57% of women agree
  41% of men agree
- A corporate wife who also must travel, entertain, and act as a sounding board is extremely important to the success of a high-level business executive.
  51% of women agree
  28% of men agree
- The lifestyle of a corporate wife is more of a job than a luxury.
  73% of women agree
  57% of men agree

Source: Reprinted from the February 2, 1998, issue of *Fortune*. Copyright © 1998 Time, Inc. Reprinted by permission.

9.48 Set up the null and alternative hypotheses needed to test whether the mean earnings per share for all target firms differs from the mean earnings per share for all bidder firms. Test these hypotheses at the 0.10, 0.05, 0.01, and 0.001 levels of significance. How much evidence is there that these means differ? Explain.

9.49 Set up the null and alternative hypotheses needed to test whether the mean debt-to-equity ratio for all target firms differs from the mean debt-to-equity ratio for all bidder firms. Test these hypotheses at the 0.10, 0.05, 0.01, and 0.001 levels of significance. How much evidence is there that these means differ? Explain.

Based on the results of this exercise and Exercise 9.48, which has more influence on whether a firm will be a target or a bidder: its earnings per share or its debt-to-equity ratio? Explain.

9.50 What impact did the September 11, 2001, terrorist attacks have on U.S. airline demand? An analysis was conducted by Ito and Lee, "Assessing the impact of the September 11 terrorist attacks on U.S. airline demand," in the *Journal of Economics and Business* (January–February 2005). They found a negative short-term effect of over 30 percent and an ongoing negative impact of over 7 percent. Suppose that we wish to test the impact by taking a random sample of 12 airline routes before and after September 11, 2001. Passenger miles (in millions) for the same routes were tracked for the 12 months prior to and the 12 months immediately following September 11, 2001. Assume that the population of all possible paired differences is normally distributed.

  a. Set up the null and alternative hypotheses needed to determine whether there was a reduction in mean airline passenger demand.

  b. Below, we present the outcomes of a paired-differences test. Use this and rejection points to test the hypotheses at the 0.10, 0.05, and 0.01 levels of significance. Has the true mean airline demand decreased?

	n	Mean	Standard Deviation
Before Sept. 11	12	117.333	26.976
After Sept. 11	12	87.583	25.518
Difference	12	29.7500	10.3056

  c. Use the p value to test the hypotheses at the 0.10, 0.05, and 0.01 levels of significance. How much evidence is there against the null hypothesis?

9.51 In the book *Essentials of Marketing Research*, Dillon, Madden, and Firtle discuss evaluating the effectiveness of a test coupon. Samples of 500 test coupons and 500 control coupons were randomly delivered to shoppers. The results indicated that 35 of the 500 control coupons

were redeemed, while 50 of the 500 test coupons were redeemed.

  a. In order to consider the test coupon for use, the marketing research organization required that the proportion of all shoppers who would redeem the test coupon be statistically shown to be greater than the proportion of all shoppers who would redeem the control coupon. Assuming that the two samples of shoppers are independent, carry out a hypothesis test at the 0.01 level of significance that will show whether this requirement is met by the test coupon. Explain your conclusion.

  b. Carry out the test of part a at the 0.10 level of significance. What do you conclude? Is your result statistically significant?

9.52 A marketing manager wishes to compare the mean prices charged for two brands of CD players. The manager conducts a random survey of retail outlets and obtains independent random samples of prices with the following results:

	Onkyo	JVC
Sample mean, $\bar{x}$	$189	$145
Sample standard deviation, s	$ 12	$ 10
Sample size	6	12

Assume normality and equal variances.

  a. Use an appropriate hypothesis test to determine whether the mean prices for the two brands differ. How much evidence is there that the mean prices differ?

  b. Use an appropriate hypothesis test to provide evidence supporting the claim that the mean price of the Onkyo CD player is more than $30 higher than the mean price of the JVC CD player. Set α equal to 0.05.

9.53 Consider the situation of Exercise 9.52. Use the sample information to test $H_0: \sigma_1^2 = \sigma_2^2$ versus $H_a: \sigma_1^2 \neq \sigma_2^2$ with $\alpha = 0.05$. Based on this test, does it make sense to use the equal-variances procedure? Explain.

9.54 **INTERNET EXERCISE**
Statistics Canada uses what it refers to as "Seasonal Adjustments" when determining the unemployment rates in Canada as a whole and for the provinces. Go to the Statistics Canada Web site (http://www.statcan.gc.ca).
  a. Determine what is meant by "seasonal adjustment."
  b. Compare and contrast the employment rates in Alberta and Manitoba. What are the differences and why do you think they exist?
  c. Compare and contrast the unemployment rates in your province and the national average. What are the differences and why do you think they exist?

CHAPTER 10
Experimental Design and Analysis of Variance

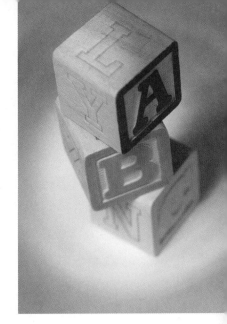

LEARNING OBJECTIVES

After reading this chapter, you should be able to

LO1 define an independent variable (IV) and a dependent variable (DV)

LO2 explain the difference between an experiment and an observational study

LO3 list the statistics that appear in an ANOVA results table and understand how they are computed

LO4 describe how pairwise comparisons are conducted

LO5 explain the term *randomized block design*

LO6 compare one-way ANOVA designs with two-way ANOVA designs

CHAPTER OUTLINE

10.1 Basic Concepts of Experimental Design

10.2 One-Way Analysis of Variance

10.3 The Randomized Block Design

10.4 Two-Way Analysis of Variance

In Chapter 9, we learned that business improvement often involves making **comparisons**. In that chapter, we presented several hypothesis-testing procedures for comparing two population means. However, business improvement often requires that we compare more than two means. For instance, we might compare the mean sales obtained by using three different advertising campaigns in order to improve a company's marketing process. Or, we might compare the mean production output obtained by using four different manufacturing process designs to improve productivity.

In this chapter, we extend the methods presented in Chapter 9 by considering statistical procedures for **comparing two or more means**. Each of the methods we discuss is called an **analysis of variance (ANOVA)** procedure. One advantage of conducting an ANOVA (over multiple comparisons between

two conditions) is that the overall Type I (α) error (as introduced in Chapter 8) is kept to a fixed level. For example, if there were three groups (as will be the case in the training method experiment case in this chapter), comparing the means would require conducting three *t* tests. If each comparison error were treated as an independent test and if the Type I error rate were set to 0.05 for each *t* test, then the overall error for this set of comparisons would be much greater than 0.05. In the ANOVA procedure, the means are compared in one analysis, keeping the Type I error level to 0.05. We also present some basic concepts of **experimental design**, which involves deciding how to collect data in a way that allows us to most effectively compare population means.

We explain the methods of this chapter in the context of three cases:

The Training Method Experiment Case: A camera manufacturer wants to improve the efficiency of packing by individuals (in terms of number of boxes packed per hour) by testing various training methods. The company uses **one-way ANOVA** to compare the effects of three different training methods to find the method that most increases packing efficiency.

The Defective Cardboard Box Case: A paper company performs an experiment to investigate the effects of four production methods on the number of defective cardboard boxes produced in an hour. The company uses a **randomized block ANOVA** to determine which production method yields the smallest mean number of defective boxes.

The Shelf Display Case: A commercial bakery supplies many supermarkets. In order to improve the effectiveness of its supermarket shelf displays, the company wishes to compare the effects of shelf display height (bottom, middle, or top) and width (regular or wide) on monthly demand. The bakery employs **two-way ANOVA** to find the display height and width combination that produces the highest monthly demand.

connect™ Practise and learn online with *Connect*. Throughout this chapter, questions and tables with online data sets are marked with ✈.

LO1

10.1 BASIC CONCEPTS OF EXPERIMENTAL DESIGN

In many statistical studies, researchers are interested in how a **factor** (the **independent variable** or **IV**) influences responses given by participants (the response measured is called the **dependent variable** or **DV**).[1] For example, a marketing company may be interested in the effects of a novel's cover on the likelihood that the novel will be purchased. The variable manipulated (cover appearance) is the independent variable, and the self-reported likelihood that the individual would buy the book is the dependent variable. If we cannot control the factor(s) being studied, we say that the data obtained are **observational**. For example, suppose that in order to study how the size of a home relates to the sale price of the home, a real estate agent randomly selects 50 recently sold homes and records the sizes and sale prices of these homes. Because the real estate agent cannot control the sizes of the randomly selected homes, we say that the data are observational.

If we can control the factors being studied, we say that the data are **experimental**. Furthermore, in this case the values, or **levels**, of the factor (or combination of factors) are called **LO2** **treatment groups** (or simply groups). The purpose of most experiments is *to compare and estimate the effects of the different treatment groups (IVs) on the response variable (DV)*. For example, suppose that an oil company wishes to study how three different gasoline types (*A*, *B*, and *C*) affect the fuel efficiency (L/100 km) obtained by a popular midsized automobile model. Here the response variable is fuel efficiency, and the company will study a single factor— gasoline type. Since the oil company can control which gasoline type is used in the midsized automobile, the data that it will collect are experimental. The levels of the factor "gasoline type" are *A*, *B*, and *C*. This type of experimental design is also described as being a 1×3 design because there is one factor or IV (gasoline type) with three levels. The model's dimensions are given in the notation as one row and three columns:

Gas *A*	Gas *B*	Gas *C*
x_1 litres per 100 km	x_2 litres per 100 km	x_3 litres per 100 km

In order to collect data in an experiment, the different IV levels are assigned to objects (people, cars, animals, or the like) that are called **experimental units**. For example, in the fuel efficiency situation, gasoline types *A*, *B*, and *C* will be compared by conducting fuel efficiency tests using a midsized automobile. The automobiles used in the tests are the experimental units.

In general, when an IV is applied to more than one experimental unit, it is said to be **replicated**. Furthermore, when the analyst controls the IVs employed and how they are applied to the experimental units, a **designed experiment** is being carried out. A commonly used, simple experimental design is called the **completely randomized experimental design**.

In a **completely randomized experimental design**, independent random samples of experimental units are assigned to the treatments.

---
[1]The independent variable is called "independent" because in an experimental condition, the independent variable is the one that is manipulated by the experimenter and is therefore independent of what the subject (or participant in the study) does. The participant's responses to the conditions set up by the experimenter are then termed as being "dependent" on the condition under which the participant was placed in the experiment.

Suppose we assign three experimental units to each of five IV levels (five groups). We can achieve a completely randomized experimental design by assigning experimental units to groups as follows. First, randomly select three experimental units and assign them to the first group. Next, randomly select three *different* experimental units from those remaining and assign them to the second group. That is, select these units from those not assigned to the first group. Third, randomly select three *different* experimental units from those not assigned to either the first or the second group. Assign these experimental units to the third group. Continue this procedure until the required number of experimental units have been assigned to each group.[2]

Once experimental units have been assigned to groups and the experiment has been completed, a value of the response variable is observed for each experimental unit. Thus, we obtain a *sample* of values of the response variable for each group. When we employ a completely randomized experimental design, we assume that each sample has been randomly selected from the population of all values of the response variable that could potentially be observed. We also assume that the different samples of response variable values are *independent* of each other. This is usually reasonable because the completely randomized design ensures that each different sample results from *measurements* being taken on *different experimental units*. Thus, we sometimes say that we are conducting an *independent-samples experiment*.

Example 10.1 Training Method Experiment Case

Great White North Cameras wants to increase the efficiency of its packers in terms of the number of camera boxes packed per hour. Clark, a human resources (HR) employee, suggests conducting an independent two-group design comparing passive video training (in which people watch a video about how to improve their efficiency) to interactive training (in which people actually pack boxes while receiving feedback from a trainer). Maggie (another HR employee) suggests adding in a third group, for comparison, that receives the basic training already used in the company (which consists of a booklet with photos explaining where the camera parts should be packed in the box and in what order). Clark agrees that this third group provides an excellent group to which to compare the other training methods and to act as a control group. So the HR department decides upon a completely randomized experimental design with three conditions in which the IV is the training condition (three levels) and the DV is the number of boxes an individual can pack per hour the day after receiving the training.

Fifteen employees are randomly selected from the pool of newly hired employees of Great White North Cameras. Of the fifteen individuals, five are randomly selected for the video training condition, five for the interactive training condition, and five for the standard training condition (the control group). In the following, the notation x_{ij} is used to denote the jth number of boxes packed per hour after receiving training type i. The data obtained are given in Table 10.1 and

TABLE **10.1** The Training Method Data

Video (Group A)	Interactive (Group B)	Standard (Group C)	
$x_{A1} = 34.0$	$x_{B1} = 35.3$	$x_{C1} = 33.3$	
$x_{A2} = 35.0$	$x_{B2} = 36.5$	$x_{C2} = 34.0$	
$x_{A3} = 34.3$	$x_{B3} = 36.4$	$x_{C3} = 34.7$	
$x_{A4} = 35.5$	$x_{B4} = 37.0$	$x_{C4} = 33.0$	
$x_{A5} = 35.8$	$x_{B5} = 37.6$	$x_{C5} = 34.9$	

[2]This method of sampling is also known as sampling without replacement. In experimental designs, it is ideal to have the same number of experimental units (subjects) in each condition. In addition, because the selection of experimental units is random, this means that each unit has an equal probability of being assigned to any of the experimental groups. It also means that different samples will result in different statistics (different means, variances, etc.).

represent the average numbers of boxes packed per hour. Examining the box plots shown next to the data, we see some evidence that the interactive training method (B) may result in the greatest efficiency in packing camera parts.

Example 10.2 The Shelf Display Case

The Tastee Bakery Company supplies a bakery product to many supermarkets in a metropolitan area. The company wishes to study the effect of the shelf display height (the IV) employed by the supermarkets on monthly sales (measured in cases of ten units each) for this product. Shelf display height has three levels: bottom (B), middle (M), and top (T). To compare these groups, the bakery uses a completely randomized experimental design. For each shelf height, six supermarkets (the experimental units) of equal sales potential are randomly selected, and each supermarket displays the product using its assigned shelf height for a month.[3] At the end of the month, sales of the bakery product (the DV or response variable) at the 18 participating stores are recorded, giving the data in Table 10.2. Here we assume that the set of sales amounts for each display height is a sample randomly selected from the population of all sales amounts that could be obtained (at supermarkets of the given sales potential) at that display height. Examining the box plots that are shown next to the sales data, we seem to have evidence that a middle display height gives the highest bakery product sales (which supports the marketing finding that products at eye level for an adult are purchased more often than are products at the top or the bottom of the shelf display).

TABLE **10.2** The Bakery Product Sales Data

| | Shelf Display Height | |
Bottom (*B*)	Middle (*M*)	Top (*T*)
58.2	73.0	52.4
53.7	78.1	49.7
55.8	75.4	50.9
55.7	76.2	54.0
52.5	78.4	52.1
58.9	82.1	49.9

Exercises for Section 10.1

CONCEPTS

10.1 Define the terms *response variable*, *factor*, and *experimental units*.

10.2 What is a completely randomized experimental design?

METHODS AND APPLICATIONS

10.3 A study compared three different display panels for use by air traffic controllers. Each display panel was tested in a simulated emergency condition; 12 highly

---

[3]Note that pure design individuals would state that this model is not a true experiment because the individuals shopping at the supermarkets are *not* randomly assigned to the conditions (in other words, people are not assigned to shop in a certain store). Equating the stores in terms of sales potential is advantageous, but it could be argued that any differences between stores could be due to uncontrollable factors (also called "third factors" or "nuisance variables"), such as unexpected construction near a store decreasing the number of shoppers. True experimentalists would then refer to this design as quasi-experimental.

TABLE 10.3 Display Panel Study Data

Display Panel		
A	B	C
21	24	40
27	21	36
24	18	35
26	19	32

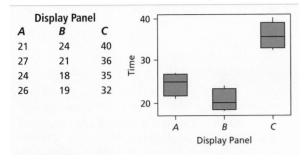

TABLE 10.4 Bottle Design Study Data

Bottle Design		
A	B	C
16	33	23
18	31	27
19	37	21
17	29	28
13	34	25

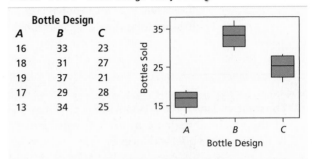

trained air traffic controllers took part in the study. Four controllers were randomly assigned to each display panel. The time (in seconds) needed to stabilize the emergency condition was recorded. The results of the study are given in Table 10.3. For this situation, identify the response variable, factor of interest, and experimental units.

10.4 A consumer preference study compares the effects of three different bottle designs (A, B, and C) on sales of a popular fabric softener. A completely randomized design is employed. Specifically, 15 supermarkets of equal sales potential are selected, and 5 of these supermarkets are randomly assigned to each bottle design. The number of bottles sold in 24 hours at each supermarket is recorded. The data obtained are displayed in Table 10.4. For this situation, identify the response variable, factor of interest, and experimental units.

10.2 ONE-WAY ANALYSIS OF VARIANCE

Suppose we wish to study the effects of p IV levels (1, 2, . . . , p) on a response variable. For any particular group, say group i, we define μ_i and σ_i to be the mean and standard deviation of the population of all possible values of the response variable that could potentially be observed for group i. Here we refer to μ_i as the **group mean i**. The goal of **one-way ANOVA** is to estimate and compare the effects of the different IV levels on the response variable. We do this by *estimating and comparing the group means* $\mu_1, \mu_2, . . . , \mu_p$. Here we assume that a sample has been randomly selected for each of the p groups by employing a completely randomized experimental design. We let n_i denote the size of the sample that has been randomly selected for group i, and we let x_{ij} denote the jth value of the response variable that is observed. It then follows that the point estimate of μ_i is $\bar{x}_i$, the average of the sample of n_i values of the response variable observed in group i. It further follows that the point estimate of σ_i is s_i, the standard deviation of the sample of n_i values of the response variable observed in group i.

VS

CHAPTER 12

Example 10.3 Training Method Experiment Case

Consider the training method case. We let μ_A, μ_B, and μ_C denote the means and σ_A, σ_B, and σ_C denote the standard deviations of the populations of all possible numbers of boxes packed per hour using training methods A (video), B (interactive), and C (reading only or control). To estimate these means and standard deviations, Great White North Cameras has employed a completely randomized experimental design and has obtained the numbers of boxes packed per hour in Table 10.1 on page 321. The means of these samples—$\bar{x}_A = 34.92$, $\bar{x}_B = 36.56$, and $\bar{x}_C = 33.98$—are the point estimates of μ_A, μ_B, and μ_C. The standard deviations of these samples—$s_A = 0.7662$, $s_B = 0.8503$, and $s_C = 0.8349$—are the point estimates of σ_A, σ_B, and σ_C. Using these point estimates, we will test to see whether there are any statistically significant differences between the means μ_A, μ_B, and μ_C. If such differences exist, we will estimate their magnitudes. This will allow Great White North Cameras to judge whether these differences have practical importance.

The one-way ANOVA formulas allow us to test for significant differences between group means and to estimate differences between group means. The validity of these formulas requires that the following assumptions hold:

Assumptions for One-Way ANOVA

1 **Constant variance:** The p populations of values of the response variable associated with the IV groups have equal variances.

2 **Normality:** The p populations of values of the response variable within each group all have normal distributions.

3 **Independence:** The samples of experimental units associated with the groups are randomly selected and independent.

The one-way ANOVA results are not very sensitive to violations of the equal-variances assumption. Studies have shown that this is particularly true when the sample sizes employed are equal (or nearly equal). Therefore, a good way to make sure that unequal variances will not be a problem is to take samples that are the same size. In addition, it is useful to compare the sample standard deviations $s_1, s_2, \ldots, s_p$ to see if they are reasonably equal. As a general rule, *the one-way ANOVA results will be approximately correct if the largest sample standard deviation is no more than twice the smallest sample standard deviation.*[4]

The normality assumption says that each of the p populations is normally distributed. This assumption is not crucial. It has been shown that the one-way ANOVA results are approximately valid for mound-shaped distributions. It is useful to construct a box plot and/or a stem-and-leaf display for each sample. If the distributions are reasonably symmetric, and if there are no outliers, the ANOVA results can be trusted for sample sizes as small as 4 or 5. As an example, consider the box-packing experiment of Examples 10.1 and 10.3. The box plots of Table 10.1 suggest that the variability of the numbers of boxes packed per hour in each of the three samples is roughly the same. Furthermore, the sample standard deviations $s_A = 0.7662$, $s_B = 0.8503$, and $s_C = 0.8349$ are reasonably equal (the largest is not even close to twice the smallest). Therefore, it is reasonable to believe that the constant-variance assumption is satisfied. Moreover, because the sample sizes are the same, unequal variances would probably not be a serious problem anyway. Many small, independent factors influence packing efficiency, so the distributions of data points for training methods A, B, and C are probably mound-shaped. In addition, the box plots of Table 10.1 indicate that each distribution is roughly symmetric with no outliers. Thus, the normality assumption probably approximately holds. Finally, because Great White North Cameras has employed a completely randomized design, the independence assumption probably holds. This is because the packing rates in the different samples were obtained for *different* employees.

Testing for significant differences between group means As a preliminary step in one-way ANOVA, we wish to determine whether there are any statistically significant differences between the group means $\mu_1, \mu_2, \ldots, \mu_p$. To do this, we test the null hypothesis

$$H_0: \mu_1 = \mu_2 = \cdots = \mu_p.$$

---

[4]The variations of the samples can also be compared by constructing a box plot for each sample (as we have done for the box-packing data in Table 10.1). Several statistical texts also employ the sample variances to test the equality of the population variances (see Bowerman and O'Connell (1990) for two of these tests). However, these tests have some drawbacks—in particular, their results are very sensitive to violations of the normality assumption. Because of this, there is controversy over whether these tests should be performed.

FIGURE 10.1   Comparing Between-Groups Variability and Within-Group Variability

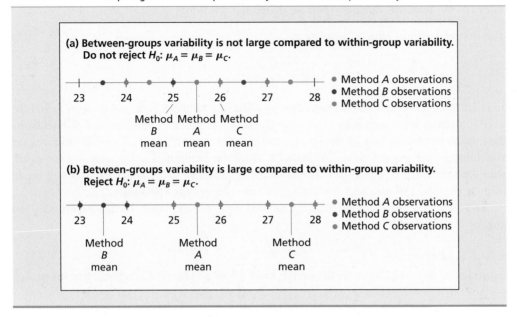

This hypothesis says that all the means are equal. We test H_0 versus the alternative hypothesis

$$H_a: \text{at least one pair of } \mu_1, \mu_2, \ldots, \mu_p \text{ differ.}$$

This alternative says that at least one group has a different mean.

To carry out such a test, we compare what we call the **between-groups** (or **between-treatments**) **variability** to the **within-group** (or **within-treatment**) **variability**. For instance, suppose we wish to study the effects of three training methods (*A*, *B*, and *C*) on mean packing efficiency, and consider Figure 10.1(a). This figure depicts three independent random samples of numbers of boxes packed per hour obtained using training methods *A* (video), *B* (interactive), and *C* (reading only or control). Observations obtained from training method *A* are plotted with blue dots (•), from method *B* with red dots (•), and from method *C* with green dots (•). Furthermore, the group means are labelled as "Method *A* mean," "Method *B* mean," and "Method *C* mean." We see that the variability of the means—that is, the **between-groups variability**—is not large compared to the variability within each sample (the **within-group variability**). In this case, the differences between the means could quite easily be the result of sampling variation. Thus, we would not have sufficient evidence to reject

$$H_0: \mu_A = \mu_B = \mu_C.$$

Next look at Figure 10.1(b), which depicts a different set of three independent random samples of packing efficiency. Here the variability of the means (the between-groups variability) is large compared to the variability within each group. This would probably provide enough evidence to tell us to reject

$$H_0: \mu_A = \mu_B = \mu_C$$

in favour of

$$H_a: \text{at least one mean is different}$$

We would conclude that at least one of training methods *A*, *B*, and *C* has a different effect on the mean number of boxes packed per hour.

In order to numerically compare the between-groups and within-group variability, we define **sums of squares** and **mean squares**. To begin, we define *n* to be the total number of experimental units employed in the one-way ANOVA, and we define $\bar{x}$ to be the overall mean of all observed values of the response variable. Then we define the following:

The **between-groups sum of squares** is

$$SSB = \sum_{i=1}^{p} n_i(\bar{x}_i - \bar{x})^2.$$

In order to compute the SSB, we calculate the difference between each group mean $\bar{x}_i$ and the overall mean $\bar{x}$, we square each of these differences, we multiply each squared difference by the number of observations for that group, and we sum over all groups. The SSB measures the variability of the group means. For instance, if all the group means ($\bar{x}_i$ values) were equal, then the SSB would be equal to 0. The more the $\bar{x}_i$ values vary, the larger the SSB will be. In other words, the SSB measures the amount of **between-groups variability**.

As an example, consider the training method data in Table 10.1. In this experiment, we employ a total of

$$n = n_A + n_B + n_C = 5 + 5 + 5 = 15$$

experimental units. Furthermore, the overall mean of the 15 observed numbers of boxes packed per hour is

$$\bar{x} = \frac{34.0 + 35.0 + \cdots + 34.9}{15} = \frac{527.3}{15} = 35.153.$$

Then

$$
\begin{aligned}
SSB &= \sum_{i=A,B,C} n_i(\bar{x}_i - \bar{x})^2 \\
&= n_A(\bar{x}_A - \bar{x})^2 + n_B(\bar{x}_B - \bar{x})^2 + n_C(\bar{x}_C - \bar{x})^2 \\
&= 5(34.92 - 35.153)^2 + 5(36.56 - 35.153)^2 + 5(33.98 - 35.153)^2 \\
&= 17.0493.
\end{aligned}
$$

Variability within a group is considered to be "noise" or random error. Because of this, within-group variability is the error term in an ANOVA.

In order to measure the within-group variability (error), we define the following quantity:

The **error sum of squares** is

$$SSE = \sum_{j=1}^{n_1} (x_{1j} - \bar{x}_1)^2 + \sum_{j=1}^{n_2} (x_{2j} - \bar{x}_2)^2 + \cdots + \sum_{j=1}^{n_p} (x_{pj} - \bar{x}_p)^2.$$

Here x_{1j} is the jth observed value of the response in the first group, x_{2j} is the jth observed value of the response in the second group, and so forth. The formula above says that we compute the SSE by calculating the squared difference between each observed value of the response and its corresponding group mean and by summing these squared differences over all the observations in the experiment.

The SSE measures the variability of the observed values of the response variable around their respective group means. For example, if there were no variability within each sample, the SSE would be equal to 0. The more the values within the groups vary, the larger the SSE will be.

As an example, in the training method study, the group means are $\bar{x}_A = 34.92$, $\bar{x}_B = 36.56$, and $\bar{x}_C = 33.98$. It follows that

$$
\begin{aligned}
SSE &= \sum_{j=1}^{n_A} (x_{Aj} - \bar{x}_A)^2 + \sum_{j=1}^{n_B} (x_{Bj} - \bar{x}_B)^2 + \sum_{j=1}^{n_C} (x_{Cj} - \bar{x}_C)^2 \\
&= [(34.0-34.92)^2 + (35.0-34.92)^2 + (34.3-34.92)^2 + (35.5-34.92)^2 + (35.8-34.92)^2] \\
&\quad + [(35.3-36.56)^2 + (36.5-36.56)^2 + (36.4-36.56)^2 + (37.0-36.56)^2 + (37.6-36.56)^2] \\
&\quad + [(33.3-33.98)^2 + (34.0-33.98)^2 + (34.7-33.98)^2 + (33.0-33.98)^2 + (34.9-33.98)^2] \\
&= 8.028.
\end{aligned}
$$

Finally, we define a sum of squares that measures the total amount of variability in the observed values of the response:

The **total sum of squares** is

$$SST = SSB + SSE.$$

The variability in the observed values of the response must come from one of two sources—the between-groups variability and the within-group variability. It follows that the SST equals the sum of the SSB and the SSE. Therefore, the SSB and SSE are said to partition the SST.

In the training method study, we see that

$$SST = SSB + SSE = 17.0493 + 8.028 = 25.0773.$$

Using the SSB and the SSE, we next define two **mean squares**:

The **between-groups mean square** is

$$MSB = \frac{SSB}{p-1}.$$

The **error mean square** is

$$MSE = \frac{SSE}{n-p}.$$

In order to decide whether there are any statistically significant differences between the group means, it makes sense to compare the amount of between-groups variability to the amount of within-group variability. This comparison suggests the following F test:

An *F* Test for Differences between Group Means

Suppose that we wish to compare p group means $\mu_1, \mu_2, \ldots, \mu_p$ and consider testing

$$H_0: \mu_1 = \mu_2 = \cdots = \mu_p$$
(all means are equal)

versus

$$H_a: \text{at least one of } \mu_1, \mu_2, \ldots, \mu_p \text{ differs}$$
(at least one mean is different).

Define the F statistic

$$F = \frac{MSB}{MSE} = \frac{SSB/(p-1)}{SSE/(n-p)}$$

and its p value to be the area under the F curve with $p - 1$ and $n - p$ degrees of freedom to the right of F. We can reject H_0 in favour of H_a at level of significance α if either of the following equivalent conditions holds:

1 $F > F_\alpha$.   2 p value $< \alpha$.

Here the F_α point is based on $p - 1$ numerator and $n - p$ denominator degrees of freedom.

A large value of F results when the SSB, which measures the between-groups variability, is large compared to the SSE, which measures the within-group variability. If F is large enough, this implies that H_0 should be rejected. The rejection point F_α tells us when F is large enough to allow us to reject H_0 at level of significance α. When F is large, the associated p value is small. If this p value is less than α, we can reject H_0 at level of significance α.

Example 10.4 Training Method Experiment Case

From the data presented in Table 10.1 on page 321, Great White North Cameras wishes to determine whether any of the training methods A, B, and C have different effects on the number of boxes packed per hour. That is, they are interested in whether or not there is a statistically significant difference between μ_A, μ_B, and μ_C. To determine this, we test the null hypothesis

$$H_0: \mu_A = \mu_B = \mu_C,$$

which says that training methods A, B, and C have the same effects on mean packing efficiency, versus the alternative

$$H_a: \text{at least one of } \mu_A, \mu_B, \text{ and } \mu_C \text{ is different,}$$

which says that at least one of training methods A, B, and C has a different effect on mean packing efficiency.

Since we have previously computed the SSB to be 17.0493 and the SSE to be 8.028, and because we are comparing $p = 3$ group means, we have

$$MSB = \frac{SSB}{p-1} = \frac{17.0493}{3-1} = 8.525$$

and

$$MSE = \frac{SSE}{n-p} = \frac{8.028}{15-3} = 0.669.$$

It follows that

$$F = \frac{MSB}{MSE} = \frac{8.525}{0.669} = 12.74.$$

In order to test H_0 at the 0.05 level of significance, we use $F_{0.05}$ with $p - 1 = 3 - 1 = 2$ numerator and $n - p = 15 - 3 = 12$ denominator degrees of freedom. Table A.7 tells us that this F point equals 3.89, so we have

$$F = 12.74 > F_{0.05} = 3.89.$$

Therefore, we reject H_0 at the 0.05 level of significance. This says we have strong evidence that at least one of the group means μ_A, μ_B, and μ_C is different. In other words, we conclude that at least one of training methods A, B, and C has a different effect on mean packing efficiency.

Figure 10.2 gives the Excel output of an ANOVA of the training method data. Note that the output gives the value $F = 12.74$ and the related p value, which equals 0.001 (rounded). Since this p value is less than 0.05, we reject H_0 at the 0.05 level of significance.

The results of an ANOVA are often summarized in what is called an **ANOVA table**. This table gives the sums of squares (SSB, SSE, SST), the mean squares (MSB and MSE), and the F statistic and its related p value for the ANOVA. The table also gives the degrees of freedom associated with each source of variation—between-groups, error, and total. Table 10.5 gives the ANOVA table for the training method experiment. Notice that in the column labelled "Sums of Squares," the SSB and SSE sum to the SST. Also notice that the lower portion of the Excel output in Figure 10.2 gives the ANOVA table of Table 10.5.

FIGURE 10.2   Excel Output of an Anova of the Training Method Data in Table 10.1

SUMMARY

Groups	Count	Sum	Average	Variance
Method A	5	174.6	34.92 [11]	0.587
Method B	5	182.8	36.56 [12]	0.723
Method C	5	169.9	33.98 [13]	0.697

ANOVA

Source of Variation	SS	df	MS	F	P-value	F crit
Between Groups	17.0493 [4]	2 [1]	8.5247 [7]	12.7424 [9]	0.0011 [10]	3.8853 [14]
Within Groups	8.0280 [5]	12 [2]	0.6690 [8]			
Total	25.0773 [6]	14 [3]				

[1] $p-1$ [2] $n-p$ [3] $n-1$ [4] SSB [5] SSE [6] SST [7] MSB [8] MSE [9] F statistic [10] p value related to F [11] $\bar{x}_A$ [12] $\bar{x}_B$ [13] $\bar{x}_C$ [14] $F_{0.05}$

TABLE **10.5** ANOVA Table for Testing $H_0: \mu_A = \mu_B = \mu_C$ in the Training Method Experiment ($p = 3$ Training Methods, $n = 15$ Observations)

LO3

Source	Degrees of Freedom	Sums of Squares	Mean Squares	F Statistic	p Value
Groups	$\begin{aligned}p - 1 &= 3 - 1\\ &= 2\end{aligned}$	$SSB = 17.0493$	$\begin{aligned}MSB &= \dfrac{SSB}{p-1}\\ &= \dfrac{17.0493}{3-1}\\ &= 8.525\end{aligned}$	$\begin{aligned}F &= \dfrac{MSB}{MSE}\\ &= \dfrac{8.525}{0.669}\\ &= 12.74\end{aligned}$	0.001
Error	$\begin{aligned}n - p &= 15 - 3\\ &= 12\end{aligned}$	$SSE = 8.028$	$\begin{aligned}MSE &= \dfrac{SSE}{n-p}\\ &= \dfrac{8.028}{15-3}\\ &= 0.669\end{aligned}$		
Total	$\begin{aligned}n - 1 &= 15 - 1\\ &= 14\end{aligned}$	$SST = 25.0773$			

Before we continue, note that if we use the ANOVA F statistic to test the equality of *two* population means, it can be shown that

1 F equals t^2, where t is the equal-variances t statistic discussed in Section 9.3 (pages 295–299) used to test the equality of the two population means.

2 The rejection point F_α, which is based on $p - 1 = 2 - 1 = 1$ and $n - p = n_1 + n_2 - 2$ degrees of freedom, equals $t^2_{\alpha/2}$, where $t_{\alpha/2}$ is the rejection point for the equal-variances t test and is based on $n_1 + n_2 - 2$ degrees of freedom.

Hence, the rejection conditions

$$F > F_\alpha \qquad \text{and} \qquad |t| > t_{\alpha/2}$$

are equivalent. It can also be shown that in this case, the p value related to F equals the p value related to t. Therefore, the ANOVA F test of the equality of p group means can be regarded as a generalization of the equal-variances t test of the equality of two group means.

Pairwise comparisons If the one-way ANOVA F test says that at least one group mean is different, then we investigate which mean is different and we estimate how large the difference is. We do this by making **pairwise comparisons** (that is, we compare group means *two at a time*). One way to make these comparisons is to compute point estimates of and confidence intervals for **pairwise differences**. For example, in the training method experiment, we would estimate the pairwise differences $\mu_A - \mu_B$, $\mu_A - \mu_C$, and $\mu_B - \mu_C$. Here, for instance, the pairwise difference $\mu_A - \mu_B$ can be interpreted as the change in mean packing efficiency achieved by changing from using training method B (interactive training) to using training method A (watching a video). Because these analyses are conducted after the fact, they are referred to as post hoc analyses.

LO4

There are two approaches to calculating confidence intervals for pairwise differences. The first involves computing the usual, or *individual*, confidence interval for each pairwise difference. Here, if we are computing $100(1 - \alpha)$ percent confidence intervals, we are $100(1 - \alpha)$ percent confident that each individual pairwise difference is contained in its respective interval. That is, the confidence level associated with each (individual) comparison is $100(1 - \alpha)$ percent, and we refer to α as the **comparisonwise error rate**. However, we are less than $100(1 - \alpha)$ percent confident that all of the pairwise differences are simultaneously contained in their respective intervals. A more conservative approach is to compute *simultaneous* confidence intervals. Such intervals make us $100(1 - \alpha)$ percent confident that all of the pairwise differences are simultaneously contained in their respective intervals. That is, when we compute simultaneous intervals, the overall confidence level associated with all the comparisons being made in the experiment is $100(1 - \alpha)$ percent, and we refer to α as the **experimentwise error rate**.

Several kinds of simultaneous confidence intervals can be computed. In this book, we present what is called the **Tukey formula** for simultaneous intervals. We do this because *if we are interested in studying all pairwise differences between group means, the Tukey formula yields the most precise (shortest) simultaneous confidence intervals.* In general, a Tukey simultaneous $100(1 - \alpha)$ percent confidence interval is longer than the corresponding individual $100(1 - \alpha)$ percent confidence interval. Thus, intuitively, we are paying a penalty for simultaneous confidence by obtaining longer intervals. One pragmatic approach to comparing group means is to first determine if we can use the more conservative Tukey intervals to make meaningful pairwise comparisons. If we cannot, then we might see what the individual intervals tell us. In the following box, we present both individual and Tukey simultaneous confidence intervals for pairwise differences. We also present the formula for a confidence interval for a single group mean, which we might use after we have used pairwise comparisons to determine the "best" group.

Estimation in One-Way ANOVA

1. Consider the **pairwise difference** $\mu_i - \mu_h$, which can be interpreted to be the change in the mean value of the response variable associated with h versus i. Then a **point estimate of the difference** $\mu_i - \mu_h$ **is** $\bar{x}_i - \bar{x}_h$, where $\bar{x}_i$ and $\bar{x}_h$ are the group means associated with i and h.

2. An **individual $100(1 - \alpha)$ percent confidence interval for $\mu_i - \mu_h$ is**

$$\left[\bar{x}_i - \bar{x}_h \pm t_{\alpha/2} \sqrt{MSE\left(\frac{1}{n_i} + \frac{1}{n_h}\right)} \right].$$

   Here the $t_{\alpha/2}$ point is based on $n - p$ degrees of freedom, and MSE is the previously defined error mean square found in the ANOVA table.

3. A **Tukey simultaneous $100(1 - \alpha)$ percent confidence interval for $\mu_i - \mu_h$ is**

$$\left[\bar{x}_i - \bar{x}_h \pm q_\alpha \sqrt{\frac{MSE}{m}} \right].$$

Here the value q_α is obtained from Table A.10, which is a table of percentage points of the studentized range. In this table, q_α is listed corresponding to values of p and $n - p$. Furthermore, we assume that the sample sizes n_i and n_h are equal to the same value, which we denote as m. If n_i and n_h are not equal, we replace $q_\alpha \sqrt{MSE/m}$ by $(q_\alpha/\sqrt{2})\sqrt{MSE[(1/n_i) + (1/n_h)]}$.

4. A **point estimate of the group mean μ_i is $\bar{x}_i$** and an **individual $100(1 - \alpha)$ percent confidence interval for μ_i** is

$$\left[\bar{x}_i \pm t_{\alpha/2} \sqrt{\frac{MSE}{n_i}} \right].$$

Here the $t_{\alpha/2}$ point is based on $n - p$ degrees of freedom.

Example 10.5 Training Method Experiment Case

In the training method experiment, we are comparing $p = 3$ group means (μ_A, μ_B, and μ_C). Furthermore, each sample is of size $m = 5$, there are a total of $n = 15$ observed packing times, and the *MSE* found in Table 10.5 is 0.669. Because $q_{0.05} = 3.77$ is the entry found in Table A.10 corresponding to $p = 3$ and $n - p = 12$, a Tukey simultaneous 95 percent confidence interval for $\mu_B - \mu_A$ is

$$\left[\bar{x}_B - \bar{x}_A \pm q_{0.05} \sqrt{\frac{MSE}{m}} \right] = \left[36.56 - 34.92 \pm 3.77 \sqrt{\frac{0.669}{5}} \right]$$

$$= [1.64 \pm 1.379]$$

$$= [0.261, 3.019].$$

Similarly, Tukey simultaneous 95 percent confidence intervals for $\mu_A - \mu_C$ and $\mu_B - \mu_C$ are, respectively,

$$[\bar{x}_A - \bar{x}_C \pm 1.379] \qquad \text{and} \qquad [\bar{x}_B - \bar{x}_C \pm 1.379]$$
$$= [34.92 - 33.98 \pm 1.379] \qquad \qquad = [36.56 - 33.98 \pm 1.379]$$
$$= [-0.439, 2.319] \qquad \qquad = [1.201, 3.959].$$

These intervals make us simultaneously 95 percent confident that

1   using interactive training (method B) compared to watching a video (method A) increases the mean number of boxes packed per hour by between 0.261 and 3.019 boxes,

2   changing the training method from reading instructions only (method C or the control group method) to showing a video (method A) might decrease the mean number of boxes packed by as much as 0.439 or might increase the mean number of boxes packed by as much as 2.319, and

3   changing the training method from reading instructions only (method C) to interactive training (method B) increases the mean number of boxes packed by between 1.201 and 3.959.

The first and third of these intervals make us 95 percent confident that μ_B is at least 0.261 boxes greater than μ_A and at least 1.201 boxes greater than μ_C. Therefore, we have strong evidence that training method B yields the highest mean number of boxes packed of the training methods tested. Furthermore, noting that $t_{0.025}$ based on $n - p = 12$ degrees of freedom is 2.179, it follows that an individual 95 percent confidence interval for μ_B is

$$\left[\bar{x}_B \pm t_{0.025}\sqrt{\frac{MSE}{n_B}}\right] = \left[36.56 \pm 2.179\sqrt{\frac{0.669}{5}}\right]$$
$$= [35.763, 37.357].$$

This interval says we can be 95 percent confident that the mean number of boxes packed by using interactive training (method B) is between 35.763 and 37.357 boxes.

We next consider testing $H_0: \mu_i - \mu_h = 0$ versus $H_a: \mu_i - \mu_h \neq 0$. The test statistic t for performing this test is calculated by dividing $\bar{x}_i - \bar{x}_h$ by $\sqrt{MSE[1/n_i + 1/n_h]}$. For example, consider testing $H_0: \mu_B - \mu_A = 0$ versus $H_a: \mu_B - \mu_A \neq 0$. Since $\bar{x}_B - \bar{x}_A = 34.92 - 36.56 = 1.64$ and $\sqrt{MSE[1/n_B + 1/n_A]} = \sqrt{0.669[1/5 + 1/5]} = 0.5173$, the test statistic t equals $1.64/0.5173 = 3.17$. This test statistic value is given in the table at the left of the following MegaStat output, as is the test statistic value for testing $H_0: \mu_B - \mu_C = 0$ ($t = 4.99$) and the test statistic value for testing $H_0: \mu_A - \mu_C = 0$ ($t = 1.82$):

Tukey simultaneous comparison t-values (d.f. = 12)	Method C 33.98	Method A 34.92	Method B 36.56
Method C 33.98			
Method A 34.92	1.82		
Method B 36.56	4.99	3.17	

critical values for experimentwise error rate:
0.05	2.67
0.01	3.56

p-values for pairwise t-tests	Method C 33.98	Method A 34.92	Method B 36.56
Method C 33.98			
Method A 34.92	0.0942		
Method B 36.56	0.0003	0.0081	

= Significant at 0.05 level
= Significant at 0.01 level
= Significant at 0.01 level

If we wish to use the Tukey simultaneous comparison procedure with an experimentwise error rate of α, we reject $H_0: \mu_i - \mu_h = 0$ in favour of $H_a: \mu_i - \mu_h \neq 0$ if the absolute value of t is greater than the rejection point $q_\alpha/\sqrt{2}$. Table A.10 tells us that $q_{0.05}$ is 3.77 and $q_{0.01}$ is 5.04. Therefore, the rejection points for experimentwise error rates of 0.05 and 0.01 are, respectively, $3.77/\sqrt{2} = 2.67$ and $5.04/\sqrt{2} = 3.56$ (see the MegaStat output). Suppose we set α equal to 0.05. Then, since the test statistic value for testing $H_0: \mu_B - \mu_A = 0$ ($t = 3.17$) and the test statistic value for testing $H_0: \mu_B - \mu_C = 0$ ($t = 4.99$) are greater than the rejection point 2.67, we reject both null hypotheses. This, along with the fact that $\bar{x}_B = 36.56$ is greater than $\bar{x}_A = 34.92$ and $\bar{x}_C = 33.98$, leads us to conclude that training method B yields the highest mean number of packed boxes of the training methods tested (note that the MegaStat output conveniently arranges the sample means in increasing order). Finally, note that the table at the right of the MegaStat output gives the p values for individual (rather than simultaneous) pairwise hypothesis tests. For example, the individual p value for testing H_0: $\mu_B - \mu_C = 0$ is 0.0003, and the individual p value for testing H_0: $\mu_B - \mu_A = 0$ is 0.0081.

In general, when we use a completely randomized experimental design, it is important to compare the groups by using experimental units that are essentially the same with respect to the characteristic under study. For example, in the training method experiment, we have tested employees of the same type (new employees who have not received training) to compare the different training methods, and in the shelf display case we have used grocery stores of the same sales potential for the bakery product to compare the shelf display heights. Sometimes, however, it is not possible to use experimental units that are essentially the same with respect to the characteristic under study. For example, suppose a chain of stores that sells audio and video equipment wishes to compare the effects of street, mall, and downtown locations on the sales volume of its stores. The experimental units in this situation are the areas where the stores are located, but these areas are not of the same sales potential because each area is populated by a different number of households. In such a situation, we must explicitly account for the differences in the experimental units. One way to do this is to use **regression analysis**, which is discussed in Chapters 11 and 12. When we use regression analysis to explicitly account for a variable (such as the number of households in the store's area) that causes differences in the experimental units, we call the variable a **covariate**. Furthermore, we say that we are performing an **analysis of covariance**. Finally, another way to deal with differing experimental units is to employ a **randomized block design**. This experimental design is discussed in Section 10.3.

To conclude this section, we note that if we fear that the normality and/or equal-variances assumptions for one-way ANOVA do not hold, we can use a nonparametric approach to compare several populations. One such approach is the Kruskal–Wallis H test, which is discussed in Section 13.4.

Exercises for Section 10.2

CONCEPTS

10.5 Explain the assumptions that must be satisfied in order to validly use the one-way ANOVA formulas.

10.6 Explain the difference between the between-groups variability and the within-group variability when performing a one-way ANOVA.

10.7 Explain why we conduct pairwise comparisons of group means.

10.8 Explain the difference between individual and simultaneous confidence intervals for a set of several pairwise differences.

METHODS AND APPLICATIONS

10.9 THE SHELF DISPLAY CASE

Consider Example 10.2, and let μ_B, μ_M, and μ_T represent the mean monthly sales when using the bottom, middle, and top shelf display heights, respectively. Figure 10.3 gives the MegaStat output of a one-way ANOVA of the bakery sales study data.

a. Test the null hypothesis that μ_B, μ_M, and μ_T are equal by setting $\alpha = 0.05$. On the basis of this test, can you conclude that the bottom, middle, and top

shelf display heights have different effects on mean monthly sales?

b. Consider the pairwise differences $\mu_M - \mu_B$, $\mu_T - \mu_B$, and $\mu_T - \mu_M$. Which display height maximizes mean sales?

10.10 Consider the display panel situation in Exercise 10.3, and let μ_A, μ_B, and μ_C represent the mean times to stabilize the emergency condition when using display panels A, B, and C, respectively. Figure 10.4 gives the MegaStat output of a one-way ANOVA of the display panel data.

a. Test the null hypothesis that μ_A, μ_B, and μ_C are equal by setting $\alpha = 0.05$. On the basis of this test, can you conclude that display panels A, B, and C have different effects on the mean time to stabilize the emergency condition?

b. Consider the pairwise differences $\mu_B - \mu_A$, $\mu_C - \mu_A$, and $\mu_C - \mu_B$. Interpret the results by describing the effects of changing from using each display panel to using each of the other panels. Which display panel minimizes the time required to stabilize the emergency condition?

FIGURE 10.3 MegaStat Output of a One-Way ANOVA of the Bakery Sales Study Data

Bakery Sales

Display Height

Bottom	Middle	Top
58.2	73.0	52.4
53.7	78.1	49.7
55.8	75.4	50.9
55.7	76.2	54.0
52.5	78.4	52.1
58.9	82.1	49.9

One factor ANOVA

	Mean	n	Std. Dev
Bottom	55.80	6	2.477
Middle	77.20	6	3.103
Top	51.50	6	1.648
Total	61.50	18	11.798

ANOVA table

Source	SS	df	MS	F	p-value
Treatment	2,273.880	2	1,136.9400	184.57	2.74E-11
Error	92.400	15	8.1000		
Total	2,366.280	17			

Post hoc analysis
Tukey Simultaneous comparison t-values (d.f. = 15)

		Top 51.50	Bottom 55.80	Middle 77.20
Top	51.50			
Bottom	55.80	3.00		
Middle	77.20	17.94	14.93	

critical values for experimentwise error rate:

0.05	2.60
0.01	3.42

p-values for pairwise t-tests

		Top 51.50	Bottom 55.80	Middle 77.20
Top	51.50			
Bottom	55.80	0.0090		
Middle	77.20	1.52E-11	2.07E-10	

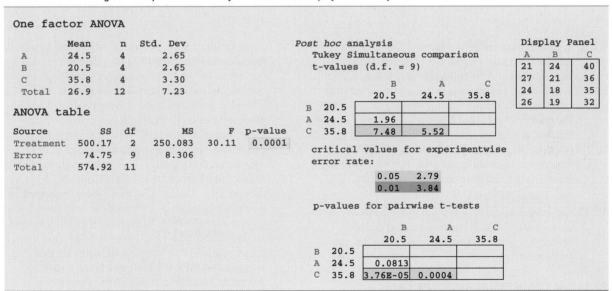

FIGURE 10.4 MegaStat Output of a One-Way ANOVA of the Display Panel Study Data

One factor ANOVA

	Mean	n	Std. Dev
A	24.5	4	2.65
B	20.5	4	2.65
C	35.8	4	3.30
Total	26.9	12	7.23

ANOVA table

Source	SS	df	MS	F	p-value
Treatment	500.17	2	250.083	30.11	0.0001
Error	74.75	9	8.306		
Total	574.92	11			

Post hoc analysis
Tukey Simultaneous comparison t-values (d.f. = 9)

		B 20.5	A 24.5	C 35.8
B	20.5			
A	24.5	1.96		
C	35.8	7.48	5.52	

critical values for experimentwise error rate:

0.05	2.79
0.01	3.84

p-values for pairwise t-tests

		B 20.5	A 24.5	C 35.8
B	20.5			
A	24.5	0.0813		
C	35.8	3.76E-05	0.0004	

Display Panel

A	B	C
21	24	40
27	21	36
24	18	35
26	19	32

10.11 Consider the bottle design study situation in Exercise 10.4, and let μ_A, μ_B, and μ_C represent mean daily sales using bottle designs *A*, *B*, and *C*, respectively. Figure 10.5 on the next page gives the Excel output of a one-way ANOVA of the bottle design study data.

a. Test the null hypothesis that μ_A, μ_B, and μ_C are equal by setting $\alpha = 0.05$. That is, test for statistically significant differences between these group means at the 0.05 level of significance. Based on this test, can you conclude that bottle designs *A*, *B*, and *C* have different effects on mean daily sales?

b. Consider the pairwise differences $\mu_B - \mu_A$, $\mu_C - \mu_A$, and $\mu_C - \mu_B$. Find a point estimate of and a Tukey simultaneous 95 percent confidence interval for each pairwise difference. Interpret the results in practical terms. Which bottle design maximizes mean daily sales?

c. Find an individual 95 percent confidence interval for each pairwise difference in part b. Interpret the results in practical terms.

d. Find a 95 percent confidence interval for each of the group means μ_A, μ_B, and μ_C. Interpret these intervals.

FIGURE 10.5 Excel Output of a One-Way ANOVA of the Bottle Design Study Data

SUMMARY							Bottles Sold		
Groups	**Count**	**Sum**	**Average**	**Variance**				Bottle Design	
DESIGN A	5	83	16.6	5.3			*A*	*B*	*C*
DESIGN B	5	164	32.8	9.2			16	33	23
DESIGN C	5	124	24.8	8.2			18	31	27
							19	37	21
ANOVA							17	29	28
Source of Variation	**SS**	**df**	**MS**	**F**	**P-Value**	**F crit**	13	34	25
Between Groups	656.1333	2	328.0667	43.35683	3.23E-06	3.88529			
Within Groups	90.8	12	7.566667						
Total	746.9333	14							

TABLE 10.6 Golf Ball Durability Test Results and a MegaStat Plot of the Results

	Brand			
Alpha	**Best**	**Century**	**Divot**	
281	270	218	364	
220	334	244	302	
274	307	225	325	
242	290	273	337	
251	331	249	355	

10.12 In order to compare the durability of four different brands of golf balls (Alpha, Best, Century, and Divot), the Canuck Golf Association randomly selects five balls of each brand and places each ball into a machine that exerts the force produced by a 250-yard (230-m) drive. The number of simulated drives needed to crack or chip each ball is recorded. The results are given in Table 10.6. The MegaStat output of a one-way ANOVA of these data is shown in Figure 10.6. Test for statistically significant differences between the group means μ_{Alpha}, μ_{Best}, μ_{Century}, and μ_{Divot}. Set $\alpha = 0.05$.

10.13 Perform pairwise comparisons of the group means in Exercise 10.12. Which brand(s) are most durable? Find a 95 percent confidence interval for each of the group means.

10.14 THE COMMERCIAL RESPONSE CASE

Advertising research indicates that when a television program is involving, individuals exposed to commercials tend to have difficulty recalling the names of the products advertised. Therefore, in order for companies to make the best use of their advertising dollars, it is important to show their most original and memorable commercials during involving programs.

In an article in the *Journal of Advertising Research*, Soldow and Principe studied the effect of program content on the response to commercials. Program content, the factor studied, had three levels: more involving programs, less involving programs, and no program (that is, commercials only). To compare these groups, Soldow and Principe employed a completely randomized experimental design. For each program content level, 29 people were randomly selected and exposed to commercials in that program content level. Then a brand recall score (measured on a continuous scale) was obtained for each person. The 29 brand recall scores for each program content level are assumed to be a sample randomly selected from the population of all brand recall scores for that program content level. The mean brand recall scores for these three groups were, respectively, $\bar{x}_1 = 1.21$, $\bar{x}_2 = 2.24$, and $\bar{x}_3 = 2.28$. Furthermore, a one-way ANOVA of the data shows that $SSB = 21.40$ and $SSE = 85.56$.

a. Define appropriate group means μ_1, μ_2, and μ_3. Then test for statistically significant differences between these group means. Set $\alpha = 0.05$.

b. Perform pairwise comparisons of the group means by computing a Tukey simultaneous 95 percent confidence interval for each of the pairwise differences $\mu_1 - \mu_2$, $\mu_1 - \mu_3$, and $\mu_2 - \mu_3$. Which type of program content results in the worst mean brand recall score?

FIGURE 10.6 MegaStat Output of a One-Way ANOVA of the Golf Ball Durability Data

ANOVA table

Source	SS	df	MS	F [6]	p-value [7]
Treatment	29,860.40 [1]	3	9,953.467 [4]	16.42	3.85E-05
Error	9,698.40 [2]	16	606.150 [5]		
Total	39,558.80 [3]	19			

Mean	n	Std. Dev	
253.6	5	24.68	Alpha
306.4	5	27.21	Best
241.8	5	21.67	Century
336.6	5	24.60	Divot
284.6	20	45.63	Total

Tukey simultaneous comparison t-values (d.f. = 16)

		Century 241.8	Alpha 253.6	Best 306.4	Divot 336.6
Century	241.8				
Alpha	253.6	0.76			
Best	306.4	4.15	3.39		
Divot	336.6	6.09	5.33	1.94	

p-values for pairwise t-tests

		Century 241.8	Alpha 253.6	Best 306.4	Divot 336.6
Century	241.8				
Alpha	253.6	0.4596			
Best	306.4	0.0008	0.0037		
Divot	336.6	1.57E-05	0.0001	0.0703	

Critical values for experimentwise error rate:

0.05	2.86
0.01	3.67

[1] SSB	[2] SSE	[3] SST	[4] MSB	[5] MSE	[6] F	[7] p value for F

10.3 THE RANDOMIZED BLOCK DESIGN

Not all experiments employ a completely randomized design. For instance, suppose that when we employ a completely randomized design, we fail to reject the null hypothesis of equality of group means because the within-groups variability (which is measured by the *SSE*) is large. This could happen because differences between the experimental units are concealing true differences between the groups. We can often remedy this by using what is called a **randomized block design**.

L05

Example 10.6 The Defective Cardboard Box Case

The Universal Paper Company manufactures cardboard boxes. The company wishes to investigate the effects of four production methods (methods 1, 2, 3, and 4) on the number of defective boxes produced in an hour. To compare the methods, the company could utilize a completely randomized design. For each of the four production methods, the company would select several (for example, three) machine operators, train each operator to use the production method to which they have been assigned, have each operator produce boxes for one hour, and record the number of defective boxes produced. The three operators using any one production method would be *different* from those using any other production method. That is, the completely randomized design would utilize a total of 12 machine operators. However, the abilities of the machine operators could differ substantially. These differences might tend to conceal any real differences between the production methods. To overcome this disadvantage, the company will employ a **randomized block experimental design**. This involves randomly selecting three machine operators and training each operator thoroughly to use all four production methods. Then each operator will produce boxes for one hour using each of the four production methods. The order in which each operator uses the four methods should be random. We record the number of defective boxes produced by each operator using each method. The advantage of the randomized block design is that the defective rates obtained by using the four methods result from employing the *same* three operators. Thus, any true differences in the effectiveness of the methods would not be concealed by differences in the operators' abilities.

When Universal Paper employs the randomized block design, it obtains the 12 defective box counts in Table 10.7 on the next page. We let x_{ij} denote the number of defective boxes produced

TABLE **10.7**   Numbers of Defective Cardboard Boxes Obtained by Production Methods 1, 2, 3, and 4 and Machine Operators 1, 2, and 3

Group (Production Method)	Block (Machine Operator) 1	2	3	Group Mean	
1	9	10	12	10.3333	
2	8	11	12	10.3333	
3	3	5	7	5.0	
4	4	5	5	4.6667	
Sample Block Mean	6.0	7.75	9.0	$\bar{x} = 7.5833$	

by machine operator j using production method i. For example, $x_{32} = 5$ says that 5 defective boxes were produced by machine operator 2 using production method 3 (see Table 10.7). In addition to the 12 defective box counts, Table 10.7 gives the sample mean of these 12 observations, which is $\bar{x} = 7.5833$, and also gives **group means** and **sample block means**. The group means are the average defective box counts obtained when using production methods 1, 2, 3, and 4. Denoting these group means as $\bar{x}_{1\bullet}, \bar{x}_{2\bullet}, \bar{x}_{3\bullet}$, and $\bar{x}_{4\bullet}$, we see from Table 10.7 that $\bar{x}_{1\bullet} = 10.3333$, $\bar{x}_{2\bullet} = 10.3333$, $\bar{x}_{3\bullet} = 5.0$, and $\bar{x}_{4\bullet} = 4.6667$. Because $\bar{x}_{3\bullet}$ and $\bar{x}_{4\bullet}$ are less than $\bar{x}_{1\bullet}$ and $\bar{x}_{2\bullet}$, we estimate that the mean number of defective boxes produced per hour by production method 3 or 4 is less than the mean number of defective boxes produced per hour by production method 1 or 2. The sample block means are the average defective box counts obtained by machine operators 1, 2, and 3. Denoting these sample block means as $\bar{x}_{\bullet 1}, \bar{x}_{\bullet 2}$, and $\bar{x}_{\bullet 3}$, we see from Table 10.7 that $\bar{x}_{\bullet 1} = 6.0$, $\bar{x}_{\bullet 2} = 7.75$, and $\bar{x}_{\bullet 3} = 9.0$. Because $\bar{x}_{\bullet 1}, \bar{x}_{\bullet 2}$, and $\bar{x}_{\bullet 3}$ differ, we have evidence that the abilities of the machine operators differ and thus that using the machine operators as blocks is reasonable.

In general, a **randomized block design** compares p IV levels (for example, production method groups) by using b blocks (for example, machine operators). Each block is used exactly once to measure the effect of each and every treatment. The advantage of the randomized block design over the completely randomized design is that we are comparing the IV levels by using the *same* experimental units. Thus, any true differences in the groups will not be concealed by differences in the experimental units.

In some experiments, a block consists of **similar or matched sets of experimental units**. For example, suppose we wish to compare the performance of business majors, science majors, and fine arts majors on a graduate school admissions test. Here the blocks might be matched sets of students. Each matched set (block) would consist of a business major, a science major, and a fine arts major selected so that each is in their last year, attends the same university, and has the same grade point average. By selecting blocks in this fashion, any true differences between majors would not be concealed by differences between classes, universities, or grade point averages.

In order to analyze the data obtained in a randomized block design, we define

x_{ij} = the value of the response variable observed when block j uses IV level i,
$\bar{x}_{i\cdot}$ = the mean of the b values of the response variable observed in group i,
$\bar{x}_{\cdot j}$ = the mean of the p values of the response variable observed when using block j,
$\bar{x}$ = the mean of the total of the bp values of the response variable that we have observed in the experiment.

The ANOVA procedure for a randomized block design partitions the **total sum of squares** (**SST**) into three components: the **between-groups sum of squares** (**SSB**), the **block sum of squares** (**SSBL**), and the **error sum of squares** (**SSE**). The formula for this partitioning is

$$SST = SSB + SSBL + SSE.$$

The steps for calculating these sums of squares, as well as what is measured by the sums of squares, can be summarized as follows:

Step 1: Calculate the SSB, which measures the amount of between-groups variability:

$$SSB = b \sum_{i=1}^{p} (\bar{x}_{i\cdot} - \bar{x})^2.$$

Step 2: Calculate the $SSBL$, which measures the amount of variability due to the blocks:

$$SSBL = p \sum_{j=1}^{b} (\bar{x}_{\cdot j} - \bar{x})^2.$$

Step 3: Calculate the SST, which measures the total amount of variability:

$$SST = \sum_{i=1}^{p} \sum_{j=1}^{b} (x_{ij} - \bar{x})^2.$$

Step 4: Calculate the SSE, which measures the amount of variability due to the error:

$$SSE = SST - SSB - SSBL.$$

These sums of squares are shown in Table 10.8, which is the ANOVA table for a randomized block design. This table also gives the degrees of freedom associated with each source of variation—groups, blocks, error, and total—as well as the mean squares and F statistics used to test the hypotheses of interest in a randomized block experiment.

Before discussing these hypotheses, we will illustrate how the entries in the ANOVA table are calculated. The sums of squares in the defective cardboard box case are calculated as follows (note that $p = 4$ production methods and $b = 3$ machine operators):

Step 1:
$$\begin{aligned}
SSB &= 3[(\bar{x}_{1\cdot} - \bar{x})^2 + (\bar{x}_{2\cdot} - \bar{x})^2 + (\bar{x}_{3\cdot} - \bar{x})^2 + (\bar{x}_{4\cdot} - \bar{x})^2] \\
&= 3[(10.3333 - 7.5833)^2 + (10.3333 - 7.5833)^2 \\
&\quad + (5.0 - 7.5833)^2 + (4.6667 - 7.5833)^2] \\
&= 90.9167.
\end{aligned}$$

TABLE 10.8 ANOVA Table for the Randomized Block Design with p Groups and b Blocks

Source of Variation	Degrees of Freedom	Sum of Squares	Mean Square	F
Groups	$p - 1$	SSB	$MSB = \dfrac{SSB}{p - 1}$	$F(groups) = \dfrac{MSB}{MSE}$
Blocks	$b - 1$	$SSBL$	$MSBL = \dfrac{SSBL}{b - 1}$	$F(blocks) = \dfrac{MSBL}{MSE}$
Error	$(p - 1)(b - 1)$	SSE	$MSE = \dfrac{SSE}{(p - 1)(b - 1)}$	
Total	$pb - 1$	SST		

FIGURE **10.7**   MegaStat Output of a Randomized Block ANOVA of the Defective Box Data

Randomized blocks ANOVA

Mean	n	Std. Dev	
6.000	4	2.944	Operator1
7.750	4	3.202	Operator2
9.000	4	3.559	Operator3
10.333	3	1.528	Method1
10.333	3	2.082	Method2
5.000	3	2.000	Method3
4.667	3	0.577	Method4
7.583	12	3.204	Total

ANOVA table

Source	SS	df	MS	F	p-value
Treatments	90.92	3	30.306	47.43	0.0001
Blocks	18.17	2	9.083	14.22	0.0053
Error	3.83	6	0.639		
Total	112.92	11			

Post hoc analysis

Tukey simultaneous comparison t-values (d.f. = 6)

		Operator1 6.000	Operator2 7.750	Operator3 9.000
Operator1	6.000			
Operator2	7.750	3.10		
Operator3	9.000	5.31	2.21	

critical values for experimentwise error rate:

0.05	3.07
0.01	4.48

p-values for pairwise t-tests

		Operator1 6.000	Operator2 7.750	Operator3 9.000
Operator1	6.000			
Operator2	7.750	0.0212		
Operator3	9.000	0.0018	0.0690	

Step 2:
$$SSBL = 4[(\bar{x}_{\bullet 1} - \bar{x})^2 + (\bar{x}_{\bullet 2} - \bar{x})^2 + (\bar{x}_{\bullet 3} - \bar{x})^2]$$
$$= 4[(6.0 - 7.5833)^2 + (7.75 - 7.5833)^2 + (9.0 - 7.5833)^2]$$
$$= 18.1667.$$

Step 3:
$$SST = (9 - 7.5833)^2 + (10 - 7.5833)^2 + (12 - 7.5833)^2$$
$$+ (8 - 7.5833)^2 + (11 - 7.5833)^2 + (12 - 7.5833)^2$$
$$+ (3 - 7.5833)^2 + (5 - 7.5833)^2 + (7 - 7.5833)^2$$
$$+ (4 - 7.5833)^2 + (5 - 7.5833)^2 + (5 - 7.5833)^2$$
$$= 112.9167.$$

Step 4:
$$SSE = SST - SSB - SSBL$$
$$= 112.9167 - 90.9167 - 18.1667$$
$$= 3.8333.$$

Figure 10.7 gives the MegaStat output of a randomized block ANOVA of the defective box data. This figure shows the above-calculated sums of squares, as well as the degrees of freedom (recall that $p = 4$ and $b = 3$), the mean squares, and the F statistics (and associated p values) used to test the hypotheses of interest.

Of main interest is the test of the null hypothesis H_0 that **no differences exist between the IV levels** on the mean value of the response variable versus the alternative hypothesis H_a that **at least one group differs from the other groups**. We can reject H_0 in favour of H_a at level of significance α if

$$F(\text{groups}) = \frac{MSB}{MSE}$$

is greater than the F_α point based on $p - 1$ numerator and $(p - 1)(b - 1)$ denominator degrees of freedom. In the defective cardboard box case, $F_{0.05}$ based on $p - 1 = 3$ numerator and $(p - 1)(b - 1) = 6$ denominator degrees of freedom is 4.76 (see Table A.7). Because

$$F(\text{groups}) = \frac{MSB}{MSE} = \frac{30.306}{0.639} = 47.43$$

is greater than $F_{0.05} = 4.76$, we reject H_0 at the 0.05 level of significance. Therefore, we have strong evidence that at least one production method has a different effect on the mean number of defective boxes produced per hour. Alternatively, we can reject H_0 in favour of H_a at level of significance α if the p value is less than α. Here the p value is the area under the curve of the F distribution (with $p - 1$ and $(p - 1)(b - 1)$ degrees of freedom) to the right of

F(treatments or groups). The MegaStat output in Figure 10.7 tells us that this p value is 0.0001 (that is, less than 0.01) for the defective box data. Therefore, we have extremely strong evidence that at least one production method has a different effect on the mean number of defective boxes produced per hour.

It is also of interest to test the null hypothesis H_0 that **no differences exist between the block effects** on the mean value of the response variable versus the alternative hypothesis H_a that **at least one block effect is different**. We can reject H_0 in favour of H_a at level of significance α if

$$F(\text{blocks}) = \frac{MSBL}{MSE}$$

is greater than the F_α point based on $b - 1$ numerator and $(p - 1)(b - 1)$ denominator degrees of freedom. In the defective cardboard box case, $F_{0.05}$ based on $b - 1 = 2$ numerator and $(p - 1)(b - 1) = 6$ denominator degrees of freedom is 5.14 (see Table A.7). Because

$$F(\text{blocks}) = \frac{MSBL}{MSE} = \frac{9.083}{0.639} = 14.22$$

is greater than $F_{0.05} = 5.14$, we reject H_0 at the 0.05 level of significance. Therefore, we have strong evidence that at least one machine operator has a different effect on the mean number of defective boxes produced per hour. Alternatively, we can reject H_0 in favour of H_a at level of significance α if the p value is less than α. Here the p value is the area under the curve of the F distribution (with $b - 1$ and $(p - 1)(b - 1)$ degrees of freedom) to the right of F(blocks). The MegaStat output tells us that this p value is 0.0053 for the defective box data. Therefore, we have very strong evidence that at least one machine operator has a different effect on the mean number of defective boxes produced per hour. This implies that using the machine operators as blocks is reasonable.

If, in a randomized block design, we conclude that at least one group mean differs, we can perform pairwise comparisons to determine how they differ.

Point Estimates and Confidence Intervals in a Randomized Block ANOVA

Consider the **difference between groups i and h on the mean value of the response variable**.

1   A *point estimate* of this difference is $\bar{x}_{i\bullet} - \bar{x}_{h\bullet}$.

2   An **individual $100(1 - \alpha)$ percent confidence interval** for this difference is

$$\left[\bar{x}_{i\bullet} - \bar{x}_{h\bullet} \pm t_{\alpha/2} s \sqrt{\frac{2}{b}} \right].$$

Here $t_{\alpha/2}$ is based on $(p - 1)(b - 1)$ degrees of freedom, and s is the square root of the MSE found in the randomized block ANOVA table.

3   A **Tukey simultaneous $100(1 - \alpha)$ percent confidence interval** for this difference is

$$\left[\bar{x}_{i\bullet} - \bar{x}_{h\bullet} \pm q_\alpha \frac{s}{\sqrt{b}} \right].$$

Here the value q_α is obtained from Table A.10, which is a table of percentage points of the studentized range. In this table, q_α is listed corresponding to values of p and $(p - 1)(b - 1)$.

Example 10.7 The Defective Cardboard Box Case

We have previously concluded that we have extremely strong evidence that at least one production method has a different mean number of defective boxes produced per hour. We have also seen that the group means are $\bar{x}_{1\bullet} = 10.3333$, $\bar{x}_{2\bullet} = 10.3333$, $\bar{x}_{3\bullet} = 5.0$, and $\bar{x}_{4\bullet} = 4.6667$. Since $\bar{x}_{4\bullet}$ is the smallest mean, we will use Tukey simultaneous 95 percent confidence intervals to compare the effect of production method 4 to the effects of production methods 1, 2, and 3. To compute these intervals, we first note that $q_{0.05} = 4.90$ is the entry in Table A.10 corresponding to $p = 4$ and $(p - 1)(b - 1) = 6$. Also note that the MSE found in the randomized block ANOVA table is 0.639 (see Figure 10.7), which implies that $s = \sqrt{0.639} = 0.7994$. It follows that a Tukey simultaneous 95 percent confidence interval for the difference between the effects of production methods 4 and 1 on the mean number of defective boxes produced per hour is

$$\left[\bar{x}_{4\bullet} - \bar{x}_{1\bullet} \pm q_{0.05}\frac{s}{\sqrt{b}} \right] = \left[4.6667 - 10.3333 \pm 4.90\left(\frac{0.7994}{\sqrt{3}}\right) \right]$$
$$= [-5.6666 \pm 2.2615]$$
$$= [-7.9281, -3.4051].$$

Furthermore, it can be verified that a Tukey simultaneous 95 percent confidence interval for the difference between the effects of production methods 4 and 2 on the mean number of defective boxes produced per hour is also $[-7.9281, -3.4051]$. Therefore, we can be 95 percent confident that changing from production method 1 or 2 to production method 4 decreases the mean number of defective boxes produced per hour by a machine operator by between 3.4051 and 7.9281 boxes. A Tukey simultaneous 95 percent confidence interval for the difference between the effects of production methods 4 and 3 on the mean number of defective boxes produced per hour is

$$[\bar{x}_{4\bullet} - \bar{x}_{3\bullet} \pm 2.2615] = [4.6667 - 5 \pm 2.2615]$$
$$= [-2.5948, 1.9282].$$

This interval tells us (with 95 percent confidence) that changing from production method 3 to production method 4 might decrease the mean number of defective boxes produced per hour by as many as 2.5948 boxes or might increase this mean by as many as 1.9282 boxes. In other words, because this interval contains 0, we cannot conclude that the effects of production methods 4 and 3 differ.

Exercises for Section 10.3

CONCEPTS

10.15 In your own words, explain why we sometimes employ the randomized block design.

10.16 How can we test to determine if the blocks we have chosen are reasonable?

METHODS AND APPLICATIONS

10.17 A marketing organization wishes to study the effects of four sales methods on weekly sales of a product. The organization employs a randomized block design in which three salespeople use each sales method. The results obtained are given in Table 10.9. Figure 10.8 on

the next page gives the Excel output of a randomized block ANOVA of the sales method data.

a. Test the null hypothesis H_0 that no differences exist between the effects of the sales methods (groups) on mean weekly sales. Set $\alpha = 0.05$. Can you conclude that the different sales methods have different effects on mean weekly sales?

b. Test the null hypothesis H_0 that no differences exist between the effects of the salespeople (blocks) on mean weekly sales. Set $\alpha = 0.05$. Can you conclude that the different salespeople have different effects on mean weekly sales?

TABLE **10.9**   Results of a Sales Method Experiment Employing a Randomized Block Design

Sales Method, i	Salesperson, j		
	A	B	C
1	32	29	30
2	32	30	28
3	28	25	23
4	25	24	23

FIGURE 10.8 Excel Output of a Randomized Block ANOVA of the Sales Method Data Given in Table 10.9

Anova: Two-Factor Without Replication

SUMMARY	Count	Sum	Average	Variance
Method 1	3	91	30.3333 $\boxed{12}$	2.3333
Method 2	3	90	30 $\boxed{13}$	4
Method 3	3	76	25.3333 $\boxed{14}$	6.3333
Method 4	3	72	24 $\boxed{15}$	1
Salesperson A	4	117	29.25 $\boxed{16}$	11.5833
Salesperson B	4	108	27 $\boxed{17}$	8.6667
Salesperson C	4	104	26 $\boxed{18}$	12.6667

ANOVA

Source of Variation	SS	df	MS	F	P-value	F crit
Rows	93.5833 $\boxed{1}$	3	31.1944 $\boxed{5}$	36.2258 $\boxed{8}$	0.0003 $\boxed{9}$	4.7571
Columns	22.1667 $\boxed{2}$	2	11.0833 $\boxed{6}$	12.8710 $\boxed{10}$	0.0068 $\boxed{11}$	5.1433
Error	5.1667 $\boxed{3}$	6	0.8611 $\boxed{7}$			
Total	120.9167 $\boxed{4}$	11				

$\boxed{1}$ SSB $\boxed{2}$ SSBL $\boxed{3}$ SSE $\boxed{4}$ SST $\boxed{5}$ MSB $\boxed{6}$ MSBL $\boxed{7}$ MSE $\boxed{8}$ F(groups) $\boxed{9}$ p value for F(groups)
$\boxed{10}$ F(blocks) $\boxed{11}$ p value for F(blocks) $\boxed{12}$ $\bar{x}_1.$ $\boxed{13}$ $\bar{x}_2.$ $\boxed{14}$ $\bar{x}_3.$ $\boxed{15}$ $\bar{x}_4.$ $\boxed{16}$ $\bar{x}_{.1}$ $\boxed{17}$ $\bar{x}_{.2}$ $\boxed{18}$ $\bar{x}_{.3}$.

TABLE 10.10 Results of a Bottle Design Experiment 📎

Bottle Design, i	Supermarket, j			
	1	2	3	4
A	16	14	1	6
B	33	30	19	23
C	23	21	8	12

TABLE 10.11 Results of a Keyboard Experiment 📎

Data Entry Specialist	Keyboard Brand		
	A	B	C
1	77	67	63
2	71	62	59
3	74	63	59
4	67	57	54

c. Use Tukey simultaneous 95 percent confidence intervals to make pairwise comparisons of the sales method effects on mean weekly sales. Which sales method(s) maximize mean weekly sales?

10.18 A consumer preference study involving three different 📎 bottle designs (A, B, and C) for the jumbo size of a new liquid laundry detergent was carried out using a randomized block experimental design, with supermarkets as blocks. Specifically, four supermarkets were supplied with all three bottle designs, which were priced the same. Table 10.10 gives the number of bottles of each design sold in a 24-hour period at each supermarket. Using these data, the SSB, SSBL, and SSE can be calculated to be 586.1667, 421.6667, and 1.8333, respectively.

a. Test the null hypothesis H_0 that no differences exist between the effects of the bottle designs on mean daily sales. Set $\alpha = 0.05$. Can you conclude that the different bottle designs have different effects on mean sales?

b. Test the null hypothesis H_0 that no differences exist between the effects of the supermarkets on mean daily sales. Set $\alpha = 0.05$. Can you conclude that the different supermarkets have different effects on mean sales?

c. Use Tukey simultaneous 95 percent confidence intervals to make pairwise comparisons of the bottle

design effects on mean daily sales. Which bottle design(s) maximize mean sales?

d. Thinking about the research design described above, what possible limitations to the design may affect the results?

10.19 To compare three brands of computer keyboards, four 📎 data entry specialists were randomly selected. Each specialist used all three keyboards to enter the same kind of text material for ten minutes, and the number of words entered per minute was recorded. The data obtained are given in Table 10.11. Using these data, the SSB, SSBL, and SSE can be calculated to be 392.6667, 143.5833, and 2.6667, respectively.

a. Test the null hypothesis H_0 that no differences exist between the effects of the keyboard brands on the mean number of words entered per minute. Set $\alpha = 0.05$.

b. Test the null hypothesis H_0 that no differences exist between the effects of the data entry specialists on the mean number of words entered per minute. Set $\alpha = 0.05$.

c. Use Tukey simultaneous 95 percent confidence intervals to make pairwise comparisons of the keyboard brand effects on the mean number of words entered per minute. Which keyboard brand maximizes the mean number of words entered per minute?

TABLE **10.12**   Broadband Subscriber Statistics per 100 Inhabitants for Exercise 10.20

	DSL	Cable	Other	Rank		DSL	Cable	Other	Rank
Denmark	17.4	9	2.8	1	France	16.7	1	0	16
Netherlands	17.2	11.1	0.5	2	Australia	13.9	2.9	0.6	17
Iceland	26.5	0	0.7	3	Germany	14.7	0.3	0.1	18
Korea	13.2	8.8	4.5	4	Spain	10.5	3.1	0.1	19
Switzerland	16.9	9	0.4	5	Italy	12.6	0	0.6	20
Finland	21.7	3.1	0.2	6	Portugal	7.9	5	0	21
Norway	20.4	3.8	0.4	7	New Zealand	10.7	0.5	0.6	22
Sweden	14.4	4.3	4	8	Czech Republic	3.9	2	3.5	23
Canada	10.8	11.5	0.1	9	Ireland	6.8	1	1.4	24
United Kingdom	14.6	4.9	0	10	Hungary	4.8	2.9	0.1	25
Belgium	11.9	7.4	0	11	Poland	3.9	1.3	0.1	26
United States	8	9.8	1.4	12	Turkey	2.9	0	0	27
Japan	11.3	2.7	4.9	13	Slovak Republic	2.2	0.5	0.2	28
Luxembourg	16	1.9	0	14	Mexico	2.1	0.7	0	29
Austria	11.2	6.3	0.2	15	Greece	2.7	0	0	30

Source: OECD Broadband Statistics to June 2006; OECD, 2006, http://www.oecd.org/document/9/0,3343,en_2649_201185_37529673_1_1_1_1,00.html.

10.20 OECD BROADBAND STATISTICS TO JUNE 2006

The Organisation for Economic Co-operation and Development (OECD) collected statistics of broadband subscribers in 30 countries around the world. Options of accessing the Internet were DSL, Cable, and Other. The data, per 100 inhabitants, are presented in Table 10.12.

To test whether or not there is a significant main effect for type of subscription, we can treat the data as a randomized block design where the IV levels are the three types of subscriptions and the blocks are the 30 countries. Figure 10.9 gives the MegaStat output of a randomized block ANOVA of the broadband statistics.

a. Test the null hypothesis H_0 that no differences exist between the three subscription types. Do the three subscription types differ?

FIGURE **10.9**   MegaStat Output of a Randomized Block ANOVA of the Internet Data for Exercise 10.20

ANOVA table

Source	SS	df	MS	F	p-value
Treatments	1,828.710 [1]	2	914.3551 [5]	58.13 [8]	1.40E-14 [9]
Blocks	659.182 [2]	29	22.7304 [6]	1.45 [10]	0.1162 [11]
Error	912.350 [3]	58	15.7302 [7]		
Total	3,400.242 [4]	89			

Post hoc analysis

Tukey simultaneous comparison t-values (d.f. = 58)

		OTHER 0.9133	CABLE 3.8267	DSL 11.5933
OTHER	0.9133			
CABLE	3.8267	2.84		
DSL	11.5933	10.43	7.58	

critical values for experimentwise error rate:

0.05	2.40
0.01	3.04

p-values for pairwise t-tests

		OTHER 0.9133	CABLE 3.8267	DSL 11.5933
OTHER	0.9133			
CABLE	3.8267	0.0061		
DSL	11.5933	6.39E-15	3.05E-10	

[1] *SSB*   [2] *SSBL*   [3] *SSE*   [4] *SST*   [5] *MSB*   [6] *MSBL*   [7] *MSE*   [8] *F*(groups)   [9] *p* value for *F*(groups)

[10] *F*(blocks)   [11] *p* value for *F*(blocks)

FIGURE 10.10 MegaStat Output of a Randomized Block ANOVA of the Vending Machine Data for Exercise 10.21

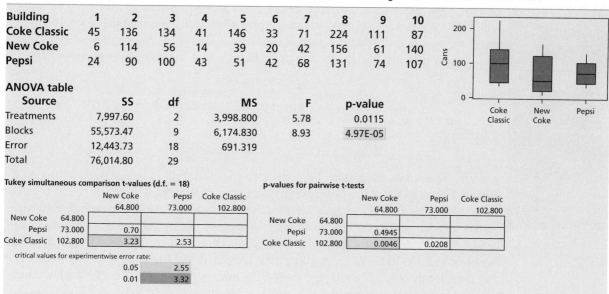

Building	1	2	3	4	5	6	7	8	9	10
Coke Classic	45	136	134	41	146	33	71	224	111	87
New Coke	6	114	56	14	39	20	42	156	61	140
Pepsi	24	90	100	43	51	42	68	131	74	107

ANOVA table

Source	SS	df	MS	F	p-value
Treatments	7,997.60	2	3,998.800	5.78	0.0115
Blocks	55,573.47	9	6,174.830	8.93	4.97E-05
Error	12,443.73	18	691.319		
Total	76,014.80	29			

Tukey simultaneous comparison t-values (d.f. = 18)

		New Coke	Pepsi	Coke Classic
		64.800	73.000	102.800
New Coke	64.800			
Pepsi	73.000	0.70		
Coke Classic	102.800	3.23	2.53	

critical values for experimentwise error rate:

0.05	2.55	
0.01	3.32	

p-values for pairwise t-tests

		New Coke	Pepsi	Coke Classic
		64.800	73.000	102.800
New Coke	64.800			
Pepsi	73.000	0.4945		
Coke Classic	102.800	0.0046	0.0208	

b. Make pairwise comparisons of the three subscription types. Which type is the most popular?

10.21 The Coca-Cola Company introduced New Coke in 1985. Within three months of this introduction, negative consumer reaction forced Coca-Cola to reintroduce the original formula of Coke as Coca-Cola Classic. Suppose that two years later, in 1987, a marketing research firm in Vancouver compared the sales of Coca-Cola Classic, New Coke, and Pepsi in public building vending machines. To do this, the marketing research firm randomly selected ten public buildings in Vancouver with both a Coke machine (selling Coke Classic and New Coke) and a Pepsi machine. The data—in number of cans sold over a given period of time—and a MegaStat randomized block ANOVA of the data are given in Figure 10.10.

a. Test the null hypothesis H_0 that no differences exist between the mean sales of Coca-Cola Classic, New Coke, and Pepsi in Vancouver public building vending machines. Set $\alpha = 0.05$.

b. Make pairwise comparisons of the mean sales of Coca-Cola Classic, New Coke, and Pepsi in Vancouver public building vending machines.

c. By the mid-1990s, the Coca-Cola Company had discontinued making New Coke and had returned to making only its original product. Is there evidence in the 1987 study that this might happen? Explain your answer.

10.4 TWO-WAY ANALYSIS OF VARIANCE

LO6

Many response variables are affected by more than one factor. Because of this, we must often conduct experiments in which we study the effects of several factors on the response. In this section, we consider studying the effects of *two* factors on a response variable. To begin, recall that in Example 10.2 we discussed an experiment in which the Tastee Bakery Company investigated the effect of shelf display height on monthly demand for one of its bakery products. This one-factor experiment is actually a simplification of a two-factor experiment carried out by the Tastee Bakery Company. We discuss this two-factor experiment in the following example.

Example 10.8 The Shelf Display Case

The Tastee Bakery Company supplies a bakery product to many supermarkets. The company wishes to study the effects of two factors—**shelf display height** and **shelf display width**—on **monthly demand** (measured in cases of ten units each) for this product. The factor "display height" is defined to have three levels: B (bottom), M (middle), and T (top). The factor "display width" is defined to have two levels: R (regular) and W (wide). The **IVs** in this experiment are **display height and display width combinations**. This design is also referred to as a 3 × 2

design because there are three levels of the display height factor (rows) and two levels of the display width factor (columns). The design could also be referred to as a 2×3 design in which the two levels of IV_1 represent the display width factor and the three levels of IV_2 represent the display height factor. Again, as stated at the start of the chapter, this notation depicts what the experimental design in which there are two rows and three columns looks like:

Display Width	Display Height		
	Bottom (*B*)	Middle (*M*)	Top (*T*)
Regular (*R*)	*RB*	*RM*	*RT*
Wide (*W*)	*WB*	*WM*	*WT*

Here, for example, the notation *RB* denotes the condition (cell) of regular width display on the bottom. For each display height and width combination, the company randomly selects a sample of $m = 3$ supermarkets (all supermarkets used in the study have equal sales potential). Each supermarket sells the product for one month using its assigned display height and width combination, and the month's demand for the product is recorded. The six samples obtained in this experiment are given in Table 10.13. We let $x_{ij,k}$ denote the monthly demand obtained at the kth supermarket that used display height i and display width j. For example, $x_{MW,2} = 78.4$ is the monthly demand obtained at the second supermarket that used a middle display height and a wide display width.

In addition to giving the six samples, Table 10.13 gives the **sample group mean** for each display height and display width combination. For example, $\bar{x}_{BR} = 55.9$ is the mean of the three demands observed at supermarkets using a bottom display height and a regular display width. The table also gives the mean demand for each level of display height (*B*, *M*, and *T*) and for each level of display width (*R* and *W*). Specifically,

$\bar{x}_{B\bullet} = 55.8 =$ the mean of the six demands observed when using a bottom display height,

$\bar{x}_{M\bullet} = 77.2 =$ the mean of the six demands observed when using a middle display height,

$\bar{x}_{T\bullet} = 51.5 =$ the mean of the six demands observed when using a top display height,

$\bar{x}_{\bullet R} = 60.8 =$ the mean of the nine demands observed when using a regular display width,

$\bar{x}_{\bullet W} = 62.2 =$ the mean of the nine demands observed when using a wide display width.

Finally, Table 10.13 gives $\bar{x} = 61.5$, which is the overall mean of the total of 18 demands observed in the experiment. Because $\bar{x}_{M\bullet} = 77.2$ is considerably larger than $\bar{x}_{B\bullet} = 55.8$ and

TABLE 10.13   Six Samples of Monthly Demands for a Bakery Product

Display Height	Display Width			
	R	*W*		
B	58.2	55.7		
	53.7	52.5		
	55.8	58.9		
	$\bar{x}_{BR} = 55.9$	$\bar{x}_{BW} = 55.7$	$\bar{x}_{B\bullet} = 55.8$	
M	73.0	76.2		
	78.1	78.4		
	75.4	82.1		
	$\bar{x}_{MR} = 75.5$	$\bar{x}_{MW} = 78.9$	$\bar{x}_{M\bullet} = 77.2$	
T	52.4	54.0		
	49.7	52.1		
	50.9	49.9		
	$\bar{x}_{TR} = 51.0$	$\bar{x}_{TW} = 52.0$	$\bar{x}_{T\bullet} = 51.5$	
	$\bar{x}_{\bullet R} = 60.8$	$\bar{x}_{\bullet W} = 62.2$	$\bar{x}_{\bullet} = 61.5$	

FIGURE **10.11** Graphical Analysis of the Bakery Demand Data

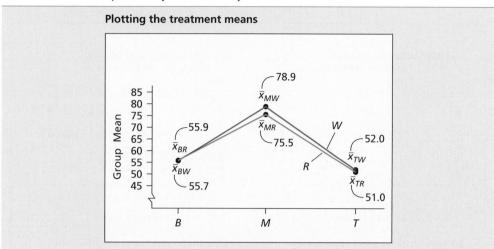

$\bar{x}_{T\bullet} = 51.5$, we estimate that mean monthly demand is highest when using a middle display height. Since $\bar{x}_{\bullet R} = 60.8$ and $\bar{x}_{\bullet W} = 62.2$ do not differ by very much, we estimate that there is little difference between the effects of a regular display width and a wide display width on mean monthly demand.

Figure 10.11 presents a graphical analysis of the bakery demand data. In this figure, we plot for each display width (R and W) the mean demand associated with changing the display height from bottom (B) to middle (M) to top (T). Note that for both the regular display width (R) and the wide display width (W), the middle display height (M) gives the highest mean monthly demand. Also note that for either a bottom, middle, or top display height, there is little difference between the effects of a regular display width and a wide display width on mean monthly demand. This sort of graphical analysis is useful in determining whether a condition called **interaction** exists.

Interaction effects In general, suppose we wish to study the effects of two factors on a response variable. We assume that the first factor, which we refer to as **factor 1** (or IV_1), has *a* **levels** (levels 1, 2, . . . , *a*). Further, we assume that the second factor, which we will refer to as **factor 2** (or IV_2), has *b* **levels** (levels 1, 2, . . . , *b*). Here a **group (or cell)** is considered to be a **combination of a level of factor 1 and a level of factor 2**. It follows that there is a total of *ab* cells, and we assume that we will employ a **completely randomized experimental design** in which we will assign *m* experimental units to each group. This procedure results in our observing *m* values of the response variable for each of the *ab* combinations, and in this case we say that we are performing a **two-factor factorial experiment**.

The method we will explain for analyzing the results of a two-factor factorial experiment is called **two-way ANOVA**. This method requires that the following assumptions hold:

Assumptions for Two-Way ANOVA

1 **Sample:** We have obtained a random sample corresponding to each IV combination, and the sample sizes in all the cells are equal.

2 **Independence:** The samples are independent because we have employed a completely randomized experimental design.

3 **Normality:** The populations of values of the response variable (DV) associated with the IVs have normal distributions with equal variances.

FIGURE 10.12   Different Possible Treatment Effects in Two-Way ANOVA

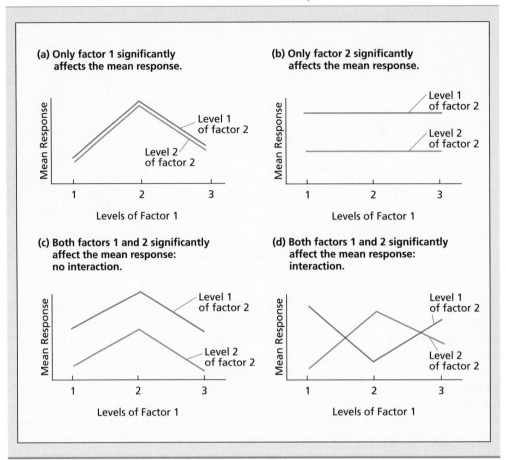

In order to understand the various ways in which factor 1 and factor 2 might affect the mean response, consider Figure 10.12. It is possible that only factor 1 significantly affects the mean response (see Figure 10.12(a)). On the other hand, it is possible that only factor 2 significantly affects the mean response (see Figure 10.12(b)). It is also possible that both factors 1 and 2 significantly affect the mean response. If this is so, these factors might affect the mean response independently (see Figure 10.12(c)), or these factors might **interact** as they affect the mean response (see Figure 10.12(d)). In general, we say that **there is interaction between factors 1 and 2 if the relationship between the mean response and one of the factors depends upon the level of the other factor**. This is clearly true in Figure 10.12(d). Note here that at levels 1 and 3 of factor 1, level 1 of factor 2 gives the highest mean response, whereas at level 2 of factor 1, level 2 of factor 2 gives the highest mean response. On the other hand, the *parallel* line plots in Figure 10.12(a), (b), and (c) indicate a lack of interaction between factors 1 and 2. To graphically check for interaction, we can plot the group means, as we have done in Figure 10.11 on the previous page. If we obtain essentially parallel line plots, then it might be reasonable to conclude that there is little or no interaction between factors 1 and 2 (this is true in Figure 10.11). On the other hand, if the line plots are not parallel (the two lines intersect), then it might be reasonable to conclude that factors 1 and 2 interact.

In addition to graphical analysis, ANOVA is a useful tool for analyzing the data from a two-factor factorial experiment. To explain the ANOVA approach to analyzing such an experiment, we define

$x_{ij,k}$ = the kth value of the response variable observed when using level i of factor 1 and level j of factor 2,

$\bar{x}_{ij}$ = the mean of the m values observed when using the ith level of factor 1 and the jth level of factor 2,

$\bar{x}_{i\bullet}$ = the mean of the bm values observed when using the ith level of factor 1,

$\bar{x}_{\bullet j}$ = the mean of the am values observed when using the jth level of factor 2,

$\bar{x}$ = the mean of the total of abm values that we have observed in the experiment.

The ANOVA procedure for a two-factor factorial experiment partitions the **total sum of squares (SST)** into four components: the **factor 1 sum of squares, SS(1)**; the **factor 2 sum of squares, SS(2)**; the **interaction sum of squares, SS(int)**; and the **error sum of squares, SSE**. The formula for this partitioning is

$$SST = SS(1) + SS(2) + SS(\text{int}) + SSE.$$

The steps for calculating these sums of squares, as well as what is measured by the sums of squares, can be summarized as follows:

Step 1: Calculate the SST, which measures the total amount of variability:

$$SST = \sum_{i=1}^{a} \sum_{j=1}^{b} \sum_{k=1}^{m} (x_{ij,k} - \bar{x})^2.$$

Step 2: Calculate the $SS(1)$, which measures the amount of variability due to the different levels of factor 1:

$$SS(1) = bm \sum_{i=1}^{a} (\bar{x}_{i\bullet} - \bar{x})^2.$$

Step 3: Calculate the $SS(2)$, which measures the amount of variability due to the different levels of factor 2:

$$SS(2) = am \sum_{j=1}^{b} (\bar{x}_{\bullet j} - \bar{x})^2.$$

Step 4: Calculate the $SS(\text{interaction})$, which measures the amount of variability due to the interaction between factors 1 and 2:

$$SS(\text{int}) = m \sum_{i=1}^{a} \sum_{j=1}^{b} (\bar{x}_{ij} - \bar{x}_{i\bullet} - \bar{x}_{\bullet j} + \bar{x})^2.$$

Step 5: Calculate the SSE, which measures the amount of variability due to the error:

$$SSE = SST - SS(1) - SS(2) - SS(\text{int}).$$

These sums of squares are shown in Table 10.14, which is called a **two-way ANOVA table**. This table also gives the degrees of freedom associated with each source of variation—factor 1, factor 2, interaction, error, and total—as well as the mean squares and F statistics used to test the hypotheses of interest in a two-factor factorial experiment.

TABLE **10.14**   Two-Way Anova Table

Source of Variation	Degrees of Freedom	Sum of Squares	Mean Square	F
Factor 1	$a - 1$	$SS(1)$	$MS(1) = \dfrac{SS(1)}{a-1}$	$F(1) = \dfrac{MS(1)}{MSE}$
Factor 2	$b - 1$	$SS(2)$	$MS(2) = \dfrac{SS(2)}{b-1}$	$F(2) = \dfrac{MS(2)}{MSE}$
Interaction	$(a-1)(b-1)$	$SS(\text{int})$	$MS(\text{int}) = \dfrac{SS(\text{int})}{(a-1)(b-1)}$	$F(\text{int}) = \dfrac{MS(\text{int})}{MSE}$
Error	$ab(m-1)$	SSE	$MSE = \dfrac{SSE}{ab(m-1)}$	
Total	$abm - 1$	SST		

Before discussing these hypotheses, we will illustrate how the entries in the ANOVA table are calculated. The sums of squares in the shelf display case are calculated as follows (note that $a = 3$, $b = 2$, and $m = 3$):

Step 1: $SST = (58.2 - 61.5)^2 + (53.7 - 61.5)^2 + (55.8 - 61.5)^2$
$\qquad\qquad + (55.7 - 61.5)^2 + \cdots + (49.9 - 61.5)^2$
$\qquad\quad = 2{,}366.28.$

Step 2: $SS(1) = 2 \cdot 3[(\bar{x}_{B\bullet} - \bar{x})^2 + (\bar{x}_{M\bullet} - \bar{x})^2 + (\bar{x}_{T\bullet} - \bar{x})^2]$
$\qquad\qquad = 6[(55.8 - 61.5)^2 + (77.2 - 61.5)^2 + (51.5 - 61.5)^2]$
$\qquad\qquad = 6(32.49 + 246.49 + 100)$
$\qquad\qquad = 2{,}273.88.$

Step 3: $SS(2) = 3 \cdot 3[(\bar{x}_{\bullet R} - \bar{x})^2 + (\bar{x}_{\bullet W} - \bar{x})^2]$
$\qquad\qquad = 9[(60.8 - 61.5)^2 + (62.2 - 61.5)^2]$
$\qquad\qquad = 9(0.49 + 0.49)$
$\qquad\qquad = 8.82.$

Step 4: $SS(\text{int}) = 3[(\bar{x}_{BR} - \bar{x}_{B\bullet} - \bar{x}_{\bullet R} + \bar{x})^2 + (\bar{x}_{BW} - \bar{x}_{B\bullet} - \bar{x}_{\bullet W} + \bar{x})^2$
$\qquad\qquad\quad + (\bar{x}_{MR} - \bar{x}_{M\bullet} - \bar{x}_{\bullet R} + \bar{x})^2 + (\bar{x}_{MW} - \bar{x}_{M\bullet} - \bar{x}_{\bullet W} + \bar{x})^2$
$\qquad\qquad\quad + (\bar{x}_{TR} - \bar{x}_{T\bullet} - \bar{x}_{\bullet R} + \bar{x})^2 + (\bar{x}_{TW} - \bar{x}_{T\bullet} - \bar{x}_{\bullet W} + \bar{x})^2]$
$\qquad\qquad = 3[(55.9 - 55.8 - 60.8 + 61.5)^2 + (55.7 - 55.8 - 62.2 + 61.5)^2$
$\qquad\qquad\quad + (75.5 - 77.2 - 60.8 + 61.5)^2 + (78.9 - 77.2 - 62.2 + 61.5)^2$
$\qquad\qquad\quad + (51.0 - 51.5 - 60.8 + 61.5)^2 + (52.0 - 51.5 - 62.2 + 61.5)^2]$
$\qquad\qquad = 3(3.36) = 10.08.$

Step 5: $SSE = SST - SS(1) - SS(2) - SS(\text{int})$
$\qquad\qquad = 2366.28 - 2273.88 - 8.82 - 10.08$
$\qquad\qquad = 73.50.$

Figure 10.13 gives the MegaStat output of a two-way ANOVA for the shelf display data. This figure shows the above-calculated sums of squares, as well as the degrees of freedom (recall that $a = 3$, $b = 2$, and $m = 3$), mean squares, and F statistics used to test the hypotheses of interest.

We first test the null hypothesis H_0 that **no interaction exists between factors 1 and 2** versus the alternative hypothesis H_a that **interaction does exist**. We can reject H_0 in favour of H_a at level of significance α if

$$F(\text{int}) = \frac{MS(\text{int})}{MSE}$$

FIGURE 10.13   MegaStat Output of a Two-Way ANOVA of the Shelf Display Data

Two factor ANOVA

			Factor 1			
Means:			Bottom	Middle	Top	
		R	55.90	75.50	51.00	60.80
	Factor 2	W	55.70	78.90	52.00	62.20
			55.80	77.20	51.50	61.50

ANOVA table

Source	SS	df	MS	F	p-value
Factor 1	2,273.880	2	1,136.9400	185.62	9.42E-10
Factor 2	8.820	1	8.8200	1.44	0.2533
Interaction	10.080	2	5.0400	0.82	0.4625
Error	73.500	12	6.1250		
Total	2,366.280	17			

is greater than the F_α point based on $(a - 1)(b - 1)$ numerator and $ab(m - 1)$ denominator degrees of freedom. In the shelf display case, $F_{0.05}$ based on $(a - 1)(b - 1) = 2$ numerator and $ab(m - 1) = 12$ denominator degrees of freedom is 3.89 (see Table A.7). Because

$$F(\text{int}) = \frac{MS(\text{int})}{MSE} = \frac{5.04}{6.12} = 0.82$$

is less than $F_{0.05} = 3.89$, we cannot reject H_0 at the 0.05 level of significance. We conclude that little or no interaction exists between shelf display height and shelf display width. That is, we conclude that the relationship between mean demand for the bakery product and shelf display height depends little (or not at all) on shelf display width. Further, we conclude that the relationship between mean demand and shelf display width depends little (or not at all) on shelf display height. Notice that these conclusions are suggested by the previously given plot of Figure 10.11 (page 345).

In general, when we conclude that little or no interaction exists between IV factors 1 and 2, we can (separately) test the significance of each of factors 1 and 2. We call this **testing the significance of the main effects** (what we do if we conclude that interaction does exist between factors 1 and 2 will be discussed at the end of this section).

To test the significance of factor 1 (the first IV), we test the null hypothesis H_0 that **no differences exist between the effects of the different levels of factor 1** on the mean response versus the alternative hypothesis H_a that **at least one level of factor 1 has a different effect**. We can reject H_0 in favour of H_a at level of significance α if

$$F(1) = \frac{MS(1)}{MSE}$$

is greater than the F_α point based on $a - 1$ numerator and $ab(m - 1)$ denominator degrees of freedom. In the shelf display case, $F_{0.05}$ based on $a - 1 = 2$ numerator and $ab(m - 1) = 12$ denominator degrees of freedom is 3.89. Because

$$F(1) = \frac{MS(1)}{MSE} = \frac{1136.94}{6.12} = 185.77$$

is greater than $F_{0.05} = 3.89$, we can reject H_0 at the 0.05 level of significance. Therefore, we have strong evidence that at least one of the bottom, middle, and top display heights has a different effect on mean monthly demand.

To test the significance of factor 2 (the second IV), we test the null hypothesis H_0 that **no differences exist between the effects of the different levels of factor 2** on the mean response versus the alternative hypothesis H_a that **at least one level of factor 2 has a different effect**. We can reject H_0 in favour of H_a at level of significance α if

$$F(2) = \frac{MS(2)}{MSE}$$

is greater than the F_α point based on $b - 1$ numerator and $ab(m - 1)$ denominator degrees of freedom. In the shelf display case, $F_{0.05}$ based on $b - 1 = 1$ numerator and $ab(m - 1) = 12$ denominator degrees of freedom is 4.75. Because

$$F(2) = \frac{MS(2)}{MSE} = \frac{8.82}{6.12} = 1.44$$

is less than $F_{0.05} = 4.75$, we cannot reject H_0 at the 0.05 level of significance. Therefore, we do not have strong evidence that the regular display width and the wide display width have different effects on mean monthly demand.

If, in a two-factor factorial experiment, we conclude that at least one level of factor 1 has a different effect or at least one level of factor 2 has a different effect, we can make pairwise comparisons to determine how the effects differ.

Point Estimates and Confidence Intervals in Two-Way ANOVA

1 Consider the **difference between the effects of levels i and i' of factor 1 on the mean value of the response variable**.

  a. A **point estimate** of this difference is $\bar{X}_{i\cdot} - \bar{X}_{i'\cdot}$.

  b. An **individual $100(1 - \alpha)$ percent confidence interval** for this difference is

$$\left[\bar{x}_{i\cdot} - \bar{x}_{i'\cdot} \pm t_{\alpha/2}\sqrt{MSE\left(\frac{2}{bm}\right)}\right],$$

    where the $t_{\alpha/2}$ point is based on $ab(m - 1)$ degrees of freedom, and MSE is the error mean square found in the two-way ANOVA table.

  c. A **Tukey simultaneous $100(1 - \alpha)$ percent confidence interval** for this difference (in the set of all possible paired differences between the effects of the different levels of factor 1) is

$$\left[\bar{x}_{i\cdot} - \bar{x}_{i'\cdot} \pm q_{\alpha}\sqrt{MSE\left(\frac{1}{bm}\right)}\right],$$

    where q_{α} is obtained from Table A.10, which is a table of percentage points of the studentized range. Here q_{α} is listed corresponding to values of a and $ab(m - 1)$.

2 Consider the **difference between the effects of levels j and j' of factor 2 on the mean value of the response variable**.

  a. A **point estimate** of this difference is $\bar{X}_{\cdot j} - \bar{X}_{\cdot j'}$.

  b. An **individual $100(1 - \alpha)$ percent confidence interval** for this difference is

$$\left[\bar{x}_{\cdot j} - \bar{x}_{\cdot j'} \pm t_{\alpha/2}\sqrt{MSE\left(\frac{2}{am}\right)}\right],$$

    where the $t_{\alpha/2}$ point is based on $ab(m - 1)$ degrees of freedom.

  c. A **Tukey simultaneous $100(1 - \alpha)$ percent confidence interval** for this difference (in the set of all possible paired differences between the effects of the different levels of factor 2) is

$$\left[\bar{x}_{\cdot j} - \bar{x}_{\cdot j'} \pm q_{\alpha}\sqrt{MSE\left(\frac{1}{am}\right)}\right],$$

    where q_{α} is obtained from Table A.10 and is listed corresponding to values of b and $ab(m - 1)$.

3 Let μ_{ij} denote the **mean value of the response variable obtained when using level i of factor 1 and level j of factor 2**. A point estimate of μ_{ij} is $\bar{X}_{ij}$, and an **individual $100(1 - \alpha)$ percent confidence interval** for μ_{ij} is

$$\left[\bar{X}_{ij} \pm t_{\alpha/2}\sqrt{\frac{MSE}{m}}\right],$$

where the $t_{\alpha/2}$ point is based on $ab(m - 1)$ degrees of freedom.

Example 10.9 The Shelf Display Case

We have previously concluded that at least two of the bottom, middle, and top display heights have different effects on mean monthly demand. Since $\bar{x}_{M\cdot} = 77.2$ is greater than $\bar{x}_{B\cdot} = 55.8$ and $\bar{x}_{T\cdot} = 51.5$, we will use Tukey simultaneous 95 percent confidence intervals to compare the effect of a middle display height to the effects of the bottom and top display heights. To compute these intervals, we first note that $q_{0.05} = 3.77$ is the entry in Table A.10 corresponding to $a = 3$ and $ab(m - 1) = 12$. Also note that the MSE found in the two-way ANOVA table is 6.12 (see Figure 10.13 on page 348). It follows that a Tukey simultaneous 95 percent confidence interval is

$$\left[\bar{x}_{M\cdot} - \bar{x}_{B\cdot} \pm q_{0.05}\sqrt{MSE\left(\frac{1}{bm}\right)}\right] = \left[77.2 - 55.8 \pm 3.77\sqrt{6.12\left(\frac{1}{2(3)}\right)}\right]$$

$$= [21.4 \pm 3.81]$$

$$= [17.59, 25.21]$$

for the difference between the effects of a middle and a bottom display height on mean monthly demand and

$$[\bar{x}_{M\cdot} - \bar{x}_{T\cdot} \pm 3.81] = [77.2 - 51.5 \pm 3.81]$$

$$= [21.89, 29.51]$$

for the difference between the effects of a middle and a top display height on mean monthly demand.

Together, these intervals make us 95 percent confident that a middle shelf display height is, on average, at least 17.6 cases sold per month better than a bottom shelf display height and at least 21.9 cases sold per month better than a top shelf display height.[5]

Next, recall that previously conducted F tests suggest that there is little or no interaction between display height and display width and that there is little difference between using a regular display width and a wide display width. However, intuitive and graphical analysis should always be used to supplement the results of hypothesis testing. In this case, note from Table 10.13 (page 344) that $\bar{x}_{MR} = 75.5$ and $\bar{x}_{MW} = 78.9$. This implies that we estimate that when we use a middle display height, changing from a regular display width to a wide display width increases mean monthly demand by 3.4 cases (or 34 units). This slight increase can be seen in Figure 10.11 (page 345) and suggests that it might be best (depending on what supermarkets charge for different display heights and widths) for the bakery to use a wide display width with a middle display height. Since $t_{0.025}$ based on $ab(m - 1) = 12$ degrees of freedom is 2.179, an individual 95 percent confidence interval for μ_{MW}, the mean demand obtained when using a middle display height and a wide display width, is

$$\left[\bar{x}_{MW} \pm t_{0.025}\sqrt{\frac{MSE}{m}} \right] = \left[78.9 \pm 2.179\sqrt{\frac{6.12}{3}} \right]$$

$$= [75.79, 82.01].$$

This interval says that when we use a middle display height and a wide display width, we can be 95 percent confident that mean demand for the bakery product will be between 75.8 and 82.0 cases per month.

If we conclude that an interaction exists between factors 1 and 2, the effects of changing the level of one IV will depend on the level of the other IV. In this case, we cannot separate the analysis of the effects of the levels of the two factors. One simple alternative procedure is to use one-way ANOVA (see Section 10.2) to compare all of the group means (the μ_{ij}'s) with the possible purpose of finding the best combination of levels of factors 1 and 2. For example, if there had been interaction in the shelf display case, we could have used one-way ANOVA to compare the six means—μ_{BR}, μ_{BW}, μ_{MR}, μ_{MW}, μ_{TR}, and μ_{TW}—to find the best combination of display height and width. Alternatively, we could study the effects of the different levels of one factor at a specified level of the other factor. This is what we did at the end of the shelf display case, when we noticed that at a middle display height, a wide display width seemed slightly more effective than a regular display width.

Finally, we might wish to study the effects of more than two factors on a response variable of interest. The ideas involved in such a study are an extension of those involved in a two-way ANOVA. Although studying more than two factors is beyond the scope of this text, a good reference is Neter, Kutner, Nachtsheim, and Wasserman (1996).

Exercises for Section 10.4

CONCEPTS

10.22 What is a treatment in the context of a two-factor factorial experiment?

10.23 Explain what we mean when we say that
   a. An interaction exists between factor 1 and factor 2.
   b. No interaction exists between the factors.

METHODS AND APPLICATIONS

10.24 An experiment is conducted to study the effects of two sales approaches—high-pressure (H) and low-pressure (L)—and to study the effects of two sales pitches (1 and 2) on the weekly sales of a product. The data in Table 10.15 on the next page are obtained by using a completely

---

[5]The 95 percent confidence level applies to all of the calculated confidence intervals simultaneously. If an interval is not included in an interpretation, then we are actually more than 95 percent confident in our statement.

TABLE **10.15**   Results of the Sales Approach Experiment

Sales Pressure	Sales Pitch 1	Sales Pitch 2
H	32	32
	29	30
	30	28
L	28	25
	25	24
	23	23

TABLE **10.16**   Results of a Two-Factor Display Panel Experiment

Display Panel	Emergency Condition 1	2	3	4
A	17	25	31	14
	14	24	34	13
B	15	22	28	9
	12	19	31	10
C	21	29	32	15
	24	28	37	19

FIGURE **10.14**   Excel Output of a Two-Way ANOVA of the Sales Approach Data

Anova: Two-Factor With Replication

SUMMARY	Pitch 1	Pitch 2	Total
High Pressure			
Count	3	3	6
Sum	91	90	181
Average	30.3333	30	30.1667 [16]
Variance	2.3333	4	2.5667
Low Pressure			
Count	3	3	6
Sum	76	72	148
Average	25.3333	24	24.6667 [17]
Variance	6.3333	1	3.4667
Total			
Count	6	6	
Sum	167	162	
Average	27.8333 [18]	27 [19]	
Variance	10.9667	12.8	

ANOVA

Source of Variation	SS	df	MS	F	P-value	F crit
Pressure	90.75 [1]	1	90.75 [6]	26.5610 [10]	0.0009 [11]	5.3177
Pitch	2.0833 [2]	1	2.0833 [7]	0.6098 [12]	0.4574 [13]	5.3177
Interaction	0.75 [3]	1	0.75 [8]	0.2195 [14]	0.6519 [15]	5.3177
Within	27.3333 [4]	8	3.4167 [9]			
Total	120.917 [5]	11				

[1] $SS(1)$	[2] $SS(2)$	[3] $SS(\text{int})$	[4] SSE	[5] SST
[6] $MS(1)$	[7] $MS(2)$	[8] $MS(\text{int})$	[9] MSE	
[10] $F(1)$	[11] p value for $F(1)$	[12] $F(2)$	[13] p value for $F(2)$	
[14] $F(\text{int})$	[15] p value for $F(\text{int})$	[16] $\bar{x}_{H\cdot}$	[17] $\bar{x}_{L\cdot}$	[18] $\bar{x}_{\cdot 1}$ [19] $\bar{x}_{\cdot 2}$

randomized design, and Figure 10.14 gives the Excel output of a two-way ANOVA of the sales experiment data.

a. Perform graphical analysis to check for interaction between sales pressure and sales pitch.
b. Test for interaction by setting $\alpha = 0.05$.
c. Test for differences in the effects of the levels of sales pressure by setting $\alpha = 0.05$. That is, test the significance of sales pressure effects with $\alpha = 0.05$.
d. Calculate and interpret a 95 percent individual confidence interval for $\mu_{H\cdot} - \mu_{L\cdot}$.
e. Test for differences in the effects of the levels of sales pitch by setting $\alpha = 0.05$. That is, test the significance of sales pitch effects with $\alpha = 0.05$.
f. Calculate and interpret a 95 percent individual confidence interval for $\mu_{\cdot 1} - \mu_{\cdot 2}$.
g. Calculate a 95 percent individual confidence interval for mean sales when using high sales pressure and sales pitch 1. Interpret this interval.

10.25 A study compared three display panels used by air traffic controllers. Each display panel was tested for four different simulated emergency conditions. Twenty-four highly trained air traffic controllers were used in the study. Two controllers were randomly assigned to each display panel–emergency condition combination. The time (in seconds) required to stabilize the emergency condition was recorded. The data in Table 10.16 were

observed. Figure 10.15 presents the MegaStat output of a two-way ANOVA of the display panel data.

a. Interpret the MegaStat interaction plot in Figure 10.15. Then test for interaction with $\alpha = 0.05$.
b. Test the significance of display panel effects with $\alpha = 0.05$.
c. Test the significance of emergency condition effects with $\alpha = 0.05$.
d. Make pairwise comparisons of display panels A, B, and C.
e. Make pairwise comparisons of emergency conditions 1, 2, 3, and 4.
f. Which display panel minimizes the time required to stabilize an emergency condition? Does your answer depend on the emergency condition? Why?
g. Calculate a 95 percent individual confidence interval for the mean time required to stabilize emergency condition 4 using display panel B.

10.26 A marketing firm has studied the effects of two factors on the response to its television advertisements. The first factor is the time of day at which the ad is run, while the second is the position of the ad within the hour. The data in Table 10.17, which were obtained by using a completely randomized experimental design, give the number of calls placed to a toll-free number following a sample broadcast of the advertisement. If

FIGURE 10.15 MegaStat Output of a Two-Way ANOVA of the Display Panel Data

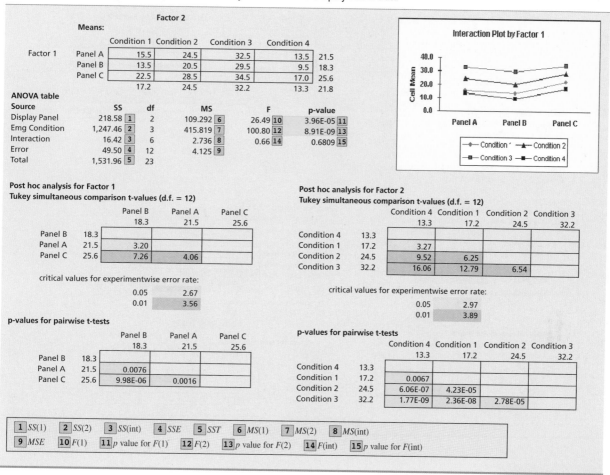

1	$SS(1)$	2	$SS(2)$	3	$SS(\text{int})$	4	SSE	5	SST	6	$MS(1)$	7	$MS(2)$	8	$MS(\text{int})$
9	MSE	10	$F(1)$	11	p value for $F(1)$	12	$F(2)$	13	p value for $F(2)$	14	$F(\text{int})$	15	p value for $F(\text{int})$		

TABLE 10.17 Results of a Two-Factor Marketing Response Experiment

| Time of Day | On the Hour | Position of Advertisement | | |
		On the Half-Hour	Early in Program	Late in Program
10:00 morning	42	36	62	51
	37	41	68	47
	41	38	64	48
4:00 afternoon	62	57	88	67
	60	60	85	60
	58	55	81	66
9:00 evening	100	97	127	105
	96	96	120	101
	103	101	126	107

we use MegaStat to analyze these data, we obtain the output in Figure 10.16 on the next page.

a. Perform graphical analysis to check for interaction between time of day and position of advertisement. Explain your conclusion. Then test for interaction with $\alpha = 0.05$.

b. Test the significance of time-of-day effects with $\alpha = 0.05$.

c. Test the significance of position of advertisement effects with $\alpha = 0.05$.

d. Make pairwise comparisons of the morning, afternoon, and evening times.

e. Make pairwise comparisons of the four advertisement positions.

f. Which time of day and advertisement position maximize consumer response? Compute a 95 percent individual confidence interval for the mean number of calls placed for this time of day–advertisement position combination.

FIGURE **10.16**   MegaStat Output of a Two-Way ANOVA of the Marketing Data

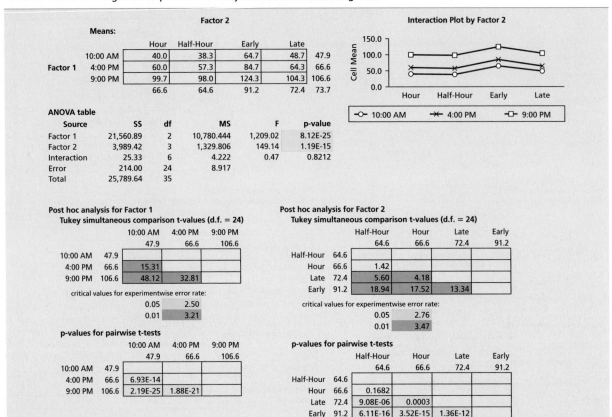

TABLE **10.18**   Results of the House Profitability Study

Supervisor	House Design		
	A	**B**	**C**
1	10.2	12.2	19.4
	11.1	11.7	18.2
2	9.7	11.6	13.6
	10.8	12.0	12.7

10.27 A small builder of speculative homes builds three basic house designs and employs two supervisors. The builder has used each supervisor to build two houses of each design and has obtained the profits given in Table 10.18 (the profits are given in thousands of dollars). Figure 10.17 presents the MegaStat output of a two-way ANOVA of the house profitability data.

a. Interpret the interaction plot in Figure 10.17. Then test for interaction with $\alpha = 0.05$. Can you (separately) test for the significance of house design and supervisor effects? Explain.

b. Which house design–supervisor combination gives the highest profit? When the six house design–supervisor combinations are analyzed using one-way ANOVA, $MSE = 0.390$. Compute a 95 percent individual confidence interval for mean profit when the best house design–supervisor combination is employed.

10.28 In the article "Humor in American, British, and German ads" (*Industrial Marketing Management*, vol. 22, 1993), McCullough and Taylor study humour in trade magazine advertisements. A sample of 665 advertisements were categorized according to two factors: nationality (American, British, or German) and industry (29 levels, ranging from accounting to travel). A panel of judges ranked the degree of humour in each advertisement on a five-point scale. When the resulting data were analyzed using two-way ANOVA, the p values for testing the significance of nationality, industry, and the interaction between nationality and industry were, respectively,

FIGURE 10.17 MegaStat Output of a Two-Way ANOVA of the House Profitability Data

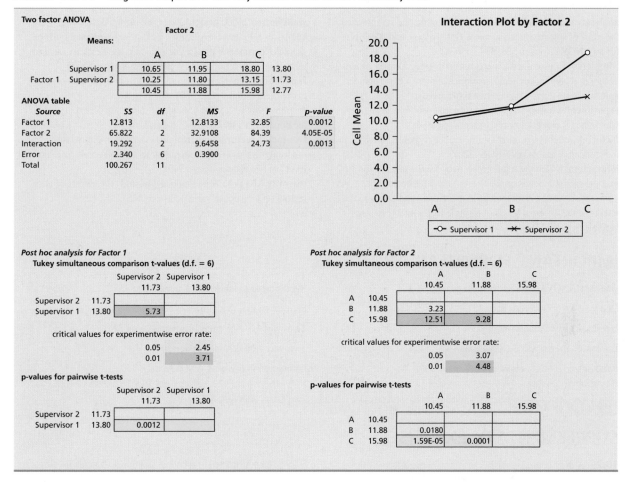

0.087, 0.000, and 0.046. Discuss why these *p* values agree with the following conclusions of the authors: "British ads were more likely to be humorous than German or American ads in the graphics industry.

German ads were least humorous in the grocery and mining industries, but funnier than American ads in the medical industry and funnier than British ads in the packaging industry."

CHAPTER SUMMARY

We began this chapter by introducing some basic concepts of **experimental design**. We saw that we carry out an experiment by setting the values of one or more **independent variables (IV)** before the values of the **response variable (dependent variable, DV)** are observed. The purpose of most experiments is to compare and estimate the effects of the various IVs on the DV. We saw that **experimental units** are assigned to IV groups, and we discussed the **completely randomized experimental design**. This design assigns independent, random samples of experimental units to the treatments.

We began studying how to analyze experimental data by discussing **one-way analysis of variance (ANOVA)**. Here we studied how one factor (with *p* levels) affects the response variable. In particular, we learned how to use this methodology to test for differences between **group means** and to estimate the size of pairwise differences between the means.

Sometimes, even if we randomly select the experimental units, differences between the experimental units conceal differences between the IVs. In such a case, we learned that we can employ a **randomized block design**. Each **block** (experimental unit or set of experimental units) is used exactly once to measure the effect of each and every IV. Because we are comparing the IVs by using the same experimental units, any true differences between the IVs will not be concealed by differences between the experimental units.

The last technique we studied in this chapter was **two-way ANOVA**. Here we studied the effects of two factors by carrying out a **two-factor factorial experiment**. If there is little or no interaction between the two factors, then we are able to separately study the significance of each of the two factors. On the other hand, if substantial interaction exists between the two factors, we study the nature of the differences between the group means.

GLOSSARY OF TERMS

analysis of variance (ANOVA) table: A table that summarizes the sums of squares, mean squares, F statistic(s), and p value(s) for an ANOVA. (pages 328, 337, and 347)

completely randomized experimental design: An experimental design in which independent, random samples of experimental units are assigned to IV conditions. (page 320)

experimental units: The entities (objects, people, and so on) to which the IV conditions are assigned. (page 320)

factor: A variable that might influence the response variable; an independent variable (IV). (page 320)

interaction: When the relationship between the mean response and one factor depends on the level of the other factor. (page 345)

one-way ANOVA: A method used to estimate and compare the effects of the different levels of a single factor on a response variable. (page 323)

randomized block design: An experimental design that compares p IV levels by using b blocks (experimental units or sets of experimental units). Each block is used exactly once to measure the effect of each IV combination. (page 335)

replication: When a treatment is applied to more than one experimental unit. (page 320)

response variable: The variable of interest in an experiment; the dependent variable (DV). (page 320)

two-factor factorial experiment: An experiment in which we randomly assign m experimental units to each combination of levels of two factors. (page 345)

two-way ANOVA: A method used to study the effects of two factors on a response variable. (page 345)

IMPORTANT FORMULAS AND TESTS

One-way ANOVA sums of squares: pages 326–327

One-way ANOVA F test: page 327

One-way ANOVA table: page 329

Estimation in one-way ANOVA: page 330

Randomized block sums of squares: page 337

Randomized block ANOVA table: page 337

Estimation in a randomized block experiment: page 339

Two-way ANOVA sums of squares: page 347

Two-way ANOVA table: page 347

Estimation in two-way ANOVA: page 350

connect Practise and learn online with *Connect*. Questions and tables with online data sets are marked with ⟡ .

SUPPLEMENTARY EXERCISES

10.29 A drug company wishes to compare the effects of three different drugs (X, Y, and Z) that are being developed to reduce cholesterol levels. Each drug is administered to six patients at the recommended dosage for six months. At the end of this period, the reduction in cholesterol level is recorded for each patient. The results are given in Table 10.19. Analyze these data using one-way ANOVA. Use the MegaStat output in Figure 10.18.

10.30 In an article in *Accounting and Finance* (the journal of the Accounting Association of Australia and New Zealand), Church and Schneider report on a study concerning auditor objectivity. A sample of 45 auditors was randomly divided into three groups: (1) the 15 auditors in group 1 designed an audit program for accounts receivable and evaluated an audit program for accounts payable designed by somebody else, (2) the 15 auditors in group 2 did the reverse, (3) the 15 auditors in group 3 (the control group) evaluated the audit programs for both accounts. All 45 auditors were

then instructed to spend an additional 15 hours investigating suspected irregularities in either or both of the audit programs. The mean additional number of hours allocated to the accounts receivable audit program by the auditors in groups 1, 2, and 3 were $\bar{x}_1 = 6.7$, $\bar{x}_2 = 9.7$, and $\bar{x}_3 = 7.6$. Furthermore, a one-way ANOVA of the data shows that $SSB = 71.51$ and $SSE = 321.3$.

a. Define appropriate group means μ_1, μ_2, and μ_3. Then test for statistically significant differences between these group means. Set $\alpha = 0.05$. Can you conclude that the different auditor groups have different effects on the mean additional time allocated to investigating the accounts receivable audit program?

b. Perform pairwise comparisons of the group means by computing a Tukey simultaneous 95 percent confidence interval for each of the pairwise differences $\mu_1 - \mu_2$, $\mu_1 - \mu_3$, and $\mu_2 - \mu_3$. Interpret the results. What do your results imply about the objectivity of auditors? What are the practical implications of this result?

10.31 The loan officers at a large bank can use three different methods for evaluating loan applications. Loan decisions can be based on (1) the applicant's balance sheet (B), (2) examination of key financial ratios (F), or (3) use of a new decision support system (D). In order to compare these three methods, four of the bank's loan officers are randomly selected. Each officer employs each of the evaluation methods for one month (the methods are employed in randomly selected orders). After a year has passed, the percentage of bad loans for each loan officer and evaluation method is determined.

TABLE **10.19**   Reduction of Cholesterol Levels ⟡

	Drug	
X	**Y**	**Z**
22	40	15
31	35	9
19	47	14
27	41	11
25	39	21
18	33	5

FIGURE **10.18**   MegaStat Output of an ANOVA of the Cholesterol Reduction Data

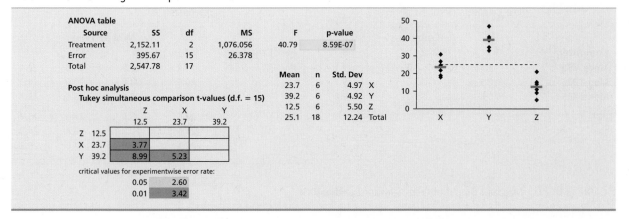

TABLE **10.20**   Results of a Loan Evaluation Experiment 🖊

Loan Officer	Loan Evaluation Method		
	B	*F*	*D*
1	8	5	4
2	6	4	3
3	5	2	1
4	4	1	0

The data obtained by using this randomized block design are given in Table 10.20. Analyze the data using a randomized block ANOVA.

10.32 In an article in the *Accounting Review*, Brown and Solomon study the effects of two factors—confirmation of accounts receivable and verification of sales transactions—on account misstatement risk by auditors. Both factors had two levels—completed or not completed—and a line plot of the treatment mean misstatement risks is shown in Figure 10.19. This line plot makes it appear that an interaction exists between the two factors. In your own words, explain what the interaction means in practical terms.

10.33 Ergonomics is the science of adjusting the work environment to meet the needs of the employee. An experiment was conducted at a Canadian university to assess the comfort level of data entry clerks. Two factors were assessed: size of keys for the entry pad ($B_1 = 1.0$ cm^2; $B_2 = 2.25$ cm^2; $B_3 = 4.0$ cm^2) and the presence or absence of armrests on the employee's chair (armrests versus no armrests). Comfort was measured using a self-report scale from 1 = not at all comfortable to 10 = completely comfortable.
   a. How many cells are in this experiment?
   b. If a total of 60 employees participated in this experiment and an equal number of employees were assigned to each condition, how many employees were in each condition?
   c. In the next column is an incomplete MegaStat output for the experiment. Using the information provided, compute and assess the corresponding significance of the three missing *F* values.
   d. What would you conclude from this experiment?

FIGURE **10.19**   Line Plot for Exercise 10.32

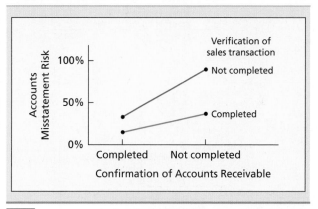

Source: "Configural information processing in auditing: The role of domain-specific knowledge," by C. E. Brown and I. Solomon, *The Accounting Review,* 66, no. 1 (January 1991), p. 105 (Figure 1). Copyright © 1991 American Accounting Association. Used with permission.

Two factor ANOVA

Means:		Factor 2		
		Armrests	No Armrests	
Factor 1	B1	7.5	6.8	7.2
	B2	2.7	6.0	4.4
	B3	2.8	2.8	2.8
		4.3	5.2	4.8

ANOVA table

Source	SS	df	MS	F	p-value
Factor 1	194.43	2	97.217		
Factor 2	11.27	1	11.267		
Interaction	45.63	2	22.817		
Error	147.40	54	2.730		
Total	398.73	59			

10.34 An information systems manager wishes to compare the execution speed (in seconds) for a standard statistical software package using three different compilers. The manager tests each compiler using three different computer models, and the data in Table 10.21 on the next page are obtained. Analyze the data (using a computer package if you wish). In particular, test for compiler effects and computer model effects, and also perform pairwise comparisons.

TABLE 10.21   Results of an Execution Speed Experiment for Three Compilers (Seconds) ✎

Computer	Compiler		
	1	**2**	**3**
Model 235	9.9	8.0	7.1
Model 335	12.5	10.6	9.1
Model 435	10.8	9.0	7.8

TABLE 10.22   Results of a Two-Factor Wheat Yield Experiment ✎

Fertilizer Type	Wheat Type			
	M	**N**	**O**	**P**
A	19.4	25.0	24.8	23.1
	20.6	24.0	26.0	24.3
	20.0	24.5	25.4	23.7
B	22.6	25.6	27.6	25.4
	21.6	26.8	26.4	24.5
	22.1	26.2	27.0	26.3

FIGURE 10.20   MegaStat Output of Crop Yields for Exercise 10.35

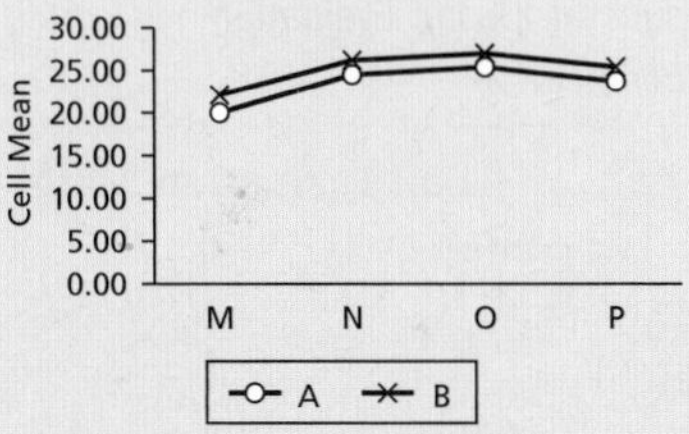

10.35 A research team at a school of agriculture carried out an experiment to study the effects of two fertilizer types (A and B) and four wheat types (M, N, O, and P) on crop yields (in tonnes per 5-ha plot). The data in Table 10.22 were obtained by using a completely randomized experimental design. Analyze these data by using the MegaStat output in Figure 10.20.

10.36 INTERNET EXERCISE

Recently people have been concerned about fuel consumption of their vehicles due to rising gasoline prices. One commonly occurring statement is that larger vehicles are far less fuel efficient than are smaller vehicles. Natural Resources Canada lists the most fuel-efficient vehicles for 2010 on their Web site at:

http://oee.nrcan.gc.ca/transportation/personal/pdfs/most-efficient-vehicles-2010.pdf.

Group the vehicles into three groups: 1 = two-seater, subcompact, and compact ($n = 3$); 2 = mid-size, full-size, and station wagon (excluding the diesel model; $n = 3$); 3 = pickup trucks and special purpose ($n = 2$).

a. Compute the mean fuel consumption value for each group for city driving and for highway driving separately.

b. Conduct a one-way ANOVA on the city driving values. What do the results tell you?

c. Conduct a one-way ANOVA on the highway driving values. What do the results tell you?

d. Based on the findings of the two analyses, what is your conclusion regarding the claim that larger vehicles are much less fuel efficient?

CHAPTER 11

Correlation Coefficient and Simple Linear Regression Analysis

LEARNING OBJECTIVES

After reading this chapter, you should be able to

LO1 define and calculate the correlation coefficient statistic and describe the two properties of the statistic

LO2 compute r^2 (eta^2) from a correlation and explain the resulting value

LO3 define what is meant by simple linear regression

LO4 list the assumptions behind linear regression

LO5 write the equation for linear regression and explain what the terms mean

LO6 define the F test in a linear regression

CHAPTER OUTLINE

11.1 Correlation Coefficient

11.2 Testing the Significance of the Population Correlation Coefficient

11.3 The Simple Linear Regression Model

11.4 Model Assumptions

11.5 The Least Squares Estimates, and Point Estimation and Prediction

11.6 Testing the Significance of the Slope and y Intercept

11.7 Confidence and Prediction Intervals

11.8 Simple Coefficients of Determination and Correlation

11.9 An F Test for the Model

11.10 Residual Analysis

11.11 Some Shortcut Formulas

Managers often make decisions by studying the relationships between variables, and process improvements can often be made by understanding how changes in one or more variables affect the process output. The basic statistic for understanding how two variables are related is the correlation coefficient (r), which is also known as the Pearson-product-moment correlation, named after its creator Karl Pearson (1857–1936). This useful statistic describes two properties of the linear relationship between variables: the direction (positive or negative) and the strength (from zero, or no relationship, to one, or a perfect relationship). The correlation coefficient is briefly discussed in this chapter. Following the discussion of the correlation statistic (note that r was originally chosen as an abbreviation for "regression"), regression analysis is covered.

Regression analysis is a statistical technique in which we use observed data to relate a variable of interest, which is called the **dependent** (or **response** or **criterion**) **variable**, to one or more **independent** (or **predictor**) **variables**. The objective is to build a **regression model**, or **prediction**

equation, that can be used to **describe**, **predict**, and **control** the dependent variable on the basis of the independent variables. For example, a company might wish to improve its marketing process. After collecting data concerning the demand for a product, the product's price, and the advertising expenditures made to promote the product, the company might use regression analysis to develop an equation to predict demand on the basis of price and advertising expenditure. Predictions of demand for various price–advertising expenditure combinations can then be used to evaluate potential changes in the company's marketing strategies. As another example, a manufacturer might use regression analysis to describe the relationship between several input variables and an important output variable. Understanding the relationships between these variables would allow the manufacturer to identify **control variables** that can be used to improve the process performance.

In this chapter, we present the simple linear regression model. Using this technique is appropriate when we are relating a dependent variable to a single independent variable and when a **straight-line model** describes the relationship between these two variables. We explain many of the methods of this chapter in the context of a new case:

The QHIC Case: The marketing department at Quality Home Improvement Centre (QHIC) uses simple linear regression analysis to predict home-upkeep expenditure on the basis of home value. Predictions of home-upkeep expenditures are used to help determine which homes should be sent advertising brochures promoting QHIC's products and services.

 Practise and learn online with *Connect*. Throughout this chapter, questions and tables with online data sets are marked with ✐.

11.1 CORRELATION COEFFICIENT

In Chapter 2, we discussed how to use a scatter plot to explore the relationship between a dependent variable y and an independent variable x. To construct a scatter plot, a sample of n pairs of values of x and y—(x_1, y_1), (x_2, y_2), . . . , (x_n, y_n)—is collected. Then each value of y is plotted against the corresponding value of x. If the plot points seem to fluctuate around a straight line, we say that there is a **linear relationship** between x and y. For example, suppose that ten sales regions of equal sales potential for a company are randomly selected. The advertising expenditures (in units of $10,000) in these ten sales regions in July of last year (x) are given in the second column of Table 11.1. The sales volumes $(y$, in units of $10,000) are then recorded for the ten sales regions in the third column of Table 11.1. A scatter plot of sales volume, y, versus advertising expenditure, x, is given in Figure 11.1 and shows a linear relationship between x and y.

A measure of the **strength of the linear relationship** between x and y is the correlation. To calculate the correlation, we begin with the **covariance** between the two variables. The **sample covariance** is calculated by using the sample of n pairs of observed values of x and y. This sample covariance is denoted as s_{xy} and defined as follows:

$$s_{xy} = \frac{\sum_{i=1}^{n} (x_i - \bar{x})(y_i - \bar{y})}{n - 1}.$$

To use this formula, we first find the mean $\bar{x}$ of the n observed values of x and the mean $\bar{y}$ of the n observed values of y. For each observed (x_i, y_i) combination, we then multiply the deviation of x_i from $\bar{x}$ by the deviation of y_i from $\bar{y}$ to form the product $(x_i - \bar{x})(y_i - \bar{y})$. Finally, we add together the n products $(x_1 - \bar{x})(y_1 - \bar{y})$, $(x_2 - \bar{x})(y_2 - \bar{y})$, . . . , $(x_n - \bar{x})(y_n - \bar{y})$ and divide the resulting sum by $n - 1$. For example, the mean of the ten advertising expenditures in Table 11.1 is $\bar{x} = 9.5$, and the mean of the ten sales volumes in Table 11.1 is $\bar{y} = 108.3$. It follows that the numerator of s_{xy} is the sum of the values of $(x_i - \bar{x})(y_i - \bar{y}) = (x_i - 9.5)(y_i - 108.3)$. Table 11.2 shows that this sum equals 365.50, which implies that the sample covariance is

$$s_{xy} = \frac{\sum (x_i - \bar{x})(y_i - \bar{y})}{n - 1} = \frac{365.50}{9} = 40.61111.$$

To interpret the covariance, consider Figure 11.2(a). This figure shows the scatter plot of Figure 11.1 with a vertical blue line drawn at $\bar{x} = 9.5$ and a horizontal red line drawn at $\bar{y} = 108.3$. The lines divide the scatter plot into four quadrants. Points in quadrant I correspond to x_i greater than $\bar{x}$ and y_i greater than $\bar{y}$ and thus give a value of $(x_i - \bar{x})(y_i - \bar{y})$ greater than 0. Points in quadrant III correspond to x_i less than $\bar{x}$ and y_i less than $\bar{y}$ and thus also give a value of $(x_i - \bar{x})(y_i - \bar{y})$ greater than 0. It follows that if s_{xy} is positive, the points with the greatest influence on $\Sigma(x_i - \bar{x})(y_i - \bar{y})$ and thus on s_{xy} must be in quadrants I and III. Therefore, a positive value of s_{xy} (as in the sales volume example) indicates a positive linear relationship between x and y. That is, as x increases, y increases.

If we further consider Figure 11.2, we see that points in quadrant II correspond to x_i less than $\bar{x}$ and y_i greater than $\bar{y}$. Points in quadrant IV correspond to x_i greater than $\bar{x}$ and y_i less than $\bar{y}$.

TABLE **11.1** The Sales Volume Data

Sales Region	Advertising Expenditure, x	Sales Volume, y
1	5	89
2	6	87
3	7	98
4	8	110
5	9	103
6	10	114
7	11	116
8	12	110
9	13	126
10	14	130

FIGURE **11.1** A Scatter Plot of Sales Volume versus Advertising Expenditure

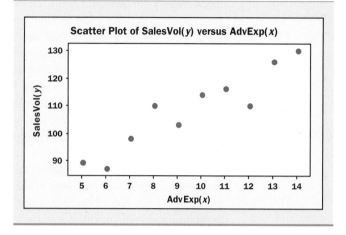

TABLE **11.2** The Calculation of the Numerator of s_{xy}

x_i	y_i	$x_i - 9.5$	$y_i - 108.3$	$(x_i - 9.5)(y_i - 108.3)$
5	89	−4.5	−19.3	86.85
6	87	−3.5	−21.3	74.55
7	98	−2.5	−10.3	25.75
8	110	−1.5	1.7	−2.55
9	103	−0.5	−5.3	2.65
10	114	0.5	5.7	2.85
11	116	1.5	7.7	11.55
12	110	2.5	1.7	4.25
13	126	3.5	17.7	61.95
14	130	4.5	21.7	97.65
Totals 95	1,083	0	0	365.50

FIGURE **11.2** Interpretation of the Sample Covariance

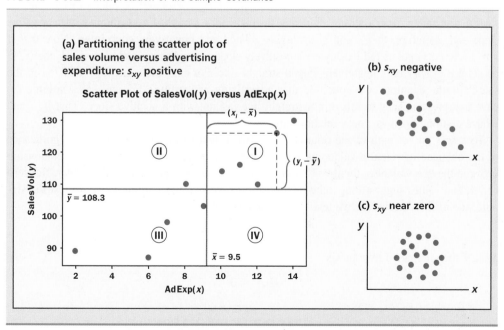

It follows that if s_{xy} is negative, the points with the greatest influence on $\Sigma(x_i - \bar{x})(y_i - \bar{y})$ and thus on s_{xy} must be in quadrants II and IV. A negative value of s_{xy} indicates a negative linear relationship between x and y. That is, as x increases, y decreases, as shown in Figure 11.2(b). For example, a negative linear relationship might exist between average hourly outdoor temperature (x) in a city during a week and the city's natural gas consumption (y) during the week. That is, as the average hourly outdoor temperature increased, the city's natural gas consumption would decrease (or, as temperatures dropped, gas consumption would increase). Finally, note that if s_{xy} is near zero, the (x_i, y_i) points will be fairly evenly distributed across all four quadrants. This indicates little or no linear relationship between x and y, as shown in Figure 11.2(c).[1]

From the previous discussion, it might seem that a large positive value for the covariance indicates that x and y have a strong positive linear relationship and a large negative value for the covariance indicates that x and y have a strong negative linear relationship. However, one problem with using the covariance as a measure of the strength of the linear relationship between x and y is that the value of the covariance depends on the units in which x and y are measured. A measure of the strength of the linear relationship between x and y that does not depend on the units in which x and y are measured is the **correlation coefficient**. The **simple correlation coefficient** is denoted as r and is defined as follows:

$$r = \frac{s_{xy}}{s_x s_y}.$$

Here s_{xy} is the previously defined sample covariance, s_x is the sample standard deviation of the sample of x values, and s_y is the sample standard deviation of the sample of y values. For the sales volume data,

$$s_x = \sqrt{\frac{\sum_{i=1}^{10}(x_i - \bar{x})^2}{9}} = 3.02765 \quad \text{and} \quad s_y = \sqrt{\frac{\sum_{i=1}^{10}(y_i - \bar{y})^2}{9}} = 14.30656.$$

Therefore, the sample correlation coefficient is

LO1

$$r = \frac{s_{xy}}{s_x s_y} = \frac{40.61111}{(3.02765)(14.30656)} = 0.93757.$$

It can be shown that the sample correlation coefficient r is always between -1 and 1. A value of r near 0 implies little linear relationship between x and y. A value of r close to 1 says that x and y have a strong tendency to relate in a straight-line fashion with a positive slope and, therefore, that x and y are highly related and **positively correlated**. A value of r close to -1 says that x and y have a strong tendency to relate in a straight-line fashion with a negative slope and, therefore, that x and y are highly related and **negatively correlated**. Note that if $r = 1$, the (x, y) points fall exactly on a positively sloped straight line, and, if $r = -1$, the (x, y) points fall exactly on a negatively sloped straight line. For example, since $r = 0.93757$ in the sales volume example, we conclude that advertising expenditure (x) and sales volume (y) have a strong tendency to relate in a straight-line fashion with a positive slope. That is, x and y have a strong positive linear relationship.

To assess the strength of the relationship between two variables, the statistical significance of the obtained correlation value can be assessed. In particular, when there is no relationship between the two variables, then $r = 0$ and the variables are independent of each other. Nonzero correlation values suggest that some relationship between x and y might exist. To test the significance of the correlation, we test the null hypothesis

$$H_0: r = 0$$

against the alternative hypothesis

$$H_a: r \neq 0.$$

---

[1]One way to remember the zero correlation is that the scatter plot looks like a circle or a zero.

TABLE 11.3   Critical Values of r, Where $df = n - 2$ and n is the Number of Pairs of Scores

Degrees of Freedom (df)	5%	1%	Degrees of Freedom (df)	5%	1%
1	0.997	1.000	24	0.388	0.496
2	0.950	0.990	25	0.381	0.487
3	0.878	0.959	26	0.374	0.478
4	0.811	0.917	27	0.367	0.470
5	0.754	0.874	28	0.361	0.463
6	0.707	0.834	29	0.355	0.456
7	0.666	0.798	30	0.349	0.449
8	0.632	0.765	31	0.325	0.418
9	0.602	0.735	32	0.304	0.393
10	0.576	0.708	33	0.288	0.372
11	0.533	0.684	34	0.273	0.354
12	0.532	0.661	35	0.250	0.325
13	0.514	0.641	36	0.232	0.302
14	0.497	0.623	37	0.217	0.283
15	0.482	0.606	38	0.205	0.267
16	0.468	0.590	39	0.195	0.254
17	0.456	0.575	40	0.174	0.228
18	0.444	0.561	41	0.159	0.208
19	0.433	0.549	42	0.138	0.181
20	0.423	0.537	43	0.113	0.148
21	0.413	0.526	44	0.098	0.128
22	0.404	0.515	45	0.088	0.115
23	0.396	0.505	46	0.062	0.081

Source: This table is adapted from Table VII of Fisher and Yates, *Statistical Tables for Biological, Agricultural and Medical Research*, published by Longman Group Ltd., London (previously published by Oliver and Boyd, Edinburgh), and by permission of Pearson Education Limited.

How large the correlation value has to be to suggest a meaningful relationship between x and y is influenced by the number of pairs of data points, as is reflected in Table 11.3.

For example, in the sales volume example, $r = 0.93757$ was obtained for ten sales regions. Here the $df = n - 2 = 10 - 2 = 8$. Looking at Table 11.3, the critical value for significance is 0.632 at 5 percent (0.05) and 0.765 at 1 percent (0.01). Because 0.93757 is greater than 0.765, we can conclude that the likelihood of obtaining the correlation of 0.93757 is less than 0.01 and that the relationship between advertising expenditure and sales volume is statistically significant at the 0.01 level.

In general, however, note that a strong positive or strong negative linear relationship between an independent variable x and a dependent variable y does not necessarily mean that we can accurately *predict* y on the basis of x. We consider predicting y on the basis of x later in this chapter.

The sample covariance s_{xy} is the point estimate of the **population covariance**, which we denote as σ_{xy}, and the sample correlation coefficient r is the point estimate of the **population correlation coefficient**, which we denote as ρ. To define σ_{xy} and ρ, let μ_x and σ_x denote the mean and the standard deviation of the population of all possible x values, and let μ_y and σ_y denote the mean and the standard deviation of the population of all possible y values. Then σ_{xy} is the average of all possible values of $(x - \mu_x)(y - \mu_y)$, and ρ equals $\sigma_{xy}/(\sigma_x\sigma_y)$. Similar to r, ρ is always between -1 and 1.

LO2

Another useful statistic derived from the correlation coefficient (r) is the **simple coefficient of determination** or eta squared (eta^2) or r squared (r^2). Eta^2 is simply the squared correlation value and tells us the amount of variance overlap between the two variables x and y. For example, if the correlation between self-reported altruistic behaviour and charity donations is 0.24, then eta^2 is $0.24 \times 0.24 = 0.0576$. Expressing this number as a percentage gives 5.76 percent. From this value, it can be concluded that 5.76 percent of the variance in charity donations overlaps with the variance in self-reported altruistic behaviour. More about r^2 and variance overlap and predicting y from x is discussed in Section 11.8.

Exercises for Section 11.1

CONCEPTS

11.1 Define the term "covariance." What would the relationship between x and y look like if there were no covariance between these two variables?

11.2 Describe what the scatterplot would look like for each correlation:
a. $r = 0.02$ **b.** $r = -0.85$ **c.** $r = 0.73$

METHODS AND APPLICATIONS

11.3 Chemical BFYR is used in the production of a cosmetic product, and chemists feel that the amount of chemical BFYR may be related to the viscosity of the cosmetic product. To verify and quantify this relationship, 24 batches of the product are produced. The amount (x) of chemical BFYR (in grams) is varied from batch to batch, and the viscosity (y) obtained for each batch is measured. For the 24 batches, the following is found:

$$\sum_{i=1}^{24} (x_i - \bar{x})(y_i - \bar{y}) = 10.2281,$$

$$s_x = 0.7053, \text{ and } s_y = 0.6515.$$

Using this information, calculate the sample covariance s_{xy} and the sample correlation coefficient r. Interpret r. What can you say about the strength of the linear relationship between x and y? (*Hint:* Refer to Table 11.3.)

11.4 Statistics Canada (http://www.statcan.gc.ca) collects data on the social behaviour of Canadians. One activity for which data are collected deals with donations to charities. Average donations (in dollars) are reported by Statistics Canada by age groups of Canadians for the year 2000, and the values are provided below for adults aged 15 and over.

Age Group	Average Donation ($)
15–24 years	118
25–34 years	229
35–44 years	242
45–54 years	338
55–64 years	316
65 years and over	308

Source: http://www40.statcan.gc.ca/l01/cst01/famil104.htm.

For these data, compute the correlation value and interpret r (use a single number to represent each age group, such as 1, 2, 3, etc.). Also compute r^2 (eta^2). Based on the r^2 (eta^2) value, what percentage of variance overlap is found between age and average donation amount?

11.2 TESTING THE SIGNIFICANCE OF THE POPULATION CORRELATION COEFFICIENT

The sample correlation coefficient (r) measures the linear relationship between the observed values of x and the observed values of y that make up the sample. A similar coefficient of linear correlation can be defined for the population of *all possible combinations of observed values of x and y*. We call this coefficient the **population correlation coefficient** and denote it by the symbol ρ (rho). We use r as the point estimate of ρ. In addition, we can carry out a hypothesis test. Here we test the null hypothesis $H_0: \rho = 0$, **which says there is no linear relationship between x and y**, against the alternative hypothesis $H_a: \rho \neq 0$, **which says there is a positive or negative linear relationship between x and y**. This test employs the test statistic

$$t = \frac{r\sqrt{n-2}}{\sqrt{1-r^2}}$$

and is based on the assumption that the population of all possible observed combinations of values of x and y has a **bivariate normal probability distribution** (see Wonnacott and Wonnacott (1981) for a discussion of this distribution). If the bivariate normal distribution assumption for the test concerning ρ is badly violated, we can use a nonparametric approach to correlation. One such approach is **Spearman's rank correlation coefficient**. This approach is discussed in Section 13.5.

Exercises for Section 11.2

CONCEPTS

11.5 Explain what is meant by the population correlation coefficient ρ.

11.6 Explain how to test H_0: $\rho = 0$ versus H_a: $\rho \neq 0$. What do you conclude if you reject H_0: $\rho = 0$?

METHODS AND APPLICATIONS

11.7 In a study conducted by the human resources department of a large organization, the correlation between job satisfaction (x) and attendance (y) was found to be 0.23 based on surveys completed by 200 employees. Assuming that the bivariate normal probability distribution assumption holds,

test H_0: $\rho = 0$ versus H_a: $\rho \neq 0$ by setting α equal to 0.001. What do you conclude about how x and y are related?

11.8 In a smaller organization, the human resources department tried to replicate the findings from the larger organization described in Exercise 11.7. Based on surveys completed by ten employees, the correlation between job satisfaction (x) and attendance (y) was again found to be 0.23. As in the previous exercise, test H_0: $\rho = 0$ versus H_a: $\rho \neq 0$. What can you conclude about the relationship between x and y based on this smaller sample of employees?

11.3 THE SIMPLE LINEAR REGRESSION MODEL

The **simple linear regression model** assumes that the relationship between the *dependent variable, which is denoted* y, and the *independent variable, denoted* x, can be approximated by a straight line. We can tentatively decide whether there is an approximate straight-line relationship between y and x by making a **scatter diagram**, or **scatter plot**, of y versus x. First, data concerning the two variables are observed in pairs. To construct the scatter plot, each value of y is plotted against its corresponding value of x. If the y values tend to increase or decrease in a straight-line fashion as the x values increase, and if there is a scattering of the (x, y) points around the straight line, then it is reasonable to describe the relationship between y and x by using the simple linear regression model.

We suppose that we have gathered n observations—each observation consists of an observed value of x and its corresponding value of y. Then we have the following:

The Simple Linear Regression Model

The **simple linear (or straight-line) regression model** is $y = \mu_{y|x} + \varepsilon = \beta_0 + \beta_1 x + \varepsilon$.

1   $\mu_{y|x} = \beta_0 + \beta_1 x$ is the **mean value** of the dependent variable y when the value of the independent variable is x.

2   β_0 is the **y intercept**. β_0 is the mean value of y when x equals zero.

3   β_1 is the **slope**. β_1 is the change (amount of increase or decrease) in the mean value of y

associated with a one-unit increase in x. If β_1 is positive, the mean value of y increases as x increases. If β_1 is negative, the mean value of y decreases as x increases.

4   ε is an error term that describes the effects on y of all factors other than the value of the independent variable x.

This model is illustrated in Figure 11.3 on the next page (note that x_0 in this figure denotes a specific value of the independent variable x). The y intercept β_0 and the slope β_1 are called **regression parameters**. Because we do not know the true values of these parameters, we must use the sample data to estimate them. We will see how this is done in Section 11.5. In later sections, we will show how to use these estimates to predict y, where $\hat{y}$ is the predicted value of y.

LO3

FIGURE **11.3**   The Simple Linear Regression Model (Here the Slope β_1 Is Positive)

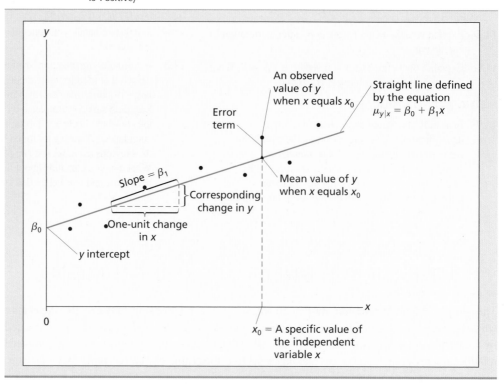

Example 11.1 The QHIC Case

Quality Home Improvement Centre (QHIC) operates five stores in a large metropolitan area. The marketing department at QHIC wishes to study the relationship between x, home value (in thousands of dollars), and y, yearly expenditure on home upkeep (in dollars). A random sample of 40 homeowners is taken and asked to estimate their expenditures during the previous year on the types of home-upkeep products and services offered by QHIC. Public city records are used to obtain the previous year's assessed values of the homeowner's homes. The resulting x and y values are given in Table 11.4(a). Because the 40 observations are for the same year (for different homes), these data are **cross-sectional** (data observed at a single point in time as opposed to time series data, which are longitudinal).

The Excel scatter plot of y versus x is given in Table 11.4(b). We see that the observed values of y tend to increase in a straight-line (or slightly curved) fashion as x increases. Assuming that $\mu_{y|x}$ and x have a straight-line relationship, it is reasonable to relate y to x by using the simple linear regression model with positive slope ($\beta_1 > 0$)

$$y = \beta_0 + \beta_1 x + \varepsilon.$$

The slope β_1 is the change (increase) in mean dollar yearly upkeep expenditure associated with each \$1,000 increase in home value. In later examples, the marketing department at QHIC will use predictions given by this simple linear regression model to help determine which homes should be sent advertising brochures promoting QHIC's products and services.

TABLE 11.4 The QHIC Upkeep Expenditure Data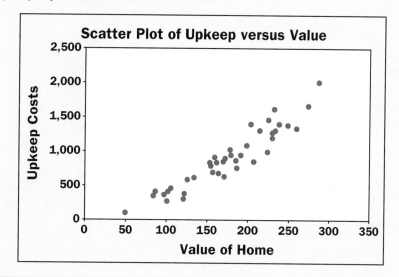

(a) The data

Home	Value of Home, x (Thousands of Dollars)	Upkeep Expenditure, y (Dollars)	Home	Value of Home, x (Thousands of Dollars)	Upkeep Expenditure, y (Dollars)
1	237.00	1,412.08	21	153.04	849.14
2	153.08	797.20	22	232.18	1,313.84
3	184.86	872.48	23	125.44	602.06
4	222.06	1,003.42	24	169.82	642.14
5	160.68	852.90	25	177.28	1,038.80
6	99.68	288.48	26	162.82	697.00
7	229.04	1,288.46	27	120.44	324.34
8	101.78	423.08	28	191.10	965.10
9	257.86	1,351.74	29	158.78	920.14
10	96.28	378.04	30	178.50	950.90
11	171.00	918.08	31	272.20	1,670.32
12	231.02	1,627.24	32	48.90	125.40
13	228.32	1,204.76	33	104.56	479.78
14	205.90	857.04	34	286.18	2,010.64
15	185.72	775.00	35	83.72	368.36
16	168.78	869.26	36	86.20	425.60
17	247.06	1,396.00	37	133.58	626.90
18	155.54	711.50	38	212.86	1,316.94
19	224.20	1,475.18	39	122.02	390.16
20	202.04	1,413.32	40	198.02	1,090.84

(b) Excel Plot of upkeep expenditure versus value of home

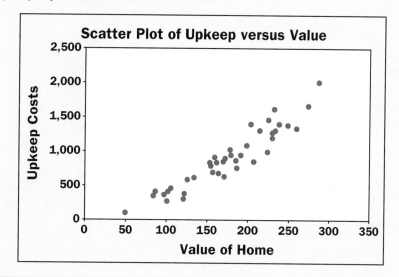

We have interpreted the slope β_1 of the simple linear regression model to be the change in the mean value of y associated with a one-unit increase in x. We sometimes refer to this change as *the effect of the independent variable x on the dependent variable y.* However, we cannot prove that a *change in an independent variable causes a change in the dependent variable.* Rather, regression can be used only to establish that the two variables relate and that the independent variable contributes information for predicting the dependent variable. For instance, regression analysis might be used to establish that as liquor sales have increased over the years, university professors' salaries have also increased. However, this does not prove that increases in liquor sales cause increases in university professors' salaries. Rather, both variables are influenced by a third variable—long-run growth in the economy.

Exercises for Section 11.3

CONCEPTS

11.9 When does the scatter plot of the values of a dependent variable y versus the values of an independent variable x suggest that the simple linear regression model

$$y = \mu_{y|x} + \varepsilon$$
$$= \beta_0 + \beta_1 x + \varepsilon$$

might appropriately relate y to x?

11.10 In the simple linear regression model, what are y, $\mu_{y|x}$, and ε?

11.11 In the simple linear regression model, define the slope β_1 and the y intercept β_0.

11.12 What is the difference between time series data and cross-sectional data?

METHODS AND APPLICATIONS

11.13 THE SERVICE TIME CASE

Accu-Copiers sells and services the Accu-500 copying machine. As part of its standard service contract, the company agrees to perform routine service on this copier. To obtain information about the time it takes to perform routine service, Accu-Copiers has collected data for 11 service calls. The data are as in Figure 11.4.

Using the Excel scatter plot of y versus x, discuss why the simple linear regression model might appropriately relate y to x.

11.14 THE SERVICE TIME CASE

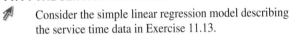

Consider the simple linear regression model describing the service time data in Exercise 11.13.

a. Interpret $\mu_{y|x = 4} = \beta_0 + \beta_1(4)$.
b. Interpret $\mu_{y|x = 6} = \beta_0 + \beta_1(6)$.
c. Interpret the slope parameter β_1.
d. Interpret the y intercept β_0. Does this interpretation make practical sense?
e. The error term ε describes the effects of many factors on service time. What are these factors? Give two specific examples.

11.15 THE FRESH DETERGENT CASE

Enterprise Industries produces Fresh, a brand of liquid laundry detergent. In order to study the relationship between price and demand for the large bottle of Fresh, the company has gathered data concerning demand for Fresh over the last 30 sales periods (each sales period is four weeks). Here, for each sales period,

y = demand for the large bottle of Fresh (in hundreds of thousands of bottles) in the sales period, and

x = the difference between the average industry price (in dollars) of competitors' similar detergents and the price (in dollars) of Fresh as offered by Enterprise Industries in the sales period.

Referring to the variable x as the price difference for brevity's sake, the data are as follows:

Fresh Detergent Demand Data					
Sales Period	y	x	Sales Period	y	x
1	7.38	−0.05	16	8.87	0.30
2	8.51	0.25	17	9.26	0.50
3	9.52	0.60	18	9.00	0.50
4	7.50	0	19	8.75	0.40
5	9.33	0.25	20	7.95	−0.05
6	8.28	0.20	21	7.65	−0.05
7	8.75	0.15	22	7.27	−0.10
8	7.87	0.05	23	8.00	0.20
9	7.10	−0.15	24	8.50	0.10
10	8.00	0.15	25	8.75	0.50
11	7.89	0.20	26	9.21	0.60
12	8.15	0.10	27	8.27	−0.05
13	9.10	0.40	28	7.67	0
14	8.86	0.45	29	7.93	0.05
15	8.90	0.35	30	9.26	0.55

FIGURE 11.4   Routine Copier Service Times for Exercise 11.13

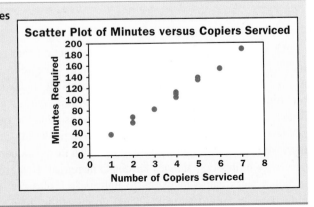

Service Call	Number of Copiers Serviced, x	Number of Minutes Required, y
1	4	109
2	2	58
3	5	138
4	7	189
5	1	37
6	3	82
7	4	103
8	5	134
9	2	68
10	4	112
11	6	154

Scatter Plot of Minutes versus Copiers Serviced

TABLE 11.5   Data for Exercises 11.17 and 11.19

(a) Direct labour cost data		(b) Dog Biscuit Sales	
Direct Labour Cost, y ($100s)	Batch Size, x	Number of Bags Sold, y	Number of Coupons Issued, x
71	5	180	23
663	62	98	11
381	35	173	20
138	12	137	17
861	83	141	15
145	14	166	21
493	46	194	24
548	52	128	13
251	23	164	19
1024	100	173	25
435	41		
772	75		

Using the Excel scatter plot of y versus x shown below, discuss why the simple linear regression model might appropriately relate y to x.

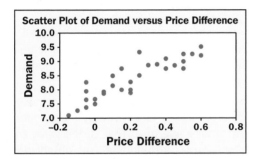

Scatter Plot of Demand versus Price Difference

11.16 THE FRESH DETERGENT CASE

Consider the simple linear regression model relating demand, y, to the price difference, x, and the Fresh demand data of Exercise 11.15.
a. Interpret $\mu_{y|x = 0.10} = \beta_0 + \beta_1(0.10)$.
b. Interpret $\mu_{y|x = -0.05} = \beta_0 + \beta_1(-0.05)$.
c. Interpret the slope parameter β_1.
d. Interpret the y intercept β_0. Does this interpretation make practical sense?
e. What factors are represented by the error term in this model? Give two specific examples.

11.17 THE DIRECT LABOUR COST CASE

An accountant wishes to predict direct labour cost (y) on the basis of the batch size (x) of a product produced in a job shop. Data for 12 production runs are given in Table 11.5(a).
a. Construct a scatter plot of y versus x.
b. Discuss whether the scatter plot suggests that a simple linear regression model might appropriately relate y to x.

11.18 THE DIRECT LABOUR COST CASE

Consider the simple linear regression model describing the direct labour cost data of Exercise 11.17.

a. Interpret $\mu_{y|x = 60} = \beta_0 + \beta_1(60)$.
b. Interpret $\mu_{y|x = 30} = \beta_0 + \beta_1(30)$.
c. Interpret the slope parameter β_1.
d. Interpret the y intercept β_0. Does this interpretation make practical sense?
e. What factors are represented by the error term in this model? Give two specific examples of these factors.

11.19 DOG BISCUIT SALES

A manufacturer of dog biscuits is interested in improving sales by providing "cents-off" coupons to customers. Ten supermarkets are used in the data collection (all of equal sales potential). The number of coupons issued (x) on the store shelf where the dog biscuits are located is varied and monthly sales of the number of bags of dog biscuits sold (y) are compiled. The data are listed in Table 11.5(b).
a. Construct a scatter plot of y versus x.
b. Discuss whether the scatter plot suggests that a simple linear regression model might appropriately relate y to x.

11.20 DOG BISCUIT SALES

Consider the simple linear regression model describing the data of Exercise 11.19.
a. Interpret $\mu_{y|x = 20} = \beta_0 + \beta_1(20)$.
b. Interpret $\mu_{y|x = 18} = \beta_0 + \beta_1(18)$.
c. Interpret the slope parameter β_1.
d. Interpret the y intercept β_0. Does this interpretation make practical sense?
e. What factors are represented by the error term in this model? Give two specific examples.

11.4 MODEL ASSUMPTIONS

Model assumptions In order to perform hypothesis tests and set up various types of intervals when using the simple linear regression model

$$y = \mu_{y|x} + \varepsilon$$
$$= \beta_0 + \beta_1 x + \varepsilon,$$

we need to make certain assumptions about the error term ε. At any given value of x, there is a population of error term values that could potentially occur. These error term values describe the different potential effects on y of all factors other than the value of x. Therefore, these error term values explain the variation in the y values that could be observed when the independent variable is x. Our statement of the simple linear regression model assumes that $\mu_{y|x}$, the mean of the population of all y values that could be observed when the independent variable is x, is $\beta_0 + \beta_1 x$. This model also implies that $\varepsilon = y - (\beta_0 + \beta_1 x)$, so this is equivalent to assuming that the mean of the corresponding population of potential error term values is 0. We make four **regression assumptions** about the simple linear regression model. These assumptions can be stated in terms of potential y values or, equivalently, in terms of potential error term values. Following tradition, we begin by stating these assumptions in terms of potential error term values:

The Regression Assumptions

LO4 1 **Error mean assumption:** At any given value of x, the population of potential error term values has a *mean equal to 0.*

2 **Constant-variance assumption:** At any given value of x, the population of potential error term values has a variance that does not depend on the value of x. That is, the different populations of potential error term values corresponding to different values of x have *equal variances.* We denote the *constant variance as σ^2.*

3 **Normality assumption:** At any given value of x, the population of potential error term values has a *normal distribution.*

4 **Independence assumption:** Any one value of the error term ε is *statistically independent* of any other value of ε. That is, the value of the error term ε corresponding to an observed value of y is statistically independent of the value of the error term corresponding to any other observed value of y.

Taken together, the first three assumptions say that at any given value of x, the population of potential error term values is *normally distributed* with *mean zero* and a *variance σ^2 that does not depend on the value of x.* Because the potential error term values cause the variation in the potential y values, these assumptions imply that the population of all y values that could be observed when the independent variable is x is *normally distributed* with *mean $\beta_0 + \beta_1 x$ and a variance σ^2 that does not depend on x.* These three assumptions are illustrated in Figure 11.5(a) (based on the data in Figure 11.5(b)). Specifically, this figure depicts the populations of y values corresponding to two x values—32.5 and 45.9. Note that these populations are shown to be normally distributed with different means (each of which is on the line of means) and with the same variance (or spread).

The independence assumption is most likely to be violated when time series data are being utilized in a regression study. This assumption says that there is no pattern of positive error terms being followed (in time) by other positive error terms, and there is no pattern of positive error terms being followed by negative error terms. That is, there is no pattern of higher than average y values being followed by other higher than average y values.

It is important to point out that the regression assumptions very seldom, if ever, hold exactly in any practical regression problem. However, it has been found that regression results are not

FIGURE 11.5 An Illustration of the Model Assumptions

(a) Model assumptions

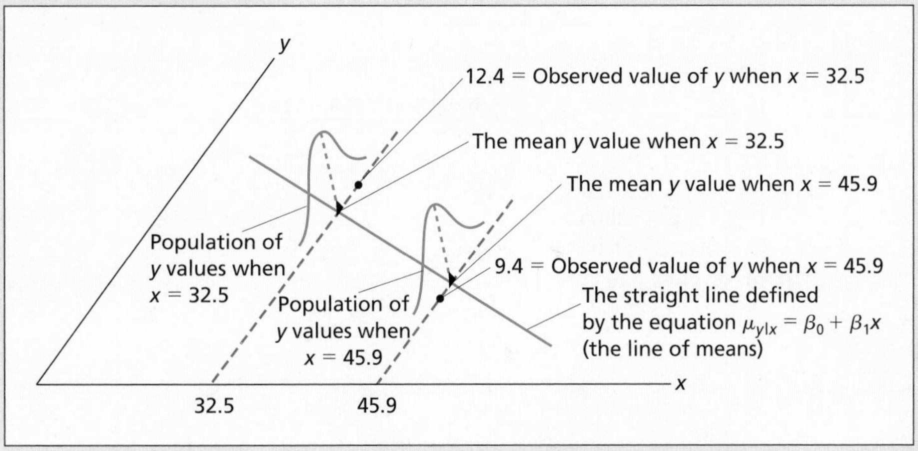
y
12.4 = Observed value of y when x = 32.5
The mean y value when x = 32.5
The mean y value when x = 45.9
Population of
y values when
x = 32.5
9.4 = Observed value of y when x = 45.9
Population of
y values when
x = 45.9
The straight line defined
by the equation $\mu_{y|x} = \beta_0 + \beta_1 x$
(the line of means)
x
32.5
45.9

(b) Data

Observation	x	y
1	28.0	12.4
2	28.0	11.7
3	32.5	12.4
4	39.0	10.8
5	45.9	9.4
6	57.8	9.5
7	58.1	8.0
8	62.5	7.5

extremely sensitive to mild departures from these assumptions. In practice, only pronounced departures from these assumptions require attention. For the examples in this chapter, we will suppose that the assumptions are valid.

When we predict an individual value of the dependent variable, we predict the error term to be 0. To see why we do this, note that the regression assumptions state that at any given value of the independent variable, the population of all error term values that can potentially occur is normally distributed with a mean equal to 0. Because we also assume that successive error terms are statistically independent, each error term has a 50 percent chance of being positive and a 50 percent chance of being negative. Therefore, it is reasonable to predict any particular error term value to be 0.

11.5 THE LEAST SQUARES ESTIMATES, AND POINT ESTIMATION AND PREDICTION

The true values of the y intercept (β_0) and slope (β_1) in the simple linear regression model are unknown. Therefore, it is necessary to use observed data to compute estimates of these regression parameters.

Consider the data and scatter plot of y versus x in Table 11.6 and Figure 11.6. The figure suggests that the simple linear regression model appropriately relates y to x. We now wish to

TABLE 11.6 Data

Observation	x	y
1	28.0	12.4
2	28.0	11.7
3	32.5	12.4
4	39.0	10.8
5	45.9	9.4
6	57.8	9.5
7	58.1	8.0
8	62.5	7.5

FIGURE 11.6 Excel Output of a Scatter Plot of y versus x

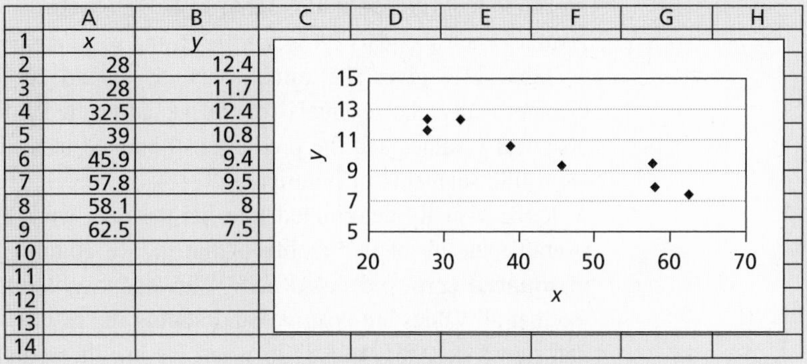
A
B
C
D
E
F
G
H
x
y
28 12.4
28 11.7
32.5 12.4
39 10.8
45.9 9.4
57.8 9.5
58.1 8
62.5 7.5
15
13
11
9
7
5
y
20
30
40
50
60
70
x

FIGURE **11.7**   Visually Fitting a Line

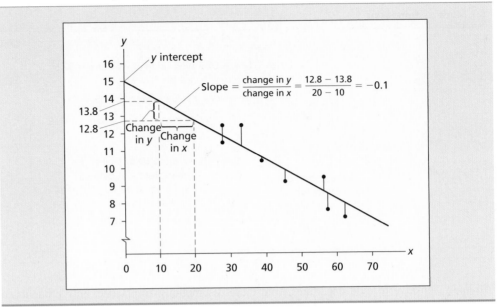

use the data in Table 11.6 to estimate the intercept β_0 and the slope β_1 of the line of means. To do this, it might be reasonable to estimate the line of means by "fitting" the "best" straight line to the plotted data in Figure 11.6. But how do we fit the best straight line? One approach would be to simply "eyeball" a line through the points. Then we could read the y intercept and slope off the visually fitted line and use these values as the estimates of β_0 and β_1. For example, Figure 11.7 shows a line that has been visually fitted to the plot of the data. We see that this line intersects the y axis at $y = 15$. Therefore, the y intercept of the line is 15. In addition, the figure shows that the slope of the line is

$$\frac{\text{change in } y}{\text{change in } x} = \frac{12.8 - 13.8}{20 - 10} = \frac{-1}{10} = -0.1.$$

Therefore, based on the visually fitted line, we estimate that β_0 is 15 and β_1 is -0.1.

In order to evaluate how "good" our point estimates of β_0 and β_1 are, consider using the visually fitted line to predict y. Denoting such a **prediction** as $\hat{y}$, a reasonable prediction of y when x is a certain value is simply the point on the visually fitted line corresponding to x. For instance, when x is 28,

$$\hat{y} = 15 - 0.1x = 15 - 0.1(28) = 12.2,$$

as shown in Figure 11.8. We can evaluate how well the visually determined line fits the points on the scatter plot by comparing each observed value of y to the corresponding predicted value of y given by the fitted line. We do this by computing the **residual, $y - \hat{y}$**. For instance, looking at the first observation in Table 11.6, we observe $y = 12.4$ and $x = 28.0$. Since the predicted y value when x equals 28 is $\hat{y} = 12.2$, the residual $y - \hat{y}$ equals $12.4 - 12.2 = 0.2$.

Table 11.7 gives the values of y, x, $\hat{y}$, and $y - \hat{y}$ for each observation in Table 11.6. Geometrically, the residuals for the visually fitted line are the vertical distances between the observed y values and the predictions obtained using the fitted line, which are depicted as the eight line segments in Figure 11.7.

If the visually determined line fits the data well, the residuals will be small. To obtain an overall measure of the quality of the fit, we compute the **sum of squared residuals** or **sum of squared errors**, denoted **SSE**. This quantity is obtained by squaring each of the residuals (so that all values are positive) and adding the results. Table 11.7 demonstrates this calculation and shows that $SSE = 4.8796$ when we use the visually fitted line to calculate predictions.

Clearly, the line shown in Figure 11.7 is not the only line that could be fitted to the observed data. Different people would obtain somewhat different visually fitted lines. However, it can

FIGURE **11.8** Using the Visually Fitted Line to Predict y When $x = 28$

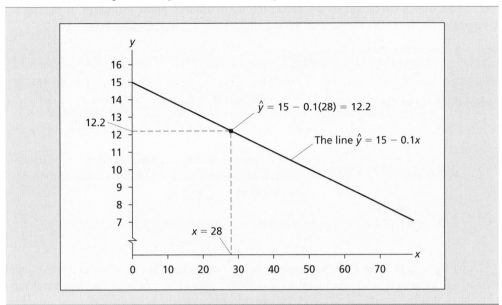

TABLE **11.7** Calculation of the *SSE* for a Line Visually Fitted to the Sample Data

y	x	$\hat{y} = 15 - 0.1x$	$y - \hat{y}$
12.4	28.0	$15 - 0.1(28.0) = 12.2$	$12.4 - 12.2 = 0.2$
11.7	28.0	$15 - 0.1(28.0) = 12.2$	$11.7 - 12.2 = -0.5$
12.4	32.5	$15 - 0.1(32.5) = 11.75$	$12.4 - 11.75 = 0.65$
10.8	39.0	$15 - 0.1(39.0) = 11.1$	$10.8 - 11.1 = -0.3$
9.4	45.9	$15 - 0.1(45.9) = 10.41$	$9.4 - 10.41 = -1.01$
9.5	57.8	$15 - 0.1(57.8) = 9.22$	$9.5 - 9.22 = 0.28$
8.0	58.1	$15 - 0.1(58.1) = 9.19$	$8.0 - 9.19 = -1.19$
7.5	62.5	$15 - 0.1(62.5) = 8.75$	$7.5 - 8.75 = -1.25$

$$SSE = \sum (y - \hat{y})^2 = (0.2)^2 + (-0.5)^2 + (0.65)^2 + \cdots + (-1.25)^2 = 4.8796$$

be shown that there is exactly one line that gives a value of the *SSE* that is smaller than the value of the *SSE* that would be given by any other line that could be fitted to the data. This line is called the **least squares regression line** and its equation is called the **least squares prediction equation**.

To show how to find the least squares line, we first write the **general form** of a straight-line prediction equation. Letting $\hat{y}$ denote the predicted value of y when the value of the independent variable is x, we write this equation as

$$\hat{y} = b_0 + b_1 x.$$

Here b_0 is *the y intercept* and b_1 is *the slope* of the line. Now suppose we have collected n observations $(x_1, y_1), (x_2, y_2), \ldots, (x_n, y_n)$, and consider a particular observation (x_i, y_i). The predicted value of y_i is

$$\hat{y}_i = b_0 + b_1 x_i$$

LO5

and the residual for this observation is

$$e_i = y_i - \hat{y}_i = y_i - (b_0 + b_1 x_i).$$

Then the **least squares line** is the line that *minimizes the sum of squared residuals*

$$SSE = \sum_{i=1}^{n} (y_i - (b_0 + b_1 x_i))^2.$$

To find this line, we find the values of the y intercept b_0 and the slope b_1 that minimize the SSE. These values of b_0 and b_1 are called the **least squares point estimates** of β_0 and β_1. Using calculus, it can be shown that these estimates are calculated as follows:[2]

The Least Squares Point Estimates

For the simple linear regression model:

1 The **least squares point estimate of the slope β_1** is $b_1 = \dfrac{SS_{xy}}{SS_{xx}}$, where

$$SS_{xy} = \sum (x_i - \bar{x})(y_i - \bar{y}) = \sum x_i y_i - \frac{\left(\sum x_i\right)\left(\sum y_i\right)}{n}$$

and $SS_{xx} = \sum (x_i - \bar{x})^2 = \sum x_i^2 - \dfrac{\left(\sum x_i\right)^2}{n}$.

2 The **least squares point estimate of the y intercept β_0** is $b_0 = \bar{y} - b_1 \bar{x}$, where

$$\bar{y} = \frac{\sum y_i}{n} \quad \text{and} \quad \bar{x} = \frac{\sum x_i}{n}.$$

Here n is the number of observations (an observation is an observed value of x and its corresponding value of y).

Using the data in Table 11.6, we illustrate below how to calculate these point estimates and how to use them to estimate mean values and predict individual values of the dependent variable. Note that the quantities SS_{xy} and SS_{xx} used to calculate the least squares point estimates are also used throughout this chapter to perform other important calculations.

Part 1: Calculating the least squares point estimates To compute the least squares point estimates of the regression parameters β_0 and β_1, we first calculate the following preliminary summations:

y_i	x_i	x_i^2	$x_i y_i$
12.4	28.0	$(28.0)^2 = 784$	$(28.0)(12.4) = 347.2$
11.7	28.0	$(28.0)^2 = 784$	$(28.0)(11.7) = 327.6$
12.4	32.5	$(32.5)^2 = 1{,}056.25$	$(32.5)(12.4) = 403$
10.8	39.0	$(39.0)^2 = 1{,}521$	$(39.0)(10.8) = 421.2$
9.4	45.9	$(45.9)^2 = 2{,}106.81$	$(45.9)(9.4) = 431.46$
9.5	57.8	$(57.8)^2 = 3{,}340.84$	$(57.8)(9.5) = 549.1$
8.0	58.1	$(58.1)^2 = 3{,}375.61$	$(58.1)(8.0) = 464.8$
7.5	62.5	$(62.5)^2 = 3{,}906.25$	$(62.5)(7.5) = 468.75$
$\sum y_i = 81.7$	$\sum x_i = 351.8$	$\sum x_i^2 = 16{,}874.76$	$\sum x_i y_i = 3{,}413.11$

Using these summations, we calculate SS_{xy} and SS_{xx} as follows:

$$SS_{xy} = \sum x_i y_i - \frac{\left(\sum x_i\right)\left(\sum y_i\right)}{n}$$

$$= 3{,}413.11 - \frac{(351.8)(81.7)}{8} = -179.6475,$$

$$SS_{xx} = \sum x_i^2 - \frac{\left(\sum x_i\right)^2}{n}$$

$$= 16{,}874.76 - \frac{(351.8)^2}{8} = 1{,}404.355.$$

It follows that the least squares point estimate of the slope β_1 is

$$b_1 = \frac{SS_{xy}}{SS_{xx}} = \frac{-179.6475}{1{,}404.355} = -0.1279.$$

---

[2]In order to simplify notation, we will often drop the limits on summations in this and subsequent chapters. That is, instead of using the summation $\sum\limits_{i=1}^{n}$, we will simply write $\sum$.

TABLE **11.8** Calculation of the *SSE* Obtained by Using the Least Squares Point Estimates

y_i	x_i	$\hat{y} = 15.84 - 0.1279x_i$	$y_i - \hat{y}$ = residual
12.4	28.0	$15.84 - 0.1279(28.0) = 12.2588$	$12.4 - 12.2588 = 0.1412$
11.7	28.0	$15.84 - 0.1279(28.0) = 12.2588$	$11.7 - 12.2588 = 20.5588$
12.4	32.5	$15.84 - 0.1279(32.5) = 11.68325$	$12.4 - 11.68325 = 0.71675$
10.8	39.0	$15.84 - 0.1279(39.0) = 10.8519$	$10.8 - 10.8519 = 20.0519$
9.4	45.9	$15.84 - 0.1279(45.9) = 9.96939$	$9.4 - 9.96939 = 20.56939$
9.5	57.8	$15.84 - 0.1279(57.8) = 8.44738$	$9.5 - 8.44738 = 1.05262$
8.0	58.1	$15.84 - 0.1279(58.1) = 8.40901$	$8.0 - 8.40901 = 20.40901$
7.5	62.5	$15.84 - 0.1279(62.5) = 7.84625$	$7.5 - 7.84625 = 20.34625$

$$SSE = \sum (y_i - \hat{y}_i)^2 = 0.1412^2 + (-0.5588)^2 + \cdots + (-0.346\,25)^2 = 2.568$$

Furthermore, because

$$\bar{y} = \frac{\sum y_i}{8} = \frac{81.7}{8} = 10.2125 \quad \text{and} \quad \bar{x} = \frac{\sum x_i}{8} = \frac{351.8}{8} = 43.975,$$

the least squares point estimate of the y intercept β_0 is

$$b_0 = \bar{y} - b_1\bar{x} = 10.2125 - (-0.1279)(43.975) = 15.84.$$

Because $b_1 = -0.1279$, we estimate that y decreases (b_1 is negative) by 0.1279 when x increases by 1. Because $b_0 = 15.84$, we estimate that y is 15.84 when x is 0.

Table 11.8 gives predictions of y for each observation obtained by using the least squares line (or prediction equation)

$$\hat{y} = b_0 + b_1x = 15.84 - 0.1279x.$$

The table also gives each of the residuals and the sum of squared residuals ($SSE = 2.568$) obtained by using this prediction equation. Notice that the SSE here, which was obtained using the least squares point estimates, is smaller than the SSE of Table 11.7, which was obtained using the visually fitted line $\hat{y} = 15 - 0.1x$. In general, the SSE obtained by using the least squares point estimates is smaller than the value of the SSE that would be obtained by using any other estimates of β_0 and β_1. Figure 11.9 illustrates the eight observed y values (the dots in the figure) and the eight predicted y values (the squares in the figure) given by the least

FIGURE **11.9** The Least Squares Line for the Sample Data

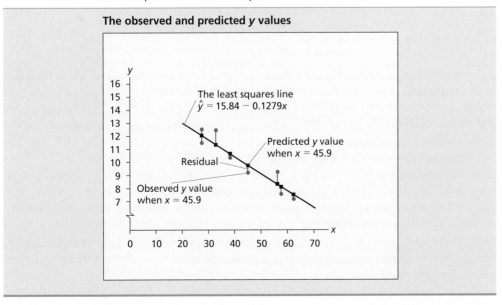

squares line. The distances between the observed and predicted values are the residuals. Therefore, when we say that the least squares point estimates minimize the *SSE*, we are saying that these estimates position the least squares line so as to minimize the sum of the squared distances between the observed and predicted *y* values. In this sense, the least squares line is the best straight line that can be fitted to the eight observed *y* values. In general, we will rely on Excel and MegaStat to compute the least squares estimates (and to perform many other regression calculations).

Part 2: Estimating a mean *y* value and predicting an individual *y* value We define the **experimental region** to be the range of the previously observed values of *x*. Referring to Table 11.6, we see that the experimental region consists of the range of *x* values from 28 to 62.5. The simple linear regression model relates *y* to *x* for values of *x* that are in the experimental region. For such values of *x*, the least squares line is the estimate of the line of means.

We now consider finding a point estimate of

$$\mu_{y|x} = \beta_0 + \beta_1 x,$$

which is the mean of all of the *y* values that could be observed for *x*. Because the least squares line is the estimate of the line of means, the point estimate of $\mu_{y|x}$ is the point on the least squares line that corresponds to the average *x* value:

$$\hat{y} = b_0 + b_1 x$$
$$= 15.84 - 0.1279x.$$

This point estimate is intuitively logical because it is obtained by replacing the unknown parameters β_0 and β_1 in the expression for $\mu_{y|x}$ by their least squares estimates b_0 and b_1.

The quantity $\hat{y}$ is also the point prediction of the individual value

$$y = \beta_0 + \beta_1 x + \varepsilon,$$

which is the *y* value corresponding to the average value of *x*. To understand why $\hat{y}$ is the point prediction of *y*, note that *y* is the sum of the mean $\beta_0 + \beta_1 x$ and the error term ε. We have already seen that $\hat{y} = b_0 + b_1 x$ is the point estimate of $\beta_0 + \beta_1 x$. We will now explain why *we should use a value of 0 for the error term ε.* Recall that we are using the average value of all of the *y*'s for a given value of *x* to estimate a single value of $\hat{y}$, so, logically, it makes sense to use the average value of all of the errors to estimate a single error. This allows us to use the average value of the errors, or 0, in place of the error term when using $\hat{y}$ as the point estimate of a single value of *y*. In the previous section, we discussed several assumptions concerning the simple linear regression model.

Now suppose a forecasted average *x* value is 40. Because 40 is in the experimental region,

$$\hat{y} = 15.84 - 0.1279(40)$$
$$= 10.72,$$

and $\hat{y}$ is (1) the point estimate of *y* when the average *x* value is 40 and (2) the point prediction of an individual *y* value when the average *x* value is 40. This says that (1) we estimate that the average of all *y* values that could be observed when *x* is 40 equals 10.72, and (2) we predict that *y* in a single observation when *x* = 40 will be 10.72. Note that Figure 11.10 illustrates $\hat{y} = 10.72$ as a square on the least squares line.

To conclude, Figure 11.11 illustrates the potential danger of using the least squares line to predict outside the experimental region. In the figure, we extrapolate the least squares line far beyond the experimental region to obtain a prediction for *x* = −10. As shown in Figure 11.6 (page 373), for values of *x* in the experimental region the observed values of *y* tend to decrease in a straight-line fashion as the values of *x* increase. However, for *x* values lower than 28, the relationship between *y* and *x* might become curved. If it does, extrapolating the straight-line prediction equation to obtain a prediction for *x* = −10 might badly underestimate *y* (see Figure 11.11).

FIGURE **11.10**   Point Estimation and Point Prediction

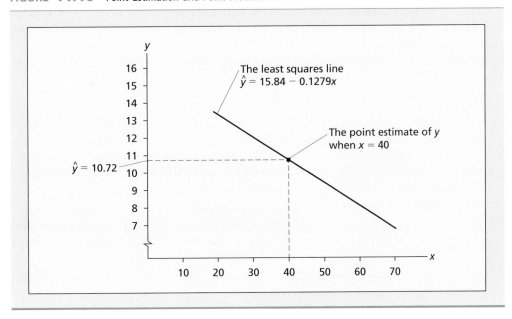

FIGURE **11.11**   The Danger of Extrapolation Outside the Experimental Region

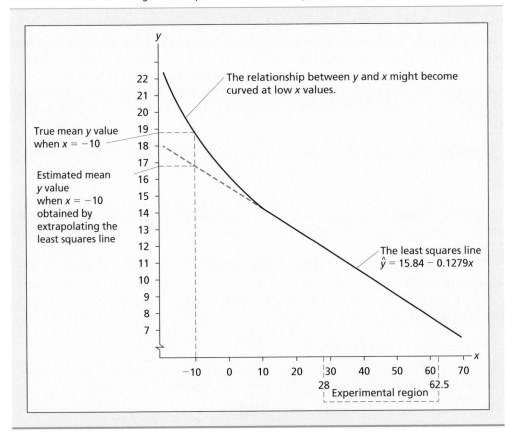

The previous situation illustrates that when we are using a least squares regression line, we should not estimate a mean value or predict an individual value unless the corresponding value of x is in the **experimental region**—the range of the previously observed values of x. Often the value $x = 0$ is not in the experimental region. In such a situation, it would not be appropriate to interpret the y intercept b_0 as the estimate of the mean value of y when x equals 0.

For example, Figure 11.12 illustrates that $x = 0$ is not in the experimental region. Therefore, it would not be appropriate to use $b_0 = 15.84$ as the point estimate of y when $x = 0$. Because it is not meaningful to interpret the y intercept in many regression situations, we often omit such interpretations.

We now present a general procedure for estimating a mean value and predicting an individual value:

Point Estimation and Point Prediction in Simple Linear Regression

Let b_0 and b_1 be the least squares point estimates of the y intercept β_0 and the slope β_1 in the simple linear regression model, and suppose that x_0, a specified value of the independent variable x, is inside the experimental region. Then

$$\hat{y} = b_0 + b_1 x_0$$

1   is the **point estimate** of the **mean value of the dependent variable** when the value of the independent variable is x_0.

2   is the **point prediction** of an **individual value of the dependent variable** when the value of the independent variable is x_0. Here we predict the error term to be 0.

Example 11.2 The QHIC Case

Consider the simple linear regression model relating yearly home-upkeep expenditure, y, to home value, x. Using the data in Table 11.4 (page 367), we can calculate the least squares point estimates of the y intercept β_0 and the slope β_1 to be $b_0 = -348.3921$ and $b_1 = 7.2583$. Because $b_1 = 7.2583$, we estimate that mean yearly upkeep expenditure increases by \$7.26 for each additional \$1,000 increase in home value. Consider a home worth \$220,000, and note that $x_0 = 220$ is in the range of previously observed values of x: 48.9 to 286.18 (see Table 11.4). It follows that

$$\hat{y} = b_0 + b_1 x_0$$
$$= -348.3921 + 7.2583(220)$$
$$= 1248.43 \ (\text{or} \ \$1,248.43)$$

is the point estimate of the mean yearly upkeep expenditure for all homes worth \$220,000 and the point prediction of a yearly upkeep expenditure for an individual home worth \$220,000.

The marketing department at QHIC wishes to determine which homes should be sent advertising brochures promoting QHIC's products and services. The prediction equation $\hat{y} = b_0 + b_1 x$ implies that the home value x corresponding to a predicted upkeep expenditure of $\hat{y}$ is

$$x = \frac{\hat{y} - b_0}{b_1} = \frac{\hat{y} - (-348.3921)}{7.2583} = \frac{\hat{y} + 348.3921}{7.2583}.$$

For instance, if we set predicted upkeep expenditure $\hat{y}$ equal to \$500, we have

$$x = \frac{\hat{y} + 348.3921}{7.2583} = \frac{500 + 348.3921}{7.2583} = 116.886 \ (\$116,886).$$

BI

Therefore, if QHIC wishes to send an advertising brochure to any home with a predicted upkeep expenditure of at least \$500, then QHIC should send this brochure to any home with a value of at least \$116,886.

The mean square error and the standard error To present statistical inference formulas in later sections, we need to be able to compute point estimates of σ^2 and σ, the constant variance and standard deviation of the error term populations. The point estimate of σ^2 is called the **mean square error** and the point estimate of σ is called the **standard error**. In the following box, we show how to compute these estimates:

The Mean Square Error and the Standard Error

If the regression assumptions are satisfied and the SSE is the sum of squared residuals:

1 The point estimate of σ^2 is the **mean square error**

$$s^2 = \frac{SSE}{n-2}.$$

2 The point estimate of σ is the **standard error**

$$s = \sqrt{\frac{SSE}{n-2}}.$$

In order to understand these point estimates, recall that σ^2 is the variance of the population of y values (for a given value of x) around the mean value $\mu_{y|x}$. Because $\hat{y}$ is the point estimate of this mean, we use

$$SSE = \sum (y_i - \hat{y}_i)^2$$

to help construct a point estimate of σ^2. We divide the SSE by $n - 2$ because doing so makes the resulting s^2 an unbiased point estimate of σ^2. Here we call $n - 2$ the **number of degrees of freedom** associated with the SSE.

Consider the data from Figure 11.5 on page 371. The calculated sum of squared residuals for these data is $SSE = 2.568$. It follows, because we have $n = 8$ observations, that the point estimate of σ^2 is the mean square error

$$s^2 = \frac{SSE}{n-2} = \frac{2.568}{8-2} = 0.428,$$

and the point estimate of σ is the standard error

$$s = \sqrt{s^2} = \sqrt{0.428} = 0.6542.$$

As another example, the standard error for the simple linear regression model describing the QHIC data is $s = 146.8970$. To conclude this section, note that in Section 11.11 we present a shortcut formula for calculating the SSE.

Exercises for Sections 11.4 and 11.5

CONCEPTS

11.21 What four assumptions are made about the simple linear regression model?

11.22 What is estimated by the mean square error, and what is estimated by the standard error?

11.23 What does the SSE measure?

11.24 What is the least squares regression line, and what are the least squares point estimates?

11.25 How can you obtain a point estimate of the mean value of the dependent variable and a point prediction of an individual value of the dependent variable?

11.26 Why is it dangerous to extrapolate outside the experimental region?

FIGURE **11.12** Flight Simulator Test Results for Exercise 11.32

(a) Flight simulator test results

Age	Errors	Age	Errors
19	7	20	8
19	8	23	5
21	6	19	3
24	5	26	2
20	6	19	7
19	7	19	8
19	8	18	7
19	6	19	6
22	3	20	9
19	9	22	9
19	9	18	8
19	8	21	9
19	6	19	6
19	4		

(b) Scatter plot of flight simulator test results

Results of Youth Training Program
$y = -0.489x + 16.417$
$R^2 = 0.220$

(c) MegaStat regression analysis of flight simulator test results

Regression Analysis

r^2 0.220		n 27
r −0.469		k 1
Std. Error 1.786		Dep. Var. Errors

ANOVA table

Source	SS	df	MS	F	p-value
Regression	22.5106	1	22.5106	7.05	0.0136
Residual	79.7857	25	3.1914		
Total	102.2963	26			

Regression output   **confidence interval**

variables	coefficients	std. error	t (df=25)	p-value	95% lower	95% upper	std. coeff.
Intercept	16.4169	3.7012	4.436	0.0002	8.7941	24.0396	0.000
Age	−0.4894	0.1843	−2.656	0.0136	−0.8688	−0.1099	−0.469

METHODS AND APPLICATIONS

11.27 THE SERVICE TIME CASE

When a least squares line is fit to the 11 observations in the service time data, we obtain $SSE = 191.7017$. Calculate s^2 and s.

11.28 THE FRESH DETERGENT CASE

When a least squares line is fit to the 30 observations in the Fresh detergent data, we obtain $SSE = 2.806$. Calculate s^2 and s.

11.29 THE DIRECT LABOUR COST CASE

When a least squares line is fit to the 12 observations in the labour cost data, we obtain $SSE = 746.7624$. Calculate s^2 and s.

11.30 DOG BISCUIT SALES

When a least squares line is fit to the ten observations in the biscuit sales data, we obtain $SSE = 888.96$. Calculate s^2 and s.

11.31 Ten sales regions of equal sales potential for a company were randomly selected. The advertising expenditures (in units of $10,000) in these ten sales regions were purposely set during July of last year at, respectively, 5, 6, 7, 8, 9, 10, 11, 12, 13, and 14. The sales volumes (in units of $10,000) were then recorded for the ten sales regions and found to be, respectively, 89, 87, 98, 110, 103, 114, 116, 110, 126, and 130. Assuming that the simple linear regression model is appropriate, it can be shown that $b_0 = 66.2121$, $b_1 = 4.4303$, and $SSE = 222.8242$. Calculate s^2 and s.

11.32 A Canadian youth training program tested 27 undergraduate students to examine the relationship between age and errors made on a flight simulator test. The average age of the participants was 20 years and the ages ranged from 18 to 26 years. The number of errors made was found for each individual. The data are presented in Figure 11.12(a). In Figure 11.12(b) and (c) are the scatter plot of the resulting data and the regression results from MegaStat. From the results given:

a. Explain the relationship between age and errors.

b. Compute s^2 and s.

c. Find the values of b_0 and b_1.

11.33 THE SERVICE TIME CASE

The following output is obtained when Excel is used to fit a least squares line to the service time data given in Exercise 11.13 (page 368).

a. Find the least squares point estimates b_0 and b_1 on the computer output and report their values. Interpret b_0 and b_1. Does the interpretation of b_0 make practical sense?

b. Use the least squares line to compute a point estimate of the mean time to service four copiers and a point prediction of the time to service four copiers on a single call.

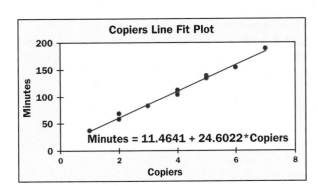

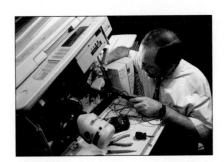

11.34 THE FRESH DETERGENT CASE

For the Fresh detergent demand data given in Exercise 11.15 (page 368), the regression equation is found to be

$$\text{Demand} = 7.814 + 2.665(\text{PriceDif}).$$

a. Use the least squares line to compute a point estimate of the mean demand in all sales periods when the price difference is 0.10 and a point prediction of the actual demand in an individual sales period when the price difference is 0.10.

b. If Enterprise Industries wishes to maintain a price difference that corresponds to a predicted demand of 850,000 bottles (that is, $\hat{y} = 8.5$), what should this price difference be?

11.35 THE DIRECT LABOUR COST CASE

The following output is obtained when Excel is used to fit a least squares line to the direct labour cost data given in Exercise 11.17 (page 369).

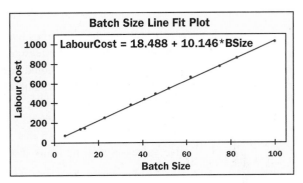

a. By using the formulas illustrated in this section and the data of Exercise 11.17, verify that $b_0 = 18.488$ and $b_1 = 10.146$, as shown on the Excel output.

b. Interpret b_0 and b_1. Does the interpretation of b_0 make practical sense?

c. Write the least squares prediction equation using x and y notation.

d. Use the least squares line to obtain a point estimate of the mean direct labour cost for all batches of size 60 and a point prediction of the direct labour cost for an individual batch of size 60.

11.36 DOG BISCUIT SALES

The least squares line for the coupons issued versus dog biscuit sales data from Exercise 11.19 (page 369) was found to be

$$\text{Sales} = 47.8 + 5.72(\text{Coupons}).$$

a. By using the formulas illustrated on pages 376 to 378 and the data of Exercise 11.19, verify that $b_0 = 47.8$ and $b_1 = 5.72$.

b. Interpret b_0 and b_1. Does the interpretation of b_0 make practical sense?

c. Write the least squares prediction equation using x and y notation.

d. Use the least squares line to obtain a point estimate of the monthly sales when 20 coupons are issued.

11.6 TESTING THE SIGNIFICANCE OF THE SLOPE AND y INTERCEPT

Testing the significance of the slope A simple linear regression model is not likely to be useful unless there is a *significant relationship between y and x*. In order to judge the significance of the relationship between y and x, we test the null hypothesis

$$H_0: \beta_1 = 0,$$

which says that there is no change in the mean value of y associated with a change in x, versus the alternative hypothesis

$$H_a: \beta_1 \neq 0,$$

which says that there is a (positive or negative) change in the mean value of y associated with a change in x. It would be reasonable to conclude that x is significantly related to y if we can be quite certain that we should reject H_0 in favour of H_a.

In order to test these hypotheses, recall that we compute the least squares point estimate b_1 of the true slope β_1 by using a sample of n observed values of the dependent variable y. Different samples of n observed y values would yield different values of the least squares point estimate b_1. It can be shown that if the regression assumptions hold, the population of all possible values of b_1 is normally distributed with a mean of β_1 and a standard deviation of

$$\sigma_{b_1} = \frac{\sigma}{\sqrt{SS_{xx}}}.$$

The standard error s is the point estimate of σ, so it follows that a point estimate of σ_{b_1} is

$$s_{b_1} = \frac{s}{\sqrt{SS_{xx}}},$$

which is called the **standard error of the estimate b_1**. Furthermore, if the regression assumptions hold, then the population of all values of

$$\frac{b_1 - \beta_1}{s_{b_1}}$$

has a t distribution with $n - 2$ degrees of freedom. It follows that if the null hypothesis $H_0: \beta_1 = 0$ is true, the population of all possible values of the test statistic

$$t = \frac{b_1}{s_{b_1}}$$

has a t distribution with $n - 2$ degrees of freedom. Therefore, we can test the significance of the regression relationship as follows:

Testing the Significance of the Regression Relationship: Testing the Significance of the Slope

Define the test statistic

$$t = \frac{b_1}{s_{b_1}}, \quad \text{where} \quad s_{b_1} = \frac{s}{\sqrt{SS_{xx}}},$$

and suppose that the regression assumptions hold. Then we can test $H_0: \beta_1 = 0$ versus a particular alternative hypothesis at significance level α (that is, by setting the probability of a Type I error equal to α) by using the appropriate rejection point rule or, equivalently, the corresponding p value.

Alternative Hypothesis	Rejection Point Condition: Reject H_0 if	p Value (Reject H_0 if p Value $< \alpha$)
$H_a: \beta_1 \neq 0$	$\lvert t \rvert > t_{\alpha/2}$	Twice the area under the t curve to the right of $\lvert t \rvert$
$H_a: \beta_1 > 0$	$t > t_\alpha$	The area under the t curve to the right of t
$H_a: \beta_1 < 0$	$t < -t_\alpha$	The area under the t curve to the left of t

Here $t_{\alpha/2}$, t_α, and all *p* values are based on $n - 2$ degrees of freedom. *If we can reject H_0: $\beta_1 = 0$ at a given value of α, then we conclude that the slope* (*or, equivalently, the regression relationship) is significant at the α level.*

We usually use the two-sided alternative $H_a: \beta_1 \neq 0$ for this test of significance. However, sometimes a one-sided alternative is appropriate. For example, we could say that if the slope β_1 is not 0, then it must be negative. A negative β_1 would say that the *y* values decrease as *x* increases. Because of this, it would be appropriate to decide that *x* is significantly related to *y* if we can reject H_0: $\beta_1 = 0$ in favour of the one-sided alternative $H_a: \beta_1 < 0$. Most computer packages (such as Excel) present results for testing a two-sided alternative hypothesis. For these reasons, we will emphasize the two-sided test.

The following should also be noted:

1   *If we can decide that the slope is significant at the 0.05 significance level*, then we have concluded that *x* is significantly related to *y* by using a test that allows a 0.05 probability of concluding that *x* is significantly related to *y* when it is not. *This is usually regarded as strong evidence that the regression relationship is significant.*

2   *If we can decide that the slope is significant at the 0.01 significance level, this is usually regarded as very strong evidence that the regression relationship is significant.*

3   The smaller the significance level α at which H_0 can be rejected, the stronger is the evidence that the regression relationship is significant.

In addition to testing the significance of the slope, it is often useful to calculate a confidence interval for β_1. We show how this is done in the following box:

A Confidence Interval for the Slope

If the regression assumptions hold, a *100(1 − α) percent confidence interval for the true slope β_1 is* $[b_1 \pm t_{\alpha/2}s_{b_1}]$. Here $t_{\alpha/2}$ is based on $n - 2$ degrees of freedom.

Example 11.3 The QHIC Case

Figure 11.13 on the next page presents the MegaStat output of a simple linear regression analysis of the QHIC data. We summarize some important quantities from the output as follows: $b_0 = -348.3921$ [1], $b_1 = 7.2583$ [2], $s = 146.897$ [8], $s_{b_1} = 0.4156$ [4], and $t = b_1/s_{b_1} = 17.466$ [6]. Since the *p* value related to $t = 17.466$ is less than 0.001 (see the MegaStat output), we can reject H_0: $\beta_1 = 0$ in favour of H_a: $\beta_1 \neq 0$ at the 0.001 level of significance. It follows that we have extremely strong evidence that the regression relationship is significant.

FIGURE 11.13 MegaStat Output of a Simple Linear Regression Analysis of the QHIC Data

Regression Analysis

r^2	0.889 [9]	n	40	
r	0.943	k	1	
Std. Error	146.897 [8]	Dep. Var.	Upkeep	

ANOVA table

Source	SS	df	MS	F [13]	p-value [14]
Regression	6,582,759.6972 [10]	1	6,582,759.6972	305.06	9.49E-20
Residual	819,995.5427 [11]	38	21,578.8301		
Total	7,402,755.2399 [12]	39			

Regression output

variables	coefficients	std. error	t (df=38)	p-value [7]	confidence interval 95% lower	95% upper
Intercept	-348.3921 [1]	76.1410 [3]	-4.576 [5]	4.95E-05	-502.5314	-194.2527
Value	7.2583 [2]	0.4156 [4]	17.466 [6]	9.49E-20	6.4170 [19]	8.0995 [19]

Predicted values for: Upkeep

Value	Predicted [15]	95% Confidence Interval [16] lower	upper	95% Prediction Interval [17] lower	upper	Leverage [18]
220	1,248.42597	1,187.78944	1,309.06251	944.92879	1,551.92315	0.042

[1] b_0 = point estimate of the y intercept [2] b_1 = point estimate of the slope [3] s_{b_0} = standard error of the estimate b_0 [4] s_{b_1} = standard error of the estimate b_1
[5] t for testing significance of the y intercept [6] t for testing significance of the slope [7] p values for t statistics [8] s = standard error [9] r^2 (eta²)
[10] Explained variation [11] SSE = unexplained variation [12] Total variation [13] F(model) statistic [14] p value for F(model) [15] $\hat{y}$ = point prediction when x = 220
[16] 95% confidence interval when x = 220 [17] 95% prediction interval when x = 220 [18] Distance value [19] 95% confidence interval for the slope β_1

The MegaStat output also tells us that a 95 percent confidence interval for the true slope β [19] is [6.4170, 8.0995]. This interval says we are 95 percent confident that mean yearly upkeep expenditure increases by between $6.42 and $8.10 for each additional $1,000 increase in home value.

Testing the significance of the y intercept We can also test the significance of the y intercept β_0. We do this by testing the null hypothesis $H_0: \beta_0 = 0$ versus the alternative hypothesis $H_a: \beta_0 \neq 0$. **If we can reject H_0 in favour of H_a by setting the probability of a Type I error equal to α, we conclude that the intercept β_0 is significant at the α level.** To carry out the hypothesis test, we use the test statistic

$$t = \frac{b_0}{s_{b_0}}, \text{ where } s_{b_0} = s\sqrt{\frac{1}{n} + \frac{\bar{x}^2}{SS_{xx}}}.$$

Here the rejection point and p value conditions for rejecting H_0 are the same as those given previously for testing the significance of the slope, except that t is calculated as b_0/s_{b_0}. For example, in Figure 11.13, $b_0 = -348.3921$ [1], $s_{b_0} = 76.1410$ [3], $t = -4.576$ [5], and p value = 0.000. Because $t = |-4.576| > t_{0.025} = 2.447$ and p value < 0.05, we can reject $H_0: \beta_0 = 0$ in favour of $H_a: \beta_0 \neq 0$ at the 0.05 level of significance. In fact, because p value < 0.001, we can also reject H_0 at the 0.001 level of significance. This provides extremely strong evidence that the y intercept β_0 does not equal 0 and thus is significant.

In general, if we fail to conclude that the intercept is significant at a level of significance of 0.05, it might be reasonable to drop the y intercept from the model. However, remember that β_0 equals the mean value of y when x equals 0. If, logically speaking, the mean value of y would not equal 0 when x equals 0, then it is common practice to include the y intercept whether or not $H_0: \beta_0 = 0$ is rejected. In fact, experience suggests that it is definitely safest, when in doubt, to include the intercept β_0.

Exercises for Section 11.6

CONCEPTS

11.37 What can you conclude if you can reject $H_0: \beta_1 = 0$ in favour of $H_a: \beta_1 \neq 0$ by setting
  a. α equal to 0.05?
  b. α equal to 0.01?

11.38 Give an example of a practical application of the confidence interval for β_1.

METHODS AND APPLICATIONS

In Exercises 11.39 through 11.42, we refer to MegaStat and Excel output of simple linear regression analyses of the data sets related to four case studies introduced in the exercises for Section 11.3. Using the appropriate output for each case study:

a. Find the least squares point estimates b_0 and b_1 of β_0 and β_1 on the output and report their values.
b. Find the *SSE* on the output and report its value.
c. Find s_{b_1} and the *t* statistic for testing the significance of the slope on the output and report their values. Show how *t* was calculated by using b_1 and s_{b_1} from the output.
d. Using the *t* statistic and an appropriate rejection point, test $H_0: \beta_1 = 0$ versus $H_a: \beta_1 \neq 0$ by setting α equal to 0.05. Is the slope (regression relationship) significant at the 0.05 level?

e. Using the *t* statistic and an appropriate rejection point, test $H_0: \beta_1 = 0$ versus $H_a: \beta_1 \neq 0$ by setting α equal to 0.01. Is the slope (regression relationship) significant at the 0.01 level?
f. Find the *p* value for testing $H_0: \beta_1 = 0$ versus $H_a: \beta_1 \neq 0$ on the output and report its value. Using the *p* value, determine whether we can reject H_0 by setting α equal to 0.10, 0.05, 0.01, and 0.001. How much evidence is there that the slope (regression relationship) is significant?
g. Calculate the 95 percent confidence interval for β_1 using numbers on the output. Interpret the interval.
h. Find s_{b_0} and the *t* statistic for testing the significance of the *y* intercept on the output and report their values. Show how *t* was calculated by using b_0 and s_{b_0} from the output.
i. Find the *p* value for testing $H_0: \beta_0 = 0$ versus $H_a: \beta_0 \neq 0$. Using the *p* value, determine whether you can reject H_0 by setting α equal to 0.10, 0.05, 0.01, and 0.001. What do you conclude?

11.39 THE SERVICE TIME CASE

The MegaStat output of a simple linear regression analysis of the data set for this case is given in Figure 11.14.

FIGURE 11.14 MegaStat Output of a Simple Linear Regression Analysis of the Service Time Data

Regression Analysis				
r^2 0.990		n 11		
r 0.995		k 1		
Std. Error 4.615		Dep. Var. Minutes (y)		

ANOVA table

Source	SS	df	MS	F	p-value
Regression	19,918.8438	1	19,918.8438	935.15	2.09E-10
Residual	191.7017	9	21.3002		
Total	20,110.5455	10			

Regression output

variables	coefficients	std. error	t (df=9)	p-value	confidence interval 95% lower	95% upper
Intercept	11.4641	3.4390	3.334	0.0087	3.6845	19.2437
Copiers (x)	24.6022	0.8045	30.580	2.09E-10	22.7823	26.4221

Predicted values for: Minutes (y)

Copiers (x)	Predicted	95% Confidence Intervals lower	upper	95% Prediction Intervals lower	upper	Leverage
1	36.066	29.907	42.226	23.944	48.188	0.348
2	60.669	55.980	65.357	49.224	72.113	0.202
3	85.271	81.715	88.827	74.241	96.300	0.116
4	109.873	106.721	113.025	98.967	120.779	0.091
5	134.475	130.753	138.197	123.391	145.559	0.127
6	159.077	154.139	164.016	147.528	170.627	0.224
7	183.680	177.233	190.126	171.410	195.950	0.381

FIGURE **11.15**   Excel Output of a Simple Linear Regression Analysis of the Fresh Detergent Demand Data

SUMMARY OUTPUT

Regression Statistics

Multiple R	0.889671764
R Square	0.791515848
Adjusted R Square	0.784069986
Standard Error	0.316560873
Observations	30

ANOVA

	df	SS	MS	F	Significance F
Regression	1	10.65268464	10.65268	106.3028	4.88134E-11
Residual	28	2.805902023	0.100211		
Total	29	13.45858667			

	Coefficients	Standard Error	t Stat	P-value	Lower 95%	Upper 95%	Lower 95.0%	Upper 95.0%
Intercept	7.814087575	0.079884322	97.81754	4.85E-37	7.650451776	7.9777234	7.65045178	7.97772337
PriceDif	2.665214492	0.258499595	10.31032	4.88E-11	2.135701482	3.1947275	2.13570148	3.1947275

FIGURE **11.16**   Excel and MegaStat Output of a Simple Linear Regression Analysis of the Direct Labour Cost Data

(a) The Excel Output

Regression Statistics

Multiple R	0.9996
R Square	0.9993
Adjusted R Square	0.9992
Standard Error	8.6415
Observations	12

ANOVA	df	SS	MS	F	Significance F
Regression	1	1,024,592.9043	1,024,592.9043	13,720.4677	5.04E-17
Residual	10	746.7624	74.6762		
Total	11	1,025,339.6667			

	Coefficients	Standard Error	t Stat	P-value	Lower 95%	Upper 95%
Intercept	18.4875	4.6766	3.9532	0.0027	8.0674	28.9076
BatchSize (x)	10.1463	0.0866	117.1344	5.04E-17	9.9533	10.3393

(b) Prediction Using MegaStat

Predicted values for: LabourCost (y)

BatchSize (x)	Predicted	95% Confidence Interval lower	upper	95% Prediction Interval lower	upper	Leverage
60	627.263	621.054	633.472	607.032	647.494	0.104

11.40 THE FRESH DETERGENT CASE

🖉   The Excel output of a simple linear regression analysis of the data set for this case is given in Figure 11.15.

11.41 THE DIRECT LABOUR COST CASE

🖉   The Excel and MegaStat outputs of a simple linear regression analysis of the data set for this case are given in Figure 11.16.

11.42 DOG BISCUIT SALES

🖉   The Excel output of a simple linear regression analysis of the data set for this case is given in Figure 11.17.

11.43 Find and interpret a 95 percent confidence interval for the slope β_1 of the simple linear regression model describing the Canadian youth training program data in Exercise 11.32 (page 380).

FIGURE **11.17**   Excel Output of a Simple Linear Regression Analysis of the Dog Biscuit Sales Data

SUMMARY OUTPUT

Regression Statistics

Multiple R	0.938803701
R Square	0.881352389
Adjusted R Square	0.866521438
Standard Error	10.54131963
Observations	10

ANOVA

	df	SS	MS	F	Significance F
Regression	1	6603.444643	6603.444643	59.42655806	5.6967E-05
Residual	8	888.9553571	111.1194196		
Total	9	7492.4			

	Coefficients	Standard Error	t Stat	P-value	Lower 95%	Upper 95%	Lower 95.0%	Upper 95.0%
Intercept	47.80357143	14.35004134	3.331249737	0.010365121	14.71229536	80.89484749	14.71229536	80.89484749
Coupons Issued	5.723214286	0.742420095	7.708862306	5.6967E-05	4.011189369	7.435239202	4.011189369	7.435239202

11.7 CONFIDENCE AND PREDICTION INTERVALS

The point on the least squares line corresponding to a particular value x_0 of the independent variable x is

$$\hat{y} = b_0 + b_1 x_0.$$

Unless we are very lucky, $\hat{y}$ will not exactly equal either the mean value of y when x equals x_0 or a particular individual value of y when x equals x_0. Therefore, we need to place bounds on how far $\hat{y}$ might be from these values. We can do this by calculating a *confidence interval for the mean value of y* and a *prediction interval for an individual value of y*.

Both of these intervals employ a quantity called the **distance value**. For simple linear regression, this quantity is calculated as follows:

The Distance Value for Simple Linear Regression

In simple linear regression, the **distance value** for a particular value x_0 of x is

$$\text{Distance value} = \frac{1}{n} + \frac{(x_0 - \bar{x})^2}{SS_{xx}}.$$

This quantity is given its name because it is a measure of the distance between the value x_0 of x and $\bar{x}$, the average of the previously observed values of x. Notice from the above formula that the farther x_0 is from $\bar{x}$, which can be regarded as the centre of the experimental region, the larger is the distance value.

We now consider establishing a confidence interval for the mean value of y when x equals a particular value x_0 (we call this mean value $\mu_{y|x_0}$). Because each possible sample of n values of the dependent variable gives values of b_0 and b_1 that differ from the values given by other samples, different samples give different values of the point estimate

$$\hat{y} = b_0 + b_1 x_0.$$

It can be shown that if the regression assumptions hold, the population of all possible values of $\hat{y}$ is normally distributed with mean $\mu_{y|x_0}$ and standard deviation

$$\sigma_{\hat{y}} = \sigma \sqrt{\text{distance value}}.$$

The point estimate of $\sigma_{\hat{y}}$ is

$$s_{\hat{y}} = s \sqrt{\text{distance value}},$$

which is called the **standard error of the estimate** $\hat{y}$. Using this standard error, we form a confidence interval as follows:

A Confidence Interval for a Mean Value of *y*

If the regression assumptions hold, a *100(1 − α) percent confidence interval for the mean value of y when the value of the independent variable is x_0 is*

$$[\hat{y} \pm t_{\alpha/2}s\sqrt{\text{distance value}}].$$

Here $t_{\alpha/2}$ is based on $n − 2$ degrees of freedom.

Data		
Observation	***x***	***y***
1	28.0	12.4
2	28.0	11.7
3	32.5	12.4
4	39.0	10.8
5	45.9	9.4
6	57.8	9.5
7	58.1	8.0
8	62.5	7.5

For the data from Table 11.6 (reproduced in the margin), suppose we wish to compute a 95 percent confidence interval for the *y* value when $x_0 = 40$. Previously, we calculated the point estimate of this mean to be

$$\hat{y} = b_0 + b_1 x_0$$
$$= 15.84 − 0.1279(40)$$
$$= 10.72.$$

Furthermore, using the information on pages 376 and 377, we compute

$$\text{Distance value} = \frac{1}{n} + \frac{(x_0 − \bar{x})^2}{SS_{xx}}$$
$$= \frac{1}{8} + \frac{(40 − 43.98)^2}{1{,}404.355}$$
$$= 0.1363.$$

Because $s = 0.6542$ (see page 372), and $t_{\alpha/2} = t_{0.025}$ based on $n − 2 = 8 − 2 = 6$ degrees of freedom equals 2.447, it follows that the desired 95 percent confidence interval is

$$[\hat{y} \pm t_{\alpha/2}s\sqrt{\text{distance value}}] = [10.72 \pm 2.447(0.6542)\sqrt{0.1363}]$$
$$= [10.72 \pm 0.59]$$
$$= [10.13, 11.31].$$

This interval says we are 95 percent confident that the *y* value that would be observed in all observations where $x = 40$ is between 10.13 and 11.31.

We develop an interval for an individual value of *y* when *x* equals a particular value x_0 by considering the **prediction error** $y − \hat{y}$. After observing each possible sample and calculating the point prediction based on that sample, we could observe any one of an infinite number of different individual values of *y* (because of different possible error terms). Therefore, an infinite number of different prediction errors could be observed. If the regression assumptions hold, it can be shown that the population of all possible prediction errors is normally distributed with mean 0 and standard deviation

$$\sigma_{(y−\hat{y})} = \sigma\sqrt{1 + \text{distance value}}.$$

The point estimate of $\sigma_{(y−\hat{y})}$ is

$$s_{(y−\hat{y})} = s\sqrt{1 + \text{distance value}},$$

which is called the **standard error of the prediction error**. Using this quantity, we obtain a **prediction interval** as follows:

A Prediction Interval for an Individual Value of *y*

If the regression assumptions hold, a *100(1 − α) percent prediction interval for an individual value of y when the value of the independent variable is x_0 is*

$$[\hat{y} \pm t_{\alpha/2}s\sqrt{1 + \text{distance value}}].$$

Here $t_{\alpha/2}$ is based on $n − 2$ degrees of freedom.

In general, the prediction interval is useful if it is important to predict an individual value of the dependent variable. A confidence interval is useful if it is important to estimate the mean value, such as when observations are affected by a very large number of values of the dependent variable when the independent variable equals a particular value. We illustrate this in the following example.

Example 11.4 The QHIC Case

Consider a home worth $220,000. We have seen that the predicted yearly upkeep expenditure for such a home is

$$\hat{y} = b_0 + b_1 x_0$$
$$= -348.3921 + 7.2583(220)$$
$$= 1248.43 \text{ (or } \$1,248.43).$$

This predicted value is given at the bottom of the MegaStat output in Figure 11.13 (page 384), which we repeat here:

Predicted values for: Upkeep

		95% Confidence Interval		95% Prediction Interval		
Value	Predicted	lower	upper	lower	upper	Leverage
220	1,248.42597	1,187.78944	1,309.06251	944.92879	1,551.92315	0.042

In addition to giving $\hat{y} = 1,248.43$, the MegaStat output also tells us that the distance value, which is given under the heading "Leverage" on the output, equals 0.042. Therefore, because s equals 146.897 (see Figure 11.13), it follows that a 95 percent prediction interval for the yearly upkeep expenditure of an individual home worth $220,000 is calculated as follows:

$$[\hat{y} \pm t_{0.025} s\sqrt{1 + \text{distance value}}]$$
$$= [1,248.43 \pm 2.024(146.897)\sqrt{1.042}]$$
$$= [944.93, 1,551.93].$$

Here $t_{0.025}$ is based on $n - 2 = 40 - 2 = 38$ degrees of freedom. Note that this interval is given on the MegaStat output.

Because there are many homes worth roughly $220,000 in the metropolitan area, QHIC is more interested in the mean upkeep expenditure for all such homes than in the individual upkeep expenditure for one such home. The MegaStat output tells us that a 95 percent confidence interval for this mean upkeep expenditure is [1,187.79, 1,309.06]. This interval says that QHIC is 95 percent confident that the mean upkeep expenditure for all homes worth $220,000 is at least $1,187.79 and no more than $1,309.06.

Exercises for Section 11.7

CONCEPTS

11.44 What does the distance value measure?

11.45 What is the difference between a confidence interval and a prediction interval?

11.46 Discuss how the distance value affects the length of a confidence interval and a prediction interval.

METHODS AND APPLICATIONS

11.47 THE SERVICE TIME CASE

The partial MegaStat regression output in Figure 11.18 on the next page for the service time data relates to predicting service times for 1, 2, 3, 4, 5, 6, and 7 copiers.

a. Report (as shown on the computer output) a point estimate of and a 95 percent confidence interval for the mean time to service four copiers.

b. Report (as shown on the computer output) a point prediction of and a 95 percent prediction interval for the time to service four copiers on a single call.

c. For this case, $n = 11$, $b_0 = 11.4641$, $b_1 = 24.6022$, and $s = 4.615$. Using this information and a distance value from the MegaStat output, hand-calculate (within rounding) the confidence interval of part a and the prediction interval of part b.

FIGURE **11.18**   Partial MegaStat Regression Output for Exercise 11.47

Predicted values for: Minutes (y)

Copiers (x)	Predicted	95% Confidence Intervals		95% Prediction Intervals		Leverage
		lower	upper	lower	upper	
1	36.066	29.907	42.226	23.944	48.188	0.348
2	60.669	55.980	65.357	49.224	72.113	0.202
3	85.271	81.715	88.827	74.241	96.300	0.116
4	109.873	106.721	113.025	98.967	120.779	0.091
5	134.475	130.753	138.197	123.391	145.559	0.127
6	159.077	154.139	164.016	147.528	170.627	0.224
7	183.680	177.233	190.126	171.410	195.950	**0.381**

d. Examine the service time data and note that there was at least one call on which Accu-Copiers serviced each of 1, 2, 3, 4, 5, 6, and 7 copiers. The 95 percent confidence intervals for the mean service times on these calls might be used to schedule future service calls. To understand this, note that a person making service calls will (in, say, a year or more) make a very large number of service calls. Some of the person's individual service times will be below, and some will be above, the corresponding mean service times. However, since the very large number of individual service times will average out to the mean service times, it seems fair to both the efficiency of the company and the person making service calls to schedule service calls by using estimates of the mean service times. Therefore, suppose you wish to schedule a call to service five copiers. Examine the MegaStat output and note that a 95 percent confidence interval for the mean time to service five copiers is [130.753, 138.197]. Since the mean time might be 138.197 minutes, it would seem fair to allow 138 minutes to make the service call. Now suppose you wish to schedule a call to service four copiers. Determine how many minutes to allow for the service call.

11.48 THE FRESH DETERGENT CASE

The partial MegaStat regression output in Figure 11.19(a) for the Fresh detergent data relates to predicting demand for future sales periods in which the price difference will be 0.10 and 0.25.

a. Report (as shown on the computer output) a point estimate of and a 95 percent confidence interval for the mean demand for Fresh in all sales periods when the price difference is 0.10.

b. Report (as shown on the computer output) a point prediction of and a 95 percent prediction interval for the actual demand for Fresh in an individual sales period when the price difference is 0.10.

c. Remembering that $s = 0.316561$ and that the distance value equals $(s_{\hat{y}}/s)^2$, use $s_{\hat{y}}$ from the computer output to hand-calculate the distance value when $x = 0.10$.

d. For this case, $n = 30$, $b_0 = 7.81409$, $b_1 = 2.6652$, and $s = 0.316561$. Using this information and your result from part c, find 99 percent confidence and

prediction intervals for mean and individual demands when $x = 0.10$.

e. Repeat parts a, b, c, and d when $x = 0.25$.

11.49 THE DIRECT LABOUR COST CASE

The partial MegaStat regression output in Figure 11.19(b) for the direct labour cost data relates to predicting direct labour cost when the batch size is 60.

a. Report (as shown on the MegaStat output) a point estimate of and a 95 percent confidence interval for the mean direct labour cost of all batches of size 60.

b. Report (as shown on the MegaStat output) a point prediction of and a 95 percent prediction interval for the actual direct labour cost of an individual batch of size 60.

c. For this case, $n = 12$, $b_0 = 18.4875$, $b_1 = 10.1463$, and $s = 8.6415$. Use this information and the distance value from the MegaStat output to compute 99 percent confidence and prediction intervals for the mean and individual labour costs when $x = 60$.

11.50 DOG BISCUIT SALES

The partial MegaStat regression output in Figure 11.19(c) for the dog biscuit sales data relates to predicting the average number of bags sold in a month when 20 coupons are issued at a supermarket.

a. Report (as shown on the MegaStat output) a point estimate of and a 95 percent confidence interval for

FIGURE 11.19 MegaStat Output for Exercises 11.48, 11.49, and 11.50

(a) Fresh detergent data for Exercise 11.48

Predicted values for: Demand

| PriceDif | Predicted | 95% Confidence Intervals | | 95% Prediction Intervals | | Leverage |
		lower	upper	lower	upper	
0.10	8.08061	7.94788	8.21334	7.41872	8.74250	0.042
0.25	8.48039	8.36042	8.60036	7.82094	9.13984	0.034

(b) Labour cost data for Exercise 11.49

Predicted values for: LabourCost (y)

| BatchSize (x) | Predicted | 95% Confidence Interval | | 95% Prediction Interval | | Leverage |
		lower	upper	lower	upper	
60	627.263	621.054	633.472	607.032	647.494	0.104

(c) Dog biscuit sales data for Exercise 11.50

Predicted values for: Sales

| Coupons Issued | Predicted | 95% Confidence Interval | | 95% Prediction Interval | | Leverage |
		lower	upper	lower	upper	
20	162.268	154.311	170.225	136.690	187.845	0.107

the mean monthly sales for all supermarkets with 20 coupons issued.

b. Report (as shown on the MegaStat output) a 95 percent prediction interval for the mean monthly sales of an individual supermarket with 20 coupons issued.

11.51 Using the sales volume data in Exercise 11.27 (page 373), find a point prediction of and a 95 percent prediction interval for sales volume when advertising expenditure is 11 (that is, $110,000).

11.8 SIMPLE COEFFICIENTS OF DETERMINATION AND CORRELATION

The simple coefficient of determination The **simple coefficient of determination** (r^2 or eta^2) was introduced in Section 11.1 and is a measure of the usefulness of a simple linear regression model. Suppose we have observed n values of the dependent variable y. However, we choose to predict y without using a predictor (independent) variable x. In such a case, the only reasonable prediction of a specific value of y, say y_i, is $\bar{y}$, which is simply the average of the n observed values $y_1, y_2, \ldots, y_n$. Here the error of prediction in predicting y_i is $y_i - \bar{y}$ and represents the prediction errors obtained when we do not use the information provided by the independent variable x.

If we decide to employ the predictor variable x and observe the values $x_1, x_2, \ldots, x_n$ corresponding to the observed values of y, then the prediction of y_i is

$$\hat{y}_i = b_0 + b_1 x_i$$

and the prediction error is $y_i - \hat{y}_i$. Using the predictor variable x decreases the prediction error in predicting y_i from $(y_i - \bar{y})$ to $(y_i - \hat{y}_i)$, or by an amount equal to

$$(y_i - \bar{y}) - (y_i - \hat{y}_i) = \hat{y}_i - \bar{y}.$$

It can be shown that in general

$$\sum (y_i - \bar{y})^2 - \sum (y_i - \hat{y}_i)^2 = \sum (\hat{y}_i - \bar{y})^2.$$

The sum of squared prediction errors obtained when we do not employ the predictor variable x, $\sum (y_i - \bar{y})^2$, is called the **total variation**. This quantity measures the total amount of variation exhibited by the observed values of y. The sum of squared prediction errors obtained when we use the predictor variable x, $\Sigma(y_i - \hat{y}_i)^2$, is called the **unexplained variation** (this is another name for the SSE). This quantity measures the amount of variation in the values of y that is not explained by the predictor variable. The quantity $\Sigma(\hat{y}_i - \bar{y})^2$ is called the **explained variation**. Using these definitions and the above equation involving these summations, we see that

$$\text{Total variation} - \text{unexplained variation} = \text{explained variation}.$$

It follows that the explained variation is the reduction in the sum of squared prediction errors that has been accomplished by using the predictor variable x to predict y. It also follows that

$$\text{Total variation} = \text{explained variation} + \text{unexplained variation}.$$

This equation implies that the explained variation represents the amount of the total variation in the observed values of y that is explained by the predictor variable x (and the simple linear regression model).

We now define the **simple coefficient of determination** to be

$$\text{eta}^2 = r^2 = \frac{\text{explained variation}}{\text{total variation}}.$$

That is, r^2 (or eta^2) is the proportion of the total variation in the n observed values of y that is explained by the simple linear regression model. Neither the explained variation nor the total variation can be negative (both quantities are sums of squares). Therefore, r^2 is greater than or equal to 0. Because the explained variation must be less than or equal to the total variation, r^2 cannot be greater than 1. The nearer r^2 is to 1, the larger is the proportion of the total variation that is explained by the model, and the greater is the utility of the model in predicting y. If the value of r^2 is not reasonably close to 1, the independent variable in the model does not provide accurate predictions of y. In such a case, a different predictor variable must be found in order to accurately predict y. It is also possible that no regression model employing a single predictor variable will accurately predict y. In this case, the model must be improved by including more than one independent variable. We will see how to do this in Chapter 12.

In the following box, we summarize the results of this section:

The Simple Coefficient of Determination, r^2 (eta^2)

For the simple linear regression model:

1 **Total variation** $= \sum(y_i - \bar{y})^2$.

2 **Explained variation** $= \sum(\hat{y}_i - \bar{y})^2$.

3 **Unexplained variation** $= \sum(y_i - \hat{y}_i)^2$.

4 **Total variation = explained variation + unexplained variation.**

5 The **simple coefficient of determination is**

$$r^2 = \frac{\text{explained variation}}{\text{total variation}}.$$

6 r^2 is the proportion of the total variation in the n observed values of the dependent variable that is explained by the simple linear regression model.

Example 11.5 The QHIC Case

In the QHIC case, it can be shown that total variation = 7,402,755.2399, explained variation = 6,582,759.6972, SSE = unexplained variation = 819,995.5427, and

$$r^2 = \frac{\text{explained variation}}{\text{total variation}} = \frac{6,582,759.6972}{7,402,755.2399} = 0.889.$$

This value of r^2 (eta^2) says that the simple linear regression model that employs home value as a predictor variable explains 88.9 percent of the total variation in the 40 observed home-upkeep expenditures.

In Section 11.11, we present some shortcut formulas for calculating the total, explained, and unexplained variations. In the previous section, r^2, the explained variation, the unexplained variation, and the total variation were calculated by Excel and MegaStat.

Exercises for Section 11.8

CONCEPTS

11.52 Discuss the meanings of the total variation, the unexplained variation, and the explained variation.

11.53 What does the simple coefficient of determination measure?

METHODS AND APPLICATIONS

In Exercises 11.54 through 11.57, we give the total variation, the unexplained variation (*SSE*), and the least squares point estimate b_1 that are obtained when simple linear regression is used to analyze the data set related to each of four previously discussed case studies. Using the information given in each exercise, find the explained variation, the simple coefficient of

determination (r^2 or eta^2), and the simple correlation coefficient (r). Interpret r^2 (eta^2).

11.54 THE SERVICE TIME CASE

Total variation = 20,110.5455, *SSE* = 191.7017, $b_1 = 24.6022$.

11.55 THE FRESH DETERGENT CASE

Total variation = 13.459, *SSE* = 2.806, $b_1 = 2.6652$.

11.56 THE DIRECT LABOUR COST CASE

Total variation = 1,025,339.6667, *SSE* = 746.7624, $b_1 = 10.1463$.

11.57 DOG BISCUIT SALES

Total variation = 7,492.4, *SSE* = 888.96, $b_1 = 5.72$.

11.9 AN *F* TEST FOR THE MODEL

In this section, we discuss an *F* test that can be used to test the significance of the regression relationship between x and y (sometimes referred to as testing the significance of the simple linear regression model). For simple linear regression, this test is another way to test the null hypothesis $H_0: \beta_1 = 0$ (the relationship between x and y is not significant) versus $H_a: \beta_1 \neq 0$ (the relationship between x and y is significant). If we can reject H_0 at level of significance α, we often say that *the simple linear regression model is significant at level of significance* α.

LO6

An *F* Test for the Simple Linear Regression Model

Suppose that the regression assumptions hold, and define the **overall *F* statistic** to be

$$F(\text{model}) = \frac{\text{explained variation}}{(\text{unexplained variation})/(n - 22)}.$$

Also define the *p* value related to *F*(model) to be the area under the curve of the *F* distribution (with 1 numerator and $n - 2$ denominator degrees of freedom) to the right of *F*(model)—see Figure 11.20(b) on the next page.

We can reject $H_0: \beta_1 = 0$ in favour of $H_a: \beta_1 \neq 0$ at level of significance α if either of the following equivalent conditions holds:

1   $F(\text{model}) > F_\alpha$.

2   *p* value $< \alpha$.

Here the point F_α is based on 1 numerator and $n - 2$ denominator degrees of freedom.

The first condition in the box says we should reject $H_0: \beta_1 = 0$ (and conclude that the relationship between x and y is significant) when *F*(model) is large. This is because a large overall *F* statistic will be obtained when the explained variation is large compared to the unexplained variation. This occurs if x is significantly related to y, which implies that the slope β_1 is not equal to 0. Figure 11.20(a) illustrates that we reject H_0 when *F*(model) is greater than F_α. As can be seen in Figure 11.20(b), when *F*(model) is large, the related

FIGURE **11.20**   An *F* Test for the Simple Linear Regression Model

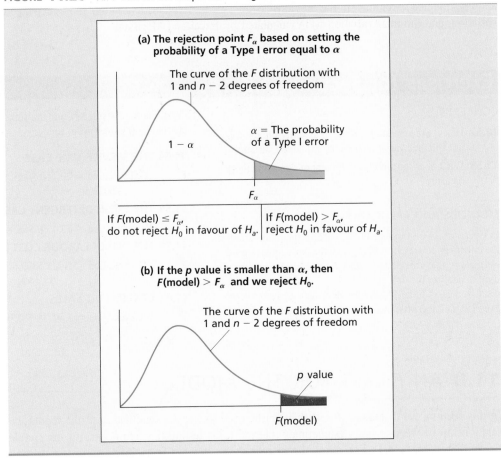

p value is small. When the *p* value is small enough (resulting from an *F*(model) statistic that is large enough), we reject H_0. Figure 11.20(b) illustrates that the second condition in the box (*p* value $< \alpha$) is an equivalent way to carry out this test.

For example, a partial Excel output of a simple linear regression analysis relating *y* to *x* is given below:

ANOVA	df	SS	MS	F	Significance F
Regression	1	22.9808	22.9808	53.6949	0.0003
Residual	6	2.5679	0.4280		
Total	7	25.5488			

Looking at this output, we see that the explained variation is 22.9808 and the unexplained variation is 2.5679. It follows that

$$F(\text{model}) = \frac{\text{explained variation}}{\text{unexplained variation}/(n-2)}$$

$$= \frac{22.9808}{2.5679/(8-2)} = \frac{22.9808}{0.4280}$$

$$= 53.69.$$

The *p* value related to *F*(model) is the area to the right of 53.69 under the curve of the *F* distribution with 1 numerator and 6 denominator degrees of freedom. This *p* value is given on the Excel output (labelled "Significance F") and is less than 0.001. If we wish to test the significance of the regression relationship with level of significance $\alpha = 0.05$, we use the rejection point $F_{0.05}$ based on 1 numerator and 6 denominator degrees of freedom. Using Table A.7, we find that $F_{0.05} = 5.99$. Since $F(\text{model}) = 53.69 > F_{0.05} = 5.99$, we can reject $H_0\colon \beta_1 = 0$ in favour of $H_a\colon \beta_1 \neq 0$ at level of significance 0.05. Alternatively, since the p value is smaller than 0.05, 0.01, and 0.001, we can reject H_0 at level of significance 0.05, 0.01, or 0.001. Therefore, we have extremely strong evidence that $H_0\colon \beta_1 = 0$ should be rejected and that the regression relationship between x and y is significant. That is, we say that we have extremely strong evidence that the simple linear model relating y to x is significant.

As another example, consider the following partial MegaStat output:

ANOVA table

Source	SS	df	MS	F	p-value
Regression	6,582,759.6972	1	6,582,759.6972	305.06	9.49E-20
Residual	819,995.5427	38	21,578.8301		
Total	7,402,755.2399	39			

This output tells us that for the QHIC simple linear regression model, $F(\text{model})$ is 305.06 and the related p value is less than 0.001. Because the p value is less than 0.001, we have extremely strong evidence that the regression relationship is significant.

Testing the significance of the regression relationship between y and x by using the overall F statistic and its related p value is equivalent to doing this test by using the t statistic ($t = b_1/s_{b_1}$) and its related p value. Specifically, it can be shown that $t^2 = F(\text{model})$ and that $(t_{\alpha/2})^2$ based on $n - 2$ degrees of freedom equals F_α based on 1 numerator and $n - 2$ denominator degrees of freedom. It follows that the rejection point conditions

$$|t| > t_{\alpha/2} \text{ and } F(\text{model}) > F_\alpha$$

are equivalent. Furthermore, the p values related to t and $F(\text{model})$ can be shown to be equal. Because these tests are equivalent, it is logical to ask why we have presented the F test. There are two reasons. First, most standard regression computer packages include the results of the F test as a part of the regression output. Second, the F test has a useful generalization in multiple regression analysis (where we employ more than one predictor variable). The F test in multiple regression is not equivalent to a t test. This is further explained in Chapter 12.

Exercises for Section 11.9

CONCEPTS

11.58 What are the null and alternative hypotheses for the F test in simple linear regression?

11.59 The F test in simple linear regression is equivalent to what other test?

METHODS AND APPLICATIONS

In Figure 11.21 on the next page, we give MegaStat and Excel outputs of simple linear regression analyses of the data sets related to four previously discussed case studies. Use the appropriate computer output to do the following for Exercises 11.60 through 11.63:

a. Use the explained variation and the unexplained variation as given on the computer output to calculate the $F(\text{model})$ statistic.

b. Use the $F(\text{model})$ statistic and the appropriate rejection point to test $H_0\colon \beta_1 = 0$ versus $H_a\colon \beta_1 \neq 0$ by setting α equal to 0.05. What do you conclude about the regression relationship between y and x?

c. Use the $F(\text{model})$ statistic and the appropriate rejection point to test $H_0\colon \beta_1 = 0$ versus $H_a\colon \beta_1 \neq 0$ by setting α equal to 0.01. What do you conclude about the regression relationship between y and x?

d. Find the p value related to $F(\text{model})$ on the computer output and report its value. Using the p value, test the significance of the regression model at the 0.10, 0.05, 0.01, and 0.001 levels of significance. What do you conclude?

e. Show that the $F(\text{model})$ statistic is (within rounding) the square of the t statistic for testing $H_0\colon \beta_1 = 0$ versus $H_a\colon \beta_1 \neq 0$. Also show that the $F_{0.05}$ rejection point is the square of the $t_{0.025}$ rejection point.

Note that in the lower right-hand corner of each output we give (in parentheses) the number of observations, n, used to perform the regression analysis and the t statistic for testing $H_0\colon \beta_1 = 0$ versus $H_a\colon \beta_1 \neq 0$.

11.60 THE SERVICE TIME CASE

The MegaStat output for this case is given in Figure 11.21(a).

FIGURE 11.21   MegaStat and Excel Outputs for Exercises 11.60 through 11.63

(a) MegaStat output for Exercise 11.60

ANOVA table

Source	SS	df	MS	F	p-value
Regression	19,918.8438	1	19,918.8438	935.15	2.09E-10
Residual	191.7017	9	21.3002		
Total	20,110.5455	10			

(n=11; t=30.580)

(b) Excel output for Exercise 11.61

ANOVA

	df	SS	MS	F	Significance F
Regression	1	10.65268	10.65268	106.3028	4.88134E-11
Residual	28	2.805902	0.100211		
Total	29	13.45859			

(n = 30; t = 10.31)

(c) Excel output for Exercise 11.62

ANOVA	df	SS	MS	F	Significance F
Regression	1	1,024,592.9043	1,024,592.9043	13,720.4677	5.04E-17
Residual	10	746.7624	74.6762		
Total	11	1,025,339.6667			

(n=12; t=117.1344)

(d) Excel output for Exercise 11.63

ANOVA

	df	SS	MS	F	Significance F
Regression	1	6603.444643	6603.444643	59.42655806	5.6967E-05
Residual	8	888.9553571	111.1194196		
Total	9	7492.4			

(N = 10, t = 7.71)

11.61 THE FRESH DETERGENT CASE

 The Excel output for this case is given in Figure 11.21(b).

11.62 THE DIRECT LABOUR COST CASE

The Excel output for this case is given in Figure 11.21(c).

11.63 DOG BISCUIT SALES

 The Excel output for this case is given in Figure 11.21(d).

11.10 RESIDUAL ANALYSIS

In this section, we explain how to check the validity of the regression assumptions. The required checks are carried out by analyzing the **regression residuals**. The residuals are defined as follows:

For any particular observed value of y, the corresponding **residual** is

$$e = y - \hat{y} = (\text{observed value of } y - \text{predicted value of } y),$$

where the predicted value of y is calculated using the **least squares prediction equation**

$$\hat{y} = b_0 + b_1 x.$$

The linear regression model $y = \beta_0 + \beta_1 x + \varepsilon$ implies that the error term ε is given by the equation $\varepsilon = y - (\beta_0 + \beta_1 x)$. Because $\hat{y}$ in the previous box is the point estimate of $\beta_0 + \beta_1 x$, we see that the residual $e = y - \hat{y}$ is the point estimate of the error term ε. If the regression assumptions are valid, then for any given value of the independent variable, the population of potential error term values will be normally distributed with mean 0 and variance σ^2 (see the regression assumptions in Section 11.4 on page 370). Furthermore, the different error terms will be statistically independent. Because the residuals provide point estimates of the error terms, we have the following:

If the regression assumptions hold, the residuals should look like they have been randomly and independently selected from normally distributed populations with mean 0 and variance σ^2.

In any real regression problem, the regression assumptions will not hold exactly. In fact, it is important to point out that mild departures from the regression assumptions do not seriously hinder our ability to use a regression model to make statistical inferences. Therefore, we are looking for pronounced, rather than subtle, departures from the regression assumptions. Because of this, we will require that the residuals only approximately fit the description just given.

Residual plots One useful way to analyze residuals is to plot them versus various criteria. The resulting plots are called **residual plots**. To construct a residual plot, we compute the residual for each observed y value. The calculated residuals are then plotted versus some criterion. To validate the regression assumptions, we make residual plots against (1) values of the independent variable x; (2) values of $\hat{y}$, the predicted value of the dependent variable; and (3) the time order in which the data have been observed (if the regression data are time series data).

We next look at an example of constructing residual plots. Then we explain how to use these plots to check the regression assumptions.

Example 11.6 The QHIC Case

Figure 11.22 gives the QHIC upkeep expenditure data and an Excel scatter plot of the data. If we use a simple linear regression model to describe the QHIC data, we find that the least squares point estimates of β_0 and β_1 are $b_0 = -348.3921$ and $b_1 = 7.2583$. The MegaStat

FIGURE **11.22** The QHIC Upkeep Expenditure Data and an Excel Scatter Plot of the Data

Home	Value of Home, x (Thousands of Dollars)	Upkeep Expenditure, y (Dollars)	Home	Value of Home, x (Thousands of Dollars)	Upkeep Expenditure, y (Dollars)
1	237.00	1,412.08	21	153.04	849.14
2	153.08	797.20	22	232.18	1,313.84
3	184.86	872.48	23	125.44	602.06
4	222.06	1,003.42	24	169.82	642.14
5	160.68	852.90	25	177.28	1,038.80
6	99.68	288.48	26	162.82	697.00
7	229.04	1,288.46	27	120.44	324.34
8	101.78	423.08	28	191.10	965.10
9	257.86	1,351.74	29	158.78	920.14
10	96.28	378.04	30	178.50	950.90
11	171.00	918.08	31	272.20	1,670.32
12	231.02	1,627.24	32	48.90	125.40
13	228.32	1,204.76	33	104.56	479.78
14	205.90	857.04	34	286.18	2,010.64
15	185.72	775.00	35	83.72	368.36
16	168.78	869.26	36	86.20	425.60
17	247.06	1,396.00	37	133.58	626.90
18	155.54	711.50	38	212.86	1,316.94
19	224.20	1,475.18	39	122.02	390.16
20	202.04	1,413.32	40	198.02	1,090.84

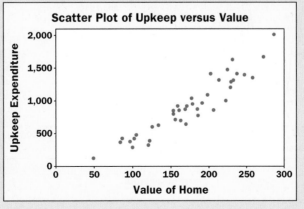

output in Figure 11.23(a) presents the predicted home-upkeep expenditures and residuals that are given by the simple linear regression model. Here each residual is computed as

$$e = y - \hat{y} = y - (b_0 + b_1x) = y - (-348.3921 + 7.2583x).$$

For instance, for the first observation (home), when $y = 1412.08$ and $x = 237.00$ (see Figure 11.22), the residual is

$$e = 1,412.08 - (-348.3921 + 7.2583(237))$$
$$= 1,412.08 - 1,371.816 = 40.264.$$

The MegaStat output in Figure 11.23(b) and (c) gives plots of the residuals for the QHIC simple linear regression model for each observation and against values of $\hat{y}$. To understand how these plots are constructed, recall that for the first observation (home), $y = 1,412.08$, $x = 237.00$, $\hat{y} = 1,371.816$, and the residual is 40.264, so the first point on the plot in Figure 11.23(b) is (237.00, 40.264). The point plotted in Figure 11.23(c) corresponding to the first observation

FIGURE 11.23   MegaStat and Excel Output of the Residuals and Residual Plots for the QHIC Simple Linear Regression Model

(a) MegaStat output of the residuals

Observation	Upkeep	Predicted	Residual	Observation	Upkeep	Predicted	Residual
1	1,412.080	1,371.816	40.264	21	849.140	762.413	86.727
2	797.200	762.703	34.497	22	1,313.840	1,336.832	−22.992
3	872.480	993.371	−120.891	23	602.060	562.085	39.975
4	1,003.420	1,263.378	−259.958	24	642.140	884.206	−242.066
5	852.900	817.866	35.034	25	1,038.800	938.353	100.447
6	288.480	375.112	−86.632	26	697.000	833.398	−136.398
7	1,288.460	1,314.041	−25.581	27	324.340	525.793	−201.453
8	423.080	390.354	32.726	28	965.100	1,038.662	−73.562
9	1,351.740	1,523.224	−171.484	29	920.140	804.075	116.065
10	378.040	350.434	27.606	30	950.900	947.208	3.692
11	918.080	892.771	25.309	31	1,670.320	1,627.307	43.013
12	1,627.240	1,328.412	298.828	32	125.400	6.537	118.863
13	1,204.760	1,308.815	−104.055	33	479.780	410.532	69.248
14	857.040	1,146.084	−289.044	34	2,010.640	1,728.778	281.862
15	775.000	999.613	−224.613	35	368.360	259.270	109.090
16	869.260	876.658	−7.398	36	425.600	277.270	148.330
17	1,396.000	1,444.835	−48.835	37	626.900	621.167	5.733
18	711.500	780.558	−69.058	38	1,316.940	1,196.602	120.338
19	1,475.180	1,278.911	196.269	39	390.160	537.261	−147.101
20	1,413.320	1,118.068	295.252	40	1,090.840	1,088.889	1.951

(b) Plot of residuals by observation   (c) Residual plot versus $\hat{y}$

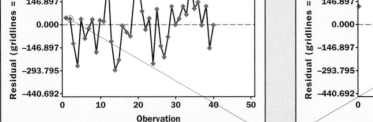

first observation

has a horizontal axis coordinate of the $\hat{y}$ value 1,371.816 and a vertical axis coordinate of the residual 40.264. Finally, note that the QHIC data are cross-sectional data, not time series data. Therefore, we cannot make a residual plot versus time.

The constant-variance assumption To check the validity of the constant-variance assumption, we examine plots of the residuals against values of x, $\hat{y}$, and time (if the regression data are time series data). When we look at these plots, the pattern of the residuals' fluctuation around 0 tells us about the validity of the constant-variance assumption. A residual plot that fans out (as in Figure 11.24(a)) suggests that the error terms are becoming more spread out as the horizontal plot value increases and that the constant-variance assumption is violated. Here we would say that an **increasing error variance** exists. A residual plot that funnels in (as in Figure 11.24(b)) suggests that the spread of the error terms is decreasing as the horizontal plot value increases and that again the constant-variance assumption is violated. In this case, we would say that a **decreasing error variance** exists. A residual plot with a horizontal band appearance (as in Figure 11.24(c)) suggests that the spread of the error terms around 0 is not changing much as the horizontal plot value increases. Such a plot tells us that the constant-variance assumption (approximately) holds.

As an example, consider the QHIC case and the residual plot in Figure 11.23(c). This plot tells us that the residuals appear to fan out as $\hat{y}$ (predicted y) increases. Also note that the scatter plot of y versus x in Figure 11.22 shows the increasing error variance—the y values appear to fan out as x increases. In fact, one might ask why we need to consider residual plots when we can simply look at scatter plots of y versus x. One answer is that, in general, because of possible differences in scaling between residual plots and scatter plots of y versus x, one of these types of plots might be more informative in a particular situation. Therefore, we should always consider both types of plots.

When the constant-variance assumption is violated, we cannot use the formulas of this chapter to make statistical inferences. Later in this section, we discuss how we can make statistical inferences when a nonconstant error variance exists.

The assumption of correct functional form If the functional form of a regression model is incorrect, the residual plots constructed by using the model often display a pattern suggesting the form of a more appropriate model. For instance, if we use a simple linear regression model when the true relationship between y and x is curved, the residual plot will have a curved appearance. Later in this section, we discuss one way to model curved relationships.

FIGURE **11.24** Residual Plots and the Constant-Variance Assumption

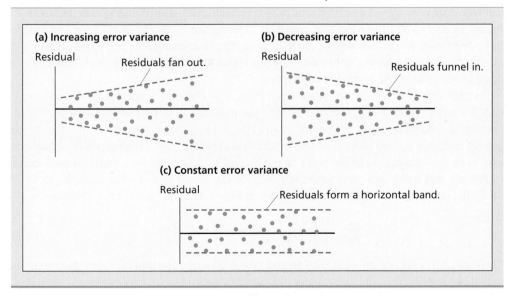

FIGURE **11.25**   Histogram and Normal Plots of the Residuals from the Simple Linear Regression Model Describing the QHIC Data

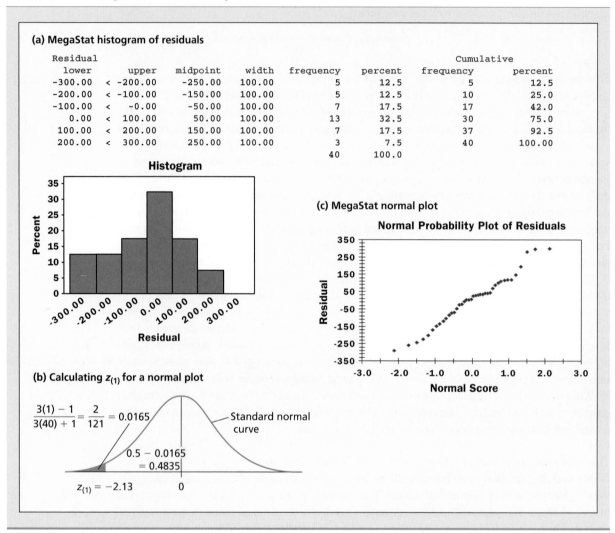

(a) MegaStat histogram of residuals

Residual lower		upper	midpoint	width	frequency	percent	Cumulative frequency	percent
-300.00	<	-200.00	-250.00	100.00	5	12.5	5	12.5
-200.00	<	-100.00	-150.00	100.00	5	12.5	10	25.0
-100.00	<	-0.00	-50.00	100.00	7	17.5	17	42.0
0.00	<	100.00	50.00	100.00	13	32.5	30	75.0
100.00	<	200.00	150.00	100.00	7	17.5	37	92.5
200.00	<	300.00	250.00	100.00	3	7.5	40	100.00
					40	100.0		

Histogram

(c) MegaStat normal plot

Normal Probability Plot of Residuals

(b) Calculating $z_{(1)}$ for a normal plot

$$\frac{3(1) - 1}{3(40) + 1} = \frac{2}{121} = 0.0165$$

Standard normal curve

$0.5 - 0.0165 = 0.4835$

$z_{(1)} = -2.13$ 0

The normality assumption If the normality assumption holds, a histogram and/or a stem-and-leaf display of the residuals should look reasonably bell-shaped and symmetric about 0. Figure 11.25(a) gives the MegaStat output of a histogram of the residuals from the simple linear regression model describing the QHIC data. The histogram looks fairly bell-shaped and symmetric about 0. However, the tails look somewhat long and heavy or thick, indicating a possible violation of the normality assumption.

Another way to check the normality assumption is to construct a **normal plot** of the residuals. To make a normal plot, we first arrange the residuals in order from smallest to largest. Letting the ordered residuals be denoted as $e_{(1)}, e_{(2)}, \ldots, e_{(n)}$, we denote the ith residual in the ordered listing as $e_{(i)}$. We plot $e_{(i)}$ on the vertical axis against a point called $z_{(i)}$ on the horizontal axis. Here $z_{(i)}$ is defined to be the point on the horizontal axis under the standard normal curve so that the area under this curve to the left of $z_{(i)}$ is $(3i - 1)/(3n + 1)$. For example, recall in the QHIC case that $n = 40$ residuals are given in Figure 11.23(a). It follows that when $i = 1$,

$$\frac{3i - 1}{3n + 1} = \frac{3(1) - 1}{3(40) + 1} = \frac{2}{121} = 0.0165.$$

Therefore, $z_{(1)}$ is the normal point with an area of 0.0165 under the standard normal curve to its left. This implies that the area under the standard normal curve between $z_{(1)}$ and 0 is $0.5 - 0.0165 = 0.4835$. Thus, as illustrated in Figure 11.25(b), $z_{(1)}$ equals -2.13. Because the smallest residual in Figure 11.23(a) is −289.044, the first point plotted is $e_{(1)} = -289.044$ on the vertical scale versus $z_{(1)} = -2.13$ on the horizontal scale. When $i = 2$, it can be verified that $(3i - 1)/(3n + 1)$ equals 0.0413 and thus that $z_{(2)} = -1.74$. Therefore, because the second-smallest residual in Figure 11.23(a) is −259.958, the second point plotted is $e_{(2)} = -259.958$ on the vertical scale versus $z_{(2)} = -1.74$ on the horizontal scale. This process is continued until the entire normal plot is constructed. The MegaStat output of this plot is given in Figure 11.25(c).

If the normality assumption holds, the expected value of the ith ordered residual $e_{(i)}$ is proportional to $z_{(i)}$. Therefore, a plot of the $e_{(i)}$ values on the horizontal scale versus the $z_{(i)}$ values on the vertical scale (or, equivalently, the $e_{(i)}$ values on the horizontal scale versus the $p_{(i)}$ values on the vertical scale) should have a straight-line appearance. That is, if the normality assumption holds, then the normal plot should have a straight-line appearance. A normal plot that does not look like a straight line (admittedly a subjective decision) indicates that the normality assumption is violated. Because the normal plot in Figure 11.25 has some curvature (particularly in the upper right portion), there is a possible violation of the normality assumption.

It is important to realize that violations of the constant-variance and correct functional form assumptions can often cause a histogram and/or a stem-and-leaf display of the residuals to look nonnormal and can cause the normal plot to have a curved appearance. Because of this, it is usually a good idea to use residual plots to check for nonconstant variance and incorrect functional form before making any final conclusions about the normality assumption. Later in this section, we discuss a procedure that sometimes remedies simultaneous violations of the constant-variance, correct functional form, and normality assumptions.

The independence assumption The independence assumption is most likely to be violated when the regression data are **time series data**—that is, data that have been collected in a time sequence. For such data, the time-ordered error terms can be **autocorrelated**. Intuitively, we say that error terms occurring over time have **positive autocorrelation** if a positive error term in time period i tends to produce, or be followed by, another positive error term in time period $i + k$ (some later time period) and if a negative error term in time period i tends to produce, or be followed by, another negative error term in time period $i + k$. In other words, positive autocorrelation exists when positive error terms tend to be followed over time by positive error terms and when negative error terms tend to be followed over time by negative error terms. Positive autocorrelation in the error terms is depicted in Figure 11.26(a), which illustrates that *positive autocorrelation can produce a cyclical error term pattern over time*. The simple linear regression model implies that a positive error term produces a greater than average value of y and a negative error term produces a smaller than average value of y. It follows that positive autocorrelation in the error terms means that greater than average values of y tend to be followed by greater than average values of y, and smaller than average values of y tend to be followed by smaller than average values of y. An example of positive autocorrelation could

FIGURE **11.26** Positive and Negative Autocorrelation

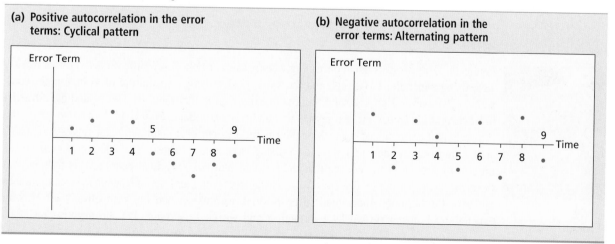

(a) Positive autocorrelation in the error terms: Cyclical pattern

(b) Negative autocorrelation in the error terms: Alternating pattern

hypothetically be provided by a simple linear regression model relating demand for a product to advertising expenditure. Here we assume that the data are time series data observed over a number of consecutive sales periods. One of the factors included in the error term of the simple linear regression model is competitors' advertising expenditure for their similar products. If, for the moment, we assume that competitors' advertising expenditure significantly affects the demand for the product, then a higher than average competitors' advertising expenditure probably causes demand for the product to be lower than average and hence probably causes a negative error term. On the other hand, a lower than average competitors' advertising expenditure probably causes the demand for the product to be higher than average and hence probably causes a positive error term. If, then, competitors tend to spend money on advertising in a cyclical fashion—spending large amounts for several consecutive sales periods (during an advertising campaign) and then spending lesser amounts for several consecutive sales periods— a negative error term in one sales period will tend to be followed by a negative error term in the next sales period, and a positive error term in one sales period will tend to be followed by a positive error term in the next sales period. In this case, the error terms would display positive autocorrelation, and thus these error terms would not be statistically independent.

Intuitively, error terms occurring over time have **negative autocorrelation** if a positive error term in time period i tends to produce, or be followed by, a negative error term in time period $i + k$ and if a negative error term in time period i tends to produce, or be followed by, a positive error term in time period $i + k$. In other words, negative autocorrelation exists when positive error terms tend to be followed over time by negative error terms and negative error terms tend to be followed over time by positive error terms. An example of negative autocorrelation in the error terms is depicted in Figure 11.26(b), which illustrates that *negative autocorrelation in the error terms can produce an alternating pattern over time*. It follows that negative autocorrelation in the error terms means that greater than average values of y tend to be followed by smaller than average values of y and smaller than average values of y tend to be followed by greater than average values of y. An example of negative autocorrelation might be provided by a retailer's weekly stock orders. Here a larger than average stock order one week might result in an oversupply and hence a smaller than average order the next week.

The **independence assumption** basically says that the time-ordered error terms display no positive or negative autocorrelation. This says that *the error terms occur in a random pattern over time*. Such a random pattern implies that the error terms (and their corresponding y values) are statistically independent.

Because the residuals are point estimates of the error terms, a residual plot versus time is used to check the independence assumption. If a residual plot versus the data's time sequence has a cyclical appearance, the error terms are positively autocorrelated and the independence assumption is violated. If a plot of the time-ordered residuals has an alternating pattern, the error terms are negatively autocorrelated, and again the independence assumption is violated. However, if a plot of the time-ordered residuals displays a random pattern, the error terms have little or no autocorrelation. In such a case, it is reasonable to conclude that the independence assumption holds.

Example 11.7

Figure 11.27(a) presents data concerning weekly sales at Folio Bookstore (Sales), Folio's weekly advertising expenditure (Adver), and the weekly advertising expenditure of Folio's main competitor (Compadv). Here the sales values are expressed in thousands of dollars, and the advertising expenditure values are expressed in hundreds of dollars. Figure 11.27(a) also gives the residuals that are obtained when MegaStat is used to perform a simple linear regression analysis relating Folio's sales to Folio's advertising expenditure. These residuals are plotted versus time in Figure 11.27(b). We see that the residual plot has a cyclical pattern. This tells us that the error terms for the model are positively autocorrelated and the independence assumption is violated. Furthermore, there tend to be positive residuals when the competitor's advertising expenditure is lower (in weeks 1 through 8 and weeks 12 through 16) and negative residuals

FIGURE 11.27   Folio Bookstore Sales and Advertising Data, and Residual Analysis

(a) The data and the MegaStat output of the residuals from a simple linear regression relating Folio's sales to Folio's advertising expenditure

Observation	Adver	Compadv	Sales	Predicted	Residual
1	18	10	22	18.7	3.3
2	20	10	27	23.0	4.0
3	20	15	23	23.0	−0.0
4	25	15	31	33.9	−2.9
5	28	15	45	40.4	4.6
6	29	20	47	42.6	4.4
7	29	20	45	42.6	2.4
8	28	25	42	40.4	1.6
9	30	35	37	44.7	−7.7
10	31	35	39	46.9	−7.9
11	34	35	45	53.4	−8.4
12	35	30	52	55.6	−3.6
13	36	30	57	57.8	−0.8
14	38	25	62	62.1	−0.1
15	41	20	73	68.6	4.4
16	45	20	84	77.3	6.7

Durbin-Watson = 0.65

(b) MegaStat output of a plot of the residuals in Figure 11.27(a) versus time

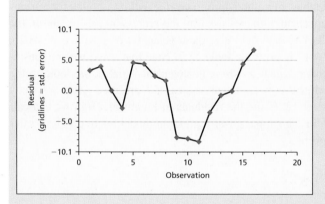

when the competitor's advertising expenditure is higher (in weeks 9 through 11). Therefore, the competitor's advertising expenditure seems to be causing the positive autocorrelation.

To conclude this example, note that the simple linear regression model relating Folio's sales to Folio's advertising expenditure has a standard error, s, of 5.038. The MegaStat residual plot in Figure 11.27(b) includes grid lines that are placed one and two standard errors above and below the residual mean of 0. All MegaStat residual plots use such grid lines to help better diagnose potential violations of the regression assumptions.

When the independence assumption is violated, various remedies can be employed. One approach is to identify which independent variable left in the error term (for example, competitors' advertising expenditure) is causing the error terms to be autocorrelated. We can then remove this independent variable from the error term and insert it directly into the regression model, forming a **multiple regression model**. (Multiple regression models are discussed in Chapter 12.)

The Durbin–Watson test One type of positive or negative autocorrelation is called **first-order autocorrelation**. It says that ε_t, the error term in time period t, is related to ε_{t-1}, the error term in time period $t - 1$. To check for first-order autocorrelation, we can use the **Durbin–Watson statistic**

$$d = \frac{\sum_{t=2}^{n} (e_t - e_{t-1})^2}{\sum_{t=1}^{n} e_t^2},$$

where $e_1, e_2, \ldots, e_n$ are the time-ordered residuals.

Small values of d lead us to conclude that there is positive autocorrelation. This is because, if d is small, the differences $(e_t - e_{t-1})$ are small. This indicates that the adjacent residuals e_t and e_{t-1} are of the same magnitude, which in turn says that the adjacent error terms ε_t and ε_{t-1} are positively correlated. Consider testing the null hypothesis H_0 **that the error terms are not autocorrelated** versus the alternative hypothesis H_a **that the error terms are positively autocorrelated**. Durbin and Watson have shown that there are points (denoted $d_{L,\alpha}$ and $d_{U,\alpha}$) such that if α is the probability of a Type I error, we have the following:

1 If $d < d_{L,\alpha}$, we reject H_0.

2 If $d > d_{U,\alpha}$, we do not reject H_0.

3 If $d_{L,\alpha} \leq d \leq d_{U,\alpha}$, the test is inconclusive.

So that the Durbin–Watson test may be easily done, tables containing the points $d_{L,\alpha}$ and $d_{U,\alpha}$ have been constructed. These tables give the appropriate $d_{L,\alpha}$ and $d_{U,\alpha}$ points for various values of α; k, the number of independent variables used by the regression model; and n, the number of observations. Tables A.12, A.13, and A.14 give these points for $\alpha = 0.05$, $\alpha = 0.025$, and $\alpha = 0.01$. A portion of Table A.12 is given in Table 11.9. Note that when we are considering a simple linear regression model, which uses *one* independent variable, we look up the points $d_{L,\alpha}$ and $d_{U,\alpha}$ under the heading "$k = 1$." Other values of k are used when we study multiple regression models in Chapter 12. Using the residuals in Figure 11.27(a), we can calculate the Durbin–Watson statistic for the simple linear regression model relating Folio's sales to Folio's advertising expenditure to be

$$d = \frac{\sum_{t=2}^{16} (e_t - e_{t-1})^2}{\sum_{t=1}^{16} e_t^2}$$

$$= \frac{(4.0 - 3.3)^2 + (0.0 - 4.0)^2 + \cdots + (6.7 - 4.4)^2}{3.3^2 + 4.0^2 + \cdots + 6.7^2}$$

$$= 0.65.$$

A MegaStat output of the Durbin–Watson statistic is given at the bottom of Figure 11.27(a) on the previous page. To test for positive autocorrelation, we note that there are $n = 16$ observations

TABLE **11.9** Critical Values for the Durbin–Watson d Statistic ($\alpha = 0.05$)

	$k = 1$		$k = 2$		$k = 3$		$k = 4$	
n	$d_{L,0.05}$	$d_{U,0.05}$	$d_{L,0.05}$	$d_{U,0.05}$	$d_{L,0.05}$	$d_{U,0.05}$	$d_{L,0.05}$	$d_{U,0.05}$
15	1.08	1.36	0.95	1.54	0.82	1.75	0.69	1.97
16	1.10	1.37	0.98	1.54	0.86	1.73	0.74	1.93
17	1.13	1.38	1.02	1.54	0.90	1.71	0.78	1.90
18	1.16	1.39	1.05	1.53	0.93	1.69	0.82	1.87
19	1.18	1.40	1.08	1.53	0.97	1.68	0.86	1.85
20	1.20	1.41	1.10	1.54	1.00	1.68	0.90	1.83

and the regression model uses $k = 1$ independent variable. Therefore, if we set $\alpha = 0.05$, Table 11.9 tells us that $d_{L,0.05} = 1.10$ and $d_{U,0.05} = 1.37$. Because $d = 0.65$ is less than $d_{L,0.05} = 1.10$, we reject the null hypothesis of no autocorrelation and conclude (at an α of 0.05) that there is positive (first-order) autocorrelation.

It can be shown that the Durbin–Watson statistic d is always between 0 and 4. Large values of d (and hence small values of $4 - d$) lead us to conclude that there is negative autocorrelation because if d is large, this indicates that the differences $(e_t - e_{t-1})$ are large. This says that the adjacent error terms ε_t and ε_{t-1} are negatively autocorrelated. Consider testing the null hypothesis H_0 **that the error terms are not autocorrelated** versus the alternative hypothesis H_a **that the error terms are negatively autocorrelated**. Durbin and Watson have shown that based on setting the probability of a Type I error equal to α, the points $d_{L,\alpha}$ and $d_{U,\alpha}$ are such that we have the following:

1   If $4 - d < d_{L,\alpha}$, we reject H_0.
2   If $4 - d > d_{U,\alpha}$, we do not reject H_0.
3   If $d_{L,\alpha} \leq 4 - d \leq d_{U,\alpha}$, the test is inconclusive.

As an example, for the Folio sales simple linear regression model, we see that

$$4 - d = 4 - 0.65 = 3.35 > d_{U,0.05} = 1.37.$$

Therefore, on the basis of setting α equal to 0.05, we do not reject the null hypothesis of no autocorrelation and conclude that there is no evidence of negative (first-order) autocorrelation.

We can also use the Durbin–Watson statistic to test for positive or negative autocorrelation. Specifically, consider testing the null hypothesis H_0 **that the error terms are not autocorrelated** versus the alternative hypothesis H_a **that the error terms are positively or negatively autocorrelated**. Durbin and Watson have shown that based on setting the probability of a Type I error equal to α, we have the following:

1   If $d < d_{L,\alpha/2}$ or $4 - d < d_{L,\alpha/2}$, we reject H_0.
2   If $d > d_{U,\alpha/2}$ and $4 - d > d_{U,\alpha/2}$, we do not reject H_0.
3   If $d_{L,\alpha/2} \leq d \leq d_{U,\alpha/2}$ or $d_{L,\alpha/2} \leq 4 - d \leq d_{U,\alpha/2}$, the test is inconclusive.

For example, consider testing for positive or negative autocorrelation in the Folio sales model. If we set α equal to 0.05, then $\alpha/2 = 0.025$, and we need to find the points $d_{L,0.025}$ and $d_{U,0.025}$ when $n = 16$ and $k = 1$. Looking up these points in Table A.13, we find that $d_{L,0.025} = 0.98$ and $d_{U,0.025} = 1.24$. Because $d = 0.65$ is less than $d_{L,0.025} = 0.98$, we reject the null hypothesis of no autocorrelation and conclude (at an α of 0.05) that there is first-order autocorrelation.

Although we have used the Folio sales model in these examples to demonstrate the Durbin–Watson tests for (1) positive autocorrelation, (2) negative autocorrelation, and (3) positive or negative autocorrelation, we must in practice choose one of these Durbin–Watson tests in a particular situation. Positive autocorrelation is more common in real time series data than is negative autocorrelation, so the Durbin–Watson test for positive autocorrelation is used more often than the other two tests. Also note that each Durbin–Watson test assumes that the population of all possible residuals at any time t has a normal distribution.

Transforming the dependent variable: A possible remedy for violations of the constant-variance, correct functional form, and normality assumptions In general, if a data or residual plot indicates that the error variance of a regression model increases as an independent variable or the predicted value of the dependent variable increases, then we can sometimes remedy the situation by transforming the dependent variable. One transformation that works well is to take each y value to a fractional power. As an example, we might use a transformation in which we take the square root (or one-half power) of each y value. Letting y^* denote the value obtained when the transformation is applied to y, we write the **square root transformation** as

$$y^* = \sqrt{y} = y^{0.5}.$$

Another commonly used transformation is the **quartic root transformation**. Here we take each y value to the one-fourth power. That is,

$$y^* = y^{0.25}.$$

In addition, we sometimes use the **logarithmic transformation**

$$y^* = \ln y,$$

which takes the natural logarithm of each y value. In general, when we take a fractional power (including the natural logarithm) of the dependent variable, the transformation tends to not only equalize the error variance but also straighten out certain types of nonlinear data plots. Specifically, if a data plot indicates that the dependent variable is increasing at an increasing rate (as in Figure 11.22 on page 397), then a fractional power transformation tends to straighten out the data plot. A fractional power transformation can also help to remedy a violation of the normality assumption. Because we cannot know which fractional power to use before we actually take the transformation, we recommend taking all of the square root, quartic root, and natural logarithm transformations and seeing which one best equalizes the error variance and (possibly) straightens out a nonlinear data plot.

Example 11.8 The QHIC Case

Consider the QHIC upkeep expenditures. In Figures 11.28, 11.29, and 11.30, we show the plots that result when we take the square root, quartic root, and natural logarithmic transformations of the upkeep expenditures and plot the transformed values versus the home values. The square root transformation seems to best equalize the error variance and straighten out the curved data plot in Figure 11.22. Note that the natural logarithm transformation seems to overtransform the data—the error variance tends to decrease as the home value increases and the data plot seems to bend down. The plot of the quartic roots indicates that the quartic root transformation also seems to overtransform the data (but not by as much as the logarithmic transformation). In general, as the fractional power gets smaller, the transformation gets stronger. Different fractional powers are best in different situations.

Because the plot in Figure 11.28 of the square roots of the upkeep expenditures versus the home values has a straight-line appearance, we consider the model

$$y^* = \beta_0 + \beta_1 x + \varepsilon, \quad \text{where} \quad y^* = y^{0.5}.$$

FIGURE **11.28** MegaStat Plot of the Square Roots of the Upkeep Expenditures versus the Home Values

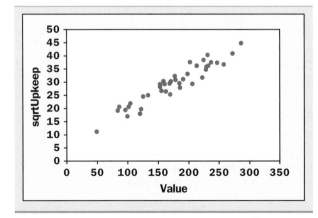

FIGURE **11.29** MegaStat Plot of the Quartic Roots of the Upkeep Expenditures versus the Home Values

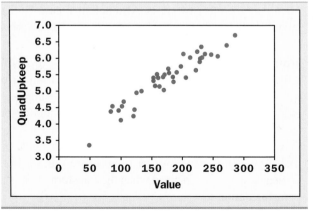

FIGURE **11.30**   MegaStat Plot of the Natural Logarithms of the Upkeep Expenditures
versus the Home Values

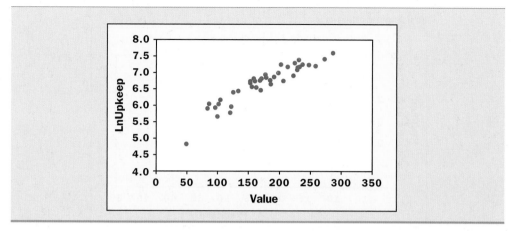

FIGURE **11.31**   MegaStat Output of a Regression Analysis of the Upkeep Expenditure Data by Using
the Model $y^* = \beta_0 + \beta_1 x + \varepsilon$, where $y^* = y^{0.5}$

Regression Analysis

r^2	0.908		n	40	
r	0.953		k	1	
Std. Error	2.325		Dep. Var.	sqrtUpkeep	

ANOVA table

Source	SS	df	MS	F	p-value
Regression	2,016.8421	1	2,016.8421	373.17	3.01E-21
Residual	205.3764	38	5.4046		
Total	2,222.2185	39			

Regression output   confidence interval

variables	coefficients	std. error	t (df=38)	p-value	95% lower	95% upper
Intercept	7.2007	1.2050	5.976	6.15E-07	4.7613	9.6401
Value	0.1270	0.0066	19.318	3.01E-21	0.1137	0.1404

Predicted values for: sqrtUpkeep

		95% Confidence Interval		95% Prediction Interval		
Value	Predicted	lower	upper	lower	upper	Leverage
220	35.1510672	34.1914370	36.1106974	30.3479388	39.9541956	0.042

The MegaStat output of a regression analysis using this transformed model is given in Figure 11.31, and the MegaStat output of an analysis of the model's residuals is given in Figure 11.32 on the next page. Note that the residual plot versus x for the transformed model in Figure 11.32 has a horizontal band appearance. Therefore, we conclude that the constant-variance and correct functional form assumptions approximately hold for the transformed model.

Because the regression assumptions approximately hold for the transformed regression model, we can use this model to make statistical inferences. Consider a home worth $220,000. Using the least squares point estimates on the MegaStat output in Figure 11.31, it follows that a point prediction of y^* for such a home is

$$\hat{y}^* = 7.2007 + 0.1270(220)$$
$$= 35.141.$$

This point prediction is given (within rounding) at the bottom of the output, as is the 95 percent prediction interval for y^*, which is [30.348, 39.954]. It follows that a point prediction of the

FIGURE **11.32**   MegaStat Output of Residual Analysis for the Upkeep Expenditure Model $y^* = \beta_0 + \beta_1 x + \varepsilon$, where $y^* = y^{0.5}$

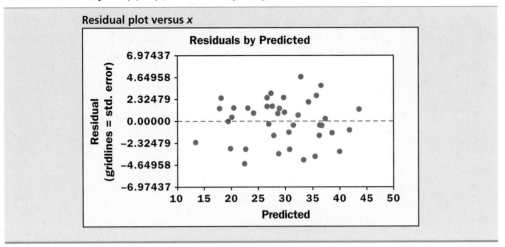

upkeep expenditure for a home worth \$220,000 is $(35.141)^2 = \$1,234.89$ and that a 95 percent prediction interval for this upkeep expenditure is $[(30.348)^2, (39.954)^2] = [\$921.00, \$1,596.32]$. Suppose that QHIC wishes to send an advertising brochure to any home that has a predicted upkeep expenditure of at least \$500. Solving the prediction equation $\hat{y}^* = b_0 + b_1 x$ for x, and noting that a predicted upkeep expenditure of \$500 corresponds to a $\hat{y}^*$ of $\sqrt{500} = 22.36068$, we obtain

$$x = \frac{\hat{y}^* - b_0}{b_1} = \frac{22.36068 - 7.2007}{0.1270} = 119.3699 \text{ (or \$119,370)}.$$

It follows that QHIC should send the advertising brochure to any home that has a value of at least \$119,370.

Recall that because there are many homes of a particular value in the metropolitan area, QHIC is interested in estimating the mean upkeep expenditure corresponding to this value. Consider all homes worth, for example, \$220,000. The output in Figure 11.31 tells us that a point estimate of the mean of the square roots of the upkeep expenditures for all such homes is 35.151 and that a 95 percent confidence interval for this mean is [34.191, 36.111]. Unfortunately, the mean of the square root is not the square root of the mean. Therefore, we cannot transform the results for the mean of the square roots back into a result for the mean of the original upkeep expenditures. This is a major drawback to transforming the dependent variable and one reason why many statisticians avoid doing this unless the regression assumptions are badly violated. In Chapter 12, we discuss other remedies for violations of the regression assumptions that do not have some of the drawbacks of transforming the dependent variable. Some of these remedies involve transforming the independent variable.

Exercises for Section 11.10

CONCEPTS

11.64 In a regression analysis, what variables should the residuals be plotted against? What types of patterns in residual plots indicate violations of the regression assumptions?

11.65 In regression analysis, how do you check the normality assumption?

11.66 What is one possible remedy for violations of the constant-variance, correct functional form, and normality assumptions?

FIGURE **11.33** MegaStat Residual Diagnostics for Exercise 11.67

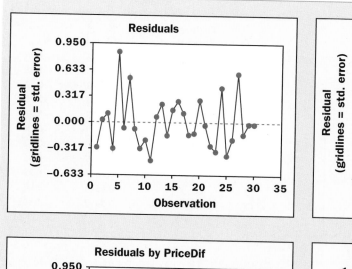

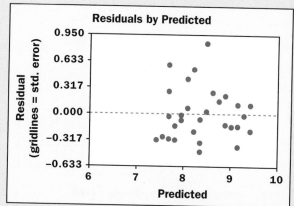

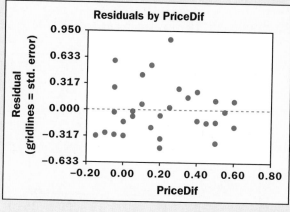

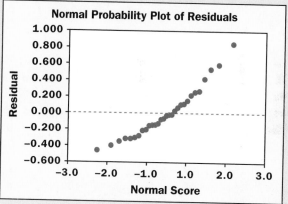

METHODS AND APPLICATIONS

11.67 THE FRESH DETERGENT CASE

Figure 11.33 gives the MegaStat output of residual diagnostics that are obtained when the simple linear regression model is fit to the Fresh detergent demand data. Interpret the diagnostics and determine if they indicate any violations of the regression assumptions.

11.68 THE SERVICE TIME CASE

The MegaStat output of the residuals given by the service time model is given in Figure 11.34 and the MegaStat output of residual plots versus x and $\hat{y}$ is given in Figure 11.35(a) and (b) on the next page. Do the plots indicate any violations of the regression assumptions?

11.69 THE SERVICE TIME CASE

Figure 11.34 gives the MegaStat output of the residuals from the simple linear regression model describing the service time data.

a. In this exercise, we construct a normal plot of the residuals from the simple linear regression model. To construct this plot, we must first arrange the residuals in order from smallest to largest. These ordered residuals are given in Table 11.10 on the next page. Denoting the ith ordered residual as

FIGURE **11.34** MegaStat Output of the Residuals for the Service Time Model

Observation	Minutes	Predicted	Residual
1	109.0	109.9	−0.9
2	58.0	60.7	−2.7
3	138.0	134.5	3.5
4	189.0	183.7	5.3
5	37.0	36.1	0.9
6	82.0	85.3	−3.3
7	103.0	109.9	−6.9
8	134.0	134.5	−0.5
9	68.0	60.7	7.3
10	112.0	109.9	2.1
11	154.0	159.1	−5.1

$e_{(i)}$ ($i = 1, 2, \ldots, 11$), we next compute for each value of i the point $z_{(i)}$. These computations are summarized in Table 11.10. Show how $z_{(4)} = -0.46$ and $z_{(10)} = 1.05$ were obtained.

b. The ordered residuals (the $e_{(i)}$'s) are plotted against the $z_{(i)}$'s on the MegaStat output of Figure 11.35(c) on the next page. Does this figure indicate a violation of the normality assumption?

FIGURE **11.35**   MegaStat Residual Plots for the Service
Time Model

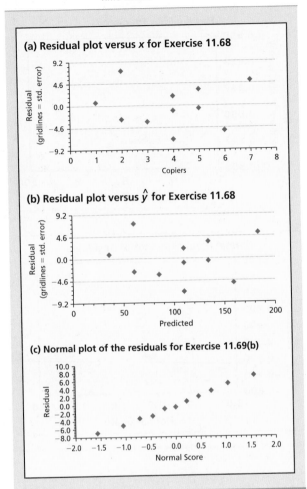

(a) Residual plot versus x for Exercise 11.68

(b) Residual plot versus $\hat{y}$ for Exercise 11.68

(c) Normal plot of the residuals for Exercise 11.69(b)

TABLE **11.10**   Ordered Residuals and Normal Plot
Calculations

i	Ordered Residual, $e_{(i)}$	$\dfrac{3i-1}{3n+1}$	$z_{(i)}$
1	−6.9	0.0588	−1.565
2	−5.1	0.1470	−1.05
3	−3.3	0.2353	−0.72
4	−2.7	0.3235	−0.46
5	−0.9	0.4118	−0.22
6	−0.5	0.5000	0
7	0.9	0.5882	0.22
8	2.1	0.6765	0.46
9	3.5	0.7647	0.72
10	5.3	0.8529	1.05
11	7.3	0.9412	1.565

FIGURE **11.36**   Residual Plot for Exercise 11.70

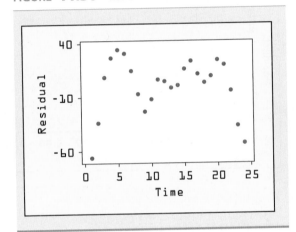

TABLE **11.11**   Sales and Advertising Data for Exercise 11.70

Month	Monthly Total Sales, y	Advertising Expenditures, x	Month	Monthly Total Sales, y	Advertising Expenditures, x
1	202.66	116.44	13	260.51	129.85
2	232.91	119.58	14	266.34	122.65
3	272.07	125.74	15	281.24	121.64
4	290.97	124.55	16	286.19	127.24
5	299.09	122.35	17	271.97	132.35
6	296.95	120.44	18	265.01	130.86
7	279.49	123.24	19	274.44	122.90
8	255.75	127.55	20	291.81	117.15
9	242.78	121.19	21	290.91	109.47
10	255.34	118.00	22	264.95	114.34
11	271.58	121.81	23	228.40	123.72
12	268.27	126.54	24	209.33	130.33

Source: "Sales and advertising data," by S. Makridakis, S. C. Wheelwright, and V. E. McGee, *Forecasting: Methods and Applications* (Copyright © 1983 John Wiley & Sons, Inc.). Reprinted by permission of John Wiley & Sons, Inc.

11.70 A simple linear regression model is employed to analyze the 24 monthly observations given in Table 11.11 on the previous page. Residuals are computed and are plotted versus time. The resulting residual plot is shown in Figure 11.36 on the previous page. Discuss why the residual plot suggests the existence of positive autocorrelation. The Durbin–Watson statistic d can be calculated to be 0.473. Test for positive (first-order) autocorrelation at $\alpha = 0.05$, and test for negative (first-order) autocorrelation at $\alpha = 0.05$.

11.71 USING A NATURAL LOGARITHM TRANSFORMATION

Western Steakhouses, a fast-food chain, opened 15 years ago. Each year since then, the number of steakhouses in operation, y, has been recorded. An analyst for the firm wishes to use these data to predict the number of steakhouses that will be in operation next year. The data are given in Figure 11.37(a), and a plot of the data is given in Figure 11.37(b). Examining the data plot, we see that the number of steakhouse openings has increased over time at an increasing rate and with increasing variation. A plot of the natural logarithms of the steakhouse values versus time (see Figure 11.37(c)) has a straight-line appearance with constant variation. Therefore, we consider the model

$$\ln y_t = \beta_0 + \beta_1 t + \varepsilon_t.$$

If we use MegaStat, we find that the least squares point estimates of β_0 and β_1 are $b_0 = 2.0701$ and $b_1 = 0.2569$. We also find that a point prediction of and a 95 percent prediction interval for the natural logarithm of the number of steakhouses in operation next year (year 16) are 6.1802 and [5.9945, 6.3659]. See the MegaStat output in Figure 11.38.

FIGURE 11.37 The Data and Data Plots for Exercise 11.71

(a) Western Steakhouse openings for the last 15 years

Year, t	Steakhouse Openings, y	Year, t	Steakhouse Openings, y
1	11	9	82
2	14	10	99
3	16	11	119
4	22	12	156
5	28	13	257
6	36	14	284
7	46	15	403
8	67		

(b) Time series plot of y versus t

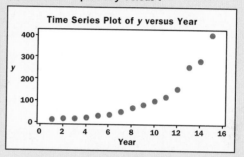

(c) Time series plot of natural logarithm of y versus t

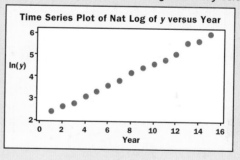

FIGURE 11.38 MegaStat Output of a Regression Analysis of the Steakhouse Data Using the Model $y^* = \beta_0 + \beta_1 x + \varepsilon$, where $y^* = \ln y$

Regression Analysis

r^2	0.996	n	15
r	0.998	k	1
Std. Error	0.076	Dep. Var.	ln(y)

ANOVA table

Source	SS	df	MS	F	p-value
Regression	18.4765	1	18.4765	3239.97	5.60E-17
Residual	0.0741	13	0.0057		
Total	18.5506	14			

Regression output

variables	coefficients	std. error	t (df=13)	p-value	confidence interval 95% lower	95% upper
Intercept	2.0701	0.0410	50.451	2.67E-16	1.9815	2.1588
Year	0.2569	0.0045	56.921	5.60E-17	0.2471	0.2666

Predicted values for: ln(y)

Year	Predicted	95% Confidence Interval lower	upper	95% Prediction Interval lower	upper	Leverage
16	6.180206	6.091562	6.268851	5.994536	6.365877	0.295

FIGURE 11.39 The Data, Data Plot, and Residual Plot for Exercise 11.72

(a) Service time data for 15 service calls

Service Time, y (Minutes)	Number of Microcomputers Serviced, x
92	3
63	2
126	6
247	8
49	2
90	4
119	5
114	6
67	2
115	4
188	6
298	11
77	3
151	10
27	1

(b) Plot of y versus x

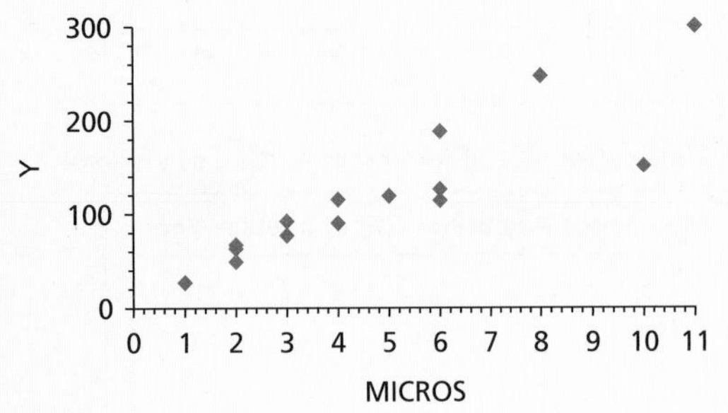

(c) The Excel residual plot

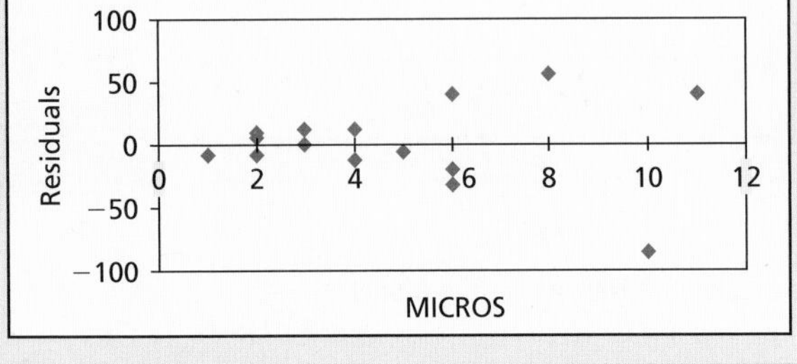

a. Use the least squares point estimates to verify the point prediction.

b. By exponentiating the point prediction and prediction interval—that is, by calculating $e^{6.1802}$ and $[e^{5.9945}, e^{6.3659}]$—find a point prediction of and a 95 percent prediction interval for the number of steakhouses in operation next year.

c. The Durbin–Watson statistic is found to be 1.88. Test for positive autocorrelation at the 0.05 level of significance.

d. The model $\ln y_t = \beta_0 + \beta_1 t + \varepsilon_t$ is called a **growth curve model** because it implies that

$$y_t = e^{(\beta_0 + \beta_1 t + \varepsilon_t)} = (e^{\beta_0})(e^{\beta_1 t})(e^{\varepsilon_t}) = \alpha_0 \alpha_1^t \eta_t,$$

where $\alpha_0 = e^{\beta_0}$, $\alpha_1 = e^{\beta_1}$, and $\eta_t = e^{\varepsilon_t}$. Here $\alpha_1 = e^{\beta_1}$ is called the **growth rate** of the y values. Noting that the least squares point estimate of β_1

is $b_1 = 0.2569$, estimate the growth rate α_1. Also interpret this growth rate by using the fact that $y_t = \alpha_0 \alpha_1^t \eta_t = (\alpha_0 \alpha_1^{t-1}) \alpha_1 \eta_t \approx (y_{t-1}) \alpha \eta_t$. This says that y_t is expected to be approximately α_1 times y_{t-1}.

11.72 THE UNEQUAL-VARIANCES SERVICE TIME CASE

Figure 11.39(a) presents data concerning the time, y, required to perform service and the number of microcomputers serviced, x, for 15 service calls. Figure 11.39(b) gives a plot of y versus x, and Figure 11.39(c) gives the Excel output of a plot of the residuals versus x for a simple linear regression model. What regression assumption appears to be violated?

11.73 THE UNEQUAL-VARIANCES SERVICE TIME CASE

Consider the simple linear regression model describing the service time data in Figure 11.39(a). Figure 11.39(c) shows that the residual plot versus x for this model fans out, indicating that the error term ε tends to become larger in magnitude as x increases. To remedy this violation of the constant-variance assumption, we divide all terms in the simple linear regression model by x. This gives the transformed model

$$\frac{y}{x} = \beta_0 \left(\frac{1}{x} \right) + \beta_1 + \frac{\varepsilon}{x} \text{ or, equivalently,}$$

$$\frac{y}{x} = \beta_0 + \beta_1 \left(\frac{1}{x} \right) + \frac{\varepsilon}{x}.$$

Figure 11.40 and Figure 11.41 give a regression output and a residual plot versus x, respectively, for this model.

a. Does the residual plot indicate that the constant-variance assumption holds for the transformed model?

b. Consider a future service call on which seven microcomputers will be serviced. Let μ_0 represent the mean service time for all service calls on which seven microcomputers will be serviced, and let y_0 represent the actual service time for an individual service call on which seven microcomputers will be serviced. The bottom of the MegaStat output in Figure 11.40 tells us that

$$\frac{\hat{y}}{7} = 24.0406 + 6.7642 \left(\frac{1}{7} \right) = 25.0069$$

is a point estimate of $\mu_0/7$ and a point prediction of $y_0/7$. Multiply this result by 7 to obtain $\hat{y}$. Multiply the ends of the confidence interval and prediction interval shown on the MegaStat output by 7. This will give a 95 percent confidence interval for μ_0 and a 95 percent prediction interval for y_0. If the number of minutes you will allow for the future service call is the upper limit of the 95 percent confidence interval for μ_0, how many minutes will you allow?

FIGURE **11.40** MegaStat Output of a Regression Analysis of the Service Time Data Using the Model $y/x = \beta_0 + \beta_1(1/x) + \varepsilon/x$

Regression Analysis

r^2	0.095		n	15
r	0.308		k	1
Std. Error	5.158		Dep. Var.	**Y/X**

ANOVA table

Source	SS	df	MS	F	p-value
Regression	36.2685	1	36.2685	1.36	0.2640
Residual	345.8857	13	26.6066		
Total	382.1542	14			

Regression output

variables	coefficients	std. error	t (df = 13)	p-value	confidence interval 95% lower	95% upper
Intercept	24.0406	2.2461	10.703	8.13E-08	19.1883	28.8929
1/X	6.7642	5.7936	1.168	0.2640	−5.7521	19.2804

Predicted values for: Y/X

1/X	Predicted	95% Confidence Intervals lower	upper	95% Prediction Intervals lower	upper	Leverage
0.1429	25.0069	21.4335	28.5803	13.3044	36.7094	0.103

FIGURE **11.41** MegaStat Residual Plot for Exercise 11.73

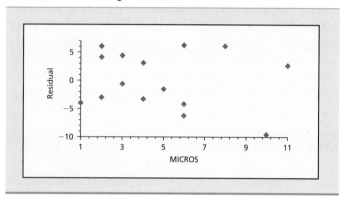

11.11 SOME SHORTCUT FORMULAS

Calculating the sum of squared residuals A shortcut formula for the sum of squared residuals is

$$SSE = SS_{yy} - \frac{SS_{xy}^2}{SS_{xx}},$$

where

$$SS_{yy} = \sum (y_i - \bar{y})^2 = \sum y_i^2 - \frac{\left(\sum y_i\right)^2}{n}.$$

For example, consider the data in Table 11.12 on the next page. If we square each of the eight observed y values and add up the resulting squared values, we find that $\sum y_i^2 = 859.91$. Also, for these data, it has been found that $\sum y_i = 81.7$, $SS_{xy} = -179.6475$, and $SS_{xx} = 1{,}404.355$. It follows that

$$SS_{yy} = \sum y_i^2 - \frac{\left(\sum y_i\right)^2}{n}$$

$$= 859.91 - \frac{81.7^2}{8} = 25.549$$

and

$$SSE = SS_{yy} - \frac{SS_{xy}^2}{SS_{xx}} = 25.549 - \frac{(-179.6475)^2}{1{,}404.355}$$
$$= 25.549 - 22.981 = 2.568.$$

Finally, note that SS_{xy}^2/SS_{xx} equals $b_1 SS_{xx}$. However, we recommend using the first of these expressions, because doing so usually gives less round-off error.

TABLE **11.12**   Data

Observation	x	y
1	28.0	12.4
2	28.0	11.7
3	32.5	12.4
4	39.0	10.8
5	45.9	9.4
6	57.8	9.5
7	58.1	8.0
8	62.5	7.5

Calculating the total, explained, and unexplained variations The **unexplained variation** is the *SSE*, and thus the shortcut formula for the *SSE* is a shortcut formula for the unexplained variation. The quantity SS_{yy} is the **total variation**, and thus the shortcut formula for SS_{yy} is a shortcut formula for the total variation. Lastly, it can be shown that the expression SS_{xy}^2/SS_{xx} equals the **explained variation** and thus is a shortcut formula for this quantity.

CHAPTER SUMMARY

In this chapter, we have discussed the **correlation coefficient (r)** and **simple linear regression analysis**, which relates a **dependent variable** to a single **independent (predictor) variable**. We began by considering the **simple linear regression model**, which employs two parameters: the **slope** and the **y intercept**. We next discussed how to compute the **least squares point estimates** of these parameters and how to use these estimates to calculate a **point estimate of the mean value of the dependent variable** and a **point prediction of an individual value** of the dependent variable. Then, after considering the assumptions behind the simple linear regression model, we discussed **testing**

the significance of the regression relationship (slope), calculating a **confidence interval** for the mean value of the dependent variable, and calculating a **prediction interval** for an individual value of the dependent variable. We next explained several measures of the utility of the simple linear regression model. These include the **simple coefficient of determination** and an **F test for the simple linear model**. We concluded this chapter by discussing using **residual analysis** to detect violations of the regression assumptions. We learned that we can sometimes remedy violations of these assumptions by **transforming** the dependent variable.

GLOSSARY OF TERMS

correlation coefficient (r): A measure of the strength of the linear relationship between x and y that does not depend on the units in which x and y are measured. (page 362)

cross-sectional data: Data that are observed at a single point in time. (page 366)

dependent variable: The variable that is being described, predicted, or controlled. (page 365)

distance value: A measure of the distance between a particular value x_0 of the independent variable x and $\bar{x}$, the average of the previously observed values of x (the centre of the experimental region). (page 387)

experimental region: The range of the previously observed values of the independent variable. (page 378)

independent variable: A variable used to describe, predict, and control the dependent variable. (page 365)

least squares point estimates: The point estimates of the slope and y intercept of the simple linear regression model that minimize the sum of squared residuals. (pages 375–376)

negative autocorrelation: The situation in which positive error terms tend to be followed over time by negative error terms and negative error terms tend to be followed over time by positive error terms. (page 402)

normal plot: A residual plot that is used to check the normality assumption. (page 400)

positive autocorrelation: The situation in which positive error terms tend to be followed over time by positive error terms and negative error terms tend to be followed over time by negative error terms. (page 401)

residual: The difference between the observed value of the dependent variable and the corresponding predicted value of the dependent variable. (pages 374, 396)

residual plot: A plot of the residuals against some criterion. The plot is used to check the validity of one or more regression assumptions. (page 397)

simple coefficient of determination: The proportion of the total variation in the observed values of the dependent variable that is explained by the simple linear regression model. (pages 363, 391)

simple correlation coefficient: A measure of the linear association between two variables. (page 362)

simple linear regression model: An equation that describes the straight-line relationship between a dependent variable and an independent variable. (page 365)

slope (of the simple linear regression model): The change in the mean value of the dependent variable that is associated with a one-unit increase in the value of the independent variable. (page 365)

time series data: Data that are observed in time sequence. (page 401)

y intercept (of the simple linear regression model): The mean value of the dependent variable when the value of the independent variable is 0. (page 365)

IMPORTANT FORMULAS AND TESTS

Simple correlation coefficient: page 362

Testing the significance of the population correlation coefficient: page 364

Simple linear regression model: page 365

Mean square error: page 371

Standard error: page 371

Least squares point estimates of β_0 and β_1: pages 375–376

Least squares line (prediction equation): page 375

The predicted value of y_i: page 375

Sum of squared residuals: pages 375, 413

The residual: page 396

Point estimate of a mean value of y: page 380

Point prediction of an individual value of y: page 308

Sampling distribution of b_1: page 382

Standard error of the estimate b_1: page 382

Testing the significance of the slope: pages 382–383

Confidence interval for the slope: page 383

Testing the significance of the y intercept: page 384

Distance value: page 387

Sampling distribution of $\hat{y}$: page 387

Standard error of $\hat{y}$: pages 387–388

Confidence interval for a mean value of y: page 388

Prediction interval for an individual value of y: page 388

Unexplained variation: page 392

Explained variation: page 392

Total variation: page 392

Simple coefficient of determination: page 392

An F test for the simple linear regression model: page 393

Durbin–Watson test: page 404

connect Practise and learn online with *Connect*. Questions and tables with online data sets are marked with 📌.

SUPPLEMENTARY EXERCISES

11.74 Consider the following data concerning the demand (y) and price (x) of a consumer product.

Demand, y	252	244	241	234	230	223
Price, x	$2.00	$2.20	$2.40	$2.60	$2.80	$3.00

    a. Plot y versus x. Does it seem reasonable to use the simple linear regression model to relate y to x?

    b. Calculate the least squares point estimates of the parameters in the simple linear regression model.

    c. Write the least squares prediction equation. Graph this equation on the plot of y versus x.

    d. Test the significance of the regression relationship between y and x.

    e. Find a point prediction of and a 95 percent prediction interval for the demand corresponding to each of the prices $2.10, $2.75, and $3.10.

11.75 In an article in *Public Roads* (1983), Bissell, Pilkington, Mason, and Woods study bridge safety (measured in accident rates per 100 million vehicles) and the difference between the width of the bridge and the width of the road-way approach (road plus shoulder):[3]

WidthDiff.	−6	−4	−2	0	2	4	6	8	10	12
Accident	120	103	87	72	58	44	31	20	12	7

The Excel output of a simple linear regression analysis relating accident to width difference is as in Figure 11.42 on the next page. Use the Excel output to do the following:

    a. Identify and interpret the least squares point estimate of the slope of the simple linear regression model.

    b. Identify and interpret the p value for testing $H_0: \beta_1 = 0$ versus $H_a: \beta_1 \neq 0$.

    c. Compute and interpret r^2 (eta^2).

---

[3]Source: "Roadway cross section and alignment," by H. H. Bissell, G. B. Pilkington II, J. M. Mason, and D. L. Woods, *Public Roads*, 46 (March 1983), pp. 132–141.

FIGURE 11.42 Excel Output for Exercise 11.75

SUMMARY OUTPUT

Regression Statistics

Multiple R	0.991786163
R Square	0.983639793
Adjusted R Square	0.981594768
Standard Error	5.336268132
Observations	10

ANOVA

	df	SS	MS	F	Significance F
Regression	1	13696.59394	13696.59394	480.9913802	1.97186E-08
Residual	8	227.8060606	28.47575758		
Total	9	13924.4			

	Coefficients	Standard Error	t Stat	P-value	Lower 95%	Upper 95%	Lower 95.0%	Upper 95.0%
Intercept	74.72727273	1.903729846	39.25308671	1.95043E-10	70.33726099	79.11728446	70.33726099	79.11728446
WidthDiff	-6.442424242	0.293751893	-21.93151568	1.97186E-08	-7.11981776	-5.765030725	-7.11981776	-5.765030725

11.76 An organizational behaviour researcher wants to predict job satisfaction with perceived control over the work environment under the hypothesis that those employees who feel that they have greater control over their work will be more satisfied with their jobs. Employees ($n = 25$) completed a self-report survey asking about job satisfaction, measured on a 1 (not at all satisfied) to 10 (completely satisfied) scale, and perceived control, measured on a 1 (no control, told what to do) to 10 (have complete control) scale. The data are reported in Table 11.13.

   a. Calculate the correlation between the control and satisfaction variables.

   b. Use the simple linear regression model and a computer to compute the model. What is the F value of the resulting model?

   c. Based on the regression analysis, how much of the variance in job satisfaction can be predicted by perceived control?

   d. What conclusions can you draw from the study?

11.77 Table 11.14 presents the public and publicly guaranteed external debt for 27 countries according to the World Bank for the second quarter of 2009. Also in Table 11.14 are the 2010 population statistics from the United Nations.

   a. Enter the data into Excel and calculate the correlation between debt and population. What is the value? How would you interpret the correlation?

   b. Analyze the data using regression analysis predicting debt (y) with population (x). How does the multiple R compare to the correlation found in part a?

   c. Calculate the residuals. Which country had the least residual value? Which country had the greatest residual value?

11.78 In analyzing the stock market, we sometimes use the model $y = \beta_0 + \beta_1 x + \varepsilon$ to relate y, the rate of return on a particular stock, to x, the rate of return on the overall stock market. When using this model, we can interpret β_1 to be the percentage point change in the mean (or expected) rate of return on the particular stock that is associated with an increase of one percentage point in the rate of return on the overall stock market.

   If regression analysis can be used to conclude (at a high level of confidence) that β_1 is greater than 1 (for

TABLE 11.13 Perceived Control and Job Satisfaction Data for 25 Employees

Employee	Control	Satisfaction
1	8	10
2	2	5
3	9	6
4	4	7
5	8	8
6	1	5
7	4	4
8	3	1
9	1	2
10	10	9
11	5	5
12	6	7
13	4	3
14	5	2
15	7	10
16	3	1
17	8	9
18	6	5
19	4	6
20	5	7
21	5	8
22	1	3
23	8	6
24	2	4
25	3	5

example, if the 95 percent confidence interval for β_1 is [1.1826, 1.4723]), this indicates that the mean rate of return on the particular stock changes more quickly than the rate of return on the overall stock market. Such a stock is called an *aggressive stock* because gains for such a stock tend to be greater than overall market gains (which occur when the market is bullish). However, losses for such a stock tend to be greater than overall market losses (which occur when the market is bearish). Aggressive stocks should be purchased if you expect the market to rise and avoided if you expect the market to fall.

TABLE **11.14** Public and Publicly Guaranteed External Debt (US$ millions) and Population for 27 Countries

Country	2009Q2	2010 Population
Albania	2,622	3,169
Algeria	3,187	35,423
Bahamas, The	473	346
Bolivia	2,569	10,031
Burkina Faso	1,771	16,287
Cambodia	2,749	15,053
Cameroon	2,002	19,958
China	67,621	1,354,146
Dominica	208	71
Ethiopia	4,365	84,976
Georgia	2,980	4,219
Ghana	4,704	24,333
Guatemala	4,784	14,377
Honduras	2,457	7,616
Kenya	7,038	40,863
Lebanon	21,103	4,255
Madagascar	2,174	20,146
Nepal	3,577	29,853
Nigeria	3,719	158,259
Pakistan	42,264	184,753
Panama	8,907	3,508
Rwanda	704	10,277
Sri Lanka	15,437	20,410
Tajikistan	1,473	7,075
Tonga	103	104
Uganda	2,046	33,796
Yemen	5,920	24,256

Debt data are in millions.
Population data are in thousands.

Source: This table has been adapted from The World Bank Table C1-Public and Publicly-Guaranteed External Debt Position (US$ millions), http://ddp-ext.worldbank.org/ext/ddpreports/ViewSharedReport?REPORT_ID=10836&REQUEST_TYPE=VIEW; and The United Nations Statistics Division Social Indicators: Indicators on Population, http://unstats.un.org/unsd/demographic/products/socind/population.htm

If regression analysis can be used to conclude (at a high level of confidence) that β_1 is less than 1 (for example, if the 95 percent confidence interval for β_1 is [0.4729, 0.7861]), this indicates that the mean rate of return on the particular stock changes more slowly than the rate of return on the overall stock market. Such a stock is called a *defensive stock*. Losses for such a stock tend to be less than overall market losses, whereas gains for such a stock tend to be less than overall market gains. Defensive stocks should be held if you expect the market to fall and sold if you expect the market to rise.

If the least squares point estimate b_1 of β_1 is nearly equal to 1, and if the 95 percent confidence interval for β_1 contains 1, this might indicate that the mean rate of return on the particular stock changes at roughly the same rate as the rate of return on the overall stock market. Such a stock is called a *neutral stock*.

In a 1984 article in *Financial Analysts Journal*, Levy considers how a stock's value of β_1 depends on the length of time for which the rate of return is calculated. Levy calculated estimated values of β_1 for return length times varying from 1 to 30 months for each of 38 aggressive stocks, 38 defensive stocks, and 68 neutral stocks. Each estimated value was based on data from 1946 to 1975. In the following table, we present the average estimate of β_1 for each stock type for different return length times:

	Average Estimate of β_1 🏹		
Return Length Time	Aggressive Stocks	Defensive Stocks	Neutral Stocks
1	1.37	0.50	0.98
3	1.42	0.44	0.95
6	1.53	0.41	0.94
9	1.69	0.39	1.00
12	1.83	0.40	0.98
15	1.67	0.38	1.00
18	1.78	0.39	1.02
24	1.86	0.35	1.14
30	1.83	0.33	1.22

Source: Reprinted by permission from "Measuring risk and performance over alternative investment horizons," by H. Levy, *Financial Analysts Journal* (March–April 1984), pp. 61–68. Copyright © 1984, CFA Institute. Reproduced and modified from *Financial Analysts Journal* with permission of CFA Institute.

Let y = average estimate of β_1 and x = return length time, and consider relating y to x for each stock type by using the simple linear regression model

$$y = \beta_0^* + \beta_1^* x + \varepsilon.$$

Here β_0^* and β_1^* are regression parameters relating y to x. We use the asterisks to indicate that these regression parameters are different from β_0 and β_1. Calculate a 95 percent confidence interval for β_1^* for each stock type. Carefully interpret each interval.

11.79 INTERNET EXERCISE

Organizations that depend on volunteers can gain information about the age, income, and other personal characteristics of people and the average number of hours that these people volunteer from the statistics reported by Statistics Canada. Go to the data file at http://www40.statcan.gc.ca/l01/cst01/famil103.htm. In Excel, enter the age groups from 1 to 6 (15–24 is group 1 and 65 and older is group 6) in the first column. In the second column, enter the corresponding average number of hours. Compute the correlation between age and average hours. What does this value tell you? Compute r^2 (eta^2) from the correlation. What can you conclude from this value? Also run a linear regression analysis with average hours as the dependent (y) variable and age as the independent (x) variable. What does the result of the regression analysis tell you? If you were asked by volunteer organizations which age groups to target to look for volunteers, which group would you suggest?

CHAPTER **12**

Multiple Regression

LEARNING OBJECTIVES

After reading this chapter, you should be able to

LO1 describe the experimental region in a multiple regression

LO2 list the assumptions for the multiple regression model

LO3 explain what is meant by the least squares point estimate of a model parameter

LO4 define the multiple coefficient of determination

LO5 compute an *F* test from the results output

LO6 distinguish between a confidence interval and a prediction interval for *y*

CHAPTER OUTLINE

Part 1 Basic Multiple Regression

12.1 The Multiple Regression Model

12.2 Model Assumptions and the Standard Error

12.3 The Least Squares Estimates, and Point Estimation and Prediction

12.4 R^2 and Adjusted R^2

12.5 The Overall *F* Test

12.6 Testing the Significance of an Independent Variable

12.7 Confidence and Prediction Intervals

Part 2 Using Squared and Interaction Terms (Optional)

12.8 The Quadratic Regression Model (Optional)

12.9 Interaction (Optional)

Part 3 Dummy Variables and Advanced Statistical Inferences (Optional)

12.10 Using Dummy Variables to Model Qualitative Independent Variables (Optional)

12.11 The Partial *F* Test: Testing the Significance of a Portion of a Regression Model (Optional)

Important Note:

Part 1 of this chapter covers basic multiple regression analysis and is the only prerequisite for Optional Parts 2 and 3. Parts 2 and 3 cover more advanced regression topics and can be read independently of each other. They can be read in any order without loss of continuity.

Often we can more accurately describe, predict, and control a dependent variable by using a regression model that employs more than one independent variable, such as when deciding on whom to hire for a position. In this situation, multiple pieces of information are preferable to a single question and answer. For example, a job candidate's past employment experience may be a good indicator of future work behaviour. If an interviewer can also add information such as a work sample or personality–job fit measures, then the hiring decision will be more sound. Such a model is called a **multiple regression model**, which is the subject of this chapter.

In order to explain the ideas of this chapter, we consider the following two cases:

The Sales Territory Performance Case: A sales manager evaluates the performance of sales representatives by using a multiple regression model that predicts sales performance on the basis of five independent variables. Salespeople whose actual performance is far worse than predicted performance will get extra training to help improve their sales techniques.

The Fresh Detergent Case: Enterprise Industries predicts future demand for Fresh liquid laundry detergent by using a multiple regression model that employs as independent variables the advertising expenditures used to promote Fresh and the difference between the price of Fresh and the average price of competing detergents.

Connect Practise and learn online with *Connect*. Throughout this chapter, questions and tables with online data sets are marked with ✈.

12.1 THE MULTIPLE REGRESSION MODEL

PART 1
Basic Multiple
Regression

Regression models that employ more than one independent variable are called **multiple regression models**.

Part 1: The data and a regression model In Chapter 11, we used a single predictor variable x to predict y. We now consider predicting y using an additional variable, x_2.

Consider the data in Table 12.1. Figure 12.1 presents a scatter plot of y versus x_1. This plot shows that y tends to decrease in a straight-line fashion as x_1 increases. This suggests that if we wish to predict y on the basis of x_1 only, the simple linear regression model

CHAPTER 17

$$y = \beta_0 + \beta_1 x_1 + \varepsilon$$

relates y to x_1. Figure 12.2 presents a scatter plot of y versus x_2. This plot shows that y tends to increase in a straight-line fashion as x_2 increases. This suggests that if we wish to predict y on the basis of x_2 only, the simple linear regression model

$$y = \beta_0 + \beta_1 x_2 + \varepsilon$$

relates y to x_2. If we wish to predict y on the basis of both x_1 and x_2, it seems reasonable to combine these models to form the model

$$y = \beta_0 + \beta_1 x_1 + \beta_2 x_2 + \varepsilon$$

to relate y to x_1 and x_2. Here we have arbitrarily placed the $\beta_1 x_1$ term first and the $\beta_2 x_2$ term second, and we have renumbered β_1 and β_2 to be consistent with the subscripts on x_1 and x_2. This regression model says that

1 β_0, β_1, and β_2 are regression parameters relating the mean value of y to x_1 and x_2.

2 ε is an error term that describes the effects on y of all factors other than x_1 and x_2.

TABLE 12.1
Sample Data

x_1	x_2	y
28.0	18	12.4
28.0	14	11.7
32.5	24	12.4
39.0	22	10.8
45.9	8	9.4
57.8	16	9.5
58.1	1	8.0
62.5	0	7.5

FIGURE 12.1 Plot of y versus x_1

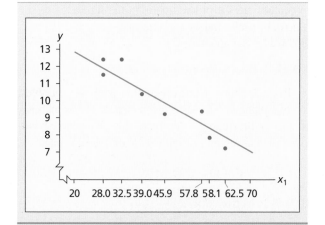

FIGURE 12.2 Plot of y versus x_2

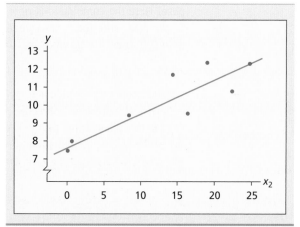

When predicting y with x_1 and x_2, ideally the correlations between y and x_1 and between y and x_2 will both be high (in either the positive or negative direction), resulting in greater prediction of y. A concern in multiple regression models is when the relationship between x_1 and x_2 is high. In a perfect world, the correlation between x_1 and x_2 would be zero so that when both were entered into a multiple regression equation, each would predict a unique proportion of the variance in y. Typically the correlation between x_1 and x_2 is not zero, resulting in some overlap between x_1 and x_2. If the correlation between x_1 and x_2 is too high, then there is evidence of **multicollinearity** and either x_1 or x_2 is redundant. Therefore, before a multiple regression analysis is conducted, the correlations between y, x_1, and x_2 should be examined.

Part 2: Interpreting the regression parameters β_0, β_1, and β_2 The exact interpretations of the parameters β_0, β_1, and β_2 are quite simple. First suppose that $x_1 = 0$ and $x_2 = 0$. Then

$$\beta_0 + \beta_1 x_1 + \beta_2 x_2 = \beta_0 + \beta_1(0) + \beta_2(0) = \beta_0.$$

So β_0 is the mean y value when $x_1 = 0$ and $x_2 = 0$. The parameter β_0 is called the **intercept** in the regression model. One might wonder whether β_0 has any practical interpretation, since it might be unlikely for x_1 and x_2 to equal zero. Indeed, sometimes the parameter β_0 and other parameters in a regression analysis do not have practical interpretations because the situations related to the interpretations are not likely to occur in practice. In fact, sometimes each parameter does not, by itself, have much practical importance. Rather, the parameters relate the mean of the dependent variable to the independent variables in an overall sense.

We next interpret β_1 and β_2 individually. To examine the interpretation of β_1, consider two observations. Suppose that for x_1, the value is c, and for x_2, the value is d. The mean y value is then

$$\beta_0 + \beta_1(c) + \beta_2(d).$$

For the second observation, suppose that the x_1 value is $c + 1$ and the x_2 value is d. The mean y value is

$$\beta_0 + \beta_1(c + 1) + \beta_2(d).$$

It is easy to see that the difference between these mean y values is β_1 because the two observations only differ in that x_1 is one greater in the second observation than in the first. In the following, we can interpret the parameter β_1 as the mean change in y associated with a one-point increase in x_1 (note that x_2 did not change in value).

The interpretation of β_2 can be established similarly. We can interpret β_2 as the change in mean y values that is associated with a one-unit increase in x_2 when x_1 does not change.

LO1

Part 3: A geometric interpretation of the regression model To interpret a multiple regression model geometrically, we begin by defining the **experimental region** to be the range of the combinations of the observed values of x_1 and x_2. From the data in Table 12.1, it is reasonable to depict the experimental region as the shaded region in Figure 12.3 on the next page. Here the combinations of x_1 and x_2 values are the ordered pairs in the figure.

We next write the mean value of y when IV_1 (independent variable one) is x_1 and IV_2 is x_2 as $\mu_{y|x_1, x_2}$ (mu of y given x_1 and x_2) and consider the equation

$$\mu_{y|x_1, x_2} = \beta_0 + \beta_1 x_1 + \beta_2 x_2,$$

which relates mean y values to x_1 and x_2. Because this is a linear equation with two variables, geometrically this equation is the equation of a plane in three-dimensional space. We sometimes refer to this plane as the **plane of means**, and we illustrate the portion of this plane corresponding to the (x_1, x_2) combinations in the experimental region in Figure 12.4 on the next page. As illustrated in this figure, the model

$$y = \mu_{y|x_1, x_2} + \varepsilon$$
$$= \beta_0 + \beta_1 x_1 + \beta_2 x_2 + \varepsilon$$

FIGURE **12.3** The Experimental Region

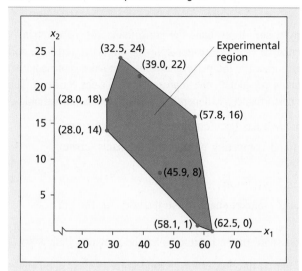

FIGURE **12.4** A Geometrical Interpretation of the Regression Model Relating y to x_1 and x_2

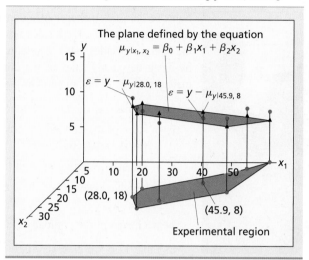

says that the error terms cause the observed y values (the red dots in the upper portion of the figure) to deviate from the mean y values (the triangles in the figure), which lie exactly on the plane of means

$$\mu_{y|x_1, x_2} = \beta_0 + \beta_1 x_1 + \beta_2 x_2.$$

For example, consider the first row of data in Table 12.1 ($y = 12.4$, $x_1 = 28.0$, $x_2 = 18$). Figure 12.4 shows that the error term for this observation is positive, causing y to be higher than $\mu_{y|28.0, 18}$ (mean y value when $x_1 = 28.0$ and $x_2 = 18$). Here factors other than x_1 and x_2 have resulted in a positive error term. As another example, the error term for row 5 in Table 12.1 ($y = 9.4$, $x_1 = 45.9$, $x_2 = 8$) is negative, so y is lower than $\mu_{y|45.9, 8}$ (mean y value when $x_1 = 45.9$ and $x_2 = 8$). Here factors other than x_1 and x_2 have resulted in a negative error term.

The model above expresses the dependent variable as a function of two independent variables. In general, we can use a multiple regression model to express a dependent variable as a function of any number of independent variables. For example, hiring decisions could be based on four independent variables, such as education, past work experience, personality, and a current work sample. The general form of a multiple regression model expresses the dependent variable y as a function of k independent variables $x_1, x_2, \ldots, x_k$. We express this general form in the following box. Here we assume that we have obtained n observations, with each observation consisting of an observed value of y and corresponding observed values of $x_1, x_2, \ldots, x_k$.

The Multiple Regression Model

The multiple regression model relating y to x_1, $x_2, \ldots, x_k$ is

$$y = \mu_{y|x_1, x_2, \ldots, x_k} + \varepsilon$$
$$= \beta_0 + \beta_1 x_1 + \beta_2 x_2 + \cdots + \beta_k x_k + \varepsilon.$$

Here

1 $\mu_{y|x_1, x_2, \ldots, x_k} = \beta_0 + \beta_1 x_1 + \beta_2 x_2 + \cdots + \beta_k x_k$ is the mean value of the dependent variable y when

the values of the independent variables are $x_1, x_2, \ldots, x_k$.

2 $\beta_0, \beta_1, \beta_2, \ldots, \beta_k$ are (unknown) **regression parameters** relating the mean value of y to x_1, $x_2, \ldots, x_k$.

3 ε is an **error term** that describes the effects on y of all factors other than the values of the independent variables $x_1, x_2, \ldots, x_k$.

Example 12.1 The Sales Territory Performance Case

Suppose the sales manager of a company wishes to evaluate the performance of the company's sales representatives. Each sales representative is solely responsible for one sales territory, and the manager decides that it is reasonable to measure the performance, y, of a sales representative by using the yearly sales of the company's product in the representative's sales territory. The manager wants to investigate how sales performance, y, depends on five independent variables:

x_1 = number of months the representative has been employed by the company,

x_2 = sales of the company's product and competing products in the sales territory (market potential),

x_3 = dollar advertising expenditure in the territory,

x_4 = weighted average of the company's market share in the territory for the previous four years,

x_5 = change in the company's market share in the territory over the previous four years.

In Table 12.2, we present values of y and x_1 through x_5 for 25 randomly selected sales representatives. To understand the values of y and x_2 in the table, note that sales of the company's product or any competing product are measured in hundreds of units of the product sold. Therefore, for example, the first sales figure of 3,669.88 in Table 12.2 means that the first randomly selected sales representative sold 366,988 units of the company's product during the year.

Plots of y versus x_1 through x_5 are given beside Table 12.2. Because each plot has an approximate straight-line appearance, it is reasonable to relate y to x_1 through x_5 by using the regression model

$$y = \beta_0 + \beta_1 x_1 + \beta_2 x_2 + \beta_3 x_3 + \beta_4 x_4 + \beta_5 x_5 + \varepsilon.$$

TABLE 12.2   Sales Territory Performance Study Data 🖋

Sales, y	Time with Company, x_1	Market Potential, x_2	Advertising, x_3	Market Share, x_4	Market Share Change, x_5
3,669.88	43.10	74,065.11	4,582.88	2.51	0.34
3,473.95	108.13	58,117.30	5,539.78	5.51	0.15
2,295.10	13.82	21,118.49	2,950.38	10.91	−0.72
4,675.56	186.18	68,521.27	2,243.07	8.27	0.17
6,125.96	161.79	57,805.11	7,747.08	9.15	0.50
2,134.94	8.94	37,806.94	402.44	5.51	0.15
5,031.66	365.04	50,935.26	3,140.62	8.54	0.55
3,367.45	220.32	35,602.08	2,086.16	7.07	−0.49
6,519.45	127.64	46,176.77	8,846.25	12.54	1.24
4,876.37	105.69	42,053.24	5,673.11	8.85	0.31
2,468.27	57.72	36,829.71	2,761.76	5.38	0.37
2,533.31	23.58	33,612.67	1,991.85	5.43	−0.65
2,408.11	13.82	21,412.79	1,971.52	8.48	0.64
2,337.38	13.82	20,416.87	1,737.38	7.80	1.01
4,586.95	86.99	36,272.00	10,694.20	10.34	0.11
2,729.24	165.85	23,093.26	8,618.61	5.15	0.04
3,289.40	116.26	26,878.59	7,747.89	6.64	0.68
2,800.78	42.28	39,571.96	4,565.81	5.45	0.66
3,264.20	52.84	51,866.15	6,022.70	6.31	−0.10
3,453.62	165.04	58,749.82	3,721.10	6.35	−0.03
1,741.45	10.57	23,990.82	860.97	7.37	−1.63
2,035.75	13.82	25,694.86	3,571.51	8.39	−0.43
1,578.00	8.13	23,736.35	2,845.50	5.15	0.04
4,167.44	58.54	34,314.29	5,060.11	12.88	0.22
2,799.97	21.14	22,809.53	3,552.00	9.14	−0.74

Plots (beside table, top to bottom): Sales vs Time; Sales vs MktPoten; Sales vs Adver; Sales vs MktShare; Sales vs Change

Source: This data set is from a research study published in "An analytical approach for evaluation of sales territory performance," by David W. Cravens, Robert B. Woodruff, and Joseph C. Stamper, *Journal of Marketing*, January 1972, 31–37. We have updated the situation in our case study to be more modern.

Here, $\mu_{y|x_1, x_2, \ldots, x_5} = \beta_0 + \beta_1 x_1 + \beta_2 x_2 + \beta_3 x_3 + \beta_4 x_4 + \beta_5 x_5$ is the mean sales in all sales territories, where the values of the five independent variables are x_1, x_2, x_3, x_4, and x_5. Furthermore, for example, the parameter β_3 equals the increase in mean sales that is associated with a \$1 increase in advertising expenditure (x_3) when the other four independent variables do not change. The main objective of the regression analysis is to help the sales manager evaluate sales performance by comparing actual performance to predicted performance.

Exercises for Section 12.1

CONCEPTS

For Exercises 12.1 through 12.5, consider the multiple regression model

$$y = \mu_{y|x_1, x_2, \ldots, x_k} + \varepsilon$$
$$= \beta_0 + \beta_1 x_1 + \beta_2 x_2 + \cdots + \beta_k x_k + \varepsilon.$$

12.1 What is y? What are $x_1, x_2, \ldots, x_k$?

12.2 Interpret $\mu_{y|x_1, x_2, \ldots, x_k}$.

12.3 What are $\beta_0, \beta_1, \beta_2, \ldots, \beta_k$?

12.4 What does the error term ε describe?

12.5 In your own words, interpret β_0, β_1, and β_2.

METHODS AND APPLICATIONS

12.6 THE WORK ATTENDANCE CASE

A human resources manager conducts a small study to examine factors that might predict employee attendance. For ten employees, the manager collects the following information:

y = attendance (in percentage of days worked),

x_1 = job satisfaction (from an opinion survey with 1 = not satisfied to 10 = very satisfied),

x_2 = commuting distance (in kilometres).

The data and data plots are provided in Table 12.3. Using these data, the manager plans to test the following model:

$$y = \mu_{y|x_1, x_2} + \varepsilon$$
$$= \beta_0 + \beta_1 x_1 + \beta_2 x_2 + \varepsilon.$$

a. Discuss why the data plots given below Table 12.3 indicate that this model might be reasonable.

b. Interpret

$$\mu_{y|x_1 = 2, x_2 = 9} = \beta_0 + \beta_1(2) + \beta_2(9).$$

c. Interpret β_0, β_1, and β_2.

d. What factors are represented by the error term in this model? Give a specific example of these factors.

12.7 THE FRESH DETERGENT CASE

Enterprise Industries produces Fresh, a brand of liquid laundry detergent. In order to more effectively manage its inventory and make revenue projections, the company would like to better predict demand for Fresh. To develop a prediction model, the company has gathered data concerning demand for Fresh over the last 30 sales periods (each sales period is defined to be a four-week

TABLE **12.3** The Work Attendance Data

Attendance (y)	Job Satisfaction (x_1)	Commuting Distance (x_2)
66	3	12
100	8	5
78	5	9
95	9	7
82	7	11
97	7	6
87	6	13
71	4	8
73	6	6
81	7	3

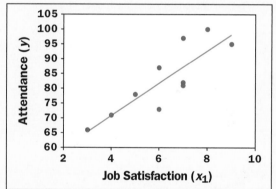

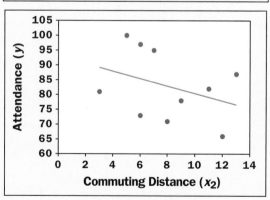

period). The demand data are presented in Table 12.4 on the next page. Here, for each sales period,

y = the demand for the large bottle of Fresh (in hundreds of thousands of bottles) in the sales period,

x_1 = the price (in dollars) of Fresh as offered by Enterprise Industries in the sales period,

TABLE **12.4**   Historical Data Concerning Demand for Fresh Detergent ✈

Sales Period	Price for Fresh, x_1	Average Industry Price, x_2	Price Difference, $x_4 = x_2 - x_1$	Advertising Expenditure for Fresh, x_3	Demand for Fresh, y	Sales Period	Price for Fresh, x_1	Average Industry Price, x_2	Price Difference, $x_4 = x_2 - x_1$	Advertising Expenditure for Fresh, x_3	Demand for Fresh, y
1	3.85	3.80	−0.05	5.50	7.38	16	3.80	4.10	0.30	6.80	8.87
2	3.75	4.00	0.25	6.75	8.51	17	3.70	4.20	0.50	7.10	9.26
3	3.70	4.30	0.60	7.25	9.52	18	3.80	4.30	0.50	7.00	9.00
4	3.70	3.70	0	5.50	7.50	19	3.70	4.10	0.40	6.80	8.75
5	3.60	3.85	0.25	7.00	9.33	20	3.80	3.75	−0.05	6.50	7.95
6	3.60	3.80	0.20	6.50	8.28	21	3.80	3.75	−0.05	6.25	7.65
7	3.60	3.75	0.15	6.75	8.75	22	3.75	3.65	−0.10	6.00	7.27
8	3.80	3.85	0.05	5.25	7.87	23	3.70	3.90	0.20	6.50	8.00
9	3.80	3.65	−0.15	5.25	7.10	24	3.55	3.65	0.10	7.00	8.50
10	3.85	4.00	0.15	6.00	8.00	25	3.60	4.10	0.50	6.80	8.75
11	3.90	4.10	0.20	6.50	7.89	26	3.65	4.25	0.60	6.80	9.21
12	3.90	4.00	0.10	6.25	8.15	27	3.70	3.65	−0.05	6.50	8.27
13	3.70	4.10	0.40	7.00	9.10	28	3.75	3.75	0	5.75	7.67
14	3.75	4.20	0.45	6.90	8.86	29	3.80	3.85	0.05	5.80	7.93
15	3.75	4.10	0.35	6.80	8.90	30	3.70	4.25	0.55	6.80	9.26

TABLE **12.5**   Hospital Labour Needs Data ✈

Hospital	Monthly X-Ray Exposures, x_1	Monthly Occupied Bed Days, x_2	Average Length of Stay, x_3	Monthly Labour Hours Required, y
1	2,463	472.92	4.45	566.52
2	2,048	1,339.75	6.92	696.82
3	3,940	620.25	4.28	1,033.15
4	6,505	568.33	3.90	1,603.62
5	5,723	1,497.60	5.50	1,611.37
6	11,520	1,365.83	4.60	1,613.27
7	5,779	1,687.00	5.62	1,854.17
8	5,969	1,639.92	5.15	2,160.55
9	8,461	2,872.33	6.18	2,305.58
10	20,106	3,655.08	6.15	3,503.93
11	13,313	2,912.00	5.88	3,571.89
12	10,771	3,921.00	4.88	3,741.40
13	15,543	3,865.67	5.50	4,026.52
14	34,703	12,446.33	10.78	11,732.17
15	39,204	14,098.40	7.05	15,414.94
16	86,533	15,524.00	6.35	18,854.45

Source: *Procedures and Analysis for Staffing Standards Development Regression Analysis Handbook* (San Diego, CA: Navy Manpower and Material Analysis Center, 1979).

x_2 = the average industry price (in dollars) of competitors' similar detergents in the sales period,

x_3 = Enterprise Industries' advertising expenditure (in hundreds of thousands of dollars) to promote Fresh in the sales period,

$x_4 = x_2 - x_1$ = the "price difference" in the sales period.

Consider relating y to x_1, x_2, and x_3 by using the model

$$y = \beta_0 + \beta_1 x_1 + \beta_2 x_2 + \beta_3 x_3 + \varepsilon.$$

a. Discuss why the data plots given under Table 12.4 indicate that this model might be reasonable.

b. Interpret

$\mu_{y|x_1 = 3.70,\, x_2 = 3.90,\, x_3 = 6.50}$

$\quad = \beta_0 + \beta_1(3.70) + \beta_2(3.90) + \beta_3(6.50).$

c. Interpret β_0, β_1, β_2, β_3, and ε in the model.

d. Discuss why the data plots given under Table 12.4 indicate that it might be reasonable to use the alternative model

$$y = \beta_0 + \beta_1 x_4 + \beta_2 x_3 + \varepsilon.$$

12.8   THE HOSPITAL LABOUR NEEDS CASE

Table 12.5 on the previous page presents data concerning the need for labour in 16 hospitals. Here

y = monthly labour hours required,

x_1 = monthly X-ray exposures,

x_2 = monthly occupied bed days (a hospital has one occupied bed day if one bed is occupied for an entire day),

x_3 = average length of patients' stay (in days).

The main objective of the regression analysis is to evaluate the performance of hospitals in terms of how many labour hours are used relative to how many labour hours are needed. Sixteen efficiently run hospitals are selected and a regression model based on efficiently run hospitals is created to evaluate the efficiency of other hospitals. Consider relating y to x_1, x_2, and x_3 by using the model

$$y = \beta_0 + \beta_1 x_1 + \beta_2 x_2 + \beta_3 x_3 + \varepsilon.$$

Discuss why the data plots given beside Table 12.5 indicate that this model might be reasonable. Interpret $\beta_0, \beta_1, \beta_2, \beta_3$, and ε in this model.

12.2 MODEL ASSUMPTIONS AND THE STANDARD ERROR

Model assumptions   In order to perform hypothesis tests and set up various types of intervals when using the multiple regression model

$$y = \beta_0 + \beta_1 x_1 + \beta_2 x_2 + \cdots + \beta_k x_k + \varepsilon,$$

we need to make certain assumptions about the error term ε. At any given combination of values of $x_1, x_2, \ldots, x_k$, there is a population of error term values that could potentially occur. These error term values describe the different potential effects on y of all factors other than the combination of values of $x_1, x_2, \ldots, x_k$. Therefore, these error term values explain the variation in the y values that could be observed at the combination of values of $x_1, x_2, \ldots, x_k$. We make the following four assumptions about the potential error term values:

Assumptions for the Multiple Regression Model

1   **Mean error value assumption:** At any given combination of values of $x_1, x_2, \ldots, x_k$, the population of potential error term values has a mean equal to 0.

2   **Constant-variance assumption:** At any given combination of values of $x_1, x_2, \ldots, x_k$, the population of potential error term values has a variance that does not depend on the combination of values of $x_1, x_2, \ldots, x_k$. That is, the different populations of potential error term values corresponding to different combinations of values of $x_1, x_2, \ldots, x_k$ have equal variances. We denote the constant variance as σ^2.

3   **Normality assumption:** At any given combination of values of $x_1, x_2, \ldots, x_k$, the population of potential error term values has a *normal distribution*.

4   **Independence assumption:** Any one value of the error term ε is *statistically independent* of any other value of ε. That is, the value of the error term ε corresponding to an observed value of y is statistically independent of the error term corresponding to any other observed value of y.

Taken together, the first three assumptions say that at any given combination of values of x_1, $x_2, \ldots, x_k$, the population of potential error term values is normally distributed with mean 0 and a variance σ^2 that does not depend on the combination of values of $x_1, x_2, \ldots, x_k$. Because the potential error term values cause the variation in the potential y values, the first three assumptions imply that at any given combination of values of $x_1, x_2, \ldots, x_k$, the population of y values that could be observed is normally distributed with mean $\beta_0 + \beta_1 x_1 + \beta_2 x_2 + \cdots + \beta_k x_k$ and a variance σ^2 that does not depend on the combination of values of $x_1, x_2, \ldots, x_k$. Furthermore, the independence assumption says that when time series data are utilized in a regression study, there are no patterns in the error term values. As in simple linear regression, only pronounced departures from the assumptions must be remedied.

LO2

The mean square error and the standard error   To present statistical inference formulas in later sections, we need to be able to compute point estimates of σ^2 and σ (the constant variance and standard deviation of the different error term populations). We show how to do this in the following box:

The Mean Square Error and the Standard Error

Suppose that the multiple regression model

$$y = \beta_0 + \beta_1 x_1 + \beta_2 x_2 + \cdots + \beta_k x_k + \varepsilon$$

utilizes k independent variables and thus has $(k + 1)$ parameters $\beta_0, \beta_1, \beta_2, \ldots, \beta_k$. Then, if the regression assumptions are satisfied and if the SSE is the sum of squared residuals for the model:

1   A point estimate of σ^2 is the **mean square error**

$$s^2 = \frac{SSE}{n - (k + 1)}.$$

2   A point estimate of σ is the **standard error**

$$s = \sqrt{\frac{SSE}{n - (k + 1)}}.$$

In order to explain these point estimates, recall that σ^2 is the variance of the population of y values (for given values of $x_1, x_2, \ldots, x_k$) around the mean value $\mu_{y|x_1, x_2, \ldots, x_k}$. Because $\hat{y}$ is the point estimate of this mean, we use $SSE = \Sigma(y_i - \hat{y}_i)^2$ to help construct a point estimate of σ^2. We divide the SSE by $n - (k + 1)$ because doing so makes the resulting s^2 an unbiased point estimate of σ^2. We call $n - (k + 1)$ the **number of degrees of freedom** associated with the SSE.

We will see in Section 12.7 that if a particular regression model gives a small standard error, then the model will give short prediction intervals and thus accurate predictions of individual y values. For example, for Table 12.6 (page 428) the SSE for the model

$$y = \beta_0 + \beta_1 x_1 + \beta_2 x_2 + \varepsilon$$

is 0.674. This model utilizes $k = 2$ independent variables and thus has $k + 1 = 3$ parameters (β_0, β_1, and β_2), so a point estimate of σ^2 is the mean square error

$$s^2 = \frac{SSE}{n - (k + 1)} = \frac{0.674}{8 - 3} = \frac{0.674}{5} = 0.1348,$$

and a point estimate of σ is the standard error $s = \sqrt{0.1348} = 0.3671$.

As another example, the SSE for the sales territory performance model

$$y = \beta_0 + \beta_1 x_1 + \beta_2 x_2 + \beta_3 x_3 + \beta_4 x_4 + \beta_5 x_5 + \varepsilon$$

is 3,516,890.0266. This model utilizes $k = 5$ independent variables and thus has $k + 1 = 6$ parameters. A point estimate of σ^2 is the mean square error

$$s^2 = \frac{SSE}{n - (k + 1)} = \frac{3,516,890.0266}{25 - 6} = 185,099.4751,$$

and a point estimate of σ is the standard error $s = \sqrt{185,099.4751} = 430.2319$. Note that these values of the SSE, s^2, and s are given on the MegaStat output in Figure 12.7 (page 430).

12.3 THE LEAST SQUARES ESTIMATES, AND POINT ESTIMATION AND PREDICTION

The regression parameters $\beta_0, \beta_1, \beta_2, \ldots, \beta_k$ in the multiple regression model are unknown. Therefore, they must be estimated from data (observations of $y, x_1, x_2, \ldots, x_k$). To see how we might do this, let $b_0, b_1, b_2, \ldots, b_k$ denote point estimates of the unknown parameters. Then a point prediction of an observed value of the dependent variable

$$y = \beta_0 + \beta_1 x_1 + \beta_2 x_2 + \cdots + \beta_k x_k + \varepsilon$$

is

$$\hat{y} = b_0 + b_1 x_1 + b_2 x_2 + \cdots + b_k x_k,$$

LO3

which is called the **least squares prediction equation**. It is obtained by replacing β_0, β_1, and β_2 by their estimates b_0, b_1, and b_2. You will notice that the error term is not present in this equation. One of the assumptions in the regression model is that the expected value of the error term is 0 (more regression assumptions were discussed in Section 12.2). Next, let y_i and $\hat{y}_i$ denote the observed and predicted values of the dependent variable for the ith observation, and define the **residual** for the ith observation to be $e_i = y_i - \hat{y}_i$. We then consider the **sum of squared residuals**

$$SSE = \sum_{i=1}^{n} (y_i - \hat{y}_i)^2.$$

If any particular values of b_0, b_1, b_2, . . . , b_k are good point estimates, they will make (for $i = 1$, 2, . . . , n) the predicted value $\hat{y}_i$ fairly close to the observed value y_i and thus will make the SSE fairly small. We define the **least squares point estimates** to be the values of b_0, b_1, b_2, . . . , b_k that minimize the SSE.

It can be shown that a formula exists for computing the least squares point estimates of the parameters in the multiple regression model. This formula is written using a branch of mathematics called **matrix algebra** and is presented in Appendix F on *Connect*. In practice, the least squares point estimates can easily be computed using many standard statistical computer packages. In our discussion of multiple regression here, we will rely on Excel and MegaStat to compute the needed estimates.

Example 12.2 The Sample Data in Table 12.1

Part 1: The least squares point estimates Consider the model of the data in Table 12.1 (reproduced in the margin):

$$y = \beta_0 + \beta_1 x_1 + \beta_2 x_2 + \varepsilon.$$

The Excel output in Figure 12.5 on the next page tells us that if we use the data to calculate the least squares point estimates of the parameters β_0, β_1, and β_2, we obtain $b_0 = 13.1087$, $b_1 = -0.0900$, and $b_2 = 0.0825$.

The point estimate $b_1 = -0.0900$ of β_1 says we estimate that y decreases (b_1 is negative) by 0.0900 when x_1 increases by one and x_2 does not change. The point estimate $b_2 = 0.0825$ of β_2 says we estimate that y increases (b_2 is positive) by 0.0825 when there is a one-unit increase in x_2 and x_1 does not change.

The equation

$$\hat{y} = b_0 + b_1 x_1 + b_2 x_2$$
$$= 13.1087 - 0.0900 x_1 + 0.0825 x_2$$

is the least squares prediction equation. We can use this equation to compute a prediction for any observed value of y. For instance, a point prediction of $y_1 = 12.4$ (when $x_1 = 28.0$ and $x_2 = 18$) is

$$\hat{y}_1 = 13.1087 - 0.0900(28.0) + 0.0825(18)$$
$$= 12.0737.$$

This results in a residual equal to

$$e_1 = y_1 - \hat{y}_1 = 12.4 - 12.0737 = 0.3263.$$

Table 12.6 on the next page gives the point prediction obtained using the least squares prediction equation and the residual for each of the eight observed y values. In addition, this table tells us

Sample Data		
x_1	x_2	y
28.0	18	12.4
28.0	14	11.7
32.5	24	12.4
39.0	22	10.8
45.9	8	9.4
57.8	16	9.5
58.1	1	8.0
62.5	0	7.5

FIGURE **12.5**   Excel Output of a Regression Analysis of the Data in
Table 12.1 Using the Model $y = \beta_0 + \beta_1 x_1 + \beta_2 x_2 + \varepsilon$

Regression Statistics

Multiple R	0.9867
R Square	0.9736 [8]
Adjusted R Square	0.9631 [9]
Standard Error	0.3671 [7]
Observations	8

ANOVA

	df	SS	MS	F	Significance F
Regression	2	24.8750 [10]	12.4375	92.3031 [13]	0.0001 [14]
Residual	5	0.6737 [11]	0.1347		
Total	7	25.5488 [12]			

	Coefficients	Standard Error [4]	t Stat [5]	P-value [6]	Lower 95% [15]	Upper 95% [15]
Intercept	13.1087 [1]	0.8557	15.3193	2.15E-05	10.9091	15.3084
X1	-0.0900 [2]	0.0141	-6.3942	0.0014	-0.1262	-0.0538
X2	0.0825 [3]	0.0220	3.7493	0.0133	0.0259	0.1391

[1] b_0 [2] b_1 [3] b_2 [4] s_{b_j} = standard error of the estimate b_j	[5] t statistics	[6] p values for t statistics	[7] s = standard error
[8] R^2 [9] Adjusted R^2 [10] Explained variation	[11] SSE = unexplained variation	[12] Total variation	[13] F(model) statistic
[14] p value for F(model) [15] 95% confidence interval for β_j			

TABLE **12.6**   The Point Predictions and Residuals Using the Least Squares Point
Estimates $b_0 = 13.1$, $b_1 = -0.0900$, and $b_2 = 0.0825$

x_1	x_2	y	$\hat{y} = b_0 + b_1 x_1 + b_2 x_2$ $= 13.1 - 0.0900 x_1 + 0.0825 x_2$	Residual, $e = y - \hat{y}$
28.0	18	12.4	12.0733	0.3267
28.0	14	11.7	11.7433	-0.0433
32.5	24	12.4	12.1632	0.2368
39.0	22	10.8	11.4131	-0.6131
45.9	8	9.4	9.6371	-0.2371
57.8	16	9.5	9.2259	0.2741
58.1	1	8.0	7.9614	0.0386
62.5	0	7.5	7.4829	0.0171

$$SSE = (0.3267)^2 + (-0.0433)^2 + \cdots + (0.0171)^2 = 0.674$$

that the sum of squared residuals (*SSE*) equals 0.674. Some of the numbers in Table 12.6 have been rounded.

The least squares prediction equation is the equation of a plane that is sometimes called the **least squares plane**. Figure 12.6 illustrates a portion of this plane—the portion that corresponds to the (x_1, x_2) combinations in the experimental region. Figure 12.6 also shows the residuals for each observation (here $n = 8$). These residuals are depicted as line segments drawn between the observed y values (the dots scattered around the least squares plane) and the predicted y values (the squares on the least squares plane). Because the least squares point estimates minimize the sum of squared residuals, we can interpret them as positioning the planar prediction equation in three-dimensional space so as to minimize the sum of squared distances between the observed and predicted y values. In this sense, we can say that the plane defined by the least squares point estimates is the best plane that can be positioned between the observed y values.

Part 2: Estimating means and predicting individual values   For combinations of values of x_1 and x_2 that are in the experimental region, the **least squares plane** is the estimate of

FIGURE 12.6 A Geometrical Interpretation of the Prediction Equation Relating $\hat{y}$ to x_1 and x_2

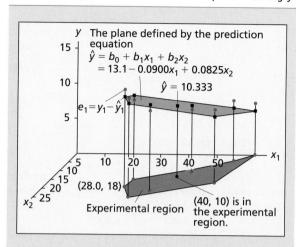

the **plane of means**. This implies that the point on the least squares plane corresponding to x_1 and x_2,

$$\hat{y} = b_0 + b_1 x_1 + b_2 x_2$$
$$= 13.1087 - 0.0900 x_1 + 0.0825 x_2,$$

is the point estimate of $\mu_{y|x_1, x_2}$, the mean of all y values that could be observed at x_1 and x_2. In addition, because we predict the error term to be 0, $\hat{y}$ is also the point prediction of $y = \mu_{y|x_1, x_2} + \varepsilon$.

Generalizing the previous example, we obtain the following:

Point Estimation and Point Prediction in Multiple Regression

Let b_0, b_1, b_2, . . . , b_k be the least squares point estimates of the parameters β_0, β_1, β_2, . . . , β_k in the multiple regression model, and suppose that x_{01}, x_{02}, . . . , x_{0k} are specified values of the independent variables x_1, x_2, . . . , x_k. If the combination of specified values is inside the experimental region, then

$$\hat{y} = b_0 + b_1 x_{01} + b_2 x_{02} + \cdots + b_k x_{0k}$$

is the **point estimate** of the **mean value of the dependent variable** when the values of the independent variables are x_{01}, x_{02}, . . . , x_{0k}. In addition, $\hat{y}$ is the **point prediction** of an **individual value of the dependent variable** when the values of the independent variables are x_{01}, x_{02}, . . . , x_{0k}. Again, you will notice that the error term is not included in the estimated multiple regression model because the expected value of the error term is 0.

Example 12.3 The Sales Territory Performance Case

Figure 12.7 on the next page presents the MegaStat output of a regression analysis of the data in Table 12.2 (page 422) using the model

$$y = \beta_0 + \beta_1 x_1 + \beta_2 x_2 + \beta_3 x_3 + \beta_4 x_4 + \beta_5 x_5 + \varepsilon.$$

On this output, x_1, x_2, x_3, x_4, and x_5 are denoted as Time, MktPoten, Adver, MktShare, and Change, respectively. The MegaStat output tells us that the least squares point estimates of the

FIGURE **12.7**   MegaStat Output of the Sales Territory Performance Data Using the Model $y = \beta_0 + \beta_1 x_1 + \beta_2 x_2 + \beta_3 x_3 + \beta_4 x_4 + \beta_5 x_5 + \varepsilon$

Regression Analysis

R^2 0.915 [6]
Adjusted R^2 0.893 [7]
R 0.957
Std. Error 430.232 [8]

n 25
k 5
Dep. Var. **Sales**

☐ = significant at 0.05 level
☐ = significant at 0.01 level

ANOVA table

Source	SS	df	MS	F	p-value
Regression	37,862,658.9002 [1]	5	7,572,531.7800	40.91 [4]	1.59E-09 [5]
Residual	3,516,890.0266 [2]	19	185,099.4751		
Total	41,379,548.9269 [3]	24			

Regression output   confidence interval [17]

variables	coefficients [9]	std. error [10]	t(df=19) [11]	p-value [12]	95% lower	95% upper
Intercept	-1,113.7879	419.8869	-2.653	0.0157	-1,992.6213	-234.9545
Time	3.6121	1.1817	3.057	0.0065	1.1388	6.0854
MktPoten	0.0421	0.0067	6.253	5.27E-06	0.0280	0.0562
Adver	0.1289	0.0370	3.479	0.0025	0.0513	0.2064
MktShare	256.9555	39.1361	6.566	2.76E-06	175.0428	338.8683
Change	324.5334	157.2831	2.063	0.0530	-4.6638	653.7307

Predicted values for: Sales

Predicted [13]	95% Confidence Interval [14]		95% Prediction Interval [15]		Leverage [16]
	lower	upper	lower	upper	
4,181.74333	3,884.90651	4,478.58015	3,233.59431	5,129.89235	0.109

---

[1] Explained variation   [2] SSE = unexplained variation   [3] Total variation   [4] F(model)   [5] p value for F(model)

[6] R^2 [7] Adjusted R^2 [8] s = standard error   [9] b_j = least squares estimate of β_j [10] s_{b_j} = standard error of the estimate b_j

[11] t statistics for testing significance of independent variables   [12] p values for t statistics   [13] $\hat{y}$ = point prediction

[14] 95% confidence interval   [15] 95% prediction interval   [16] Distance value   [17] 95% confidence interval for β_j

model parameters are $b_0 = -1,113.7879$, $b_1 = 3.6121$, $b_2 = 0.0421$, $b_3 = 0.1289$, $b_4 = 256.9555$, and $b_5 = 324.5334$. These estimates give the least squares prediction equation

$$\hat{y} = -1,113.7879 + 3.6121 x_1 + 0.0421 x_2 + 0.1289 x_3 + 256.9555 x_4 + 324.5334 x_5.$$

Recalling that the sales values in Table 12.2 are measured in hundreds of units of the product sold, the point estimate $b_3 = 0.1289$ says we estimate that mean sales increase by 0.1289 hundreds of units—that is, by 12.89 units—for each dollar increase in advertising expenditure when the other four independent variables do not change. If the company sells each unit for $1.10, this implies that we estimate that mean sales revenue increases by ($1.10)(12.89) = $14.18 for each dollar increase in advertising expenditure when the other four independent variables do not change. The other β values in the model can be interpreted similarly.

Consider a sales representative for whom Time = 85.42, MktPoten = 35,182.73, Adver = 7,281.65, MktShare = 9.64, and Change = 0.28. The point prediction of the sales corresponding to this combination of values of the independent variables is

$$\hat{y} = -1,113.7879 + 3.6121(85.42) + 0.0421(35,182.73)$$
$$+ 0.1289(7,281.65) + 256.9555(9.64) + 324.5334(0.28)$$
$$= 4,181.74 \text{ (or } 418,174 \text{ units)},$$

which is given on the MegaStat output. The actual sales for the sales representative were 3,087.52. This sales figure is 1,094.22 less than the point prediction $\hat{y} = 4,181.74$. Later, when we study prediction intervals in multiple regression (see Section 12.6), we will be able to determine whether there is strong evidence that this sales figure is unusually low.

12.4 R^2 AND ADJUSTED R^2

The multiple coefficient of determination, R^2 In this section, we discuss several ways to assess the utility of a multiple regression model. We first discuss a quantity called the **multiple coefficient of determination**, which is denoted R^2. The formulas for R^2 and other related quantities are given in the following box:

The Multiple Coefficient of Determination, R^2

For the multiple regression model:

1 **Total variation** $= \Sigma(y_i - \bar{y})^2$.

2 **Explained variation** $= \Sigma(\hat{y}_i - \bar{y})^2$.

3 **Unexplained variation** $= \Sigma(y_i - \hat{y}_i)^2$.

4 **Total variation** = explained variation

　　　　　　　　+ unexplained variation.

5 The **multiple coefficient of determination** is

$$R^2 = \frac{\text{explained variation}}{\text{total variation}}.$$

6 R^2 is the proportion of the total variation in the n observed values of the dependent variable that is explained by the overall regression model.

7 **Multiple correlation coefficient** $= R = \sqrt{R^2}$.

For example, consider the model

$$y = \beta_0 + \beta_1 x_1 + \beta_2 x_2 + \varepsilon$$

and the following Excel output from the data in Table 12.1:

SUMMARY OUTPUT	Data:	x1	x2	y
		28	18	12.4
Regression Statistics		28	14	11.7
Multiple R	0.986727	32.5	24	12.4
R Square	0.97363	39	22	10.8
Adjusted R Square	0.963081	45.9	8	9.4
Standard Error	0.367078	57.8	16	9.5
Observations	8	58.1	1	8
		62.5	0	7.5

ANOVA

	df	SS	MS	F	Significance F
Regression	2	24.87502	12.43751	92.30309	0.000112926
Residual	5	0.673732	0.134746		
Total	7	25.54875			

	Coefficients	Standard Error	t Stat	P-value	Lower 95%	Upper 95%	Lower 95.0%	Upper 95.0%
Intercept	13.10874	0.855698	15.31935	2.15E-05	10.90909894	15.308375	10.9090989	15.3083755
x1	−0.090014	0.014077	−6.394229	0.001386	−0.12620082	−0.0538269	−0.1262008	−0.0538269
x2	0.082495	0.022003	3.749337	0.013303	0.025935717	0.1390542	0.02593572	0.13905423

This output tells us that the total variation (SS Total), explained variation (SS Regression), and unexplained variation (SS Residual) for the model are, respectively, 25.54875, 24.87502, and 0.673732. The output also tells us that the multiple coefficient of determination is

$$R^2 = \frac{\text{explained variation}}{\text{total variation}} = \frac{24.87502}{25.54875} = 0.97363.$$

The multiple correlation coefficient is $R = \sqrt{0.97363} = 0.986727$. The rounded value of $R^2 = 0.974$ says that the two-independent-variable model explains 97.4 percent of the total variation in the eight observed y values.

As another example, consider the sales territory performance model

$$y = \beta_0 + \beta_1 x_1 + \beta_2 x_2 + \beta_3 x_3 + \beta_4 x_4 + \beta_5 x_5 + \varepsilon$$

and the following MegaStat output:

Regression Analysis

R^2	0.915			
Adjusted R^2	0.893		n	25
R	0.957		k	5
Std. Error	430.232		Dep. Var.	Sales

ANOVA table

Source	SS	df	MS	F	p-value
Regression	37,862,658.9002	5	7,572,531.7800	40.91	1.59E-09
Residual	3,516,890.0266	19	185,099.4751		
Total	41,379,548.9269	24			

This output tells us that the total, explained, and unexplained variations for the model are, respectively, 41,379,548.9269, 37,862,658.9002, and 3,516,890.0266. The MegaStat output also tells us that R^2 equals 0.915.

Adjusted R^2 Even if the independent variables in a regression model are unrelated to the dependent variable, they will make R^2 somewhat greater than 0. To avoid overestimating the importance of the independent variables, many analysts recommend calculating an *adjusted* multiple coefficient of determination.

Adjusted R^2

The **adjusted multiple coefficient of determination (adjusted R^2)** is

$$\overline{R}^2 = \left(R^2 - \frac{k}{n-1}\right)\left(\frac{n-1}{n-(k+1)}\right),$$

where R^2 is the multiple coefficient of determination, n is the number of observations, and k is the number of independent variables in the model under consideration.

Note that subtracting $k/(n - 1)$ from R^2 helps avoid overestimating the importance of the k independent variables. Furthermore, multiplying $[R^2 - (k/(n - 1))]$ by $(n - 1)/(n - (k + 1))$ makes $\overline{R}^2$ equal to 1 when R^2 equals 1.

As an example, consider the model of Table 12.1:

$$y = \beta_0 + \beta_1 x_1 + \beta_2 x_2 + \varepsilon.$$

From the Excel output on the previous page, $R^2 = 0.97363$. So it follows that

$$\overline{R}^2 = \left(R^2 - \frac{k}{n-1}\right)\left(\frac{n-1}{n-(k+1)}\right)$$

$$= \left(0.97363 - \frac{2}{8-1}\right)\left(\frac{8-1}{8-(2+1)}\right)$$

$$= 0.96309,$$

which is also given on the Excel output. Similarly, in addition to telling us that $R^2 = 0.915$ for the five-independent-variable sales territory performance model, the MegaStat output tells us that $\overline{R}^2 = 0.893$ for this model.

If R^2 is less than $k/(n - 1)$ (which can happen), then $\overline{R}^2$ will be negative. In this case, statistical software systems set $\overline{R}^2$ equal to 0. Historically, R^2 and $\overline{R}^2$ have been popular measures of model utility—possibly because they are unitless and between 0 and 1. In general, we want R^2 and $\overline{R}^2$ to be near 1. However, sometimes even if a regression model has an R^2 and an $\overline{R}^2$ that are near 1, the model may still not be able to predict accurately. We will discuss assessing a model's ability to predict accurately, as well as using R^2 and $\overline{R}^2$ to help choose a regression model, as we proceed through this chapter.

12.5 THE OVERALL *F* TEST

Another way to assess the utility of a regression model is to test the significance of the regression relationship between y and $x_1, x_2, \ldots, x_k$. For the multiple regression model, we test the null hypothesis H_0: $\beta_1 = \beta_2 = \cdots = \beta_k = 0$, which says that *none of the independent variables $x_1, x_2, \ldots, x_k$ is significantly related to y (the regression relationship is not significant)*, versus the alternative hypothesis H_a: at least one of $\beta_1, \beta_2, \ldots, \beta_k$ does not equal 0, which says that *at least one of the independent variables is significantly related to y (the regression relationship is significant)*. If we can reject H_0 at level of significance α, we say that *the multiple regression model is significant at level of significance α*. We carry out the test as follows:

LO5

An *F* Test for the Multiple Regression Model

Suppose that the regression assumptions hold and that the multiple regression model has $(k + 1)$ parameters, and consider testing

$$H_0: \beta_1 = \beta_2 = \cdots = \beta_k = 0$$

versus

H_a: at least one of $\beta_1, \beta_2, \ldots, \beta_k$ does not equal 0.

We define the **overall *F* statistic** to be

$$F(\text{model}) = \frac{\text{explained variation}/k}{\text{unexplained variation}/[n - (k + 1)]}.$$

The *p* value related to $F(\text{model})$ is the area under the curve of the F distribution (with k and $[n - (k + 1)]$ degrees of freedom) to the right of $F(\text{model})$. We can reject H_0 in favour of H_a at level of significance α if either of the following equivalent conditions holds:

1. $F(\text{model}) > F_{\alpha}$.
2. *p* value $< \alpha$.

Here the point F_{α} is based on k numerator and $n - (k + 1)$ denominator degrees of freedom.

Condition 1 is intuitively reasonable because a large value of $F(\text{model})$ would be caused by an explained variation that is large relative to the unexplained variation. This would occur if at least one independent variable in the regression model significantly affected y, which would imply that H_0 is false and H_a is true. For example, consider the model

$$y = \beta_0 + \beta_1 x_1 + \beta_2 x_2 + \varepsilon$$

from the sample data in Table 12.1 and the following Excel output:

ANOVA	df	SS	MS	F	Significance F
Regression	2	24.8750	12.4375	92.3031	0.0001
Residual	5	0.6737	0.1347		
Total	7	25.5488			

This output tells us that the explained and unexplained variations for this model are, respectively, 24.8750 and 0.6737. It follows, since there are $k = 2$ independent variables, that

$$F(\text{model}) = \frac{\text{explained variation}/k}{\text{unexplained variation}/[n - (k + 1)]}$$

$$= \frac{24.8750/2}{0.6737/[8 - (2 + 1)]} = \frac{12.4375}{0.1347}$$

$$= 92.33.$$

The p value related to $F(\text{model})$ is the area to the right of 92.33 under the curve of the F distribution with $k = 2$ numerator and $n - (k + 1) = 8 - 3 = 5$ denominator degrees of freedom. The Excel output says this p value is less than 0.001.

If we wish to test the significance of the regression model at level of significance $\alpha = 0.05$, we use the rejection point $F_{0.05}$ based on 2 numerator and 5 denominator degrees of freedom. Using Table A.7, we find that $F_{0.05} = 5.79$. Because $F(\text{model}) = 92.30 > F_{0.05} = 5.79$, we can reject H_0 in favour of H_a at level of significance 0.05. Alternatively, the p value is smaller than 0.001, so we can reject H_0 at level of significance 0.001, and we have extremely strong evidence that the model is significant and that at least one of the independent variables x_1 and x_2 in the model is significantly related to y.

Similarly, consider the following MegaStat output based on the Sales Territory Performance case:

ANOVA table

Source	SS	df	MS	F	p-value
Regression	37,862,658.9002	5	7,572,531.7800	40.91	1.59E-09
Residual	3,516,890.0266	19	185,099.4751		
Total	41,379,548.9269	24			

This output tells us that $F(\text{model}) = 40.91$ and that the p value related to $F(\text{model})$ is less than 0.001, suggesting that we have extremely strong evidence that at least one of the five independent variables in this model is significantly related to sales territory performance.

If the overall F test tells us that at least one independent variable in a regression model is significant, we next attempt to decide which independent variables are significant. In the next section, we discuss one way to do this.

Exercises for Sections 12.2, 12.3, 12.4, and 12.5

CONCEPTS

12.9 What is estimated by the mean square error? the standard error?

12.10 In the multiple regression model, what sum of squared deviations do the least squares point estimates minimize?

12.11 When using the multiple regression model, how do you obtain a point estimate of the mean value of the dependent variable and a point prediction of an individual value of the dependent variable?

12.12 a. What do R^2 and $\overline{R}^2$ measure?
   b. How do R^2 and $\overline{R}^2$ differ?

12.13 What is the purpose of the overall F test?

METHODS AND APPLICATIONS

In Exercises 12.14 to 12.16, we give MegaStat and Excel outputs of regression analyses of the data sets related to three case studies introduced in Section 12.1. The outputs are shown in Figure 12.8. In each exercise, we give the regression model and the number of observations, n, used to perform the regression analysis under consideration. Using the appropriate model, sample size n, and output:

a. Report the SSE as shown on the output. Calculate s^2 from the SSE and other numbers.

b. Report the total variation and the explained variation as shown on the output.

c. Report R^2 and $\overline{R}^2$ as shown on the output. Interpret R^2 and $\overline{R}^2$. Show how $\overline{R}^2$ has been calculated from R^2 and other numbers.

d. Calculate the $F(\text{model})$ statistic by using the explained variation, the unexplained variation, and other relevant quantities. Find $F(\text{model})$ on the output to check your answer.

FIGURE 12.8   Output for Exercises 12.14, 12.15, and 12.16

(a) MegaStat output for Exercise 12.14

Regression Analysis

R^2	0.732			
Adjusted R^2	0.655	n	10	
R	0.855	k	2	
Std. Error	6.802	Dep. Var.	**Attendance (y)**	

ANOVA table

Source	SS	df	MS	F	p-value
Regression	884.0887	2	442.0443	9.55	0.0100
Residual	323.9113	7	46.2730		
Total	1,208.0000	9			

(b) MegaStat output for Exercise 12.15

Regression Analysis

R^2	0.894			
Adjusted R^2	0.881	n	30	
R	0.945	k	3	
Std. Error	0.235	Dep. Var.	**Demand (y)**	

ANOVA table

Source	SS	df	MS	F	p-value
Regression	12.0268	3	4.0089	72.80	8.88E-13
Residual	1.4318	26	0.0551		
Total	13.4586	29			

(c) Excel output for Exercise 12.16

Regression Statistics

Multiple R	0.9981
R Square	0.9961
Adjusted R Square	0.9952
Standard Error	387.1598
Observations	16

ANOVA	df	SS	MS	F	Significance F
Regression	3	462,327,889.4	154,109,296.5	1,028.1309	9.92E-15
Residual	12	1,798,712.2	149,892.7		
Total	15	464,126,601.6			

e. Use the *F*(model) statistic and the appropriate rejection point to test the significance of the linear regression model under consideration by setting α equal to 0.05.

f. Use the *F*(model) statistic and the appropriate rejection point to test the significance of the linear regression model under consideration by setting α equal to 0.01.

g. Find the *p* value related to *F*(model) on the output. Using the *p* value, test the significance of the linear regression model by setting $\alpha = 0.10, 0.05, 0.01,$ and 0.001. What do you conclude?

12.14 THE WORK ATTENDANCE CASE

Model: $y = \beta_0 + \beta_1 x_1 + \beta_2 x_2 + \varepsilon$.

Sample size: $n = 10$.

12.15 THE FRESH DETERGENT CASE

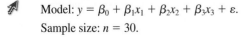   Model: $y = \beta_0 + \beta_1 x_1 + \beta_2 x_2 + \beta_3 x_3 + \varepsilon$.

Sample size: $n = 30$.

12.16 THE HOSPITAL LABOUR NEEDS CASE

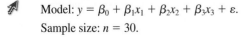   Model: $y = \beta_0 + \beta_1 x_1 + \beta_2 x_2 + \beta_3 x_3 + \varepsilon$.

Sample size: $n = 16$.

12.17 THE WORK ATTENDANCE CASE

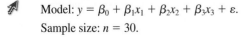   Figure 12.9 on the next page gives the Excel output of a regression analysis of the work attendance study data in Table 12.3 (page 423) using the model

$$y = \beta_0 + \beta_1 x_1 + \beta_2 x_2 + \varepsilon.$$

On the Excel output, find the values of b_0, b_1, and b_2 (the least squares point estimates of β_0, β_1, and β_2). Report and interpret b_0, b_1, and b_2.

FIGURE **12.9**   Excel Output of a Regression Analysis of the Work Attendance Data Using the Model $y = \beta_0 + \beta_1x_1 + \beta_2x_2 + \varepsilon$

SUMMARY OUTPUT

Regression Statistics

Multiple R	0.85548904
R Square	0.73186149
Adjusted R Square	0.65525049
Standard Error	6.80242938
Observations	10

ANOVA

	df	SS	MS	F	Significance F
Regression	2	884.0886821	442.0443	9.552955	0.00998291
Residual	7	323.9113179	46.27305		
Total	9	1208			

	Coefficients	Standard Error	t Stat	P-value	Lower 95%	Upper 95%
Intercept	44.6631219	13.50112214	3.308104	0.012975	12.73806393	76.5881799
Job Satis (x1)	5.74060008	1.437002571	3.994843	0.005224	2.342631377	9.13856878
Commute Dist (x2)	0.3431447	0.806379492	0.425537	0.683222	-1.563638436	2.24992784

FIGURE **12.10**   MegaStat Output of a Regression Analysis of the Fresh Detergent Demand Data Using the Model $y = \beta_0 + \beta_1x_1 + \beta_2x_2 + \beta_3x_3 + \varepsilon$

Regression Analysis

R^2 0.894
Adjusted R^2 0.881   n 30
R 0.945   k 3
Std. Error 0.235   Dep. Var. **Demand (y)**

ANOVA table

Source	SS	df	MS	F	p-value
Regression	12.0268	3	4.0089	72.80	8.88E-13
Residual	1.4318	26	0.0551		
Total	13.4586	29			

Regression output   confidence interval

variables	coefficients	std. error	t (df = 26)	p-value	95% lower	95% upper
Intercept	7.5891	2.4450	3.104	0.0046	2.5633	12.6149
Price (x1)	-2.3577	0.6379	-3.696	0.0010	-3.6690	-1.0464
IndPrice (x2)	1.6122	0.2954	5.459	1.01E-05	1.0051	2.2193
AdvExp (x3)	0.5012	0.1259	3.981	0.0005	0.2424	0.7599

Predicted values for: Demand (y)

				95% Confidence Interval		95% Prediction Interval		
Price (x1)	IndPrice (x2)	AdvExp (x3)	Predicted	lower	upper	lower	upper	Leverage
3.7	3.9	6.5	8.4107	8.3143	8.5070	7.9188	8.9025	0.040

12.18 THE FRESH DETERGENT CASE

Figure 12.10 gives the MegaStat output of a regression analysis of the Fresh detergent demand data in Table 12.4 (page 424) using the model

$$y = \beta_0 + \beta_1x_1 + \beta_2x_2 + \beta_3x_3 + \varepsilon.$$

a. Find (on the output) and report the values of b_0, b_1, b_2, and b_3, the least squares point estimates of β_0, β_1, β_2, and β_3. Interpret b_0, b_1, b_2, and b_3.

b. Consider the demand for Fresh detergent in a future sales period when Enterprise Industries' price for Fresh will be $x_1 = 3.70$, the average price of competitors' similar detergents will be $x_2 = 3.90$, and Enterprise Industries' advertising expenditure for Fresh will be $x_3 = 6.50$. The point prediction of this demand is given at the bottom of the MegaStat output. Report this point prediction and show how it was calculated.

FIGURE 12.11 Excel and MegaStat Output of a Regression Analysis of the Hospital Labour Needs Data Using the Model $y = \beta_0 + \beta_1x_1 + \beta_2x_2 + \beta_3x_3 + \varepsilon$

(a) The Excel output

Regression Statistics

Multiple R	0.9981
R Square	0.9961
Adjusted R Square	0.9952
Standard Error	387.1598
Observations	16

ANOVA

	df	SS	MS	F	Significance F
Regression	3	462,327,889.4	154,109,296.5	1,028.1309	9.92E-15
Residual	12	1,798,712.2	149,892.7		
Total	15	464,126,601.6			

	Coefficients	Standard Error	t Stat	P-value	Lower 95%	Upper 95%
Intercept	1,946.8020	504.1819	3.8613	0.0023	848.2840	3,045.3201
XRay (x1)	0.0386	0.0130	2.9579	0.0120	0.0102	0.0670
BedDays (x2)	1.0394	0.0676	15.3857	2.91E-09	0.8922	1.1866
LengthStay (x3)	-413.7578	98.5983	-4.1964	0.0012	-628.5850	-198.9306

(b) Prediction using MegaStat

Predicted values for: LabourHours

XRay (x1)	BedDays (x2)	LengthStay (x3)	Predicted	95% Confidence Interval lower	95% Confidence Interval upper	95% Prediction Interval lower	95% Prediction Interval upper	Leverage
56,194	14,077.88	6.89	15,896.2473	15,378.0313	16,414.4632	14,906.2361	16,886.2584	0.3774

12.19 THE HOSPITAL LABOUR NEEDS CASE

Figure 12.11 gives the Excel and MegaStat output of a regression analysis of the hospital labour needs data in Table 12.5 (page 424) using the model

$$y = \beta_0 + \beta_1x_1 + \beta_2x_2 + \beta_3x_3 + \varepsilon.$$

Note that the variables x_1, x_2, and x_3 are denoted as XRay, BedDays, and LengthStay on the output.

a. Find (on the output) and interpret b_0, b_1, b_2, and b_3, the least squares point estimates of β_0, β_1, β_2, and β_3.

b. Consider a hospital for which XRay = 56,194, BedDays = 14,077.88, and LengthStay = 6.89.

A point prediction of the labour hours corresponding to this combination of values of the independent variables is given on the MegaStat output. Report this point prediction and show how it was calculated.

c. If the actual number of labour hours used by the hospital was $y = 17,207.31$, how does this y value compare with the point prediction?

12.6 TESTING THE SIGNIFICANCE OF AN INDEPENDENT VARIABLE

Consider the multiple regression model

$$y = \beta_0 + \beta_1x_1 + \beta_2x_2 + \cdots + \beta_kx_k + \varepsilon.$$

In order to gain information about which of the independent variables significantly affect y, we can test the significance of a single independent variable. We arbitrarily refer to this variable as x_j and assume that it is multiplied by the parameter β_j. For example, if $j = 1$, we are testing the significance of x_1, which is multiplied by β_1; if $j = 2$, we are testing the significance of x_2, which is multiplied by β_2. To test the significance of x_j, we test the null hypothesis H_0: $\beta_j = 0$. We usually test H_0 versus the alternative hypothesis H_a: $\beta_j \neq 0$. *It is reasonable to conclude that x_j is significantly related to y in the regression model under consideration if H_0*

can be rejected in favour of H_a at a small level of significance. Here the phrase "in the regression model under consideration" is very important because whether x_j is significantly related to y in a particular regression model can depend on what other independent variables are included in the model.

Testing the significance of x_j in a multiple regression model is similar to testing the significance of the slope in the simple linear regression model (recall we test $H_0: \beta_1 = 0$ in simple regression). If the regression assumptions hold, the population of all possible values of the least squares point estimate b_j is normally distributed with mean β_j and standard deviation σ_{b_j}. The point estimate of σ_{b_j} is called the **standard error of the estimate b_j** and is denoted s_{b_j}. The formula for s_{b_j} involves matrix algebra and is discussed in Appendix F on *Connect*. In our discussion here, we will rely on MegaStat and Excel to compute s_{b_j}. If the regression assumptions hold, the population of all possible values of

$$\frac{b_j - \beta_j}{s_{b_j}}$$

has a t distribution with $n - (k + 1)$ degrees of freedom. It follows that if the null hypothesis $H_0: \beta_j = 0$ is true, the population of all possible values of the test statistic

$$t = \frac{b_j}{s_{b_j}}$$

has a t distribution with $n - (k + 1)$ degrees of freedom. Therefore, we can test the significance of x_j as follows:

Testing the Significance of the Independent Variable x_j

Define the test statistic

$$t = \frac{b_j}{s_{b_j}}$$

and suppose that the regression assumptions hold.

Then we can test $H_0: \beta_j = 0$ versus a particular alternative hypothesis at significance level α by using the appropriate rejection point rule or, equivalently, the corresponding p value.

Alternative Hypothesis	Rejection Point Rule: Reject H_0 if	p Value (Reject H_0 if p Value $< \alpha$)
$H_a: \beta_j \neq 0$	$|t| > t_{\alpha/2}$	Twice the area under the t curve to the right of $|t|$
$H_a: \beta_j > 0$	$t > t_\alpha$	The area under the t curve to the right of t
$H_a: \beta_j < 0$	$t < -t_\alpha$	The area under the t curve to the left of t

Here $t_{\alpha/2}$, t_α, and all p values are based on $n - (k + 1)$ degrees of freedom.

As in testing $H_0: \beta_1 = 0$ in simple linear regression, we usually use the two-sided alternative hypothesis $H_a: \beta_j \neq 0$ unless we have theoretical reasons to believe that β_j has a particular (plus or minus) sign (referred to as a one-tailed prediction). Moreover, MegaStat and Excel present the results for the two-sided test.

It is customary to test the significance of every independent variable in a regression model. Generally speaking, we have the following:

1   If we can reject $H_0: \beta_j = 0$ at the 0.05 level of significance, we have strong evidence that the independent variable x_j is significantly related to y in the regression model.

2   If we can reject $H_0: \beta_j = 0$ at the 0.01 level of significance, we have very strong evidence that x_j is significantly related to y in the regression model.

3   The smaller the significance level α at which H_0 can be rejected, the stronger is the evidence that x_j is significantly related to y in the regression model.

Example 12.4 The Sales Territory Performance Case

Consider the sales territory performance model

$$y = \beta_0 + \beta_1 x_1 + \beta_2 x_2 + \beta_3 x_3 + \beta_4 x_4 + \beta_5 x_5 + \varepsilon.$$

Because the MegaStat output in Figure 12.12 tells us that the p values associated with Time, MktPoten, Adver, and MktShare are all less than 0.01, we have very strong evidence that these variables are significantly related to y and, thus, are important in this model. The p value associated with Change is 0.0530, suggesting weaker evidence that this variable is important.

FIGURE **12.12** MegaStat Output of t Statistics and p Values for the Sales Territory Performance Model

Regression output					confidence interval	
variables	coefficients	std. error	t (df=19)	p-value	95% lower	95% upper
Intercept	−1,113.7879	419.8869	−2.653	0.0157	−1,992.6213	−234.9545
Time	3.6121	1.1817	3.057	0.0065	1.1388	6.0854
MktPoten	0.0421	0.0067	6.253	5.27E-06	0.0280	0.0562
Adver	0.1289	0.0370	3.479	0.0025	0.0513	0.2064
MktShare	256.9555	39.1361	6.566	2.76E-06	175.0428	338.8683
Change	324.5334	157.2831	2.063	0.0530	−4.6638	653.7307

The following box demonstrates how to calculate a confidence interval for a regression parameter. In Section 12.7, confidence and prediction intervals are discussed.

A Confidence Interval for the Regression Parameter β_j

If the regression assumptions hold, a $100(1 - \alpha)$ percent confidence interval for B_j is

$$[b_j \pm t_{\alpha/2} s_{b_j}].$$

Here $t_\alpha/2$ is based on $n - (k + 1)$ degrees of freedom.

Exercises for Section 12.6

CONCEPTS

12.20 What do you conclude about x_j if you can reject $H_0: \beta_j = 0$ in favour of $H_a: \beta_j \neq 0$ by setting
a. α equal to 0.05?
b. α equal to 0.01?

12.21 Give an example of a practical application of the confidence interval for β_j.

METHODS AND APPLICATIONS

In Exercises 12.22 through 12.24, we refer to MegaStat and Excel outputs of regression analyses of the data sets related to three case studies introduced in Section 12.1. The outputs are given in Figure 12.13 on the next page. Using the appropriate output, do the following for *each parameter* β_j in the model under consideration:

a. Find b_j, s_{b_j}, and the t statistic for testing $H_0: \beta_j = 0$ on the output, and report their values. Show how t was calculated by using b_j and s_{b_j}.

b. Using the t statistic and appropriate rejection points, test $H_0: \beta_j = 0$ versus $H_a: \beta_j \neq 0$ by setting α equal to 0.05. Which independent variables are significantly related to y in the model with $\alpha = 0.05$?

c. Using the t statistic and appropriate rejection points, test $H_0: \beta_j = 0$ versus $H_a: \beta_j \neq 0$ by setting α equal to 0.01. Which independent variables are significantly related to y in the model with $\alpha = 0.01$?

d. Find the p value for testing $H_0: \beta_j = 0$ versus $H_a: \beta_j \neq 0$ on the output. Using the p value, determine whether you can reject H_0 by setting α equal to 0.10, 0.05, 0.01, and 0.001. What do you conclude about the significance of the independent variables in the model?

e. Calculate the 95 percent confidence interval for β_j. Discuss one practical application of this interval.

f. Calculate the 99 percent confidence interval for β_j. Discuss one practical application of this interval.

FIGURE **12.13**   *t* Statistics and *p* Values for Three Case Studies

(a) MegaStat output for the work attendance case (sample size: *n* = 10)

Regression output variables	coefficients	std. error	t (df=7)	p-value	confidence interval 95% lower	95% upper
Intercept	44.6631	13.5011	3.308	0.0130	12.7381	76.5882
Job Satis (x1)	5.7406	1.4370	3.995	0.0052	2.3426	9.1386
Commute Dist (x2)	0.3431	0.8064	0.426	0.6832	-1.5636	2.2499

(b) MegaStat output for the Fresh detergent case (sample size: *n* = 30)

Regression output variables	coefficients	std. error	t (df=26)	p-value	confidence interval 95% lower	95% upper
Intercept	7.5891	2.4450	3.104	0.0046	2.5633	12.6149
Price (x1)	−2.3577	0.6379	−3.696	0.0010	−3.6690	−1.0464
IndPrice (x2)	1.6122	0.2954	5.459	1.01E-05	1.0051	2.2193
AdvExp (x3)	0.5012	0.1259	3.981	0.0005	0.2424	0.7599

(c) Excel output for the hospital labour needs case (sample size: *n* = 16)

	Coefficients	Standard Error	t Stat	P-value	Lower 95%	Upper 95%
Intercept	1,946.8020	504.1819	3.8613	0.0023	848.2840	3,045.3201
XRay (x1)	0.0386	0.0130	2.9579	0.0120	0.0102	0.0670
BedDays (x2)	1.0394	0.0676	15.3857	2.91E-09	0.8922	1.1866
LengthStay (x3)	−413.7578	98.5983	−4.1964	0.0012	−628.5850	−198.9306

12.22 THE WORK ATTENDANCE CASE

Use the MegaStat output in Figure 12.13(a) to do parts a through f for each of β_0, β_1, and β_2.

12.23 THE FRESH DETERGENT CASE

 Use the MegaStat output in Figure 12.13(b) to do parts a through f for each of β_0, β_1, β_2, and β_3.

12.24 THE HOSPITAL LABOUR NEEDS CASE

Use the Excel output in Figure 12.13(c) to do parts a through f for each of β_0, β_1, β_2, and β_3.

12.7 CONFIDENCE AND PREDICTION INTERVALS

In this section, we show how to use the multiple regression model to find a **confidence interval for a mean value of *y*** and a **prediction interval for an individual value of *y***. We first present an example of these intervals, and then we discuss the logic behind and formulas used to compute the intervals.

Example 12.5 The Sales Territory Performance Case

Consider a sales representative for whom Time = 85.42, MktPoten = 35,182.73, Adver = 7,281.65, MktShare = 9.64, and Change = 0.28. We saw in Example 12.3 that the point prediction of the sales corresponding to this combination of values of the independent variables is

$$\hat{y} = -1,113.7879 + 3.6121(85.42) + 0.0421(35,182.73)$$
$$+ 0.1289(7,281.65) + 256.9555(9.64) + 324.5334(0.28)$$
$$= 4,181.74 \text{ (or } 418,174 \text{ units)}.$$

This point prediction is given at the bottom of the MegaStat output in Figure 12.7, which we repeat here:

Predicted values for: Sales

| Predicted | 95% Confidence Interval | | 95% Prediction Interval | | Leverage |
	lower	upper	lower	upper	
4,181.74333	3,884.90651	4,478.58015	3,233.59431	5,129.89235	0.109

In addition to giving $\hat{y} = 4,181.74$, the MegaStat output tells us that a 95 percent prediction interval for y is $[3,233.59, 5,129.89]$. Furthermore, the actual sales y for the representative were 3,087.52. This actual sales figure is less than the point prediction $\hat{y} = 4,181.74$ and is less than the lower bound of the 95 percent prediction interval for y, $[3,233.59, 5,129.89]$. Therefore, we conclude that there is strong evidence that the actual performance of the representative is less than the predicted performance.

In general,

$$\hat{y} = b_0 + b_1 x_{01} + \cdots + b_k x_{0k}$$

is the *point estimate of the mean value of* y when the values of the independent variables are $x_{01}, x_{02}, \ldots, x_{0k}$. Calling this mean value $\mu_{y|x_{01}, x_{02}, \ldots, x_{0k}}$, if the regression assumptions hold, the population of all possible values of $\hat{y}$ is normally distributed with mean $\mu_{y|x_{01}, x_{02}, \ldots, x_{0k}}$ and standard deviation

$$\sigma_{\hat{y}} = \sigma \sqrt{\text{distance value}}.$$

The formula for the distance value involves matrix algebra and is given in Appendix F on *Connect*. We will soon see how to use the MegaStat output to find the distance value. It can be shown that the farther the values $x_{01}, x_{02}, \ldots, x_{0k}$ are from the centre of the experimental region, the larger is the distance value. We regard the centre of the experimental region to be the point $(\bar{x}_1, \bar{x}_2, \ldots, \bar{x}_k)$, where $\bar{x}_1$ is the average of the observed x_1 values, $\bar{x}_2$ is the average of the observed x_2 values, and so forth. Because s is the point estimate of σ, the point estimate of $\sigma_{\hat{y}}$ is

$$s_{\hat{y}} = s \sqrt{\text{distance value}},$$

which is called the **standard error of the estimate** $\hat{y}$. Using this standard error, we can form a confidence interval:

LO6

A Confidence Interval for a Mean Value of *y*

If the regression assumptions hold, a $100(1 - \alpha)$ percent confidence interval for the mean value of *y* when the values of the independent variables are $x_{01}, x_{02}, \ldots, x_{0k}$ is

$$[\hat{y} \pm t_{\alpha/2} s \sqrt{\text{distance value}}].$$

Here $t_{\alpha/2}$ is based on $n - (k + 1)$ degrees of freedom.

To develop an interval for an individual value of y, we consider the prediction error $y - \hat{y}$. If the regression assumptions hold, the population of all possible prediction errors is normally distributed with mean 0 and standard deviation

$$\sigma_{(y-\hat{y})} = \sigma \sqrt{1 + \text{distance value}}.$$

The point estimate of $\sigma_{(y-\hat{y})}$ is

$$s_{(y-\hat{y})} = s \sqrt{1 + \text{distance value}},$$

which is called the **standard error of the prediction error**. Using this standard error, we can form a prediction interval:

A Prediction Interval for an Individual Value of *y*

If the regression assumptions hold, a **100(1 − α) percent prediction interval for an individual value of *y*** when the values of the independent variables are $x_{01}, x_{02}, \ldots, x_{0k}$ is

$$[\hat{y} \pm t_{\alpha/2} s\sqrt{1 + \text{distance value}}].$$

Here $t_{\alpha/2}$ is based on $n - (k + 1)$ degrees of freedom.

Recall that the farther the values $x_{01}, x_{02}, \ldots, x_{0k}$ are from the centre of the experimental region, the larger is the distance value. It follows that the farther the values $x_{01}, x_{02}, \ldots, x_{0k}$ are from the centre of the experimental region, the longer (less precise) are the confidence intervals and prediction intervals provided by a regression model.

For example, the MegaStat output in Example 12.5 tells us that $\hat{y} = 4,181.74$. This output also tells us that the distance value, which is given under the heading "Leverage" on the output, equals 0.109. Therefore, since *s* for the five-variable sales territory performance model equals 430.232, it follows that the 95 percent prediction interval given on the MegaStat output of Example 12.5 was calculated as follows:

$$[\hat{y} \pm t_{0.025} s\sqrt{1 + \text{distance value}}]$$
$$= [4,181.74 \pm 2.093(430.232)\sqrt{1 + 0.109}]$$
$$= [3,233.59, 5,129.89].$$

Here $t_{0.025} = 2.093$ is based on $n - (k + 1) = 25 - 6 = 19$ degrees of freedom.

Exercises for Section 12.7

CONCEPTS

12.25 What does the distance value measure?

12.26 How is the distance value obtained from a MegaStat output?

METHODS AND APPLICATIONS

12.27 THE WORK ATTENDANCE CASE

The MegaStat output in Figure 12.14(a) relates to predictions based on two different employee cases.

a. Report (as shown on the output) the predicted attendance and the 95 percent prediction interval for an employee who is very satisfied with the job and lives close to work. (*Hint:* Recall that satisfaction ranged from 1 = not satisfied to 10 = very satisfied.)

b. Report (as shown on the output) the predicted attendance and the 95 percent prediction interval for an employee who is dissatisfied with the job and who lives 8 km from work.

c. Comparing the results of the two predictions, which has the larger distance value?

FIGURE **12.14**   MegaStat Outputs for Exercises 12.27, 12.28, and 12.29

(a) Output for Exercise 12.27

Predicted values for: Attendance (*y*)

Job Satis (x1)	Commute Dist (x2)	Predicted	95% Confidence Intervals lower	upper	95% Prediction Intervals lower	upper	Leverage
8	2	91.274	80.085	102.463	71.680	110.868	0.484
2	8	58.889	43.739	74.040	36.792	80.987	0.887

(b) Output for Exercise 12.28

Predicted	95% Confidence Interval lower	upper	95% Prediction Interval lower	upper	Leverage
8.4107	8.3143	8.5070	7.9188	8.9025	0.040

(c) Output for Exercise 12.29

Predicted	95% Confidence Interval lower	upper	95% Prediction Interval lower	upper	Leverage
15,896.2473	15,378.0313	16,414.4632	14,906.2361	16,886.2584	0.3774

12.28 THE FRESH DETERGENT CASE

Consider the demand for Fresh detergent in a future sales period when Enterprise Industries' price for Fresh will be $x_1 = 3.70$, the average price of competitors' similar detergents will be $x_2 = 3.90$, and Enterprise Industries' advertising expenditure for Fresh will be $x_3 = 6.50$. A 95 percent prediction interval for this demand is given on the MegaStat output in Figure 12.14(b).

a. Find and report the 95 percent prediction interval on the output. If Enterprise Industries plans to have in inventory the number of bottles implied by the upper limit of this interval, it can be very confident that it will have enough bottles to meet demand for Fresh in the future sales period. How many bottles is this? If we multiply the number of bottles implied by the lower limit of the prediction interval by the price of Fresh ($3.70), we can be very confident that the resulting dollar amount will be the minimal revenue from Fresh in the future sales period. What is this dollar amount?

b. Calculate a 99 percent prediction interval for the demand for Fresh in the future sales period. *Hint:* $n = 30$.

c. Recall that the data plots given at the bottom of Table 12.4 (page 424) suggest that the model $y = \beta_0 + \beta_1 x_4 + \beta_2 x_3 + \varepsilon$ might appropriately relate demand for Fresh (y) to the price difference

($x_4 = x_2 - x_1$) and advertising expenditure (x_3). The 95 percent prediction interval given by this model for the demand for Fresh in the future sales period is [7.89034, 8.88523]. Is this interval shorter or longer than the interval of part a? What does this imply about which model might best predict y?

12.29 THE HOSPITAL LABOUR NEEDS CASE

Consider a hospital for which XRay = 56,194, BedDays = 14,077.88, and LengthStay = 6.89. A 95 percent prediction interval for the labour hours corresponding to this combination of values of the independent variables is given on the MegaStat output in Figure 12.14(c). Find and report the prediction interval on the output. Then use this interval to determine if the actual number of labour hours used by the hospital ($y = 17,207.31$) is unusually low or high.

12.8 THE QUADRATIC REGRESSION MODEL (OPTIONAL)

**PART 2
Using Squared and Interaction Terms (Optional)**

One useful form of the multiple regression model is what we call the **quadratic regression model**. Assuming that we have obtained n observations—each consisting of an observed value of y and a corresponding value of x—the model is as follows:

The Quadratic Regression Model

The **quadratic regression model** relating y to x is

$$y = \beta_0 + \beta_1 x + \beta_2 x^2 + \varepsilon,$$

where

1   $\beta_0 + \beta_1 x + \beta_2 x^2$ is $\mu_{y|x}$, the mean value of the dependent variable y when the value of the independent variable is x.

2   β_0, β_1, and β_2 are (unknown) **regression parameters** relating the mean value of y to x.

3   ε is an error term that describes the effects on y of all factors other than x and x^2.

The quadratic equation $\mu_{y|x} = \beta_0 + \beta_1 x + \beta_2 x^2$ that relates $\mu_{y|x}$ to x is the equation of a **parabola**. Two parabolas are shown in Figure 12.15(a) and (b) on the next page and help to interpret the parameters β_0, β_1, and β_2. Here β_0 is the **y intercept** of the parabola (the value of $\mu_{y|x}$ when $x = 0$). Furthermore, β_1 is the **shift parameter** of the parabola: the value of β_1 shifts the parabola to the left or right. Specifically, increasing the value of β_1 shifts the parabola to

FIGURE 11.15 The Mean Value of the Dependent Variable Changing in a Quadratic Fashion as x Increases ($\mu_{y|x} = \beta_0 + \beta_1 x + \beta_2 x^2$)

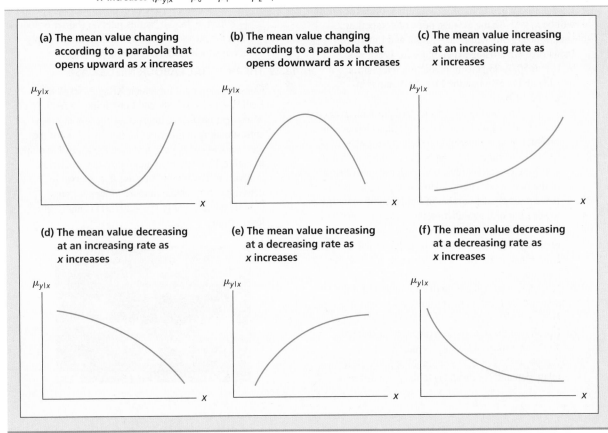

the left. Lastly, β_2 is the **rate of curvature** of the parabola. If β_2 is greater than 0, the parabola opens upward (see Figure 12.15(a)). If β_2 is less than 0, the parabola opens downward (see Figure 12.15(b)). If a scatter plot of y versus x shows points scattered around a parabola, or a part of a parabola (some typical parts are shown in Figure 12.15(c), (d), (e), and (f)), then the quadratic regression model might appropriately relate y to x.

Example 12.6 The Stress and Work Motivation Case

Stress is typically a difficult psychological variable to measure. Although the word *stress* usually has negative connotations, some stress may actually be motivating in the workplace. Stress researchers have suggested that too little stress and too much stress result in lower work performance, but a moderate amount of stress is motivating and improves work performance (so the pattern/correlation would be nonlinear in nature). To test this hypothesis, a human resources (HR) department administers a stress questionnaire to 15 employees in which people rate their stress level on a 0 (no stress) to 4 (high stress) scale. Work performance is measured as the average number of projects completed by the employee per year, averaged over the last five years (in order to improve the reliability of the measure). Table 12.7(a) gives the results of the test. Here the dependent variable y is productivity (in projects per year) and the independent variable x is the self-reported stress level.

Table 12.7(b) gives a scatter plot of y versus x. Because the scatter plot has the appearance of a quadratic curve (that is, part of a parabola), it seems reasonable to relate y to x by using the quadratic model

$$y = \beta_0 + \beta_1 x + \beta_2 x^2 + \varepsilon.$$

TABLE 12.7 The Stress and Work Motivation Study Data, and a Scatter Plot of the Data ✐

(a) The data

Self-Reported Stress Level, x	Productivity, y (Projects per Year)
0	25.8
0	26.1
0	25.4
1	29.6
1	29.2
1	29.8
2	32.0
2	31.4
2	31.7
3	31.7
3	31.5
3	31.2
4	29.4
4	29.0
4	29.5

(b) Scatter plot of y versus x

FIGURE 12.16 MegaStat Output of a Regression Analysis of the Stress and Motivation Data Using the Quadratic Model

Regression Analysis

R^2	0.986		
Adjusted R^2	0.983	n	15
R	0.993	k	2
Std. Error	0.286	Dep. Var.	Productivity, y (projects per year)

ANOVA table

Source	SS	df	MS	F	p-value
Regression	67.9152	2	33.9576	414.92	8.39E-12
Residual	0.9821	12	0.0818		
Total	68.8973	14			

Regression output

variables	coefficients	std. error	t (df=12)	p-value	confidence interval 95% lower	95% upper
Intercept	25.7152	0.1554	165.431	1.60E-21	25.3766	26.0539
Stress Level, x	4.9762	0.1841	27.025	4.05E-12	4.5750	5.3774
x2	−1.0190	0.0441	−23.085	2.60E-11	−1.1152	−0.9229

Predicted values for: Productivity, y (projects per year)

Stress Level, x	x2	Predicted	95% Confidence Interval lower	upper	95% Prediction Interval lower	upper	Leverage
2.44	5.936	31.8081	31.5648	32.0514	31.1390	32.4772	0.152

Figure 12.16 gives the MegaStat output of a regression analysis of the data using this quadratic model. Here the squared term x^2 is denoted as x2 on the output. The output tells us that the least squares point estimates of the model parameters are $b_0 = 25.7152$, $b_1 = 4.9762$, and $b_2 = -1.0190$. These estimates give us the least squares prediction equation

$$\hat{y} = 25.7152 + 4.9762x - 1.0190x^2.$$

This is the equation of the best quadratic curve that can be fitted to the data plotted in Table 12.7(b). The output also tells us that the p values related to x and x^2 are less than 0.001. This implies that we have extremely strong evidence that each of these model components is significant. The fact that x^2 seems significant confirms the graphical evidence that there is a quadratic relationship between y and x. Once we have such confirmation, we usually retain the linear term x in the model no matter what the size of its p value. The reason is that geometrical considerations indicate that it is best to use both x and x^2 to model a quadratic relationship.

The HR department wishes to find the value of x that results in the highest productivity score. Using calculus, it can be shown that the value $x = 2.44$ maximizes predicted productivity, suggesting that, in theory, productivity will be highest for an individual worker who scores between 2 and 3 on the stress scale. This will result in a predicted productivity score equal to

$$\hat{y} = 25.7152 + 4.9762(2.44) - 1.01905(2.44)^2$$
$$= 31.7901 \text{ average projects completed per year.}$$

Note that $\hat{y} = 31.8081$ is given at the bottom of the output in Figure 12.16. In addition, the output tells us that a 95 percent confidence interval for the mean productivity score that would be obtained by all of the employees is [31.5648, 32.0514]. The output also tells us that a 95 percent prediction interval for the average number of projects completed by an individual employee is [31.1390, 32.4772].

We now consider a model that employs both a linear and a quadratic term for one independent variable and also employs another linear term for a second independent variable.

Example 12.7 The Fresh Detergent Case

Enterprise Industries produces Fresh, a brand of liquid laundry detergent. In order to more effectively manage its inventory and make revenue projections, the company would like to better predict demand for Fresh. To develop a prediction model, the company has gathered data concerning demand for Fresh over the last 30 sales periods (each sales period is defined to be a four-week period). The demand data are presented in Table 12.8. Here, for each sales period,

  y = the demand for the large bottle of Fresh (in hundreds of thousands of bottles) in the
       sales period,

  x_1 = the price (in dollars) of Fresh as offered by Enterprise Industries in the sales period,

  x_2 = the average industry price (in dollars) of competitors' similar detergents in the sales period,

  x_3 = Enterprise Industries' advertising expenditure (in hundreds of thousands of dollars) to
       promote Fresh in the sales period,

  $x_4 = x_2 - x_1$ = the price difference in the sales period.

To begin our analysis, suppose that Enterprise Industries believes on theoretical grounds that the single independent variable x_4 adequately describes the effects of x_1 and x_2 on y. That is, perhaps demand for Fresh depends more on how the price for Fresh compares to competitors' prices than it does on the absolute levels of the prices for Fresh and other competing detergents. This makes sense since most consumers must buy a certain amount of detergent no matter what the price is (we will examine the validity of using x_4 to predict y more fully in Exercise 12.33 on page 450). For now, we will build a prediction model utilizing x_3 and x_4.

Figure 12.17 presents scatter plots of y versus x_4 and y versus x_3. The plot in Figure 12.17(a) indicates that y tends to increase in a straight-line fashion as x_4 increases. This suggests that the simple linear model

$$y = \beta_0 + \beta_1 x_4 + \varepsilon$$

might appropriately relate y to x_4. The plot in Figure 12.17(b) indicates that y tends to increase in a curved fashion as x_3 increases. Since this curve appears to have the shape of Figure 12.15(c), this suggests that the quadratic model

$$y = \beta_0 + \beta_1 x_3 + \beta_2 x_3^2 + \varepsilon$$

might appropriately relate y to x_3.

TABLE 12.8 Historical Data, Including Price Differences, Concerning Demand for Fresh Detergent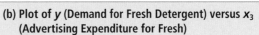

Sales Period	Price for Fresh, x_1 (Dollars)	Average Industry Price, x_2 (Dollars)	Price Difference, $x_4 = x_2 - x_1$ (Dollars)	Advertising Expenditure for Fresh, x_3 (Hundreds of Thousands of Dollars)	Demand for Fresh, y (Hundreds of Thousands of Bottles)
1	3.85	3.80	−0.05	5.50	7.38
2	3.75	4.00	0.25	6.75	8.51
3	3.70	4.30	0.60	7.25	9.52
4	3.70	3.70	0	5.50	7.50
5	3.60	3.85	0.25	7.00	9.33
6	3.60	3.80	0.20	6.50	8.28
7	3.60	3.75	0.15	6.75	8.75
8	3.80	3.85	0.05	5.25	7.87
9	3.80	3.65	−0.15	5.25	7.10
10	3.85	4.00	0.15	6.00	8.00
11	3.90	4.10	0.20	6.50	7.89
12	3.90	4.00	0.10	6.25	8.15
13	3.70	4.10	0.40	7.00	9.10
14	3.75	4.20	0.45	6.90	8.86
15	3.75	4.10	0.35	6.80	8.90
16	3.80	4.10	0.30	6.80	8.87
17	3.70	4.20	0.50	7.10	9.26
18	3.80	4.30	0.50	7.00	9.00
19	3.70	4.10	0.40	6.80	8.75
20	3.80	3.75	−0.05	6.50	7.95
21	3.80	3.75	−0.05	6.25	7.65
22	3.75	3.65	−0.10	6.00	7.27
23	3.70	3.90	0.20	6.50	8.00
24	3.55	3.65	0.10	7.00	8.50
25	3.60	4.10	0.50	6.80	8.75
26	3.65	4.25	0.60	6.80	9.21
27	3.70	3.65	−0.05	6.50	8.27
28	3.75	3.75	0	5.75	7.67
29	3.80	3.85	0.05	5.80	7.93
30	3.70	4.25	0.55	6.80	9.26

FIGURE 12.17 Scatter Plots of the Fresh Demand Data

(a) Plot of y (Demand for Fresh Detergent) versus x_4 (Price Difference)

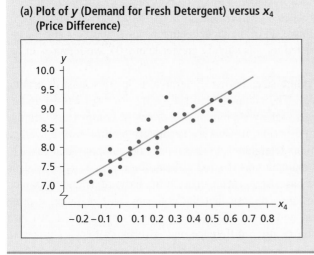

(b) Plot of y (Demand for Fresh Detergent) versus x_3 (Advertising Expenditure for Fresh)

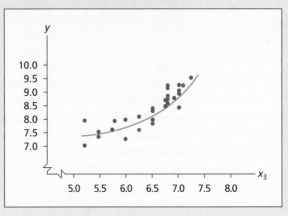

FIGURE **12.18**   Excel and MegaStat Output of a Regression Analysis of the Fresh Demand Data in Table 12.8 Using the Model $y = \beta_0 + \beta_1 x_4 + \beta_2 x_3 + \beta_3 x_3^2 + \varepsilon$

(a) The Excel output

Regression Statistics

Multiple R	0.9515
R Square	0.9054
Adjusted R Square	0.8945
Standard Error	0.2213
Observations	30

ANOVA	df	SS	MS	F	Significance F
Regression	3	12.1853	4.0618	82.9409	1.94E-13
Residual	26	1.2733	0.0490		
Total	29	13.4586			

	Coefficients	Standard Error	t Stat	P-value	Lower 95%	Upper 95%
Intercept	17.3244	5.6415	3.0709	0.0050	5.7282	28.9206
PriceDif (x4)	1.3070	0.3036	4.3048	0.0002	0.6829	1.9311
AdvExp (x3)	-3.6956	1.8503	-1.9973	0.0564	-7.4989	0.1077
x3Sq	0.3486	0.1512	2.3060	0.0293	0.0379	0.6594

(b) Prediction using MegaStat

Predicted values for: Y

	95% Confidence Interval		95% Prediction Interval		
Predicted	lower	upper	lower	upper	Leverage
8.29330	8.17378	8.41281	7.82298	8.76362	0.069

To construct a prediction model based on both x_3 and x_4, it seems reasonable to combine these two models to form the regression model

$$y = \beta_0 + \beta_1 x_4 + \beta_2 x_3 + \beta_3 x_3^2 + \varepsilon.$$

Here we have arbitrarily ordered the x_4, x_3, and x_3^2 terms in the combined model, and we have renumbered the subscripts on the β's appropriately. In the combined model,

$$\beta_0 + \beta_1 x_4 + \beta_2 x_3 + \beta_3 x_3^2$$

is the mean demand for Fresh when the price difference is x_4 and the advertising expenditure is x_3. The error term describes the effects on demand of all factors other than x_4 and x_3.

Figure 12.18(a) presents the Excel output of a regression analysis of the Fresh demand data using the combined model. The output tells us that the least squares point estimates of the model parameters are $b_0 = 17.3244$, $b_1 = 1.3070$, $b_2 = -3.6956$, and $b_3 = 0.3486$. The output also tells us that the p values related to x_4, x_3, and x_3^2 are 0.0002, 0.0564, and 0.0293. Therefore, we have strong evidence that each of the model components x_4 and x_3^2 is significant. Furthermore, although the p value related to x_3 is slightly greater than 0.05, we retain x_3 in the model because x_3^2 is significant.

In order to predict demand in a future sales period, Enterprise Industries must determine future values of x_3 and $x_4 = x_2 - x_1$. The company can set x_1 (its price for Fresh) and x_3 (its advertising expenditure) and feels that by examining the prices of competitors' similar products immediately prior to a future period, it can very accurately predict x_2 (the average industry price for competitors' similar detergents). Furthermore, the company can react to any change in competitors' price to maintain any desired price difference $x_4 = x_2 - x_1$. This is an advantage of predicting on the basis of x_4 rather than on the basis of x_1 and x_2 (which the company cannot control). Therefore, suppose that the company will maintain a price difference of \$0.20 ($x_{04} = 0.20$) and will spend \$650,000 on advertising ($x_{03} = 6.50$) in a future sales period. This combination of price difference and advertising expenditure is in the experimental region defined by the data in Table 12.8. A point prediction of demand in the future sales period is

$$\hat{y} = 17.3244 + 1.3070x_{04} - 3.6956x_{03} + 0.3486x_{03}^2$$
$$= 17.3244 + 1.3070(0.20) - 3.6956(6.50) + 0.3486(6.50)^2$$
$$= 8.29330 \text{ (or } 829,330 \text{ bottles)}.$$

This quantity, in addition to being the point prediction of demand in a single sales period when the price difference is \$0.20 and the advertising expenditure is \$650,000, is also the point estimate of the mean of all possible demands when $x_4 = 0.20$ and $x_3 = 6.50$. Note that $\hat{y} = 8.29330$ is given on the MegaStat output of Figure 12.18(b). The output also gives a 95 percent confidence interval for mean demand when x_4 equals 0.20 and x_3 equals 6.50, which is [8.17378, 8.41281], and a 95 percent prediction interval for an individual demand when x_4 equals 0.20 and x_3 equals 6.50, which is [7.82298, 8.76362]. This latter interval says we are 95 percent confident that the actual demand in the future sales period will be between 782,298 bottles and 876,362 bottles. The upper limit of this interval can be used for inventory control. It says that if Enterprise Industries plans to have 876,362 bottles on hand to meet demand in the future sales period, then the company can be very confident that it will have enough bottles. The lower limit of the interval can be used to better understand Enterprise Industries' cash flow situation. It says the company can be very confident that it will sell at least 782,298 bottles in the future sales period. Therefore, for example, if the average competitors' price is \$3.90 and thus Enterprise Industries' price is \$3.70, the company can be very confident that its minimum revenue from the large bottle of Fresh in the future period will be at least 782,298 × \$3.70 = \$2,894,502.60.

One cautionary note about the quadratic regression model is that the bend (or bends) in the scatter plot of x and y should reflect an overall pattern and not simply be due to the influence of a few extreme cases, or outliers. An **outlier** is an observation that is well separated from the rest of the data. An observation that would cause some important aspect of the regression analysis (for example, the least squares point estimates or the standard error s) to substantially change if it were removed from the data set is called **influential**. An observation may be an outlier with respect to its y value and/or its x values, but an outlier may or may not be influential. We illustrate these ideas by considering Figure 12.19, which is a hypothetical plot of the values of a dependent variable y against an independent variable x. Observation 1 in this figure is outlying with respect to its y value. However, it is not outlying with respect to its x value, because its x value is near the middle of the other x values. Moreover, observation 1 may not be influential because there are several observations with similar x values and non-outlying y values, which will keep the least squares point estimates from being excessively influenced by observation 1. Observation 2 in Figure 12.19 is outlying with respect to its x

FIGURE **12.19**   Data Plot Illustrating Outlying and Influential Observations

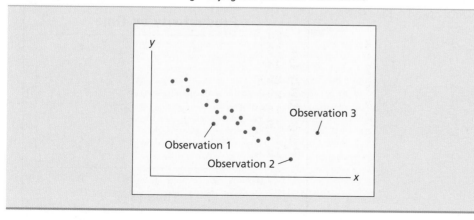

value, but since its y value is consistent with the regression relationship displayed by the non-outlying observations, it is probably not influential. Observation 3, however, is probably influential, because it is outlying with respect to its x value and because its y value is not consistent with the regression relationship displayed by the other observations. Observation 3 might also give the impression that there is a curved relationship between x and y.

What should we do about outlying and influential observations? We recommend first dealing with outliers with respect to their y values, because they affect the overall fit of the model. Often when we decide what to do with such outliers, other problems become much less important or disappear. In general, we should first check to see if the y value in question was recorded correctly. If it was recorded incorrectly, it should be corrected and the regression should be rerun. If it cannot be corrected, we should consider discarding the corresponding observation and rerunning the regression.

Exercises for Section 12.8

CONCEPTS

12.30 When does a scatter plot suggest the use of the quadratic regression model?

12.31 In the quadratic regression model, what are y, $\beta_0 + \beta_1 x + \beta_2 x^2$, and ε?

METHODS AND APPLICATIONS

12.32 A line manager of a distribution company is interested in investigating the relationship between the length of a shift and the productivity of the employees. Employees at this company are required to package products to be sent to retailers. The manager collects the average number of shipments completed for each hour of an eight-hour shift (the lunch hour is not counted) and reports the data in Table 12.9.

  a. Based on the scatter plot of the data given in Table 12.9, describe the relationship between the length of a shift and the productivity of the employees.

  b. The manager decides that to test the regression equation, the time variable should be squared (becoming x^2). The manager does this transformation and tests the model

$$y = \beta_0 + \beta_1 x_1 + \beta_2 x_1^2 + \varepsilon.$$

The Excel output of the regression analysis is presented in Figure 12.20. Do the p values for the independent variables in this model indicate that these independent variables are significant? Explain your answer.

12.33 THE FRESH DETERGENT CASE

Consider the demand for Fresh detergent in a future sales period when Enterprise Industries' price for Fresh will be $x_1 = 3.70$, the average price of competitors' similar detergents will be $x_2 = 3.90$, the price difference $x_4 = x_2 - x_1$ will be 0.20, and Enterprise Industries' advertising expenditure for Fresh will be $x_3 = 6.50$. You saw in Example 12.7 that the 95 percent prediction interval for this demand given by the model

$$y = \beta_0 + \beta_1 x_4 + \beta_2 x_3 + \beta_3 x_3^2 + \varepsilon$$

is [7.82298, 8.76362]. The 95 percent prediction interval for this demand given by the model

$$y = \beta_0 + \beta_1 x_1 + \beta_2 x_2 + \beta_3 x_3 + \beta_4 x_3^2 + \varepsilon$$

TABLE **12.9**   Productivity by Time of Shift

Productivity (y)	Time (x_1)
22	1
25	2
13	3
12	4
11	5
18	6
27	7
26	8

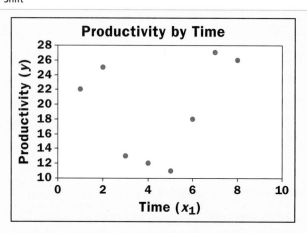

FIGURE **12.20** Excel Output of a Regression Analysis of the Work Productivity Data Using the Model $y = \beta_0 + \beta_1 x_1 + \beta_2 x_1^2 + \varepsilon$

SUMMARY OUTPUT

Regression Statistics

Multiple R	0.82433
R Square	0.67952
Adjusted R Square	0.551328
Standard Error	4.439541
Observations	8

ANOVA	df	SS	MS	F	Significance F
Regression	2	208.952381	104.4762	5.300797	0.058143683
Residual	5	98.54761905	19.70952		
Total	7	307.5			

	Coefficients	Standard Error	t Stat	P-value	Lower 95%	Upper 95%	Lower 95.0%	Upper 95.0%
Intercept	32.53571	6.193801762	5.252947	0.003318	16.614066	48.457363	16.614066	48.4573626
Time (x1)	−9.02381	3.157860114	−2.857571	0.035507	−17.1413341	−0.9062849	−17.1413341	−0.90628494
TimeSQ (x2)	1.071429	0.34251802	3.128094	0.026013	0.190959409	1.9518977	0.19095941	1.95189773

TABLE **12.10** Pop-Canada's Focus Group Results 🖎

Rated Taste, y	Caramel Colour, x_1	Maple Syrup, x_2
27.4	0	0
28.0	0	0
28.6	0	0
29.6	1	0
30.6	1	0
28.6	2	0
29.8	2	0
32.0	0	1
33.0	0	1
33.3	1	1
34.5	1	1
32.3	0	2
33.5	0	2
34.4	1	2
35.0	1	2
35.6	1	2
33.3	2	2
34.0	2	2
34.7	2	2
33.4	1	3
32.0	2	3
33.0	2	3

is [7.84139, 8.79357]. Which interval is shorter? Based on this, which model seems better?

12.34 Pop-Canada is trying to decide on the right 🖎 combination of two independent variables— x_1, caramel colour (0, 1, or 2 units), and x_2, maple syrup flavouring (0, 1, 2, or 3 units)—to improve the taste of its beverages. Taste tests were carried out using focus groups across Canada. The combinations of x_1 and x_2 used in the experiment, along with the corresponding values of y, are given in Table 12.10.

FIGURE **12.21**   MegaStat Output of a Regression Analysis of the Pop-Canada Data Using
the Model $y = \beta_0 + \beta_1 x_1 + \beta_2 x_1^2 + \beta_3 x_2 + \beta_4 x_2^2 + \varepsilon$

Regression Analysis

R^2	0.947		
Adjusted R^2	0.935	n	22
R	0.973	k	4
Std. Error	0.631	Dep. Var.	Y

ANOVA table

Source	SS	df	MS	F	p-value
Regression	120.7137	4	30.1784	75.90	1.30E-10
Residual	6.7590	17	0.3976		
Total	127.4727	21			

Regression output

variables	coefficients	std. error	t (df = 17)	p-value	confidence interval 95% lower	95% upper
Intercept	28.1589	0.2902	97.040	9.01E-25	27.5467	28.7711
X1	3.3133	0.5896	5.619	3.07E-05	2.0693	4.5573
X1SQ	−1.4111	0.2816	−5.012	0.0001	−2.0051	−0.8170
X2	5.2752	0.4129	12.776	3.83E-10	4.4041	6.1463
X2SQ	−1.3964	0.1509	−9.257	4.74E-08	−1.7146	−1.0781

Predicted values for: Y

Predicted	95% Confidence Interval lower	upper	95% Prediction Interval lower	upper	Leverage
35.0261	34.4997	35.5525	33.5954	36.4568	0.157

a. Discuss why the data plots given beside Table 12.10 indicate that the model

$$y = \beta_0 + \beta_1 x_1 + \beta_2 x_1^2 + \beta_3 x_2 + \beta_4 x_2^2 + \varepsilon$$

might appropriately relate y to x_1 and x_2.

b. If we use MegaStat to analyze the data in Table 12.10 by using the model in part a, we obtain the output in Figure 12.21. Noting from Table 12.10 that the combination of one unit of caramel colour and two units of maple syrup seems to maximize rated taste, assume that Pop-Canada will use this combination to make its beverage. The estimation and prediction results at the bottom of the MegaStat output are for the combination $x_1 = 1$ and $x_2 = 2$.

(1) Use the computer output to find and report a point estimate of and a 95 percent confidence interval for the mean rated taste obtained by all samples of the beverage when it is made using one unit of caramel colour and two units of maple syrup.

(2) Use the computer output to find and report a point prediction of and a 95 percent prediction interval for the rated taste that would be obtained by an individual sample of the beverage when it is made using one unit of caramel colour and two units of maple syrup.

12.9 INTERACTION (OPTIONAL)

Multiple regression models often contain **interaction variables**. We form an interaction variable by multiplying two independent variables together. For instance, if a regression model includes the independent variables x_1 and x_2, then we can form the interaction variable $x_1 x_2$. It is appropriate to employ an interaction variable if the relationship between the mean value of the dependent variable y and one of the independent variables is dependent on (that is, is different depending on) the value of the other independent variable. We explain the concept of interaction in the following example.

Example 12.8 Froid Frozen Foods Experiment

Part 1: The data and data plots Froid Frozen Foods has designed an experiment to study the effects of two types of advertising expenditures on sales of one of its lines of frozen foods. Twenty-five sales regions of equal sales potential were selected. Different combinations of $x_1 =$ radio expenditures (measured in units of $1,000) and $x_2 =$ print expenditures (measured in

TABLE 12.11 Froid Frozen Foods Sales Volume Data

Sales Region	Radio Expenditures, x_1	Print Expenditures, x_2	Sales Volume, y	Sales Region	Radio Expenditures, x_1	Print Expenditures, x_2	Sales Volume, y
1	1	1	3.27	14	3	4	17.99
2	1	2	8.38	15	3	5	19.85
3	1	3	11.28	16	4	1	9.46
4	1	4	14.50	17	4	2	12.61
5	1	5	19.63	18	4	3	15.50
6	2	1	5.84	19	4	4	17.68
7	2	2	10.01	20	4	5	21.02
8	2	3	12.46	21	5	1	12.23
9	2	4	16.67	22	5	2	13.58
10	2	5	19.83	23	5	3	16.77
11	3	1	8.51	24	5	4	20.56
12	3	2	10.14	25	5	5	21.05
13	3	3	14.75				

FIGURE 12.22 Plot of y versus x_1 (Plot Character Is the Corresponding Value of x_2): The Larger x_2 Is, the Smaller Is the Slope of the Straight Line Relating y to x_1

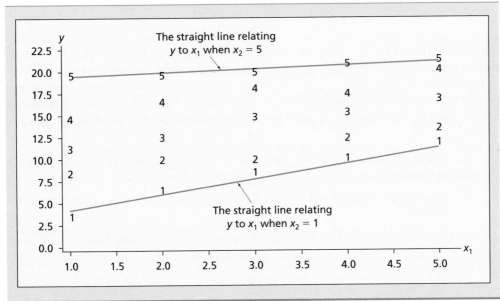

units of $1,000) were specified and randomly assigned to the sales regions. Table 12.11 shows the expenditure combinations along with the associated values of sales volume, measured in units of $10,000 and denoted y, for the sales regions during August of last year.

To help decide whether an interaction exists between x_1 and x_2, we can plot the data in Table 12.11. To do this, we first plot y versus x_1. In constructing this plot, we make the plot character for each point the corresponding value of x_2 ($x_2 = 1, 2, 3, 4, 5$). The resulting plot (shown in Figure 12.22) is called a **plot of y versus x_1 for the different "levels" of x_2**. Looking at this plot, we see that the straight line relating y to x_1 when $x_2 = 5$ appears to have a smaller slope than does the line relating y to x_1 when $x_2 = 1$. That is, the rate of increase of the line corresponding to $x_2 = 5$ is less steep than the rate of increase of the line corresponding to $x_2 = 1$. Examining the entire data plot, we see that Figure 12.22 might suggest that the larger x_2 is, the smaller is the slope of the straight line relating y to x_1.

In Figure 12.23 on the next page, we plot y versus x_2 for the different levels of x_1 ($x_1 = 1, 2, 3, 4, 5$). Here the plot character for each point is the corresponding value of x_1. We see that the straight line relating y to x_2 when $x_1 = 5$ appears to have a smaller slope than does the straight

FIGURE 12.23 Plot of y versus x_2 (Plot Character Is the Corresponding Value of x_1):
The Larger x_1 Is, the Smaller Is the Slope of the Straight Line Relating y to x_2

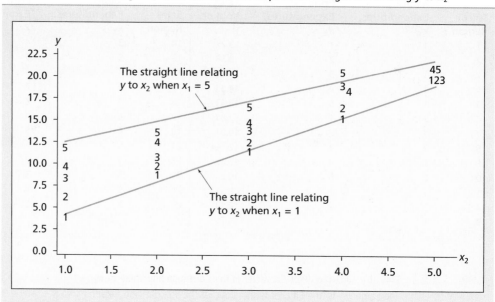

line relating y to x_2 when $x_1 = 1$. Looking at the entire data plot, we see that Figure 12.23 might suggest that the larger x_1 is, the smaller is the slope of the straight line relating y to x_2.

In summary, Figures 12.22 and 12.23 seem to imply that the more money is spent on one type of advertising, the smaller is the slope of the straight line relating sales volume to the amount spent on the other type of advertising. This says that there is an interaction between x_1 and x_2 because

1 The relationship between y and x_1 (the slope of the line relating y to x_1) is different for different values of x_2.

2 The relationship between y and x_2 (the slope of the line relating y to x_2) is different for different values of x_1.

An interaction between x_1 and x_2 makes sense because as Froid Frozen Foods spends more money on one type of advertising, increases in spending on the other type of advertising might become less effective.

Part 2: Modelling the interaction between x_1 and x_2 The regression model

$$y = \beta_0 + \beta_1 x_1 + \beta_2 x_2 + \varepsilon$$

cannot describe the interaction between x_1 and x_2 because this model says that mean sales volume equals

$$\beta_0 + \beta_1 x_1 + \beta_2 x_2 = (\beta_0 + \beta_1 x_1) + \beta_2 x_2.$$

This implies that for any particular value of x_1, the slope of the straight line relating the mean value of y to x_2 will always be β_2. That is, no matter what the value of x_1 is, the slope of the line relating mean y to x_2 is always the same. This rules out the possibility of describing the relationships illustrated in Figure 12.23 by using the above model. The model also says that mean sales volume equals

$$\beta_0 + \beta_1 x_1 + \beta_2 x_2 = (\beta_0 + \beta_2 x_2) + \beta_1 x_1.$$

This implies that no matter what the value of x_2 is, the slope of the line relating mean y to x_1 is always the same (here the slope equals β_1). This rules out the possibility of describing the relationships illustrated in Figure 12.22 by using the above model. In short, we say that the above model assumes *no interaction* between x_1 and x_2.

In order to model the interaction between x_1 and x_2, we can use the **cross-product term** or **interaction term** x_1x_2. Therefore, we consider the model

$$y = \beta_0 + \beta_1 x_1 + \beta_2 x_2 + \beta_3 x_1 x_2 + \varepsilon.$$

This model says that mean sales volume equals

$$\beta_0 + \beta_1 x_1 + \beta_2 x_2 + \beta_3 x_1 x_2,$$

which can be rewritten as $(\beta_0 + \beta_1 x_1) + (\beta_2 + \beta_3 x_1)x_2$. *This implies that the slope of the line relating mean y to x_2, which is $\beta_2 + \beta_3 x_1$, will be different for different values of x_1.* This allows the **interaction model** to describe relationships such as those illustrated in Figure 12.23. Furthermore, for this model the mean sales volume

$$\beta_0 + \beta_1 x_1 + \beta_2 x_2 + \beta_3 x_1 x_2$$

can also be rewritten as $(\beta_0 + \beta_2 x_2) + (\beta_1 + \beta_3 x_2)x_1$. *This implies that the slope of the line relating mean y to x_1, which is $\beta_1 + \beta_3 x_2$, will be different for different values of x_2.* This allows the interaction model to describe relationships such as those illustrated in Figure 12.22. In short, we say that the model employing the term x_1x_2 assumes that *an interaction exists* between x_1 and x_2.

Part 3: Statistical inference Figure 12.24 gives the MegaStat output of a regression analysis of the data in Table 12.11 by using the model

$$y = \beta_0 + \beta_1 x_1 + \beta_2 x_2 + \beta_3 x_1 x_2 + \varepsilon.$$

Because all of the p values related to the intercept and the independent variables are less than 0.01, we have very strong evidence that each of β_0, x_1, x_2, and x_1x_2 is significant in the above model. In particular, the very small p value related to x_1x_2 confirms that an interaction exists between x_1 and x_2, as was originally suggested by the plots in Figures 12.22 and 12.23.

FIGURE 12.24 MegaStat Output of a Regression Analysis of the Sales Volume Data in Table 12.11 by Using the Model $y = \beta_0 + \beta_1 x_1 + \beta_2 x_2 + \beta_3 x_1 x_2 + \varepsilon$

Regression Analysis

R^2	0.986		
Adjusted R^2	0.984	n	25
R	0.993	k	3
Std. Error	0.626	Dep. Var.	**y**

ANOVA table

Source	SS	df	MS	F	p-value
Regression	590.4057	3	196.8019	502.67	1.05E-19
Residual	8.2218	21	0.3915		
Total	598.6275	24			

Regression output

variables	coefficients	std. error	t (df=21)	p-value	confidence interval 95% lower	95% upper
Intercept	−2.3497	0.6883	−3.414	0.0026	−3.7811	−0.9183
x1	2.3611	0.2075	11.377	1.93E-10	1.9295	2.7927
x2	4.1831	0.2075	20.157	3.21E-15	3.7515	4.6147
x1x2	−0.3489	0.0626	−5.576	1.56E-05	−0.4790	−0.2188

Predicted values for: y

x1	x2	x1x2	Predicted	95% Confidence Interval lower	upper	95% Prediction Interval lower	upper	Leverage
2	5	10	19.79900	19.24693	20.35107	18.38550	21.21250	0.180

(If there were little or no interaction between x_1 and x_2, the term x_1x_2 would be nonsignificant since it would not help us to model the data.)

Next, suppose that Froid Frozen Foods will spend $2,000 on radio advertising ($x_1 = 2$) and $5,000 on print advertising ($x_2 = 5$) in a future month in a particular sales region. If there are no trend, seasonal, or other time-related influences affecting monthly sales volume, then it is reasonable to believe that the regression relationship between y and x_1 and x_2 that we have developed probably applies to the future month and particular sales region. It follows that

$$\hat{y} = -2.3497 + 2.3611(2) + 4.1831(5) - 0.3489(2)(5)$$
$$= 19.799 \text{ (or \$197,990)}$$

is a point estimate of mean sales volume when $2,000 is spent on radio advertising and $5,000 is spent on print advertising. In addition, $\hat{y}$ is a point prediction of the individual sales volume that will be observed in the future month in the particular sales region. In addition, the output in Figure 12.24 tells us that the 95 percent confidence interval for mean sales volume is [19.24693, 20.35107] and the 95 percent prediction interval for an individual sales volume is [18.38550, 21.21250]. This prediction interval says we are 95 percent confident that the individual sales volume in the future month in the particular sales region will be between $183,855 and $212,125. In Exercise 12.37 (on page 459), we will continue this example.

It is easy to construct data plots to check for interaction in the Froid Frozen Foods example because the company has carried out a designed experiment. In many regression problems, however, we do not carry out a designed experiment, and the data are unstructured. In such a case, it may not be possible to construct the data plots needed to detect an interaction between independent variables. For example, if we consider the Fresh demand data in Table 12.8 (page 447), we might suspect that there is an interaction between x_3 (advertising expenditure) and x_4 (the price difference). That is, we might suspect that the relationship between mean demand for Fresh and advertising expenditure is different for different levels of the price difference. For instance, increases in advertising expenditures might be more effective at some price differences than at others. To detect such an interaction, we can use t statistics and p values related to potential interaction terms. We illustrate this in the following example.

Example 12.9 The Fresh Detergent Case

Part 1: An interaction model and statistical inference In Example 12.7, we considered the Fresh demand model

$$y = \beta_0 + \beta_1 x_4 + \beta_2 x_3 + \beta_3 x_3^2 + \varepsilon.$$

We might logically suspect that there is an interaction between x_4 (price difference) and x_3 (advertising expenditure), so we include the interaction term x_4x_3 in this model as follows:

$$y = \beta_0 + \beta_1 x_4 + \beta_2 x_3 + \beta_3 x_3^2 + \beta_4 x_4 x_3 + \varepsilon.$$

Figure 12.25(a) presents the Excel output obtained by using this model to perform a regression analysis of the Fresh demand data. This output shows that each of the p values for testing the independent variables is less than 0.05. Therefore, we have strong evidence that each of x_4, x_3, x_3^2, and x_4x_3 is significant. In particular, since the p value related to x_4x_3 is 0.0361, we have strong evidence that the interaction variable x_4x_3 is important.

Suppose again that Enterprise Industries wishes to predict demand for Fresh in a future sales period when the price difference will be $0.20 ($x_4 = 0.20$) and the advertising expenditure for

FIGURE 12.25 Excel and MegaStat Output of a Regression Analysis of the Fresh Demand Data by Using the Interaction Model $y = \beta_0 + \beta_1 x_4 + \beta_2 x_3 + \beta_3 x_3^2 + \beta_4 x_4 x_3 + \varepsilon$

(a) The Excel output

Regression Statistics

Multiple R	0.9596
R Square	0.9209
Adjusted R Square	0.9083
Standard Error	0.2063
Observations	30

ANOVA	df	SS	MS	F	Significance F
Regression	4	12.3942	3.0985	72.7771	2.11E-13
Residual	25	1.0644	0.0426		
Total	29	13.4586			

	Coefficients	Standard Error	t Stat	P-value	Lower 95%	Upper 95%
Intercept	29.1133	7.4832	3.8905	0.0007	13.7013	44.5252
PriceDif (x4)	11.1342	4.4459	2.5044	0.0192	1.9778	20.2906
AdvExp (x3)	−7.6080	2.4691	−3.0813	0.0050	−12.6932	−2.5228
x3sq	0.6712	0.2027	3.3115	0.0028	0.2538	1.0887
x4x3	−1.4777	0.6672	−2.2149	0.0361	−2.8518	−0.1037

(b) Prediction using MegaStat

Predicted values for: Y

Predicted	95% Confidence Interval		95% Prediction Interval		Leverage
	lower	upper	lower	upper	
8.32725	8.21121	8.44329	7.88673	8.76777	0.075

Fresh will be \$650,000 ($x_3 = 6.50$). Using the least squares point estimates in Figure 12.25, the needed point prediction is

$$\hat{y} = 29.1133 + 11.1342(0.20) - 7.6080(6.50) + 0.6712(6.50)^2$$
$$-1.4777(0.20)(6.50)$$
$$= 8.32533 \text{ (or 832,533 bottles)}.$$

This point prediction is given (within rounding) on the MegaStat output of Figure 12.25(b), which also tells us that the 95 percent confidence interval for mean demand when x_4 equals 0.20 and x_3 equals 6.50 is [8.21121, 8.44329] and the 95 percent prediction interval for an individual demand when x_4 equals 0.20 and x_3 equals 6.50 is [7.88673, 8.76777]. Notice that this prediction interval is shorter than the 95 percent prediction interval—[7.82298, 8.76362]—obtained using the model that omits the interaction term $x_4 x_3$ and predicts y on the basis of x_4, x_3, and x_3^2. This is another indication that it is useful to include the interaction variable $x_4 x_3$ in the model.

Part 2: The nature of the interaction between x_3 and x_4 To understand the exact nature of the interaction between x_3 and x_4, consider the prediction equation

$$\hat{y} = 29.1133 + 11.1342x_4 - 7.6080x_3 + 0.6712x_3^2 - 1.4777x_4 x_3$$

obtained by using the Fresh demand interaction model. If we set x_4 equal to 0.10 and place this value of x_4 into the prediction equation, we obtain

$$\hat{y} = 29.1133 + 11.1342x_4 = 7.6080x_3 + 0.6712x_3^2 - 1.4777x_4 x_3$$
$$= 29.1133 + 11.1342(0.10) - 7.6080x_3 + 0.6712x_3^2 - 1.4777(0.10)x_3$$
$$= 30.2267 - 7.7558x_3 + 0.6712x_3^2.$$

FIGURE **12.26**   Interaction between x_4 and x_3 in the Fresh Detergent Case

(a) Calculating values of predicted demand when x_4 equals 0.10

x_3	$\hat{y} = 30.2267 - 7.7558x_3 + 0.6712x_3^2$
6.0	$\hat{y} = 30.2267 - 7.7558(6.0) + 0.6712(6.0)^2 = 7.86$
6.4	$\hat{y} = 30.2267 - 7.7558(6.4) + 0.6712(6.4)^2 = 8.08$
6.8	$\hat{y} = 30.2267 - 7.7558(6.8) + 0.6712(6.8)^2 = 8.52$

(b) Calculating values of predicted demand when x_4 equals 0.30

x_3	$\hat{y} = 32.4535 - 8.0513x_3 + 0.6712x_3^2$
6.0	$\hat{y} = 32.4535 - 8.0513(6.0) + 0.6712(6.0)^2 = 8.31$
6.4	$\hat{y} = 32.4535 - 8.0513(6.4) + 0.6712(6.4)^2 = 8.42$
6.8	$\hat{y} = 32.4535 - 8.0513(6.8) + 0.6712(6.8)^2 = 8.74$

(c) Illustrating the interaction

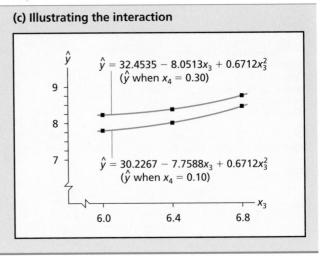

This quadratic equation shows us how predicted demand changes as advertising expenditure x_3 increases when the price difference is 0.10. Next we set x_4 equal to 0.30. If we place this value of x_4 into the Fresh prediction equation, we obtain

$$\hat{y} = 29.1133 + 11.1342x_4 - 7.6080x_3 + 0.6712x_3^2 - 1.4777x_4x_3$$
$$= 29.1133 + 11.1342(0.30) - 7.6080x_3 + 0.6712x_3^2 - 1.4777(0.30)x_3$$
$$= 32.4535 - 8.0513x_3 + 0.6712x_3^2.$$

This quadratic equation shows us how predicted demand changes as advertising expenditure x_3 increases when the price difference is 0.30.

In Figure 12.26(a) and (b), we calculate three points (predicted demands) on each of these quadratic curves. Figure 12.26(c) shows graphs of the two quadratic curves with the predicted demands plotted on these graphs. Comparing these graphs, we see that predicted demand is higher when x_4 equals 0.30 than when x_4 equals 0.10. This makes sense—predicted demand should be higher when Enterprise Industries has a larger price advantage. Furthermore, for each curve we see that predicted demand increases at an increasing rate as x_3 increases. However, the rate of increase in predicted demand is slower when x_4 equals 0.30 than when x_4 equals 0.10—this is the effect of the interaction between x_3 and x_4.

This type of interaction is logical because when the price difference is large (the price for Fresh is low relative to the average industry price), the mean demand for Fresh will be high (assuming the quality of Fresh is comparable to competing brands). Thus, with mean demand already high because many consumers are buying Fresh on the basis of price, there may be little opportunity for increased advertising expenditure to increase mean demand. However, when the price difference is smaller, there may be more potential consumers who are not buying Fresh who can be convinced to do so by increased advertising. Thus, when the price difference is smaller, increased advertising expenditure is more effective than it is when the price difference is larger.

It should be noted that this type of interaction between x_4 and x_3 was estimated from the observed Fresh demand data in Table 12.8. This is because we obtained the least squares point estimates using these data. We can only hypothesize the reasons behind the interaction and should point out that this type of interaction can be assumed to exist only for values of x_4 and x_3 inside the experimental region. Examination of the Fresh demand data shows that Fresh was being sold at either a price advantage (when the price of Fresh is lower than the average industry price) or a slight price disadvantage (when the price of Fresh is slightly higher than the average industry price). However, if Fresh were sometimes sold at a large price disadvantage, the type of interaction that exists between x_4 and x_3 might be different. In such a case, increases in advertising expenditure might be very ineffective because most consumers will not wish to buy a product with a much higher price.

A final comment is in order. If a p value indicates that an interaction term (say, x_1x_2) is significant, then it is usual practice to retain the corresponding linear terms (x_1 and x_2) in the model no matter what the size of their p values. The reason is that doing so can be shown to give a model that will better describe the interaction between x_1 and x_2.

Exercises for Section 12.9

CONCEPTS

12.35 If a regression model utilizes the independent variables x_1 and x_2, how do we form an interaction variable involving x_1 and x_2?

12.36 What is meant when we say that interaction exists between two independent variables?

METHODS AND APPLICATIONS

12.37 Consider the Froid Frozen Foods sales volume model

$$y = \beta_0 + \beta_1 x_1 + \beta_2 x_2 + \beta_3 x_1 x_2 + \varepsilon.$$

a. You saw in Example 12.8 that $\beta_1 + \beta_3 x_2$ is the slope of the line relating the mean y to x_1 at a given value of x_2. This slope is the increase in mean sales volume (in units of $10,000) obtained by increasing radio advertising by $1,000 when print advertising is x_2 thousand dollars. Using $b_1 = 2.3611$ and $b_3 = -0.3489$ from the MegaStat output in Figure 12.24 (page 455), a point estimate of the slope $\beta_1 + \beta_3 x_2$ is $2.3611 - 0.3489 x_2$. Calculate this point estimate for each of the values 1, 2, 3, 4, and 5 of x_2. Interpret the five point estimates.

b. You saw in Example 12.8 that $\beta_2 + \beta_3 x_1$ is the slope of the line relating mean y to x_2 at a given value of x_1. This slope is the increase in mean sales volume (in units of $10,000) obtained by increasing print advertising by $1,000 when radio advertising is x_1 thousand dollars. Using $b_2 = 4.1831$ and $b_3 = -0.3489$ from the MegaStat output in

Figure 12.24, a point estimate of the slope $\beta_2 + \beta_3 x_1$ is $4.1831 - 0.3489 x_1$. Calculate this point estimate for each of the values 1, 2, 3, 4, and 5 of x_1. Interpret the five point estimates.

c. By comparing the five point estimates calculated in part b with the five point estimates calculated in part a, discuss why it is reasonable to conclude that increasing print advertising expenditures is more effective than increasing radio advertising expenditures.

12.38 Managers who are transferred to a different country sometimes experience stress in the new environment, a state referred to as culture shock. To try to alleviate this state, a study is conducted on 30 managers. Before their departure, managers are given books (maximum ten) and videos (maximum five) detailing the culture that they will be working in. The number of books read and the number of videos watched are recorded. After six months in the new environment, managers self-report their level of culture shock on a 10-point scale, where 1 = feeling perfectly comfortable with the new environment and 10 = experiencing great distress (lower scores reflect less culture shock). The data for this study are reported in Table 12.12.

a. Figure 12.27(a) on the next page presents the Excel output of the regression analysis predicting culture shock with books read (x_1) and videos watched (x_2). Based on the result, do books and videos significantly reduce culture shock? Write the resulting regression equation.

TABLE **12.12** Self-Reported Culture Shock and Prior Number of Books Read and Videos Watched

Culture Shock (y)	Books (x₁)	Videos (x₂)	Culture Shock (y)	Books (x₁)	Videos (x₂)
8	1	1	8	2	1
2	10	4	7	2	3
3	9	5	1	10	4
4	8	4	2	9	5
5	6	1	9	0	1
6	1	2	5	3	2
1	9	5	3	2	3
9	0	1	9	1	0
2	9	5	1	9	5
5	4	1	8	1	3
3	8	3	7	1	2
4	5	4	2	9	5
6	2	2	10	1	1
7	1	2	3	7	5
2	10	5	2	10	4

FIGURE 12.27 Excel Output of a Regression Analysis of the Culture Shock Data

(a) Excel output of the regression analysis

SUMMARY OUTPUT

Regression Statistics	
Multiple R	0.930435
R Square	0.865709
Adjusted R Square	0.855761
Standard Error	1.076052
Observations	30

ANOVA

	df	SS	MS	F	Significance F
Regression	2	201.537	100.7685	87.02788	1.69E-12
Residual	27	31.26297	1.157888		
Total	29	232.8			

	Coefficients	Standard Error	t Stat	P-value	Lower 95%	Upper 95%	Lower 95.0%	Upper 95.0%
Intercept	8.843314	0.414223	21.34916	1.93E-18	7.993399	9.693229	7.993399	9.693229
Books (x1)	-0.478789	0.093215	-5.136386	2.11E-05	-0.670051	-0.287528	-0.670051	-0.287528
Videos (x2)	-0.555967	0.215487	-2.580047	0.015639	-0.998109	-0.113824	-0.998119	-0.113824

(b) Excel analysis of joint effect

SUMMARY OUTPUT

Regression Statistics	
Multiple R	0.94186076
R Square	0.88710169
Adjusted R Square	0.87407496
Standard Error	1.00542235
Observations	30

ANOVA

	df	SS	MS	F	Significance F
Regression	3	206.5172735	68.83909	68.09858	1.92E-12
Residual	26	26.28272647	1.010874		
Total	29	232.8			

	Coefficients	Standard Error	t Stat	P-value	Lower 95%	Upper 95%	Lower 95.0%	Upper 95.0%
Intercept	9.9909913	0.645871131	15.46902	1.25E-14	8.663383	11.318599	8.6633833	11.3185993
Books (x1)	-0.8315653	0.181236103	-4.588298	9.97E-05	-1.204102	-0.459029	-1.2041017	-0.45902893
Videos (x2)	-1.0985413	0.316690341	-3.468818	0.001836	-1.749508	-0.447575	-1.749508	-0.44757451
x1x2	0.11203898	0.050476874	2.21961	0.035376	0.008282	0.2157957	0.0082822	0.21579575

b. To investigate the possible interaction effects of books (x_1) and videos (x_2), a further analysis was conducted examining the joint effect of both (x_1x_2). The results of this analysis are presented in Figure 12.27(b). By combining books and videos, how well is culture shock predicted? Write the resulting regression equation.

c. Compare and contrast the results from the two analyses. Which is a stronger predictor of culture shock? Based on these findings, what would you suggest would be the best method to reduce culture shock for managers transferred to other countries?

PART 3 Dummy Variables and Advanced Statistical Inferences (Optional)

12.10 USING DUMMY VARIABLES TO MODEL QUALITATIVE INDEPENDENT VARIABLES (OPTIONAL)

While the levels (or values) of a quantitative independent variable are numerical, the levels of a **qualitative** independent variable are defined by describing them. For instance, the type of sales technique used by a door-to-door salesperson is a qualitative independent variable. Here we might define three different levels—high pressure, medium pressure, and low pressure.

We can model the effects of the different levels of a qualitative independent variable by using what we call **dummy variables** (also called **indicator variables**). Such variables are usually defined so that they take on two values—either 0 or 1. To see how we use dummy variables, we begin with an example.

Example 12.10

Part 1: The data and data plots Suppose that Electronics World, a chain of stores that sells audio and video equipment, has gathered the data in Table 12.13. These data concern store sales volume in July of last year (y, measured in thousands of dollars), the number of households in the store's area (x, measured in thousands), and the location of the store (on a suburban street or in a suburban shopping mall—a qualitative independent variable). Figure 12.28 gives a data plot of y versus x. Stores with a street location are plotted as solid dots, while stores with a mall location are plotted as asterisks. Notice that the line relating y to x for mall locations has a higher y intercept than does the line relating y to x for street locations.

Part 2: A dummy variable model In order to model the effects of the street and shopping mall locations, we define a dummy variable denoted D_M as follows:

$$D_M = \begin{cases} 1 & \text{if a store is in a mall location,} \\ 0 & \text{otherwise.} \end{cases}$$

Using this dummy variable, we consider the regression model

$$y = \beta_0 + \beta_1 x + \beta_2 D_M + \varepsilon.$$

This model and the definition of D_M imply the following:

1 For a street location, mean sales volume equals

$$\beta_0 + \beta_1 x + \beta_2 D_M = \beta_0 + \beta_1 x + \beta_2(0)$$
$$= \beta_0 + \beta_1 x.$$

2 For a mall location, mean sales volume equals

$$\beta_0 + \beta_1 x + \beta_2 D_M = \beta_0 + \beta_1 x + \beta_2(1)$$
$$= (\beta_0 + \beta_2) + \beta_1 x.$$

TABLE **12.13** The Electronics World Sales Volume Data

Store	Number of Households, x	Location	Sales Volume, y
1	161	Street	157.27
2	99	Street	93.28
3	135	Street	136.81
4	120	Street	123.79
5	164	Street	153.51
6	221	Mall	241.74
7	179	Mall	201.54
8	204	Mall	206.71
9	214	Mall	229.78
10	101	Mall	135.22

FIGURE **12.28** Plot of the Sales Volume Data and a Geometrical Interpretation of the Model $y = \beta_0 + \beta_1 x + \beta_2 D_M + \varepsilon$

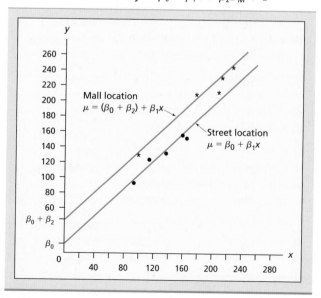

FIGURE 12.29   Excel Output of a Regression Analysis of the Sales Volume Data Using the Model $y = \beta_0 + \beta_1 x + \beta_2 D_M + \varepsilon$

Regression Statistics	
Multiple R	0.9913
R Square	0.9827
Adjusted R Square	0.9778
Standard Error	7.3288
Observations	10

ANOVA	df	SS	MS	F	Significance F
Regression	2	21,411.7977	10,705.8989	199.3216	6.75E-07
Residual	7	375.9817	53.7117		
Total	9	21,787.7795			

	Coefficients	Standard Error	t Stat	P-value	Lower 95%	Upper 95%
Intercept	17.3598	9.4470	1.8376	0.1087	−4.9788	39.6985
Households (x)	0.8510	0.0652	13.0439	3.63E-06	0.6968	1.0053
DummyMall	29.2157	5.5940	5.2227	0.0012	15.9881	42.4434

Thus, the dummy variable allows us to model the situation illustrated in Figure 12.28. Here the lines relating mean sales volume to x for street and mall locations have different y intercepts—β_0 and $(\beta_0 + \beta_2)$—and the same slope, β_1. Note that β_2 is the difference between the mean monthly sales volume for stores in mall locations and the mean monthly sales volume for stores in street locations, when all these stores have the same number of households in their areas. That is, we can say that β_2 represents the effect on mean sales of a mall location compared to a street location. The Excel output in Figure 12.29 tells us that the least squares point estimate of β_2 is $b_2 = 29.2157$. This says that for any given number of households in a store's area, we estimate that the mean monthly sales volume in a mall location is \$29,215.70 greater than the mean monthly sales volume in a street location.

Part 3: A dummy variable model for comparing three locations   In addition to the data concerning street and mall locations in Table 12.13, Electronics World has also collected data concerning downtown locations. The complete data set is given in Table 12.14 and plotted in Figure 12.30. Here stores with a downtown location are plotted as open circles. A model describing these data is

$$y = \beta_0 + \beta_1 x + \beta_2 D_M + \beta_3 D_D + \varepsilon.$$

TABLE 12.14   The Complete Electronics World Sales Volume Data

Store	Number of Households, x	Location	Sales Volume, y
1	161	Street	157.27
2	99	Street	93.28
3	135	Street	136.81
4	120	Street	123.79
5	164	Street	153.51
6	221	Mall	241.74
7	179	Mall	201.54
8	204	Mall	206.71
9	214	Mall	229.78
10	101	Mall	135.22
11	231	Downtown	224.71
12	206	Downtown	195.29
13	248	Downtown	242.16
14	107	Downtown	115.21
15	205	Downtown	197.82

FIGURE 12.30   Plot of the Complete Electronics World Sales Volume Data and a Geometrical Interpretation of the Model $y = \beta_0 + \beta_1 x + \beta_2 D_M + \beta_3 D_D + \varepsilon$

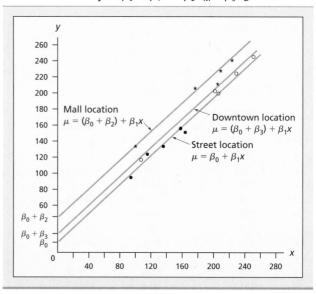

The dummy variable D_M is as previously defined and the dummy variable D_D is defined as follows:

$$D_D = \begin{cases} 1 & \text{if a store is in a downtown location,} \\ 0 & \text{otherwise.} \end{cases}$$

Then we have the following:

1 For a street location, mean sales volume equals

$$\beta_0 + \beta_1 x + \beta_2 D_M + \beta_3 D_D = \beta_0 + \beta_1 x + \beta_2(0) + \beta_3(0)$$
$$= \beta_0 + \beta_1 x.$$

2 For a mall location, mean sales volume equals

$$\beta_0 + \beta_1 x + \beta_2 D_M + \beta_3 D_D = \beta_0 + \beta_1 x + \beta_2(1) + \beta_3(0)$$
$$= (\beta_0 + \beta_2) + \beta_1 x.$$

3 For a downtown location, mean sales volume equals

$$\beta_0 + \beta_1 x + \beta_2 D_M + \beta_3 D_D = \beta_0 + \beta_1 x + \beta_2(0) + \beta_3(1)$$
$$= (\beta_0 + \beta_3) + \beta_1 x.$$

The dummy variables allow us to model the situation illustrated in Figure 12.30. Here the lines relating mean sales volume to x for street, mall, and downtown locations have different y-intercepts—β_0, $(\beta_0 + \beta_2)$, and $(\beta_0 + \beta_3)$—and the same slope, β_1. Note that β_2 represents the effect on mean sales of a mall location compared to a street location, and β_3 represents the effect on mean sales of a downtown location compared to a street location. Furthermore, the difference between β_2 and β_3, $\beta_2 - \beta_3$, represents the effect on mean sales of a mall location compared to a downtown location.

Part 4: Comparing the three locations Figure 12.31 gives the MegaStat output of a regression analysis of the sales volume data using the dummy variable model. The output tells us

FIGURE 12.31 MegaStat Output of a Regression Analysis of the Sales Volume Data Using the Model
$$y = \beta_0 + \beta_1 x + \beta_2 D_M + \beta_3 D_D + \varepsilon$$

Regression Analysis

R^2	0.987		
Adjusted R^2	0.983	n	15
R	0.993	k	3
Std. Error	6.349	Dep. Var.	**Sales**

ANOVA table

Source	SS	df	MS	F	p-value
Regression	33,268.6953	3	11,089.5651	275.07	1.27E-10
Residual	443.4650	11	40.3150		
Total	33,712.1603	14			

Regression output

					confidence interval	
variables	coefficients	std. error	t (df=11)	p-value	95% lower	95% upper
Intercept	14.9777	6.1884	2.420	0.0340	1.3570	28.5984
DM	28.3738	4.4613	6.360	0.0001	18.5545	38.1930
DD	6.8638	4.7705	1.439	0.1780	−3.6360	17.3635
Households	0.8686	0.0405	21.452	2.52E-10	0.7795	0.9577

Predicted values for: Sales

				95% Confidence Interval		95% Prediction Interval		
DM	DD	Households	Predicted	lower	upper	lower	upper	Leverage
1	0	200	217.06913	210.65476	223.48351	201.69240	232.44586	0.211

that the least squares point estimate of β_2 is $b_2 = 28.3738$. This says that for any given number of households in a store's area, we estimate that the mean monthly sales volume in a mall location is \$28,373.80 greater than the mean monthly sales volume in a street location. Furthermore, the output tells us that a 95 percent confidence interval for β_2 is [18.5545, 38.1930], so we are 95 percent confident that for any given number of households in a store's area, the mean monthly sales volume in a mall location is between \$18,554.50 and \$38,193.00 greater than the mean monthly sales volume in a street location. The output also shows that the t statistic for testing H_0: $\beta_2 = 0$ versus H_a: $\beta_2 \neq 0$ equals 6.360 and that the related p value is 0.001. Therefore, we have very strong evidence that there is a difference between the mean monthly sales volumes in mall and street locations.

We next note that the output in Figure 12.31 shows that the least squares point estimate of β_3 is $b_3 = 6.8638$. Therefore, we estimate that for any given number of households in a store's area, the mean monthly sales volume in a downtown location is \$6,863.80 greater than the mean monthly sales volume in a street location. Furthermore, the output shows that a 95 percent confidence interval for β_3 is [−3.6360, 17.3635]. This says we are 95 percent confident that for any given number of households in a store's area, the mean monthly sales volume in a downtown location is between \$3,636.00 less than and \$17,363.50 greater than the mean monthly sales volume in a street location. The output also shows that the t statistic and p value for testing H_0: $\beta_3 = 0$ versus H_a: $\beta_3 \neq 0$ are, respectively, 1.439 and 0.1780. Therefore, we do not have strong evidence that there is a difference between the mean monthly sales volumes in downtown and street locations.

Finally, note that since $b_2 = 28.3738$ and $b_3 = 6.8638$, the point estimate of $\beta_2 - \beta_3$ is $b_2 - b_3 = 28.3738 - 6.8638 = 21.51$. Therefore, we estimate that the mean monthly sales volume in a mall location is \$21,510 higher than the mean monthly sales volume in a downtown location. Near the end of this section, we will show how to compare the mall and downtown locations by using a confidence interval and a hypothesis test. We will find that there is very strong evidence that the mean monthly sales volume in a mall location is higher than the mean monthly sales volume in a downtown location. In summary, the mall location seems to give a higher mean monthly sales volume than either the street or the downtown location.

Part 5: Predicting future sales volume Suppose that Electronics World wishes to predict the sales volume in a future month for an individual store that has 200,000 households in its area and is located in a shopping mall. The point prediction of this sales volume is (since $D_M = 1$ and $D_D = 0$ when a store is in a shopping mall)

$$\hat{y} = b_0 + b_1(200) + b_2(1) + b_3(0)$$
$$= 14.9777 + 0.8686(200) + 28.3738(1)$$
$$= 217.07.$$

This point prediction is given at the bottom of the output in Figure 12.31(a). The corresponding 95 percent prediction interval, which is [201.69, 232.45], says we are 95 percent confident that the sales volume in a future sales period for an individual mall store that has 200,000 households in its area will be between \$201,690 and \$232,450.

Part 6: Interaction models Consider the Electronics World data for street and mall locations given in Table 12.13 (page 461) and the model

$$y = \beta_0 + \beta_1 x + \beta_2 D_M + \beta_3 x D_M + \varepsilon.$$

This model uses the **cross-product**, or **interaction**, term $x D_M$ and implies the following:

1   For a street location, mean sales volume equals (since $D_M = 0$)

$$\beta_0 + \beta_1 x + \beta_2(0) + \beta_3 x(0) = \beta_0 + \beta_1 x.$$

2   For a mall location, mean sales volume equals (since $D_M = 1$)

$$\beta_0 + \beta_1 x + \beta_2(1) + \beta_3 x(1) = (\beta_0 + \beta_2) + (\beta_1 + \beta_3)x.$$

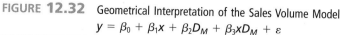

FIGURE 12.32 Geometrical Interpretation of the Sales Volume Model

$$y = \beta_0 + \beta_1 x + \beta_2 D_M + \beta_3 x D_M + \varepsilon$$

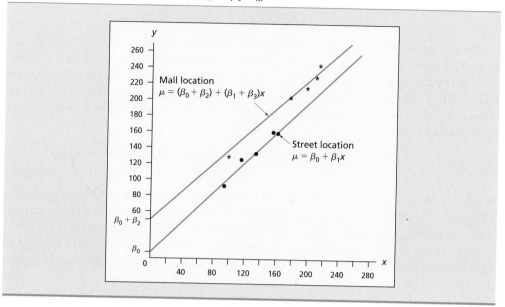

FIGURE 12.33 MegaStat Output Using the Interaction Model $y = \beta_0 + \beta_1 x + \beta_2 DM + \beta_3 x DM + \varepsilon$

Regression Analysis

R^2	0.984			
Adjusted R^2	0.975	n	10	
R	0.992	k	3	
Std. Error	7.709	Dep. Var.	**Sales**	

ANOVA table

Source	SS	df	MS	F	p-value
Regression	21,431.1861	3	7,143.7287	120.20	9.53E-06
Residual	356.5933	6	59.4322		
Total	21,787.7795	9			

Regression output

variables	coefficients	std. error	t (df = 6)	p-value	confidence interval 95% lower	95% upper
Intercept	7.9004	19.3142	0.409	0.6967	−39.3598	55.1607
X	0.9207	0.1399	6.579	0.0006	0.5783	1.2631
DM	42.7297	24.3812	1.753	0.1302	−16.9290	102.3885
XDM	−0.0917	0.1606	−0.571	0.5886	−0.4846	0.3012

As illustrated in Figure 12.32, if we use this model, then the straight lines relating mean sales volume to x for street and mall locations have *different y intercepts* and *different slopes*. Therefore, we say that this model assumes an *interaction* between x and store location. Such a model is appropriate if the relationship between mean sales volume and x depends on (that is, is different for) the street and mall store locations. In general, an interaction exists between two independent variables if the relationship between (for example, the slope of the line relating) the mean value of the dependent variable and one of the independent variables depends upon the value (or level) of the other independent variable. Figure 12.33 gives the MegaStat output of a regression analysis of the sales volume data using the interaction model. Here D_M and $x D_M$ are labelled as DM and XDM, respectively, on the output. The output tells us that the p value related to the significance of $x D_M$ is 0.5886. This large p value tells us that the interaction term is not important. It follows that the no-interaction model seems best.

Next consider the Electronics World data for street, mall, and downtown locations given in Table 12.14 (page 462). In modelling these data, if we believe that an interaction exists between the number of households in a store's area and store location, we might consider using the model

$$y = \beta_0 + \beta_1 x + \beta_2 D_M + \beta_3 D_D + \beta_4 x D_M + \beta_5 x D_D + \varepsilon.$$

Similar to Figure 12.32, this model implies that the straight lines relating mean sales volume to x for the street, mall, and downtown locations have *different y intercepts* and *different slopes*. If we perform a regression analysis of the sales volume data using this interaction model, we find that the p values related to the significance of $x D_M$ and $x D_D$ are large: -0.5334 and 0.8132, respectively. Because these interaction terms are not significant, it seems best to employ the no-interaction model.

In general, if we wish to model the effect of a qualitative independent variable with a levels, we use $a - 1$ dummy variables. The parameter multiplied by a particular dummy variable expresses the effect of the level represented by that dummy variable with respect to the effect of the level that is not represented by a dummy variable. For example, if we wish to compare the effects on sales, y, of four different types of advertising campaigns—television (T), radio (R), magazine (M), and mailed coupons (C)—we might employ the model

$$y = \beta_0 + \beta_1 D_T + \beta_2 D_R + \beta_3 D_M + \varepsilon.$$

This model does not use a dummy variable to represent the mailed coupon advertising campaign. The parameter β_1 is the difference between mean sales when a television advertising campaign is used and mean sales when a mailed coupon advertising campaign is used. The interpretations of β_2 and β_3 follow similarly. As another example, if we wish to employ a confidence interval and a hypothesis test to compare the mall and downtown locations in the Electronics World example, we can use the model

$$y = \beta_0 + \beta_1 x + \beta_2 D_S + \beta_3 D_M + \varepsilon.$$

Here the dummy variable D_M is as previously defined, and

$$D_S = \begin{cases} 1 & \text{if a store is in a street location,} \\ 0 & \text{otherwise.} \end{cases}$$

Because this model does not use a dummy variable to represent the downtown location, the parameter β_2 expresses the effect on mean sales of a street location compared to a downtown location, and the parameter β_3 expresses the effect on mean sales of a mall location compared to a downtown location.

The Excel output of the least squares point estimates of the parameters of this model is as follows:

	Coefficients	Standard Error	t Stat	P-value	Lower 95%	Upper 95%
Intercept	21.8415	8.5585	2.5520	0.0269	3.0044	40.6785
Households (x)	0.8686	0.0405	21.4520	2.52E-10	0.7795	0.9577
DummyStreet	−6.8638	4.7705	−1.4388	0.1780	−17.3635	3.6360
DummyMall	21.5100	4.0651	5.2914	0.0003	12.5628	30.4572

Because the least squares point estimate of β_3 is $b_3 = 21.51$, we estimate that for any given number of households in a store's area, the mean monthly sales volume in a mall location is $\$21,510$ higher than the mean monthly sales volume in a downtown location. The Excel output tells us that a 95 percent confidence interval for β_3 is [12.5628, 30.4572]. Therefore, we are 95 percent confident that for any given number of households in a store's area, the mean monthly sales volume in a mall location is between $\$12,562.80$ and $\$30,457.20$ greater than the mean monthly sales volume in a downtown location. The output also shows that the t

statistic and p value for testing $H_0: \beta_3 = 0$ versus $H_a: \beta_3 \neq 0$ in this model are, respectively, 5.2914 and 0.0003. Therefore, we have extremely strong evidence that there is a difference between the mean monthly sales volumes in mall and downtown locations.

   In some situations, dummy variables represent the effects of unusual events or occurrences that may have an important effect on the dependent variable. For instance, suppose we wish to build a regression model relating quarterly sales of automobiles (y) to automobile prices (x_1), fuel prices (x_2), and personal income (x_3). If an autoworkers' strike occurred in a particular quarter that had a major effect on automobile sales, then we might define a dummy variable D_S to be equal to 1 if an autoworkers' strike occurs and 0 otherwise. The least squares point estimate of the regression parameter multiplied by D_S would estimate the effect of the strike on mean auto sales. Finally, dummy variables can be used to model the impact of regularly occurring *seasonal* influences on time series data—for example, the effect of the hot summer months on soft drink sales. This is discussed in Chapter 16.

Exercises for Section 12.10

CONCEPTS

12.39 What is a qualitative independent variable?

12.40 How are dummy variables used to model the effects of a qualitative independent variable?

12.41 What does the parameter multiplied by a dummy variable express?

METHODS AND APPLICATIONS

12.42 Neter, Kutner, Nachtsheim, and Wasserman (1996) relate the speed, y, with which a particular insurance innovation is adopted to the size of the insurance firm, x, and the type of firm. The dependent variable y is measured by the number of months elapsed between the time the first firm adopted the innovation and the time the firm being considered adopted the innovation. The size of the firm, x, is measured by the total assets of the firm, and the type of firm—a qualitative independent variable—is either a mutual company or a stock company. The data in Table 12.15 are observed.
   a. Discuss why the data plot below indicates that the model

$$y = \beta_0 + \beta_1 x + \beta_2 D_S + \varepsilon$$

might appropriately describe the observed data. Here D_S equals 1 if the firm is a stock company and 0 if the firm is a mutual company.

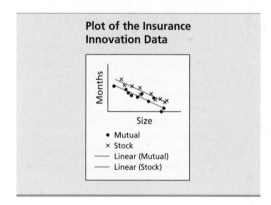

Plot of the Insurance Innovation Data

- Mutual
× Stock
— Linear (Mutual)
— Linear (Stock)

b. The model of part a implies that the mean adoption time of an insurance innovation by mutual companies with asset size x equals

$$\beta_0 + \beta_1 x + \beta_2(0) = \beta_0 + \beta_1 x$$

and that the mean adoption time by stock companies

TABLE 12.15   The Insurance Innovation Data

Firm	Number of Months Elapsed, y	Size of Firm (Millions of Dollars), x	Type of Firm	Firm	Number of Months Elapsed, y	Size of Firm (Millions of Dollars), x	Type of Firm
1	17	151	Mutual	11	28	164	Stock
2	26	92	Mutual	12	15	272	Stock
3	21	175	Mutual	13	11	295	Stock
4	30	31	Mutual	14	38	68	Stock
5	22	104	Mutual	15	31	85	Stock
6	0	277	Mutual	16	21	224	Stock
7	12	210	Mutual	17	20	166	Stock
8	19	120	Mutual	18	13	305	Stock
9	4	290	Mutual	19	30	124	Stock
10	16	238	Mutual	20	14	246	Stock

FIGURE **12.34**   Excel Output of a Regression Analysis of the Insurance Innovation Data Using the Model
$$y = \beta_0 + \beta_1 x + \beta_2 D_S + \varepsilon$$

Regression Statistics	
Multiple R	0.9461
R Square	0.8951
Adjusted R Square	0.8827
Standard Error	3.2211
Observations	20

ANOVA	df	SS	MS	F	Significance F
Regression	2	1,504.4133	752.2067	72.4971	4.77E-09
Residual	17	176.3867	10.3757		
Total	19	1,680.8			

	Coefficients	Standard Error	t Stat	P-value	Lower 95%	Upper 95%
Intercept	33.8741	1.8139	18.6751	9.15E-13	30.0472	37.7010
Size of Firm (x)	−0.1017	0.0089	−11.4430	2.07E-09	−0.1205	−0.0830
DummyStock	8.0555	1.4591	5.5208	3.74E-05	4.9770	11.1339

with asset size x equals

$$\beta_0 + \beta_1 x + \beta_2(1) = \beta_0 + \beta_1 x + \beta_2$$

The difference between these two means equals the model parameter β_2. In your own words, interpret β_2. Does this interpretation make practical sense?

c. Figure 12.34 presents the Excel output of a regression analysis of the insurance innovation data using the model of part a. Using the output, test $H_0: \beta_2 = 0$ versus $H_a: \beta_2 \neq 0$ by setting $\alpha = 0.05$ and 0.01. Interpret the result of this test. Does this interpretation make practical sense? Also use the computer output to find, report, and interpret a 95 percent confidence interval for β_2.

d. If we add the interaction term $x D_S$ to the model of part a, we find that the p value related to this term is 0.9821. What does this imply?

12.43 THE SHELF DISPLAY CASE

The Tastee Bakery Company supplies a bakery product to many supermarkets in a metropolitan area. The company wishes to study the effect of the height of the shelf display employed by the supermarkets on monthly sales, y (measured in cases of ten units each), for this product. Shelf display height has three levels—bottom (B), middle (M), and top (T). For each shelf display height, six supermarkets of equal sales potential will be randomly selected, and each supermarket will display the product using its assigned shelf height for a month. At the end of the month, sales of the bakery product at the 18 participating stores will be recorded. When the experiment is carried out, the data in Table 12.16 are obtained. Here we assume that the set of sales amounts for each display height is a sample that has been randomly selected from the population of all sales amounts that could be obtained (at supermarkets of the given sales potential) when using that display height. To compare the population mean sales amounts μ_B, μ_M, and μ_T that would be obtained by using the bottom,

TABLE **12.16**   Bakery Sales Study Data (Sales in Cases)

Shelf Display Height		
Bottom, B	Middle, M	Top, T
58.2	73.0	52.4
53.7	78.1	49.7
55.8	75.4	50.9
55.7	76.2	54.0
52.5	78.4	52.1
58.9	82.1	49.9

middle, and top display heights, we use the following dummy variable regression model:

$$y = \beta_B + \beta_M D_M + \beta_T D_T + \varepsilon.$$

Here D_M equals 1 if a middle display height is used and 0 otherwise; D_T equals 1 if a top display height is used and 0 otherwise. Figure 12.35 presents the MegaStat output of a regression analysis of the bakery sales study data using this model.[1]

a. By using the definitions of the dummy variables, show that

$$\mu_B = \beta_B, \ \mu_M = \beta_B + \beta_M, \text{ and } \mu_T = \beta_B + \beta_T.$$

b. Use the overall F statistic to test $H_0: \beta_M = \beta_T = 0$ or, equivalently, $H_0: \mu_B = \mu_M = \mu_T$. Interpret the result of this test. Does this interpretation make practical sense?

c. Show that your results in part a imply that

$$\mu_M - \mu_B = \beta_M, \ \mu_T - \mu_B = \beta_T,$$
$$\text{and } \mu_M - \mu_T = \beta_M - \beta_T.$$

Then use the least squares point estimates of the model parameters to find a point estimate of each of the three differences in means. Also find a 95 percent confidence interval for and test the significance of each of the first two differences in means. Interpret your results.

---

[1] In general, the regression approach of this exercise produces the same comparisons of several population means that are produced by **one-way analysis of variance** (see Section 10.2). In Appendix G on *Connect*, we discuss the regression approach to **two-way analysis of variance** (see Section 10.4).

FIGURE **12.35**   MegaStat Output of a Dummy Variable Regression Analysis of the Bakery Sales Data in Table 12.16

Regression Analysis

R^2	0.961	n	18
Adjusted R^2	0.956	k	2
R	0.980	Dep. Var.	Sales (y)
Std. Error	2.482		

ANOVA table

Source	SS	df	MS	F	p-value
Regression	2,273.8800	2	1,136.9400	184.57	2.74E-11
Residual	92.4000	15	6.1600		
Total	2,366.2800	17			

Regression output

					confidence interval	
variables	coefficients	std. error	t (df=15)	p-value	95% lower	95% upper
Intercept	55.8000	1.0132	55.071	9.96E-19	53.6403	57.9597
Middle	21.4000	1.4329	14.934	2.07E-10	18.3457	24.4543
Top	−4.3000	1.4329	−3.001	0.0090	−7.3543	−1.2457

Predicted values for: Sales (y)

			95% Confidence Interval		95% Prediction Interval		
Middle	Top	Predicted	lower	upper	lower	upper	Leverage
1	0	77.2000	75.0403	79.3597	71.4860	82.9140	0.167

d. Find a point estimate of mean sales when using a middle display height, a 95 percent confidence interval for mean sales when using a middle display height, and a 95 percent prediction interval for sales at an individual supermarket that employs a middle display height (see the bottom of the output in Figure 12.35).

e. Consider the alternative model

$$y = \beta_T + \beta_B D_B + \beta_M D_M + \varepsilon.$$

Here D_B equals 1 if a bottom display height is used and 0 otherwise. The output of the least squares point estimates of the parameters of this model is as follows:

	Coefficients	Standard Error	t Stat	P-value
Intercept	51.5	1.013246	50.82677	3.3E-18
Middle	25.7	1.432946	17.93508	1.52E-11
Bottom	4.3	1.432946	3.000812	0.008958

Because β_M expresses the effect of the middle display height with respect to the effect of the top display height, β_M equals $\mu_M - \mu_T$. Use the output to calculate a 95 percent confidence interval for and test the significance of $\mu_M - \mu_T$. Interpret your results.

12.44 THE FRESH DETERGENT CASE

Recall from Exercise 12.7 (on pages 423 and 424) that Enterprise Industries has observed the historical data in Table 12.4 (page 424) concerning y (demand for Fresh liquid laundry detergent), x_1 (the price of Fresh), x_2 (the average industry price of competitors' similar detergents), and x_3 (Enterprise Industries' advertising expenditure for Fresh). To ultimately increase the demand for Fresh, Enterprise Industries' marketing department is comparing the effectiveness of three different advertising campaigns. These campaigns are denoted as campaigns A, B, and C. Campaign A consists entirely of television

TABLE **12.17**   Advertising Campaigns Used by Enterprise Industries

Sales Period	Advertising Campaign	Sales Period	Advertising Campaign
1	B	16	B
2	B	17	B
3	B	18	A
4	A	19	B
5	C	20	B
6	A	21	C
7	C	22	A
8	C	23	A
9	B	24	A
10	C	25	A
11	A	26	B
12	C	27	C
13	C	28	B
14	A	29	C
15	B	30	C

commercials, campaign B consists of a balanced mixture of television and radio commercials, and campaign C consists of a balanced mixture of television, radio, newspaper, and magazine advertisements. To conduct the study, Enterprise Industries has randomly selected one advertising campaign to be used in each of the 30 sales periods in Table 12.4. Although each of campaigns A, B, and C should be used in 10 of the 30 sales periods, Enterprise Industries has made previous commitments to the advertising media involved in the study. As a result, campaigns A, B, and C were randomly assigned to, respectively, 9, 11, and 10 sales periods. Furthermore, advertising was done in only the first three weeks of each sales period, so that the carryover effect of the campaign used in a sales period to the next sales period would be minimized. Table 12.17 lists the campaigns used in the sales periods.

FIGURE **12.36**   MegaStat Output of a Dummy Variable Regression Model Analysis of the Fresh Demand Data

Regression Analysis

	R^2 0.960		
	Adjusted R^2 0.951	n 30	
	R 0.980	k 5	
	Std. Error 0.150	Dep. Var. **Demand**	

ANOVA table

Source	SS	df	MS	F	p-value
Regression	12.9166	5	2.5833	114.39	6.24E-16
Residual	0.5420	24	0.0226		
Total	13.4586	29			

Regression output

					confidence interval	
variables	coefficients	std. error	t (df = 24)	p-value	95% lower	95% upper
Intercept	8.7154	1.5849	5.499	1.18E-05	5.4443	11.9866
X1	−2.7680	0.4144	−6.679	6.58E-07	−3.6234	−1.9127
X2	1.6667	0.1913	8.711	6.77E-09	1.2718	2.0616
X3	0.4927	0.0806	6.110	2.60E-06	0.3263	0.6592
DB	0.2695	0.0695	3.880	0.0007	0.1262	0.4128
DC	0.4396	0.0703	6.250	1.85E-06	0.2944	0.5847

Predicted values for: Demand

	95% Confidence Interval		95% Prediction Interval			
Predicted	lower	upper	lower	upper	Leverage	
8.61621	8.51380	8.71862	8.28958	8.94285	0.109	

To compare the effectiveness of advertising campaigns A, B, and C, we define two dummy variables. Specifically, we define the dummy variable D_B to equal 1 if campaign B is used in a sales period and 0 otherwise. Furthermore, we define the dummy variable D_C to equal 1 if campaign C is used in a sales period and 0 otherwise. Figure 12.36 presents the MegaStat output of a regression analysis of the Fresh demand data by using the model

$$y = \beta_0 + \beta_1 x_1 + \beta_2 x_2 + \beta_3 x_3 + \beta_4 D_B + \beta_5 D_C + \varepsilon.$$

a. In this model, the parameter β_4 represents the effect on mean demand of advertising campaign B compared to advertising campaign A, and the parameter β_5 represents the effect on mean demand of advertising campaign C compared to advertising campaign A. Use the regression output to find and report a point estimate of each of the above effects and to test the significance of each of the above effects. Also find and report a 95 percent confidence interval for each of the above effects. Interpret your results.

b. The prediction results at the bottom of the MegaStat output correspond to a future period

when the price of Fresh will be $x_1 = 3.70$, the competitor's average price of similar detergents will be $x_2 = 3.90$, the advertising expenditure for Fresh will be $x_3 = 6.50$, and advertising campaign C will be used. Show how $\hat{y} = 8.61621$ is calculated. Then find, report, and interpret a 95 percent confidence interval for mean demand and a 95 percent prediction interval for an individual demand when $x_1 = 3.70$, $x_2 = 3.90$, $x_3 = 6.50$, and campaign C is used.

c. Consider the alternative model

$$y = \beta_0 + \beta_1 x_1 + \beta_2 x_2 + \beta_3 x_3 + \beta_4 D_A + \beta_5 D_C + \varepsilon.$$

Here D_A equals 1 if advertising campaign A is used and 0 otherwise. Describe the effect represented by the regression parameter β_5.

d. The MegaStat output of the least squares point estimates of the parameters of the model of part c is as in Figure 12.37. Use the MegaStat output to test the significance of the effect represented by β_5 and find a 95 percent confidence interval for β_5. Interpret your results.

FIGURE **12.37**   MegaStat Output for Exercise 12.44(d)

Regression output

					confidence interval	
variables	coefficients	std. error	t (df = 23)	p-value	95% lower	95% upper
Intercept	8.9849	1.5971	5.626	8.61E-06	5.6888	12.2811
X1	−2.7680	0.4144	−6.679	6.58E-07	−3.6234	−1.9127
X2	1.6667	0.1913	8.711	6.77E-09	1.2718	2.0616
X3	0.4927	0.0806	6.110	2.60E-06	0.3263	0.6592
DA	−0.2695	0.0695	−3.880	0.0007	−0.4128	−0.1262
DC	0.1701	0.0669	2.543	0.0179	0.0320	0.3081

FIGURE **12.38** MegaStat Output of a Regression Analysis of the Fresh Demand Data Using the Model
$$y = \beta_0 + \beta_1 x_1 + \beta_2 x_2 + \beta_3 x_3 + \beta_4 D_B + \beta_5 D_C + \beta_6 x_3 D_B + \beta_7 x_3 D_C + \varepsilon$$

Regression output

variables	coefficients	std. error	t (df = 22)	p-value	confidence interval 95% lower	95% upper
Intercept	8.7619	1.7071	5.133	3.82E-05	5.2216	12.3021
X1	−2.7895	0.4339	−6.428	1.81E-06	−3.6894	−1.8895
X2	1.6365	0.2062	7.938	6.72E-08	1.2089	2.0641
X3	0.5160	0.1288	4.007	0.0006	0.2489	0.7831
DB	0.2539	0.8722	0.291	0.7737	−1.5550	2.0628
DC	0.8435	0.9739	0.866	0.3958	−1.1762	2.8631
X3DB	0.0030	0.1334	0.023	0.9822	−0.2736	0.2797
X3DC	−0.0629	0.1502	−0.419	0.6794	−0.3744	0.2486

Predicted values for: Demand

Predicted	95% Confidence Interval lower	upper	95% Prediction Interval lower	upper	Leverage	
8.61178	8.50372	8.71984	8.27089	8.95266	0.112	

R^2 0.960
Adjusted R^2 0.948
R 0.980
Std. Error 0.156

12.45 THE FRESH DETERGENT CASE

Figure 12.38 presents the MegaStat output of a regression analysis of the Fresh demand data using the model

$$y = \beta_0 + \beta_1 x_1 + \beta_2 x_2 + \beta_3 x_3 + \beta_4 D_B + \beta_5 D_C \\ + \beta_6 x_3 D_B + \beta_7 x_3 D_C + \varepsilon,$$

where the dummy variables D_B and D_C are defined as in Exercise 12.44.

a. This model assumes that there is an interaction between advertising expenditure, x_3, and type of advertising campaign. What do the p values related to the significance of the cross-product terms $x_3 D_B$

and $x_3 D_C$ say about the need for these interaction terms and about whether there is an interaction between x_3 and the type of advertising campaign?

b. The prediction results at the bottom of Figure 12.38 are for a future sales period in which $x_1 = 3.70$, $x_2 = 3.90$, $x_3 = 6.50$, and advertising campaign C will be used. Use the output to find and report a point prediction of and a 95 percent prediction interval for Fresh demand in such a sales period. Is the 95 percent prediction interval given by this model shorter or longer than the 95 percent prediction interval given by the model that utilizes D_B and D_C in Exercise 12.44? What are the implications of this comparison?

12.11 THE PARTIAL *F* TEST: TESTING THE SIGNIFICANCE OF A PORTION OF A REGRESSION MODEL (OPTIONAL)

We now present a **partial F test** that allows us to test the significance of a set of independent variables in a regression model. That is, we can use this F test to test the significance of a *portion* of a regression model. For example, in the Electronics World situation, we employed the dummy variable model

$$y = \beta_0 + \beta_1 x + \beta_2 D_M + \beta_3 D_D + \varepsilon.$$

It might be useful to test the significance of the dummy variables D_M (mall location) and D_D (downtown location). We can do this by testing the null hypothesis

$$H_0: \beta_2 = \beta_3 = 0,$$

which says that neither dummy variable significantly affects y, versus the alternative hypothesis

$$H_a: \text{at least one of } \beta_2 \text{ and } \beta_3 \text{ does not equal } 0,$$

which says that at least one of the dummy variables significantly affects y. Because β_2 and β_3 represent the effects of the mall and downtown locations with respect to the street location, the null hypothesis says that the effects of the mall, downtown, and street locations on mean sales volume do not differ (nonsignificant dummy variables). The alternative hypothesis says that at least two locations have different effects on mean sales volume (at least one significant dummy variable).

In general, consider the regression model

$$y = \beta_0 + \beta_1 x_1 + \cdots + \beta_g x_g + \beta_{g+1} x_{g+1} + \cdots + \beta_k x_k + \varepsilon.$$

Suppose we wish to test the null hypothesis

$$H_0: \beta_{g+1} = \beta_{g+2} = \cdots = \beta_k = 0,$$

which says that none of the independent variables $x_{g+1}, x_{g+2}, \ldots, x_k$ affect y, versus the alternative hypothesis

$$H_a: \text{at least one of } \beta_{g+1}, \beta_{g+2}, \ldots, \beta_k \text{ does not equal } 0,$$

which says that at least one of the independent variables $x_{g+1}, x_{g+2}, \ldots, x_k$ affects y. If we can reject H_0 in favour of H_a by specifying a *small* probability of a Type I error, then it is reasonable to conclude that at least one of $x_{g+1}, x_{g+2}, \ldots, x_k$ *significantly* affects y. In this case, we use t statistics and other techniques to determine which of $x_{g+1}, x_{g+2}, \ldots, x_k$ significantly affect y. To test H_0 versus H_a, consider the following two models:

Complete model: $y = \beta_0 + \beta_1 x_1 + \cdots + \beta_g x_g + \beta_{g+1} x_{g+1} + \cdots + \beta_k x_k + \varepsilon.$

Reduced model: $y = \beta_0 + \beta_1 x_1 + \cdots + \beta_g x_g + \varepsilon.$

Here the complete model is assumed to have k independent variables, the reduced model is the complete model under the assumption that H_0 is true, and $(k - g)$ denotes the number of regression parameters we have set equal to 0 in the statement of H_0.

To carry out this test, we calculate SSE_C, **the unexplained variation for the complete model**, and SSE_R, **the unexplained variation for the reduced model**. The appropriate test statistic is based on the difference

$$SSE_R - SSE_C,$$

which is called the **drop in the unexplained variation attributable to the independent variables** $x_{g+1}, x_{g+2}, \ldots, x_k$. In the following box, we give the formula for the test statistic and show how to carry out the test:

The Partial F Test: An F Test for a Portion of a Regression Model

Suppose that the regression assumptions hold and consider testing

$$H_0: \beta_{g+1} = \beta_{g+2} = \cdots = \beta_k = 0$$

versus

$$H_a: \text{at least one of } \beta_{g+1}, \beta_{g+2}, \ldots, \beta_k \text{ does not equal } 0.$$

We define the **partial F statistic** to be

$$F = \frac{(SSE_R - SSE_C)/(k - g)}{SSE_C/[n - (k + 1)]}.$$

Also define the p value related to F to be the area under the curve of the F distribution (with $k - g$ and $n - (k + 1)$ degrees of freedom) to the right of F. Then we can reject H_0 in favour of H_a at level of significance α if either of the following equivalent conditions holds:

1 $F > F_\alpha$.

2 p value $< \alpha$.

Here the point F_α is based on $k - g$ numerator and $n - (k + 1)$ denominator degrees of freedom.

It can be shown that the "extra" independent variables $x_{g+1}, x_{g+2}, \ldots, x_k$ will always explain some of the variation in the observed y values and, therefore, will always make SSE_C somewhat smaller than SSE_R. Condition 1 says that we should reject H_0 if

$$F = \frac{(SSE_R - SSE_C)/(k - g)}{SSE_C/[n - (k + 1)]}$$

is large. This is reasonable because a large value of F would result from a large value of $(SSE_R - SSE_C)$, which would be obtained if at least one of the independent variables $x_{g+1}, x_{g+2}, \ldots, x_k$ makes SSE_C substantially smaller than SSE_R. This would suggest that H_0 is false and H_a is true.

Before looking at an example, we should point out that testing the significance of a single independent variable by using a partial F test is equivalent to carrying out this test by using the previously discussed t test (see Section 12.6).[2]

Example 12.11   Store Locations

In Example 12.10 (pages 461–466), we used the dummy variable model

$$y = \beta_0 + \beta_1 x + \beta_2 D_M + \beta_3 D_D + \varepsilon$$

to make pairwise comparisons of the street, mall, and downtown store locations by carrying out a t test for each of the parameters β_2, β_3, and $\beta_2 - \beta_3$. There is a theoretical problem with this because although we can set the probability of a Type I error equal to 0.05 for each individual test, it is possible that the probability of falsely rejecting H_0 in *at least one* of these tests is greater than 0.05 (note that the type I error is additive). Because of this problem, some people feel that before making pairwise comparisons we should test for overall differences between the effects of the locations by testing the null hypothesis

$$H_0: \beta_2 = \beta_3 = 0,$$

which says that the street, mall, and downtown locations have the same effects on mean sales volume (no differences between locations), versus the alternative hypothesis

$$H_a: \text{at least one of } \beta_2 \text{ and } \beta_3 \text{ does not equal } 0,$$

which says that at least two locations have different effects on mean sales volume.

To carry out this test, we consider the following:

Complete model: $y = \beta_0 + \beta_1 x + \beta_2 D_M + \beta_3 D_D + \varepsilon.$

For this complete model (which has $k = 3$ independent variables), we obtain an unexplained variation equal to $SSE_C = 443.4650$. The reduced model is the complete model when H_0 is true. Therefore, we obtain

Reduced model: $y = \beta_0 + \beta_1 x + \varepsilon.$

For this model, the unexplained variation is $SSE_R = 2{,}467.8067$. Noting that two parameters (β_2 and β_3) are set equal to 0 in the statement of H_0, we have $k - g = 2$. Therefore, the needed partial F statistic is

$$
\begin{aligned}
F &= \frac{(SSE_R - SSE_C)/(k - g)}{SSE_C/[n - (k + 1)]} \\
&= \frac{(2{,}467.8067 - 443.4650)/2}{443.4650/(15 - 4)} \\
&= 25.1066.
\end{aligned}
$$

---

[2]When we test $H_0: \beta_j = 0$ versus $H_a: \beta_j \neq 0$ using a partial F test,

$$F = t^2 \text{ and } F_\alpha = (t_{\alpha/2})^2.$$

Here $t_{\alpha/2}$ is based on $n - (k + 1)$ degrees of freedom, and F_α is based on 1 numerator and $n - (k + 1)$ denominator degrees of freedom. Hence, the rejection conditions

$$|t| > t_{\alpha/2} \text{ and } F > F_\alpha$$

are equivalent. In this case the p value related to t equals the p value related to F.

We compare F to $F_{0.01} = 7.21$, which is based on $k - g = 2$ numerator and $n - (k + 1) = 15 - 4 = 11$ denominator degrees of freedom. Since

$$F = 25.1066 > 7.21,$$

we can reject H_0 at the 0.01 level of significance, and we have very strong statistical evidence that at least two locations have different effects on mean sales volume. Having reached this conclusion, it makes sense to compare the effects of specific pairs of locations. We have already done this in Example 12.10. It should also be noted that even if H_0 were not rejected, pairwise comparisons could still be made in order to test specific a priori hypotheses.

Exercises for Section 12.11

CONCEPTS

12.46 When we perform a partial F test, what are the complete and reduced models?

12.47 When we perform a partial F test, what is $(k - g)$? What is $n - (k + 1)$?

METHODS AND APPLICATIONS

THE FRESH DETERGENT CASE ✍

In Exercises 12.48 through 12.50, you will perform partial F tests by using the following three Fresh detergent models:

Model 1: $y = \beta_0 + \beta_1 x_1 + \beta_2 x_2 + \beta_3 x_3 + \varepsilon$,

Model 2: $y = \beta_0 + \beta_1 x_1 + \beta_2 x_2 + \beta_3 x_3 + \beta_4 D_B + \beta_5 D_C + \varepsilon$,

Model 3: $y = \beta_0 + \beta_1 x_1 + \beta_2 x_2 + \beta_3 x_3 + \beta_4 D_B + \beta_5 D_C + \beta_6 x_3 D_B + \beta_7 x_3 D_C + \varepsilon$.

The values of the SSE for models 1, 2, and 3 are, respectively, 1.4318, 0.5420, and 0.5347.

12.48 In Model 2, test H_0: $\beta_4 = \beta_5 = 0$ by setting α equal to 0.05 and 0.01. Interpret your results.

12.49 In Model 3, test H_0: $\beta_4 = \beta_5 = \beta_6 = \beta_7 = 0$ by setting α equal to 0.05 and 0.01. Interpret your results.

12.50 In Model 3, test H_0: $\beta_6 = \beta_7 = 0$ by setting α equal to 0.05 and 0.01. Interpret your results.

CHAPTER SUMMARY

In this chapter, we have discussed **multiple regression analysis**. We began by considering the **multiple regression model**. We next discussed the **least squares point estimates** of the model parameters, the assumptions behind the model, and some ways to judge **overall model utility**—the **standard error**, the **multiple coefficient of determination**, the **adjusted multiple coefficient of determination**, and the **overall F test**. Then we considered testing the significance of a single independent variable in a multiple regression model, calculating a **confidence interval** for the mean value of the dependent variable, and calculating a **prediction interval** for an individual value of the dependent variable. We continued this chapter by discussing using **squared terms** to model **quadratic** relationships, using **cross-product terms** to model **interaction**, and using **dummy variables** to model **qualitative** independent variables. We concluded this chapter by examining how to use the **partial F test** to evaluate a portion of a regression model.

GLOSSARY OF TERMS

dummy variable: A variable that takes on the value 0 or 1 and is used to describe the effects of the different levels of a qualitative independent variable in a regression model. (page 460)
experimental region: The range of the previously observed combinations of values of the independent variables. (page 420)
influential observation: An observation that causes the least squares point estimates (or other aspects of the regression analysis) to be substantially different from what they would be if the observation were removed from the data. (page 449)

interaction: The situation in which the relationship between the mean value of the dependent variable and an independent variable is dependent on the value of another independent variable. (page 452)
multiple regression model: An equation that describes the relationship between a dependent variable and more than one independent variable. (page 419)
outlier: An observation that is well separated from the rest of the data with respect to its y value and/or its x values. (page 449)

IMPORTANT FORMULAS AND TESTS

The multiple regression model: page 421

Point prediction of an individual value of y: page 426

Mean square error: page 426

Standard error: page 426

The least squares point estimates: page 427

Point estimate of a mean value of y: page 427

Total variation: page 431

Explained variation: page 431

Unexplained variation: page 431

Multiple coefficient of determination: page 431

Multiple correlation coefficient: page 431

Adjusted multiple coefficient of determination: page 432

An F test for the linear regression model: page 433

Testing the significance of an independent variable: page 438

Confidence interval for β_j: page 439

Sampling distribution of $\hat{y}$ (and the distance value): page 441

Confidence interval for a mean value of y: page 441

Prediction interval for an individual value of y: page 442

The quadratic regression model: page 443

The partial F test: page 472

Mc Graw Hill connect™ Practise and learn online with *Connect.* Questions and tables with online data sets are marked with 🐎 .

SUPPLEMENTARY EXERCISES

12.51 In a September 1982 article in *Business Economics,* Allmon related y = Crest toothpaste sales in a given year (in thousands of dollars) to x_1 = Crest advertising budget in the year (in thousands of dollars), x_2 = ratio of Crest's advertising budget to Colgate's advertising budget in the year, and x_3 = U.S. personal disposable income in the year (in billions of dollars). The data analyzed are given in Table 12.18. When we perform a regression analysis of these data using the model

$$y = \beta_0 + \beta_1 x_1 + \beta_2 x_2 + \beta_3 x_3 + \varepsilon,$$

we find that the least squares point estimates of the model parameters and their associated p values (given in parentheses) are $b_0 = 30{,}626 \ (0.156)$, $b_1 = 3.893 \ (0.094)$, $b_2 = -29{,}607 \ (0.245)$, and $b_3 = 86.52 \ (< 0.001)$. Suppose it was estimated at the end of 1979 that in 1980 the advertising budget for Crest would be 28,000, the ratio of Crest's advertising budget to Colgate's advertising budget

would be 1.56, and the U.S. personal disposable income would be 1,821.7. Using the model, we would obtain a point prediction of about 251,057, thus giving the 95 percent prediction interval [221,986, 280,128] for Crest sales in 1980. Show how the point prediction was calculated.

12.52 The trend in home-building in recent years has been to emphasize open spaces and great rooms, rather than smaller living rooms and family rooms. A builder of speculative homes (Oxford Homes) in London, Ontario, had been building such homes, but these homes had been taking many months to sell and selling for substantially less than the asking price. In order to determine what types of homes would attract residents of the community, the builder contacted a statistician. The statistician went to a local real estate agency and obtained the data in Table 12.19 on the next page. This table presents the sales price y, total floor area x_1, number of rooms x_2, number of

TABLE **12.18** Crest Toothpaste Sales Data 🐎

Year	Crest Sales, y	Crest Budget, x_1	Ratio, x_2	U.S. Personal Disposable Income, x_3	
1967	105,000	16,300	1.25	547.9	
1968	105,000	15,800	1.34	593.4	
1969	121,600	16,000	1.22	638.9	
1970	113,750	14,200	1.00	695.3	
1971	113,750	15,000	1.15	751.8	
1972	128,925	14,000	1.13	810.3	
1973	142,500	15,400	1.05	914.5	
1974	126,000	18,250	1.27	998.3	
1975	162,000	17,300	1.07	1,096.1	
1976	191,625	23,000	1.17	1,194.4	
1977	189,000	19,300	1.07	1,311.5	
1978	210,000	23,056	1.54	1,462.9	
1979	224,250	26,000	1.59	1,641.7	

Source: "Advertising and sales relationships for toothpaste: Another look," by C. I. Allmon, *Business Economics* (September 1982), pp. 17, 58. Reprinted by permission. Copyright © 1982 National Association for Business Economics.

TABLE **12.19**   Measurements Taken on 63 Single-Family Residences

Residence	Sales Price, y (× $1,000)	Floor area x_1	Rooms, x_2	Bedrooms, x_3	Age, x_4	Residence	Sales Price, y (× $1,000)	Floor area x_1	Rooms, x_2	Bedrooms, x_3	Age, x_4
1	53.5	1,008	5	2	35	33	63.0	1,053	5	2	24
2	49.0	1,290	6	3	36	34	60.0	1,728	6	3	26
3	50.5	860	8	2	36	35	34.0	416	3	1	42
4	49.9	912	5	3	41	36	52.0	1,040	5	2	9
5	52.0	1,204	6	3	40	37	75.0	1,496	6	3	30
6	55.0	1,204	5	3	10	38	93.0	1,936	8	4	39
7	80.5	1,764	8	4	64	39	60.0	1,904	7	4	32
8	86.0	1,600	7	3	19	40	73.0	1,080	5	2	24
9	69.0	1,255	5	3	16	41	71.0	1,768	8	4	74
10	149.0	3,600	10	5	17	42	83.0	1,503	6	3	14
11	46.0	864	5	3	37	43	90.0	1,736	7	3	16
12	38.0	720	4	2	41	44	83.0	1,695	6	3	12
13	49.5	1,008	6	3	35	45	115.0	2,186	8	4	12
14	105.0	1,950	8	3	52	46	50.0	888	5	2	34
15	152.5	2,086	7	3	12	47	55.2	1,120	6	3	29
16	85.0	2,011	9	4	76	48	61.0	1,400	5	3	33
17	60.0	1,465	6	3	102	49	147.0	2,165	7	3	2
18	58.5	1,232	5	2	69	50	210.0	2,353	8	4	15
19	101.0	1,736	7	3	67	51	60.0	1,536	6	3	36
20	79.4	1,296	6	3	11	52	100.0	1,972	8	3	37
21	125.0	1,996	7	3	9	53	44.5	1,120	5	3	27
22	87.9	1,874	5	2	14	54	55.0	1,664	7	3	79
23	80.0	1,580	5	3	11	55	53.4	925	5	3	20
24	94.0	1,920	5	3	14	56	65.0	1,288	5	3	2
25	74.0	1,430	9	3	16	57	73.0	1,400	5	3	2
26	69.0	1,486	6	3	27	58	40.0	1,376	6	3	103
27	63.0	1,008	5	2	35	59	141.0	2,038	12	4	62
28	67.5	1,282	5	3	20	60	68.0	1,572	6	3	29
29	35.0	1,134	5	2	74	61	139.0	1,545	6	3	9
30	142.5	2,400	9	4	15	62	140.0	1,993	6	3	4
31	92.2	1,701	5	3	15	63	55.0	1,130	5	2	21
32	56.0	1,020	6	3	16						

bedrooms x_3, and age x_4 for each of 63 single-family residences recently sold in the community. When we perform a regression analysis of these data using the model

$$y = \beta_0 + \beta_1 x_1 + \beta_2 x_2 + \beta_3 x_3 + \beta_4 x_4 + \varepsilon,$$

we find that the least squares point estimates of the model parameters and their associated p values (given in parentheses) are $b_0 = 10.3676$ (0.3710), $b_1 = 0.0500$ (< 0.001), $b_2 = 6.3218$ (0.0152), $b_3 = -11.1032$ (0.0635), and $b_4 = -0.4319$ (0.0002). Discuss why the estimates $b_2 = 6.3218$ and $b_3 = -11.1032$ suggest that it might be more profitable when building a house with a specified floor area (1) to include both a (smaller) living room and a family room rather than a (larger) great room and (2) to not increase the number of bedrooms (at the cost of another type of room) that would normally be included in a house with the specified floor area.

Note: Based on the statistical results, the builder realized that there are many families with children in London and that the parents in such families would rather have one living area for the children (the family room) and a

separate living area for themselves (the living room). The builder started modifying the open-space homes accordingly and greatly increased profits.

12.53 Interest in e-book readers has been growing in Canada. Typical prices for these readers range from $140 to $270. A researcher decides to examine how age, gender, and price influence interest in purchasing an e-book reader and surveys 29 adults who do not own an e-book reader. Of these 29 adults, 15 are men and 14 are women. Each individual is given the same advertisement for an e-book reader, each with a randomly set price (x_2), falling between $140 and $270. Individuals provide their age (x_1) and are asked to report how interested (y) they are in an e-book reader (from 1 = not at all interested to 10 = very interested). The data are reported in Table 12.20.

a. Using a computer, perform the multiple regression analysis for all participants and summarize the results.

b. Perform the multiple regression analyses separately for men (M) and women (F). How do the results differ between men and women?

TABLE **12.20** Data for Exercise 12.53

Interest (y)	Age (x_1)	Price (x_2)	Gender
8	18	140	M
7	48	181	M
5	65	225	M
9	22	170	M
1	59	220	M
6	48	252	M
5	63	199	M
7	29	177	M
8	31	140	M
10	24	153	M
9	19	144	M
8	30	160	M
6	33	200	M
7	25	188	M
9	67	155	F
2	19	265	F
3	20	250	F
6	80	184	F
5	40	233	F
4	32	256	F
8	66	162	F
9	70	156	F
10	69	139	F
1	21	260	F
3	26	257	F
2	31	233	F
8	59	155	F
7	64	188	F
6	48	173	F

TABLE **12.21** Restaurant Data

Table Number	Average Satisfaction (y)	Average Bill (x_1)	Average Item (x_2)
1	2	33.21	1.1
2	2	55.01	1.35
3	2	22.75	1.2
4	3	47.31	1.1
5	2	37.12	1.18
6	4	9.18	1.25
7	3	20.06	1.25
8	3	49.63	1.57
9	2	46.87	1.4
10	2	24.16	1.45
11	3	26.15	1.48
12	4	33.03	1.9
13	3	33.49	1.85
14	5	19.12	1.8
15	5	18.65	1.58
16	2	64.28	1.5
17	2	48.64	0.93
18	4	17.13	1.6
19	2	62.79	1.4
20	2	54.65	1.3
21	3	59.98	1.62
22	2	41.18	1.13
23	2	34.44	1.28
24	3	41.89	1.45
25	3	31.36	1.21

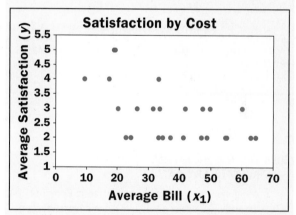

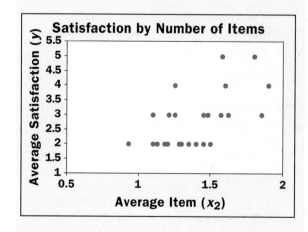

12.54 RESTAURANT SATISFACTION DATA

The owner of a restaurant wants to investigate customer satisfaction. Over the course of an evening, customers are asked to complete a satisfaction card with scores ranging from 1 (not at all satisfied) to 5 (extremely satisfied). The average satisfaction ratings are compiled for each table of guests ($n = 25$ tables). Also measured is the average price of the meal per person (x_1) and the average number of items ordered per person (x_2). The data are presented in Table 12.21, along with the scatter plots. The results of the regression analysis are presented in Figure 12.39 on the next page.

a. Describe the relationship between satisfaction and average price.

b. Describe the relationship between satisfaction and number of items.

c. Are price and number of items significant predictors of satisfaction?

d. Write the resulting regression equation.

FIGURE **12.39**   Restaurant Satisfaction Data

Regression Statistics	
Multiple R	0.772805226
R Square	0.597227917
Adjusted R Square	0.560612273
Standard Error	0.634643272
Observations	25

ANOVA	df	SS	MS	F	Significance F
Regression	2	13.13901417	6.569507	16.310731	4.53E-05
Residual	22	8.860985826	0.402772		
Total	24	22			

	Coefficients	Standard Error	t Stat	P-value	Lower 95%	Upper 95%	Lower 95.0%	Upper 95.0%
Intercept	1.144082814	0.841244082	1.359989	0.18760824	−0.600553	2.888718	−0.600553	2.888718
Avg Bill (x1)	−0.031821898	0.008386506	−3.794417	0.00099447	−0.049214	−0.014429	−0.049214	−0.014429
Avg Item (x2)	2.037227195	0.529363909	3.848444	0.00087221	0.939392	3.135062	0.939392	3.135062

FIGURE **12.40**   Testing an Interaction in the Restaurant Data

Regression Statistics	
Multiple R	0.793082
R Square	0.62898
Adjusted R Square	0.575977
Standard Error	0.623449
Observations	25

ANOVA	df	SS	MS	F	Significance F
Regression	3	13.83754992	4.61251664	11.86688	9.26483E-05
Residual	21	8.16245008	0.388688099		
Total	24	22			

	Coefficients	Standard Error	t Stat	P-value	Lower 95%	Upper 95%	Lower 95.0%	Upper 95.0%
Intercept	−1.941907	2.445820453	−0.793969428	0.436094	−7.028269623	3.144456	−7.02827	3.144456
Avg Bill (x1)	0.054431	0.064865471	0.839143126	0.41084	−0.08046374	0.189327	−0.080464	0.189327
Avg Item (x2)	4.183635	1.683434061	2.485179192	0.021454	0.682741912	7.684529	0.682742	7.684529
x1x2	−0.060513	0.045138978	−1.340582963	0.194379	-0.154384204	0.033359	−0.154384	0.033359

12.55 TESTING AN INTERACTION IN THE RESTAURANT DATA

As a follow-up to the regression analysis in Exercise 12.54, the restaurant owner would like to see if the interaction of average cost (x_1) and average number of items ordered (x_2) adds to the regression equation. Thus, the x_1x_2 variable is computed and is added to the analysis. The results are presented in Figure 12.40.

a. Does the interaction term add to the prediction of sales?

b. How do the results of Figures 12.39 and 12.40 differ?

12.56 DEMONSTRATING THE EFFECTS OF AN OUTLIER IN THE SALES TERRITORY DATA

In Example 12.1 at the beginning of the chapter, a sales manager was investigating sales based on a variety of predictors. In this exercise, suppose that the manager is only interested in predicting sales (y) based on number of months with the company (x_1) and advertising expenditures (x_3). The regression results of the original sample with the two predictors are given in Figure 12.41(a). One additional salesperson has been added to the data set

compiled by the manager in Table 12.2. This employee is considered to be of exceptional ability. She has only been with the company for five months, has spent only $250.00 in advertising, and yet has had $6,978.85 in sales. When this employee is added to the regression analysis, the new results are calculated and the regression results are presented in Figure 12.41(b).

a. How does adding this exceptional employee to the analysis change the results?

b. How do the results of Figure 12.41(a) and 12.41(b) differ?

c. Write the resulting regression equations.

d. If the manager asked your opinion, what would you suggest regarding the inclusion of the exceptional employee into the regression analysis?

12.57 THE FRESH DETERGENT CASE

Recall from Exercise 12.44 (pages 469–470) that Enterprise Industries has advertised Fresh liquid laundry detergent by using three different advertising campaigns—advertising campaign A (television commercials),

FIGURE 12.41 Regression Results for Exercise 12.56

(a) Regression results of original sales territory data

Regression Statistics

Multiple R	0.771585
R Square	0.5953435
Adjusted R Square	0.5585565
Standard Error	872.41841
Observations	25

ANOVA	df	SS	MS	F	Significance F
Regression	2	24635043.52	12317522	16.18355	4.76379E-05
Residual	22	16744505.4	761113.9		
Total	24	41379548.93			

	Coefficients	Standard Error	t Stat	P-value	Lower 95%	Upper 95%	Lower 95.0%	Upper 95.0%
Intercept	1703.672	355.1447204	4.797121	8.62E-05	967.1461647	2440.198	967.14616	2440.1989
Time with Company, x1	7.651244	2.118531925	3.611578	0.001548	3.257673016	12.04482	3.257673	12.0448151
Advertising, x3	0.22957	0.068380534	3.357242	0.002847	0.087757269	0.371383	0.0877573	0.37138267

(b) Regression results of sales territory data with new employee included

Regression Statistics

Multiple R	0.506732
R Square	0.256778
Adjusted R Square	0.192149
Standard Error	1319.386
Observations	26

ANOVA	df	SS	MS	F	Significance F
Regression	2	13832798	6916399	3.973159	0.032950855
Residual	23	40037955	1740781		
Total	25	53870752			

	Coefficients	Standard Error	t Stat	P-value	Lower 95%	Upper 95%	Lower 95.0%	Upper 95.0%
Intercept	2416.529	500.4962	4.828266	7.14E-05	1381.174916	3451.883	1381.175	3451.883
Time with Company, x1	6.335721	3.183677	1.990064	0.0586	-0.250207207	12.92165	-0.25021	12.92165
Advertising, x3	0.133716	0.100039	1.336636	0.194414	-0.073230523	0.340662	-0.07323	0.340662

advertising campaign B (a balanced mixture of television and radio commercials), and advertising campaign C (a balanced mixture of television, radio, newspaper, and magazine advertisements). To compare the effectiveness of these advertising campaigns, consider the model

$$y = \beta_0 + \beta_1 x_4 + \beta_2 x_3 + \beta_3 x_3^2 + \beta_4 x_4 x_3 + \beta_5 D_B + \beta_6 D_C + \varepsilon.$$

Here, y is demand for Fresh, x_4 is the price difference, x_3 is Enterprise Industries' advertising expenditure for Fresh, D_B equals 1 if advertising campaign B is used in a sales period and 0 otherwise, and D_C equals 1 if advertising campaign C is used in a sales period and 0 otherwise. If we use this model to perform a regression analysis of the data in Table 12.22 on the next page, we obtain the partial MegaStat output in Figure 12.42(a) on the next page.

a. In the above model, the parameter β_5 represents the effect on mean demand of advertising campaign B compared to advertising campaign A, and the parameter β_6 represents the effect on mean demand of advertising campaign C compared to advertising campaign A. Use the regression output to find a point estimate of and test the significance of each of the above effects. Also

find a 95 percent confidence interval for each of the above effects. Interpret your results.

b. Consider the alternative model

$$y = \beta_0 + \beta_1 x_4 + \beta_2 x_3 + \beta_3 x_3^2 + \beta_4 x_4 x_3 + \beta_5 D_A + \beta_6 D_C + \varepsilon.$$

Here D_A equals 1 if advertising campaign A is used and 0 otherwise. The MegaStat output of the least squares point estimates of the parameters of this model is as in Figure 12.42(b). Noting that β_6 represents the effect on mean demand of advertising campaign C compared to advertising campaign B, find a point estimate of and a 95 percent confidence interval for this effect. Also test the significance of this effect. Interpret your results.

c. Consider the alternative model

$$y = \beta_0 + \beta_1 x_4 + \beta_2 x_3 + \beta_3 x_3^2 + \beta_4 x_4 x_3 + \beta_5 D_B + \beta_6 D_C + \beta_7 x_3 D_B + \beta_8 x_3 D_C + \varepsilon.$$

The MegaStat output of the least squares point estimates of the parameters of this model is as in Figure 12.42(c).

TABLE **12.22**   Fresh Advertising Data

Price x_1	IndPrice x_2	PriceDif x_4	AdvExp x_3	Demand y	AdCamp	DA	DB	DC
3.85	3.80	−0.05	5.50	7.38	B	0	1	0
3.75	4.00	0.25	6.75	8.51	B	0	1	0
3.70	4.30	0.60	7.25	9.52	B	0	1	0
3.70	3.70	0.00	5.50	7.50	A	1	0	0
3.60	3.85	0.25	7.00	9.33	C	0	0	1
3.60	3.80	0.20	6.50	8.28	A	1	0	0
3.60	3.75	0.15	6.75	8.75	C	0	0	1
3.80	3.85	0.05	5.25	7.87	C	0	0	1
3.80	3.65	−0.15	5.25	7.10	B	0	1	0
3.85	4.00	0.15	6.00	8.00	C	0	0	1
3.90	4.10	0.20	6.50	7.89	A	1	0	0
3.90	4.00	0.10	6.25	8.15	C	0	0	1
3.70	4.10	0.40	7.00	9.10	C	0	0	1
3.75	4.20	0.45	6.90	8.86	A	1	0	0
3.75	4.10	0.35	6.80	8.90	B	0	1	0
3.80	4.10	0.30	6.80	8.87	B	0	1	0
3.70	4.20	0.50	7.10	9.26	B	0	1	0
3.80	4.30	0.50	7.00	9.00	A	1	0	0
3.70	4.10	0.40	6.80	8.75	B	0	1	0
3.80	3.75	−0.05	6.50	7.95	B	0	1	0
3.80	3.75	−0.05	6.25	7.65	C	0	0	1
3.75	3.65	−0.10	6.00	7.27	A	1	0	0
3.70	3.90	0.20	6.50	8.00	A	1	0	0
3.55	3.65	0.10	7.00	8.50	A	1	0	0
3.60	4.10	0.50	6.80	8.75	A	1	0	0
3.65	4.25	0.60	6.80	9.21	B	0	1	0
3.70	3.65	−0.05	6.50	8.27	C	0	0	1
3.75	3.75	0.00	5.75	7.67	B	0	1	0
3.80	3.85	0.05	5.80	7.93	C	0	0	1
3.70	4.25	0.55	6.80	9.26	C	0	0	1

Let $\mu_{[d, a, A]}$, $\mu_{[d,a,B]}$, and $\mu_{[d,a,C]}$ denote the mean demands for Fresh when the price difference is d; the advertising expenditure is a; and we use advertising campaigns A, B, and C, respectively. The model of this part implies that

$$\mu_{[d,a,A]} = \beta_0 + \beta_1 d + \beta_2 a + \beta_3 a^2 + \beta_4 da$$
$$+ \beta_5(0) + \beta_6(0) + \beta_7 a(0) + \beta_8 a(0),$$

$$\mu_{[d,a,B]} = \beta_0 + \beta_1 d + \beta_2 a + \beta_3 a^2 + \beta_4 da$$
$$+ \beta_5(1) + \beta_6(0) + \beta_7 a(1) + \beta_8 a(0),$$

$$\mu_{[d,a,C]} = \beta_0 + \beta_1 d + \beta_2 a + \beta_3 a^2 + \beta_4 da$$
$$+ \beta_5(0) + \beta_6(1) + \beta_7 a(0) + \beta_8 a(1),$$

Using these equations, verify that $\mu_{[d,a,C]} - \mu_{[d,a,A]}$ equals $\beta_6 + \beta_8 a$. Then, using the least squares point estimates, show that a point estimate of $\mu_{[d,a,C]} - \mu_{[d,a,A]}$ equals 0.3266 when $a = 6.2$ and 0.4080 when $a = 6.6$. Also verify that $\mu_{[d,a,C]} - \mu_{[d,a,B]}$

equals $\beta_6 - \beta_5 + \beta_8 a - \beta_7 a$. Using the least squares point estimates, show that a point estimate of $\mu_{[d,a,C]} - \mu_{[d,a,B]}$ equals 0.14266 when $a = 6.2$ and 0.18118 when $a = 6.6$. Discuss why these results imply that the larger advertising expenditure a is, the larger is the improvement in mean sales obtained by using advertising campaign C rather than advertising campaign A or B.

d. The prediction results given at the bottom of the MegaStat outputs in Figure 11.42(a) and (c) correspond to a future period when the price difference will be $x_4 = 0.20$, the advertising expenditure will be $x_3 = 6.50$, and campaign C will be used. Which model—the first model or the third model of this exercise—gives the shortest 95 percent prediction interval for Fresh demand? Using all of the results in this exercise, discuss why there might be a small amount of interaction between advertising expenditure and advertising campaign.

FIGURE 12.42   MegaStat Output for Exercise 12.57

(a) Partial MegaStat output for Exercise 12.57

Regression output

variables	coefficients	std. error	t (df = 23)	p-value	confidence interval 95% lower	95% upper
Intercept	25.6127	4.7938	5.343	2.00E-05	15.6960	35.5294
X4	9.0587	3.0317	2.988	0.0066	2.7871	15.3302
X3	−6.5377	1.5814	−4.134	0.0004	−9.8090	−3.2664
X3SQ	0.5844	0.1299	4.500	0.0002	0.3158	0.8531
X43	−1.1565	0.4557	−2.538	0.0184	−2.0992	−0.2137
DB	0.2137	0.0622	3.438	0.0022	0.0851	0.3423
DC	0.3818	0.0613	6.233	2.33E-06	0.2551	0.5085

Predicted values for: Y

Predicted	95% Confidence Interval lower	upper	95% Prediction Interval lower	upper	Leverage	
8.50068	8.40370	8.59765	8.21322	8.78813	0.128	

R^2 0.971
Adjusted R^2 0.963
R 0.985
Std. Error 0.131

(b) MegaStat output of least squares point estimates for Exercise 12.57(b)

Regression output

variables	coefficients	std. error	t (df = 23)	p-value	confidence interval 95% lower	95% upper
Intercept	25.8264	4.7946	5.387	1.80E-05	15.9081	35.7447
X4	9.0587	3.0317	2.988	0.0066	2.7871	15.3302
X3	−6.5377	1.5814	−4.134	0.0004	−9.8090	−3.2664
X3SQ	0.5844	0.1299	4.500	0.0002	0.3158	0.8531
X43	−1.1565	0.4557	−2.538	0.0184	−2.0992	−0.2137
DA	−0.2137	0.0622	−3.438	0.0022	−0.3423	−0.0851
DC	0.1681	0.0637	2.638	0.0147	0.0363	0.2999

(c) MegaStat output of least squares point estimates for Exercise 12.57(c)

Regression output

variables	coefficients	std. error	t (df = 21)	p-value	confidence interval 95% lower	95% upper	
Intercept	28.6873	5.1285	5.594	1.50E-05	18.0221	39.3526	R^2 0.974
X4	10.8253	3.2988	3.282	0.0036	3.9651	17.6855	Adjusted R^2 0.964
X3	−7.4115	1.6617	−4.460	0.0002	−10.8671	−3.9558	R 0.987
X3SQ	0.6458	0.1346	4.798	0.0001	0.3659	0.9257	Std. Error 0.129
X43	−1.4156	0.4929	−2.872	0.0091	−2.4406	−0.3907	
DB	−0.4807	0.7309	−0.658	0.5179	−2.0007	1.0393	n 30
DC	−0.9351	0.8357	−1.119	0.2758	−2.6731	0.8029	k 8
X3DB	0.1072	0.1117	0.960	0.3480	−0.1251	0.3395	Dep. Var. Y
X3DC	0.2035	0.1288	1.580	0.1291	−0.0644	0.4714	

Predicted values for: Y

Predicted	95% Confidence Interval lower	upper	95% Prediction Interval lower	upper	Leverage
8.51183	8.41229	8.61136	8.22486	8.79879	0.137

12.58 INTERNET EXERCISE

Statistics Canada (http://www.statcan.gc.ca) is conducting an ongoing study of Canadian Internet use. In the study description (http://www.statcan.gc.ca/daily-quotidien/100805/dq100705c-eng.htm), click on the link "Definitions, data sources and methods: survey number 4432" near the bottom of the page. Read the section dealing with data accuracy and explain how multiple regression techniques could be used to help detect possible outliers.

CHAPTER 13
Nonparametric Methods

LEARNING OBJECTIVES

After reading this chapter, you should be able to

LO1 state the difference between a nonparametric method and a parametric method

LO2 explain how the sign test is used to examine the population median

LO3 identify and understand the different conditions required in order to compute a Wilcoxon rank sum test

LO4 understand when to use the Kruskal–Wallis *H* test and be able to conduct the test properly

LO5 compute Spearman's rank correlation coefficient and test the value for significance

CHAPTER OUTLINE

13.1 The Sign Test: A Hypothesis Test about the Median

13.2 The Wilcoxon Rank Sum Test

13.3 The Wilcoxon Signed Ranks Test

13.4 Comparing Several Populations Using the Kruskal–Wallis *H* Test

13.5 Spearman's Rank Correlation Coefficient

LO1 **Parametric** statistics, such as the *t* test, correlation, multiple regression, and analysis of variance, require that the data being analyzed be of the interval or ratio level of measurement. All of these procedures also assume that the sampled populations are normally distributed (or mound-shaped and not highly skewed to the right (positively) or left (negatively)). When the level of measurement is qualitative (nominal or ordinal) and/ or when the assumptions of the population's distribution are not satisfied, then **nonparametric** methods can be used. Specifically, we consider four nonparametric tests that can be used in place of the *t* and *F* tests. These four nonparametric tests are the **sign test**, the **Wilcoxon rank sum test**, the **Wilcoxon signed ranks test**, and the **Kruskal–Wallis *H* test**. These tests require no assumptions about the shapes of the sampled populations. In addition, these nonparametric tests are usually better than the *t* and *F* tests at correctly finding statistically significant differences in the presence of outliers and extreme skewness. We also consider a fifth nonparametric test, **Spearman's rank order correlation coefficient**, which can be used in place of Pearson's product moment correlation.

Each nonparametric test discussed in this chapter theoretically assumes that each sampled population under consideration is described by a continuous probability distribution. However, in most situations, each nonparametric technique is slightly **statistically conservative** if the sampled population is described by a discrete probability distribution. This means, for example, that a nonparametric hypothesis test has a slightly smaller chance of falsely rejecting the null hypothesis than the specified *α* value seems to indicate if the sampled population is described by a discrete probability distribution. Furthermore, because each nonparametric technique is based essentially on **ranking** the observed sample values, and not on the exact sizes of the sample values, it can be used to analyze any type of data that can be ranked. This includes ordinal data and quantitative data. To conclude this introduction, note that *t* and *F* tests are more powerful (better at correctly finding statistically significant differences) than nonparametric tests when the sampled populations are normally distributed.

13.1 THE SIGN TEST: A HYPOTHESIS TEST ABOUT THE MEDIAN

If a population is highly skewed to the right or left (positively or negatively skewed), then the population median might be a better measure of central tendency than the population mean. Furthermore, if the sample size is small and the population is highly skewed or clearly not mound-shaped, then the t test for the population might not be valid. For these reasons, when we have taken a small sample and if it is possible that the sampled population might be far from being normally distributed, it is sometimes useful to use a hypothesis test about the population median. This test, called the **sign test**, is valid for any sample size and population shape. To illustrate the sign test, we consider the following example.

LO2

Example 13.1 Digital Music Player Lifetime

A leading digital music player is advertised to have a median lifetime (or time to failure) of 6,000 hours of continuous play. The developer of a new digital music player wishes to show that the median lifetime of the new player exceeds 6,000 hours of continuous play. To this end, the developer randomly selects 20 new players and tests them in continuous play until each fails. Figure 13.1(a) presents the 20 lifetimes obtained (expressed in hours and arranged in increasing order), and Figure 13.1(b) shows a stem-and-leaf display of these lifetimes. The stem-and-leaf display and the three low lifetimes of 5, 947, and 2,142 suggest that the population of all lifetimes might be highly skewed to the left (i.e., negatively skewed). In addition, the sample size is small. Therefore, it might be reasonable to use the sign test.

In order to show that the population median lifetime, M_d, of the new digital music player exceeds 6,000 (hours), recall that this median divides the population of ordered lifetimes into two equal parts. It follows that if more than half of the individual population lifetimes exceed 6,000, the population median, M_d, exceeds 6,000. Let p denote the proportion of the individual population lifetimes that exceed 6,000. Then we can reject $H_0: M_d = 6,000$ in favour of $H_a: M_d > 6,000$ if we can reject $H_0: p = 0.5$ in favour of $H_a: p > 0.5$. Let x denote the total number of lifetimes that exceed 6,000 in a random sample of 20 lifetimes. If $H_0: p = 0.5$ is true, then x is a binomial random variable where $n = 20$ and $p = 0.5$. This says that if $H_0: p = 0.5$ is true, then we would expect $\mu_x = np = 20(0.5) = 10$ of the 20 lifetimes to exceed 6,000. Considering the 20 lifetimes

FIGURE 13.1 The Digital Music Player Lifetime Data and Associated Statistical Analyses

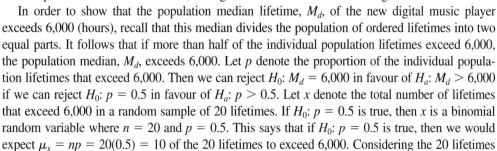

(a) The digital music player lifetime data

5	947	2,142	4,867	5,840	6,085	6,238	6,411	6,507	6,687
6,827	6,985	7,082	7,176	7,285	7,410	7,563	7,668	7,724	7,846

(c) MegaStat output of the sign test of $H_0: M_d = 6,000$ versus $H_a: M_d > 6,000$

Sign Test

6,000 hypothesized value	5 below	binomial
6,757 median Lifetime	0 equal	0.0207 p-value (one-tailed, upper)
20 n	15 above	

(b) A stem-and-leaf display

0	005
0	947
1	
1	
2	142
2	
3	
3	
4	
4	867
5	
5	840
6	085 238 411
6	507 687 827 985
7	082 176 285 410
7	563 668 724 846

we have actually observed, we note that 15 of these 20 lifetimes exceed 6,000. The p value for testing H_0: $p = 0.5$ versus H_a: $p > 0.5$ is the probability, computed assuming that H_0: $p = 0.5$ is true, of observing a sample result that is as large as or larger than the sample result we have actually observed. The p value is calculated as follows:

$$p \text{ value} = P(x \geq 15) = \sum_{x=15}^{20} \frac{20!}{x!(20-x)!} (0.5)^x (0.5)^{20-x}.$$

Using the binomial distribution table in Table A.1 (see section in the margin), we find that

$$\begin{aligned}
p \text{ value} &= P(x \geq 15) \\
&= P(x = 15) + P(x = 16) + P(x = 17) + P(x = 18) \\
&\quad + P(x = 19) + P(x = 20) \\
&= 0.0148 + 0.0046 + 0.0011 + 0.0002 + 0.0000 + 0.0000 \\
&= 0.0207.
\end{aligned}$$

This says that if H_0: $p = 0.5$ is true, then the probability that at least 15 out of 20 lifetimes would exceed 6,000 is only 0.0207. Therefore, we have strong evidence against H_0: $p = 0.5$ and in favour of H_a: $p > 0.5$. That is, we have strong evidence that H_0: $M_d = 6,000$ is false and H_a: $M_d > 6,000$ is true. This implies that it is reasonable to conclude that the median lifetime of the new digital music player exceeds the advertised median lifetime of the market's leading digital music player. Figure 13.1(c) presents the MegaStat output of the sign test of H_0: $M_d = 6,000$ versus H_a: $M_d > 6,000$. In addition, the output tells us that a point estimate of the population median lifetime is the sample median of 6,757 hours.

Binomial Probabilities (n equal to 20)

$n = 20$	p	
	0.50	
0.0000		20
0.0000		19
0.0002		18
0.0011		17
0.0046		16
0.0148		15
0.0370		14
0.0739		13
0.1201		12
0.1602		11
0.1762		10
0.1602		9
0.1201		8
0.0739		7
0.0370		6
0.0148		5
0.0046		4
0.0011		3
0.0002		2
0.50		$x \uparrow$

Source: Computed by D. K. Hildebrand. Found in D. K. Hildebrand and L. Ott, *Statistical Thinking for Managers*, 3rd ed. (Boston, MA: PWS-KENT Publishing Company, 1991).

We summarize how to carry out the sign test in the following box:

The Sign Test for a Population Median

Suppose we have randomly selected a sample of size n from a population, and suppose we wish to test the null hypothesis H_0: $M_d = M_0$ versus one of H_a: $M_d < M_0$, H_a: $M_d > M_0$, and H_a: $M_d \neq M_0$, where M_d denotes the population median. Define the test statistic S as follows:

1　If the alternative is H_a: $M_d < M_0$, then $S =$ the number of sample measurements less than M_0.

2　If the alternative is H_a: $M_d > M_0$, then $S =$ the number of sample measurements greater than M_0.

3　If the alternative is H_a: $M_d \neq M_0$, then $S =$ the larger of S_1 and S_2, where S_1 is the number of sample measurements less than M_0 and S_2 is the number of sample measurements greater than M_0.

Furthermore, define x to be a binomial variable with parameters n and $p = 0.5$. Then we can test H_0: $M_d = M_0$ versus a particular alternative hypothesis at level of significance α by using the appropriate p value.

Alternative Hypothesis	p Value (Reject H_0 if p Value $< \alpha$)
H_a: $M_d < M_0$	The probability that x is greater than or equal to S
H_a: $M_d > M_0$	The probability that x is greater than or equal to S
H_a: $M_d \neq M_0$	Twice the probability that x is greater than or equal to S

Here we can use Table A.1 to find the p value.

Note that when we take a large sample, we can use the normal approximation to the binomial distribution to implement the sign test. Here, when the null hypothesis H_0: $M_d = M_0$ (or H_0: $p = 0.5$) is true, the binomial variable x is approximately normally distributed with mean $np = n(0.5) = 0.5n$ and standard deviation $\sqrt{np(1-p)} = \sqrt{n(0.5)(1-0.5)} = 0.5\sqrt{n}$. The test is based on the test statistic

$$z = \frac{S - 0.5 - 0.5n}{0.5\sqrt{n}},$$

where S is as defined in the previous box and where we subtract 0.5 from S as a correction for continuity. This motivates the following test:

The Large-Sample Sign Test for a Population Median

Suppose we have taken a large sample (for this test, $n \geq 10$). Define S as in the previous box, and define the test statistic

$$z = \frac{S - 0.5 - 0.5n}{0.5\sqrt{n}}.$$

We can test $H_0: M_d = M_0$ versus a particular alternative hypothesis at level of significance α by using the appropriate rejection point rule or, equivalently, the corresponding p value.

Alternative Hypothesis	Rejection Point Rule: Reject H_0 if	p Value (Reject H_0 if p Value $< \alpha$)
$H_a: M_d > M_0$	$z > z_\alpha$	The area under the standard normal curve to the right of z
$H_a: M_d < M_0$	$z > z_\alpha$	The area under the standard normal curve to the right of z
$H_a: M_d \neq M_0$	$z > z_{\alpha/2}$	Twice the area under the standard normal curve to the right of z

Example 13.2 Large-Sample Sign Test for Digital Music Player Lifetime

Consider Example 13.1. Because the sample size $n = 20$ is greater than 10, we can use the large-sample sign test to test $H_0: M_d = 6,000$ versus $H_a: M_d > 6,000$. Because $S = 15$ is the number of digital music player lifetimes that exceed $M_0 = 6,000$, the test statistic z is

$$z = \frac{S - 0.5 - 0.5n}{0.5\sqrt{n}} = \frac{15 - 0.5 - 0.5(20)}{0.5\sqrt{20}} = 2.01.$$

The p value for the test is the area under the standard normal curve to the right of $z = 2.01$, which is $0.5 - 0.4778 = 0.0222$. Because this p value is less than 0.05, we have strong evidence that $H_a: M_d > 6,000$ is true. Also note that the large-sample, approximate p value of 0.0222 given by the normal distribution is fairly close to the exact p value of 0.0207 given by the binomial distribution (see Figure 13.1(c) on page 483).

To conclude this section, consider the DVD recorder rating example discussed in Chapter 2. In this example, the manufacturer of a DVD recorder has randomly selected a sample of 20 purchasers who have owned the recorder for one year. Each purchaser in the sample is asked to rank their satisfaction with the recorder along the following 10-point scale:

The stem-and-leaf display below gives the 20 ratings obtained:

```
 1   0
 2
 3   0
 4
 5   00
 6
 7   0
 8   000000
 9   00000
10   0000
```

Let M_d denote the median rating that would be given by all purchasers who have owned the DVD recorder for one year. Below is the MegaStat output of the sign test of H_0: $M_d = 7.5$ versus H_a: $M_d > 7.5$:

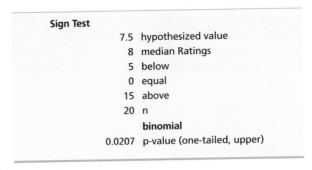

Sign Test	
7.5	hypothesized value
8	median Ratings
5	below
0	equal
15	above
20	n
	binomial
0.0207	p-value (one-tailed, upper)

Because the *p* value of 0.0207 is less than 0.05, we have strong evidence that the population median rating exceeds 7.5. Furthermore, note that the sign test has reached this conclusion by showing that *more than 50 percent* of all DVD recorder ratings exceed 7.5. It follows, since a rating exceeding 7.5 is the same as a rating being at least 8 (because of the discrete nature of the ratings), that we have strong evidence that the population median rating is at least 8.

Exercises for Section 13.1

CONCEPTS

13.1 What is a nonparametric test? Why would such a test be particularly useful when we must take a small sample?

13.2 When we perform the sign test, we use the sample data to compute a *p* value. What probability distribution is used to compute the *p* value? Explain.

METHODS AND APPLICATIONS

13.3 Consider the following sample of five chemical yields:

801   814   784   836   820

   a. Use this sample to test H_0: $M_d = 800$ versus H_a: $M_d \neq 800$ by setting $\alpha = 0.01$.

   b. Use this sample to test H_0: $M_d = 750$ versus H_a: $M_d > 750$ by setting $\alpha = 0.05$.

13.4 Consider the following sample of seven bad debt ratios:

7%   4%   6%   7%   5%   4%   9%

Use this sample and the MegaStat output in Figure 13.2 to test the null hypothesis that the median bad debt ratio

equals 3.5 percent versus the alternative hypothesis that the median bad debt ratio exceeds 3.5 percent by setting α equal to 0.05.

13.5 A local newspaper randomly selects 20 patrons of the Springwood Restaurant on a given Saturday night and has each patron rate the quality of their meal as 5 (excellent), 4 (good), 3 (average), 2 (poor), or 1 (unsatisfactory). When the results are summarized, it is found that there are sixteen ratings of 5, three ratings of 4, and one rating of 3. Let M_d denote the population median rating that would be given by all possible patrons of the restaurant on the Saturday night.

   a. Test H_0: $M_d = 4.5$ versus H_a: $M_d > 4.5$ by setting $\alpha = 0.05$.

   b. Reason that your conclusion in part a implies that you have very strong evidence that the median rating that would be given by all possible patrons is 5.

13.6 Suppose that a particular type of plant has a median growing height of 20 cm in a specified time period when the best plant food currently on the market is used as directed. The developer of a new plant food

FIGURE 13.2 MegaStat Output for Exercise 13.4

Sign Test	
3.5	hypothesized value
6	median
0	below
0	equal
7	above
7	n
	binomial
0.0078	p-value (one-tailed, upper)

TABLE **13.1** Results of a Taste Test of Coke versus Pepsi ✎

Customer	Preference (Coke or Pepsi)	Value (Sign)
1	Coke	+1
2	Pepsi	−1
3	Pepsi	−1
4	Coke	+1
5	Coke	+1
6	Pepsi	−1
7	Coke	+1
8	Coke	+1
9	Pepsi	−1

Sign Test	0 hypothesized value	4 below	binomial
9 n	1 median Value (sign)	0 equal	1.0000 p-value (two-tailed)
		5 above	

wishes to show that it increases the median growing height. If a stem-and-leaf display indicates that the population of all growing heights using the new plant food is markedly nonnormal, it would be appropriate to use the sign test to test $H_0: M_d = 20$ versus $H_a: M_d > 20$. Here M_d denotes the population median growing height when the new plant food is used. Suppose that 13 out of 15 sample plants grown using the new plant food reach a height of more than 20 cm. Test $H_0: M_d = 20$ versus $H_a: M_d > 20$ by using the large-sample sign test.

13.7 ✎ A common application of the sign test deals with analyzing consumer preferences. For instance, suppose that a blind taste test is administered to nine randomly selected convenience store customers. Each participant is asked to express a preference for either Coke or Pepsi after tasting unidentified samples of each soft drink. The sample results are expressed by recording +1 for each consumer who prefers Coke and −1 for each consumer who prefers Pepsi. Note that sometimes, rather than recording either +1 or −1, we simply record the sign + or −, hence the name "sign test." If a consumer is unable to rank the two brands, 0 is recorded, and these observations are eliminated from the analysis.

The null hypothesis in this application says that there is no difference in preferences for Coke and Pepsi.

If this null hypothesis is true, then the number of +1 values in the population of all preferences should equal the number of −1 values, which implies that the median preference is $M_d = 0$ (and that the proportion p of +1 values equals 0.5). The alternative hypothesis says that there is a significant difference in preferences (or that there is a significant difference in the number of +1 values and −1 values in the population of all preferences). This implies that the median preference does not equal 0 (and that the proportion p of +1 values does not equal 0.5).

a. Table 13.1 gives the results of the taste test administered to the nine randomly selected consumers. If we consider testing $H_0: M_d = 0$ versus $H_a: M_d \neq 0$, where M_d is the median of the (+1 and −1) preference rankings, determine the values of S_1, S_2, and S for the sign test needed to test H_0 versus H_a. Identify the value of S on the MegaStat output.

b. Use the value of S to find the p value for testing $H_0: M_d = 0$ versus $H_a: M_d \neq 0$. Then use the p value to test H_0 versus H_a by setting α equal to 0.10, 0.05, 0.01, and 0.001. How much evidence is there of a difference in the preferences for Coke and Pepsi? What do you conclude?

13.2 THE WILCOXON RANK SUM TEST

We can use t tests to compare two population means in an independent-samples experiment. If the sampled populations are far from normally distributed and the sample sizes are small, these tests are not valid. In such a case, a nonparametric method should be used to compare the populations.

We have seen that the mean of a population measures the **central tendency**, or **location**, of the probability distribution describing the population. Thus, for instance, if a t test provides strong evidence that μ_1 is greater than μ_2, we might conclude that the probability distribution of population 1 is *shifted to the right* of the probability distribution of population 2. The nonparametric test for comparing the locations of two populations is not (necessarily) a test about the difference between population means. Rather, it is a more general test to detect whether the probability distribution of population 1 is shifted to the right (or left) of the probability

LO3

distribution of population 2.[1] Furthermore, *the nonparametric test is valid for any shapes that might describe the sampled populations.*

In this section, we present the **Wilcoxon rank sum test** (also called the **Mann–Whitney test**), which is used to compare the locations of two populations when *independent samples* are selected. To perform this test, we first combine all of the observations in both samples into a single set, and we rank these observations from smallest to largest, with the smallest observation receiving rank 1, the next smallest observation receiving rank 2, and so forth. The sum of the ranks of the observations in each sample is then calculated. If the probability distributions of the two populations are identical, we would expect the sum of the ranks for sample 1 to roughly equal the sum of the ranks for sample 2. However, if, for example, the sum of the ranks for sample 1 is substantially larger than the sum of the ranks for sample 2, this would suggest that the probability distribution of population 1 is shifted to the right of the probability distribution of population 2. We explain how to carry out the Wilcoxon rank sum test in the following box:

The Wilcoxon Rank Sum Test

Let D_1 and D_2 denote the probability distributions of populations 1 and 2, and assume that we randomly select independent samples of sizes n_1 and n_2 from populations 1 and 2. Rank the $n_1 + n_2$ observations in the two samples from the smallest (rank 1) to the largest (rank $n_1 + n_2$). Here, if two or more observations are equal, we assign to each tied observation a rank equal to the average of the consecutive ranks that would otherwise be assigned to the tied observations. Let T_1 denote the sum of the ranks of the observations in sample 1, and let T_2 denote the sum of the ranks of the observations in sample 2. Furthermore, define the **test statistic T** to be T_1 if $n_1 \leq n_2$ and T_2 if $n_1 > n_2$. Then, we can test

H_0: D_1 and D_2 are identical probability distributions

versus a particular alternative hypothesis at level of significance α by using the appropriate rejection point rule.

Alternative Hypothesis	Rejection Point Rule: Reject H_0 if
H_a: D_1 is shifted to the right of D_2	$T \geq T_U$ if $n_1 \leq n_2$ $T \leq T_L$ if $n_1 > n_2$
H_a: D_1 is shifted to the left of D_2	$T \leq T_L$ if $n_1 \leq n_2$ $T \geq T_U$ if $n_1 > n_2$
H_a: D_1 is shifted to the right or left of D_2	$T \leq T_L$ or $T \geq T_U$

The first two alternative hypotheses above are **one-sided**, while the third alternative hypothesis is **two-sided**. Values of the rejection points T_U and T_L are given in Table A.15 for values of n_1 and n_2 from 3 to 10.

Table 13.2 repeats a portion of Table A.15. This table gives the rejection point (T_U or T_L) for testing a one-sided alternative hypothesis at level of significance $\alpha = 0.05$ and the rejection points (T_U and T_L) for testing a two-sided alternative hypothesis at level of significance $\alpha = 0.10$.

TABLE 13.2 A Portion of the Wilcoxon Rank Sum Table Rejection Points for $\alpha = 0.05$ (One-Sided); $\alpha = 0.10$ (Two-Sided)

n_1	3		4		5		6		7		8		9		10	
n_2	T_L	T_U	T_L	T_U	T_L	T_U	T_L	T_U	T_L	T_U	T_L	T_U	T_L	T_U	T_L	T_U
3	6	15	7	17	7	20	8	22	9	24	9	27	10	29	11	31
4	7	17	12	24	13	27	14	30	15	33	16	36	17	39	18	42
5	7	20	13	27	19	36	20	40	22	43	24	46	25	50	26	54
6	8	22	14	30	20	40	28	50	30	54	32	58	33	63	35	67
7	9	24	15	33	22	43	30	54	39	66	41	71	43	76	46	80
8	9	27	16	36	24	46	32	58	41	71	52	84	54	90	57	95
9	10	29	17	39	25	50	33	63	43	76	54	90	66	105	69	111
10	11	31	18	42	26	54	35	67	46	80	57	95	69	111	83	127

$\alpha = 0.05$ one-sided; $\alpha = 0.10$ two-sided

---

[1] To be precise, we say that the probability distribution of population 1 is shifted to the right (or left) of the probability distribution of population 2 if there is more than a 50 percent chance that a randomly selected observation from population 1 will be greater than (or less than) a randomly selected observation from population 2.

The rejection points are tabulated according to n_1 and n_2, the sizes of the samples taken from populations 1 and 2, respectively. For instance, as shown in Table 13.2, if we have taken a sample of size $n_1 = 10$ from population 1 and a sample of size $n_2 = 7$ from population 2, then for a one-sided test with $\alpha = 0.05$, we use $T_U = 80$ or $T_L = 46$. Similarly, if $n_1 = 10$ and $n_2 = 7$, we use $T_U = 80$ and $T_L = 46$ for a two-sided test with $\alpha = 0.10$.

Example 13.3 Train Speeds

The Railway Association of Canada (see http://www.railcan.ca) reports that passenger trains travel at an average speed of 160 km/h and freight trains at 105 km/h. One complaint that many city commuters have about the train system is that the flow of traffic is interrupted by trains passing through the city on level crossings. Wait times were assessed within a city for those waiting at passenger rail crossovers (ten measures taken) versus freight crossovers (seven measures taken). The resulting wait times (in seconds) are given in Figure 13.3. The box plots indicate that the population of all possible wait times for the two populations of train types (passenger and freight) might be skewed to the right. A Wilcoxon rank sum test will be conducted on the data.

Because passenger trains travel at 55 km/h faster than freight trains in Canada, it was predicted that wait times would be shorter for passenger train crossings than for freight train crossings. Therefore, the null hypothesis is

H_0: the crossing wait times will be the same for passenger and freight trains

versus the alternative hypothesis of

H_a: the wait times will be shorter for passenger trains than for freight trains.

To perform the test, rank the $n_1 + n_2 = 10 + 7 = 17$ wait times in the two samples as shown in Figure 13.3(a). Note that two wait times of 145 seconds are tied as the sixth and seventh wait times, so these values are each assigned the average rank of 6.5. The sum of the ranks in wait times is $T_1 = 72.5$ for the passenger trains and $T_2 = 80.5$ for the freight trains. Because $n_1 = 10$ is greater than $n_2 = 7$, the summary box states that the test statistic is $T_2 = 80.5$ and that H_0 can be rejected in favour of H_a at the 0.05 significance level if T is greater than or equal to T_U. Because $T_2 = 80.5$ is greater than $T_U = 80$ (see Table 13.2 on the next page), we

FIGURE 13.3 Analysis of Passenger and Freight Train Level Crossing Times

(a) Wait times (in seconds)

Passenger		Freight		
Time	Rank	Time	Rank	
48	1	109	4	
97	2	145	6.5	
103	3	196	10	
117	5	273	13	
145	6.5	289	14	
151	8	417	16	
179	9	505	17	
220	11		$T_2 = 80.5$	
257	12			
294	15			
	$T_1 = 72.5$			

Box Plots of Passenger and Freight Times

(b) MegaStat output of the Wilcoxon rank sum test for the wait times

Wilcoxon - Mann/Whitney Test

n	sum of ranks	
10	72.5	Passenger
7	80.5	Freight
17	153	total
	0.0485	p-value (one-tailed, lower)

can conclude at the 0.05 level of significance that the passenger wait times are shifted to the left and are therefore "systematically less than" the wait times for freight trains. This might result because passenger trains travel faster than freight trains. Of course it might also result from freight trains being longer than passenger trains, but that is for another study!

Figure 13.3(b) presents the MegaStat output of the Wilcoxon rank sum test for the wait times. In general, MegaStat gives T_1, the sum of the ranks of the observations in sample 1, and T_2, the sum of the ranks for sample 2. In this example, n_1 is greater than n_2 and thus the correct test statistic is T_2.

In addition, MegaStat gives the p value related to the hypothesis test, which is 0.0485.

As another example, suppose that on a given Saturday night a local newspaper randomly selects 20 patrons from each of two restaurants and has each patron rate the quality of their meal as 5 (excellent), 4 (good), 3 (average), 2 (poor), or 1 (unsatisfactory). The following results are obtained:

Rating	Restaurant 1 Patrons	Restaurant 2 Patrons	Total Patrons	Ranks Involved	Average Rank	Restaurant 1 Rank Sum	Restaurant 2 Rank Sum
5	15	5	20	21–40	30.5	(15)(30.5) = 457.5	(5)(30.5) = 152.5
4	4	11	15	6–20	13	(4)(13) = 52	(11)(13) = 143
3	1	2	3	3, 4, 5	4	(1)(4) = 4	(2)(4) = 8
2	0	1	1	2	2	(0)(2) = 0	(1)(2) = 2
1	0	1	1	1	1	(0)(1) = 0	(1)(1) = 1
						$T_1 = 513.5$	$T_2 = 306.5$

Suppose that we wish to test

H_0: the probability distributions of all possible Saturday night meal ratings for restaurants 1 and 2 are identical

versus

H_a: the probability distribution of all possible Saturday night meal ratings for restaurant 1 is shifted to the right or left of the probability distribution of all possible Saturday night meal ratings for restaurant 2.

Because there are only five numerical ordinal ratings, there are many ties. The above table shows how we determine the sum of the ranks for each sample. Because $n_1 = 20$ and $n_2 = 20$, we cannot obtain rejection points by using Table A.15 (which gives rejection points for sample sizes up to $n_1 = 10$ and $n_2 = 10$). However, we can use a large-sample, normal approximation, which is valid if both n_1 and n_2 are at least 10. The normal approximation involves making two modifications. First, we replace the test statistic T in the previously given summary box by a standardized value of the test statistic. This standardized value, denoted z, is calculated by subtracting the mean $\mu_T = n_i(n_1 + n_2 + 1)/2$ from the test statistic T and then dividing the resulting difference by the standard deviation $\sigma_T = \sqrt{n_1 n_2 (n_1 + n_2 + 1)/12}$. Here n_i in the expression for μ_T equals n_1 if the test statistic T is T_1 and n_2 if T is T_2. Second, when testing a one-sided alternative hypothesis, we replace the rejection points T_U and T_L by the normal points z_α and $-z_\alpha$. When testing a two-sided alternative hypothesis, we replace T_U and T_L by $z_{\alpha/2}$ and $-z_{\alpha/2}$. For the current example, $n_1 = n_2$, and thus the test statistic T is $T_1 = 513.5$. Furthermore,

$$\mu_T = \frac{n_1(n_1 + n_2 + 1)}{2} = \frac{20(20 + 20 + 1)}{2} = 410,$$

$$\sigma_T = \sqrt{\frac{n_1 n_2 (n_1 + n_2 + 1)}{12}} = \sqrt{\frac{20(20)(41)}{12}} = 36.968455,$$

and

$$z = \frac{T - \mu_T}{\sigma_T} = \frac{513.5 - 410}{36.968455} = 2.7997.$$

Because we are testing a "shifted right or left" (that is, a two-sided) alternative hypothesis, we reject the null hypothesis if $T \leq T_L$ or $T \geq T_U$. Stated in terms of standardized values, we reject the null hypothesis if $z < -z_{\alpha/2}$ or $z > z_{\alpha/2}$ (here we use strict inequalities to be consistent with other normal distribution rejection point conditions). If we set $\alpha = 0.01$, we use the rejection points $-z_{0.005} = -2.575$ and $z_{0.005} = 2.575$. Because $z = 2.7997$ is greater than $z_{0.005} = 2.575$, we reject the null hypothesis at the 0.01 level of significance. Therefore, we have very strong evidence that there is a systematic difference between the Saturday night meal ratings at restaurants 1 and 2. Looking at the original data, we would estimate that Saturday night meal ratings are higher at restaurant 1.

We will conclude this section with a final comment. When there are ties, an adjusted formula for σ_T takes the ties into account. If (as in the restaurant example) we ignore the formula, the results we obtain are statistically conservative. Therefore, if we rejected the null hypothesis by using the unadjusted formula, we would reject the null hypothesis by using the adjusted formula.

Exercises for Section 13.2

CONCEPTS

13.8 Explain the circumstances under which to use the Wilcoxon rank sum test.

13.9 Identify the parametric test corresponding to the Wilcoxon rank sum test. What assumption is needed for the validity of this parametric test (and not needed for the Wilcoxon rank sum test)?

METHODS AND APPLICATIONS

13.10 A loan officer at a bank wishes to compare the mortgage rates charged at banks with the mortgage rates of brokers. Two independent random samples of bank mortgage rates and broker mortgage rates are obtained, with the results in Figure 13.4(a) on the next page.

Because both samples are small, the bank officer is uncertain about the shape of the distributions of bank and broker mortgage rates. Therefore, the Wilcoxon rank sum test will be used to compare the two types of mortgage rates.

    a. Let D_1 be the distribution of bank mortgage rates and D_2 be the distribution of broker mortgage rates. Carry out the Wilcoxon rank sum test to determine whether D_1 and D_2 are identical versus the alternative that D_1 is shifted to the right or left of D_2. Use $\alpha = 0.05$.

    b. Carry out the Wilcoxon rank sum test to determine whether D_1 is shifted to the right of D_2. Use $\alpha = 0.025$. What do you conclude?

13.11 A company collected employee absenteeism data (in hours per year) at two of its manufacturing plants. The data were obtained by randomly selecting one sample from all of the employees at the first plant and another, independent, sample from all of the employees at the second plant. For each randomly selected employee, absenteeism records were used to determine the exact number of hours the employee had been absent during

the past year. The results in Figure 13.4(b) on the next page were obtained.

Use a Wilcoxon rank sum test and the MegaStat output in Figure 13.4(c) to determine whether absenteeism is different at the two plants. Use $\alpha = 0.05$.

13.12 Kevin travels frequently to Winnipeg, Manitoba, from London, Ontario. He uses either ExecuAir or EconoAir. He realizes that flight delays are inevitable but would prefer to give his business to the airline with the best on-time arrival record. The number of minutes that his flight arrived late for the last seven trips is given below. Negative numbers mean that the flight was early.

> **ExecuAir:** 2, −1, 4, −5, 3, 7, −2
> **EconoAir:** −3, 6, 8, 9, 10 −7, 5

Is there evidence to suggest that ExecuAir is superior to EconoAir in terms of its on-time arrival record? Use the Wilcoxon rank sum test and test at $\alpha = 0.05$.

13.13 Moore (2000) reports on a study by Boo (1997), who asked the following question of 303 randomly selected people at fairs:

> How often do you think people become sick because of food they consume prepared at outdoor fairs and festivals?

The possible responses were 5 (always), 4 (often), 3 (more often than not), 2 (once in a while), and 1 (very rarely). The data in Figure 13.4(d) on the next page were obtained.

The computer output at the right of the data presents the results of a Wilcoxon rank sum test that attempts to determine if men and women systematically differ in their responses. Here the normal approximation has been used to calculate the p value of 0.0009. What do you conclude?

FIGURE **13.4**   Data and Output for Exercises 13.10, 13.11, and 13.13

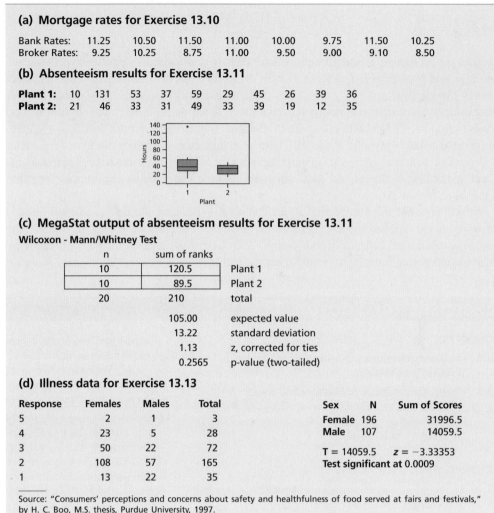

(a) Mortgage rates for Exercise 13.10

| Bank Rates: | 11.25 | 10.50 | 11.50 | 11.00 | 10.00 | 9.75 | 11.50 | 10.25 |
| Broker Rates: | 9.25 | 10.25 | 8.75 | 11.00 | 9.50 | 9.00 | 9.10 | 8.50 |

(b) Absenteeism results for Exercise 13.11

| **Plant 1:** | 10 | 131 | 53 | 37 | 59 | 29 | 45 | 26 | 39 | 36 |
| **Plant 2:** | 21 | 46 | 33 | 31 | 49 | 33 | 39 | 19 | 12 | 35 |

(c) MegaStat output of absenteeism results for Exercise 13.11

Wilcoxon - Mann/Whitney Test

n	sum of ranks	
10	120.5	Plant 1
10	89.5	Plant 2
20	210	total
	105.00	expected value
	13.22	standard deviation
	1.13	z, corrected for ties
	0.2565	p-value (two-tailed)

(d) Illness data for Exercise 13.13

Response	Females	Males	Total
5	2	1	3
4	23	5	28
3	50	22	72
2	108	57	165
1	13	22	35

Sex	N	Sum of Scores
Female	196	31996.5
Male	107	14059.5

$T = 14059.5$ $z = -3.33353$
Test significant at 0.0009

Source: "Consumers' perceptions and concerns about safety and healthfulness of food served at fairs and festivals," by H. C. Boo, M.S. thesis, Purdue University, 1997.

13.3 THE WILCOXON SIGNED RANKS TEST

We can use a *t* test to compare two population means in a paired-differences experiment. If the sample size is small and the population of paired differences is far from normally distributed, this test is not valid and we should use a nonparametric test. In this section, we present the **Wilcoxon signed ranks test**, which is a nonparametric test for comparing two populations when a **paired-differences experiment** has been carried out.

The Wilcoxon Signed Ranks Test

Let D_1 and D_2 denote the probability distributions of populations 1 and 2, and assume that we have randomly selected n matched pairs of observations from populations 1 and 2. Calculate the paired differences of the n matched pairs by subtracting each paired population 2 observation from the corresponding population 1 observation, and rank the absolute values of the n paired differences from the smallest (rank 1) to the largest (rank n). Here paired differences equal to 0 are eliminated, and the number n of paired differences is reduced accordingly. Furthermore, if two or more absolute paired differences are equal, we assign to each tied absolute paired difference a rank equal to the average of the consecutive ranks that would otherwise be assigned to the tied absolute paired differences. Let

$T^- =$ the sum of the ranks associated with the negative paired differences

and

$T^+ =$ the sum of the ranks associated with the positive paired differences.

We can test

H_0: D_1 and D_2 are identical probability distributions

versus a particular alternative hypothesis at level of significance α by using the appropriate test statistic and the corresponding rejection point rule.

Alternative Hypothesis	Test Statistic	Rejection Point Rule: Reject H_0 if
H_a: D_1 is shifted to the right of D_2	T^-	$T^- \leq T_0$
H_a: D_1 is shifted to the left of D_2	T^+	$T^+ \leq T_0$
H_a: D_1 is shifted to the right or left of D_2	$T =$ the smaller of T^- and T^+	$T \leq T_0$

The first two alternative hypotheses above are **one-sided**, while the third alternative hypothesis is **two-sided**. Values of the rejection point T_0 are given in Table A.16 for values of n from 5 to 50.

Table 13.3 repeats a portion of Table A.16. This table gives the rejection point T_0 for testing one-sided and two-sided alternative hypotheses at several different values of α. The rejection points are tabulated according to n, the number of paired differences. For instance, Table 13.3 shows that if we are analyzing ten paired differences, the rejection point for testing a one-sided alternative hypothesis at the 0.01 level of significance is equal to $T_0 = 5$. This table also shows that we would use the rejection point $T_0 = 5$ to test a two-sided alternative hypothesis at level of significance $\alpha = 0.02$.

TABLE **13.3** A Portion of the Wilcoxon Signed Ranks Table

One-Sided	Two-Sided	$n = 5$	$n = 6$	$n = 7$	$n = 8$	$n = 9$	$n = 10$
$\alpha = 0.05$	$\alpha = 0.10$	1	2	4	6	8	11
$\alpha = 0.025$	$\alpha = 0.05$		1	2	4	6	8
$\alpha = 0.01$	$\alpha = 0.02$			0	2	3	5
$\alpha = 0.005$	$\alpha = 0.01$				0	2	3
		$n = 11$	$n = 12$	$n = 13$	$n = 14$	$n = 15$	$n = 16$
$\alpha = 0.05$	$\alpha = 0.10$	14	17	21	26	30	36
$\alpha = 0.025$	$\alpha = 0.05$	11	14	17	21	25	30
$\alpha = 0.01$	$\alpha = 0.02$	7	10	13	16	20	24
$\alpha = 0.005$	$\alpha = 0.01$	5	7	10	13	16	19

Example 13.4 The Repair Cost Comparison Case

Consider the automobile repair cost data given in Figure 13.5(a) on the next page. If we think that the population of all possible paired differences of repair cost estimates at garages 1 and 2 may be far from normally distributed, we can perform the Wilcoxon signed ranks test. Here we test

H_0: the probability distributions of the populations of all possible repair cost estimates at garages 1 and 2 are identical

versus

H_a: the probability distribution of repair cost estimates at garage 1 is shifted to the left of the probability distribution of repair cost estimates at garage 2.

FIGURE 13.5   Analysis of Repair Cost Estimates at Two Garages

(a) Sample of $n = 7$ Paired Differences of the Repair Cost Estimates at Garages 1 and 2 (Cost Estimates in Hundreds of Dollars)

Sample of $n = 7$ Damaged Cars	Repair Cost Estimates at Garage 1	Repair Cost Estimates at Garage 2	Sample of $n = 7$ Paired Differences	Absolute Paired Differences	Ranks
Car 1	$ 7.1	$ 7.9	$d_1 = -0.8$	0.8	4
Car 2	9.0	10.1	$d_2 = -1.1$	1.1	5
Car 3	11.0	12.2	$d_3 = -1.2$	1.2	6
Car 4	8.9	8.8	$d_4 = 0.1$	0.1	1
Car 5	9.9	10.4	$d_5 = -0.5$	0.5	2
Car 6	9.1	9.8	$d_6 = -0.7$	0.7	3
Car 7	10.3	11.7	$d_7 = -1.4$	1.4	7

(b) MegaStat output of the Wilcoxon signed ranks test

Wilcoxon Signed Rank Test

variables:	Garage1 - Garage2
1	sum of positive ranks
27	sum of negative ranks
7	n
14.00	expected value
5.92	standard deviation
−2.20	z
0.0140	p-value (one-tailed, lower)

To perform this test, we find the absolute value of each paired difference, and we assign ranks to the absolute differences (see Figure 13.5(a)). Because of the form of the alternative hypothesis (see the preceding summary box), we use the test statistic

$$T^+ = \text{the sum of the ranks associated with the positive paired differences.}$$

Because 0.1 is the only positive paired difference, and because the rank associated with this difference equals 1, we find that $T^+ = 1$ (see Figure 13.5(b)). The alternative hypothesis is one-sided, and we are analyzing $n = 7$ paired differences. Table 13.3 tells us that we can test H_0 versus H_a at the 0.05, 0.025, and 0.01 levels of significance by setting the rejection point T_0 equal to 4, 2, and 0, respectively. The rejection point condition is $T^+ \le T_0$. It follows that since $T^+ = 1$ is less than or equal to 4 and 2 but not less than or equal to 0, we can reject H_0 in favour of H_a at the 0.05 and 0.025 levels of significance, but not at the 0.01 level of significance. Therefore, we have strong evidence that the probability distribution of repair cost estimates at garage 1 is shifted to the left of the probability distribution of repair cost estimates at garage 2. That is, the repair cost estimates at garage 1 seem to be systematically lower than the repair cost estimates at garage 2.

Notice that in Example 13.4 the nonparametric Wilcoxon signed ranks test would not allow us to reject H_0 in favour of H_a at the 0.01 level of significance. On the other hand, a **parametric** paired-differences t test would allow us to reject H_0: $\mu_1 - \mu_2 = 0$ in favour of H_a: $\mu_1 - \mu_2 < 0$ at the 0.01 level of significance when the mean of garage 1 (9.329) is compared with the mean of garage 2 (10.129), as shown in the MegaStat output in Figure 13.6:

In general, *a parametric test is often more powerful* than the analogous nonparametric test. That is, the parametric test often allows us to reject H_0 at smaller values of α. Therefore, if

FIGURE **13.6** MegaStat Output of a Paired-Differences
Test for the Repair Cost Estimates

Hypothesis Test: Paired Observations

0.0000	hypothesized value
9.3286	mean Garage1
10.1286	mean Garage2
−0.8000	mean difference (Garage1 - Garage2)
0.5033	std. dev.
0.1902	std. error
7	n
6	df
−4.21	t
0.0057	p-value (two-tailed)

the assumptions for the parametric test are satisfied—for example, if, when we are using small samples, the sampled populations are approximately normally distributed—it is preferable to use the parametric test. *The advantage of nonparametric tests is that they can be used without assuming that the sampled populations have the shapes of any particular probability distributions,* which can be important when the sampled populations are approximately normally distributed.

Finally, if the sample size n is at least 25, we can use a large-sample approximation of the Wilcoxon signed ranks test. This is done by making two modifications. First, we replace the test statistic (T^- or T^+) by a standardized value of the test statistic. This standardized value is calculated by subtracting the mean $n(n + 1)/4$ from the test statistic (T^- or T^+) and then dividing the resulting difference by the standard deviation $\sqrt{n(n + 1)(2n + 1)/24}$. Second, when testing a one-sided alternative hypothesis, we replace the rejection point T_0 by the normal point $-z_\alpha$. When testing a two-sided alternative hypothesis, we replace T_0 by $-z_{\alpha/2}$.

Exercises for Section 13.3

CONCEPTS

13.14 Explain the circumstances under which to use the Wilcoxon signed ranks test.

13.15 Identify the parametric test corresponding to the Wilcoxon signed ranks test. What assumption is needed for the validity of the parametric test (but not for the Wilcoxon signed ranks test)?

METHODS AND APPLICATIONS

13.16 A consumer advocacy group is concerned about the ability of tax preparation firms to correctly prepare complex returns. To test the performance of tax preparers in two different tax preparation firms—Speedy Tax and Discount Tax—the group designed a tax case for a family with a gross annual income of $150,000 involving several thorny tax issues. In a "tax-off" competition, the advocacy group randomly selected independent samples of ten preparers from each firm and asked each preparer to compute the tax liability for the test case. The preparers' returns were collected, and the group computed the difference between each preparer's computed tax and the actual tax that should have been computed. The data in Table 13.4 on the next page consist of the resulting two sets of tax computation errors, one for preparers from Speedy Tax and the other for preparers from Discount

Tax. Fully interpret the MegaStat output in Table 13.4 of a Wilcoxon signed ranks test analysis of these data.

13.17 Table 13.5 on the next page lists the number of permanent residents in Canada by source country for the years 2008 and 2009 as published by Citizenship and Immigration Canada. Enter the data into Excel and conduct the Wilcoxon–Mann/Whitney test (using MegaStat). Based on the output, would you suggest that there has been a significant change in the pattern of immigration from the ten countries listed? Explain your answer.

13.18 A human resources director wishes to assess the benefits of sending a company's managers to an innovative management course. Twelve of the company's managers are randomly selected to attend the course, and a psychologist interviews each participating manager before and after taking the course. Based on these interviews, the psychologist rates the manager's leadership ability on a 1-to-100 scale. The pretest and posttest leadership scores for each of the 12 managers are given in Table 13.6 on the next page.

a. Let D_1 be the distribution of leadership scores before taking the course and D_2 be the distribution of leadership scores after taking the course. Carry out the Wilcoxon signed ranks test to test whether

TABLE **13.4**   Tax Computation Errors and MegaStat Output for Exercise 13.7

Speedy Tax Errors	Discount Tax Errors	Difference
857	156	701
920	200	720
1,090	202	888
1,594	390	1,204
1,820	526	1,294
1,943	749	1,194
1,987	911	1,076
2,008	920	1,088
2,083	2,145	−62
2,439	2,602	−163

Wilcoxon Signed Rank Test

			No.	Label	Data	Rank
variables:	Speedy - Discount		1		701	3
52	sum of positive ranks		2		720	4
3	sum of negative ranks		3		888	5
			4		1204	9
10	n		5		1294	10
27.50	expected value		6		1194	8
9.81	standard deviation		7		1076	6
2.50	z		8		1088	7
0.0125	p-value (two-tailed)		9		−62	1
			10		−163	2

D_1 and D_2 are identical (that is, the course has no effect on leadership scores) versus the alternative that D_2 is shifted to the right or left of D_1 (that is, the course affects leadership scores). Use $\alpha = 0.05$.

b. Carry out the Wilcoxon signed ranks test to determine whether D_2 is shifted to the right of D_1. Use $\alpha = 0.05$. What do you conclude?

13.19 In a study examining the difference in attitudes between preexposure and postexposure to an advertisement, ten people were tested. The data obtained and the related MegaStat output are shown in Table 13.7. Use the Wilcoxon signed ranks test and the MegaStat output to determine whether the distributions of preexposure and postexposure attitude scores are different. Use $\alpha = 0.05$.

TABLE **13.5**   Permanent Residents in Canada by Top Ten Source Countries (Number of People)

	2008	2009
China	29,337	29,049
Philippines	23,726	27,277
India	24,548	26,122
United States	11,216	9,723
United Kingdom	9,243	9,566
France	6,384	7,300
Pakistan	8,052	6,214
Iran	6,010	6,065
Korea, Republic of	7,246	5,864
Morocco	3,906	5,222

Source: http://www.cic.gc.ca/english/resources/statistics/facts2009/permanent/10.asp.

TABLE **13.6**   Pretest and Posttest Leadership Scores

Manager	Pretest Score	Posttest Score	Difference
1	35	54	−19
2	27	43	−16
3	51	53	−2
4	38	50	−12
5	32	42	−10
6	44	58	−14
7	33	35	−2
8	26	39	−13
9	40	47	−7
10	50	48	2
11	36	41	−5
12	31	37	−6

TABLE **13.7** Preexposure and Postexposure Attitude Scores for an Advertising Study

Subject	Preexposure Attitudes (A_1)	Postexposure Attitudes (A_2)	Attitude Change (d_i)	Wilcoxon Signed Rank Test
				variables: Pre. Attitudes(A1) - Post. Attitudes(A2)
1	50	53	3	
2	25	27	2	0 sum of positive ranks
3	30	38	8	45 sum of negative ranks
4	50	55	5	
5	60	61	1	
6	80	85	5	9 n
7	45	45	0	
8	30	31	1	22.50 expected value
9	65	72	7	7.89 standard deviation
10	70	78	8	−2.85 z, corrected for ties
				0.0043 p-value (two-tailed)

Source: *Essentials of Marketing Research*, by W. R. Dillon, T. J. Madden, and N. H. Firtle (Burr Ridge, IL: Richard D. Irwin, 1993), p. 435. Copyright © 1993. Reprinted by permission of McGraw-Hill Companies, Inc.

13.4 COMPARING SEVERAL POPULATIONS USING THE KRUSKAL–WALLIS *H* TEST

If we fear that the normality and/or equal-variances assumptions for one-way ANOVA do not hold, we can use a nonparametric approach to compare several populations. One such approach is the **Kruskal–Wallis *H* test**, which compares the locations of three or more populations by using independent random samples and a completely randomized experimental design.

In general, suppose we wish to use the Kruskal–Wallis *H* test to compare the locations of *p* populations by using *p* independent samples of observations randomly selected from these populations. We first rank all of the observations in the *p* samples from smallest to largest. If n_i denotes the number of observations in the *i*th sample, we are ranking a total of $n = (n_1 + n_2 + \cdots + n_p)$ observations. Furthermore, we assign tied observations the average of the consecutive ranks that would otherwise be assigned to the tied observations. Next we calculate the sum of the ranks of the observations in each sample. Letting T_i denote the rank sum for the *i*th sample, we obtain the rank sums $T_1, T_2, \ldots, T_p$. For example, suppose that a company wants to decrease the culture shock experienced by managers who work on a project in a foreign country for a year. Three types of enculturation training methods are assessed using the experimental method, and learning of the new culture is tested using a standard test. Training type *A* uses information about the new culture only (books, videotapes, etc.). Training type *B* is interactive and includes behavioural modelling with an instructor from the new culture. Training type *C* is the control group, which receives no information or behavioural modelling. Fifteen managers in total are tested with five being randomly assigned to each of the three training types. The resulting data are presented in Table 13.8 on the next page, in which higher scores represent greater learning about the new culture on the standard test (rank values are given in brackets). If we sum the ranks in each sample, we find that $T_1 = 37.5$, $T_2 = 63$, and $T_3 = 19.5$. Note that although the box plots in Table 13.8 do not indicate any serious violations of the normality or equal-variances assumptions, the samples are quite small, and thus we cannot be sure that these assumptions approximately hold. Therefore, it is reasonable to compare training types *A*, *B*, and *C* by using the Kruskal–Wallis *H* test.

L04

TABLE **13.8**   The Training Type Results and Rank Sums

Training Type A	Training Type B	Training Type C	
34.0 (3.5)	35.3 (9)	33.3 (2)	
35.0 (8)	36.5 (13)	34.0 (3.5)	
34.3 (5)	36.4 (12)	34.7 (6)	
35.5 (10)	37.0 (14)	33.0 (1)	
35.8 (11)	37.6 (15)	34.9 (7)	
$T_1 = 37.5$	$T_2 = 63$	$T_3 = 19.5$	

The Kruskal–Wallis *H* Test

Consider testing the null hypothesis H_0 that the p populations under consideration are identical versus the alternative hypothesis H_a that at least two populations differ in location (that is, are shifted either to the left or to the right of one another). We can reject H_0 in favour of H_a at level of significance α if the **Kruskal–Wallis *H* statistic**

$$H = \frac{12}{n(n+1)} \sum_{i=1}^{p} \frac{T_i^2}{n_i} - 3(n+1)$$

is greater than the χ_α^2 point based on $p - 1$ degrees of freedom. Here, for this test to be valid, there should be five or more observations in each sample. Furthermore, the number of ties should be small relative to the total number of observations. Values of χ_α^2 are given in Table A.18.

A Chi-Square Table: Value of χ_α^2

df	$\chi_{0.10}^2$	$\chi_{0.05}^2$
1	2.70554	3.84146
2	4.60517	5.99147
3	6.25139	7.81473
4	7.77944	9.48773
5	9.23635	11.0705
6	10.6446	12.5916
7	12.0170	14.0671
8	13.3616	15.5073
9	14.6837	16.9190
10	15.9871	18.3070

In this training type case, $\chi_{0.05}^2$ based on $p - 1 = 2$ degrees of freedom is 5.99147 (see the section of the table in the margin). Furthermore, in this example, $n = n_1 + n_2 + n_3 = 15$, so the Kruskal–Wallis H statistic is

$$H = \frac{12}{15(15+1)} \left[\frac{37.5^2}{5} + \frac{63^2}{5} + \frac{19.5^2}{5} \right] - 3(15+1)$$

$$= \frac{1}{20} \left[\frac{1{,}406.25}{5} + \frac{3{,}969}{5} + \frac{380.25}{5} \right] - 48 = 9.555.$$

Because $H = 9.555 > \chi_{0.05}^2 = 5.99147$, we can reject H_0 at the 0.05 level of significance. Therefore, we have strong evidence that at least two of the three populations of test scores differ in location. Figure 13.7 presents the MegaStat output of the Kruskal–Wallis H test in this training type case.

To conclude this section, we note that if the Kruskal–Wallis H test leads us to conclude that the p populations differ in location, there are various procedures for comparing pairs of populations. A simple procedure is to use the Wilcoxon rank sum test to compare pairs of populations. For example, if we use this test to make separate, *two-sided* comparisons of (1) training types A and B, (2) training types A and C, and (3) training types B and C, and if we set α equal to 0.05 for each comparison, we find that the test scores given by training type B differ systematically from the scores given by training types A and C. Examining the scores in Table 13.8, we would estimate that training type B results in the highest test scores. One problem, however, with using the Wilcoxon rank sum test to make pairwise comparisons is that it is difficult to know how to set α for each comparison. Therefore, some practitioners prefer to make *simultaneous* pairwise comparisons (such as given by the Tukey simultaneous confidence intervals discussed in Chapter 10). Gibbons (1985) discusses a nonparametric approach for making simultaneous pairwise comparisons.

FIGURE **13.7** MegaStat Output of the Kruskal–Wallis *H* Test in the Training Method Experiment

Kruskal–Wallis Test

Median	n	Avg. Rank	
35.00	5	7.50	Type A
36.50	5	12.60	Type B
34.00	5	3.90	Type C
35.00	15		Total

9.572	H (corrected for ties)
2	d.f.
0.0083	p-value

multiple comparison values for avg. ranks
6.77 (0.05)   8.30 (0.01)

No.	Label	Data	Rank		No.	Label	Data	Rank
1	Type A	34	3.5		9	Type B	37	14
2	Type A	35	8		10	Type B	38	15
3	Type A	34	5		11	Type C	33	2
4	Type A	36	10		12	Type C	34	3.5
5	Type A	36	11		13	Type C	35	6
6	Type B	35	9		14	Type C	33	1
7	Type B	37	13		15	Type C	35	7
8	Type B	36	12					

Exercises for Section 13.4

CONCEPTS

13.20 Explain the circumstances under which to use the Kruskal–Wallis *H* test.

13.21 Identify the parametric test corresponding to the Kruskal–Wallis *H* test.

13.22 What assumptions are needed for the validity of the parametric test identified in Exercise 13.21 that are not needed for the Kruskal–Wallis *H* test?

METHODS AND APPLICATIONS

In each of Exercises 13.23 through 13.26, use the given independent samples to perform the Kruskal–Wallis *H* test of the null hypothesis H_0 that the corresponding populations are identical versus the alternative hypothesis H_a that at least two populations differ in location. Note that we previously analyzed each of these data sets using the one-way ANOVA *F* test in Chapter 10.

13.23 Use the Kruskal–Wallis *H* test to compare display panels *A*, *B*, and *C* using the data in Table 13.9. Use $\alpha = 0.05$.

13.24 Use the Kruskal–Wallis *H* test to compare bottle designs *A*, *B*, and *C* using the data in Table 13.10. Use $\alpha = 0.01$.

13.25 Use the Kruskal–Wallis *H* test and the MegaStat output in Figure 13.8 on the next page to compare the bottom (*B*), middle (*M*), and top (*T*) display heights using the data in Table 13.11 on the next page. Use $\alpha = 0.05$. Then repeat the analysis if the first sales value for the middle display height is found to be incorrect and must be removed from the data set.

TABLE **13.9** Display Panel Study Data (Time, in Seconds, Required to Stabilize Air Traffic Emergency Condition)

	Display Panel	
A	*B*	*C*
21	24	40
27	21	36
24	18	35
26	19	32
25	20	37

TABLE **13.10** Bottle Design Study Data (Sales during a 24-Hour Period)

	Bottle Design	
A	*B*	*C*
16	33	23
18	31	27
19	37	21
17	29	28
13	34	25

FIGURE 13.8   MegaStat Output of the Kruskal–Wallis *H* Test for the Bakery Sales Data

Kruskal-Wallis Test

Median	n	Avg. Rank	
55.75	6	9.17	Bottom
77.15	6	15.50	Middle
51.50	6	3.83	Top
55.75	18		Total

14.363	H
2	d.f.
0.0008	p-value

multiple comparison values for avg. ranks
7.38 (0.05)   9.05 (0.01)

No.	Label	Data	Rank
1	Bottom	58	11
2	Bottom	54	7
3	Bottom	56	10
4	Bottom	56	9
5	Bottom	53	6
6	Bottom	59	12
7	Middle	73	13
8	Middle	78	16
9	Middle	75	14
10	Middle	76	15
11	Middle	78	17
12	Middle	82	18
13	Top	52	5
14	Top	50	1
15	Top	51	3
16	Top	54	8
17	Top	52	4
18	Top	50	2

13.26 Use the Kruskal–Wallis *H* test to compare golf ball brands Alpha, Best, Century, and Divot using the data in Table 13.12. Use $\alpha = 0.01$ and the MegaStat output to the right in Table 13.12.

13.27 A statistics professor at a local university believes that the amount of time that students spend studying depends on the term the student is studying in. Fall, winter, and spring terms were considered. Students were randomly selected during three different times of year during a one-year period and asked to estimate the number of hours spent studying per week. Here are the students' estimates:

> **Fall:** 5, 2, 6, 9, 4, 7, 5, 3
> **Winter:** 9, 7, 12, 11, 8, 10, 6, 11, 5, 9
> **Spring:** 6, 9, 5, 8, 8, 5, 3, 4, 7

Conduct a Kruskal–Wallis test at the $\alpha = 0.05$ level of significance. Based on the results of the hypothesis test, is there evidence to suggest that the average study times are not all the same, that is, that the amount of time studying differs throughout the school year?

TABLE 13.11   Bakery Sales Study Data (Sales in Cases)

	Shelf Display Height	
Bottom (*B*)	Middle (*M*)	Top (*T*)
58.2	73.0	52.4
53.7	78.1	49.7
55.8	75.4	50.9
55.7	76.2	54.0
52.5	78.4	52.1
58.9	82.1	49.9

TABLE 13.12   Golf Ball Durability Test Results

	Brand				Kruskal–Wallis Test				
Alpha	Best	Century	Divot		Median	n	Avg. Rank	13.834	H
281	270	218	364		251.00	5	6.80 Alpha	3	d.f.
220	334	244	302		307.00	5	13.40 Best	0.0031	p-value
274	307	225	325		244.00	5	4.80 Century		
242	290	273	337		337.00	5	17.00 Divot		
251	331	249	355		277.50	20	Total		

13.5 SPEARMAN'S RANK CORRELATION COEFFICIENT

In Chapter 11, we showed how to test the significance of a population correlation coefficient. This test is based on the assumption that the population of all possible combinations of values of *x* and *y* has a bivariate normal probability distribution. If we fear that this assumption is

TABLE **13.13**   Electronics World Sales Volume Data and Ranks for 15 Stores

Store	Number of Households, x	Sales Volume, y	x Rank	y Rank	Difference, d	d^2
1	161	157.27	6	7	−1	1
2	99	93.28	1	1	0	0
3	135	136.81	5	5	0	0
4	120	123.79	4	3	1	1
5	164	153.51	7	6	1	1
6	221	241.74	13	14	−1	1
7	179	201.54	8	10	−2	4
8	204	206.71	9	11	−2	4
9	214	229.78	12	13	−1	1
10	101	135.22	2	4	−2	4
11	231	224.71	14	12	2	4
12	206	195.29	11	8	3	9
13	248	242.16	15	15	0	0
14	107	115.21	3	2	1	1
15	205	197.82	10	9	1	1

$$\Sigma d^2 = 32$$

violated, we can use a nonparametric approach. One such approach is **Spearman's rank correlation coefficient**,[2] which is denoted r_s.

To illustrate, suppose that Electronics World, a chain of stores that sells audio and video equipment, has gathered the data in Table 13.13. The company wishes to study the relationship between store sales volume in July of last year (y, measured in thousands of dollars) and the number of households in the store's area (x, measured in thousands). Spearman's rank correlation coefficient is found by first ranking the values of x and y separately (ties are treated by averaging the tied ranks). To calculate r_s, we use the formula[3]

$$r = \frac{\Sigma xy - \dfrac{\Sigma x \Sigma y}{n}}{\sqrt{\left(\Sigma x^2 - \dfrac{(\Sigma x)^2}{n_1}\right)\left(\Sigma y^2 - \dfrac{(\Sigma y^2)}{n_2}\right)}}$$

for r and replace the x and y values in that formula by their ranks. If there are no ties in the ranks, this formula can be calculated by the simple equation

$$r_s = 1 - \frac{6\Sigma d_i^2}{n(n^2 - 1)},$$

where d_i is the difference between the x rank and the y rank for the ith observation (if there are few ties in the ranks, this formula is approximately valid). To deal with a tie, sum the tied ranks and divide the sum by the number of ties to create an "average" rank value to assign to the tied cases. For example, Table 13.13 gives the ranks of x and y, the difference between the ranks, and the squared difference for each of the $n = 15$ stores in the Electronics World example. Because the sum of the squared differences is 32, we calculate r_s to be

$$r_s = 1 - \frac{6(32)}{15(225 - 1)} = 0.9429.$$

---

[2]Charles Spearman was the advisor of Karl Pearson, who developed the correlation coefficient described in Chapter 11.
[3]*Note:* As with the correlation coefficient, $n_1 = n_2$.

Equivalently, if we have MegaStat analyze the data, we obtain the following output:

Spearman Coefficient of Rank Correlation

	X	Y
X	1.000	
Y	0.943	1.000

15 sample size

± 0.514 critical value 0.05 (two-tail)
± 0.641 critical value 0.01 (two-tail)

X	Y	X	Y
6	7	12	13
1	1	2	4
5	5	14	12
4	3	11	8
7	6	15	15
13	14	3	2
8	10	10	9
9	11		

This large positive value of r_s says that there is a strong positive rank correlation between the numbers of households and sales volumes in the sample.

LO5   In general, let ρ_s denote the **population rank correlation coefficient**—the rank correlation coefficient for the population of all possible (x, y) values. We can test the significance of ρ_s by using **Spearman's rank correlation test**.

Spearman's Rank Correlation Test

Let r_s denote Spearman's rank correlation coefficient. Then we can test H_0: $\rho_s = 0$ versus a particular alternative hypothesis at level of significance α by using the appropriate rejection point rule.

Alternative Hypothesis	Rejection Point Rule: Reject H_0 if
H_a: $\rho_s > 0$	$r_s > r_\alpha$
H_a: $\rho_s < 0$	$r_s < -r_\alpha$
H_a: $\rho_s \neq 0$	$\mid r_s \mid > r_{\alpha/2}$

Table A.17 gives values of the rejection points r_α, $-r_\alpha$, and $r_{\alpha/2}$ for values of n from 5 to 30. Note that for this test to be valid, the number of ties encountered in ranking the observations should be small relative to the number of observations.

A portion of Table A.17 is reproduced here as Table 13.14. To illustrate using this table, suppose in the Electronics World example that we wish to test H_0: $\rho_s = 0$ versus H_a: $\rho_s > 0$ by setting $\alpha = 0.05$. Because there are $n = 15$ stores, Table 13.14 tells us that we use the rejection point $r_{0.05} = 0.441$. Because $r_s = 0.9429$ is greater than this rejection point, we can reject H_0: $\rho_s = 0$ in favour of H_a: $\rho_s > 0$ at $\alpha = 0.05$. Therefore, we have strong evidence that in July of last year, the sales volume of an Electronics World store was positively correlated with the number of households in the store's area.

TABLE **13.14** Critical Values for Spearman's Rank Correlation Coefficient

n	$\alpha = 0.05$	$\alpha = 0.025$	$\alpha = 0.01$	$\alpha = 0.005$
10	0.564	0.648	0.745	0.794
11	0.523	0.623	0.736	0.818
12	0.497	0.591	0.703	0.780
13	0.475	0.566	0.673	0.745
14	0.457	0.545	0.646	0.716
15	0.441	0.525	0.623	0.689
16	0.425	0.507	0.601	0.666
17	0.412	0.490	0.582	0.645
18	0.399	0.476	0.564	0.625
19	0.388	0.462	0.549	0.608
20	0.377	0.450	0.534	0.591

TABLE **13.15** Rankings of 12 Midsize Cars by Two Automobile Magazines

Car	Magazine 1 Ranking	Magazine 2 Ranking
1	5	7
2	1	1
3	4	5
4	7	4
5	6	6
6	8	10
7	9	8
8	12	11
9	2	3
10	3	2
11	10	12
12	11	9

To illustrate testing a two-sided alternative hypothesis, consider Table 13.15. This table presents the rankings of $n = 12$ midsize cars given by two automobile magazines. Here each magazine has ranked the cars from 1 (best) to 12 (worst) on the basis of overall ride. Because the two magazines sometimes have differing views, we cannot theorize about whether their rankings would be positively or negatively correlated. Therefore, we will test $H_0: \rho_s = 0$ versus $H_a: \rho_s \neq 0$. The summary box tells us that to perform this test at level of significance α, we use the rejection point $r_{\alpha/2}$. To look up $r_{\alpha/2}$ in Table A.17 (or Table 13.14), we replace the symbol α by the symbol $\alpha/2$. For example, consider setting $\alpha = 0.05$. Then, since $\alpha/2 = 0.025$, we look in Table 13.14 for the value 0.025. Because there are $n = 12$ cars, we find that $r_{0.025} = 0.591$. Spearman's rank correlation coefficient for the car-ranking data can be calculated to be 0.8951. Because $r_s = 0.8951$ is greater than $r_{0.025} = 0.591$, we reject H_0 at the 0.05 level of significance. Therefore, we conclude that the midsize car ride rankings given by the two magazines are correlated. Furthermore, because $r_s = 0.8951$, we estimate that these rankings are positively correlated.

To conclude this section, we make two comments. First, the car-ranking example illustrates that Spearman's rank correlation coefficient and test can be used when the raw measurements of the x and/or y variables are themselves **ranks**. Ranks are measurements of an ordinal variable, and Spearman's nonparametric approach applies to ordinal variables. Second, it can be shown that if the sample size n is at least 10, then we can carry out an approximation to Spearman's rank correlation test by replacing r_s by the t statistic

$$t = \frac{r_s \sqrt{n - 2}}{\sqrt{1 - r_s^2}}$$

and by replacing the rejection points r_α, $-r_\alpha$, and $r_{\alpha/2}$ by the t points t_α, $-t_\alpha$, and $t_{\alpha/2}$ (with $n - 2$ degrees of freedom). Table A.17 gives r_α points for sample sizes up to $n = 30$. However, if the sample size exceeds 30, we can use the z points z_α, $-z_\alpha$, and $z_{\alpha/2}$ in place of the corresponding t points.

(BI)

Exercises for Section 13.5

CONCEPTS

13.28 Explain the circumstances under which to use Spearman's rank correlation coefficient.

13.29 Write the formula that is used to compute Spearman's rank correlation coefficient in each case.

a. There are no (or few) ties in the ranks of the x and y values.

b. There are many ties in the ranks of the x and y values.

METHODS AND APPLICATIONS

13.30 A sales manager ranks ten people at the end of their training on the basis of their sales potential. A year later, the number of units sold by each person is determined. The data and MegaStat output in Table 13.16(a) are obtained. Note that the manager's ranking of 1 is "best."

a. Find r_s on the MegaStat output and use Table 13.14 to find the critical value for testing H_0: $\rho_s = 0$ versus H_a: $\rho_s \neq 0$ at the 0.05 level of significance. Do you reject H_0?

b. The MegaStat output gives approximate critical values for $\alpha = 0.05$ and $\alpha = 0.01$. Do these approximate critical values, which are based on the t distribution, differ by much from the exact critical values in Table 13.14 (recall that $n = 10$)?

13.31 Use the MegaStat output in Table 13.16(b) to find r_s, and then test H_0: $\rho_s = 0$ versus H_a: $\rho_s > 0$ for the service time data in Table 13.16(b).

TABLE 13.16 Data and MegaStat Output for Exercises 13.30 and 13.31

(a) Training data and MegaStat output for Exercise 13.30

Person	1	2	3	4	5	6	7	8	9	10
Manager's Ranking, x	7	4	2	6	1	10	3	5	9	8
Units Sold, y	770	630	820	580	720	440	690	810	560	470

	MgrRank, x	UnitSold, y
MgrRank, x	1.000	
UnitSold, y	−0.721	1.000

±0.632 critical value 0.05 (two-tail)
±0.765 critical value 0.01 (two-tail)

10 sample size

(b) Service time data and MegaStat output for Exercise 13.31

Copiers Serviced, x	4	2	5	7	1	3	4	5	2	4	6
Minutes Required, y	109	58	138	189	37	82	103	134	68	112	154

Spearman Coefficient of Rank Correlation

	Copiers, x	Minutes, y
Copiers, x	1.000	
Minutes, y	0.986	1.000

11 sample size

± 0.602 critical value 0.05 (two-tail)
± 0.735 critical value 0.01 (two-tail)

Copiers, x	Minutes, y
6	6
2.5	2
8.5	9
11	11
1	1
4	4
6	5
8.5	8
2.5	3
6	7
10	10

CHAPTER SUMMARY

The validity of many of the inference procedures presented in this book requires that various assumptions be met. Often, for instance, a normality assumption is required. In this chapter, we have learned that when the needed assumptions are not met, we must employ a **nonparametric method**. Such a method does not require any assumptions about the shape(s) of the distribution(s) of the sampled population(s).

We first presented the **sign test**, which is a hypothesis test about a population median. This test is useful when we have taken a sample from a population that may not be normally distributed. We next presented two nonparametric tests for comparing the locations of two populations. The first such test, the **Wilcoxon rank sum test**, is appropriate when an **independent-samples experiment** has been carried out. The second, the

Wilcoxon signed ranks test, is appropriate when a **paired-differences experiment** has been carried out. Both of these tests can be used without assuming that the sampled populations have the shapes of any particular probability distributions. We then discussed the **Kruskal–Wallis H test**, which is a nonparametric test for comparing the locations of several populations by using independent samples. This test, which employs the chi-square distribution, can be used when the normality and/or equal-variances assumptions for one-way ANOVA do not hold. Finally, we presented a nonparametric approach for testing the significance of a population correlation coefficient. Here we saw how to compute **Spearman's rank correlation coefficient**, and we discussed how to use this quantity to test the significance of the population correlation coefficient.

GLOSSARY OF TERMS

Kruskal–Wallis H test: A nonparametric test for comparing the locations of three or more populations by using independent random samples. (page 497)

nonparametric test: A hypothesis test that requires no assumptions about the distribution(s) of the sampled population(s). (page 482)

sign test: A hypothesis test about a population median that requires no assumptions about the sampled population. (page 483)

Spearman's rank correlation coefficient: A correlation coefficient computed using the ranks of the observed values of two variables, x and y. (page 501)

Wilcoxon rank sum test: A nonparametric test for comparing the locations of two populations when an independent-samples experiment has been carried out. (page 488)

Wilcoxon signed ranks test: A nonparametric test for comparing the locations of two populations when a paired-differences experiment has been carried out. (page 492)

IMPORTANT FORMULAS AND TESTS

Sign test for a population median: page 484

Large-sample sign test: page 485

Wilcoxon rank sum test: page 488

Wilcoxon rank sum test (large-sample approximation): page 490

Wilcoxon signed ranks test: pages 492–493

Wilcoxon signed ranks test (large-sample approximation): page 495

Kruskal–Wallis H test: page 498

Kruskal–Wallis H statistic: page 498

Spearman's rank correlation coefficient: page 501

Spearman's rank correlation test: page 502

connect™ Practise and learn online with *Connect*. Questions and tables with online data sets are marked with ✎.

SUPPLEMENTARY EXERCISES

13.32 A marketing research firm wishes to compare the prices charged by two supermarket chains—Miller's and Albert's. The research firm, using a standardized one-week shopping list, makes identical purchases at ten of each chain's stores. The stores for each chain are randomly selected, and all purchases are made during a single week.

The shopping expenses obtained at the two chains are given below.

Miller's

$119.25	$121.32	$122.34	$120.14	$122.19
$123.71	$121.72	$122.42	$123.63	$122.44

Albert's

$111.99	$114.88	$115.11	$117.02	$116.89
$116.62	$115.38	$114.40	$113.91	$111.87

Because the sample sizes are small, there might be reason to doubt that the populations of expenses at the two chains are normally distributed. Therefore, use a Wilcoxon rank sum test to determine whether expenses at Miller's and Albert's differ. Use $\alpha = 0.05$.

13.33 A drug company wishes to compare the effects of three different drugs (X, Y, and Z) that are being developed to reduce cholesterol levels. Each drug is administered to six patients at the recommended dosage for six months. At the end of this period, the reduction in cholesterol level is recorded for each patient. The results are given in Table 13.17 on the next page. Assuming that the three samples are independent, use a nonparametric test to see whether the effects of the three drugs differ. Use $\alpha = 0.05$.

TABLE **13.17** Reduction of Cholesterol Levels Using Three Drugs

	Drug	
X	**Y**	**Z**
22	40	15
31	35	9
19	47	14
27	41	11
25	39	21
18	33	5

13.34 Table 13.18 lists the monthly receipts for restaurants, caterers, and taverns by province for June 2010 in millions of dollars. Also listed in Table 13.18 is the population of each province in July 2009, in thousands. Enter the data into Excel and compute both the Pearson correlation coefficient (from Chapter 11) and the Spearman rank correlation coefficient. How do the two values differ? Which statistic do you feel is most appropriate and why?

13.35 During 2009, a company implemented a number of policies aimed at reducing the ages of its customers'

accounts. In order to assess the effectiveness of these measures, the company randomly selects ten customer accounts. The average age of each account is determined for each of the years 2009 and 2010. These data are given in Table 13.19. Use a nonparametric technique to attempt to show that average account ages have decreased from 2009 to 2010. Use $\alpha = 0.05$.

13.36 The following data represent the total number of people employed and the total revenue (in thousands of dollars) of the Canadian film and video distribution and videocassette wholesaling industry for the years 2000 to 2005. Compute the Spearman rank correlation coefficient for these two variables. What does the resulting value tell you about the relationship between the number of employees and total revenue?

Year	Employed	Revenue ($1,000s)
2000/01	3,592	2,813,116
2001/02	3,900	3,036,646
2002/03	4,033	3,278,386
2003/04	3,972	3,437,629
2004/05	4,152	359,617

Source: http://www40.statcan.gc.ca/l01/cst01/arts15-eng.htm.

TABLE **13.18** Monthly Receipts for Restaurants, Caterers, and Taverns for June 2010 and Population Values by Province for July 2009

Province	Receipts ($1,000,000s)	Population (1,000s)
Newfoundland and Labrador	52	509
Prince Edward Island	14	141
Nova Scotia	106	938
New Brunswick	82	750
Quebec	797	7,829
Ontario	1,570	13,069
Manitoba	122	1,222
Saskatchewan	120	1,030
Alberta	573	3,688
British Columbia	654	4,455

Source: http://www40.statcan.gc.ca/l01/cst01/econ92-eng.htm, http://www40.statcan.gc.ca/l01/cst01/demo02a-eng.htm.

TABLE **13.19** Average Account Ages in 2009 and 2010 for Ten Randomly Selected Accounts

Account	Average Age of Account in 2009 (Days)	Average Age of Account in 2010 (Days)
1	35	27
2	24	19
3	47	40
4	28	30
5	41	33
6	33	25
7	35	31
8	51	29
9	18	15
10	28	21

13.37 A loan officer wishes to compare the interest rates being charged for 48-month fixed-rate auto loans and 48-month variable-rate auto loans. Two independent, random samples of auto loan rates are selected. A sample of eight 48-month fixed-rate auto loans had the following loan rates:

10.29% 9.75% 9.50% 9.99% 9.75%
9.99% 11.40% 10.00%

A sample of five 48-month variable-rate auto loans had loan rates as follows:

9.59% 8.75% 8.99% 8.50% 9.00%

Perform a nonparametric test to determine whether loan rates for 48-month fixed-rate auto loans differ from loan rates for 48-month variable-rate auto loans. Use $\alpha = 0.05$. Explain your conclusion.

13.38 A large bank wishes to limit the median debt-to-equity ratio for its portfolio of commercial loans to 1.5. The bank randomly selects 15 of its commercial loan accounts. Audits result in the following debt-to-equity ratios:

1.31	1.05	1.45	1.21	1.19
1.78	1.37	1.41	1.22	1.11
1.46	1.33	1.29	1.32	1.65

Can it be concluded that the median debt-to-equity ratio is less than 1.5 at the 0.05 level of significance? Explain.

13.39 INTERNET EXERCISE

Go to the Web site http://lib.stat.cmu.edu/DASL/Datafiles/Heliumfootball.html. Carry out the Wilcoxon signed ranks test to determine whether the distributions of the distances for air-filled and helium-filled footballs are different. Use $\alpha = 0.05$.

CHAPTER 14
Chi-Square Tests

LEARNING OBJECTIVES

After reading this chapter, you should be able to

LO1 describe the type of data used in a chi-square goodness of fit test

LO2 conduct a chi-square goodness of fit test

LO3 compute the degrees of freedom and examine the significance of the chi-square test statistic

LO4 explain the purpose of a control variable in a chi-square goodness of fit test

LO5 describe how a chi-square goodness of fit test can be used to test the assumption that the sample was drawn from a normal population

LO6 explain how graphs may be used to demonstrate the relationship between variables

CHAPTER OUTLINE

In this chapter, we present two useful hypothesis tests based on the **chi-square distribution**. First, we consider the **chi-square goodness of fit test**. This test evaluates whether data falling into several categories do so with a hypothesized set of probabilities. Second, we discuss the **chi-square test for independence**. Here data are classified on two dimensions and are summarized in a **contingency table**. The test for independence then evaluates whether the cross-classified (or cross-tabulated) variables are independent of each other. If we conclude that the variables are not independent, then we have established that the variables in question are related, and we must then investigate the nature of the relationship.

14.1 CHI-SQUARE GOODNESS OF FIT TESTS

Multinomial probabilities Sometimes we collect count data in order to study how the counts are distributed among several **categories** or **cells**. As an example, we might study consumer preferences for four different brands of a product. To do this, we select a random sample of consumers, and we ask each survey participant to indicate a brand preference. We then count the number of consumers who prefer each of the four brands. Here we have four categories (brands), and we study the distribution of the counts in each category in order to see which brands are preferred.

LO1

VS

CHAPTER 13

We often use categorical data[1] to carry out a statistical inference. For instance, suppose that a major wholesaler in London, Ontario, carries four different brands of microwave ovens. Historically, consumer behaviour in London has resulted in the market shares shown in Table 14.1. The wholesaler plans to begin doing business in a new territory—Edmonton, Alberta. To study whether its policies for stocking the four brands of ovens in London can also be used in Edmonton, the wholesaler compares consumer preferences for the four ovens in Edmonton with the historical market shares observed in London. A random sample of 400 consumers in Edmonton gives the preferences shown in Table 14.2.

To compare consumer preferences in London and Edmonton, we must consider a **multinomial experiment**. This is similar to the binomial experiment. However, a binomial experiment concerns count data that can be classified into two categories, while a multinomial experiment concerns count data that are classified into more than two categories. Specifically, the assumptions for the multinomial experiment are as follows:

The Multinomial Experiment

1. We perform an experiment in which we carry out n identical trials and in which there are k possible outcomes on each trial.

2. The probabilities of the k outcomes are denoted $p_1, p_2, \ldots, p_k$, where $p_1 + p_2 + \cdots + p_k = 1$. These probabilities stay the same from trial to trial.

3. The trials in the experiment are independent.

4. The results of the experiment are observed frequencies (counts) of the number of trials that result in each of the k possible outcomes. The frequencies are denoted $f_1, f_2, \ldots, f_k$. That is, f_1 is the number of trials resulting in the first possible outcome, f_2 is the number of trials resulting in the second possible outcome, and so forth.

Notice that the scenario that defines a multinomial experiment is similar to that which defines a binomial experiment. In fact, a binomial experiment is simply a multinomial experiment in which k equals 2 (there are two possible outcomes on each trial).

In general, the probabilities $p_1, p_2, \ldots, p_k$ are unknown, and we estimate their values. Or, we compare estimates of these probabilities with a set of specified values. We now look at an example.

TABLE **14.1** Market Shares for Four Microwave Oven Brands in London, Ontario

Brand	Market Share
1	20%
2	35%
3	30%
4	15%

TABLE **14.2** Brand Preferences for Four Microwave Ovens in Edmonton, Alberta

Brand	Observed Frequency (Number of Consumers Sampled Who Prefer the Brand)
1	102
2	121
3	120
4	57

[1]Note that categorical data are the same as nominal data (as described in the four levels of measurement in Chapter 1).

Example 14.1   The Microwave Oven Preference Case

Suppose the microwave oven wholesaler wishes to compare consumer preferences in Edmonton with the historical market shares in London. If the consumer preferences in Edmonton are substantially different, the wholesaler will consider changing its policies for stocking the ovens. Here we will define

p_1 = the proportion of Edmonton consumers who prefer brand 1,

p_2 = the proportion of Edmonton consumers who prefer brand 2,

p_3 = the proportion of Edmonton consumers who prefer brand 3,

p_4 = the proportion of Edmonton consumers who prefer brand 4.

Remembering that the historical market shares for brands 1, 2, 3, and 4 in London are 20 percent, 35 percent, 30 percent, and 15 percent, we test the null hypothesis

$$H_0: p_1 = 0.20, \quad p_2 = 0.35, \quad p_3 = 0.30, \quad \text{and} \quad p_4 = 0.15,$$

which says that consumer preferences in Edmonton are consistent with the historical market shares in London. We test H_0 versus

H_a: the null hypothesis is not supported (at least one of the percentages is different).

To test H_0, we must compare the observed frequencies given in Table 14.2 with the **expected frequencies** for the brands calculated on the assumption that H_0 is true. For instance, if H_0 is true, we would expect $400(0.20) = 80$ of the 400 Edmonton consumers surveyed to prefer brand 1. Denoting this expected frequency for brand 1 as E_1, the expected frequencies for brands 2, 3, and 4 when H_0 is true are $E_2 = 400(0.35) = 140$, $E_3 = 400(0.30) = 120$, and $E_4 = 400(0.15) = 60$. Recalling that Table 14.2 gives the observed frequency for each brand, we have $f_1 = 102, f_2 = 121, f_3 = 120$, and $f_4 = 57$. We now compare the observed and expected frequencies by computing a **chi-square statistic** as follows:

LO2

$$\chi^2 = \sum_{i=1}^{k=4} \frac{(f_i - E_i)^2}{E_i}$$

$$= \frac{(102 - 80)^2}{80} + \frac{(121 - 140)^2}{140} + \frac{(120 - 120)^2}{120} + \frac{(57 - 60)^2}{60}$$

$$= \frac{484}{80} + \frac{361}{140} + \frac{0}{120} + \frac{9}{60} = 8.7786.$$

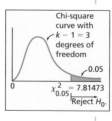

The more the observed frequencies differ from the expected frequencies, the larger χ^2 will be and the more doubt will be cast on the null hypothesis. If the chi-square statistic is large enough (beyond a rejection point), then we reject H_0.

To find an appropriate rejection point, it can be shown that when the null hypothesis is true, the sampling distribution of the χ^2 statistic is approximately a χ^2 distribution with $k - 1 = 4 - 1 = 3$ degrees of freedom. If we wish to test H_0 at the 0.05 level of significance, we reject H_0 if and only if

$$\chi^2_{\text{obtained}} > \chi^2_{0.05}.$$

LO3

Table A.18 tells us that the $\chi^2_{0.05}$ point corresponding to $k - 1 = 3$ degrees of freedom equals 7.81473. Therefore,

$$\chi^2_{\text{obtained}} = 8.7786 > \chi^2_{0.05} = 7.81473,$$

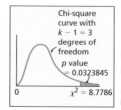

and we reject H_0 at the 0.05 level of significance. The p value for this hypothesis test is the area under the curve of the chi-square distribution with 3 degrees of freedom to the right of $\chi^2 = 8.7786$. This p value can be calculated to be 0.0323845. Because this p value is less than 0.05, we can reject H_0 at the 0.05 level of significance.

We conclude that consumer preferences in Edmonton for the four brands of ovens are not consistent with the historical market shares in London. Based on this conclusion, the wholesaler should consider changing its stocking policies for microwave ovens when it enters the Edmonton market. To study how to change its policies, the wholesaler might compute a 95 percent confidence interval for, say, the proportion of consumers in Edmonton who prefer brand 2. Computing this confidence interval involves the expression used for computing a population proportion (introduced in Chapter 7):

$$\left[\hat{p} \pm z_{\alpha/2} \sqrt{\frac{\hat{p}(1 - \hat{p})}{n}} \right].$$

For brand 2, $\hat{p}_2 = 121/400 = 0.3025$, so this interval is

$$\left[\hat{p}_2 \pm z_{0.025} \sqrt{\frac{\hat{p}_2(1 - \hat{p}_2)}{n}} \right] = \left[0.3025 \pm 1.96 \sqrt{\frac{0.3025(1 - 0.3025)}{400}} \right]$$

$$= [0.2575, 0.3475].$$

Because this entire interval is below 0.35, it suggests that (1) the market share for brand 2 ovens in Edmonton will be smaller than the 35 percent market share that this brand commands in London, and (2) fewer brand 2 ovens (on a percentage basis) should be stocked in Edmonton. For brand 1, the interval is found to be [0.2125, 0.2977], which is greater then the historic 0.20, suggesting market shares may be larger for brand 1. The confidence interval for brand 3 is [0.2551, 0.3449], which contains the historic 0.30, suggesting the same level of interest. For brand 4, the interval is [0.1082, 0.1768], which contains the historic 0.15, suggesting, as is the case for brand 3, the same level of interest in Edmonton as in London.

In the following box, we give a general chi-square goodness of fit test for multinomial probabilities:

A Goodness of Fit Test for Multinomial Probabilities

Consider a **multinomial experiment** in which each of n randomly selected items is classified into one of k groups. We let

f_i = the number of items classified into group i (that is, the ith observed frequency),

$E_i = np_i$
= the expected number of items that would be classified into group i if p_i is the probability of a randomly selected item being classified into group i (that is, the ith expected frequency).

If we wish to test

H_0: the values of the multinomial probabilities are $p_1, p_2, \ldots, p_k$—that is, the probability of a randomly selected item being classified into group 1 is p_1, the probability of a randomly selected item being classified into group 2 is p_2, and so forth,

versus

H_a: at least one of the multinomial probabilities is not equal to the value stated in H_0,

we define the **chi-square goodness of fit statistic** to be

$$\chi^2 = \sum_{i=1}^{k} \frac{(f_i - E_i)^2}{E_i}.$$

Also, we define the p value related to χ^2 to be the area under the curve of the chi-square distribution with $k - 1$ degrees of freedom to the right of χ^2.

Then we can reject H_0 in favour of H_a at level of significance α if either of the following equivalent conditions holds:

1   $\chi^2 > \chi_\alpha^2$.

2   p value $< \alpha$.

Here the χ_α^2 point is based on $k - 1$ degrees of freedom.

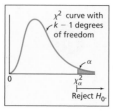

This test is based on the fact that when H_0 is true, the sampling distribution of χ^2 is approximately a chi-square distribution with $k - 1$ degrees of freedom if the sample size n is large. *It is generally agreed that n should be considered large if all of the "expected cell frequencies" (E_i values) are at least 5.* Furthermore, research implies that this condition on the E_i values can be somewhat relaxed. For example, Moore and McCabe (1993) indicate that *it is reasonable to use the chi-square approximation if the number of groups (k) exceeds 4, the average of the E_i values is at least 5, and the smallest E_i value is at least 1.* In Example 14.1, all of the E_i values are much larger than 5. Therefore, the chi-square test is valid.

LO4

Using control variables A control variable is an additional factor added to the model to examine if the pattern of the data changes or stays the same when this additional factor is considered. For example, in the microwave oven case, say the researcher examined the sex of the people tested in Edmonton. If an equal number of men and women were tested, then there were 200 of each (the total sample was 400). Suppose the observed brand preferences were found to be as follows:

Brand	Men	Women
1	41	61
2	68	53
3	58	62
4	33	24
sum	200	200

Then separate chi-square analyses could be conducted for the men and women. To compute the expected frequency values, it should be remembered that the total number within each sex is now 200. So the expected frequency is now $0.20(200) = 40$ for Brand 1, $0.35(200) = 70$ for Brand 2, $0.30(200) = 60$ for Brand 3, and 30 for Brand 4. Calculating the chi-square values with these data results in $\chi^2 = 0.4488$ for men and $\chi^2 = 16.4202$ for women. As stated above, for 3 degrees of freedom, $\chi^2_{0.05} = 7.81473$, which is greater than the obtained value for men but less than the obtained value for women. From these results we can conclude that the pattern of brand preferences differs for women in Edmonton but not for men in Edmonton.

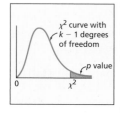

Test for homogeneity A special version of the chi-square goodness of fit test for multinomial probabilities is called a **test for homogeneity**. This involves testing the null hypothesis that all of the multinomial probabilities are equal. For instance, in the microwave oven situation, we would test

$$H_0: p_1 = p_2 = p_3 = p_4 = 0.25,$$

which would say that no single brand of microwave oven is preferred over any of the other brands (equal preferences). If this null hypothesis is rejected in favour of

$$H_a: \text{at least one of } p_1, p_2, p_3 \text{ and } p_4 \text{ exceeds } 0.25,$$

we would conclude that there is a preference for one or more of the brands. Here each of the expected cell frequencies equals $0.25(400) = 100$. Remembering that the observed cell frequencies are $f_1 = 102, f_2 = 121, f_3 = 120,$ and $f_4 = 57$, the chi-square statistic is

$$
\begin{aligned}
\chi^2 &= \sum_{i=1}^{4} \frac{(f_i - E_i)^2}{E_i} \\
&= \frac{(102 - 100)^2}{100} + \frac{(121 - 100)^2}{100} + \frac{(120 - 100)^2}{100} + \frac{(57 - 100)^2}{100} \\
&= 0.04 + 4.41 + 4 + 18.49 = 26.94.
\end{aligned}
$$

A Chi-Square Table: Values of χ^2_α

df	$\chi^2_{0.10}$	$\chi^2_{0.05}$
1	2.70554	3.84146
2	4.60517	5.99147
3	6.25139	7.81473
4	7.77944	9.48773
5	9.23635	11.0705
6	10.6446	12.5916
7	12.0170	14.0671
8	13.3616	15.5073
9	14.6837	16.9190
10	15.9871	18.3070
11	17.2750	19.6751
12	18.5494	21.0261
13	19.8119	22.3621

Because $\chi^2 = 26.94$ is greater than $\chi^2_{0.05} = 7.81473$ (see the section of Table A.18 in the margin with $k - 1 = 4 - 1 = 3$ degrees of freedom), we reject H_0 at level of significance 0.05.

TABLE **14.3** A Sample of 49 Test Scores

30.8	30.9	32.0	32.3	32.6
31.7	30.4	31.4	32.7	31.4
30.1	32.5	30.8	31.2	31.8
31.6	30.3	32.8	30.6	31.9
32.1	31.3	32.0	31.7	32.8
33.3	32.1	31.5	31.4	31.5
31.3	32.5	32.4	32.2	31.6
31.0	31.8	31.0	31.5	30.6
32.0	30.4	29.8	31.7	32.2
32.4	30.5	31.1	30.6	

FIGURE **14.1** MegaStat Output of a Stem-and-Leaf Display of the 49 Test Scores

Stem and Leaf plot for Scores

stem unit = 1
leaf unit = 0.1

Frequency	Stem	Leaf
1	29	8
4	30	1344
7	30	5666889
9	31	001233444
11	31	55566777889
10	32	0001122344
6	32	556788
1	33	3
49		

We conclude that preferences for the four brands are not equal and that at least one brand is preferred to the others.

Normal distributions We have seen that many statistical methods are based on the assumption that a random sample has been selected from a normally distributed population. We can check the validity of the normality assumption by using frequency distributions, stem-and-leaf displays, histograms, and normal plots. Another approach is to use a chi-square goodness of fit test to check the normality assumption.

Consider the sample of 49 test scores given in Table 14.3. The stem-and-leaf display of these scores (in Figure 14.1) is symmetrical and bell-shaped. This suggests that the sample of test scores has been randomly selected from a normally distributed population. In this example, we use a chi-square goodness of fit test to check the normality of the scores.

To perform this test, we first divide the number line into intervals (or categories). One way to do this is to use the class boundaries typical of a histogram. Table 14.4 gives these intervals and also gives observed frequencies (counts of the number of scores in each interval). The chi-square test is done by comparing these observed frequencies with the expected frequencies in the rightmost column of Table 14.4. To explain how the expected frequencies are calculated, we first use the sample mean $\bar{x} = 31.55$ and the sample standard deviation $s = 0.8$ of the 49 scores as point estimates of the population mean μ and population standard deviation σ. Then, for example, consider p_1, the probability that a randomly selected score will be in the first

L05

TABLE **14.4** Observed and Expected Cell Frequencies for a Chi-Square Goodness of Fit Test for Testing the Normality of the 49 Test Scores in Table 14.3

Interval	Observed Frequency (f_i)	p_i If the Population of Scores Is Normally Distributed	Expected Frequency, $E_i = np_i = 49p_i$
Less than 30.35	3	$p_1 = P(\text{score} < 30.35) = 0.0668$	$E_1 = 49(0.0668) = 3.2732$
[30.35, 30.95]	9	$p_2 = P(30.35 < \text{score} < 30.95) = 0.1598$	$E_2 = 49(0.1598) = 7.8302$
[30.95, 31.55]	12	$p_3 = P(30.95 < \text{score} < 31.55) = 0.2734$	$E_3 = 49(0.2734) = 13.3966$
[31.55, 32.15]	13	$p_4 = P(31.55 < \text{score} < 32.15) = 0.2734$	$E_4 = 49(0.2734) = 13.3966$
[32.15, 32.75]	9	$p_5 = P(32.15 < \text{score} < 32.75) = 0.1598$	$E_5 = 49(0.1598) = 7.8302$
Greater than 32.75	3	$p_6 = P(\text{score} > 32.75) = 0.0668$	$E_6 = 49(0.0668) = 3.2732$

interval (less than 30.35) in Table 14.4 if the population of all scores is normally distributed. We estimate p_1 to be

$$p_1 = P(\text{score} < 30.35) = P\left(z < \frac{30.35 - 31.55}{0.8}\right)$$

$$= P(z < -1.5) = 0.5 - 0.4332 = 0.0668.$$

If the scores are normally distributed, then we would expect that 6.68 percent of the 49 observations would fall in that interval. Therefore, it follows that $E_1 = 49p_1 = 49(0.0668) = 3.2732$ is the expected frequency for the first interval under the normality assumption. Next, if we consider p_2, the probability that a randomly selected score will be in the second interval in Table 14.4 if the population of all scores is normally distributed, we estimate p_2 to be

$$p_2 = P(30.35 < \text{score} < 30.95) = P\left(\frac{30.35 - 31.55}{0.8} < z < \frac{30.95 - 31.55}{0.8}\right)$$

$$= P(-1.5 < z < -0.75) = 0.4332 - 0.2734 = 0.1598.$$

It follows that $E_2 = 49p_2 = 49(0.1598) = 7.8302$ is the expected frequency for the second interval under the normality assumption. The other expected frequencies are computed similarly. In general, p_i is the probability that a randomly selected score will be in interval i if the population of all possible scores is normally distributed with mean 31.55 and standard deviation 0.8, and E_i is the expected number of the 49 scores that would be in interval i if the population of all possible scores has this normal distribution.

It seems reasonable to reject the null hypothesis

$$H_0: \text{the population of all scores is normally distributed}$$

in favour of the alternative hypothesis

$$H_a: \text{the population of all scores is not normally distributed}$$

if the observed frequencies in Table 14.4 differ substantially from the corresponding expected frequencies. We compare the observed frequencies with the expected frequencies under the normality assumption by computing the chi-square statistic

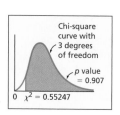

Chi-square curve with 3 degrees of freedom

p value $= 0.907$

$0 \quad \chi^2 = 0.55247$

$$\chi^2 = \sum_{i=1}^{6} \frac{(f_i - E_i)^2}{E_i}$$

$$= \frac{(3 - 3.2732)^2}{3.2732} + \frac{(9 - 7.8302)^2}{7.8302} + \frac{(12 - 13.3966)^2}{13.3966}$$

$$+ \frac{(13 - 13.3966)^2}{13.3966} + \frac{(9 - 7.8302)^2}{7.8302} + \frac{(3 - 3.2732)^2}{3.2732}$$

$$= 0.55247.$$

Because we have estimated $m = 2$ parameters (μ and σ) in computing the expected frequencies (E_i values), the sampling distribution of χ^2 is approximately a chi-square distribution with $k - 1 - m = 6 - 1 - 2 = 3$ degrees of freedom. Therefore, we can reject H_0 at level of significance α if

$$\chi^2 > \chi^2_\alpha,$$

where the χ^2_α point is based on $k - 1 - m = 6 - 1 - 2 = 3$ degrees of freedom. If we wish to test H_0 at the 0.05 level of significance, Table A.18 tells us that $\chi^2_{0.05} = 7.81473$. Therefore, because

$$\chi^2 = 0.55247 < \chi^2_{0.05} = 7.81473,$$

we cannot reject H_0 at the 0.05 level of significance, and we cannot reject the hypothesis that the population of all scores is normally distributed. Therefore, it is probably reasonable to assume that the population of all test scores is approximately normally distributed and that inferences based on this assumption are valid. Finally, the p value for this test, which is the area under the chi-square curve with 3 degrees of freedom to the right of $\chi^2 = 0.55247$, can be shown to equal 0.907. Because this p value is large (much greater than 0.05), we have little evidence to support rejecting the null hypothesis (normality).

Note that although some of the expected cell frequencies in Table 14.4 are not at least 5, the number of classes (groups) is 6 (which exceeds 4), the average of the expected cell frequencies is at least 5, and the smallest expected cell frequency is at least 1. Therefore, it is reasonable to consider the result of this chi-square test valid. If we choose to base the chi-square test on the more restrictive assumption that all of the expected cell frequencies are at least 5, then we can combine adjacent cell frequencies as follows:

Original f_i Values	Original p_i Values	Original E_i Values	Combined E_i Values	Combined p_i Values	Combined f_i Values
3	0.0668	3.2732 ⎫	11.1034	0.2266	12
9	0.1598	7.8302 ⎭			
12	0.2734	13.3966	13.3966	0.2734	12
13	0.2734	13.3966	13.3966	0.2734	13
9	0.1598	7.8302 ⎫	11.1034	0.2266	12
3	0.0668	3.2732 ⎭			

When we use these combined cell frequencies, the chi-square approximation is based on $k - 1 - m = 4 - 1 - 2 = 1$ degree of freedom. We find that $\chi^2 = 0.30214$ and p value $= 0.582545$. Because this p value is much greater than 0.05, we cannot reject the hypothesis of normality at the 0.05 level of significance.

In the test score example, we based the intervals employed in the chi-square goodness of fit test on the class boundaries typical of a histogram. Another way to establish intervals for such a test is to compute the sample mean $\bar{x}$ and the sample standard deviation s and to use intervals based on the empirical rule as follows:

Interval 1: less than $\bar{x} - 2s$

Interval 2: $\bar{x} - 2s$ to less than $\bar{x} - s$

Interval 3: $\bar{x} - s$ to less than $\bar{x}$

Interval 4: $\bar{x}$ to less than $\bar{x} + s$

Interval 5: $\bar{x} + s$ to less than $\bar{x} + 2s$

Interval 6: greater than $\bar{x} + 2s$

However, care must be taken to ensure that each of the expected frequencies is large enough (using the previously discussed criteria).

No matter how the intervals are established, we use $\bar{x}$ as an estimate of the population mean μ and s as an estimate of the population standard deviation σ when we calculate the expected frequencies (E_i values). Because we are estimating $m = 2$ population parameters, the rejection point χ^2_α is based on $k - 1 - m = k - 1 - 2 = k - 3$ degrees of freedom, where k is the number of intervals employed.

In the following box, we summarize how to carry out this chi-square test:

A Goodness of Fit Test for a Normal Distribution

1 We will test the following null and alternative hypotheses:

H_0: the population has a normal distribution,

H_a: the population does not have a normal distribution.

2 Select a random sample of size n and compute the sample mean $\bar{x}$ and sample standard deviation s.

3 Define k intervals for the test. Two ways to do this are to use the classes of a histogram of the data or to use intervals based on the empirical rule.

4 Record the observed frequency (f_i) for each interval.

5 Calculate the expected frequency (E_i) for each interval under the normality assumption. Do this by computing the probability that a normal variable with mean $\bar{x}$ and standard deviation s is within the interval and by multiplying this probability by n. Make sure that each expected frequency is large enough. If necessary, combine intervals to make the expected frequencies large enough.

6 Calculate the chi-square statistic

$$\chi^2 = \sum_{i=1}^{k} \frac{(f_i - E_i)^2}{E_i},$$

and define the p value for the test to be the area under the curve of the chi-square distribution with $k - 3$ degrees of freedom to the right of χ^2.

7 Reject H_0 in favour of H_a at level of significance α if either of the following equivalent conditions holds:

a. $\chi^2 > \chi^2_\alpha$.   b. p value $< \alpha$.

Here the χ^2_α point is based on $k - 3$ degrees of freedom.

While chi-square goodness of fit tests are often used to verify that it is reasonable to assume that a random sample has been selected from a normally distributed population, such tests can also check other distribution forms. For instance, we might verify that it is reasonable to assume that a random sample has been selected from a Poisson distribution. In general, *the number of degrees of freedom for the chi-square goodness of fit test will equal $k - 1 - m$, where k is the number of intervals or categories employed in the test and m is the number of population parameters that must be estimated to calculate the needed expected frequencies.*

Exercises for Section 14.1

CONCEPTS

14.1 Describe the characteristics that define a multinomial experiment.

14.2 Give the conditions that the expected cell frequencies must meet in order to validly carry out a chi-square goodness of fit test.

14.3 Explain the purpose of a goodness of fit test.

14.4 When performing a chi-square goodness of fit test, why does a large value of the chi-square statistic provide evidence that H_0 should be rejected?

14.5 Define a control variable and describe what might happen to the analysis when a control variable is introduced.

14.6 State two ways to obtain intervals for a goodness of fit test of normality.

METHODS AND APPLICATIONS

14.7 The proportions of yearly sales across a province in Canada for five popular fruits (apples, oranges, bananas, peaches, and grapefruit, in terms of units sold to each person per year) were found to be 36 percent, 26 percent, 21 percent, 9 percent, and 8 percent, respectively. Suppose

that a new survey of 1,000 shoppers in a city in that province was conducted and the following purchase frequencies were found:

Apples	Oranges	Bananas	Peaches	Grapefruit
391	202	275	53	79

a. Show that it is appropriate to carry out a chi-square test using these data.

b. Test to determine whether the city market shares differ from those of the province. Use $\alpha = 0.05$.

14.8 Last rating period, the percentages of viewers watching several channels in a certain time period in a major TV market were as follows:

Station 1 (News)	Station 2 (News)	Station 3 (Sitcom)	Station 4 (News)	Others
15%	19%	22%	16%	28%

Suppose that in the current rating period, a survey of 2,000 viewers gives the following frequencies:

Station 1 (News)	Station 2 (News)	Station 3 (Sitcom)	Station 4 (News)	Others
182	536	354	151	777

TABLE **14.5** Peanut Butter Purchase Data

Brand	Size	Number of Purchases by Household Panel	Market Shares
Jif	18 oz.	3,165	20.10%
Jif	28	1,892	10.10
Jif	40	726	5.42
Peter Pan	10	4,079	16.01
Skippy	18	6,206	28.56
Skippy	28	1,627	12.33
Skippy	40	1,420	7.48
Total		19,115	

Goodness of Fit Test

obs	expected	O − E	$(O − E)^2/E$	% of chisq
3,165	3,842.115	−677.115	119.331	13.56
1,892	1,930.615	−38.615	0.772	0.09
726	1,036.033	−310.033	92.777	10.54
4,079	3,060.312	1,018.689	339.092	38.52
6,206	5,459.244	746.756	102.147	11.60
1,627	2,356.880	−729.880	226.029	25.68
1,420	1,429.802	−9.802	0.067	0.01
19,115	19,115.000	0.000	880.216	100.00

880.22 chisquare   6 df   7.10E-187   *p*-value

Source: Reprinted with permission from *The Journal of Marketing Research*, published by the American Marketing Association. "Do household scanner data provide representative inferences from brand choices? A comparison with store data," by S. Gupta et al., *The Journal of Marketing Research*, Vol. 33, p. 393 (Table 6).

a. Show that it is appropriate to carry out a chi-square test using these data.

b. Test to determine whether the viewing shares in the current rating period differ from those in the last rating period at the 0.10 level of significance. What do you conclude?

14.9 In the *Journal of Marketing Research* (November 1996), Gupta studied the extent to which the purchase behaviour of scanner panels is representative of overall brand preferences. A scanner panel is a sample of households whose purchase data are recorded when a magnetic identification card is presented at a store checkout. Table 14.5 gives peanut butter purchase data collected by the ACNielsen Company using a panel of 2,500 households in Sioux Falls, South Dakota. The data were collected over 102 weeks. The table also gives the market shares obtained by recording all peanut butter purchases at the same stores during the same period.

a. Show that it is appropriate to carry out a chi-square test.

b. Test to determine whether the purchase behaviour of the panel of 2,500 households is consistent with the purchase behaviour of the population of all peanut butter purchasers. Assume here that purchase decisions by panel members are reasonably independent, and set $\alpha = 0.05$.

14.10 A warehouse manager wants to investigate the productivity of her employees. It is expected that an employee will complete 100 orders in one day. Five employees are assessed and the following data are collected:

Employee	Orders Completed
A	120
B	88
C	93
D	117
E	97

a. Calculate the chi-square value.

b. What are the degrees of freedom?

c. Based on the results, are employees performing as expected?

14.11 Using the data from Exercise 14.10, age of the employee was included as a control variable. If employees *A* and *D* represent younger employees, how does the chi-square value change? What would you conclude about the younger employees' performance?

14.12 Using the data from Exercise 14.10, age of the employee was included as a control variable. If employees *B*, *C*, and *E* represent older employees, how does the chi-square value change? What would you conclude about the older employees' performance?

14.13 The purchase frequencies for six different brands of digital cameras are observed at an electronics store over one month:

Brand	Purchase Frequency
A	131
B	273
C	119
D	301
E	176
F	200

a. Carry out a test of homogeneity for these data with $\alpha = 0.025$.

b. Interpret the results of your test.

14.14 A wholesaler has recently developed a computerized sales invoicing system. Prior to implementing this system, a manual system was used. The distribution of the number of errors per invoice for the manual system is as follows:

Errors per Invoice	0	1	2	3	More Than 3
Percentage of Invoices	87%	8%	3%	1%	1%

FIGURE **14.2**   Excel Output for Exercise 14.14

pi	Ei	fi	(f-E)^2/E	
0.87	435	479	4.4506	
0.08	40	10	22.5000	
0.03	15	8	3.2667	
0.01	5	2	1.8000	
0.01	5	1	3.2000	
	Chi-Square		35.21724	p-value 0.0000001096

After implementation of the computerized system, a random sample of 500 invoices gives the following error distribution:

Errors per Invoice	0	1	2	3	More Than 3
Number of Invoices	479	10	8	2	1

a. Show that it is appropriate to carry out a chi-square test using these data.

b. Use the Excel output in Figure 14.2 to determine whether the error percentages for the computerized system differ from those for the manual system at the 0.05 level of significance. What do you conclude?

14.15 Consider the sample of 65 payment times given in Table 14.6. Use these data to carry out a chi-square goodness of fit test to test whether the population of all payment times is normally distributed by doing the following:

a. It can be shown that $\bar{x} = 18.1077$ and $s = 3.9612$ for the payment time data. Use these values to compute the following intervals.
   (1) Less than $\bar{x} - 2s$.
   (2) $\bar{x} - 2s$ to less than $\bar{x} - s$.
   (3) $\bar{x} - s$ to less than $\bar{x}$.

(4) $\bar{x}$ to less than $\bar{x} + s$.
(5) $\bar{x} + s$ to less than $\bar{x} + 2s$.
(6) Greater than $\bar{x} + 2s$.

b. Assuming that the population of all payment times is normally distributed, find the probability that a randomly selected payment time will be contained in each of the intervals in part a. Use these probabilities to compute the expected frequency under the normality assumption for each interval.

c. Verify that the average of the expected frequencies is at least 5 and that the smallest expected frequency is at least 1. What does this tell you?

d. Formulate the null and alternative hypotheses for the chi-square test of normality.

e. For each interval in part a, find the observed frequency. Then calculate the chi-square statistic needed for the chi-square test of normality.

f. Use the chi-square statistic to test normality at the 0.05 level of significance. What do you conclude?

14.16 Consider the sample of 60 bottle design ratings given in Table 14.7. Use these data to carry out a chi-square goodness of fit test to determine whether the population of all bottle design ratings is normally distributed. Use $\alpha = 0.05$, and note that $\bar{x} = 30.35$ and $s = 3.1073$ for the 60 bottle design ratings.

TABLE **14.6**   A Sample of Payment Times (in Days) for 65 Randomly Selected Invoices

22	29	16	15	18	17	12	13	17	16	15
19	17	10	21	15	14	17	18	12	20	14
16	15	16	20	22	14	25	19	23	15	19
18	23	22	16	16	19	13	18	24	24	26
13	18	17	15	24	15	17	14	18	17	21
16	21	25	19	20	27	16	17	16	21	

TABLE **14.7**   A Sample of Bottle Design Ratings (Composite Scores for a Systematic Sample of 60 Shoppers)

34	33	33	29	26	33	28	25	32	33
32	25	27	33	22	27	32	33	32	29
24	30	20	34	31	32	30	35	33	31
32	28	30	31	31	33	29	27	34	31
31	28	33	31	32	28	26	29	32	34
32	30	34	32	30	30	32	31	29	33

14.2 A CHI-SQUARE TEST FOR INDEPENDENCE

One way to study the relationship between two variables is to classify multinomial count data on two scales (or dimensions) by setting up a contingency table.

Example 14.2 The Client Satisfaction Case

A financial institution sells three kinds of investment products—a stock fund, a bond fund, and a tax-deferred annuity. The company is examining whether customer satisfaction depends on the type of investment product purchased. To do this, 100 clients are randomly selected from the population of clients who have purchased shares in exactly one of the funds. The company records the fund type purchased by these clients and asks each sampled client to rate their level of satisfaction with the fund as high, medium, or low. Table 14.8 gives the survey results.

We can look at the data in Table 14.8 in an organized way by constructing a **contingency table** (also called a **two-way cross-classification table**). Such a table classifies the data on

TABLE 14.8 Results of a Customer Satisfaction Survey Given to 100 Randomly Selected Clients Who Invest in One of Three Fund Types—a Bond Fund, a Stock Fund, or a Tax-Deferred Annuity 🖉

Client	Fund Type	Level of Satisfaction	Client	Fund Type	Level of Satisfaction	Client	Fund Type	Level of Satisfaction
1	BOND	HIGH	35	STOCK	HIGH	69	BOND	MED
2	STOCK	HIGH	36	BOND	MED	70	TAXDEF	MED
3	TAXDEF	MED	37	TAXDEF	MED	71	TAXDEF	MED
4	TAXDEF	MED	38	TAXDEF	LOW	72	BOND	HIGH
5	STOCK	LOW	39	STOCK	HIGH	73	TAXDEF	MED
6	STOCK	HIGH	40	TAXDEF	MED	74	TAXDEF	LOW
7	STOCK	HIGH	41	BOND	HIGH	75	STOCK	HIGH
8	BOND	MED	42	BOND	HIGH	76	BOND	HIGH
9	TAXDEF	LOW	43	BOND	LOW	77	TAXDEF	LOW
10	TAXDEF	LOW	44	TAXDEF	LOW	78	BOND	MED
11	STOCK	MED	45	STOCK	HIGH	79	STOCK	HIGH
12	BOND	LOW	46	BOND	HIGH	80	STOCK	HIGH
13	STOCK	HIGH	47	BOND	MED	81	BOND	MED
14	TAXDEF	MED	48	STOCK	HIGH	82	TAXDEF	MED
15	TAXDEF	MED	49	TAXDEF	MED	83	BOND	HIGH
16	TAXDEF	LOW	50	TAXDEF	MED	84	STOCK	MED
17	STOCK	HIGH	51	STOCK	HIGH	85	STOCK	HIGH
18	BOND	HIGH	52	TAXDEF	MED	86	BOND	MED
19	BOND	MED	53	STOCK	HIGH	87	TAXDEF	MED
20	TAXDEF	MED	54	TAXDEF	MED	88	TAXDEF	LOW
21	TAXDEF	MED	55	STOCK	LOW	89	STOCK	HIGH
22	BOND	HIGH	56	BOND	HIGH	90	TAXDEF	MED
23	TAXDEF	MED	57	STOCK	HIGH	91	BOND	HIGH
24	TAXDEF	LOW	58	BOND	MED	92	TAXDEF	HIGH
25	STOCK	HIGH	59	TAXDEF	LOW	93	TAXDEF	LOW
26	BOND	HIGH	60	TAXDEF	LOW	94	TAXDEF	LOW
27	TAXDEF	LOW	61	STOCK	MED	95	STOCK	HIGH
28	BOND	MED	62	BOND	LOW	96	BOND	HIGH
29	STOCK	HIGH	63	STOCK	HIGH	97	BOND	MED
30	STOCK	HIGH	64	TAXDEF	MED	98	STOCK	HIGH
31	BOND	MED	65	TAXDEF	MED	99	TAXDEF	MED
32	TAXDEF	MED	66	TAXDEF	LOW	100	TAXDEF	MED
33	BOND	HIGH	67	STOCK	HIGH			
34	STOCK	MED	68	BOND	HIGH			

FIGURE **14.3**   MegaStat Output of a Contingency Table of Fund Type versus
Level of Client Satisfaction (See the Survey Results in Table 14.8)

Cross-tabulation

			Satisfaction Rating			
			HIGH	MED	LOW	Total
F	**BOND**	Observed	15	12	3	30
		% of row	50.0%	40.0%	10.0%	100.0%
u		% of column	37.5%	30.0%	15.0%	30.0%
n		% of total	15.0%	12.0%	3.0%	30.0%
d	**STOCK**	Observed	24	4	2	30
		% of row	80.0%	13.3%	6.7%	100.0%
T		% of column	60.0%	10.0%	10.0%	30.0%
y		% of total	24.0%	4.0%	2.0%	30.0%
p	**TAXDEF**	Observed	1	24	15	40
e		% of row	2.5%	60.0%	37.5%	100.0%
		% of column	2.5%	60.0%	75.0%	40.0%
		% of total	1.0%	24.0%	15.0%	40.0%
	Total	Observed	40	40	20	100
		% of row	40.0%	40.0%	20.0%	100.0%
		% of column	100.0%	100.0%	100.0%	100.0%
		% of total	40.0%	40.0%	20.0%	100.0%

46.44^a chi-square
4   df
$2.00E-09^b$ p-value

[a]Chi-square statistic.
[b]*p* value for chi-square.

two dimensions—type of fund and degree of client satisfaction. Figure 14.3 gives the MegaStat output of a contingency table of fund type versus level of satisfaction. This table consists of a row for each fund type and a column for each level of satisfaction. Together, the rows and columns form a "cell" for each fund type–satisfaction level combination. That is, there is a cell for each **contingency** with respect to fund type and satisfaction level. A **cell frequency** for each cell, which is the red number at the top of the cell, is reported. This is a count (observed frequency) of the number of surveyed clients with the cell's fund type–satisfaction level combination. For instance, 15 of the surveyed clients invest in the bond fund and report high satisfaction, while 24 of the surveyed clients invest in the tax-deferred annuity and report medium satisfaction. In addition to the cell frequencies, the output also gives the following:

Row totals (at the far right of the table): These are counts of the numbers of clients who invest in each fund type. These row totals tell us that

1   30 clients invest in the bond fund.
2   30 clients invest in the stock fund.
3   40 clients invest in the tax-deferred annuity.

Column totals (at the bottom of the table): These are counts of the numbers of clients who report high, medium, and low satisfaction. These column totals tell us that

1   40 clients report high satisfaction.
2   40 clients report medium satisfaction.
3   20 clients report low satisfaction.

Overall total (the bottom right entry in the table): This tells us that a total of 100 clients were surveyed.

Besides the row and column totals, the output lists **row and total percentages** (directly below the row and column totals). For example, 30.00 percent of the surveyed clients invest in the bond fund, and 20.00 percent of the surveyed clients report low satisfaction. In addition to a cell frequency, the output gives a **row percentage**, a **column percentage**, and a **cell percentage** for each cell (these are below the cell frequency in each cell). For instance, looking at the bond fund–high satisfaction cell, we see that the 15 clients in this cell make up 50.0 percent of the 30 clients who invest in the bond fund, and they make up 37.5 percent of the 40 clients who report high satisfaction. In addition, these 15 clients make up 15.0 percent of the 100 clients surveyed.

Looking at the contingency table, it appears that the level of client satisfaction may be related to the fund type. We see that higher satisfaction ratings seem to be reported by stock and bond fund investors, while holders of tax-deferred annuities report lower satisfaction ratings. To carry out a formal statistical test, we can test the null hypothesis

H_0: fund type and level of client satisfaction are independent

versus

H_a: fund type and level of client satisfaction are dependent.

In order to perform this test, we compare the counts (or **observed cell frequencies**) in the contingency table with the counts that would appear in the contingency table if we assumed that fund type and level of satisfaction were independent. Because these latter counts are computed by assuming independence, we call them the **expected cell frequencies under the independence assumption**. To illustrate how to calculate these expected cell frequencies, we consider the cell corresponding to the bond fund and high client satisfaction. We first use the data in the contingency table to compute an estimate of the probability that a randomly selected client invests in the bond fund. Denoting this probability as p_B, we estimate p_B by dividing the row total for the bond fund by the total number of clients surveyed. That is, denoting the row total for the bond fund as r_B and letting n denote the total number of clients surveyed, the estimate of p_B is $r_B/n = 30/100 = 0.3$. Next we compute an estimate of the probability that a randomly selected client will report high satisfaction. Denoting this probability as p_H, we estimate p_H by dividing the column total for high satisfaction by the total number of clients surveyed. That is, denoting the column total for high satisfaction as c_H, the estimate of p_H is $c_H/n = 40/100 = 0.4$. Next, assuming that investing in the bond fund and reporting high satisfaction are **independent**, we compute an estimate of the probability that a randomly selected client invests in the bond fund and reports high satisfaction. Denoting this probability as p_{BH}, we can compute its estimate. If two events A and B are statistically independent, then the probability of A and B equals $P(A)P(B)$. It follows that if we assume that investing in the bond fund and reporting high satisfaction are independent, we can compute an estimate of p_{BH} by multiplying the estimate of p_B by the estimate of p_H. That is, the estimate of p_{BH} is $(r_B/n)(c_H/n) = (0.3)(0.4) = 0.12$. Finally, we compute an estimate of the expected cell frequency under the independence assumption. Denoting the expected cell frequency as E_{BH}, the estimate of E_{BH} is

$$\hat{E}_{BH} = n\left(\frac{r_B}{n}\right)\left(\frac{c_H}{n}\right) = 100(0.3)(0.4) = 12.$$

Noting that the expression for $\hat{E}_{BH}$ can be written as

$$\hat{E}_{BH} = n\left(\frac{r_B}{n}\right)\left(\frac{c_H}{n}\right) = \frac{r_B c_H}{n},$$

we can generalize to obtain a formula for the estimated expected cell frequency for any cell in the contingency table. Letting $\hat{E}_{ij}$ denote the estimated expected cell frequency corresponding to row i and column j in the contingency table, we see that

$$\hat{E}_{ij} = \frac{r_i c_j}{n},$$

where r_i is the row total for row i and c_j is the column total for column j. For example, for the fund type–satisfaction level contingency table, we obtain

$$\hat{E}_{SL} = \frac{r_S c_L}{n} = \frac{30(20)}{100} = \frac{600}{100} = 6$$

and

$$\hat{E}_{TM} = \frac{r_T c_M}{n} = \frac{40(40)}{100} = \frac{1{,}600}{100} = 16.$$

Intuitively, these estimated expected cell frequencies tell us what the contingency table looks like if fund type and level of client satisfaction are independent.

To test the null hypothesis of independence, we will compute a chi-square statistic that compares the observed cell frequencies with the estimated expected cell frequencies calculated assuming independence. Letting f_{ij} denote the observed cell frequency for cell ij, we compute

$$\chi^2 = \sum_{\text{all cells}} \frac{(f_{ij} - \hat{E}_{ij})^2}{\hat{E}_{ij}}$$

$$= \frac{(f_{BH} - \hat{E}_{BH})^2}{\hat{E}_{BH}} + \frac{(f_{BM} - \hat{E}_{BM})^2}{\hat{E}_{BM}} + \cdots + \frac{(f_{TL} - \hat{E}_{TL})^2}{\hat{E}_{TL}}$$

$$= \frac{(15 - 12)^2}{12} + \frac{(12 - 12)^2}{12} + \frac{(3 - 6)^2}{6} + \frac{(24 - 12)^2}{12} + \frac{(4 - 12)^2}{12}$$

$$+ \frac{(2 - 6)^2}{6} + \frac{(1 - 16)^2}{16} + \frac{(24 - 16)^2}{16} + \frac{(15 - 8)^2}{8}$$

$$= 46.4375.$$

If the value of the chi-square statistic is large, this indicates that the observed cell frequencies differ substantially from the expected cell frequencies calculated by assuming independence. Therefore, the larger the value of chi-square, the more doubt is cast on the null hypothesis of independence.

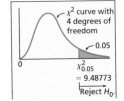

To find an appropriate rejection point, we let r denote the number of rows in the contingency table and c denote the number of columns. Then, when the null hypothesis of independence is true, the sampling distribution of χ^2 is approximately a χ^2 distribution with $(r - 1)(c - 1) = (3 - 1)(3 - 1) = 4$ degrees of freedom. If we test H_0 at the 0.05 level of significance, we reject H_0 if and only if

$$\chi^2 > \chi^2_{0.05}.$$

Table A.18 tells us that the $\chi^2_{0.05}$ point corresponding to $(r - 1)(c - 1) = 4$ degrees of freedom equals 9.48773, so

$$\chi^2 = 46.4375 > \chi^2_{0.05} = 9.48773,$$

and we reject H_0 at the 0.05 level of significance. We conclude that fund type and level of client satisfaction are not independent.

In the following box, we summarize how to carry out a chi-square test for independence:

A Chi-Square Test for Independence

Suppose that each of n randomly selected elements is classified on two dimensions, and suppose that the result of the two-way classification is a **contingency table with r rows and c columns**. Let

f_{ij} = the cell frequency corresponding to row i and column j of the contingency table (that is, the number of elements classified in row i and column j),

r_i = the row total for row i in the contingency table,

c_j = the column total for column j in the contingency table,

$$\hat{E}_{ij} = \frac{r_i c_j}{n}$$

= the estimated expected number of elements that would be classified in row i and column j of the contingency table if the two classifications are statistically independent.

If we wish to test

H_0: the two classifications are statistically independent

versus

H_a: the two classifications are statistically dependent,

we define the test statistic

$$\chi^2 = \sum_{\text{all cells}} \frac{(f_{ij} - \hat{E}_{ij})^2}{\hat{E}_{ij}}.$$

Also, we define the p value related to χ^2 to be the area under the curve of the chi-square distribution with $(r - 1)(c - 1)$ degrees of freedom to the right of χ^2.

Then we can reject H_0 in favour of H_a at level of significance α if either of the following equivalent conditions holds:

1 $\chi^2 > \chi^2_\alpha$.

2 p value $< \alpha$.

Here the χ^2_α point is based on $(r - 1)(c - 1)$ degrees of freedom.

LO6

This test is based on the fact that when the null hypothesis of independence is true, the sampling distribution of χ^2 is approximately a chi-square distribution with $(r - 1)(c - 1)$ degrees of freedom if the sample size n is large. *It is generally agreed that n should be considered large if all of the estimated expected cell frequencies ($\hat{E}_{ij}$ values) are at least 5. Moore and McCabe (1993) indicate that it is reasonable to use the chi-square approximation if the number of cells (rc) exceeds 4, the average of the $\hat{E}_{ij}$ values is at least 5, and the smallest $\hat{E}_{ij}$ value is at least 1.*

Again consider the MegaStat output of Figure 14.3 (page 520), which gives the contingency table of fund type versus level of client satisfaction. The chi-square statistic (= 46.438) for testing the null hypothesis of independence, as well as the related p value, are listed. We see that this p value is less than 0.001. It follows that we can reject

H_0: fund type and level of client satisfaction are independent

at the 0.05 level of significance because the p value is less than 0.05.

In order to study the nature of the dependency between the classifications in a contingency table, it is often useful to plot the row and/or column percentages. As an example, Figure 14.4

FIGURE 14.4 Plots of Row Percentages versus Investment Type for the Contingency Table in Figure 14.3

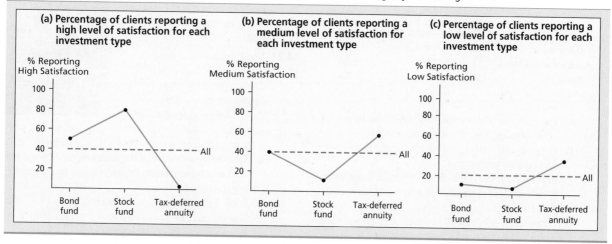

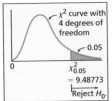

χ^2 curve with 4 degrees of freedom

0.05

$\chi^2_{0.05}$ = 9.48773

Reject H_0.

gives plots of the row percentages in the contingency table of Figure 14.3. For instance, the column in this contingency table corresponding to a high level of satisfaction tells us that 40.00 percent of the surveyed clients report a high level of satisfaction. If fund type and level of satisfaction really were independent, then we would expect roughly 40 percent of the clients in each of the three categories—bond fund participants, stock fund participants, and tax-deferred annuity holders—to report a high level of satisfaction. That is, we would expect the row percentages in the high satisfaction column to be roughly 40 percent in each row. However, Figure 14.4(a) gives a plot of the percentages of clients reporting a high level of satisfaction for each investment type (that is, the figure plots the three row percentages in the high satisfaction column). We see that these percentages vary considerably. Noting that the dashed line in the figure is the 40 percent reporting a high level of satisfaction for the overall group, we see that the percentage of stock fund participants reporting high satisfaction is 80 percent. This is far above the 40 percent we would expect if independence existed. On the other hand, the percentage of tax-deferred annuity holders reporting high satisfaction is only 2.5 percent—way below the expected 40 percent if independence existed. In a similar fashion, Figure 14.4(b) and (c) plots the row percentages for the medium and low satisfaction columns in the contingency table. These plots indicate that stock fund participants report medium and low levels of satisfaction less frequently than the overall group of clients, and that tax-deferred annuity participants report medium and low levels of satisfaction more frequently than the overall group of clients. Note that the chi-square test for independence can be used to test the equality of several population proportions.

BI

Exercises for Section 14.2

CONCEPTS

14.17 What is the purpose of summarizing data in the form of a two-way contingency table?

14.18 When performing a chi-square test for independence, how are the cell frequencies under the independence assumption calculated? Why are these frequencies calculated?

METHODS AND APPLICATIONS

14.19 A marketing research firm wishes to study the relationship between wine consumption and whether a person likes to watch professional tennis on television. One hundred randomly selected people are asked whether they drink wine and whether they watch tennis. The following results are obtained:

	Watch Tennis	Do Not Watch Tennis	Totals
Drink Wine	16	24	40
Do Not Drink Wine	4	56	60
Totals	20	80	100

    a. For each row and column total, calculate the corresponding row or column percentage.
    b. For each cell, calculate the corresponding cell, row, and column percentages.
    c. Test the hypothesis that whether people drink wine is independent of whether people watch tennis. Set $\alpha = 0.05$.
    d. Given the results of the chi-square test, does it make sense to advertise wine during a televised tennis

match (assuming that the ratings for the tennis match are high enough)? Explain.

14.20 A random sample of Canadian university undergraduate students were given a questionnaire in order to learn whether or not they would consider seeking a graduate degree. Male and female students were questioned and their responses were as follows:

Pursue a Graduate Degree	Male	Female	Total
Yes	79	121	200
No	86	114	200
Total	165	235	400

At $\alpha = 0.05$, test the hypothesis that the decision to pursue a graduate degree is independent of sex for these university students.

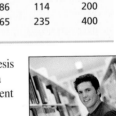

14.21 The Labour Force Survey conducted by Statistics Canada provides employment figures for men and women. Table 14.9 provides the 2009 values (in thousands) reported for men and women who were employed full-time and part-time separately.
    a. Test the hypothesis that the relationship between sex and employment status is independent by computing the chi-square value.
    b. Looking at the percentage values in Table 14.9, what conclusions can you draw for men versus women in terms of patterns of employment?

TABLE **14.9**   Employment by Sex Statistics for Canadians in 2009 🖋

		Men	Women	Total
Full-time	Count	7,726	5,902	13,628
	Expected Count	7,095.5	6,532.5	
	Percent within employ	56.7	43.3	
	Percent within sex	88.1	73.1	
	Percent of Total	45.9	35	
Part-time	Count	1,046	2,174	3,220
	Expected Count	1,676.5	1,543.5	
	Percent within employ	32.5	67.5	
	Percent within sex	11.9	26.9	
	Percent of Total	6.2	12.9	
Total	Count	8,772	8,076	16,848

Source: Adapted from the Statistics Canada Cansim database, http://cansim2.statcan.ca, table number 282–0002, 2010-01-29.

TABLE **14.10**   A Contingency Table Relating Delivery Time and Computer-Assisted Ordering 🖋

Computer-Assisted Ordering	Delivery Time			Row Total
	Below Industry Average	Equal to Industry Average	Above Industry Average	
No	4	12	8	24
Yes	10	4	2	16
Column Total	14	16	10	40

14.22 In the book *Essentials of Marketing Research*, Dillon, Madden, and Firtle discuss the relationship between delivery time and computer-assisted ordering. A sample of 40 firms shows that 16 use computer-assisted ordering, while 24 do not. Furthermore, past data are used to categorize each firm's delivery times as below the industry average, equal to the industry average, or above the industry average. The results obtained are given in Table 14.10.

a. Test the hypothesis that delivery time performance is independent of whether computer-assisted ordering is used. What do you conclude by setting $\alpha = 0.05$?

b. Verify that a chi-square test is appropriate.

c. Is there a difference in delivery-time performance between firms using computer-assisted ordering and those not using computer-assisted ordering?

d. Carry out graphical analysis to investigate the relationship between delivery-time performance and computer-assisted ordering. Describe the relationship.

14.23 A television station wishes to study the relationship between viewership of its 11 P.M. news program and viewer age (18 years or less, 19 to 35, 36 to 54, 55 or older). A sample of 250 television viewers in each age group is randomly selected, and the number who watch the station's 11 P.M. news is found for each sample. The results are given in Table 14.11.

a. Let p_1, p_2, p_3, and p_4 be the proportions of all viewers in each age group who watch the station's 11 P.M. news. If these proportions are equal, then whether a viewer watches the station's 11 P.M. news is independent of the viewer's age group. Therefore, we can test the null hypothesis H_0 that p_1, p_2, p_3, and p_4 are equal by carrying out a chi-square test for independence. Perform this test by setting $\alpha = 0.05$.

b. Compute a 95 percent confidence interval for the difference between p_1 and p_4.

TABLE **14.11**   A Summary of the Results of a TV Viewership Study 🖋

Watch 11 P.M. News?	Age Group				Total
	18 or Less	19 to 35	36 to 54	55 or Older	
Yes	37	48	56	73	214
No	213	202	194	177	786
Total	250	250	250	250	1,000

CHAPTER SUMMARY

In this chapter, we presented two hypothesis tests that employ the **chi-square distribution**. In Section 14.1, we discussed a **chi-square goodness of fit test**. Here we considered a situation in which we study how count data are distributed among various categories. In particular, we considered a **multinomial experiment** in which randomly selected items are classified into several groups, and we saw how to perform a goodness of fit test for the multinomial probabilities associated with these groups. We also explained how to perform a goodness of fit test for normality. In Section 14.2,

we presented a **chi-square test for independence**. Here we classify count data on two dimensions, and we summarize the cross-classification in the form of a **contingency table**. We use the cross-classified data to test whether the two classifications are **statistically independent**, which is really a way to see whether the classifications are related. We also learned that we can use graphical analysis to investigate the nature of the relationship between the classifications.

GLOSSARY OF TERMS

chi-square test for independence: A test to determine whether two classifications are independent. (pages 522–523)

contingency table: A table that summarizes data that have been classified on two dimensions or scales. (page 509)

goodness of fit test for multinomial probabilities: A test to determine whether multinomial probabilities are equal to a specific set of values. (page 511)

goodness of fit test for normality: A test to determine if a sample has been randomly selected from a normally distributed population. (pages 515–516)

homogeneity (test for): A test of the null hypothesis that all multinomial probabilities are equal. (page 512)

multinomial experiment: An experiment that concerns count data that are classified into more than two categories. (page 509)

IMPORTANT FORMULAS AND TESTS

A goodness of fit test for multinomial probabilities: page 511

A test for homogeneity: page 512

A goodness of fit test for a normal distribution: pages 515–516

A chi-square test for independence: pages 522–523

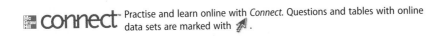 Practise and learn online with *Connect*. Questions and tables with online data sets are marked with  .

SUPPLEMENTARY EXERCISES

14.24 Leonard has just handed in his statistics midterm exam. It was a multiple choice exam with 50 questions. He is curious, and a little worried, about the distribution of his responses. On a scrap piece of paper, he recorded the number of As, Bs, Cs, and Ds he selected. The results are as follows:

A	B	C	D
10	14	17	9

a. At $\alpha = 0.05$, carry out a test of homogeneity for these data.

b. Leonard believes that the answers to any multiple choice test should be distributed evenly. Is this true in his case?

14.25 An occupant traffic study was carried out to aid in the remodelling of a large building on a university campus. The building has five entrances, and the choice of entrance was recorded for a random sample of 300 people entering the building. The results obtained are given in the following table:

Entrance				
I	II	III	IV	V
30	91	97	40	42

Test the null hypothesis that the five entrances are equally used by setting α equal to 0.05. Find a 95 percent confidence interval for the proportion of all people who use Entrance III.

TABLE **14.12** Auditor and Client Positions Regarding Earnings-Increasing Changes in Accounting Standards ✐

(a) Auditor Positions

	Large Firms	Small Firms	Total
In Favour	13	130	143
Opposed	10	24	34
Total	23	154	177

(b) Client Positions

	Large Firms	Small Firms	Total
In Favour	12	120	132
Opposed	11	34	45
Total	23	154	177

Source: "Auditor lobbying for accounting standards: The case of banks and savings and loan associations," by Heidi Hylton Meier, Pervaiz Alam, and Michael A. Pearson, *Accounting and Business Research*, 23, no. 92 (1993), pp. 477–487.

14.26 In a 1993 article in Accounting and Business Research, Meier, Alam, and Pearson studied auditor lobbying on several proposed U.S. accounting standards that affect banks and savings and loan associations. As part of this study, the authors investigated auditors' positions regarding proposed changes in accounting standards that would increase client firms' reported earnings. It was hypothesized that auditors would favour such proposed changes because their clients' managers would receive higher compensation (salary, bonuses, and so on) when client earnings were reported to be higher. Table 14.12 summarizes auditor and client positions (in favour or opposed) regarding proposed changes in accounting standards that would increase client firms' reported earnings. Here the auditor and client positions are cross-classified versus the size of the client firm.

a. Test to determine whether auditor positions regarding earnings-increasing changes in accounting standards depend on the size of the client firm. Use $\alpha = 0.05$.

b. Test to determine whether client positions regarding earnings-increasing changes in accounting standards depend on the size of the client firm. Use $\alpha = 0.05$.

c. Carry out a graphical analysis to investigate a possible relationship between (1) auditor positions and the size of the client firm and (2) client positions and the size of the client firm.

d. Does the relationship between position and the size of the client firm seem to be similar for both auditors and clients? Explain.

14.27 Consider the situation of Exercise 14.26. Table 14.13 summarizes auditor positions regarding proposed changes in accounting standards that would decrease client firms' reported earnings. Determine whether the relationship between auditor position and the size of the client firm is the same for earnings-decreasing changes in accounting standards as it is for earnings-increasing changes in accounting standards. Justify your answer using both a statistical test and a graphical analysis.

14.28 In the book *Business Research Methods* (5th ed.), Cooper and Emory discuss a market researcher for an automaker who is studying consumer preferences for styling features of larger sedans. Buyers, who were

TABLE **14.13** Auditor Positions Regarding Earnings-Decreasing Changes in Accounting Standards ✐

	Large Firms	Small Firms	Total
In Favour	27	152	179
Opposed	29	154	183
Total	56	306	362

Source: "Auditor lobbying for accounting standards: The case of banks and savings and loan associations," by Heidi Hylton Meier, Pervaiz Alam, and Michael A. Pearson, *Accounting and Business Research*, 23, no. 92 (1993), pp. 477–487.

classified as first-time buyers or repeat buyers, were asked to express their preference for one of two types of styling—European styling or Japanese styling. Of 40 first-time buyers, 8 preferred European styling and 32 preferred Japanese styling. Of 60 repeat buyers, 40 preferred European styling and 20 preferred Japanese styling.

a. Set up a contingency table for these data.

b. Test the hypothesis that buyer status (repeat versus first-time) and styling preference are independent at the 0.05 level of significance. What do you conclude?

c. Carry out a graphical analysis to investigate the nature of any relationship between buyer status and styling preference. Describe the relationship.

14.29 The manager of a chain of three drug stores wishes to investigate the level of coupon redemption at its stores. All three stores have the same sales volume. Therefore, the manager will randomly sample 200 customers at each store with regard to coupon usage. The survey results are given below. Test the hypothesis that redemption level and location are independent with $\alpha = 0.01$.

Coupon Redemption Level	Store Location			Total
	Midtown	North Side	South Side	
High	69	97	52	218
Medium	101	93	76	270
Low	30	10	72	112
Total	200	200	200	600

14.30 THE VIDEO GAME SATISFACTION RATING CASE

Consider the sample of 65 customer satisfaction ratings given in Table 14.14. Carry out a chi-square goodness of fit test of normality for the population of all customer satisfaction ratings. Recall that we previously calculated $\overline{X} = 42.95$ and $s = 2.6424$ for the 65 ratings.

14.31 In Major League Baseball, the World Series is held every year (barring any strikes) to determine a champion. Here is a summary of the results of the World Series played from the years 1903 to 2005:

Result (Best of 7)	4-0	4-1	4-2	4-3
Frequency	19	21	22	35

Test at $\alpha = 0.05$ whether or not these data are compatible with the model that each World Series game is an independent trial with $p = P(\text{American League wins}) = P(\text{National League wins}) = 0.5$. This is a tricky question. You need to consider two scenarios. That is, the National League or the American League could win the World Series in each case (in four games, five games, six games, or seven games). In order to determine the probability that a series will be won in n games, remember that a team will have to win three games in $n - 1$ games and then win its fourth game in the nth game.

14.32 At a local casino, a dice game is played such that the shooter bets on the number of sixes they will roll with three dice. The payout is proportional to the number of sixes actually rolled. A player has been rolling the dice for a few hours. The observed frequencies for the number of sixes rolled are as follows:

Number of Sixes Rolled	0	1	2	3
Frequency	45	40	14	1

The casino has become quite suspicious of this person, and they have hired you to analyze the data. Conduct the appropriate chi-square goodness of fit test to see whether or not something out of the ordinary is occurring with this player. That is, check to see whether or not this player is using fair dice. Run the test using $\alpha = 0.05$. What do you conclude?

14.33 A random sample of police records was obtained and the following table shows the number of crimes committed in a midsized Canadian city for each day of the week:

Day	Number of Crimes
Sunday	79
Monday	68
Tuesday	54
Wednesday	69
Thursday	81
Friday	97
Saturday	118

Use a chi-square goodness of fit test to determine whether or not the number of crimes committed in this

TABLE 14.14 A Sample of 65 Customer Satisfaction Ratings

39	46	42	40	45	44	44	44	45
45	44	46	46	46	41	46	46	
38	40	40	41	43	38	48	39	
42	39	47	43	47	43	44	41	
42	40	44	39	43	36	41	44	
41	42	43	43	41	44	45	42	
38	45	45	46	40	44	44	47	
42	44	45	45	43	45	44	43	

city is uniformly distributed over a seven-day week. Test this hypothesis at $\alpha = 0.05$.

14.34 The leading or first digit of legitimate records, such as invoices or expense claims, tends to follow a distribution that is referred to as Benford's law. The distribution is given as follows:

Leading Digit	Probability
1	0.301
2	0.176
3	0.125
4	0.097
5	0.079
6	0.067
7	0.058
8	0.051
9	0.046

Suppose that you suspect that your purchasing manager, who does not know about this law, is faking invoices and redirecting money to their own account. You investigate by taking a random sample of 81 invoices to an auditor. Here are the observed counts for the leading digits on these invoices:

Leading Digit	1	2	3	4	5	6	7	8	9
Observed Frequency	11	11	6	9	7	11	11	4	11

Is there evidence to suggest that these invoices have been faked? Conduct a chi-square goodness of fit test at $\alpha = 0.05$ to test whether or not these invoices follow Benford's law.

14.35 INTERNET EXERCISE

There are many different types of lotteries in Canada, but a popular one is Lotto 6/49. The player chooses six numbers from a list of numbers ranging from 1 to 49. In order to win the jackpot, players must match all six of their selected numbers with the six numbers drawn. A player may also win a prize for as few as two matched numbers (plus the bonus number).

Go to the Web site http://www.lottolore.com/l649stat.html to obtain draw statistics for all Lotto 6/49 draws from June 12, 1982, to the most recent draw. Perform a chi-square goodness of fit test to determine whether or not the numbers forming the winning combination come up with equal probability, that is, with probability 6/49 in this case. Use a p value to run this test and test at the 0.05 level of significance. You will have to use linear interpolation here as the chi-square table does not have a row for $df = 48$. Ignore the statistics involving the bonus numbers for this exercise, and just use the data in the regular column.

Hint: It would be best to use a spreadsheet to conduct this test. Cut and paste the data from the Web site into Excel or some other spreadsheet program and modify them so that you have only the numbers you need (just the regularly drawn numbers), and then set up the chi-square test statistic calculation and run the test.

Note: We have simplified this example. In order to calculate a more accurate p value, you would have to run computer simulations. The real model is more complex than the one described above. The above chi-square test does not account for the fact that the balls are drawn without replacement.

CHAPTER **15**
Decision Theory

LEARNING OBJECTIVES

After reading this chapter, you should be able to

LO1 understand the various states of nature when making a decision

LO2 identify alternatives

LO3 calculate the payoffs for each alternative

LO4 understand the differences in making decisions in the three degrees of uncertainty—certainty, uncertainty, and risk

LO5 know when to use the maximin criterion and the maximax criterion

LO6 use the expected monetary value criterion

LO7 construct a decision tree

LO8 use posterior analysis to determine the best alternative for each of several sampling results

LO9 carry out preposterior analysis to assess the value of sample information and calculate the expected value of this information

LO10 identify a risk seeker, a risk averter, and a risk neutral based on the shape of the utility curve

LO11 understand the meaning of utility and when and how it is used to make decisions

CHAPTER OUTLINE

15.1 Introduction to Decision Theory

15.2 Decision Making Using Posterior Probabilities

15.3 Introduction to Utility Theory

15.4 Decision Making Using Utility Theory

Businesses face difficult decisions on a regular basis. Should a business expand into a new area? Should a plant be closed or retooled? Should a new product be marketed or an old one improved? Individuals must also regularly make difficult decisions. Should you buy stocks, bonds, GICs, or mutual funds? Should you lock in your mortgage rate at a higher but fixed rate, or should you float with a lower but more variable rate? Should you put money in the parking meter or take a chance?

In this chapter, we study some probabilistic methods that can help a decision maker to make intelligent decisions. In Section 15.1, we formally introduce **decision theory**. We discuss the elements of a decision problem, and we present

strategies for making decisions when we face various levels of uncertainty. We also show how to construct a **decision tree**, which is a diagram that can help us analyze a decision problem, and we show how the concept of **expected value** can help us make decisions. In Section 15.2, we show how to use **sample information** to help us make decisions, and we demonstrate how to assess the worth of sample information in order to decide whether the sample information should be obtained. In Section 15.3, we introduce **utility theory**, and in Section 15.4, we explain how utility theory can be used to help make decisions. Many of this chapter's concepts are presented in the context of the following case:

15.1 INTRODUCTION TO DECISION THEORY

Suppose that a real estate developer is proposing to develop a condominium complex on an exclusive parcel of lakefront property. The developer wishes to choose among three possible options: building a large complex, building a medium-sized complex, and building a small complex. The profitability of each option depends on the level of demand for condominium units after the complex has been built. For simplicity, the developer considers only two possible levels of demand: high and low; the developer must choose whether to build a large, medium, or small complex based on its beliefs about whether demand for condominium units will be high or low.

The real estate developer's situation requires a decision. **Decision theory** is a general approach that helps decision makers make intelligent choices. A decision theory problem typically involves the following elements:

1 **States of nature:** A set of potential future conditions that affect the results of the decision. For instance, the level of demand (high or low) for condominium units will affect profits after the developer chooses to build a large, medium, or small complex. Thus, we have two states of nature: high demand and low demand.   **LO1**

2 **Alternatives:** Several alternative actions for the decision maker to choose from. For example, the real estate developer can choose among building a large, a medium, and a small condominium complex. Therefore, the developer has three alternatives: large, medium, and small.   **LO2**

3 **Payoffs:** A payoff for each alternative under each potential state of nature. The payoffs are often summarized in a **payoff table**. For instance, Table 15.1 on the next page gives a payoff table for the condominium complex situation. This table gives the profit[1] for each alternative under the different states of nature. For example, the payoff table tells us that if the developer builds a large complex and demand for units turns out to be high, a profit of $22 million will be realized. However, if the developer builds a large complex and demand for units turns out to be low, a loss of $11 million will be suffered.   **LO3**

Once the states of nature have been identified, the alternatives have been listed, and the payoffs have been determined, we evaluate the alternatives by using a **decision criterion**. How this is done depends on the **degree of uncertainty** associated with the states of nature. Here there are three possibilities:

1 **Certainty:** We know for certain which state of nature will actually occur.

2 **Uncertainty:** We have no information about the likelihoods of the various states of nature.   **LO4**

3 **Risk:** The likelihood (probability) of each state of nature can be estimated.

Decision making under certainty In the unlikely event that we know for certain which state of nature will actually occur, we simply choose the alternative that gives the best payoff for that

---

[1]Here profits are really present values representing current dollar values of expected future income minus costs.

TABLE **15.1** A Payoff Table for the Condominium Complex Situation

Alternatives	States of Nature	
	Low Demand	High Demand
Small Complex	$8 million	$8 million
Medium Complex	$5 million	$15 million
Large Complex	−$11 million	$22 million

state of nature. For instance, in the condominium complex situation, if we know that demand for units will be high, then the payoff table (see Table 15.1) tells us that the best alternative is to build a large complex and that this choice will yield a profit of $22 million. On the other hand, if we know that demand for units will be low, then the payoff table tells us that the best alternative is to build a small complex and that this choice will yield a profit of $8 million.

Of course, we rarely (if ever) know for certain which state of nature will actually occur. However, analyzing the payoff table in this way often provides insight into the nature of the problem. For instance, examining the payoff table tells us that if we know that demand for units will be low, building either a small complex or a medium complex will be far superior to building a large complex (which would yield an $11 million loss).

Decision making under uncertainty This is the exact opposite of certainty. Here we have no information about how likely the different states of nature are. That is, we have no idea how to assign probabilities to the different states of nature.

In such a case, several approaches are possible; we will discuss two commonly used methods. The first is called the **maximin criterion**.

LO5

Maximin: Find the worst possible payoff for each alternative, and then choose the alternative that yields the maximum worst possible payoff (or the best worst-case scenario).

For instance, to apply the maximin criterion to the condominium complex situation, we proceed as follows (see Table 15.1):

1 If a small complex is built, the worst possible payoff is $8 million.

2 If a medium complex is built, the worst possible payoff is $5 million.

3 If a large complex is built, the worst possible payoff is −$11 million.

Because the maximum of these worst possible payoffs is $8 million, the developer should choose to build a small complex.

The maximin criterion is a **pessimistic approach** because it considers the worst possible payoff for each alternative. When an alternative is chosen using the maximin criterion, the actual payoff obtained may be higher than the maximum worst possible payoff. However, using the maximin criterion assures a **guaranteed minimum** payoff.

A second approach is called the **maximax criterion**.

LO5

Maximax: Find the best possible payoff for each alternative, and then choose the alternative that yields the maximum best possible payoff.

To apply the maximax criterion to the condominium complex situation, we proceed as follows (see Table 15.1):

1 If a small complex is built, the best possible payoff is $8 million.

2 If a medium complex is built, the best possible payoff is $15 million.

3 If a large complex is built, the best possible payoff is $22 million.

Because the maximum of these best possible payoffs is $22 million, the developer should choose to build a large complex.

The maximax criterion is an **optimistic approach** because we always choose the alternative that yields the highest possible payoff. This is a "go-for-broke" strategy, and the actual payoff obtained may be far less than the highest possible payoff. For example, in the condominium complex situation, if a large complex is built and demand for units turns out to be low, an $11 million loss will be suffered (instead of a $22 million profit).

Decision making under risk In this case, we can estimate the probability of occurrence for each state of nature. Thus, we have a situation in which we have more information about the states of nature than in the case of uncertainty and less information than in the case of certainty. Here a commonly used approach is to use the **expected monetary value criterion**. This involves computing the expected monetary payoff for each alternative and choosing the alternative with the largest expected payoff.

LO6

The expected value criterion can be employed by using **prior probabilities**. As an example, suppose that in the condominium complex situation the developer assigns prior probabilities of 0.7 and 0.3 to high and low demands, respectively. We find the expected monetary value for each alternative by multiplying the probability of occurrence for each state of nature by the payoff associated with the state of nature and by summing these products. Referring to the payoff table in Table 15.1, the expected monetary values are as follows:

Small complex: Expected value $= 0.3(\$8\text{ million}) + 0.7(\$8\text{ million}) = \$8$ million.

Medium complex: Expected value $= 0.3(\$5\text{ million}) + 0.7(\$15\text{ million}) = \$12$ million.

Large complex: Expected value $= 0.3(-\$11\text{ million}) + 0.7(\$22\text{ million}) = \$12.1$ million.

Choosing the alternative with the highest expected monetary value, the developer would choose to build a large complex.

Remember that the expected payoff is not necessarily equal to the actual payoff that will be realized. Rather, the expected payoff is the long-run average payoff that would be realized if many identical decisions were made. For instance, the expected monetary payoff of $12.1 million for a large complex is the average payoff that would be obtained if many large condominium complexes were built. Thus, the expected monetary value criterion is best used when many similar decisions will be made.

Using a decision tree It is often convenient to depict the alternatives, states of nature, payoffs, and probabilities (in the case of risk) in the form of a **decision tree** or **tree diagram**. The diagram is made up of **nodes** and **branches**. We use square nodes to denote decision points and circular nodes to denote chance events. The branches emanating from a decision point represent alternatives, and the branches emanating from a circular node represent the possible states of nature. Figure 15.1 on the next page presents a decision tree for the condominium complex situation (in the case of risk as described previously). Notice that the payoffs are shown at the rightmost end of each branch and the probabilities associated with the various states of nature are given in parentheses corresponding to each branch emanating from a chance node. The expected monetary values for the alternatives are shown below the chance nodes. The double slashes placed through the small complex and medium complex branches indicate that these alternatives would not be chosen (because of their lower expected payoffs) and that the large complex alternative would be selected.

LO7

A decision tree is particularly useful when a problem involves a sequence of decisions. For instance, in the condominium complex situation, if demand turns out to be small, it might be possible to improve payoffs by selling the condominiums at lower prices. Figure 15.2 on the next page shows a decision tree in which, after a decision to build a small, medium, or large condominium complex is made, the developer can choose to either keep the same prices or charge lower prices for condominium units. In order to analyze the decision tree, we start with the last (rightmost) decision to be made. For each decision, we choose the alternative that gives the highest payoff. For instance, if the developer builds a large complex and demand turns out to be low, the developer should lower prices (as indicated by the double slash through the same prices alternative). If decisions are followed by chance events, we choose the alternative that gives the highest expected monetary value. For example, again looking at Figure 15.2, we see that a medium complex should now be built because of its highest expected monetary value ($0.3(\$12\text{ million}) + 0.7(\$15\text{ million}) = \$14.1$ million). This is indicated by the double slashes drawn through the small and large complex alternatives. Looking at the entire decision tree in Figure 15.2, we see that the developer should build a medium complex and should sell condominium units at lower prices if demand turns out to be low.

FIGURE 15.1 A Decision Tree for the Condominium Complex Situation

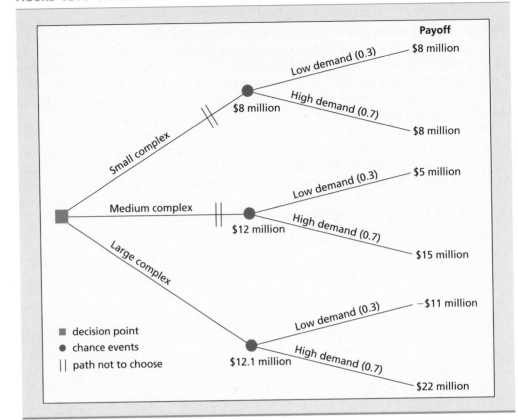

Payoff

Small complex
$8 million
Low demand (0.3) — $8 million
High demand (0.7) — $8 million

Medium complex
$12 million
Low demand (0.3) — $5 million
High demand (0.7) — $15 million

Large complex
$12.1 million
Low demand (0.3) — −$11 million
High demand (0.7) — $22 million

■ decision point
● chance events
|| path not to choose

LO7

FIGURE 15.2 A Decision Tree with Sequential Decisions

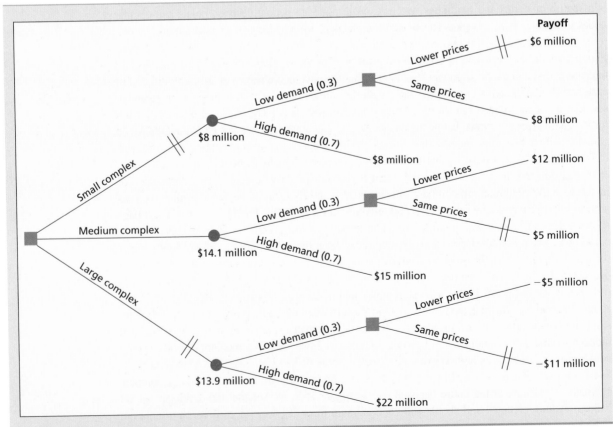

Payoff

Small complex
$8 million
Low demand (0.3)
Lower prices || $6 million
Same prices $8 million
High demand (0.7) — $8 million

Medium complex
$14.1 million
Low demand (0.3)
Lower prices $12 million
Same prices || $5 million
High demand (0.7) — $15 million

Large complex
$13.9 million
Low demand (0.3)
Lower prices — $5 million
Same prices || −$11 million
High demand (0.7) — $22 million

LO7

Sometimes it is possible to determine exactly which state of nature will occur in the future. For example, in the condominium complex situation, the level of demand for units might depend on whether a new resort casino is built in the area. While the developer may have prior probabilities concerning whether the casino will be built, it might be feasible to postpone a decision about the size of the condominium complex until a final decision about the resort casino has been made.

If we can find out exactly which state of nature will occur, we say we have obtained **perfect information**. There is usually a cost involved in obtaining this information (if it can be obtained at all). For instance, we might have to acquire an option on the lakefront property on which the condominium complex is to be built in order to postpone a decision about the size of the complex. Or perfect information might be acquired by conducting some sort of research that must be paid for. A question that arises here is whether it is worth the cost to obtain perfect information. We can answer this question by computing the **expected value of perfect information**, which we denote as the **EVPI**. The EVPI is defined as follows:

EVPI = expected payoff under certainty − expected payoff under risk.

For instance, in the condominium complex situation depicted in the decision tree of Figure 15.1, we found that the expected payoff under risk is $12.1 million (which is the expected payoff associated with building a large complex). To find the expected payoff under certainty (maximum expected payoff) we find the highest payoff under each state of nature. Referring to Table 15.1, we see that if demand is low, the highest payoff is $8 million (when we build a small complex), and if demand is high, the highest payoff is $22 million (when we build a large complex). Because the prior probabilities of high and low demand are, respectively, 0.7 and 0.3, the expected payoff under certainty is 0.7($22 million) + 0.3($8 million) = $17.8 million. Therefore, the expected value of perfect information is $17.8 million − $12.1 million = $5.7 million. This is the maximum amount of money that the developer should be willing to pay to obtain perfect information. That is, the land option should be purchased if it costs $5.7 million or less. Then, if the casino is not built (and demand is low), a small condominium complex should be built; if the casino is built (and demand is high), a large condominium complex should be built. On the other hand, if the land option costs more than $5.7 million, the developer should choose the alternative with the highest expected payoff (which would mean building a large complex—see Figure 15.1).

Finally, another approach to dealing with risk involves assigning what we call **utilities** to monetary values. These utilities reflect the decision maker's attitude toward risk: that is, is the decision maker a risk avoider or a risk taker? Here the decision maker chooses the alternative that **maximizes expected utility**. The reader interested in this approach is referred to Section 15.3.

Exercises for Section 15.1

CONCEPTS

15.1 Explain the differences between decision making under certainty, decision making under uncertainty, and decision making under risk.

15.2 Explain how to use the
  a. Maximin criterion.
  b. Maximax criterion.
  c. Expected monetary value criterion.

15.3 Explain how to find the expected value of perfect information (EVPI).

METHODS AND APPLICATIONS

Exercises 15.4 through 15.9 refer to a capacity-planning problem in which a company must choose to build a small, medium, or large production facility. The payoff obtained will depend on whether future demand is low, moderate, or high, and the payoffs are as given in the following table: ✐

Alternatives	Possible Future Demand		
	Low	Moderate	High
Small Facility	$12[a]	$12	$12
Medium Facility	9	14	14
Large Facility	−4	2	18

[a]Present value in $ millions.

15.4 Find the best alternative (and the resulting payoff) in the given payoff table if it is known with certainty that demand will be
  a. Low. **b.** Medium. **c.** High.

15.5 Given the payoff table, find the alternative that would be chosen using the maximin criterion.

15.6 Given the payoff table, find the alternative that would be chosen using the maximax criterion.

15.7 Suppose that the company assigns prior probabilities of 0.3, 0.5, and 0.2 to low, moderate, and high demand, respectively.
   a. Find the expected monetary value for each alternative (small, medium, and large).
   b. What is the best alternative using the expected monetary value criterion?

15.8 Construct a decision tree for the information in the payoff table assuming that the prior probabilities of low, moderate, and high demand are, respectively, 0.3, 0.5, and 0.2.

15.9 For the information in the payoff table, find
   a. The expected payoff under certainty.
   b. The expected value of perfect information, EVPI.

15.10 Figure 15.3 gives a decision tree presented in the book *Production/Operations Management* by Stevenson. Use this tree diagram to do the following:
   a. Find the expected monetary value for each alternative (subcontract, expand, and build).
   b. Determine the alternative that should be selected in order to maximize the expected monetary value.

15.11 A firm wishes to choose the location for a new factory. Profits obtained will depend on whether a new railroad spur is constructed to serve the town in which the new factory will be located. The payoff table on the next page summarizes the relevant information.

FIGURE 15.3   Decision Tree for Exercise 15.10

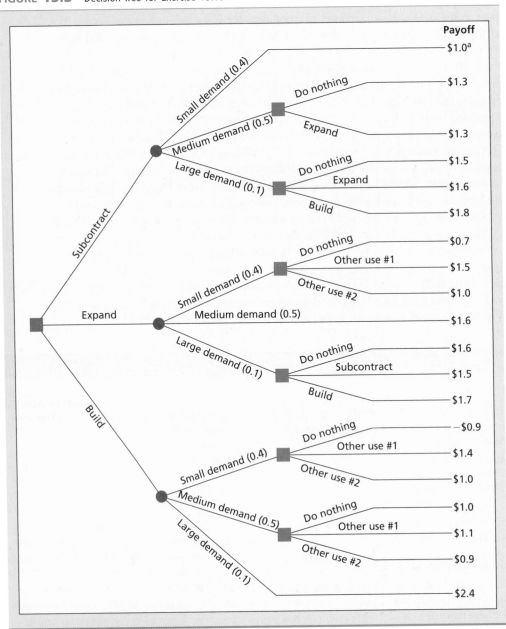

[a]Net present value in millions.

Alternatives	New Railroad Spur Built	No New Railroad Spur
Location *A*	$1[a]	$14
Location *B*	2	10
Location *C*	4	6

[a]Profits in $ millions.

Determine the location that should be chosen if the firm uses
  a. The maximin criterion.
  b. The maximax criterion.

15.12 Refer to the information given in Exercise 15.11. Use the probabilities of 0.60 for a new railroad spur and 0.40 for no new railroad spur.
  a. Compute the expected monetary value for each location.
  b. Find the location that should be selected using the expected monetary value criterion.
  c. Compute the expected value of perfect information (EVPI).

15.13 Construct a decision tree for the information given in Exercises 15.11 and 15.12.

15.14 Jimmy faces some major decisions about expanding his small pub, Bumpy's Pub and Grill. After careful consideration, he determines that his decision tree reduces to the following (profit values are in $1000s). The costs for all scenarios have already been deducted:

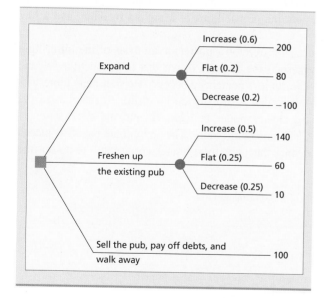

a. Using the expected monetary value criterion, what is Jimmy's best strategy?
b. A lot of people would elect to take $100,000 and walk away. Can you explain why?

15.15 When Robert drives to school each day, he has to choose a parking space. The map shows that he can turn right to enter the main parking lot, M, where parking spots are always available, or he can proceed straight to the Western Sciences building, W, where he works. There is a 30 percent chance that he can find a spot in a small parking lot behind the Western Sciences Centre. If he does not find a spot, he can always park at a parking meter in front of the building, at a cost of $10 per day. He could choose not to put money in the meter and risk getting a $35 ticket. He estimates that people are ticketed for this reason about 10 percent of the time. For both parts of this question, use the expected monetary value criterion.

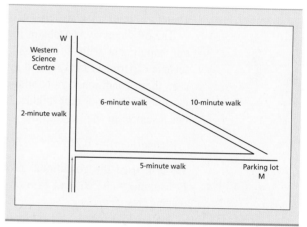

a. The times that it takes to drive the various routes are given in the map above. Note also that it takes Robert 10 minutes to walk from parking lot M to his building. If we consider that Robert's time is worth $30 per hour, what is his best strategy?
b. Now suppose that Robert faces an additional penalty if he does not put money in the meter. Suppose that 50 percent of those that get a ticket also get towed at a cost of $80 (on top of the $35 ticket), plus an hour of his time. Now what should Robert do? What is the cost of that decision?

15.2 DECISION MAKING USING POSTERIOR PROBABILITIES

We have seen that the expected monetary value criterion tells us to choose the alternative with the highest expected payoff. In Section 15.1, we computed expected payoffs by using prior probabilities. When we use the expected monetary value criterion to choose the best alternative based on expected values computed using prior probabilities, we call this **prior decision analysis**. Often, however, sample information can be obtained to help us make decisions.

In such a case, we compute expected values by using **posterior probabilities**, and we call the analysis **posterior decision analysis**. In the following example, we demonstrate how to carry out posterior analysis.

Example 15.1 **The Oil-Drilling Case (Posterior Probabilities)**

An oil company needs to decide whether to drill for oil on a particular site, and the company has assigned prior probabilities to the states of nature $S_1 \equiv$ no oil, $S_2 \equiv$ some oil, and $S_3 \equiv$ much oil of 0.7, 0.2, and 0.1, respectively. Figure 15.4 gives a decision tree and payoff table for a **prior analysis** of the oil-drilling situation. Here, using the prior probabilities, the expected monetary value associated with drilling is

$$0.7(-\$700,000) + 0.2(\$500,000) + 0.1(\$2,000,000) = -\$190,000,$$

while the expected monetary value associated with not drilling is

$$0.7(0) + 0.2(0) + 0.1(0) = 0.$$

Therefore, prior analysis tells us that the oil company should not drill.

The oil company can obtain more information about the drilling site by performing a seismic experiment with three possible readings: low, medium, and high. The accuracy of the seismic experiment is expressed by the conditional probabilities in Figure 15.5(a), and we have used these conditional probabilities to update the prior probabilities of no oil, some oil, and much oil to posterior probabilities in the probability revision tables in Figure 15.5(b), (c), and (d). For instance, in Figure 15.5(b), we found that

$$P(\text{none}|\text{high}) = 0.21875, \quad P(\text{some}|\text{high}) = 0.03125, \quad \text{and} \quad P(\text{much}|\text{high}) = 0.75.$$

We also used the conditional probabilities in Figure 15.5(a) to compute $P(\text{high}) = 0.128$, $P(\text{medium}) = 0.226$, and $P(\text{low}) = 0.646$, the probabilities of a high, a medium, and a low reading, respectively.

LO8

Figure 15.6 (page 540) presents a decision tree for a **posterior analysis** of the oil-drilling problem. The leftmost decision node represents the decision of whether to conduct the seismic experiment. The upper branch (no seismic survey) contains a second decision node representing the alternatives in our decision problem (that is, drill or do not drill). At the ends of the drill and do not drill branches we have chance nodes that branch into the three states of nature—no oil (none), some oil (some), and much oil (much). The appropriate payoff is placed at the rightmost end of each branch, and since this uppermost branch corresponds to no seismic

FIGURE 15.4   A Decision Tree and Payoff Table for a Prior Analysis of the Oil-Drilling Case

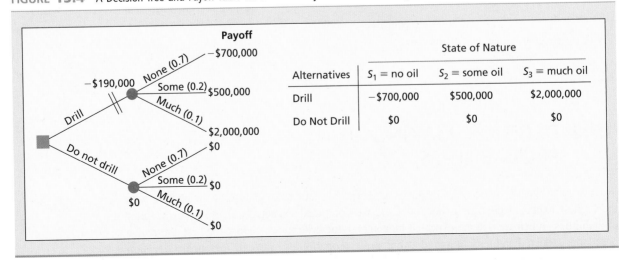

	State of Nature		
Alternatives	$S_1 \equiv$ no oil	$S_2 \equiv$ some oil	$S_3 \equiv$ much oil
Drill	-$700,000	$500,000	$2,000,000
Do Not Drill	$0	$0	$0

FIGURE **15.5** A Tree Diagram and Probability Revision Tables in the Oil-Drilling Example

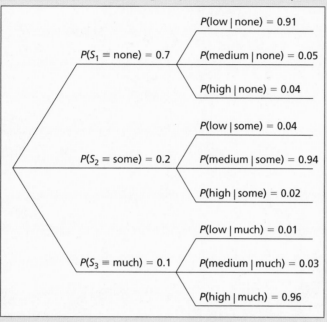

(a) A tree diagram illustrating the prior and conditional probabilities

(b) A probability revision table for calculating the probability of a high reading and the posterior probabilities of no oil (S_1), some oil (S_2), and much oil (S_3) given a high reading

S_j	$P(S_j)$	$P(\text{high} \mid S_j)$	$P(S_j \cap \text{high}) = P(S_j)P(\text{high} \mid S_j)$	$P(S_j \mid \text{high}) = P(S_j \cap \text{high})/P(\text{high})$
$S_1 \equiv$ none	$P(\text{none}) = 0.7$	$P(\text{high} \mid \text{none}) = 0.04$	$P(\text{none} \cap \text{high}) = 0.7(0.04) = 0.028$	$P(\text{none} \mid \text{high}) = 0.028/0.128 = 0.21875$
$S_2 \equiv$ some	$P(\text{some}) = 0.2$	$P(\text{high} \mid \text{some}) = 0.02$	$P(\text{some} \cap \text{high}) = 0.2(0.02) = 0.004$	$P(\text{some} \mid \text{high}) = 0.004/0.128 = 0.03125$
$S_3 \equiv$ much	$P(\text{much}) = 0.1$	$P(\text{high} \mid \text{much}) = 0.96$	$P(\text{much} \cap \text{high}) = 0.1(0.96) = 0.096$	$P(\text{much} \mid \text{high}) = 0.096/0.128 = 0.75$
Total	1		$P(\text{high}) = 0.028 + 0.004 + 0.096 = 0.128$	1

(c) A probability revision table for calculating the probability of a medium reading and the posterior probabilities of no oil (S_1), some oil (S_2), and much oil (S_3) given a medium reading

S_j	$P(S_j)$	$P(\text{medium} \mid S_j)$	$P(S_j \cap \text{medium}) = P(S_j)P(\text{medium} \mid S_j)$	$P(S_j \mid \text{medium}) = P(S_j \cap \text{medium})/P(\text{medium})$
$S_1 \equiv$ none	$P(\text{none}) = 0.7$	$P(\text{medium} \mid \text{none}) = 0.05$	$P(\text{none} \cap \text{medium}) = 0.7(0.05) = 0.035$	$P(\text{none} \mid \text{medium}) = 0.035/0.226 = 0.15487$
$S_2 \equiv$ some	$P(\text{some}) = 0.2$	$P(\text{medium} \mid \text{some}) = 0.94$	$P(\text{some} \cap \text{medium}) = 0.2(0.94) = 0.188$	$P(\text{some} \mid \text{medium}) = 0.188/0.226 = 0.83186$
$S_3 \equiv$ much	$P(\text{much}) = 0.1$	$P(\text{medium} \mid \text{much}) = 0.03$	$P(\text{much} \cap \text{medium}) = 0.1(0.03) = 0.003$	$P(\text{much} \mid \text{medium}) = 0.003/0.226 = 0.01327$
Total	1		$P(\text{medium}) = 0.035 + 0.188 + 0.003 = 0.226$	1

(d) A probability revision table for calculating the probability of a low reading and the posterior probabilities of no oil (S_1), some oil (S_2), and much oil (S_3) given a low reading

S_j	$P(S_j)$	$P(\text{low} \mid S_j)$	$P(S_j \cap \text{low}) = P(S_j)P(\text{low} \mid S_j)$	$P(S_j \mid \text{low}) = P(S_j \cap \text{low})/P(\text{low})$
$S_1 \equiv$ none	$P(\text{none}) = 0.7$	$P(\text{low} \mid \text{none}) = 0.91$	$P(\text{none} \cap \text{low}) = 0.7(0.91) = 0.637$	$P(\text{none} \mid \text{low}) = 0.637/0.646 = 0.98607$
$S_2 \equiv$ some	$P(\text{some}) = 0.2$	$P(\text{low} \mid \text{some}) = 0.04$	$P(\text{some} \cap \text{low}) = 0.2(0.04) = 0.008$	$P(\text{some} \mid \text{low}) = 0.008/0.646 = 0.01238$
$S_3 \equiv$ much	$P(\text{much}) = 0.1$	$P(\text{low} \mid \text{much}) = 0.01$	$P(\text{much} \cap \text{low}) = 0.1(0.01) = 0.001$	$P(\text{much} \mid \text{low}) = 0.001/0.646 = 0.00155$
Total	1		$P(\text{low}) = 0.637 + 0.008 + 0.001 = 0.646$	1

survey, the probabilities in parentheses for the states of nature are the prior probabilities. The expected payoff associated with drilling (which we found to be −$190,000) is shown at the chance node for the drill branch, and the expected payoff associated with not drilling (which we found to be $0) is shown at the chance node for the do not drill branch.

The lower branch of the decision tree (seismic survey) has an extra chance node that branches into the three possible outcomes of the seismic experiment—low, medium, and high. The probabilities of these outcomes are shown corresponding to the low, medium, and

FIGURE **15.6**   A Decision Tree for a Posterior Analysis of the Oil-Drilling Case

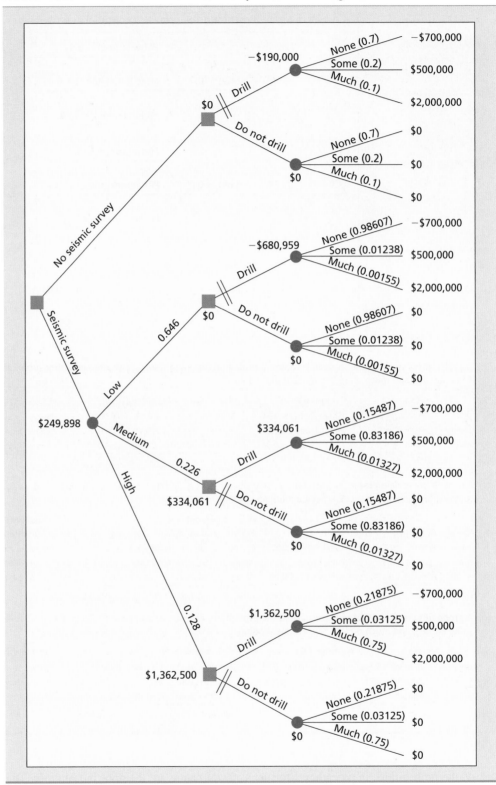

high branches. From the low, medium, and high branches, the tree branches into alternatives (drill and do not drill) and from alternatives into states of nature (none, some, and much). However, the probabilities in parentheses written beside the none, some, and much branches are the posterior probabilities that we computed in the probability revision tables in Figure 15.5 (previous page). This is because advancing to the end of a particular branch in the lower part of the decision tree is conditional; that is, it depends on obtaining a particular experimental result (low, medium, or high).

We can now use the decision tree to determine the alternative (drill or do not drill) that should be selected given that the seismic experiment has been performed and has resulted in a particular outcome. First, suppose that the seismic experiment results in a high reading. Looking at the branch of the decision tree corresponding to a high reading, the expected monetary values associated with the drill and do not drill alternatives are as follows:

Drill: $0.21875(-\$700,000) + 0.03125(\$500,000) + 0.75(\$2,000,000) = \$1,362,500.$

Do not drill: $0.21875(0) + 0.03125(0) + 0.75(0) = \$0.$

These expected monetary values are placed on the decision tree corresponding to the drill and do not drill alternatives. They tell us that if the seismic experiment results in a high reading, then the company should drill and the expected payoff will be $1,362,500. The double slash placed through the do not drill branch (at the very bottom of the decision tree) blocks off that branch and indicates that the company should drill if a high reading is obtained.

Next suppose that the seismic experiment results in a medium reading. Looking at the branch corresponding to a medium reading, the expected monetary values are as follows:

Drill: $0.15487(-\$700,000) + 0.83186(\$500,000) + 0.01327(\$2,000,000) = \$334,061.$

Do not drill: $0.15487(\$0) + 0.83186(\$0) + 0.01327(\$0) = \$0.$

Therefore, if the seismic experiment results in a medium reading, the oil company should drill, and the expected payoff will be $334,061.

Finally, suppose that the seismic experiment results in a low reading. Looking at the branch corresponding to a low reading, the expected monetary values are as follows:

Drill: $0.98607(-\$700,000) + 0.01238(\$500,000) + 0.00155(\$2,000,000) = -\$680,959.$

Do not drill: $0.98607(\$0) + 0.01238(\$0) + 0.00155(\$0) = \$0.$

Therefore, if the seismic experiment results in a low reading, the oil company should not drill on the site.

We can summarize the results of our posterior analysis as follows:

Outcome of Seismic Experiment	Probability of Outcome	Decision	Expected Payoff
High	0.128	Drill	$1,362,500
Medium	0.226	Drill	$334,061
Low	0.646	Do not drill	$0

If we carry out the seismic experiment, we now know what action should be taken for each possible outcome (low, medium, or high). However, there is a cost involved when we conduct the seismic experiment. If, for instance, it costs $100,000 to perform the seismic experiment, we need to investigate whether it is worth it to perform the experiment. This will depend on the expected worth of the information provided by the experiment. Naturally, we must decide whether the experiment is worth it *before* our posterior analysis is actually done. Therefore, when we assess the worth of the sample information, we say that we are performing a **preposterior analysis**.

In order to assess the worth of the sample information, we compute the **expected payoff of sampling**. To calculate this result, we find the expected payoff and the probability of each sample outcome (that is, at each possible outcome of the seismic experiment). Looking at the decision tree in Figure 15.6, we find the following:

Experimental Outcome	Expected Payoff	Probability
Low	$0	0.646
Medium	$334,061	0.226
High	$1,362,500	0.128

Therefore, the **expected payoff of sampling**, which is denoted **EPS**, is

$$EPS = 0.646(\$0) + 0.226(\$334,061) + 0.128(\$1,362,500) = \$249,898.$$

To find the worth of the sample information, we compare the expected payoff of sampling to the **expected payoff of no sampling**, which is denoted **EPNS**. The EPNS is the expected payoff of the alternative that we would choose by using the expected monetary value criterion with the prior probabilities. When we summarized our prior analysis in the tree diagram of Figure 15.4 (page 538), we found that (based on the prior probabilities) we should choose not to drill and that the expected payoff of this action is \$0. Therefore, EPNS = \$0.

We compare the EPS and the EPNS by computing the **expected value of sample information**, which is denoted **EVSI** and is defined to be the expected payoff of sampling minus the expected payoff of no sampling. Therefore,

$$EVSI = EPS - EPNS = \$249,898 - \$0 = \$249,898.$$

The EVSI is the expected gain from conducting the seismic experiment, and the oil company should pay no more than this amount to carry out the seismic experiment. If the experiment costs \$100,000, then it is worth the expense to conduct the experiment. Moreover, the difference between the EVSI and the cost of sampling is called the **expected net gain of sampling**, which is denoted **ENGS**. Here

$$ENGS = EVSI - \$100,000 = \$249,898 - \$100,000 = \$149,898.$$

As long as the ENGS is greater than \$0, it is worth it to carry out the seismic experiment. That is, the oil company should carry out the seismic experiment before it chooses whether or not to drill. Then, as discussed earlier, our posterior analysis says that if the experiment gives a medium or a high reading, the oil company should drill, and if the experiment gives a low reading, the oil company should not drill.

Exercises for Section 15.2

CONCEPTS

15.16 Explain what is meant by each of the following and describe the purpose of each:
  a. Prior analysis.
  b. Posterior analysis.
  c. Preposterior analysis.

15.17 Define and interpret each of the following:
  a. Expected payoff of sampling, EPS.
  b. Expected payoff of no sampling, EPNS.
  c. Expected value of sample information, EVSI.
  d. Expected net gain of sampling, ENGS.

METHODS AND APPLICATIONS

Exercises 15.18 through 15.23 refer to the following situation.

In the book *Making Hard Decisions: An Introduction to Decision Analysis* (2nd ed.), Clemen presents an example in which an investor wishes to choose to invest money in (1) a high-risk stock, (2) a low-risk stock, or (3) a savings account. The payoffs received from the two stocks will depend on the behaviour of the stock market—that is, whether the market goes up, stays the same, or goes down over the investment period. In addition, in order to obtain more information about the market behaviour

that might be anticipated during the investment period, the investor can hire an economist as a consultant to predict the future market behaviour. The results of the consultation will be one of the following three possibilities: (1) economist says "up," (2) economist says "flat" (the same), and (3) economist says "down." The conditional probabilities that express the ability of the economist to accurately forecast market behaviour are given in the following table:

Economist's Prediction	Future Market State		
	Up	Flat	Down
Up	0.80	0.15	0.20
Flat	0.10	0.70	0.20
Down	0.10	0.15	0.60

For instance, using this table we see that P(economist says "up" | market up) = 0.80. Figure 15.7 gives an incomplete decision tree for the investor's situation. Notice that this decision tree gives all relevant payoffs and also gives the prior probabilities of up, flat, and down, which are, respectively, 0.5, 0.3, and 0.2.

FIGURE 15.7 An Incomplete Decision Tree for the Investor's Decision Problem of Exercises 15.18 through 15.23

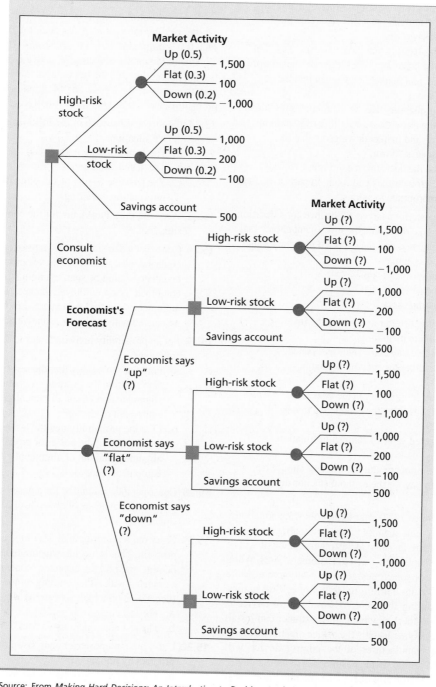

Source: From *Making Hard Decisions: An Introduction to Decision Analysis,* 2nd ed., by R. T. Clemen. Copyright © 1996. Reprinted with permission of Brooks/Cole, an imprint of the Wadsworth Group, a division of Thomson Learning. Fax 800-730-2215.

15.18 Identify and list each of the following for the investor's decision problem:
  a. The investor's alternative actions.
  b. The states of nature.
  c. The possible results of sampling (that is, of information gathering).

15.19 Write out the payoff table for the investor's decision problem.

15.20 Carry out a prior analysis of the investor's decision problem. That is, determine the investment choice that should be made and find the expected monetary value of that choice assuming that the investor does not consult the economist about future stock market behaviour.

15.21 Set up probability revision tables to do the following:

    a. Find the probability that the economist says "up" and find the posterior probabilities of market up, market flat, and market down given that the economist says "up."

    b. Find the probability that the economist says "flat," and find the posterior probabilities of market up, market flat, and market down given that the economist says "flat."

    c. Find the probability that the economist says "down," and find the posterior probabilities of market up, market flat, and market down given that the economist says "down."

    d. Reproduce the decision tree of Figure 15.7 and insert the probabilities you found in parts a, b, and c in their appropriate locations.

15.22 Carry out a posterior analysis of the investor's decision problem. That is, determine the investment choice that should be made and find the expected monetary value of that choice assuming

    a. The economist says "up."

    b. The economist says "flat."

    c. The economist says "down."

15.23 Carry out a preposterior analysis of the investor's decision problem by finding

    a. The expected monetary value associated with consulting the economist, that is, the EPS.

    b. The expected monetary value associated with not consulting the economist, that is, the EPNS.

    c. The expected value of sample information, EVSI.

    d. The maximum amount the investor should be willing to pay for the economist's consulting advice.

Exercises 15.24 through 15.30 refer to the following situation.

A firm designs and manufactures automatic electronic control devices that are installed at customers' plant sites. The control devices are shipped by truck to customers' sites. While in transit, the devices sometimes get out of alignment. More specifically, a device has a prior probability of 0.10 of getting out of alignment during shipment. When a control device is delivered to the customer's plant site, the customer can install the device. If the customer installs the device and the device is in alignment, the manufacturer of the control device will realize a profit of $15,000. If the customer installs the device and the device is out of alignment, the manufacturer must dismantle, realign, and reinstall the device for the customer. This procedure costs $3,000, and therefore the manufacturer will realize a profit of $12,000. As an alternative to customer installation, the manufacturer can send two engineers to the customer's plant site to check the alignment of the control device, realign the device if necessary before installation, and supervise the installation. Because it is less costly to realign the device before it is installed, sending the engineers costs $500. Therefore, if the engineers are sent to assist with the installation, the manufacturer realizes a profit of $14,500 (this is true whether or not the engineers must realign the device at the site).

Before a control device is installed, a piece of test equipment can be used by the customer to check the device's alignment. The test equipment has two readings, "in" and "out" of alignment. Given that the control device is in alignment, there is a 0.8 probability that the test equipment will read "in." Given that the control device is out of alignment, there is a 0.9 probability that the test equipment will read "out."

15.24 Identify and list each of the following for the control device situation:

    a. The firm's alternative actions.

    b. The states of nature.

    c. The possible results of sampling (that is, of information gathering).

15.25 Write out the payoff table for the control device situation.

15.26 Construct a decision tree for a prior analysis of the control device situation. Then determine whether the engineers should be sent, assuming that the piece of test equipment is not employed to check the device's alignment. Also find the expected monetary value associated with the best alternative action.

15.27 Set up probability revision tables to do the following:

    a. Find the probability that the test equipment reads "in" and find the posterior probabilities of in alignment and out of alignment given that the test equipment reads "in."

    b. Find the probability that the test equipment reads "out" and find the posterior probabilities of in alignment and out of alignment given that the test equipment reads "out."

15.28 Construct a decision tree for a posterior and a preposterior analysis of the control device situation.

15.29 Carry out a posterior analysis of the control device problem. That is, decide whether the engineers should be sent, and find the expected monetary value associated with either sending or not sending (depending on which is best) the engineers assuming

    a. The test equipment reads "in."

    b. The test equipment reads "out."

15.30 Carry out a preposterior analysis of the control device problem by finding

    a. The expected monetary value associated with using the test equipment, that is, the EPS.

    b. The expected monetary value associated with not using the test equipment, that is, the EPNS.

    c. The expected value of sample information, EVSI.

    d. The maximum amount that should be paid for using the test equipment.

15.3 INTRODUCTION TO UTILITY THEORY

Suppose that a decision maker is trying to decide whether to invest in one of two opportunities—Investment 1 or Investment 2—or not to invest in either of these opportunities. As shown in Table 15.2(a), (b), and (c), the expected profits associated with Investment 1, Investment 2, and no investment are $32,000, $28,000, and $0. Thus, if the decision maker uses expected profit as a decision criterion and decides to choose no more than one investment, the decision maker should choose Investment 1. However, as discussed earlier, the expected profit for an investment is the long-run average profit that would be realized if many identical investments could be made. If the decision maker will make only a limited number of investments (perhaps because of limited capital), they will not realize the expected profit. For example, a single undertaking of Investment 1 will result in a profit of $50,000, a profit of $10,000, or a loss of $20,000. Some decision makers might prefer a single undertaking of Investment 2, because the potential loss is only $10,000. Other decision makers might be unwilling to risk $10,000 and would choose no investment.

There is a way to combine the various profits and probabilities and the decision maker's individual attitude toward risk to make a decision that is best for the decision maker. The method is based on a theory of utility discussed by Von Neumann and Morgenstern in *Theory of Games and Economic Behavior*. This theory says that if a decision maker agrees with certain assumptions about rational behaviour, then the decision maker should replace the profits in the various investments by **utilities** and choose the investment that gives the **highest expected utility**. To find the utility of a particular profit, we first arrange the profits from largest to smallest. The utility of the largest profit is 1 and the utility of the smallest profit is 0. The utility of any particular intermediate profit is the probability, call it u, such that the decision maker is **indifferent** between (1) getting the particular intermediate profit with certainty and

LO10

TABLE **15.2** Three Possible Investments and Their Expected Utilities

(a) Investment 1 profits

Profit	Probability
$50,000	0.7
$10,000	0.1
−$20,000	0.2

Expected profit = 50,000(0.7) + 10,000(0.1) + (−20,000)(0.2) = 32,000

(b) Investment 2 profits

Profit	Probability
$40,000	0.6
$30,000	0.2
−$10,000	0.2

Expected profit = 40,000(0.6) + 30,000(0.2) + (−10,000)(0.2) = 28,000

(c) No investment profit

Profit	Probability
$0	1

Expected profit = 0(1) = 0

(d) Utilities

Profit	Utility
$50,000	1
$40,000	0.95
$30,000	0.90
$10,000	0.75
$0	0.60
−$10,000	0.45
−$20,000	0

(e) A utility curve

Profit (in units of $1,000)

(f) Investment 1 utilities

Utility	Probability
1	0.7
0.75	0.1
0	0.2

Expected utility = 1(0.7) + 0.75(0.1) + 0(0.2) = 0.775

(g) Investment 2 utilities

Utility	Probability
0.95	0.6
0.90	0.2
0.45	0.2

Expected utility = 0.95(0.6) + 0.90(0.2) + 0.45(0.2) = 0.84

(h) No investment utility

Utility	Probability
0.60	1

Expected utility = 0.60(1) = 0.60

A risk averter's curve:

A risk seeker's curve:

A risk neutral's curve:

(2) playing a lottery (or game) in which the probability of getting the highest profit is u and the probability of getting the smallest profit is $1 - u$. Table 15.2(d) arranges the profits in Table 15.2(a), (b), and (c) in increasing order and gives a specific decision maker's utility for each profit. The utility of 0.95 for $40,000 means that the decision maker is indifferent between (1) getting $40,000 with certainty and (2) playing a lottery in which the probability of getting $50,000 is 0.95 and the probability of losing $20,000 is 0.05. The utilities for the other profits are interpreted similarly. Table 15.2(f), (g), and (h) shows the investments with profits replaced by utilities. Because Investment 2 has the highest expected utility, the decision maker should choose Investment 2.

Table 15.2(e) shows a plot of the specific decision maker's utilities versus the profits. The curve connecting the plot points is the **utility curve** for the decision maker. This curve is an example of a **risk averter's curve**. In general, a risk averter's curve portrays a rapid increase in utility for initial amounts of money followed by a gradual levelling off for larger amounts of money. This curve is appropriate for many individuals or businesses because the marginal value of each additional dollar is not as great once a large amount of money has been earned. A risk averter's curve is shown in the page margin, as are a **risk seeker's curve** and a **risk neutral's curve**. The risk seeker's curve represents an individual who is willing to take large risks to have the opportunity to make large profits. The risk neutral's curve represents an individual for whom each additional dollar has the same value. It can be shown that this individual should choose the investment with the highest expected profit.

To conclude this section, we would like to point out that when a decision maker is risk neutral, there is no difference between using expected monetary value and expected utility. This is not the case for risk seekers and risk averters.

Exercises for Section 15.3

CONCEPTS

15.31 What is a utility?

15.32 What is a risk averter? a risk seeker? a risk neutral?

METHODS AND APPLICATIONS

15.33 Suppose that a decision maker has the opportunity to invest in an oil-drilling operation that has a 0.3 chance of yielding a profit of $1,000,000, a 0.4 chance of yielding a profit of $400,000, and a 0.3 chance of yielding a profit of −$100,000. Also suppose that the decision maker's utilities for $400,000 and $0 are 0.9 and 0.7. Explain the meanings of these utilities.

15.34 Judy is wondering whether or not to purchase real estate. The value of the house she buys at the end of one year will depend on the state of the market. She

estimates that for each $200,000 she invests, the possible value of the real estate at year's end is as follows:

Value at Year's End	Capital Gain	Probability
$280,000	$80,000	0.30
$250,000	$50,000	0.40
$210,000	$10,000	0.10
$150,000	−$50,000	0.20

Her utility values for the above capital gains are 0.9, 0.7, 0.3, and 0, respectively. Calculate Judy's expected utility.

15.4 DECISION MAKING USING UTILITY THEORY

LO11

In the face of uncertainty, one should maximize one's **expected utility**, rather than money, in order to make decisions. In Section 15.3, we learned about the utility function. This is a function that describes a person's level of satisfaction or happiness. If we convert each dollar value or payoff into utility values, we can proceed as we did in Section 15.3 and choose the option that yields the highest expected utility. Making decisions based on a person's utility function takes into account that person's risk tolerance. In Section 15.3, we looked at three possible investments and their expected utilities. Consider another investment example.

Example 15.2 To Buy Stocks or Not To Buy Stocks? (Based on Expected Utility)

Ken is deciding whether to invest $10,000 in the stock market or lend the money privately at a rate of 12 percent per year. Assume that there is no chance of the borrower defaulting on the loan. Ken is knowledgeable when it comes to the stock market and has done some research. Based on market activity in the past 100 years, he estimates that there is a 60 percent chance that the market will be bullish next year and hence give him a return of 25 percent; a 20 percent chance that the market will be steady and offer a return of 5 percent; and a 20 percent chance that the market will be bearish, in which case he will lose 10 percent.

We will determine his best investment decision in two ways: first by maximizing expected monetary value and then by maximizing expected utility.

Here is the decision tree with monetary payoffs:

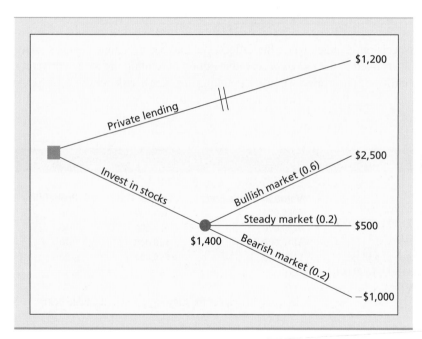

In order to make a decision based on expected utility, we need to convert the dollar values to utility values. This is somewhat arbitrary, and the numbers will vary from person to person, but here is one possibility for Ken:

LO11

	Payoff	Utility	Probability
Bullish Market	$2,500	1.00	0.6
Private Lending	$1,200	0.80	1.0
Steady Market	$500	0.60	0.2
Bearish Market	−$1,000	0	0.2

Remember that the best scenario is assigned a utility value of 1 and the worst scenario is assigned a value of 0. The other two options are assigned values based on personal feelings.

Here is the decision tree with the utility values in place:

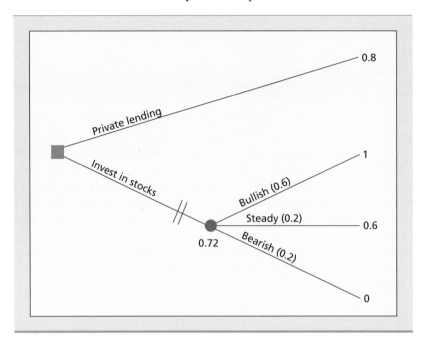

We see that our decision changes when the criteria for making decisions changes. Why is this? Our decision changed to the more conservative option of lending the money privately when maximizing utility because now we are accounting for Ken's risk tolerance. Money is not all that matters here. Peace of mind seems to be the deciding factor when using expected utility.

Exercises for Section 15.4

CONCEPTS

15.35 If a person is a risk averter, in which interval will the greatest change in utility lie: $0 to $500,000, $500,000 to $1,000,000, or $1,000,000 to $1,500,000?

15.36 If a person is a risk seeker, in which interval will the greatest change in utility lie: $0 to $500,000, $500,000 to $1,000,000, or $1,000,000 to $1,500,000?

METHODS AND APPLICATIONS

15.37 Consider Exercise 15.33 in Section 15.3. Find the expected utility of the oil-drilling operation. Find the expected utility of not investing. What should the decision maker do to maximize expected utility?

15.38 Judy is wondering whether or not to borrow $200,000 in order to invest in the real estate market. Assume that she has saved enough money to cover the closing costs of the sale. Once she sells her house, she must pay off the amount of the loan plus 12 percent interest. She can receive a tax credit for a portion of the interest paid. Specifically, she can write off $1 in taxes for every $2 in interest she pays, so that only half the interest is an expense to her. If the real estate rises in value, the increase in value will be a tax-free capital gain, but no profit is guaranteed due to the interest costs. She estimates that for each $200,000 she invests, the possible value of the real estate at year's end is as follows:

Value at Year's End	Capital Gain	Probability
$280,000	$80,000	0.30
$250,000	$50,000	0.40
$210,000	$10,000	0.10
$150,000	−$50,000	0.20

Selected utility values for Judy are given in the table below:

Net Gain (in $1,000s)	Utility[a]
$200	1.00
150	0.96
100	0.89
50	0.80
0	0.62
−50	0.37
−100	0

[a]If intermediate utility values are needed, use linear interpolation.

a. Is Judy a risk seeker, a risk averter, or a risk neutral? Graph her utility curve to answer that question.

b. Should Judy borrow $200,000 or not? Choose the option that maximizes her expected utility.

CHAPTER SUMMARY

We began this chapter with an introduction to decision theory. We saw that a decision problem involves **states of nature**, **alternatives**, **payoffs**, and **decision criteria**, and we considered three degrees of uncertainty—**certainty**, **uncertainty**, and **risk**. In the case of certainty, we know which state of nature will actually occur. Here we simply choose the alternative that gives the best payoff. In the case of uncertainty, we have no information about the likelihood of the different states of nature. Here we discussed two commonly used decision criteria—the **maxi-min criterion** and the **maxi-max criterion**. In the case of risk, we are able to estimate the probability of occurrence for each state of nature. In this case, we learned how to use the **expected monetary value criterion**. We also learned how to construct a **decision tree** in Section 15.1, and we saw how to use such a tree to analyze a decision problem. In Section 15.2, we learned how to make decisions by using posterior probabilities. We explained how to perform a **posterior analysis** to determine the best alternative for each of several sampling results. Then we showed how to carry out a **preposterior analysis**, which allows us to assess the worth of sample information. In particular, we saw how to obtain the **expected value of sample information**. This quantity is the expected gain from sampling, which tells us the maximum amount we should be willing to pay for sample information. In Section 15.3, we introduced **utility theory**, and in Section 15.4, we showed how utility theory can be used to help make decisions.

GLOSSARY OF TERMS

alternatives: Several different actions for a decision maker to choose from. (page 531)

certainty: When we know for sure which state of nature will actually occur. (page 531)

decision criterion: A rule used to make a decision. (page 531)

decision theory: An approach that helps decision makers make intelligent choices. (page 531)

decision tree: A diagram consisting of nodes and branches that depicts the information for a decision problem. (page 533)

expected monetary value criterion: A decision criterion in which one computes the expected monetary payoff for each alternative and then chooses the alternative yielding the largest expected payoff. (page 533)

expected net gain of sampling: The difference between the expected value of sample information and the cost of sampling. If this quantity is positive, it is worth it to perform sampling. (page 542)

expected value of perfect information: The difference between the expected payoff under certainty and the expected payoff under risk. (page 535)

expected value of sample information: The difference between the expected payoff of sampling and the expected payoff of no sampling. This measures the expected gain from sampling. (page 542)

maximax criterion: A decision criterion in which one finds the best possible payoff for each alternative and then chooses the alternative that yields the maximum best possible payoff. (page 532)

maximin criterion: A decision criterion in which one finds the worst possible payoff for each alternative and then chooses the alternative that yields the maximum worst possible payoff. (page 532)

payoff table: A tabular summary of the payoffs in a decision problem. (page 531)

perfect information: Information that tells us exactly which state of nature will occur. (page 535)

posterior decision analysis: Using a decision criterion based on posterior probabilities to choose the best alternative in a decision problem. (page 538)

preposterior analysis: When we assess the worth of sample information before performing a posterior decision analysis. (page 541)

prior decision analysis: Using a decision criterion based on prior probabilities to choose the best alternative in a decision problem. (page 537)

risk: When the likelihood (probability) of each state of nature can be estimated. (page 531)

states of nature: A set of potential future conditions that will affect the results of a decision. (page 531)

uncertainty: When we have no information about the likelihoods of the various states of nature. (page 531)

utility: A measure of monetary value based on an individual's attitude toward risk. (page 535)

IMPORTANT FORMULAS

Maximin criterion: page 532

Maximax criterion: page 532

Expected value of perfect information: page 535

Expected payoff of sampling: page 542

Expected value of sample information: page 542

Expected net gain of sampling: page 542

SUPPLEMENTARY EXERCISES

15.39 In the book *Making Hard Decisions: An Introduction to Decision Analysis*, Clemen presents a decision tree for a research and development decision (note that payoffs are given in millions of dollars, which is denoted by M). Based on this decision tree (shown in Figure 15.8), answer the following:

   a. Should development of the research project be continued or stopped? Justify your answer by using relevant calculations, and explain your reasoning.

   b. If development is continued and if a patent is awarded, should the new technology be licensed, or should the company develop production and marketing to sell the product directly? Justify your answer by using relevant calculations, and explain your reasoning.

15.40 On any given day, the probability that a river is polluted by a carbon tetrachloride spill is 0.10. Each day, a test is conducted to determine whether the river is polluted by carbon tetrachloride. This test has proven correct 80 percent of the time. Suppose that on a particular day the test indicates carbon tetrachloride pollution. What is the probability that such pollution actually exists?

15.41 In the book *Production/Operations Management*, Stevenson presents a decision tree concerning a firm's decision about the size of a production facility. This decision tree is given in Figure 15.9 (payoffs are given in millions of dollars). Use the decision tree to determine which alternative (build small or build large) should be chosen in order to maximize the expected monetary payoff. What is the expected monetary payoff associated with the best alternative?

15.42 Consider the decision tree in Figure 15.9 and the situation described in Exercise 15.41. Suppose that a marketing research study can be done to obtain more information about whether demand will be high or low. The marketing research study will result in one of two outcomes: favourable (indicating that demand will be high) or unfavourable (indicating that demand will be low). The accuracy of marketing research studies like the one to be carried out can be expressed by the conditional probabilities in the following table:

Study Outcome	True Demand	
	High	Low
Favourable	0.9	0.2
Unfavourable	0.1	0.8

For instance, $P(\text{favourable} \mid \text{high}) = 0.9$ and $P(\text{unfavourable} \mid \text{low}) = 0.8$. Given the prior probabilities and payoffs in Figure 15.9, do the following:

   a. Carry out a posterior analysis. Find the best alternative (build small or build large) for each possible study result (favourable or unfavourable), and find the associated expected payoffs.

   b. Carry out a preposterior analysis. Determine the maximum amount that should be paid for the marketing research study.

15.43 A marketing major will interview for an internship with a major consumer products manufacturer/distributor. Before the interview, the marketing major feels that the chances of being offered an internship are 40 percent. Suppose that of the students who have been offered internships with this company, 90 percent had good interviews, and that of the students who have not been offered internships, 50 percent had good interviews. If the marketing major has a good interview, what is the probability that they will be offered an internship?

FIGURE 15.8 A Decision Tree for a Research and Development Decision

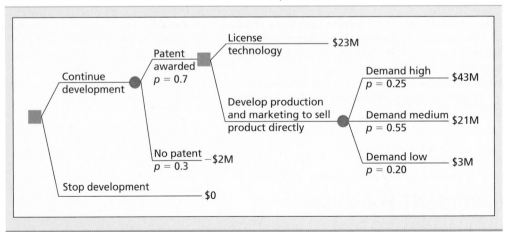

FIGURE **15.9** A Decision Tree for a Production Facility Decision

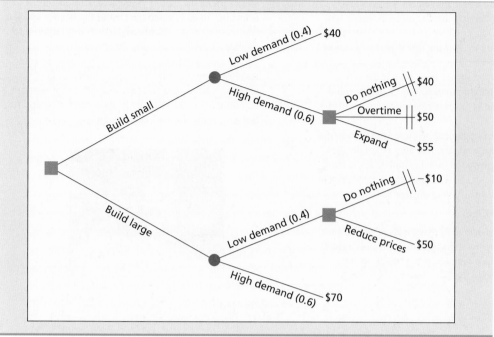

Source: Reprinted with permission from *Production/Operations Management*, 6th ed., by W. J. Stevenson, p. 70.
Copyright © 1999 by The McGraw-Hill Companies, Inc.

15.44 THE OIL-DRILLING CASE

Again consider the oil-drilling case that was described in Example 15.1 (pages 538–542). Recall that the oil company wishes to decide whether to drill and that the prior probabilities of no oil, some oil, and much oil are P(none) = 0.7, P(some) = 0.2, and P(much) = 0.1. Suppose that instead of performing the seismic survey to obtain more information about the site, the oil company can perform a cheaper magnetic experiment with two possible results: a high reading and a low reading. The past performance of the magnetic experiment can be summarized as follows:

Magnetic Experiment Result	State of Nature		
	None	Some	Much
Low Reading	0.8	0.4	0.1
High Reading	0.2	0.6	0.9

Here, for example, P(low | none) = 0.8 and P(high | some) = 0.6. Recalling that the payoffs associated with no oil, some oil, and much oil are −$700,000, $500,000, and $2,000,000, respectively, do the following:
a. Draw a decision tree for this decision problem.
b. Carry out a posterior analysis. Find the best alternative (drill or do not drill) for each possible result of the magnetic experiment (low or high), and find the associated expected payoffs.
c. Carry out a preposterior analysis. Determine the maximum amount that should be paid for the magnetic experiment.

15.45 Suppose that you are given the following two options:
(i) Toss a fair die once:
  • If you roll an even number, you get $1,500,000.
  • If you roll an odd number, you get $0.

(ii) Take $500,000 for certain.
a. Before you perform any calculations, make a choice. If you polled members of your class randomly, do you think that everyone would choose the same option? Why or why not?
b. Now determine the optimal decision using
  (1) Expected monetary value.
  (2) Expected utility.

Do your results in part b agree with any reasons you came up with in part a?

15.46 In an exercise in the book *Production/Operations Management*, Stevenson considers a theme park whose lease is about to expire. The theme park's management wishes to decide whether to renew its lease for another ten years or relocate near the site of a new motel complex. The town planning board is debating whether to approve the motel complex. A consultant estimates the payoffs of the theme park's alternatives under each state of nature, as shown in the following payoff table:

Theme Park Options	Motel Approved	Motel Rejected
Renew Lease	$500,000	$4,000,000
Relocate	$5,000,000	$100,000

a. What alternative should the theme park choose if it uses the maximax criterion? What is the resulting payoff of this choice?
b. What alternative should the theme park choose if it uses the maximin criterion? What is the resulting payoff of this choice?

15.47 Again consider the situation described in Exercise 15.46, and suppose that management believes that there is a 0.35 probability that the motel complex will be approved.

   a. Draw a decision tree for the theme park's decision problem.

   b. Which alternative should be chosen if the theme park uses the maximum expected monetary value criterion? What is the expected monetary payoff for this choice?

   c. Suppose that management is offered the option of a temporary lease while the planning board decides whether to approve the motel complex. If the lease costs $100,000, should the theme park's management sign the lease? Justify your answer.

15.48 INTERNET EXERCISE

Have you ever considered opening a franchise? Go to http://canada.franchiseopportunities.com/ and explore the possibilities. Deciding to open a franchise comes with some risk. Go to the Tim Hortons Web site (http://www.timhortons.com/en/join/franchise_ca.html) and examine the factors associated with opening a franchise. In addition to the cost of the licence and the franchise cost, the interested party is also required to finance a building (and possibly property as well). Create a decision tree to assess the possible payoffs and losses involved in opening a franchise. This exercise will require you to research sales projections and finance costs. Be realistic about your assumptions, but have some fun with this exercise.

CHAPTER 16
Time Series Forecasting

LEARNING OBJECTIVES

After reading this chapter, you should be able to

LO1 define when a time series represents a trend, a seasonal pattern, or a cyclical pattern, or is irregular

LO2 describe how you would use a time series regression model to assess if a trend is present in a data set

LO3 demonstrate when you would use multiplicative decomposition methods versus exponential smoothing

LO4 explain how forecast errors can be calculated

LO5 describe how the Canadian Consumer Price Index is computed and what information it provides

CHAPTER OUTLINE

16.1 Time Series Components and Models

16.2 Time Series Regression: Basic Models

16.3 Time Series Regression: More Advanced Models (Optional)

16.4 Multiplicative Decomposition

16.5 Exponential Smoothing

16.6 Forecast Error Comparisons

16.7 Index Numbers

Demand for some products changes over time. For example, Canadians tend to be in the market for lawn mowers more in the summer than in the winter, whereas the opposite pattern exists for snow blowers. How suppliers meet these changing demands is the focus of this chapter, which deals with **time series** analyses, or collecting observations on a variable of interest in **time order**. In this chapter, we discuss developing and using **univariate time series models**, which forecast future values of a time series *solely on the basis of past values of the time series*. Univariate time series models often forecast future time series values by extrapolating the **trend** and/or **seasonal patterns** exhibited by the past values of the time series. To illustrate these ideas, we consider several cases in this chapter, including the following:

The DVD Player Sales Case: By extrapolating an upward trend in past sales of the X-12 DVD player, Smith's Department Stores forecasts future sales of this product. The forecasts help the department store chain to better implement its inventory and financial policies.

The Traveller's Rest Case: By extrapolating an upward trend and the seasonal behaviour of its past hotel room occupancies, Traveller's Rest forecasts future hotel room occupancies. The forecasts help the hotel chain to more effectively hire help and acquire supplies.

LO1   **16.1** TIME SERIES COMPONENTS AND MODELS

In order to identify patterns in time series data, it is often convenient to think of such data as consisting of several components: **trend**, **cycle**, **seasonal variations**, and **irregular fluctuations**. **Trend** refers to the upward or downward movement that characterizes a time series over time. Thus, trend reflects the long-run growth or decline in the time series. Trend movements can represent a variety of factors. For example, long-run movements in the sales of a particular industry might be determined by changes in consumer tastes, increases in total population, and increases in per capita income. **Cycle** refers to recurring up-and-down movements around trend levels. These fluctuations can last from two to ten years, or even longer, measured from peak to peak or trough to trough. One of the common cyclical fluctuations found in time series data is the **business cycle**, which is represented by fluctuations in the time series caused by recurrent periods of prosperity and recession. **Seasonal variations** are periodic patterns in a time series that complete themselves within a calendar year or less and then are repeated on a regular basis. Seasonal variations often occur yearly. For example, soft drink sales and hotel room occupancies are annually higher in the summer months, while department store sales are annually higher during the winter holiday season. Seasonal variations can also last less than one year. For example, daily restaurant patronage might exhibit within-week seasonal variation, with daily patronage higher on Fridays and Saturdays. **Irregular fluctuations** are erratic time series movements that follow no recognizable or regular pattern. Such movements represent what is left over in a time series after trend, cycle, and seasonal variations have been accounted for.

Time series that exhibit trend, seasonal, and cyclical components are illustrated in Figure 16.1. In Figure 16.1(a), a time series of sales observations that has an essentially straight-line or linear trend is plotted. Figure 16.1(b) portrays a time series of sales observations that contains a seasonal pattern that repeats annually, with higher sales in the winter months. Figure 16.1(c) exhibits a time series of agricultural yields that is cyclical, repeating a cycle about once every ten years.

Time series models attempt to identify significant patterns in the components of a time series. Then, assuming that these patterns will continue into the future, time series models extrapolate these patterns to forecast future time series values. In Section 16.2 and optional Section 16.3, we discuss forecasting by **time series regression models**, which assume that the time series components remain essentially constant over time. If a time series exhibits increasing (or decreasing) seasonal variation, then we use the **multiplicative decomposition** model discussed in Section 16.4. If the time series components are changing slowly over time, then it is appropriate to forecast using **exponential smoothing**. This approach is discussed in Section 16.5. If the time series components might be changing fairly quickly over time, it is appropriate to forecast by using the **Box–Jenkins methodology**. This advanced approach is discussed in Appendix I (on *Connect*).

FIGURE **16.1**   Time Series Exhibiting Trend, Seasonal, and Cyclical Components

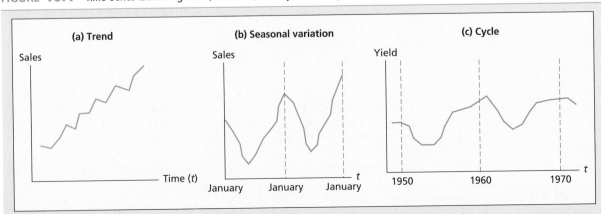

16.2 TIME SERIES REGRESSION: BASIC MODELS

Modelling trend components We begin this section with two examples.

Example 16.1 The Cod Catch Case

The Coast City Seafood Company owns a fleet of fishing trawlers and operates a fish-processing plant. In order to forecast its minimum and maximum possible revenues from cod sales and plan the operations of its fish-processing plant, the company wants to make both point forecasts and prediction interval forecasts of its monthly cod catch (measured in tonnes). The company has recorded monthly cod catch for the previous two years (years 1 and 2). The cod history is given in Table 16.1. A runs plot (or time series plot) shows that the cod catches appear to randomly fluctuate around a constant average level (see the plot in Figure 16.2). Because the company subjectively believes that this data pattern will continue in the future, it seems reasonable to use the **no-trend** regression model

$$y_t = \beta_0 + \varepsilon_t$$

LO2

to forecast cod catch in future months. It can be shown that for the no-trend regression model the least squares point estimate b_0 of β_0 is $\bar{y}$, the average of the n observed time series values. Because the average $\bar{y}$ of the $n = 24$ observed cod catches is 351.29, it follows that $\hat{y}_t = b_0 = 351.29$ is the point prediction of the cod catch (y_t) in any future month. Furthermore, it can be shown that a $100(1 - \alpha)$ percent prediction interval for any future y_t value described by the no trend model is $[\hat{y}_t \pm t_{\alpha/2}s\sqrt{1 + (1/n)}]$. Here s is the sample standard deviation of the n observed time series values, and $t_{\alpha/2}$ is based on $n - 1$ degrees of freedom. For example, because s can be calculated to be 33.82 for the $n = 24$ cod catches, and because $t_{0.025}$ based on $n - 1 = 23$ degrees of freedom is 2.069, it follows that a 95 percent prediction interval for the cod catch in any future month is $[351.29 \pm 2.069(33.82)\sqrt{1 + (1/24)}]$, or [279.92, 422.66].

TABLE **16.1** Cod Catch (in Tonnes)

Month	Year 1	Year 2
Jan.	362	276
Feb.	381	334
Mar.	317	394
Apr.	297	334
May	399	384
Jun.	402	314
Jul.	375	344
Aug.	349	337
Sep.	386	345
Oct.	328	362
Nov.	389	314
Dec.	343	365

FIGURE **16.2** Plot of Cod Catch versus Time

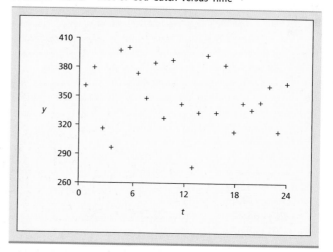

Example 16.2 The DVD Player Sales Case

For the last two years, Smith's Department Stores has carried a new type of DVD player called the X-12. Sales of this product have generally increased over these two years. Smith's inventory policy attempts to ensure that stores will have enough DVD players to meet practically all demand for the product, while at the same time ensuring that Smith's does not needlessly tie up its money by ordering more DVD players than can be sold. In order to implement this inventory policy in future months, Smith's requires both point predictions and prediction intervals for total monthly demand.

The monthly demand data for the last two years are given in Table 16.2. A runs plot of the demand data is shown in Figure 16.3. The demands appear to randomly fluctuate around an average level that increases over time in a linear fashion. Furthermore, Smith's believes that this trend will continue for at least the next year. Thus, it is reasonable to use the **linear trend** regression model

$$y_t = \beta_0 + \beta_1 t + \varepsilon_t$$

to forecast sales in future months. Notice that this model is just a simple linear regression model in which the time period, t, plays the role of the independent variable. The least squares point estimates of β_0 and β_1 can be calculated to be $b_0 = 198.028986$ and $b_1 = 8.074348$. Therefore, for example, point forecasts of product demand in January and February of year 3 (time periods 25 and 26) are, respectively,

$$\hat{y}_{25} = 198.028986 + 8.074348(25) = 399.9 \quad \text{and}$$
$$\hat{y}_{26} = 198.028986 + 8.074348(26) = 408.0.$$

Note that the Excel output under Table 16.2 gives these point forecasts. In addition, it can be shown using either the formulas for simple linear regression or a computer software package that a 95 percent prediction interval for demand is [328.6, 471.2] in time period 25 and [336.0, 479.9] in time period 26. These prediction intervals can help Smith's implement its inventory policy. For instance, if Smith's stocks 471 DVD players in January of year 3, we can be reasonably sure that monthly demand will be met.

TABLE 16.2 DVD Player Sales Data

Month	Year 1	Year 2
Jan.	197	296
Feb.	211	276
Mar.	203	305
Apr.	247	308
May	239	356
Jun.	269	393
Jul.	308	363
Aug.	262	386
Sep.	258	443
Oct.	256	308
Nov.	261	358
Dec.	288	384

A	B	C	D
358	23		
384	24		
399.8877	25	USING TREND	
407.962	26		

FIGURE 16.3 Plot of DVD Player Sales versus Time

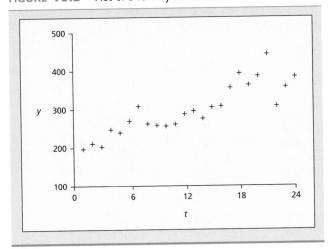

Example 16.1 illustrates that the intercept β_0 can be used to model a lack of trend over time, and Example 16.2 illustrates that the expression $\beta_0 + \beta_1 t$ can model a linear trend over time. In addition, as will be illustrated in the exercises, the expression $\beta_0 + \beta_1 t + \beta_2 t^2$ can model a quadratic trend over time.

Modelling seasonal components We next consider how to forecast time series described by trend and seasonal components.

Example 16.3 The Bike Sales Case

Table 16.3 presents quarterly sales of the TRK-50 mountain bike for the previous four years at a bicycle shop in Switzerland. Figure 16.4 shows that the bike sales exhibit a linear trend and a strong seasonal pattern, with bike sales being higher in the spring and summer quarters than in the winter and fall quarters. If we let y_t denote the number of TRK-50 mountain bikes sold in time period t at the Swiss bike shop, then a regression model describing y_t is

$$y_t = \beta_0 + \beta_1 t + \beta_{Q2}Q_2 + \beta_{Q3}Q_3 + \beta_{Q4}Q_4 + \varepsilon_t.$$

Here the expression $\beta_0 + \beta_1 t$ models the linear trend evident in Figure 16.4. Q_2, Q_3, and Q_4 are dummy variables defined for quarters 2, 3, and 4. Specifically, Q_2 equals 1 if quarterly bike sales were observed in quarter 2 (spring) and 0 otherwise, Q_3 equals 1 if quarterly bike sales were observed in quarter 3 (summer) and 0 otherwise, and Q_4 equals 1 if quarterly bike sales were observed in quarter 4 (fall) and 0 otherwise. Note that we have not defined a dummy variable for quarter 1 (winter). It follows that the regression parameters β_{Q2}, β_{Q3}, and β_{Q4} compare quarters 2, 3, and 4 with quarter 1. Intuitively, for example, β_{Q4} is the difference, excluding trend, between the level of the time series (y_t) in quarter 4 (fall) and the level of the time series in quarter 1 (winter). A positive β_{Q4} implies that, excluding trend, bike sales in the fall can be expected to be higher than bike sales in the winter. A negative β_{Q4} implies that, excluding trend, bike sales in the fall can be expected to be lower than bike sales in the winter.

Figure 16.5 on the next page gives the Excel output of a regression analysis of the quarterly bike sales by using the dummy variable model. An example of the Excel input columns using dummy coding is provided in the margin. The output tells us that the linear trend and the seasonal dummy variables are significant (every t statistic has a related p value less than 0.01). Also notice that the least squares point estimates of β_{Q2}, β_{Q3}, and β_{Q4} are, respectively, $b_{Q2} = 21$, $b_{Q3} = 33.5$, and $b_{Q4} = 4.5$. It follows that, excluding trend, expected bike sales in quarter 2 (spring), quarter 3 (summer), and quarter 4 (fall) are estimated to be, respectively, 21, 33.5, and 4.5 bikes greater than expected bike sales in quarter 1 (winter). Furthermore, using all of the least squares point estimates in Figure 16.5, we can compute point forecasts of bike sales in quarters 1 through 4 of next year (periods 17 through 20) as follows:

$$\hat{y}_{17} = b_0 + b_1(17) + b_{Q2}(0) + b_{Q3}(0) + b_{Q4}(0) = 8.75 + 0.5(17) = 17.250,$$
$$\hat{y}_{18} = b_0 + b_1(18) + b_{Q2}(1) + b_{Q3}(0) + b_{Q4}(0) = 8.75 + 0.5(18) + 21 = 38.750,$$
$$\hat{y}_{19} = b_0 + b_1(19) + b_{Q2}(0) + b_{Q3}(1) + b_{Q4}(0) = 8.75 + 0.5(19) + 33.5 = 51.750,$$
$$\hat{y}_{20} = b_0 + b_1(20) + b_{Q2}(0) + b_{Q3}(0) + b_{Q4}(1) = 8.75 + 0.5(20) + 4.5 = 23.250.$$

Quarter	Time	Q2	Q3	Q4	BikeSales
1	1	0	0	0	10
2	2	1	0	0	31
3	3	0	1	0	43
4	4	0	0	1	16
1	5	0	0	0	11
2	6	1	0	0	33
3	7	0	1	0	45
4	8	0	0	1	17
1	9	0	0	0	13
2	10	1	0	0	34
3	11	0	1	0	48
4	12	0	0	1	19
1	13	0	0	0	13
2	14	1	0	0	37
3	15	0	1	0	51
4	16	0	0	1	21

TABLE **16.3** Quarterly Sales of the TRK-50 Mountain Bike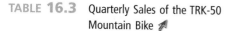

Year	Quarter	t	Sales, y_t
1	1 (winter)	1	10
	2 (spring)	2	31
	3 (summer)	3	43
	4 (fall)	4	16
2	1	5	11
	2	6	33
	3	7	45
	4	8	17
3	1	9	13
	2	10	34
	3	11	48
	4	12	19
4	1	13	15
	2	14	37
	3	15	51
	4	16	21

FIGURE **16.4** Plot of TRK-50 Bike Sales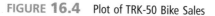

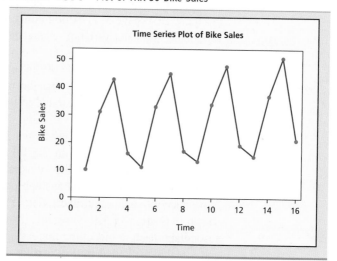

FIGURE 16.5   Excel Output of an Analysis of the Quarterly Bike Sales by Using Dummy Variable Regression

SUMMARY OUTPUT

Regression Statistics

Multiple R	0.999164927
R Square	0.998330551
Adjusted R Square	0.997723479
Standard Error	0.674199862
Observations	16

ANOVA

	df	SS	MS	F	Significance F
Regression	4	2990	747.5	1644.5	3.43916E-15
Residual	11	5	0.454545		
Total	15	2995			

	Coefficients	Standard Error	t Stat	P-value	Lower 95%	Upper 95%	Lower 95.0%	Upper 95.0%
Intercept	8.75	0.428063823	20.44088	4.23E-10	7.807837402	9.6921626	7.807837402	9.692162598
Time	0.5	0.037688918	13.2665	4.12E-08	0.417047209	0.58295279	0.417047209	0.582952791
Q2	21	0.478218759	43.91296	1.04E-13	19.94744708	22.0525529	19.94744708	22.05255292
Q3	33.5	0.48265365	69.40795	6.89E-16	32.43768594	34.5623141	32.43768594	34.56231406
Q4	4.5	0.489955935	9.184499	1.72E-06	3.421613713	5.57838629	3.421613713	5.578386287

We next consider Table 16.4, which presents a time series of hotel room occupancies observed by Traveller's Rest, a corporation that operates four hotels. The analysts in the operating division of the corporation were asked to develop a model that could be used to obtain short-term forecasts (up to one year) of the number of occupied rooms in the hotels. These forecasts were needed by various personnel to assist in hiring additional help during the summer months, ordering materials that have long delivery lead times, budgeting of local advertising expenditures, and so on. The available historical data consisted of the number of occupied rooms during each day for the previous 14 years. Because it was desired to obtain monthly forecasts, these data were reduced to monthly averages by dividing each monthly total by the number of days in the month. The monthly room averages for the previous 14 years are the time series values given in Table 16.4. A runs plot of these values in Figure 16.6 shows that the monthly room averages follow a strong trend and have a seasonal pattern with one major and several minor peaks during the year. Note that the major peak each year occurs during the high summer travel months of June, July, and August.

Although the quarterly bike sales and monthly hotel room averages both exhibit seasonal variation, they exhibit different kinds of seasonal variation. The quarterly bike sales plotted in Figure 16.4 (page 557) exhibit **constant seasonal variation**. In general, constant seasonal variation is seasonal variation where the magnitude of the seasonal swing does not depend on the level of the time series. On the other hand, **increasing seasonal variation** is seasonal variation where the magnitude of the seasonal swing increases as the level of the time series increases. Figure 16.6 shows that the monthly hotel room averages exhibit increasing seasonal variation. We have illustrated in the bike sales case that we can use **dummy variables** to model constant seasonal variation. The number of dummy variables that we use is, in general, the number of seasons minus 1. For example, if we model quarterly data, we use three dummy variables (as in the bike sales case). If we model monthly data, we use 11 dummy variables (this will be illustrated in optional Section 16.3). If a time series exhibits increasing seasonal variation, one approach is to first use a **fractional power transformation** to produce a transformed time series exhibiting constant seasonal variation. Then, as will be shown in Section 16.3, we use dummy variables to model the constant seasonal variation. A second approach to modelling increasing seasonal variation is to use a **multiplicative model** and a technique called **multiplicative decomposition**. This approach, which is intuitive, is discussed in Section 16.4.

TABLE **16.4** Monthly Hotel Room Averages

t	y_t	t	y_t	t	y_t	t	y_t	t	y_t	t	y_t	t	y_t	t	y_t
1	501	22	587	43	785	64	657	85	645	106	759	127	1,067	148	827
2	488	23	497	44	830	65	680	86	602	107	643	128	1,038	149	788
3	504	24	558	45	645	66	759	87	601	108	728	129	812	150	937
4	578	25	555	46	643	67	878	88	709	109	691	130	790	151	1,076
5	545	26	523	47	551	68	881	89	706	110	649	131	692	152	1,125
6	632	27	532	48	606	69	705	90	817	111	656	132	782	153	840
7	728	28	623	49	585	70	684	91	930	112	735	133	758	154	864
8	725	29	598	50	553	71	577	92	983	113	748	134	709	155	717
9	585	30	683	51	576	72	656	93	745	114	837	135	715	156	813
10	542	31	774	52	665	73	645	94	735	115	995	136	788	157	811
11	480	32	780	53	656	74	593	95	620	116	1,040	137	794	158	732
12	530	33	609	54	720	75	617	96	698	117	809	138	893	159	745
13	518	34	604	55	826	76	686	97	665	118	793	139	1,046	160	844
14	489	35	531	56	838	77	679	98	626	119	692	140	1,075	161	833
15	528	36	592	57	652	78	773	99	649	120	763	141	812	162	935
16	599	37	578	58	661	79	906	100	740	121	723	142	822	163	1,110
17	572	38	543	59	584	80	934	101	729	122	655	143	714	164	1,124
18	659	39	565	60	644	81	713	102	824	123	658	144	802	165	868
19	739	40	648	61	623	82	710	103	937	124	761	145	748	166	860
20	758	41	615	62	553	83	600	104	994	125	768	146	731	167	762
21	602	42	697	63	599	84	676	105	781	126	885	147	748	168	877

FIGURE **16.6** Plot of the Monthly Hotel Room Averages versus Time

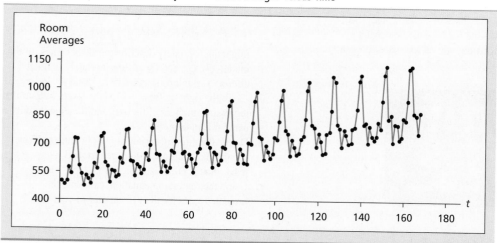

Exercises for Section 16.2

CONCEPTS

16.1 Discuss how to model no trend and a linear trend.

16.2 Discuss the difference between constant seasonal variation and increasing seasonal variation.

16.3 Discuss how to use dummy variables to model constant seasonal variation.

METHODS AND APPLICATIONS

16.4 CANADIAN TIRE SALES

Table 16.5 on the next page provides the consolidated quarterly results from Canadian Tire's *2010 Second Quarter Report to Shareholders.*

In this report, Canadian Tire states that "the second and fourth quarters of each year are typically when we experience stronger revenues and earnings in our retail businesses because of the seasonal nature" of their merchandise.

a. Plot the values and determine if you agree with their statement from the data provided.

b. Demonstrate that a linear regression model would not be the best fit to the data.

16.5 THE WATCH SALES CASE

The past 20 monthly sales figures for a new type of watch sold at Lambert's Discount Stores are given in Table 16.6 on the next page.

TABLE 16.5 Net Earnings (in $ millions) for Canadian Tire

Year	Quarter	Time	Net Earnings
2008	3	1	109.1
2008	4	2	101.5
2009	1	3	49.7
2009	2	4	103.7
2009	3	5	85.4
2009	4	6	96.2
2010	1	7	49.4
2010	2	8	119.9

Source: http://corp.canadiantire.a/EN/Investors/FinancialReports/
Quarterly Reports Library/CTC_2010–Q2.pdf.

TABLE 16.6 Watch Sales Values

Month	Sales	Month	Sales
1	298	11	356
2	302	12	371
3	301	13	399
4	351	14	392
5	336	15	425
6	361	16	411
7	407	17	455
8	351	18	457
9	357	19	465
10	346	20	481

A	B	C	D
465	19		
481	20		
472.1105	21	USING	TREND

a. Plot the watch sales values versus time and discuss why the plot indicates that the model

$$y_t = \beta_0 + \beta_1 t + \varepsilon_t$$

might appropriately describe these values.

b. The least squares point estimates of β_0 and β_1 can be calculated to be $b_0 = 290.089474$ and $b_1 = 8.667669$. Use b_0 and b_1 to show that a point forecast of watch sales in period 21 is $\hat{y}_{21} = 472.1$ (see the Excel output in Table 16.6). Use the formulas of simple linear regression analysis or a computer software package to show that a 95 percent prediction interval for watch sales in period 21 is [421.5, 522.7].

16.6 THE AIR CONDITIONER SALES CASE

Quarterly sales of the Bargain 8000-BTU Air Conditioner at the Bargain Department Stores chain over the past three years are given in Table 16.7.

a. Plot sales versus time and discuss why the plot indicates that the model

$$y_t = \beta_0 + \beta_1 t + \beta_{Q2}Q_2 + \beta_{Q3}Q_3 + \beta_{Q4}Q_4 + \varepsilon_t$$

might appropriately describe the sales values. In this model, Q_2, Q_3, and Q_4 are appropriately defined dummy variables for quarters 2, 3, and 4.

To the right of Table 16.7 is the Excel output of a regression analysis of the air conditioner sales data using this model.

b. Define the dummy variables Q_2, Q_3, and Q_4. Then use the Excel output to find, report, and interpret the least squares point estimates of β_{Q2}, β_{Q3}, and β_{Q4}.

c. Using the regression equation, calculate the projected sales for the first quarter of year 4.

TABLE 16.7 Air Conditioner Sales

Year	Quarter	Sales
1	1	2,915
	2	8,032
	3	10,411
	4	2,427
2	1	4,381
	2	9,138
	3	11,386
	4	3,382
3	1	5,105
	2	9,894
	3	12,300
	4	4,013

SUMMARY OUTPUT

Regression Statistics

Multiple R	0.999224341
R Square	0.998449283
Adjusted R Square	0.997563159
Standard Error	177.9879109
Observations	12

ANOVA

	df	SS	MS	F	Significance F
Regression	4	142781674.8	35695419	1126.76	6.60013E-10
Residual	7	221757.875	31679.7		
Total	11	143003432.7			

	Coefficients	Standard Error	t Stat	P-value	Lower 95%	Upper 95%	Lower 95.0%	Upper 95.0%
Intercept	2957.572917	129.4115123	22.85402	7.78E-08	2651.563535	3263.582	2651.563535	3263.582298
Q2	4652.447917	146.1755631	31.82781	7.81E-09	4306.797882	4998.098	4306.797882	4998.097951
Q3	6761.5625	148.6936049	45.47312	6.5E-10	6409.958247	7113.167	6409.958247	7113.166753
Q4	-1565.3229217	152.7981553	-10.244438	1.82E-05	-1926.632882	-1204.013	-1926.632882	-1204.012951
Time	235.21875	15.73205735	14.95156	1.44E-06	198.0183723	272.4191	198.0183723	272.4191277

16.7 In Table 16.8 are the data for the production of eggs in Canada for the years 2004 to 2008 from Statistics Canada. Enter the data into Excel, and then use a linear trend regression model in MegaStat to estimate the production of eggs for Canada for 2009 and 2010.

TABLE **16.8** Egg Production for Canada

Year	Quantity (Thousands of Dozens)
2004	546,820
2005	577,217
2006	580,258
2007	577,415
2008	579,882

16.3 TIME SERIES REGRESSION: MORE ADVANCED MODELS (OPTIONAL)

Example 16.4 The Traveller's Rest Case

Consider taking the square roots, quartic roots, and natural logarithms of the monthly hotel room averages in Table 16.4 (page 559). If we do this and plot the resulting three sets of transformed values versus time, we find that the quartic root transformation best equalizes the seasonal variation. Figure 16.7 presents a plot of the quartic roots of the monthly hotel room averages versus time. Letting y_t denote the hotel room average observed in time period t, it follows that a regression model describing the quartic root of y_t is

$$y_t^{0.25} = \beta_0 + \beta_1 t + \beta_{M1} M_1 + \beta_{M2} M_2 + \cdots + \beta_{M11} M_{11} + \varepsilon_t.$$

LO3

The expression $\beta_0 + \beta_1 t$ models the linear trend evident in Figure 16.7. Furthermore, M_1, M_2, ..., M_{11} are dummy variables defined for January (month 1) through November (month 11). For example, M_1 equals 1 if a monthly room average was observed in January, and 0 otherwise; M_2 equals 1 if a monthly room average was observed in February, and 0 otherwise. Note that we have not defined a dummy variable for December (month 12). It follows that the regression parameters $\beta_{M1}, \beta_{M2}, \ldots, \beta_{M11}$ compare January through November with December. Intuitively, for example, β_{M1} is the difference, excluding trend, between the level of the time series ($y_t^{0.25}$) in January and the level of the time series in December. A positive β_{M1} implies that, excluding trend, the value of the time series in January can be expected to be greater than the value in December. A negative β_{M1} implies that, excluding trend, the value of the time series in January can be expected to be smaller than the value in December.

Figure 16.8 on the next page gives relevant portions of the MegaStat output of a regression analysis of the hotel room data using the quartic root dummy variable model. The MegaStat output tells us that the linear trend and the seasonal dummy variables are significant (every

FIGURE **16.7** Plot of the Quartic Roots of the Monthly Hotel Room Averages versus Time

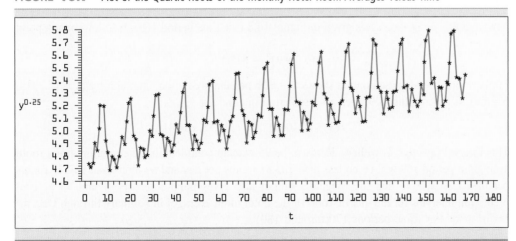

FIGURE **16.8** MegaStat Output of an Analysis of the Quartic Roots of the Room
Averages Using Dummy Variable Regression (TFY2 $= y_t^{0.25}$)

Regression output variables	coefficients	std. error	t (df = 155)	p-value	confidence interval 95% lower	95% upper
Intercept	4.807318	0.00846255	568.070	4.06E-259	4.7906	4.8240
t	0.003515	0.00004449	79.009	3.95E-127	0.0034	0.0036
M1	−0.052467	0.01055475	−4.971	1.75E-06	−0.0733	−0.0316
M2	−0.140790	0.01055278	−13.342	1.59E-27	−0.1616	−0.1199
M3	−0.107103	0.01055100	−10.151	7.02E-19	−0.1279	−0.0863
M4	0.049882	0.01054940	4.728	5.05E-06	0.0290	0.0707
M5	0.025417	0.01054800	2.410	0.0171	0.0046	0.0463
M6	0.190170	0.01054678	18.031	6.85E-40	0.1693	0.2110
M7	0.382455	0.01054575	36.266	1.28E-77	0.3616	0.4033
M8	0.413370	0.01054490	39.201	2.41E-82	0.3925	0.4342
M9	0.071417	0.01054424	6.773	2.47E-10	0.0506	0.0922
M10	0.050641	0.01054377	4.803	3.66E-06	0.0298	0.0715
M11	−0.141943	0.01054349	−13.463	7.47E-28	−0.1628	−0.1211

Durbin-Watson = 1.26

Predicted values for: TFY2

t	Predicted	95% Confidence Intervals lower	upper	95% Prediction Intervals lower	upper	Leverage
169	5.3489	5.3322	5.3656	5.2913	5.4065	0.092
170	5.2641	5.2474	5.2808	5.2065	5.3217	0.092
171	5.3013	5.2846	5.3180	5.2437	5.3589	0.092
172	5.4618	5.4451	5.4785	5.4042	5.5194	0.092
173	5.4409	5.4241	5.4576	5.3833	5.4984	0.092
174	5.6091	5.5924	5.6258	5.5515	5.6667	0.092
175	5.8049	5.7882	5.8216	5.7473	5.8625	0.092
176	5.8394	5.8226	5.8561	5.7818	5.8969	0.092
177	5.5009	5.4842	5.5176	5.4433	5.5585	0.092
178	5.4837	5.4669	5.5004	5.4261	5.5412	0.092
179	5.2946	5.2779	5.3113	5.2370	5.3522	0.092
180	5.4400	5.4233	5.4568	5.3825	5.4976	0.092

t statistic has a related p value less than 0.05). In addition, although not shown on the output, $R^2 = 0.988$. Now consider time period 169, which is January of next year and which therefore implies that $M_1 = 1$ and that all the other dummy variables equal 0. Using the least squares point estimates in Figure 16.8, we compute a point forecast of $y_{169}^{0.25}$ to be

$$b_0 + b_1(169) + b_{M1}(1) = 4.807318 + 0.003515(169) + (-0.052467)(1)$$
$$= 5.3489.$$

Note that this point forecast is given in Figure 16.8 (see time period 169). It follows that a point forecast of y_{169} is

$$(5.3489)^4 = 818.57.$$

Furthermore, the MegaStat output shows that a 95 percent prediction interval for $y_{169}^{0.25}$ is [5.2913, 5.4065]. It follows that a 95 percent prediction interval for y_{169} is

$$[(5.2913)^4, (5.4065)^4] = [783.88, 854.41].$$

This interval says that Traveller's Rest can be 95 percent confident that the monthly hotel room average in period 169 will be no less than 783.88 rooms per day and no more than 854.41 rooms per day. Lastly, note that the MegaStat output also gives point forecasts of and 95 percent prediction intervals for the quartic roots of the hotel room averages in February through December of next year (time periods 170 through 180).

The validity of the regression methods just illustrated requires that the independence assumption be satisfied. However, when time series data are analyzed, this assumption is often violated. It is quite common for the time-ordered error terms to exhibit **positive** or **negative autocorrelation**. We can use residual plots to check for these kinds of autocorrelation.

One type of positive or negative autocorrelation is called **first-order autocorrelation**. It says that ε_t, the error term in time period t, is related to ε_{t-1}, the error term in time period $t - 1$, by the equation

$$\varepsilon_t = \phi\varepsilon_{t-1} + a_t.$$

Here we assume that ϕ (phi) is the correlation coefficient that measures the relationship between error terms separated by one time period, and a_t is an error term (often called a **random shock**) that satisfies the usual regression assumptions. To check for positive or negative first-order autocorrelation, we can use the **Durbin–Watson statistic, d**, which was discussed in Section 11.10. For example, it can be verified that this statistic shows no evidence of positive or negative first-order autocorrelation in the error terms of the DVD player sales model or in the error terms of the bike sales model. However, note from the MegaStat output in Figure 16.8 that the Durbin–Watson statistic for the dummy variable regression model describing the quartic roots of the hotel room averages is $d = 1.26$. Because the dummy variable regression model uses $k = 12$ independent variables, and because most statistical tables do not give the **Durbin–Watson critical points** corresponding to $k = 12$, we cannot test for autocorrelation using these tables. However, it can be shown that $d = 1.26$ is quite small and indicates **positive autocorrelation** in the error terms. One approach to dealing with first-order autocorrelation in the error terms is to predict future values of the error terms by using the model $\varepsilon_t = \phi\varepsilon_{t-1} + a_t$. Of course the error term ε_t could be related to more than just the previous error term ε_{t-1}. It could be related to any number of previous error terms. The **autoregressive error term model of order q**,

$$\varepsilon_t = \phi_1\varepsilon_{t-1} + \phi_2\varepsilon_{t-2} + \cdots + \phi_q\varepsilon_{t-q} + a_t,$$

relates ε_t, the error term in time period t, to the previous error terms, $\varepsilon_{t-1}, \varepsilon_{t-2}, \ldots, \varepsilon_{t-q}$. Here ϕ_1, $\phi_2, \ldots, \phi_q$ are unknown parameters, and a_t is an error term (random shock) with mean 0 that satisfies the regression assumptions. The **Box–Jenkins methodology** can be used to systematically identify an autoregressive error term model that relates ε_t to an appropriate number of past error terms. More generally, the Box–Jenkins methodology can be employed to predict future time series values (y_t) by using a procedure that combines the autoregressive error term model of order q with the model

$$y_t = \beta_0 + \beta_1 y_{t-1} + \beta_2 y_{t-2} + \cdots + \beta_p y_{t-p} + \varepsilon_t.$$

This latter model, which is called the **autoregressive observation model of order p**, expresses the observation y_t in terms of the previous observations, $y_{t-1}, y_{t-2}, \ldots, y_{t-p}$, and an error term ε_t. The Box–Jenkins methodology, which is discussed in Appendix I on *Connect*, identifies which previous observations and which previous error terms describe y_t.

Although sophisticated techniques such as the Box–Jenkins methodology can be quite useful, studies show that the regression techniques discussed in Section 16.2 and in this section often provide accurate forecasts, even if we ignore the autocorrelation in the error terms. In fact, whenever we observe time series data, we should determine whether trend and/or seasonal effects exist. For example, the Fresh demand data in Table 16.9 on the next page are time series data observed over 30 consecutive four-week sales periods. Although we can predict demand for Fresh detergent on the basis of price difference and advertising expenditure, this demand could also be affected by a linear or quadratic trend over time and/or by seasonal effects (for example, more laundry detergent might be sold in summer sales periods when children are home from school; see Figure 16.9(a) and (b) on the next page). If we try using trend equations and dummy variables to search for trend and seasonal effects, we find that these effects do not exist in the Fresh demand data. However, in the supplementary exercises (see Exercise 16.38), we present a situation where we use trend equations and seasonal dummy variables, as well as **causal variables** such as price difference and advertising expenditure, to predict demand for a fishing lure.

TABLE **16.9** Historical Data, Including Price Differences, Concerning Demand for Fresh Detergent

Sales Period	Price for Fresh, x_1 (Dollars)	Average Industry Price, x_2 (Dollars)	Price Difference, $x_4 = x_2 - x_1$ (Dollars)	Advertising Expenditure for Fresh, x_3 (Hundreds of Thousands of Dollars)	Demand for Fresh, y (Hundreds of Thousands of Bottles)
1	3.85	3.80	−0.05	5.50	7.38
2	3.75	4.00	0.25	6.75	8.51
3	3.70	4.30	0.60	7.25	9.52
4	3.70	3.70	0	5.50	7.50
5	3.60	3.85	0.25	7.00	9.33
6	3.60	3.80	0.20	6.50	8.28
7	3.60	3.75	0.15	6.75	8.75
8	3.80	3.85	0.05	5.25	7.87
9	3.80	3.65	−0.15	5.25	7.10
10	3.85	4.00	0.15	6.00	8.00
11	3.90	4.10	0.20	6.50	7.89
12	3.90	4.00	0.10	6.25	8.15
13	3.70	4.10	0.40	7.00	9.10
14	3.75	4.20	0.45	6.90	8.86
15	3.75	4.10	0.35	6.80	8.90
16	3.80	4.10	0.30	6.80	8.87
17	3.70	4.20	0.50	7.10	9.26
18	3.80	4.30	0.50	7.00	9.00
19	3.70	4.10	0.40	6.80	8.75
20	3.80	3.75	−0.05	6.50	7.95
21	3.80	3.75	−0.05	6.25	7.65
22	3.75	3.65	−0.10	6.00	7.27
23	3.70	3.90	0.20	6.50	8.00
24	3.55	3.65	0.10	7.00	8.50
25	3.60	4.10	0.50	6.80	8.75
26	3.65	4.25	0.60	6.80	9.21
27	3.70	3.65	−0.05	6.50	8.27
28	3.75	3.75	0	5.75	7.67
29	3.80	3.85	0.05	5.80	7.93
30	3.70	4.25	0.55	6.80	9.26

FIGURE **16.9** Scatter Plots of the Fresh Demand Data

(a) Plot of y (Demand for Fresh Detergent) versus x_4 (Price Difference)

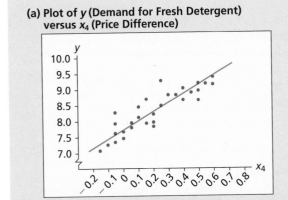

(b) Plot of y (Demand for Fresh Detergent) versus x_3 (Advertising Expenditure for Fresh)

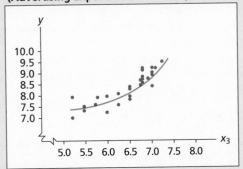

Exercises for Section 16.3

CONCEPTS

16.8 What transformations can be used to transform a time series exhibiting increasing seasonal variation into a time series exhibiting constant seasonal variation?

16.9 What is the purpose of an autoregressive error term model?

METHODS AND APPLICATIONS

16.10 Table 16.10 gives the monthly international passenger totals over the last 11 years for an airline company. A plot of these passenger totals reveals an upward trend with increasing seasonal variation, and the natural logarithmic transformation is found to best equalize the seasonal variation (see Figure 16.10(a) and (b)). Figure 16.10(c) gives the Excel output of a regression analysis of the monthly international passenger totals by using the model

$$\ln y_t = \beta_0 + \beta_1 t + \beta_{M1}M_1 + \beta_{M2}M_2$$
$$+ \cdots + \beta_{M11}M_{11} + \varepsilon_t.$$

Here $M_1, M_2, \ldots, M_{11}$ are appropriately defined dummy variables for January (month 1) through November (month 11). Using the results presented in the output, compose the regression equation.

16.11 Use the Durbin–Watson statistic given at the bottom of the Excel output in Figure 16.10(c) to test for positive autocorrelation.

TABLE **16.10**   Monthly International Passenger Totals (Thousands of Passengers) 🖊

Year	Jan.	Feb.	Mar.	Apr.	May	Jun.	Jul.	Aug.	Sep.	Oct.	Nov.	Dec.
1	112	118	132	129	121	135	148	148	136	119	104	118
2	115	126	141	135	125	149	170	170	158	133	114	140
3	145	150	178	163	172	178	199	199	184	162	146	166
4	171	180	193	181	183	218	230	242	209	191	172	194
5	196	196	236	235	229	243	264	272	237	211	180	201
6	204	188	235	227	234	264	302	293	259	229	203	229
7	242	233	267	269	270	315	364	347	312	274	237	278
8	284	277	317	313	318	374	413	405	355	306	271	306
9	315	301	356	348	355	422	465	467	404	347	305	336
10	340	318	362	348	363	435	491	505	404	359	310	337
11	360	342	406	396	420	472	548	559	463	407	362	405

Source: *FAA Statistical Handbook of Civil Aviation* (several annual issues). These data were originally presented by Box and Jenkins (1976). We have updated the situation in this exercise to be more modern.

FIGURE **16.10**   Analysis of the Monthly International Passenger Totals

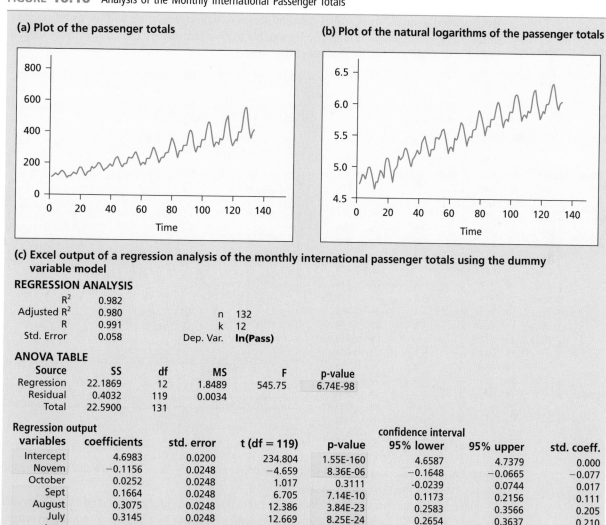

(a) Plot of the passenger totals

(b) Plot of the natural logarithms of the passenger totals

(c) Excel output of a regression analysis of the monthly international passenger totals using the dummy variable model

REGRESSION ANALYSIS

R²	0.982		
Adjusted R²	0.980	n	132
R	0.991	k	12
Std. Error	0.058	Dep. Var.	**ln(Pass)**

ANOVA TABLE

Source	SS	df	MS	F	p-value
Regression	22.1869	12	1.8489	545.75	6.74E-98
Residual	0.4032	119	0.0034		
Total	22.5900	131			

Regression output

variables	coefficients	std. error	t (df = 119)	p-value	confidence interval 95% lower	95% upper	std. coeff.
Intercept	4.6983	0.0200	234.804	1.55E-160	4.6587	4.7379	0.000
Novem	−0.1156	0.0248	−4.659	8.36E-06	−0.1648	−0.0665	−0.077
October	0.0252	0.0248	1.017	0.3111	-0.0239	0.0744	0.017
Sept	0.1664	0.0248	6.705	7.14E-10	0.1173	0.2156	0.111
August	0.3075	0.0248	12.386	3.84E-23	0.2583	0.3566	0.205
July	0.3145	0.0248	12.669	8.25E-24	0.2654	0.3637	0.210
June	0.2141	0.0248	8.624	3.32E-14	0.1650	0.2633	0.143
May	0.0916	0.0248	3.687	0.0003	0.0424	0.1407	0.061
April	0.0956	0.0248	3.848	0.0002	0.0464	0.1448	0.064
March	0.1462	0.0248	5.885	3.76E-08	0.0970	0.1954	0.098
Feb	0.0012	0.0249	0.048	0.9615	−0.0480	0.0504	0.001
Jan	0.0187	0.0249	0.752	0.4534	−0.0305	0.0679	0.012
Time	0.0103	0.00013350	76.985	2.32E-103	0.0100	0.0105	0.947

Durbin-Watson = 0.43

16.4 MULTIPLICATIVE DECOMPOSITION

When a time series exhibits increasing (or decreasing) seasonal variation, we can use the **multiplicative decomposition method** to decompose the time series into its **trend, seasonal, cyclical,** and **irregular** components. This is illustrated in the following example.

Example 16.5   The Tasty Cola Case

The Discount Cola Shop owns and operates ten soft drink stores and sells Tasty Cola, a soft drink introduced just three years ago and gaining in popularity. Discount Cola orders Tasty Cola from the regional distributor. To better implement its inventory policy, Discount Cola needs to forecast monthly Tasty Cola sales (in hundreds of cases).

Discount Cola has recorded monthly Tasty Cola sales for the previous three years. This time series is given in Table 16.11 and plotted in Figure 16.11. Notice that, in addition to having a linear trend, the Tasty Cola sales time series possesses seasonal variation, with sales of the soft drink being greatest in the summer and early fall months and lowest in the winter months. Because, furthermore, the seasonal variation seems to be increasing, we will see as we progress through this example that it might be reasonable to conclude that y_t, the sales of Tasty Cola in period t, is described by the **multiplicative model**

$$y_t = TR_t \times SN_t \times CL_t \times IR_t.$$

TABLE **16.11**   Monthly Sales of Tasty Cola
(in Hundreds of Cases)

Year	Month	t	Sales, y_t	Year	Month	t	Sales, y_t
1	1 (Jan.)	1	189	2	7	19	831
	2 (Feb.)	2	229		8	20	960
	3 (Mar.)	3	249		9	21	1,152
	4 (Apr.)	4	289		10	22	759
	5 (May)	5	260		11	23	607
	6 (Jun.)	6	431		12	24	371
	7 (Jul.)	7	660	3	1	25	298
	8 (Aug.)	8	777		2	26	378
	9 (Sep.)	9	915		3	27	373
	10 (Oct.)	10	613		4	28	443
	11 (Nov.)	11	485		5	29	374
	12 (Dec.)	12	277		6	30	660
2	1	13	244		7	31	1,004
	2	14	296		8	32	1,153
	3	15	319		9	33	1,388
	4	16	370		10	34	904
	5	17	313		11	35	715
	6	18	556		12	36	441

FIGURE **16.11**   Monthly Sales of Tasty Cola
(in Hundreds of Cases)

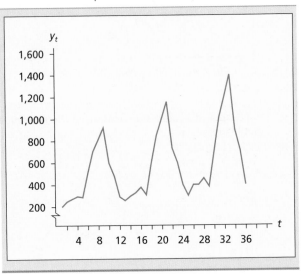

Here TR_t, SN_t, CL_t, and IR_t represent the trend, seasonal, cyclical, and irregular components, respectively, of the time series in time period t.

Table 16.12 summarizes the calculations needed to find estimates—denoted tr_t, sn_t, cl_t, and ir_t—of TR_t, SN_t, CL_t, and IR_t. As shown in the table, we begin by calculating **moving averages** and **centred moving averages**. The purpose of computing these averages is to eliminate seasonal variations and irregular fluctuations from the data. The first moving average of the first 12 Tasty Cola sales values is

$$\frac{189 + 229 + 249 + 289 + 260 + 431 + 660 + 777 + 915 + 613 + 485 + 277}{12}$$

$$= 447.833.$$

TABLE 16.12 Tasty Cola Sales and the Multiplicative Decomposition Method ✐

$t,$ Time Period	$y_t,$ Tasty Cola Sales	First Step, 12-Period Moving Average	$tr_t \times cl_t,$ Centred Moving Average	$sn_t \times ir_t,$ $\dfrac{y_t}{tr_t \times cl_t}$	$sn_t,$ Table 16.12	$d_t,$ $\dfrac{y_t}{sn_t}$	$tr_t,$ 380.163 $+9.489t$	$tr_t \times sn_t,$ Multiply tr_t by sn_t	$cl_t \times ir_t,$ $\dfrac{y_t}{tr_t \times sn_t}$	$cl_t,$ 3-Period Moving Average	$ir_t,$ $\dfrac{y_t}{tr_t \times sn_t \times cl_t}$
1 (Jan.)	189				0.493	383.37	389.652	192.10	0.9839		
2	229				0.596	384.23	399.141	237.89	0.9626	0.9902	0.9721
3	249				0.595	418.49	408.630	243.13	1.0241	1.0010	1.0231
4	289				0.680	425	418.119	284.32	1.0165	1.0396	0.9778
5	260				0.564	460.99	427.608	241.17	1.0781	1.0315	1.0452
6	431	447.833			0.986	437.12	437.097	430.98	1.0000	1.0285	0.9723
7	660	452.417	450.125	1.466	1.467	449.9	446.586	655.14	1.0074	1.0046	1.0028
8	777	458	455.2085	1.707	1.693	458.95	456.075	772.13	1.0063	1.0004	1.0059
9	915	463.833	460.9165	1.985	1.990	459.79	465.564	926.47	0.9876	0.9937	0.9939
10	613	470.583	467.208	1.312	1.307	469.01	475.053	620.89	0.9873	0.9825	1.0049
11	485	475	472.7915	1.026	1.029	471.33	489.542	498.59	0.9727	0.9648	1.0082
12	277	485.417	480.2085	0.577	0.600	461.67	494.031	296.42	0.9345	0.9634	0.9700
13 (Jan.)	244	499.667	492.542	0.495	0.493	494.97	503.520	248.24	0.9829	0.9618	1.0219
14	296	514.917	507.292	0.583	0.596	496.64	513.009	305.75	0.9681	0.9924	0.9755
15	319	534.667	524.792	0.608	0.595	536.13	522.498	310.89	1.0261	1.0057	1.0203
16	370	546.833	540.75	0.684	0.680	544.12	531.987	361.75	1.0228	1.0246	0.9982
17	313	557	551.9165	0.567	0.564	554.97	541.476	305.39	1.0249	1.0237	1.0012
18	556	564.833	560.9165	0.991	0.986	563.89	550.965	543.25	1.0235	1.0197	1.0037
19	831	569.333	567.083	1.465	1.467	566.46	560.454	822.19	1.0107	1.0097	1.0010
20	960	576.167	572.75	1.676	1.693	567.04	569.943	964.91	0.9949	1.0016	0.9933
21	1,152	580.667	578.417	1.992	1.990	578.89	579.432	1,153.07	0.9991	0.9934	1.0057
22	759	586.75	583.7085	1.300	1.307	580.72	588.921	769.72	0.9861	0.9903	0.9958
23	607	591.833	589.2915	1.030	1.029	589.89	598.410	615.76	0.9858	0.9964	0.9894
24	371	600.5	596.1665	0.622	0.600	618.33	607.899	364.74	1.0172	0.9940	1.0233
25 (Jan.)	298	614.917	607.7085	0.490	0.493	604.46	617.388	304.37	0.9791	1.0027	0.9765
26	378	631	622.9585	0.607	0.596	634.23	626.877	373.62	1.0117	0.9920	1.0199
27	373	650.667	640.8335	0.582	0.595	626.89	636.366	378.64	0.9851	1.0018	0.9833
28	443	662.75	656.7085	0.675	0.680	651.47	645.855	439.18	1.0087	1.0030	1.0057
29	374	671.75	667.25	0.561	0.564	663.12	655.344	369.61	1.0119	1.0091	1.0028
30	660	677.583	674.6665	0.978	0.986	669.37	664.833	655.53	1.0068	1.0112	0.9956
31	1,004				1.467	684.39	674.322	989.23	1.0149	1.0059	1.0089
32	1,153				1.693	681.04	683.811	1,157.69	0.9959	1.0053	0.9906
33	1,388				1.990	697.49	693.300	1,379.67	1.0060	0.9954	1.0106
34	904				1.307	691.66	702.789	918.55	0.9842	0.9886	0.9955
35	715				1.029	694.85	712.278	732.93	0.9755	0.9927	0.9827
36	441				0.600	735	721.707	433.06	1.0183		

Here we use a 12-period moving average because the Tasty Cola time series data are monthly (12 time periods or "seasons" per year). If the data were quarterly, we would compute a four-period moving average. The second moving average is obtained by dropping the first sales value (y_1) from and including the next sales value (y_{13}) in the average. Thus, we obtain

$$\frac{229 + 249 + 289 + 260 + 431 + 660 + 777 + 915 + 613 + 485 + 277 + 244}{12}$$

$$= 452.417.$$

The third moving average is obtained by dropping y_2 from and including y_{14} in the average. We obtain

$$\frac{249 + 289 + 260 + 431 + 660 + 777 + 915 + 613 + 485 + 277 + 244 + 296}{12} = 458.$$

Successive moving averages are computed similarly until we include y_{36} in the last moving average. Note that we use the term "moving average" here because, as we calculate these averages, we move along by dropping the most remote observation in the previous average and including the next observation in the new average.

The first moving average corresponds to a time that is midway between periods 6 and 7, the second moving average corresponds to a time that is midway between periods 7 and 8, and so forth. In order to obtain averages corresponding to time periods in the original Tasty Cola time series, we calculate *centred moving averages*. The centred moving averages are 2-period moving averages of the previously computed 12-period moving averages. Thus, the first centred moving average is

$$\frac{447.833 + 452.417}{2} = 450.125.$$

The second centred moving average is

$$\frac{452.417 + 458}{2} = 455.2085.$$

Successive centred moving averages are calculated similarly. The 12-period moving averages and centred moving averages for the Tasty Cola sales time series are given in Table 16.12 (previous page).

If the original moving averages had been computed using an odd number of time series values, the centring procedure would not have been necessary. For example, if we had three seasons per year, we would compute three-period moving averages. Then the first moving average would correspond to period 2, the second moving average would correspond to period 3, and so on. However, most seasonal time series are quarterly, monthly, or weekly, so the centring procedure is necessary.

The centred moving average in time period t is considered to equal $tr_t \times cl_t$, the estimate of $TR_t \times CL_t$, because the averaging procedure is assumed to have removed seasonal variations (note that each moving average is computed using exactly one observation from each season) and (short-term) irregular fluctuations. The (longer-term) trend effects and cyclical effects—that is, $tr_t \times cl_t$—remain.

Because the model

$$y_t = TR_t \times SN_t \times CL_t \times IR_t$$

implies that

$$SN_t \times IR_t = \frac{y_t}{TR_t \times CL_t},$$

it follows that the estimate $sn_t \times ir_t$ of $SN_t \times IR_t$ is

$$sn_t \times ir_t = \frac{y_t}{tr_t \times cl_t}.$$

Noting that the values of $sn_t \times ir_t$ are calculated in Table 16.12, we can find sn_t by grouping the values of $sn_t \times ir_t$ by months and calculating an average, $\overline{sn}_t$, for each month. These monthly averages are given for the Tasty Cola data in Table 16.13. The monthly averages are then normalized so that they sum to the number of time periods in a year. Denoting the number of time periods in a year by L (for instance, $L = 4$ for quarterly data and $L = 12$ for monthly data), we accomplish the normalization by multiplying each value of $\overline{sn}_t$ by the quantity

$$\frac{L}{\sum \overline{sn}_t} = \frac{12}{0.4925 + 0.595 + \cdots + 0.5995}$$

$$= \frac{12}{11.9895} = 1.0008758.$$

This normalization process results in the estimate $sn_t = 1.0008758(\overline{sn}_t)$, which is the estimate of SN_t. These calculations are summarized in Table 16.13.

TABLE **16.13** Estimation of the Seasonal Factors

		$sn_t \times ir_t = y_t/$ $(tr_t \times cl_t)$			$sn_t =$
		Year 1	Year 2	$\overline{sn}_t$	$1.0008758(\overline{sn}_t)$
1	Jan.	0.495	0.490	0.4925	0.493
2	Feb.	0.583	0.607	0.595	0.596
3	Mar.	0.608	0.582	0.595	0.595
4	Apr.	0.684	0.675	0.6795	0.680
5	May	0.567	0.561	0.564	0.564
6	Jun.	0.991	0.978	0.9845	0.986
7	Jul.	1.466	1.465	1.4655	1.467
8	Aug.	1.707	1.676	1.6915	1.693
9	Sep.	1.985	1.992	1.9885	1.990
10	Oct.	1.312	1.300	1.306	1.307
11	Nov.	1.026	1.030	1.028	1.029
12	Dec.	0.577	0.622	0.5995	0.600

FIGURE **16.12** Plot of Tasty Cola Sales and Deseasonalized Sales

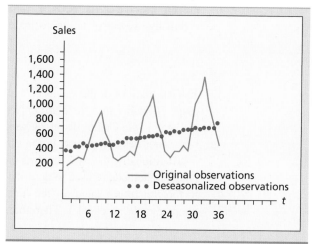

Having calculated the values of sn_t and placed them in Table 16.12 (page 567), we next define the **deseasonalized observation** in time period t to be

$$d_t = \frac{y_t}{sn_t}.$$

Deseasonalized observations are computed to better estimate the trend component TR_t. Dividing y_t by the estimated seasonal factor removes the seasonality from the data and allows us to better understand the nature of the trend. The deseasonalized observations are calculated in Table 16.12 and plotted in Figure 16.12. Since the deseasonalized observations have a straight-line appearance, it seems reasonable to assume a linear trend,

$$TR_t = \beta_0 + \beta_1 t.$$

We estimate TR_t by fitting a straight line to the deseasonalized observations. That is, we compute the least squares point estimates of the parameters in the simple linear regression model relating the dependent variable, d_t, to the independent variable, t:

$$d_t = \beta_0 + \beta_1 t + \varepsilon_t.$$

We obtain $b_0 = 380.163$ and $b_1 = 9.489$. It follows that the estimate of TR_t is

$$tr_t = b_0 + b_1 t = 380.163 + 9.489t.$$

The values of tr_t are calculated in Table 16.12. Note that, for example, although $y_{22} = 759$ (the Tasty Cola sales in period 22 (October of year 2)) is larger than $tr_{22} = 588.921$ (the estimated trend in period 22), $d_{22} = 580.72$ is smaller than $tr_{22} = 588.921$. This implies that on a deseasonalized basis, Tasty Cola sales were slightly down in October of year 2. This might have been caused by a slightly colder October than usual.

Thus far, we have found estimates sn_t and tr_t of SN_t and TR_t. Because the model

$$y_t = TR_t \times SN_t \times CL_t \times IR_t$$

implies that

$$CL_t \times IR_t = \frac{y_t}{TR_t \times SN_t},$$

it follows that the estimate of $CL_t \times IR_t$ is

$$cl_t \times ir_t = \frac{y_t}{tr_t \times sn_t}.$$

Moreover, experience has shown that when considering either monthly or quarterly data, we can average out ir_t and thus calculate the estimate, cl_t, of CL_t by computing a three-period moving average of the $cl_t \times ir_t$ values.

Finally, we calculate the estimate, ir_t, of IR_t by using the equation

$$ir_t = \frac{cl_t \times ir_t}{cl_t} = \frac{y_t}{tr_t \times sn_t \times cl_t}.$$

The calculations of the values cl_t and ir_t for the Tasty Cola data are summarized in Table 16.12 (page 567). Because there are only three years of data, and because most of the values of cl_t are near 1, we cannot discern a well-defined cycle. Furthermore, examining the values of ir_t, we cannot detect a pattern in the estimates of the irregular factors.

Traditionally, the estimates tr_t, sn_t, cl_t, and ir_t obtained by using the multiplicative decomposition method are used to describe the time series. However, we can also use these estimates to forecast future values of the time series. If there is no pattern in the irregular component, we predict IR_t to equal 1. Therefore, the point forecast of y_t is

$$\hat{y}_t = tr_t \times sn_t \times cl_t$$

if a well-defined cycle exists and can be predicted. The point forecast is

$$\hat{y}_t = tr_t \times sn_t$$

if a well-defined cycle does not exist or if CL_t cannot be predicted, as in the Tasty Cola example. Because values of $tr_t \times sn_t$ have been calculated in column 9 of Table 16.12, these values are the point forecasts of the $n = 36$ historical Tasty Cola sales values. Furthermore, we present in Table 16.14 point forecasts of future Tasty Cola sales in the 12 months of year 4. Recalling that the estimated trend equation is $tr_t = 380.163 + 9.489t$ and that the estimated seasonal factor for August is 1.693 (see Table 16.13 (previous page)), it follows, for example, that the point forecast of Tasty Cola sales in period 44 (August of year 4) is

$$\hat{y}_{44} = tr_{44} \times sn_{44}$$
$$= (380.163 + 9.489(44))(1.693)$$
$$= 797.699(1.693)$$
$$= 1350.50.$$

Although there is no theoretically correct prediction interval for y_t, a *fairly accurate approximate $100(1 - \alpha)$ percent prediction interval for y_t* is obtained by computing an interval that is centred at $\hat{y}_t$ and has a length equal to the length of the $100(1 - \alpha)$ percent prediction

TABLE 16.14   Forecasts of Future Values of Tasty Cola Sales Calculated Using the Multiplicative Decomposition Method 📎

t	sn_t	$tr_t = 380.163 + 9.489t$	Point Prediction, $\hat{y}_t = tr_t \times sn_t$	Approximate 95% Prediction Interval	y_t
37	0.493	731.273	360.52	[333.72, 387.32]	352
38	0.596	740.762	441.48	[414.56, 468.40]	445
39	0.595	750.252	446.40	[419.36, 473.44]	453
40	0.680	759.741	516.62	[489.45, 543.79]	541
41	0.564	769.231	433.85	[406.55, 461.15]	457
42	0.986	778.720	767.82	[740.38, 795.26]	762
43	1.467	788.209	1,156.30	[1,128.71, 1,183.89]	1,194
44	1.693	797.699	1,350.50	[1,322.76, 1,378.24]	1,361
45	1.990	807.188	1,606.30	[1,578.41, 1,634.19]	1,615
46	1.307	816.678	1,067.40	[1,039.35, 1,095.45]	1,059
47	1.029	826.167	850.12	[821.90, 878.34]	824
48	0.600	835.657	501.39	[473, 529.78]	495

FIGURE **16.13**   A Plot of the Observed and Forecast Tasty Cola Sales Values

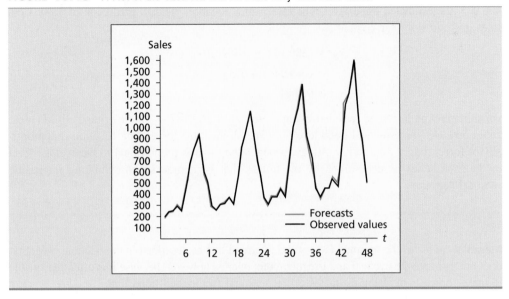

interval for the *deseasonalized observation* d_t. Here the interval for d_t is obtained by using the model

$$d_t = TR_t + \varepsilon_t$$
$$= \beta_0 + \beta_1 t + \varepsilon_t.$$

For instance, if a 95 percent prediction interval for d_{44} is [769.959, 825.439], with length equal to $825.439 - 769.959 = 55.48$, it follows that an approximate 95 percent prediction interval for y_{44} is

$$\left[\hat{y}_{44} \pm \frac{55.48}{2} \right] = [1350.50 \pm 27.74]$$
$$= [1322.76, 1378.24].$$

In Table 16.14 (previous page), we give the approximate 95 percent prediction intervals (calculated by the above method) for Tasty Cola sales in the 12 months of year 4.

Next suppose we actually observe Tasty Cola sales in year 4, and these sales are as given in Table 16.14. In Figure 16.13, we plot the observed and forecast sales for all 48 sales periods. In practice, the comparison of the observed and forecast sales in years 1 through 3 would be used by the analyst to determine whether the forecasting equation adequately fits the historical data. An adequate fit (as indicated by Figure 16.13, for example) might prompt an analyst to use this equation to calculate forecasts for future time periods. One reason that the Tasty Cola forecasting equation

$$\hat{y}_t = tr_t \times sn_t$$
$$= (380.163 + 9.489t)sn_t$$

provides reasonable forecasts is that this equation multiplies tr_t by sn_t. Therefore, as the average level of the time series (determined by the trend) increases, the seasonal swing of the time series increases, which is consistent with the data plots in Figures 16.11 (page 566) and 16.13. For example, note from Table 16.13 (page 569) that the estimated seasonal factor for August is 1.693. The forecasting equation yields a prediction of Tasty Cola sales in August of year 1 equal to

$$\hat{y}_8 = [380.163 + 9.489(8)]1.693$$
$$= (456.075)(1.693)$$
$$= 772.13.$$

This implies a seasonal swing of $772.13 - 456.075 = 316.055$ (hundreds of cases) above 456.075, the estimated trend level. The forecasting equation yields a prediction of Tasty Cola sales in August of year 2 equal to

$$\hat{y}_{20} = [380.163 + 9.489(20)]1.693$$
$$= (569.943)(1.693)$$
$$= 964.91,$$

which implies an increased seasonal swing of $964.91 - 569.943 = 394.967$ (hundreds of cases) above 569.943, the estimated trend level. In general, then, the forecasting equation is appropriate for forecasting a time series with a seasonal swing that is proportional to the average level of the time series as determined by the trend—that is, a time series exhibiting increasing seasonal variation.

MegaStat estimates the seasonal factors and the trend line as described in this section. MegaStat does not estimate the cyclical and irregular components, however, because it is often reasonable to make forecasts by using estimates of the seasonal factors and trend line.

Exercises for Section 16.4

CONCEPTS

16.12 Explain how the multiplicative decomposition model estimates seasonal factors.

16.13 Explain how the multiplicative decomposition method estimates the trend effect.

16.14 Discuss how the multiplicative decomposition method makes point forecasts of future time series values.

METHODS AND APPLICATIONS 📝

Exercises 16.15 through 16.19 are based on the following situation: International Machinery produces a tractor and wishes to use *quarterly* tractor sales data observed in the last four years to predict quarterly tractor sales next year. The MegaStat output in Figure 16.14 gives the tractor sales data and the estimates of the seasonal factors and trend line for the data.

FIGURE 16.14 MegaStat Output of Tractor Sales Data for Exercises 16.15 through 16.19

t	Year	Quarter	Sales, y	Centred Moving Average	Ratio to Centred Moving Average	Seasonal Indexes	Sales, y, Deseasonalized
1	1	1	293			1.191	245.9
2	1	2	392			1.521	257.7
3	1	3	221	275.125	0.803	0.804	275.0
4	1	4	147	302.000	0.487	0.484	303.9
5	2	1	388	325.250	1.193	1.191	325.7
6	2	2	512	338.125	1.514	1.521	336.6
7	2	3	287	354.125	0.810	0.804	357.1
8	2	4	184	381.500	0.482	0.484	380.4
9	3	1	479	405.000	1.183	1.191	402.0
10	3	2	640	417.375	1.533	1.521	420.7
11	3	3	347	435.000	0.798	0.804	431.8
12	3	4	223	462.125	0.483	0.484	461.0
13	4	1	581	484.375	1.199	1.191	487.7
14	4	2	755	497.625	1.517	1.521	496.3
15	4	3	410			0.804	510.2
16	4	4	266			0.484	549.9

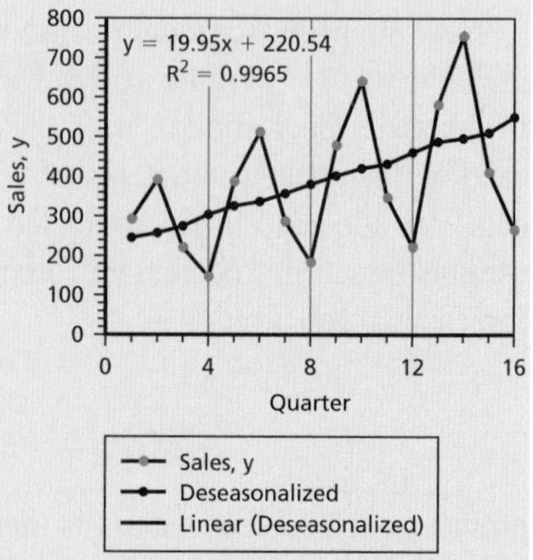

Calculation of Seasonal Indexes

	1	2	3	4	
1			0.803	0.487	
2	1.193	1.514	0.810	0.482	
3	1.183	1.533	0.798	0.483	
4	1.199	1.517			
mean:	1.192	1.522	0.804	0.484	4.001
adjusted:	1.191	1.521	0.804	0.484	4.000

16.15 Find and identify the four seasonal factors for quarters 1, 2, 3, and 4.

16.16 What type of trend is indicated by the plot of the deseasonalized data?

16.17 What is the equation of the estimated trend that has been calculated using the deseasonalized data?

16.18 Compute a point forecast of tractor sales (based on trend and seasonal factors) for each of the quarters next year.

16.19 Compute an approximate 95 percent prediction interval forecast of tractor sales for each of the quarters next year. Use the fact that the half-lengths of 95 percent prediction intervals for the deseasonalized sales values in the four quarters of next year are 14, 14.4, 14.6, and 15.

16.20 Use the deasonalization method in MegaStat to analyze the quarterly bicycle sales data given in Table 16.3.
  a. What are the quarterly seasonal factors?
  b. If a straight line is fitted to the deseasonalized values, what is the estimate of the trend?

16.5 EXPONENTIAL SMOOTHING

In ongoing forecasting systems, forecasts of future time series values are made for succeeding periods. At the end of each period, the estimates of the time series parameters and the forecasting equation need to be updated to account for the most recent observation. This updating accounts for possible changes in the parameters that may occur over time. In addition, such changes may imply that unequal weights should be applied to the time series observations when the estimates of the parameters are updated.

Simple exponential smoothing We begin by assuming that a time series is appropriately described by the no-trend equation

$$y_t = \beta_0 + \varepsilon_t.$$

When the parameter β_0 remains constant over time, we have seen that it is reasonable to forecast future values of y_t by using regression analysis (see Example 16.1 (page 555)). In such a case, the least squares point estimate of β_0 is

$$b_0 = \bar{y} = \text{the average of the observed time series values.}$$

When we compute the point estimate b_0, we are *equally weighting* each of the previously observed time series values $y_1, y_2, \ldots, y_n$.

When the value of the parameter β_0 is slowly changing over time, the equal-weighting scheme may not be appropriate. Instead, it may be desirable to weight recent observations more heavily than remote observations. **Simple exponential smoothing** is a forecasting method that applies unequal weights to the time series observations. This unequal weighting is accomplished by using a **smoothing constant** that determines how much weight is attached to each observation. The most recent observation is given the most weight. More distantly past observations are given successively smaller weights. The procedure allows the forecaster to update the estimate of β_0 so that changes in the value of this parameter can be detected and incorporated into the forecasting equation. We illustrate simple exponential smoothing in the following example.

Example 16.6 The Cod Catch Case

Consider the cod catch data of Example 16.1 (Table 16.1, page 555). The plot of these data in Figure 16.2 on page 555 suggests that the no-trend model

$$y_t = \beta_0 + \varepsilon_t$$

may appropriately describe the cod catch series. The parameter β_0 could also be slowly changing over time.

We begin the simple exponential smoothing procedure by calculating an initial estimate of the average level, β_0, of the series. This estimate is denoted S_0 and is computed by averaging the first six time series values. We obtain

$$S_0 = \frac{\sum_{t=1}^{6} y_t}{6} = \frac{362 + 381 + \cdots + 402}{6} = 359.67.$$

Note that because simple exponential smoothing attempts to track changes over time in the average level β_0 by using newly observed values to update the estimates of β_0, we use only six of the $n = 24$ time series observations to calculate the initial estimate of β_0. If we do this, then 18 observations remain to tell us how β_0 may be changing over time. Experience has shown that, in general, it is reasonable to calculate initial estimates in exponential smoothing procedures by using half of the historical data. However, it can be shown that in simple exponential smoothing, using six observations is reasonable (it would not, however, be reasonable to use a very small number of observations, because doing so might make the initial estimate so different from the true value of β_0 that the exponential smoothing procedure would be adversely affected).

Next assume that at the end of time period $T - 1$ we have an estimate S_{T-1} of β_0. Then, assuming that in time period T we obtain a new observation y_T, we can update S_{T-1} to S_T, which is an estimate made in period T of β_0. We compute the updated estimate by using the **smoothing equation**

$$S_T = \alpha y_T + (1 - \alpha)S_{T-1}.$$

Here α is a smoothing constant between 0 and 1. The updating equation says that S_T, the estimate made in time period T of β_0, equals a fraction, α (for example, 0.1), *of the newly* observed time series observation y_T plus a fraction, $1 - \alpha$ (for example, 0.9), of S_{T-1}, the estimate made in time period $T - 1$ of β_0. The more the average level of the process is changing, the more a newly observed time series value should influence our estimate, and thus the larger the smoothing constant α should be set. In the following, we use historical data to determine an appropriate value of α.

We will now begin with the initial estimate $S_0 = 359.67$ and update this initial estimate by applying the smoothing equation to the 24 observed cod catches. To do this, we arbitrarily set α equal to 0.02, and to judge the appropriateness of this choice of α we calculate **one-period-ahead** forecasts of the historical cod catches as we carry out the smoothing procedure. Because the initial estimate of β_0 is $S_0 = 359.67$, it follows that 360 is the rounded forecast made at time 0 for y_1, the value of the time series in period 1. Because we see from Table 16.15 that $y_1 = 362$, we have a forecast error of $362 - 360 = 2$. Using $y_1 = 362$, we can update S_0 to S_1, an estimate made in period 1 of the average level of the time series, by using the equation

$$\begin{aligned} S_1 &= \alpha y_1 + (1 - \alpha)S_0 \\ &= 0.02(362) + 0.98(359.67) = 359.72. \end{aligned}$$

Because this implies that 360 is the rounded forecast made in period 1 for y_2, and because we see from Table 16.15 that $y_2 = 381$, we have a forecast error of $381 - 360 = 21$. Using $y_2 = 381$, we can update S_1 to S_2, an estimate made in period 2 of β_0, by using the equation

$$\begin{aligned} S_2 &= \alpha y_2 + (1 - \alpha)S_1 \\ &= 0.02(381) + 0.98(359.72) = 360.14. \end{aligned}$$

This implies that 360 is the rounded forecast made in period 2 for y_3. We see from Table 16.15 that $y_3 = 317$, resulting in a forecast error of $317 - 360 = -43$. This procedure is continued through all 24 periods of historical data. The results are summarized in Table 16.15. Using the

TABLE 16.15 One-Period-Ahead Forecasting of the Historical Cod Catch Time Series Using Simple Exponential Smoothing with $\alpha = 0.02$ 🖉

Year	Month	Actual Cod Catch, y_T	Smoothed Estimate, S_T ($S_0 = 359.67$)	Forecast Made Last Period	Forecast Error	Squared Forecast Error
1	Jan.	362	359.72	360	2	4
	Feb.	381	360.14	360	21	441
	Mar.	317	359.28	360	−43	1,849
	Apr.	297	358.03	359	−62	3,844
	May	399	358.85	358	41	1,681
	Jun.	402	359.71	359	43	1,849
	Jul.	375	360.02	360	15	225
	Aug.	349	359.80	360	−11	121
	Sep.	386	360.32	360	26	676
	Oct.	328	359.68	360	−32	1,024
	Nov.	389	360.26	360	29	841
	Dec.	343	359.92	360	−17	289
2	Jan.	276	358.24	360	−84	7,056
	Feb.	334	357.75	358	−24	576
	Mar.	394	358.48	358	36	1,296
	Apr.	334	357.99	358	−24	576
	May	384	358.51	358	26	676
	Jun.	314	357.62	359	−45	2,025
	Jul.	344	357.35	358	−14	196
	Aug.	337	356.94	357	−20	400
	Sep.	345	356.70	357	−12	144
	Oct.	362	356.81	357	5	25
	Nov.	314	355.95	357	−43	1,849
	Dec.	365	356.13	356	9	81

results in this table, we find that for $\alpha = 0.02$, the sum of squared forecast errors is 27,744. To find a "good" value of α, we evaluate the sum of squared forecast errors for values of α ranging from 0.02 to 0.30 in increments of 0.02 (in most exponential smoothing applications, the value of the smoothing constant used is between 0.01 and 0.30). When we do this, we find that $\alpha = 0.02$ minimizes the sum of squared forecast errors. Since this minimizing value of α is small, it appears to be best to apply small weights to new observations, which tells us that the level of the time series is not changing very much.

In general, simple exponential smoothing is carried out as follows:

Simple Exponential Smoothing

1 Suppose that the time series $y_1, \ldots, y_n$ is described by the equation

$$y_t = \beta_0 + \varepsilon_t,$$

where the average level, β_0, of the process may be slowly changing over time. Then the estimate S_T of β_0 made in time period T is given by the **smoothing equation**

$$S_T = \alpha y_T + (1 - \alpha)S_{T-1},$$

where α is a smoothing constant between 0 and 1 and S_{T-1} is the estimate of β_0 made in time period $T - 1$.

2 A point forecast made in time period T for any future value of the time series is S_T.

3 If we observe y_{T+1} in time period $T + 1$, we can update S_T to S_{T+1} by using the equation

$$S_{T+1} = \alpha y_{T+1} + (1 - \alpha)S_T,$$

and a point forecast made in time period $T + 1$ for any future value of the time series is S_{T+1}.

Example 16.7 The Cod Catch Case

In Example 16.6 (pages 573–575), we saw that $\alpha = 0.02$ is a "good" value of the smoothing constant when forecasting the 24 observed cod catches in Table 16.15 (page 575). Therefore, we will use simple exponential smoothing with $\alpha = 0.02$ to forecast future monthly cod catches. From Table 16.15, we see that $S_{24} = 356.13$ is the estimate made in month 24 of the average level β_0 of the monthly cod catches. It follows that the point forecast made in month 24 of any future monthly cod catch is 356.13 tonnes of cod. Now, assuming that we observe a cod catch in January of year 3 of $y_{25} = 384$, we can update S_{24} to S_{25} by using the equation

$$S_{25} = \alpha y_{25} + (1 - \alpha)S_{24}$$
$$= 0.02(384) + 0.98(356.13)$$
$$= 356.69.$$

This implies that the point forecast made in month 25 of any future monthly cod catch is 356.69 tonnes of cod.

By using the smoothing equation

$$S_T = \alpha y_T + (1 - \alpha)S_{T-1},$$

it can be shown that S_T, the estimate made in time period T of the average level β_0 of the time series, can be expressed as

$$S_T = \alpha y_T + \alpha(1 - \alpha)y_{T-1} + \alpha(1 - \alpha)^2 y_{T-2}$$
$$+ \cdots + \alpha(1 - \alpha)^{T-1}y_1 + (1 - \alpha)^T S_0.$$

LO3

The coefficients measuring the contributions of the observations $y_T, y_{T-1}, y_{T-2}, \ldots, y_1$—that is, $\alpha, \alpha(1 - \alpha), \alpha(1 - \alpha)^2, \ldots, \alpha(1 - \alpha)^{T-1}$—decrease *exponentially* with time. For this reason, we refer to this procedure as simple exponential smoothing.

Because the coefficients measuring the contributions of $y_T, y_{T-1}, y_{T-2}, \ldots, y_1$ are decreasing exponentially, the most recent observation, y_T, makes the largest contribution to the current estimate of β_0. Older observations make smaller and smaller contributions to this estimate. Thus, remote observations are **damped out** of the current estimate of β_0 as time advances. The rate at which remote observations are damped out depends on the smoothing constant α. For values of α near 1, remote observations are damped out quickly. For example, if $\alpha = 0.9$, we obtain coefficients 0.9, 0.09, 0.009, 0.0009, ... For values of α near 0, remote observations are damped out more slowly (if $\alpha = 0.1$, we obtain coefficients 0.1, 0.09, 0.081, 0.0729, ...). The choice of a smoothing constant α is usually made by simulated forecasting of a historical data set, as illustrated in Example 16.6.

Computer software packages can be used to implement exponential smoothing. These packages choose the smoothing constant (or constants) in different ways and also compute approximate prediction intervals in different ways. Optimally, the user should carefully investigate how the computer software package implements exponential smoothing. At a minimum, the user should not trust the forecasts given by the software package if they seem illogical.

Figure 16.15 gives the MegaStat output of using simple exponential smoothing to forecast in month 24 the cod catches in future months. The point forecast of the cod catch in any future month is 356. Looking at the data in Figure 16.15(b), these forecasts seem intuitively reasonable.

Holt–Winters' models Various extensions of simple exponential smoothing can be used to forecast time series that are described by models different from the model

$$y_t = \beta_0 + \varepsilon_t.$$

FIGURE **16.15** Example of Using Simple Exponential Smoothing to Forecast the Cod Catches

(a) The graphical forecasts

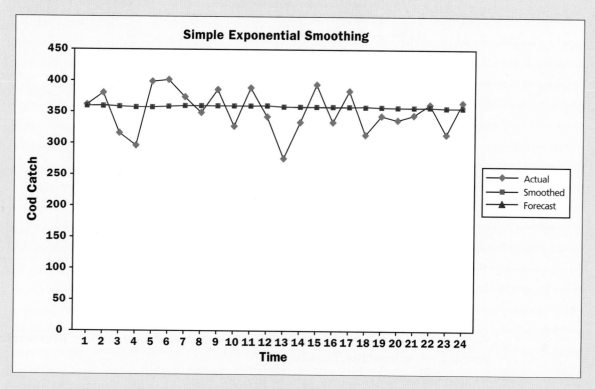

(b) The numerical forecasts of the cod catch in month 25 (and any other future month)

Simple Exponential Smoothing

		Alpha 0.02		
t	CodCatch	Smoothed	Forecast	% error
		359.7 *		
1	362	359.7	360	0.6
2	381	360.1	360	5.5
3	317	359.3	360	−13.6
4	297	358.0	359	−20.9
5	399	358.9	358	10.3
6	402	359.7	359	10.7
7	375	360.0	360	4.0
8	349	359.8	360	−3.2
9	386	360.3	360	6.7
10	328	359.7	360	−9.8
11	389	360.3	360	7.5
12	343	359.9	360	−5.0
13	276	358.2	360	−30.4
14	334	357.8	358	−7.2
15	394	358.5	358	9.1
16	334	358.0	358	−7.2
17	384	358.5	358	6.8
18	314	357.6	359	−14.3
19	344	357.3	358	−4.1
20	337	356.9	357	−5.9
21	345	356.7	357	−3.5
22	362	356.8	357	1.4
23	314	356.0	357	−13.7
24	365	356.1	356	2.5
			356	

1,156.0 Mean Squared Error
8.5% Mean Absolute Percent Error
45.8% Percent Positive Errors

* initial value - mean of first six data values

FIGURE 16.16 MegaStat Output of Using Double Exponential Smoothing to Forecast DVD Player Sales

For example, **Holt–Winters' double exponential smoothing** can forecast time series that are described by the linear trend model

$$y_t = \beta_0 + \beta_1 t + \varepsilon_t.$$

Here we assume that β_0 and β_1 (and thus the linear trend) may be changing slowly over time. To implement Holt–Winters' double exponential smoothing, we find initial estimates of β_0 and β_1 and then use updating equations to track changes in these estimates. The updating equation for the estimate of β_0 uses a smoothing constant that MegaStat calls **alpha**, and the updating equation for the estimate of β_1 uses a smoothing constant that MegaStat calls **beta**. We show in Figure 16.16 the MegaStat output of using double exponential smoothing to forecast the sales of the X-12 DVD player.

Exercises for Section 16.5

CONCEPTS

16.21 In general, when it is appropriate to use exponential smoothing?

16.22 What is the purpose of the smoothing constant in exponential smoothing?

16.23 What are the differences between the types of time series forecast by simple exponential smoothing and double exponential smoothing?

METHODS AND APPLICATIONS

16.24 THE COD CATCH CASE

Consider Table 16.15 (page 575). Verify that S_3, an estimate made in period 3 of β_0, is 359.28. Also verify that the one-period-ahead forecast error for period 4 is -62, as shown in Table 16.15.

16.25 THE LUMBER PRODUCTION CASE

Figure 16.17 gives the MegaStat output of using simple exponential smoothing to forecast yearly lumber production. Use the output to find and report the point prediction of the total lumber production in a future year.

16.26 THE WATCH SALES CASE

Figure 16.18 gives the MegaStat output of using double exponential smoothing in month 20 to forecast watch sales in month 21. Here we have used MegaStat's default option that sets each of the smoothing constants alpha and beta equal to 0.02. Find and report the point prediction of watch sales in month 21.

FIGURE **16.17** MegaStat Output of Using Simple Exponential Smoothing to Forecast Lumber Production

Simple Exponential Smoothing

Alpha
0.02

t	Production	Smoothed	Forecast	% error	t	Production	Smoothed	Forecast	% error
		35,239.7 *			19	38,902	35,409.3	35,338	9.2
1	35,404	35,243.0	35,240	0.5	20	37,858	35,458.3	35,409	6.5
2	37,462	35,287.3	35,243	5.9	21	32,926	35,407.6	35,458	27.7
3	32,901	35,239.6	35,287	−7.3	22	35,697	35,413.4	35,408	0.8
4	33,178	35,198.4	35,240	−6.2	23	34,548	35,396.1	35,413	22.5
5	34,449	35,183.4	35,198	−2.2	24	32,087	35,329.9	35,396	−10.3
6	38,044	35,240.6	35,183	7.5	25	37,515	35,373.6	35,330	5.8
7	36,762	35,271.0	35,241	4.1	26	38,629	35,438.8	35,374	8.4
8	36,742	35,300.4	35,271	4.0	27	32,019	35,370.4	35,439	−10.7
9	33,385	35,262.1	35,300	−5.7	28	35,710	35,377.1	35,370	1.0
10	34,171	35,240.3	35,262	−3.2	29	36,693	35,403.5	35,377	3.6
11	36,124	35,258.0	35,240	2.4	30	37,153	35,438.5	35,403	4.7
12	38,658	35,326.0	35,258	8.8				35,438	
13	32,901	35,277.5	35,326	−7.4				4,188,430.4	Mean Squared Error
14	36,356	35,299.1	35,277	3.0				5.0%	Mean Absolute Percent Error
15	37,166	35,336.4	35,299	5.0					
16	35,733	35,344.3	35,336	1.1				63.3%	Percent Positive Errors
17	35,791	35,353.3	35,344	1.2					
18	34,592	35,338.0	35,353	−2.2			* initial value - mean of first six data values		

FIGURE **16.18** MegaStat Output of Using Double Exponential Smoothing to Forecast Watch Sales

Two-factor Exponential Smoothing

		Alpha 0.02	Beta 0.02								
t	Sales	Smoothed	Trend	Forecast	% error	t	Sales	Smoothed	Trend	Forecast	% error
		278.1	13.3 *			14	392	456.7	13.2	458	−16.8
1	298	291.1	13.3	291	2.3	15	425	469.1	13.2	470	−10.6
2	302	304.0	13.3	304	−0.7	16	411	480.6	13.1	482	−17.3
3	301	316.7	13.3	317	−5.3	17	455	493.2	13.1	494	−8.6
4	351	330.4	13.3	330	6.0	18	457	505.0	13.1	506	−10.7
5	336	343.8	13.3	344	−2.4	19	465	516.9	13.1	518	−11.4
6	361	357.1	13.3	357	1.1	20	481	529.0	13.1	530	−10.2
7	407	370.7	13.3	370	9.1					542	
8	351	383.3	13.3	384	−9.4					2,003.6	Mean Squared Error
9	357	396.2	13.3	397	−11.2						
10	346	408.7	13.3	410	−18.5					9.9%	Mean Absolute Percent Error
11	356	420.7	13.3	422	−18.5						
12	371	432.7	13.2	434	−17.0					20.0%	Percent Positive Errors
13	399	445.1	13.2	446	−11.8			* initial values - estimated by linear trend of first six values			

16.6 FORECAST ERROR COMPARISONS

A forecast error is the difference (or deviation) between the actual value (y_t) and the predicted value ($\hat{y}_t$). Forecast errors can be used to compare forecast values generated by various prediction methods, in that the model with the smallest error value is the best predicting model. Table 16.16 on the next page gives the actual values of Tasty Cola sales in periods 37 through 48 and the multiplicative decomposition method point forecast values. Three criteria by which to compare forecasting methods are the **mean absolute deviation (MAD)**, the **mean squared deviation (MSD)**, and the **percentage error (PE)**.

TABLE **16.16**   Forecast Errors Given by the Multiplicative Decomposition Method in the Tasty Cola Case 🖋

t	y_t	$\hat{y}_t$	$y_t - \hat{y}_t$	abs($y_t - \hat{y}_t$)	$(y_t - \hat{y}_t)^2$	$(y_t - \hat{y}_t)/y_t$*100	abs(PE)
37	352	360.52	−8.52	8.52	72.5904	−2.42045455	2.420455
38	445	441.48	3.52	3.52	12.3904	0.791011236	0.791011
39	453	446.4	6.6	6.6	43.56	1.456953642	1.456954
40	541	516.62	24.38	24.38	594.3844	4.506469501	4.50647
41	457	433.85	23.15	23.15	535.9225	5.065645514	5.065646
42	762	767.82	−5.82	5.82	33.8724	−0.76377953	0.76378
43	1194	1156.3	37.7	37.7	1421.29	3.157453936	3.157454
44	1361	1350.5	10.5	10.5	110.25	0.77149155	0.771492
45	1615	1606.3	8.7	8.7	75.69	0.53869969	0.5387
46	1059	1067.4	−8.4	8.4	70.56	−0.79320113	0.793201
47	824	850.12	−26.12	26.12	682.2544	−3.16990291	3.169903
48	495	501.39	−6.39	6.39	40.8321	−1.29090909	1.290909

To calculate the MAD, we find the absolute value of each forecast error and then average the absolute values:

$$\text{MAD} = \frac{\sum \text{abs}(y_t - \hat{y}_t)}{t}$$

For example, if we find the absolute value of each of the 12 forecast errors given by the multiplicative decomposition method in Table 16.16, sum the 12 absolute values, and divide the sum by 12, we find that the MAD is 14.15.

To calculate the MSD, we find the squared value of each forecast error and then average the squared values:

$$\text{MSD} = \frac{\sum (y_t - \hat{y}_t)^2}{t}$$

For example, if we find the squared value of each of the 12 forecast errors given by the multiplicative decomposition method in Table 16.16, sum the 12 squared values, and divide the sum by 12, we find that the MSD is 307.80. Note, however, that the MSD is the average of the **squared forecast errors**. It follows that the MSD, unlike the MAD, penalizes a forecasting method much more for large forecast errors than for small forecast errors. Therefore, the forecasting method that gives the smallest MSD may not be the forecasting method that gives the smallest MAD.

The MAD and the MSD provide estimates of the forecasting errors, but the values may not be easily interpretable. In contrast, the PE provides a more interpretable value. To calculate the PE, subtract the forecasted value from the observed value, divide the result by the observed value, and multiply by 100:

$$\text{PE} = \frac{y_t - \hat{y}_t}{t} \times 100$$

A PE value is computed for each forecasted value. For example, in Table 16.16, the PE values are given in the second-last column. Two further statistics may then be generated using the PE values: the **mean percentage error (MPE)** and the **mean absolute percentage error (MAPE)**. To compute the MPE, sum the PE values and divide by the number of PE values (number of time estimates). For the Tasty Cola data, the MPE is 0.65. Because negative values will have a cancelling effect on positive values, many researchers prefer the MAPE, which is the average of the absolute PE values. These values are given in the last column of Table 16.16. For these data, the MAPE is 2.06 percent, suggesting that the forecasted values are "off" by about 2 percent on average.

LO4

Exercises for Section 16.6

CONCEPTS

16.27 What is the MAD? What is the MSD? What is the MAPE? How are these quantities used?

16.28 Why does the MSD penalize a forecasting method much more for large forecast errors than for small forecast errors?

METHODS AND APPLICATIONS

Exercises 16.29 and 16.30 compare two forecasting methods—method A and method B. Suppose that method A gives the point forecasts 57, 61, and 70 of three future time series values. Method B gives the point forecasts 59, 65, and 73 of these three future values. The three future values turn out to be 60, 64, and 67.

16.29 Calculate the MAD, the MSD, and the MAPE for method A. Calculate the MAD, the MSD and the MAPE for method B.

16.30 Which method—method A or method B—gives the smaller MAD? the smaller MSD? The smaller MAPE?

16.7 INDEX NUMBERS

We often wish to compare a value of a time series to another value of the time series. For example, Statistics Canada reported in May 2009 that "Consumer prices rose 0.1% in the 12 months to May 2009, down from the 0.4% increase in April. The slowdown in the 12-month Consumer Price Index (CPI) was primarily the result of an 18.3% year-over-year price drop for energy products. Excluding energy, the CPI rose 2.3%." In order to make such comparisons, we must describe the time series. We have seen (in Section 16.4) that time series decomposition can be employed to describe a time series. Another way to describe time-related data is to use **index numbers**.

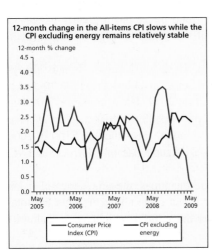

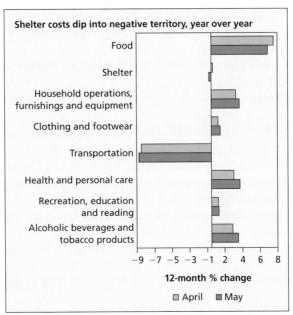

Source: Statistics Canada, *Latest release from the Consumer Price Index*; http://www.statcan.gc.ca/subjects-sujets/cpi-ipc/cpi-ipc-eng.htm; accessed June 18, 2009.

When we compare time series values to the same previous value, we say that the previous value is in the **base time period** and successive comparisons of time series values to the value in the base period form a sequence of **index numbers**. More formally, a **simple index number** (or **simple index**) is defined as follows:

A **simple index** is obtained by dividing the current value of a time series by the value of the time series in the base time period and multiplying this ratio by 100. That is, if y_t denotes the current value and y_0 denotes the value in the base time period, then the **simple index number** is

$$\frac{y_t}{y_0} \times 100.$$

FIGURE **16.19** Bank of Canada Inflation Calculator

How to use the Calculator

Enter any dollar amount, and the years you wish to compare, then click the CALCULATE button.

YEARS MUST BE IN THE RANGE 1914- 2010.
COMMAS AND SPACES CAN BE USED IN THE DOLLAR AMOUNT.

A "basket" of goods and services that cost:	\$ 100.00	in 2000
...would cost:	\$ 121.64	in 2010
CALCULATE Clear		
Per cent change: %	21.64	
Number of Years:	10	
Average Annual Rate of Inflation/ % Decline in the Value of Money:	1.98	
CPI for first year:	(Nov 2000) 96.6	
CPI for second year:	(Nov 2010) 117.5	
	2002 CPI = 100.0	

Data Source: *Statistics Canada*, CONSUMER PRICE INDEXES FOR CANADA, MONTHLY, 1914-2006 (V41690973 series.)

Source: Statistics Canada, *Consumer Price Indexes for Canada, Monthly, 1914–2006* (V41690973 series);
http://www.bankofcanada.ca/en/rates/inflation_calc.html.

LO5   The time series values used to construct an index are often **quantities** or **prices**. In Canada, the CPI was originally tabulated by the Department of Labour in the early 1990s. The monthly CPI is compiled by Statistics Canada and represents the retail price of 600 goods and services considered to be "a representative shopping basket" that encompasses an average household's costs, such as food, clothing, and housing. Each item in the basket is weighted based on the purchasing patterns of consumers, and the sum is computed. As explained by the Bank of Canada (see http://www.bankofcanada.ca/en/backgrounders/bg-i4.html), purchasing food typically costs more than buying clothing, so an increase in food prices has a greater weight or impact on the consumer. The CPI is then used for cost-of-living adjustments and represents a measure of inflation.

In Canada, the CPI is computed against a base year of 1992 (and the base year is always set to \$100; previously the base year was 1986). The Bank of Canada has an online "Inflation Calculator" (see Figure 16.19), which uses CPI indexes from 1914. For example, a \$100 bag of groceries and services in 1914 would be equivalent to \$1,945.00 in 2010 with an average annual inflation rate of 3.14 percent (over 96 years). For a shorter time interval, \$100 in 2000 would be equivalent to \$121.94 in 2010 with the average inflation rate of 2.00 percent over these years.

Because the CPI deals with prices, and these values are quantities, the time series of index values can also be called a **quantity index**. In addition, because the CPI represents the total sum of expenditures, it is also referred to as an **aggregate price index**, computed as follows:

An **aggregate price index** is

$$\left(\frac{\sum p_t}{\sum p_0} \right) \times 100,$$

where $\sum p_t$ is the sum of the prices in the current time period and $\sum p_0$ is the sum of the prices in the base year.

In addition, as mentioned above, Statistics Canada weights the items in the CPI calculations based on the relative importance of the items. For example, weights given by Statistics Canada for CPI items are listed in Table 16.17. In this table, the sum of the weights is 100. As can be seen in Table 16.17, shelter has a greater weight than food, which in turn has over three times the weight of clothing and footwear. This weighting means that the CPI could also be referred to as a **weighted aggregate price index**.

TABLE **16.17** Relative Importance Weights for the Canadian CPI for August 2010 ✎

Item	Relative Importance
All-items	100.00
Food	17.0
Shelter	26.6
Household operations and furnishings	11.1
Clothing and footwear	5.4
Transportation	19.9
Health and personal care	4.7
Recreation, education, and reading	12.2
Alcoholic beverages and tobacco products	3.1

Source: http://www.statcan.gc.ca/pub/62-001-x/62-001-x2010008-eng.pdf.

Two versions of this kind of index are commonly used. The first version is called a **Laspeyres index**. Here the quantities that are specified for the base year are also employed for all succeeding time periods. In general, we have the following:

A **Laspeyres index** is

$$\frac{\sum p_t q_0}{\sum p_0 q_0} \times 100,$$

where p_0 represents a base period price, q_0 represents a base period quantity, and p_t represents a current period price.

Because the Laspeyres index employs the base period quantities in all succeeding time periods, this index allows for ready comparison of prices for identical quantities of goods purchased. Such an index is useful as long as the base quantities provide a reasonable representation of consumption patterns in succeeding time periods. However, purchasing patterns can sometimes change drastically as consumer preferences change or as dramatic price changes occur. If consumption patterns in the current period are very different from the quantities specified in the base period, then a Laspeyres index can be misleading because it relates to quantities of goods that few people would purchase.

A second version of the weighted aggregate price index is called a **Paasche index**. Here we update the quantities so that they reflect consumption patterns in the current time period.

A **Paasche index** is

$$\frac{\sum p_t q_t}{\sum p_0 q_t} \times 100,$$

where p_0 represents a base period price, p_t represents a current period price, and q_t represents a current period quantity.

Because the Paasche index uses quantities from the current period, it reflects current buying habits. However, the Paasche index requires quantity data for each year, which can be difficult to obtain. Furthermore, although each period is compared to the base period, it is difficult to compare the index at other points in time. This is because different quantities are used in different periods, and thus changes in the index are affected by changes in both prices and quantities.

Exercises for Section 16.7

CONCEPTS

16.31 Explain the difference between a simple index and an aggregate index.

16.32 Explain the difference between a Laspeyres index and a Paasche index.

METHODS AND APPLICATIONS

16.33 Following are the statistics for new motor vehicle sales in Canada between 2005 and 2009 as reported by Statistics Canada:

Year	2005	2006	2007	2008	2009
Sales (1,000s)	1,630	1,666	1,690	1,674	1,485

Source: http://www.statcan.gc.ca/pub/63-007-x/63-007-x2010007-eng.pdf.

a. By using the year 2005 as the base year, construct a simple index for the new motor vehicle sales data.
b. Interpret the index in each of the years 2008 and 2009.
c. Plot the values and assess the overall pattern.

16.34 Below are the statistics for the production of building materials (sawn lumber) in Canada between 2004 and 2008, as reported by Statistics Canada.

Production of building materials

	2004	2005	2006	2007	2008
			Sawn lumber		
			Thousand cubic metres		
Total	84,589.6	82,888.9	80,870.4	72,042.6	57,250.1

Note: Standard Classification of Goods (*SCG*).
Source: Statistics Canada CANSIM, table (for fee) 303-0009 and Catalogue no. 35-003-X. Last modified: 2009-06-30.

a. By using 2004 as the base year, calculate a simple index for sawn lumber production.
b. What is the overall trend in the production values?
c. What is a possible reason for the trend in the production of sawn lumber?

16.35 In the following table, we present the average prices of three precious metals—gold, silver, and platinum—for the years 1988 through 1996:

Year	Gold Price ($US/Fine Oz.)	Silver Price ($US/Fine Oz.)	Platinum Price ($US/Troy Oz.)
1988	438	6.53	523
1989	383	5.50	507
1990	385	4.82	467
1991	363	4.04	371
1992	345	3.94	360
1993	361	4.30	374
1994	385	5.29	411
1995	368	5.15	425
1996	390	5.30	410

Source: Through 1994, U.S. Bureau of Mines; thereafter, U.S. Geological Survey, *Minerals Yearbook* and *Mineral Commodities Summaries*, as presented in *Statistical Abstract of the United States*, 1997, p. 701.

a. By using the year 1988 as the base year, construct a simple index for each of gold, silver, and platinum.
b. Using the three indexes you constructed in part a, describe price trends for gold, silver, and platinum from 1988 to 1996.
c. By using the year 1988 as the base year, construct an aggregate price index for these precious metals. Using the aggregate price index, describe trends for precious metals prices from 1988 to 1996.
d. By using the year 1990 as the base year, construct an aggregate price index for these precious metals.

16.36 In the following table, we present prices for three commonly used products—bread, fruits, and beverages—for the years 2000 through 2006.

Year	Bread ($ per Loaf)	Fruits ($ per kg)	Beverages ($ per L)
2000	$1.22	$1.71	$0.66
2001	$1.20	$1.64	$0.67
2002	$1.19	$1.74	$0.68
2003	$1.17	$2.04	$0.69
2004	$1.17	$1.85	$0.69
2005	$1.21	$1.55	$0.69
2006	$1.29	$2.25	$0.69

a. Consider a large family that consumes 1,850 loaves of bread, 150 kg of fruits, and 1,700 L of beverages every year. Construct the Laspeyres index for these food products using 2000 as the base year. Then describe how food prices have changed for this family over this period.
b. Consider a large family with the following food consumption pattern from 2000 to 2006.

Year	Bread (Loaves)	Fruits (kg)	Beverages (L)
2000	2,200	150	1,500
2001	2,100	150	1,600
2002	2,000	150	1,700
2003	1,950	150	1,800
2004	1,950	150	2,000
2005	1,900	150	2,100
2006	1,750	150	2,250

Construct the Paasche index for these food products using 2000 as the base year. How does the Paasche index compare to the Laspeyres index you constructed in part a?

CHAPTER SUMMARY

In this chapter, we have discussed using **univariate time series** models to forecast future time series values. We began by seeing that it can be useful to think of a time series as consisting of **trend**, **seasonal**, **cyclical**, and **irregular components**. If these components remain **constant** over time, then it is appropriate to describe and forecast the time series by using a **time series regression model**. We discussed using such models to describe **no trend**, a **linear trend**, a **quadratic trend**, and **constant seasonal variation** (by utilizing dummy variables). We also considered various transformations that transform **increasing seasonal variation** into constant seasonal variation, and we saw that we can use the Durbin–Watson test to check for **first-order autocorrelation**. As an alternative to using a transformation and

dummy variables to model increasing seasonal variation, we can use the **multiplicative decomposition method**. We discussed this intuitive method and saw how to calculate approximate prediction intervals when using it. We then turned to a consideration of **exponential smoothing**, which is appropriate to use if the components of a time series may be **changing slowly** over time. Specifically, we discussed **simple exponential smoothing** and **Holt–Winters' double exponential smoothing**. We next considered how to compare forecasting methods by using the **mean absolute deviation (MAD)**, the **mean squared deviation (MSD)**, and the **percentage error (PE)**. We concluded this chapter by showing how to use **index numbers** to describe time-related data.

GLOSSARY OF TERMS

cyclical variation: Recurring up-and-down movements of a time series around trend levels that last more than one calendar year (often two to ten years) from peak to peak or trough to trough. (page 554)

deseasonalized time series: A time series that has had the effect of seasonal variation removed. (pages 569–572)

exponential smoothing: A forecasting method that weights recent observations more heavily than remote observations. (page 573)

index number: A number that compares a value of a time series to another value of the time series. (page 581)

irregular component: What is left over in a time series after trend, cycle, and seasonal variations have been accounted for. (page 566)

moving averages: Averages of successive groups of time series observations. (page 566)

seasonal variation: Periodic patterns in a time series that repeat themselves within a calendar year and are then repeated yearly. (page 554)

smoothing constant: A number that determines how much weight is attached to each observation when using exponential smoothing. (page 553)

time series: A set of observations that has been collected in time order. (page 553)

trend: The long-run upward or downward movement that characterizes a time series over a period of time. (page 554)

univariate time series model: A model that predicts future values of a time series solely on the basis of past values of the time series. (page 553)

IMPORTANT FORMULAS AND TESTS

No trend: page 555

Linear trend: page 556

Quadratic trend: page 556

Modelling constant seasonal variation by using dummy variables: pages 557–558

The multiplicative decomposition method: pages 556–572

Simple exponential smoothing: page 575

Double exponential smoothing: page 578

Mean absolute deviation (MAD): page 580

Mean squared deviation (MSD): page 580

Mean absolute percentage error (MAPE): page 580

Simple index: page 581

Aggregate price index: page 582

Laspeyres index: page 583

Paasche index: page 583

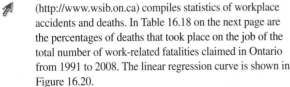 Practise and learn online with *Connect.* Questions and tables with online data sets are marked with 🖋.

SUPPLEMENTARY EXERCISES

16.37 The Workplace Safety Insurance Board of Ontario 🖋 (http://www.wsib.on.ca) compiles statistics of workplace accidents and deaths. In Table 16.18 on the next page are the percentages of deaths that took place on the job of the total number of work-related fatalities claimed in Ontario from 1991 to 2008. The linear regression curve is shown in Figure 16.20.

a. Would you state that the percentages of deaths on the job have decreased significantly?

b. Enter the raw data into a statistical package and forecast the predicted values for the next five years. How would you assess the accuracy of these predicted numbers?

TABLE **16.18** Percentage of Fatalities Claimed That Represent Death on the Job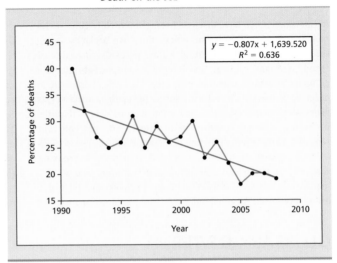

Year	Percentage of Deaths	Year	Percentage of Deaths
1991	40	2000	27
1992	32	2001	30
1993	27	2002	23
1994	25	2003	26
1995	26	2004	22
1996	31	2005	18
1997	25	2006	20
1998	29	2007	20
1999	26	2008	19

Source: http://www.wsib.on.ca/wsib/wsibsite.nsf/Public/AnnualReports.

FIGURE **16.20** Percentage of Fatalities Claimed That Represent Death on the Job

TABLE **16.19** Sales of the Bass Grabber (in Tens of Thousands of Lures)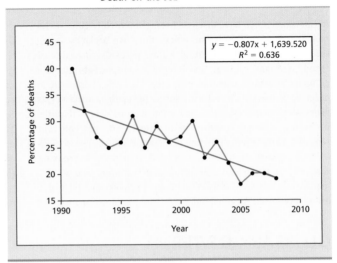

Period, t	Sales, y_t	Price, x_1	Average Industry Price, x_2	Advertising Expenditure, x_3
1	4.797	3.85	3.80	5.50
2	6.297	3.75	4.00	6.75
3	8.010	3.70	4.30	7.25
4	7.800	3.70	3.70	5.50
5	9.690	3.60	3.85	7.00
6	10.871	3.60	3.80	6.50
7	12.425	3.60	3.75	6.75
8	10.310	3.80	3.85	5.25
9	8.307	3.80	3.65	5.25
10	8.960	3.85	4.00	6.00
11	7.969	3.90	4.10	6.50
12	6.276	3.90	4.00	6.25
13	4.580	3.70	4.10	7.00
14	5.759	3.75	4.20	6.90
15	6.586	3.75	4.10	6.80
16	8.199	3.80	4.10	6.80
17	9.630	3.70	4.20	7.10
18	9.810	3.80	4.30	7.00
19	11.913	3.70	4.10	6.80
20	12.879	3.80	3.75	6.50
21	12.065	3.80	3.75	6.25
22	10.530	3.75	3.65	6.00
23	9.845	3.70	3.90	6.50
24	9.524	3.55	3.65	7.00
25	7.354	3.60	4.10	6.80
26	4.697	3.65	4.25	6.80
27	6.052	3.70	3.65	6.50
28	6.416	3.75	3.75	5.75
29	8.253	3.80	3.85	5.80
30	10.057	3.70	4.25	6.80

16.38 Alluring Tackle, a manufacturer of fishing equipment, makes the Bass Grabber, a type of fishing lure. The company would like to develop a prediction model that can be used to obtain point forecasts and prediction interval forecasts of the sales of the Bass Grabber. The sales (in tens of thousands of lures) of the Bass Grabber in sales period t, where each sales period is defined to last four weeks, are denoted by the symbol y_t

and are believed to be partially determined by one or more of the independent variables x_1 = the price in period t of the Bass Grabber as offered by Alluring Tackle (in dollars), x_2 = the average industry price in period t of competitors' similar lures (in dollars), and x_3 = the advertising expenditure in period t of Alluring Tackle to promote the Bass Grabber (in tens of thousands of dollars). The data in Table 16.19 have been observed over the past 30 sales periods, and a plot of these data indicates that sales of the Bass Grabber have been increasing in a linear fashion over time and have been seasonal, with sales of the lure being greatest in the spring and summer, when most recreational fishing takes place. Alluring Tackle believes that this pattern will continue in the future. Hence, remembering that each year consists of 13 four-week seasons, a possible regression model for predicting y_t would relate y_t to x_1, x_2, x_3, t, and the seasonal dummy variables $S_2, S_3, \ldots, S_{13}$. Here, for example, S_2 equals 1 if sales period t is the second four-week season, and 0 otherwise. As another example, S_{13} equals 1 if sales period t is the 13th four-week season, and 0 otherwise. If we calculate the least squares point estimates of the parameters of the model, we obtain the following prediction equation (the t statistic for the importance of each independent variable is given in parentheses under the independent variable):

$$\hat{y}_t = 0.1776 + 0.4071x_1 - 0.7837x_2 + 0.9934x_3 + 0.0435t$$
$$\quad\;\; (0.05) \quad\;\; (0.42) \quad\;\; (-1.51) \quad\;\; (4.89) \quad\;\; (6.49)$$
$$+\; 0.7800S_2 + 2.373S_3 + 3.488S_4 + 3.805S_5$$
$$\quad\;\; (3.16) \qquad (9.28) \qquad (12.88) \qquad (13.01)$$
$$+\; 5.673S_6 + 6.738S_7 + 6.097S_8 + 4.301S_9$$
$$\quad\;\; (19.41) \quad\;\; (23.23) \quad\;\; (21.47) \quad\;\; (14.80)$$
$$+\; 3.856S_{10} + 2.621S_{11} + 0.9969S_{12} - 1.467S_{13}.$$
$$\quad\;\; (13.89) \qquad (9.24) \qquad (3.50) \qquad (-4.70)$$

a. For sales period 31, which is the fifth season of the year, x_1 will be 3.80, x_2 will be 3.90, and x_3 will be 6.80. Using these values, it can be shown that a point prediction of and a 95 percent prediction interval for sales of the Bass Grabber are, respectively, 10.578 and [9.683, 11.473]. Using the given prediction equation, verify that the point prediction is 10.578.

b. Some t statistics indicate that some of the independent variables might not be important. Using the regression techniques of Chapter 12, try to find a better model for predicting sales of the Bass Grabber.

16.39 In the next column are the total exports (in thousands of Canadian dollars) of mining exports to the United Kingdom from Canada between 2005 and 2009, as reported by Industry Canada from their Trade Data Online (TDO) feature (http://www.ic.gc.ca).

a. Describe the trend in exports over the timespan plotted.

b. Using MegaStat, predict the 2010 export value.

Canadian Trade with the United Kindom:
Total Exports in Mining (Excluding Oil and Gas)

Year	Amount
2005	2,959,387
2006	3,950,007
2007	3,865,555
2008	6,120,554
2009	6,833,459

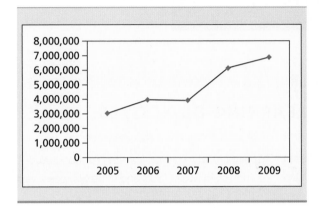

16.40 INTERNET EXERCISE

Below are the CPI values for Canada for the month of January from 1989 to 2008, as reported by Statistics Canada.

Year	Jan. CPI	Year	Jan. CPI
1989	72.7	1999	91.5
1990	76.7	2000	93.5
1991	82	2001	96.3
1992	83.3	2002	97.6
1993	85	2003	102
1994	86.1	2004	103.3
1995	86.6	2005	105.3
1996	88	2006	108.2
1997	89.9	2007	109.4
1998	90.9	2008	111.8

a. Plot the values and assess whether or not a linear trend is occurring.

b. Enter the data into a spreadsheet and do a regression analysis to calculate the predicted CPI value for January 2009 and January 2010.

c. Go to the Statistics Canada Web site (http://www.statcan.gc.ca) and determine the actual CPI values. How accurate were the predictions made by the regression analysis?

CHAPTER **17**
Process Improvement Using Control Charts

In this chapter, we explain how to use **control charts** to improve business processes. A control chart is a graphical device that helps us determine when a process is out of control. The information provided by a control chart helps us discover the causes of unusual process variations. When such causes have been identified, we attempt to remove them in order to reduce the amount of process variation. By doing so, we improve the process.

We begin this chapter by trying to explain the meaning of quality, and then we trace the history of the U.S. quality movement. Then we study control charts for monitoring the level and variability of a process and for monitoring the fraction of nonconforming (or defective) units produced. We also discuss how to evaluate the *process capability*. That is, we show how to assess a process's ability to produce individual items that meet customer requirements (*specifications*). In particular, we explain the concept of six sigma capability, which was introduced by Motorola Inc.

In order to demonstrate the ideas of this chapter, we employ three case studies:

The Hole Location Case: A manufacturer of automobile air conditioner compressors uses control charts to reduce variation in the locations of a hose connection hole that is punched in the outer housing (or shell) of the compressor.

The Hot Chocolate Temperature Case: The food service staff at a university dining hall wish to avoid possible litigation by making sure that they do not serve excessively hot beverages. The staff use control charts to find and eliminate causes of unusual variations in hot chocolate temperatures.

The Camshaft Case: An automobile manufacturer wishes to improve the process it uses to harden a part in a camshaft assembly. The manufacturer uses control charts and process capability studies to reduce the sources of process variation that are responsible for a 12 percent rework rate and a 9 percent scrap rate. After the process variation is reduced, virtually all of the hardened parts meet specifications. (*Note:* this case is included in the supplementary exercises.)

 Practise and learn online with *Connect*. Throughout this chapter, questions and tables with online data sets are marked with 🖊.

17.1 QUALITY: ITS MEANING AND A HISTORICAL PERSPECTIVE

What is quality? It is not easy to define quality, and a number of different definitions have been proposed. One definition that makes sense is **fitness for use**. Here the user of a product or service can be an individual, a manufacturer, a retailer, or the like. For instance, an individual who purchases a television or a digital video recorder (DVR) expects the unit to be defect free and to provide years of reliable, high-performance service. If the TV or DVR performs as desired, it is fit for use. Another definition of quality that makes sense says that quality is the extent to which customers feel that a product or service exceeds their needs and expectations. For instance, if the DVR purchaser believes the unit exceeds all the needs and expectations they had for the DVR when it was purchased, then the customer is satisfied with the unit's quality.

Three types of quality can be considered: **quality of design**, **quality of conformance**, and **quality of performance**. Quality of design has to do with intentional differences between goods and services with the same basic purpose. For instance, all DVRs are built to perform the same function—record and play back recorded shows. However, DVRs differ with respect to various design characteristics—picture sharpness, size of hard drive, digital effects, ease of use, and so forth. A given level of design quality may satisfy some consumers and not others. The product design will specify a set of **tolerances (specifications)** that must be met. For example, the design of a DVR sets forth many specifications regarding electronic and physical characteristics that must be met if the unit is to operate acceptably. Quality of conformance is the ability of a process to meet the specifications set forth by the design. Quality of performance is how well the product or service actually performs in the marketplace. Companies must find out how well customers' needs are met and how reliable products are by conducting after-sales research.

The marketing research arm of a company must determine what the customer seeks in each of these dimensions. Consumer research is used to develop a product or service concept—a combination of design characteristics that exceeds the expectations of a large number of consumers. This concept is translated into a design. The design includes specifications that, if met, will satisfy the consumer's wants and needs. A production process is then developed to meet the design specifications. In order to do this, variables that can control the process must be identified, and the relationships between input variables and final quality characteristics must be understood. The manufacturer expresses quality characteristics as measurable variables that can be tracked and used to monitor and improve the performance of the process. Service call analysis often leads to product or service redesigns in order to improve the product or service concept. It is extremely important that the initial design be a good one so that excessive redesigns and customer dissatisfaction can be avoided.

History of the quality movement In the 1700s and 1800s, master craftspeople and their apprentices were responsible for designing and building products. Quantities of goods produced were small, and product quality was controlled by expert quality of work. Master craftspeople had a great deal of pride in their work, and quality was not a problem. However, the introduction of mass production in the late 1800s and early 1900s changed things. Production processes became very complex, with many workers (rather than one skilled craftsperson) responsible for the final product. Inevitably, product quality characteristics displayed variation. In particular, Henry Ford developed the moving assembly line at Ford Motor Company. As assembly line manufacturing spread, quality became a problem. Production managers were rewarded for meeting production quotas, and quality suffered. To make mass-produced products more consistent, inspectors were hired to check product quality. However, 100 percent inspection proved to be costly, and people started to look for alternatives.

Much of the early work in quality control was done at Bell Telephone (now known as American Telephone and Telegraph or AT&T). The Bell System and Western Electric, the manufacturing arm of Bell Telephone, formed the Inspection Engineering Department to deal with quality problems. In 1924, Walter Shewhart of Bell Telephone Laboratories introduced the concept of statistical quality control—controlling the quality of mass-produced goods. Shewhart believed that variation always exists in manufactured products, and that the variation can be studied, monitored, and controlled using statistics. In particular, Shewhart developed a statistical tool called the **control chart**. Such a chart is a graph that can tell a company when a process needs to be adjusted and when the process should be left alone. In the late 1920s, Harold F. Dodge and Harold G. Romig, also of Bell Telephone Laboratories, introduced **statistical acceptance sampling**, a statistical sampling technique that enables a company to accept or reject a quantity of goods (called a **lot**) without inspecting the entire lot. By the mid-1930s, Western Electric was heavily using **statistical quality control (SQC)** to improve quality, increase productivity, and reduce inspection costs. However, these statistical methods were not widely adopted outside Bell Telephone.

During World War II, statistical quality control became widespread. Faced with the task of producing large quantities of high-quality war matériel, industry turned to statistical methods, failure analysis, vendor certification, and early product design. The U.S. War Department required that suppliers of war matériel employ acceptance sampling, and its use became commonplace. Statistical control charts were also used, although not as widely as acceptance sampling.

In 1946, the **American Society for Quality Control (ASQC)** (now called the American Society for Quality) was established to encourage the use of quality improvement methods. The organization sponsors training programs, seminars, and publications dealing with quality issues. In spite of the efforts of the ASQC, however, interest in quality in U.S. industry diminished after the war. U.S. businesses had little competition in the world market—Europe and Japan were rebuilding their shattered economies. Tremendous emphasis was placed on increased production because firms were often unable to meet the demand for their products. Profits were high, and the concern for quality waned. As a result, postwar U.S. managers did not understand the importance of quality and process improvement, and they were not informed about quality improvement techniques.

However, events in Japan took a different turn. After the war, Japanese industrial capacity was crippled. Productivity was very low, and products were of notoriously bad quality. In those days, products stamped "Made in Japan" were generally considered to be "cheap junk." The man credited with turning this situation around is W. Edwards Deming. Deming, born in 1900, earned a Ph.D. in mathematical physics from Yale University in 1927. He then went to work in a U.S. Department of Agriculture–affiliated laboratory. Deming, who had learned statistics while studying physics, applied statistics to experiments conducted at the laboratory. Through this work, Deming was introduced to Walter Shewhart, who explained his theories about using statistical control charts to improve quality and productivity. During World War II, Deming was largely responsible for teaching 35,000 U.S. engineers and technical people how to use statistics to improve the quality of war matériel. After the war, the Allied command sent a group of the engineers to Japan. Their mission was to improve the Japanese communication system. In doing so, the engineers employed the statistical methods they had learned, and Deming's work was brought to the attention of the Union of Japanese Scientists and Engineers (JUSE). Deming, who had started his own consulting firm in 1946, was asked by the JUSE to help increase Japanese productivity. In July 1950, Deming travelled to Japan and gave a series of lectures titled "Elementary Principles of the Statistical Control of Quality" to a group of 230 Japanese managers. Deming taught the Japanese how to use statistics to determine how well a system can perform and how to design process improvements to make the system operate better and more efficiently. He also taught the Japanese that the more quality a producer builds into a product, the less it costs. Realizing the serious nature of their economic crisis, the Japanese adopted Deming's ideas as a philosophy of doing business. Through Deming, the Japanese found that by listening to the wants and needs of consumers and by using statistical methods for process improvement in production, they could export high-quality products to the world market.

Although U.S. businesses were making only feeble attempts to improve product quality in the 1950s and 1960s, they were able to maintain a dominant competitive position. Many U.S. companies focused more on marketing and financial strategies than on product and production. But Japanese and other foreign competitors were making inroads. By the 1970s, the quality of many Japanese and European products (for instance, automobiles, television sets, and electronic equipment) became far superior to their U.S.-made counterparts. Also, rising prices made consumers more quality conscious—people expected high quality if they were going to pay high prices. As a result, the market shares of U.S. firms rapidly decreased. Many U.S. firms were severely injured or went out of business.

Meanwhile, Deming continued teaching and preaching quality improvement. While Deming was famous in Japan, he was relatively unknown in the United States until 1980. In June 1980, Deming was featured in an NBC television documentary titled "If Japan Can, Why Can't We?" This program, written and narrated by then–NBC correspondent Lloyd Dobyns, compared Japanese and U.S. industrial productivity and credited Deming for Japan's success. Within days, demand for Deming's consulting services skyrocketed. Deming consulted with many major U.S. firms. Among these firms are The Ford Motor Company, General Motors Corporation, and The Procter & Gamble Company. Ford, for instance, began consulting with Deming in 1981. Donald Petersen, who was Ford's chairman and chief executive officer at the time, became a Deming disciple. By following the Deming philosophy, Ford, which was losing $U.S. 2 billion yearly in 1980, attempted to create a quality culture. The quality of Ford products was greatly improved, and the company again became profitable. The 1980s saw many U.S. companies adopt a philosophy of continuous improvement of quality and productivity in all areas of their businesses—manufacturing, accounting, sales, finance, personnel, marketing, customer service, maintenance, and so forth. This overall approach of applying quality principles to all company activities is called **total quality management (TQM)** or **total quality control (TQC)**. It is becoming an important management strategy in North American business. Dr. Deming taught seminars on quality improvement for managers and statisticians until his death on December 20, 1993. Deming's work resulted in widespread changes in both the structure of the world economy and the ways in which North American businesses are managed.

The fundamental ideas behind Deming's approach to quality and productivity improvement are contained in his **14 points**. These are a set of managerial principles that, if followed, Deming believed would enable a company to improve quality and productivity, reduce costs, and compete effectively in the world market. We briefly summarize the 14 points in Table 17.1 on the next page. For more complete discussions of these points, see Bowerman and O'Connell (1996), Deming (1986), Walton (1986), Scherkenbach (1986), and Gitlow, Gitlow, Oppenheim, and Oppenheim (1989). Deming stressed that implementation of the 14 points requires both changes in management philosophy and the use of statistical methods. In addition, Deming believed that it is necessary to follow all of the points, not just some of them.

In 1988, the first Malcolm Baldrige National Quality Awards were presented. These awards, presented by the U.S. Commerce Department, are named for the late Malcolm Baldrige, who was Commerce Secretary during the administration of U.S. president Ronald Reagan. The awards were established to promote quality awareness, to recognize quality achievements by U.S. companies, and to publicize successful quality strategies. The Malcolm Baldrige National Quality Award Consortium, formed by the ASQC and the American Productivity and Quality Centre, administers the award. The Baldrige award has become one of the most prestigious

TABLE **17.1** W. Edwards Deming's 14 Points

1 **Create constancy of purpose toward improvement of product and service with a plan to become competitive, stay in business, and provide jobs.**
Devise a plan for the long-term success of the company based on quality improvement.

2 **Adopt a new philosophy.**
Do not tolerate commonly accepted mistakes, delays, defective materials, and defective quality of work.

3 **Cease dependence on mass inspection.**
Quality cannot be inspected into a product. It must be built into the product through process improvement.

4 **End the practice of awarding business on the basis of price tag.**
Do not buy from the lowest bidder without taking the quality of goods purchased into account. Purchasing should be based on lowest total cost (including the cost of bad quality).

5 **Improve constantly and forever the system of production and service to improve quality and productivity, and thus constantly decrease costs.**
Constantly seek to improve every aspect of the business.

6 **Institute training.**
Workers should know how to do their jobs and should know how their jobs affect quality and the success of the company.

7 **Institute leadership.**
The job of management is leadership, not mere supervision. Leadership involves understanding the work that needs to be done and fostering process improvement.

8 **Drive out fear, so that everyone may work more effectively for the company.**
Workers should not be afraid to express ideas, to ask questions, or to take appropriate action.

9 **Break down organizational barriers.**
Barriers that damage the company performance (such as competition between staff areas, poor communication, disputes between labour and management, and so on) must be removed so that everyone can work for the good of the company.

10 **Eliminate slogans, exhortations, and arbitrary numerical goals and targets for the workforce that urge the workers to achieve new levels of productivity and quality without providing methods.**
Slogans and numerical goals (such as production quotas) are counterproductive unless management provides methods for achieving them.

11 **Eliminate work standards and numerical quotas.**
Work standards and numerical quotas that specify the quantity of goods to be produced while quality is ignored are counterproductive and should be eliminated.

12 **Remove barriers that rob employees of their pride of quality in their work.**
While workers want to do a good job and have pride in their work, bad management practices often rob workers of their pride. Barriers that rob workers of pride (such as inadequate instructions, cheap materials, poor maintenance, and so on) must be removed.

13 **Institute a vigorous program of education and self-improvement.**
Education and training are necessary for everyone if continuous improvement is to be achieved.

14 **Take action to accomplish the transformation.**
A management structure that is committed to continuous improvement must be put in place.

honours in American business. Annual awards are given in three categories—manufacturing, service, and small business. Winners include companies such as Motorola Inc., Xerox Corporation Business Products and Systems, the Commercial Nuclear Fuel Division of Westinghouse Electric Corporation, Milliken and Company, Cadillac Division, General Motors Corporation, Ritz Carlton Hotels, and AT&T Consumer Communications.

Finally, the 1990s saw the adoption of an international quality standards system called **ISO 9000**. More than 90 countries around the globe have adopted the ISO 9000 standards for their companies, as have many multinational corporations (including AT&T, 3M, IBM, Motorola, and DuPont). As a brief introduction to ISO 9000, we quote "Is ISO 9000 for You?" published by CEEM Information Systems:

What Is ISO 9000?

ISO 9000 is a series of international standards for quality assurance management systems. It establishes the organizational structure and processes for assuring that the production of goods or services meets a consistent and agreed-upon level of quality for a company's customers.

The ISO 9000 series is unique in that it applies to a very wide range of organizations and industries encompassing both the manufacturing and service sectors.

> **Why Is ISO 9000 Important?**
>
> *ISO 9000 is important for two reasons.* First . . . the discipline imposed by the standard for processes influencing your quality management systems can enhance your company's quality consistency. Whether or not you decide to register your company to ISO 9000 standards, your implementing such discipline can achieve greater efficiency in your quality control systems.
>
> Second . . . more and more companies, both here at home and internationally, are requiring their suppliers to be ISO 9000 registered. To achieve your full market potential in such industries, registration is becoming essential. Those companies who become registered have a distinct competitive advantage, and sales growth in today's demanding market climate requires every advantage you can muster.[1]

Clearly, quality has finally become a crucially important issue in North American business. The quality revolution now affects every area in business. But the Japanese continue to mount new challenges. For years, the Japanese have used **designed statistical experiments** to develop new processes, find and remedy process problems, improve product performance, and improve process efficiency. Much of this work is based on the insights of Genichi Taguchi, a Japanese engineer. His methods of experimental design, the **Taguchi methods**, have been heavily used in Japan since the 1960s. Although Taguchi's methodology is controversial in statistical circles, the use of experimental design gives the Japanese a considerable advantage over U.S. competitors because it enables them to design a high level of quality into a product before production begins. Some U.S. manufacturers have begun to use experimental design techniques to design quality into their products. It will be necessary for many more U.S. companies to do so in order to remain competitive in the future—a challenge for the 21st century.

17.2 STATISTICAL PROCESS CONTROL AND CAUSES OF PROCESS VARIATION

Statistical process control Statistical process control (SPC) is a systematic method for analyzing process data (quality characteristics) in which we monitor and study the **process variation**. The goal is to stabilize the process and to reduce the amount of process variation. The ultimate goal is **continuous process improvement**. We often use SPC to monitor and improve manufacturing processes. However, SPC is also commonly used to improve service quality. For instance, we might use SPC to reduce the time it takes to process a loan application, or to improve the accuracy of an order entry system.

Before the widespread use of SPC, quality control was based on an **inspection** approach. Here the product is first made, and then the final product is inspected to eliminate defective items. This is called **action on the output** of the process. The emphasis here is on detecting defective product that has already been produced. This is costly and wasteful because if defective product is produced, the bad items must be (1) scrapped, (2) reworked or reprocessed (that is, fixed), or (3) downgraded (sold off at a lower price). In fact, the cost of bad quality (scrap, rework, and so on) can be tremendously high. It is not unusual for this cost to be as high as 10 percent to 30 percent or more of a company's dollar sales.

In contrast to the inspection approach, SPC emphasizes integrating quality improvement into the process. Here the goal is *preventing bad quality by taking appropriate action on the process.* In order to accomplish this goal, we must decide when actions on the process are needed. The focus of much of this chapter is to show how such decisions can be made.

Causes of process variation In order to understand SPC methodology, we must realize that the variations we observe in quality characteristics are caused by different sources. These sources include factors such as equipment (machines and the like), materials, people, methods

LO1

LO2

[1]Source: CEEM Information Services, "Is ISO 9000 for You?" 1993.

and procedures, the environment, and so forth. Here we must distinguish between **usual process variation** and **unusual process variation**. Usual process variation results from what we call **common causes of process variation**.

Common causes are sources of variation that can influence all process observations. That is, these sources of variation are inherent to the current process design.

Common cause variation can be substantial. For instance, obsolete or poorly maintained equipment, a poorly designed process, and inadequate instructions for workers are examples of common causes that might significantly influence all process output. As an example, suppose that we are filling 500-mL jars with strawberry jam. A 25-year-old, obsolete filler machine might be a common cause of process variation that influences all the jar fills. While (in theory) it might be possible to replace the filler machine with a new model, we might have chosen not to do so, and the obsolete filler causes all the jar fills to exhibit substantial variation.

Common causes also include small influences that would cause slight variation even if all conditions are held as constant as humanly possible. For example, in the jar fill situation, small variations in the speed at which jars move under the filler valves, slight floor vibrations, and small differences between filler valve settings would always influence the jar fills even when conditions were held as constant as possible. Sometimes these small variations are described as being due to chance.

Together, the important and unimportant common causes of variation determine the **usual process variability**. That is, these causes determine the amount of variation that exists when the process is operating routinely. We can reduce the amount of common cause variation by removing some of the important common causes. *Reducing common cause variation is usually a management responsibility.* For instance, replacing obsolete equipment, redesigning a plant or process, or improving plant maintenance requires management action.

In addition to common cause variation, processes are affected by a different kind of variation called **assignable cause variation** (sometimes also called **special cause** or **specific cause variation**).

Assignable causes are sources of unusual process variation. These are intermittent or permanent changes in the process that are not common to all process observations and that may cause important process variation. Assignable causes are usually of short duration, but they can be persistent or recurring conditions.

For example, in the jar-filling situation, one of the filler valves may become clogged so that some jars are being substantially underfilled (or perhaps not filled at all). Or a relief operator might incorrectly set the filler so that all jars are being substantially overfilled for a short period of time. As another example, suppose that a bank wishes to study the length of time customers must wait before being served by a teller. If a customer has forgotten their bank card, this might cause a temporary delay that increases the waiting time for other customers. Notice that assignable causes such as these can often be remedied by local supervision—for instance, by a production line supervisor, a machine operator, a head bank teller, or the like. *One objective of SPC is to detect and eliminate assignable causes of process variation.* By doing this, we reduce the amount of process variation. This results in improved quality.

It is important to point out that an assignable cause could be beneficial—that is, it could be an unusual process variation resulting in unusually good process performance. In such a situation, we wish to discover the root cause of the variation, and then we wish to incorporate this condition into the process if possible. For instance, suppose we find that a process performs unusually well when a raw material purchased from a particular supplier is used. It might be desirable to purchase as much of the raw material as possible from this supplier.

When a process exhibits only common cause variation, it will operate in a stable fashion. That is, in the absence of any unusual process variations, the process will display a constant amount of variation around a constant mean. On the other hand, if assignable causes are affecting the process, then the process will not be stable—unusual variations will cause the process mean or variability to change over time. Then we have the following:

1 When a process is influenced only by *common cause variation, the process will be in statistical control.*

2 When a process is influenced by *one or more assignable causes, the process will not be in statistical control.*

In general, in order to bring a process into statistical control, we must find and eliminate undesirable assignable causes of process variation, and we should (if feasible) build desirable assignable causes into the process. When we have done these things, the process is what we call a **stable, common cause system**. This means that the process operates in a *consistent* fashion and is *predictable*. Since there are no unusual process variations, the process (as currently configured) is doing all that it can be expected to do.

When a process is in statistical control, management can evaluate the **process capability**. That is, it can assess whether the process can produce output meeting customer or producer requirements. If it does not, action by local supervision will not remedy the situation—remember that the assignable causes (the sources of process variation that can be dealt with by local supervision) have already been removed. Rather, some fundamental change will be needed in order to reduce common cause variation. For instance, perhaps a new, more modern filler machine must be purchased and installed. This will require action by management.

Finally, the SPC approach is really a philosophy of doing business. It is an entire firm or organization that is focused on a single goal: continuous quality and productivity improvement. The impetus for this philosophy must come from management. Unless management is supportive and directly involved in the ongoing quality improvement process, the SPC approach will not be successful.

Exercises for Section 17.2

CONCEPTS

17.1 A television show aired recently about businesses such as grocery stores and restaurants and the waste they produce. During the economic downturn of 2008, a lot of families have had to make sacrifices and go without to make ends meet. Sometimes that means going without a meal or not eating properly. With grocery stores and restaurants throwing out unsaleable, but usable, product, many people were becoming upset. The main question was, "Why couldn't these places donate their unsaleable product to shelters or food banks?" Provide some arguments to support both sides.

17.2 Write a paragraph explaining how common causes of process variation differ from assignable causes of process variation.

METHODS AND APPLICATIONS

17.3 In this exercise, we consider several familiar processes. In each case, describe several common causes and

several assignable causes that might result in variation in the given quality characteristic.
  a. Process: getting ready for school or work in the morning.
     Quality characteristic: the time it takes to get ready.
  b. Process: driving, walking, or otherwise commuting from your home to school or work. Quality characteristic: the time it takes to commute.
  c. Process: studying for and taking a statistics exam. Quality characteristic: the score received on the exam.
  d. Process: starting your car in the morning. Quality characteristic: the time it takes to start your car.

17.4 Form a group of three or four students in your class. As a group project, select a familiar process and determine a variable that measures the quality of some aspect of the output of this process. Then list some common causes and assignable causes that might result in variation of the variable you have selected for the process. Discuss your lists in class.

17.3 SAMPLING A PROCESS, RATIONAL SUBGROUPING, AND CONTROL CHARTS

In order to find and eliminate assignable causes of process variation, we sample output from the process. To do this, we first decide which **process variables**—that is, which process characteristics—will be studied. Several graphical techniques (sometimes called *prestatistical tools*) are used here. For example, Pareto charts (see Section 2.5) help identify problem areas and

opportunities for improvement. The goal is to identify process variables that can be studied in order to decrease the gap between customer expectations and process performance.

Whenever possible and economical, it is best to study a **quantitative**, rather than a **categorical** (or **qualitative**), process variable. For example, suppose we are filling 500-mL jars with strawberry jam, and suppose specifications state that each jar should contain between 498.5 mL and 501.5 mL of jam. If we record the fill of each sampled jar by simply noting that the jar either meets specifications (the fill is between 498.5 mL and 501.5 mL) or does not meet specifications, then we are studying a **categorical (or qualitative) process variable**. However, if we measure and record the amount of strawberry jam contained in the jar (say, to the nearest tenth of a millilitre), then we are studying a **quantitative process variable**. Actually measuring the fill is best because this tells us *how close* we are to the specification limits and thus provides more information. As we will soon see, this additional information often allows us to decide whether to take action on a process by using a relatively small number of measurements.

When we study a quantitative process variable, we say that we are employing **measurement data**. To analyze such data, we take a series of samples (usually called **subgroups**) over time. Each subgroup consists of a set of several measurements; subgroup sizes between two and six are often used. Summary statistics (for example, means and ranges) for each subgroup are calculated and are plotted versus time. By comparing plot points, we hope to discover when unusual process variations are taking place.

Each subgroup is typically observed over a short period of time—a period of time in which the process operating characteristics do not change much. That is, we employ **rational subgroups**.

Rational Subgroups

LO3 Rational subgroups are selected so that *if process changes of practical importance exist, the chance that these changes will occur between subgroups is maximized and the chance that these changes will occur within subgroups is minimized.*

In order to obtain rational subgroups, we must determine the frequency with which subgroups will be selected. For example, we might select a subgroup once every 15 minutes, once an hour, or once a day. In general, we should observe subgroups often enough to detect important process changes. For instance, suppose we wish to study a process, and suppose we feel that workers' shift changes (which take place every eight hours) may be an important source of process variation. In this case, rational subgroups can be obtained by selecting a subgroup during each eight-hour shift. Here shift changes will occur *between* subgroups. Therefore, if shift changes are an important source of variation, the rational subgroups will enable us to observe the effects of these changes by comparing plot points for different subgroups (shifts). However, in addition, suppose hourly machine resets are made, and we feel that these resets may also be an important source of process variation. In this case, rational subgroups can be obtained by selecting a subgroup during each hour. Here machine resets will occur *between* subgroups, and we will be able to observe their effects by comparing plot points for different subgroups (hours). If in this situation we selected one subgroup in each eight-hour shift, we would not obtain rational subgroups. This is because hourly machine resets would occur *within* subgroups, and we would not be able to observe the effects of these resets by comparing plot points for different shifts. In general, it is very important to try to identify important sources of variation (potential assignable causes such as shift changes, resets, and so on) before deciding how subgroups will be selected.

Once we determine the sampling frequency, we need to determine the **subgroup size**—that is, the number of measurements that will be included in each subgroup—and how we will actually select the measurements in each subgroup. It is recommended that the *subgroup size be held constant*. Denoting this constant subgroup size as *n*, we typically choose *n* to be from 2 to 6, with $n = 4$ or 5 being a frequent choice. To illustrate how we can actually select the subgroup measurements, suppose we select a subgroup of 5 units every hour from the output of a machine that produces 100 units per hour. We can select these units by using a **consecutive**, **periodic**, or **random** sampling process. If we employed consecutive sampling, we would select five consecutive units produced by the machine at the beginning of (or at some time during) each hour. Here **production conditions**—machine operator, machine setting, raw material batch, and so forth—*will be as constant as possible within the subgroup.* Such a subgroup provides a "freeze-frame picture" of the process at a particular point in time. Thus the *chance of variations occurring within the subgroups is minimized.* If we used periodic sampling, we would select five units periodically through each hour. For example, since the machine produces 100 units per hour, we could select the 1st, 21st, 41st, 61st, and 81st units produced. If we used random sampling, we would use a random number table to randomly select 5 of the 100 units produced during each hour. If production conditions are really held fairly constant during each hour, then consecutive, periodic, and random sampling will each provide a similar representation of the process. If production conditions vary considerably during each hour, and if we are able to recognize this variation by using a periodic or random sampling procedure, this tells us that we should be sampling the process more often than once an hour. Of course, if we are using periodic or random sampling every hour, we might not realize that the process operates with considerably less variation during shorter periods (perhaps because we have not used a consecutive sampling procedure). We therefore might not recognize the extent of the hourly variation.

Lastly, it is important to point out that we *must also take subgroups for a period of time that is long enough to give potential sources of variation a chance to show up.* If, for instance, different batches of raw materials are suspected to be a significant source of process variation, and if we receive new batches every few days, we may need to collect subgroups for several weeks in order to assess the effects of the batch-to-batch variation. *A statistical rule of thumb says that we require at least 20 subgroups of size 4 or 5 in order to judge statistical control and in order to obtain reasonable estimates of the process mean and variability.* However, practical considerations may require the collection of much more data.

We now look at two more concrete examples of subgrouped data.

Example 17.1 The Hole Location Case[2] (Subgroup Measurements)

A manufacturer produces automobile air conditioner compressor shells. The compressor shell is basically the outer metal housing of the compressor. Several holes of various sizes must be punched into the shell to accommodate hose connections that must be made to the compressor. If any one of these holes is punched in the wrong location, the compressor shell becomes a piece of scrap metal (at considerable cost to the manufacturer). Figure 17.1(a) illustrates a compressor shell (note the holes that have been punched in the housing). Experience with the hole-punching process suggests that substantial changes (machine resets, equipment lubrication, and so forth) can occur quite frequently—as often as two or three times an hour. Because we wish to observe the impact of these changes if and when they occur, rational subgroups are obtained by selecting a subgroup every 20 minutes or so. Specifically, about every 20 minutes, five compressor shells are consecutively selected from the process output. For each shell selected, a measurement that helps to specify the location of a particular hole in the compressor shell is made. The measurement is taken by measuring from one of the edges of the compressor shell (called the trim edge) to the bottom of the hole (see Figure 17.1(a)). Obviously, it is not possible to measure to the centre of the hole because you cannot tell where it is! The target value for the measured dimension is 3.00 cm. Of course, the manufacturer would like as little variation around the target as possible. Figure 17.1(b) gives the measurements obtained for 20 subgroups that were selected between 8 A.M. and 2:20 P.M. on a particular day. Here a subgroup consists of the five measurements labelled 1 through 5 in a single row in the table.

---

[2]The data for this case were obtained from a metal fabrication plant located in the Cincinnati, Ohio, area. For confidentiality, we have agreed to withhold the company's name. Also, the measurement unit has been changed to centimetres.

FIGURE **17.1**   The Compressor Shell and the Hole Location Data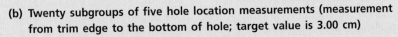

(a) Holes punched in a compressor shell for hose connections

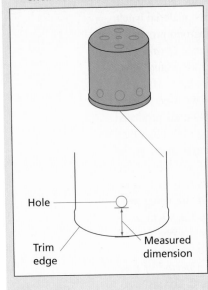

Hole

Trim edge

Measured dimension

(b) Twenty subgroups of five hole location measurements (measurement from trim edge to the bottom of hole; target value is 3.00 cm)

Time	Subgroup	Measurement 1	2	3	4	5	Mean	Range
8:00 A.M.	1	3.05	3.02	3.04	3.09	3.05	3.05	0.07
8:20 A.M.	2	3.00	3.04	2.98	2.99	2.99	3.00	0.06
8:40 A.M.	3	3.07	3.06	2.94	2.97	3.01	3.01	0.13
9:00 A.M.	4	3.02	2.96	3.01	2.98	3.02	2.998	0.06
9:20 A.M.	5	3.01	2.98	3.04	3.01	3.01	3.01	0.06
9:40 A.M.	6	3.01	3.02	2.99	2.97	2.96	2.99	0.06
10:00 A.M.	7	3.03	2.98	2.92	3.17	2.96	3.012	0.25
10:20 A.M.	8	3.05	3.03	2.96	3.01	2.97	3.004	0.09
10:40 A.M.	9	2.99	2.96	3.01	3.00	2.95	2.982	0.06
11:00 A.M.	10	3.02	3.02	2.98	3.03	3.02	3.014	0.05
11:20 A.M.	11	2.97	2.96	2.96	3.00	3.04	2.986	0.08
11:40 A.M.	12	3.06	3.04	3.02	3.10	3.05	3.054	0.08
12:00 P.M.	13	2.99	3.00	3.04	2.96	3.02	3.002	0.08
12:20 P.M.	14	3.00	3.01	2.99	3.00	3.01	3.002	0.02
12:40 P.M.	15	3.02	2.96	3.04	2.95	2.97	2.988	0.09
1:00 P.M.	16	3.02	3.02	3.04	2.98	3.03	3.018	0.06
1:20 P.M.	17	3.01	2.87	3.09	3.02	3.00	2.998	0.22
1:40 P.M.	18	3.05	2.96	3.01	2.97	2.98	2.994	0.09
2:00 P.M.	19	3.02	2.99	3.00	2.98	3.00	2.998	0.04
2:20 P.M.	20	3.00	3.00	3.01	3.05	3.01	3.014	0.05

Notice that Figure 17.1(b) also gives the mean, $\bar{x}$, and the range, R, of the measurements in each subgroup. In the next section, we will see how to use the subgroup means and ranges to detect when unusual process variations have taken place.

Example 17.2 The Hot Chocolate Temperature Case[3] (Subgroup Measurements)

Since 1994, a number of consumers have filed and won large claims against fast-food chains as a result of being scalded by excessively hot beverages such as coffee, tea, and hot chocolate. Because of such litigation, the food service staff at a university dining hall wish to study the temperature of the hot chocolate dispensed by its hot chocolate machine. The dining hall staff believe that there might be substantial variations in hot chocolate temperatures from meal to meal. Therefore, it is decided that at least one subgroup of hot chocolate temperatures will be observed during each meal—breakfast (6:30 A.M. to 10 A.M.), lunch (11 A.M. to 1:30 P.M.), and dinner (5 P.M. to 7:30 P.M.). In addition, since the hot chocolate machine is heavily used during most meals, the dining hall staff also believe that hot chocolate temperatures might vary substantially from the beginning to the end of a single meal. It follows that the staff will obtain rational subgroups by selecting a subgroup a half hour after the beginning of each meal and another subgroup a half hour before the end of each meal. Specifically, each subgroup will be selected by pouring three cups of hot chocolate over a ten-minute time span using periodic sampling (the second cup will be poured five minutes after the first, and the third cup will be poured five minutes after the second). The temperature of the hot chocolate will be measured by a candy thermometer (to the nearest tenth of a degree Celsius) immediately after each cup is poured.

---

[3]The data for this case were collected for a student's term project with the cooperation of the Food Service at Miami University, Oxford, Ohio. Temperatures have been converted to degrees Celsius.

TABLE **17.2** Twenty-four Subgroups of Three Hot Chocolate Temperatures (Measurements to the Nearest Tenth of a Degree Celsius) ✐

Day	Meal	Subgroup	Temperature 1	2	3	Subgroup Mean, $\bar{x}$	Subgroup Range, R
Monday	Breakfast	1	61.1°	60.0°	59.4°	60.17°	1.70°
		2	60.6	58.9	60.0	59.83	1.70
	Lunch	3	61.7	63.3	63.9	62.97	2.20
		4	63.3	65.0	63.9	64.07	1.70
	Dinner	5	56.1	61.1	60.0	59.07	5.00
		6	58.9	59.4	60.6	59.63	1.70
Tuesday	Breakfast	7	62.8	61.7	60.0	61.50	2.80
		8	59.4	62.2	62.8	61.47	3.40
	Lunch	9	59.4	60.6	63.9	61.30	4.50
		10	65.6	62.2	63.9	63.90	3.40
	Dinner	11	58.9	57.2	58.3	58.13	1.70
		12	62.8	60.6	62.2	61.87	2.20
Wednesday	Breakfast	13	58.9	62.8	59.4	60.37	3.90
		14	62.8	57.8	60.6	60.40	5.00
	Lunch	15	60.0	59.4	60.0	59.80	0.60
		16	61.1	61.7	62.8	61.87	1.70
	Dinner	17	62.2	61.1	60.6	61.30	1.60
		18	58.3	60.0	63.3	60.53	5.00
Thursday	Breakfast	19	51.7	53.9	57.2	54.27	5.50
		20	56.7	59.4	57.8	57.97	2.70
	Lunch	21	62.8	60.6	63.3	62.23	2.70
		22	63.9	63.3	64.4	63.87	1.10
	Dinner	23	60.0	61.7	59.4	60.37	2.30
		24	59.4	59.4	61.7	60.17	2.30

Table 17.2 gives the results for 24 subgroups of three hot chocolate temperatures taken at each meal served at the dining hall over a four-day period. Here a subgroup consists of the three temperatures labelled 1 through 3 in a single row in the table. The table also gives the mean, $\bar{x}$, and the range, R, of the temperatures in each subgroup. In the next section, we will use the subgroup means and ranges to detect unusual process variations (that is, to detect assignable causes).

Subgrouped data are used to determine when assignable causes of process variation exist. Typically, we analyze subgrouped data by plotting summary statistics for the subgroups versus time. The resulting plots are often called **graphs of process performance**. For example, the subgroup means and the subgroup ranges of the hole location measurements in Figure 17.1(b) are plotted in time order on graphs of process performance in the Excel output of Figure 17.2 on the next page. The subgroup means ($\bar{x}$ values) and ranges (R values) are plotted on the vertical axis, while the time sequence (in this case, the subgroup number) is plotted on the horizontal axis. The $\bar{x}$ values and R values for corresponding subgroups are lined up vertically. The plot points on each graph are connected by line segments as a visual aid. However, the lines between the plot points do not really say anything about the process performance between the observed subgroups. Notice that the subgroup means and ranges vary over time.

If we consider the plot of subgroup means, very high and very low points are undesirable—they represent large deviations from the target hole location dimension (3.00 cm). If we consider the plot of subgroup ranges, very high points are undesirable (high variation in the hole location dimensions), while very low points are desirable (little variation in the hole location dimensions).

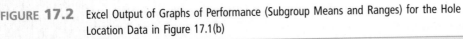

FIGURE 17.2   Excel Output of Graphs of Performance (Subgroup Means and Ranges) for the Hole
Location Data in Figure 17.1(b)

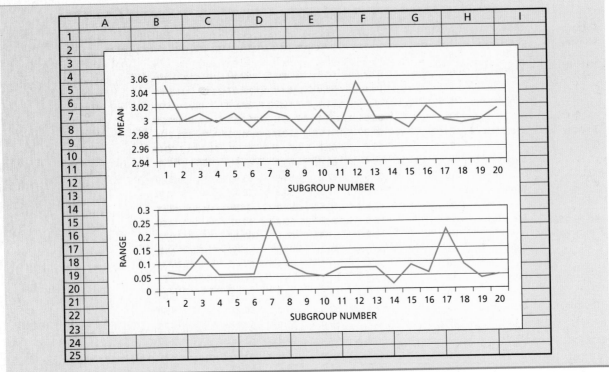

We now wish to answer a very basic question. *Is the variation that we see on the graphs of performance due to the usual process variation (that is, due to common causes), or is the variation due to one or more assignable causes (unusual variations)?* It is possible that unusual variations have occurred and that action should be taken to reduce the variation in production conditions. It is also possible that the variation in the plot points is caused by common causes and that (given the current configuration of the process) production conditions have been held as constant as possible. For example, do the high points on the $\bar{x}$ plot in Figure 17.2 suggest that one or more assignable causes have increased the hole location dimensions enough to warrant corrective action? As another example, do the high points on the R plot suggest that excess variability in the hole location dimensions exists and that corrective action is needed? Or does the lowest point on the R plot indicate that an improvement in process performance (reduction in variation) has occurred due to an assignable cause?

We can answer these questions by converting the graphs of performance shown in Figure 17.2 into **control charts**. In general, by converting graphs of performance into control charts, we can (with only a small chance of being wrong) determine whether observed process variations are unusual (due to assignable causes). That is, the purpose of a control chart is to monitor a process so we can take corrective action in response to assignable causes when it is needed. This is called **statistical process monitoring**. The use of "seat-of-the-pants intuition" has not been found to be a particularly effective way to decide whether observed process performance is unusual. By using a control chart, we can reduce our chances of making two possible errors—(1) taking action when none is needed and (2) not taking action when action is needed (just like Type I and Type II errors in hypothesis testing).

LO4   A control chart employs a **centre line** (denoted **CNL**) and two control limits—an **upper control limit** (denoted **UCL**) and a **lower control limit** (denoted **LCL**). The centre line represents the average performance of the process when it is in a state of statistical control— that is, when only common cause variation exists. The upper and lower control limits are horizontal lines situated above and below the centre line. These control limits are established so that when the process is in control, almost all plot points will be between the upper and lower limits. In practice, the control limits are used as follows:

1   If all observed plot points are *between the LCL and the UCL* (and if no unusual patterns of points exist—this will be explained later), we have no evidence that assignable causes exist and we assume that the process is in **statistical control**. In this case, *only common causes of process variation exist*, and *no action to remove assignable causes is taken on the process*. If we were to take such action, we would be *unnecessarily tampering* with the process.

2   If we observe one or more plot points *outside the control limits*, then we have evidence that the process is *out of control due to one or more assignable causes*. Here *we must take action on the process* to remove these assignable causes.

In the next section, we begin to discuss how to construct control charts. Before doing this, however, we must emphasize the importance of *documenting* a process while the subgroups of data are being collected. The time at which each subgroup is taken is recorded, and the name of the person who collected the data is also recorded. Any process changes (machine resets, adjustments, shift changes, operator changes, and so on) must be documented. Any potential sources of variation that may significantly affect the process output should be noted. If the process is not well documented, it will be very difficult to identify the root causes of unusual variations that may be detected when we analyze the subgroups of data.

17.4 $\bar{x}$ AND R CHARTS

The most commonly used control charts for **measurement data** are $\bar{x}$ **and R charts** (such charts are often called **variables control charts**). **Subgroup means** are plotted versus time on the $\bar{x}$ chart, while **subgroup ranges** are plotted on the R chart. The $\bar{x}$ chart monitors the **process mean** or **level** (we wish to run near a desired target level). The R chart is used to monitor the amount of **variability** around the process level (we desire as little variability as possible around the target). Note here that we employ two control charts and that *it is important to use the two charts together*. If we do not use both charts, we will not get all the information needed to improve the process.

CHAPTER 21

Before seeing how to construct $\bar{x}$ and R charts, we should mention that it is also possible to monitor the process variability by using a chart for **subgroup standard deviations**. Such a chart is called an *s* **chart**. However, the overwhelming majority of practitioners use R charts rather than *s* charts. This is partly for historical reasons. When control charts were developed, electronic calculators and computers did not exist. It was, therefore, much easier to compute a subgroup range than it was to compute a subgroup standard deviation. For this reason, the use of R charts has persisted. Some people also feel that it is easier for factory personnel (some of whom may have little mathematical background) to understand and relate to the subgroup range. In addition, while the standard deviation (which is computed using all the measurements in a subgroup) is a better measure of variability than the range (which is computed using only two measurements), the R chart usually suffices. This is because $\bar{x}$ and R charts usually employ small subgroups—as mentioned previously, subgroup sizes are often between two and six. For such subgroup sizes, it can be shown that using subgroup ranges is almost as effective as using subgroup standard deviations.

To construct $\bar{x}$ and R charts, suppose we have observed rational subgroups of n measurements over successive time periods (hours, shifts, days, or the like). We first calculate the mean, $\bar{x}$, and range, R, for each subgroup, and we construct graphs of performance for the $\bar{x}$ values and for the R values (as in Figure 17.2). In order to calculate centre lines and control limits, let $\bar{x}$ denote the mean of the subgroup of n measurements that is selected in a particular time period. Furthermore, assume that the population of all process measurements that could be observed in any time period is normally distributed with mean μ and standard deviation σ, and also assume successive process measurements are statistically independent.[4] Then if μ and

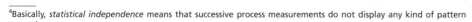

[4]Basically, *statistical independence* means that successive process measurements do not display any kind of pattern over time.

FIGURE **17.3**   An Illustration of $\bar{x}$ Chart Control Limits with the Process Mean, μ, and Process Standard Deviation, σ, Known

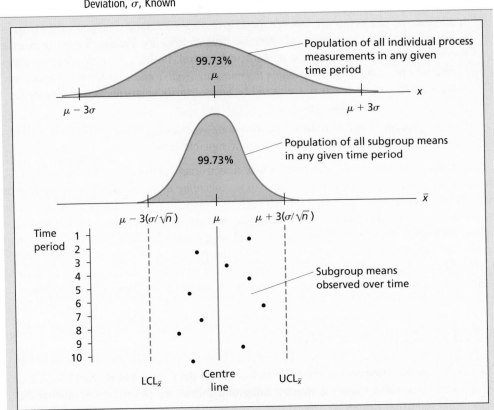

σ stay constant over time, the sampling distribution of subgroup means in any time period is normally distributed with mean μ and standard deviation $\sigma/\sqrt{n}$. It follows that (in any time period) 99.73 percent of all possible values of the subgroup mean $\bar{x}$ are in the interval

$$[\mu - 3(\sigma/\sqrt{n}), \mu + 3(\sigma/\sqrt{n})].$$

This fact is illustrated in Figure 17.3. It follows that we can set a centre line and control limits for the $\bar{x}$ chart as follows:

$$\text{Centre line} = \mu,$$
$$\text{Upper control limit} = \text{UCL}_{\bar{x}} = \mu + 3(\sigma/\sqrt{n}),$$
$$\text{Lower control limit} = \text{LCL}_{\bar{x}} = \mu - 3(\sigma/\sqrt{n}).$$

LO4

If an observed subgroup mean is inside these control limits, we have no evidence to suggest that the process is out of control. However, if the subgroup mean is outside these limits, we conclude that μ and/or σ have changed and that the process is out of control. The $\bar{x}$ chart limits are illustrated in Figure 17.3.

If the process is in control, and thus μ and σ stay constant over time, it follows that μ and σ are the mean and standard deviation of all possible process measurements. For this reason, we call μ the **process mean** and σ the **process standard deviation**. Since in most real situations we do not know the true values of μ and σ, we must estimate these values. If the process is in control, an appropriate estimate of the process mean μ is

$$\bar{\bar{x}} = \text{the mean of all observed subgroup means}$$

($\bar{\bar{x}}$ is pronounced "x double bar"). It follows that the centre line for the $\bar{x}$ chart is

$$\text{Centre line}_{\bar{x}} = \bar{\bar{x}}.$$

TABLE **17.3**   Control Chart Constants for $\bar{x}$ and R Charts

Subgroup Size, n	Chart for Averages ($\bar{x}$)	Chart for Ranges (R)		
	Factor for Control Limits, A_2	Divisor for Estimate of Standard Deviation, d_2	Factors for Control Limits	
			D_3	D_4
2	1.880	1.128	—	3.267
3	1.023	1.693	—	2.574
4	0.729	2.059	—	2.282
5	0.577	2.326	—	2.114
6	0.483	2.534	—	2.004
7	0.419	2.704	0.076	1.924
8	0.373	2.847	0.136	1.864
9	0.337	2.970	0.184	1.816
10	0.308	3.078	0.223	1.777
11	0.285	3.173	0.256	1.744
12	0.266	3.258	0.283	1.717
13	0.249	3.336	0.307	1.693
14	0.235	3.407	0.328	1.672
15	0.223	3.472	0.347	1.653
16	0.212	3.532	0.363	1.637
17	0.203	3.588	0.378	1.622
18	0.194	3.640	0.391	1.608
19	0.187	3.689	0.403	1.597
20	0.180	3.735	0.415	1.585
21	0.173	3.778	0.425	1.575
22	0.167	3.819	0.434	1.566
23	0.162	3.858	0.443	1.557
24	0.157	3.895	0.451	1.548
25	0.153	3.931	0.459	1.541

To obtain control limits for the $\bar{x}$ chart, we compute

$$\bar{R} = \text{the mean of all observed subgroup ranges.}$$

It can be shown that an appropriate estimate of the process standard deviation σ is $\bar{R}/d_2$, where d_2 is a constant that depends on the subgroup size n. Although we do not present a development of d_2 here, it intuitively makes sense that for a given subgroup size, our best estimate of the process standard deviation should be related to the average of the subgroup ranges, $\bar{R}$. The number d_2 relates these quantities. Values of d_2 are given in Table 17.3 for subgroup sizes $n = 2$ through $n = 25$. At the end of this section, we further discuss why we use $\bar{R}/d_2$ to estimate the process standard deviation.

Substituting the estimate $\bar{\bar{x}}$ of μ and the estimate $\bar{R}/d_2$ of σ into the limits

$$\mu + 3(\sigma/\sqrt{n}) \quad \text{and} \quad \mu - 3(\sigma/\sqrt{n}),$$

we obtain

$$\text{UCL}_{\bar{x}} = \bar{\bar{x}} + 3\left(\frac{\bar{R}/d_2}{\sqrt{n}}\right) = \bar{\bar{x}} + \left(\frac{3}{d_2\sqrt{n}}\right)\bar{R},$$

$$\text{LCL}_{\bar{x}} = \bar{\bar{x}} - 3\left(\frac{\bar{R}/d_2}{\sqrt{n}}\right) = \bar{\bar{x}} - \left(\frac{3}{d_2\sqrt{n}}\right)\bar{R}.$$

Finally, we define

$$A_2 = \frac{3}{d_2\sqrt{n}}$$

and rewrite the control limits as

$$\text{UCL}_{\bar{x}} = \bar{\bar{x}} + A_2\bar{R} \quad \text{and} \quad \text{LCL}_{\bar{x}} = \bar{\bar{x}} - A_2\bar{R}.$$

Here we call A_2 a **control chart constant**. As the formula for A_2 implies, this control chart constant depends on the subgroup size, n. Values of A_2 are given in Table 17.3 for subgroup sizes $n = 2$ through $n = 25$.

The centre line for the R chart is

$$\text{Centre line}_R = \bar{R}.$$

Furthermore, assuming normality, it can be shown that there are control chart constants D_4 and D_3 so that

$$\text{UCL}_R = D_4\bar{R} \quad \text{and} \quad \text{LCL}_R = D_3\bar{R}.$$

Here the control chart constants D_4 and D_3 also depend on the subgroup size, n. Values of D_4 and D_3 are given in Table 17.3 for subgroup sizes $n = 2$ through $n = 25$. We summarize the centre lines and control limits for $\bar{x}$ and R charts in the following box:

$\bar{x}$ and R Chart Centre Lines and Control Limits

$\text{Centre line}_{\bar{x}} = \bar{\bar{x}}$,

$\text{UCL}_{\bar{x}} = \bar{\bar{x}} + A_2\bar{R}$,

$\text{LCL}_{\bar{x}} = \bar{\bar{x}} - A_2\bar{R}$,

$\text{Centre line}_R = \bar{R}$,

$\text{UCL}_R = D_4\bar{R}$,

$\text{LCL}_R = D_3\bar{R}$,

where $\bar{\bar{x}}$ = the mean of all subgroup means,

$\bar{R}$ = the mean of all subgroup ranges,

and A_2, D_4, and D_3 are control chart constants that depend on the subgroup size (see Table 17.3). When D_3 is not listed, the R chart does not have a lower control limit.[5]

Example 17.3 The Hole Location Case (Calculations and Control Charts)

Consider the hole location data for air conditioner compressor shells given in Figure 17.1 (page 598). In order to calculate $\bar{x}$ and R chart control limits for these data, we compute

$$\bar{\bar{x}} = \text{the average of the 20 subgroup means}$$
$$= \frac{3.05 + 3.00 + \cdots + 3.014}{20} = 3.0062,$$

$$\bar{R} = \text{the average of the 20 subgroup ranges}$$
$$= \frac{0.07 + 0.06 + \cdots + 0.05}{20} = 0.085.$$

Looking at Table 17.3, we see that when the subgroup size is $n = 5$, the control chart constants needed for $\bar{x}$ and R charts are $A_2 = 0.577$ and $D_4 = 2.114$. It follows that the centre lines and control limits are

$$\text{Centre line}_{\bar{x}} = \bar{\bar{x}} = 3.0062,$$
$$\text{UCL}_{\bar{x}} = \bar{\bar{x}} + A_2\bar{R} = 3.0062 + 0.577(0.085) = 3.0552,$$
$$\text{LCL}_{\bar{x}} = \bar{\bar{x}} + A_2\bar{R} = 3.0062 - 0.577(0.085) = 2.9572,$$
$$\text{Centre line}_R = \bar{R} = 0.085,$$
$$\text{UCL}_R = D_4\bar{R} = 2.114(0.085) = 0.1797.$$

---

[5]When D_3 is not listed, the theoretical lower control limit for the R chart is negative. In this case, some practitioners prefer to say that the LCL_R equals 0. Others prefer to say that the LCL_R does not exist because a range, R, equal to 0 does not indicate that an assignable cause exists and because it is impossible to observe a negative range below LCL_R. We prefer the second alternative. In practice, it makes no difference.

FIGURE **17.4**   MegaStat Output of Quality Control Process Charts for the Hole Location Data

		Mean	Range
Sample size	5		
Number of samples	20		
Upper Control Limit, UCL		3.0552	0.1797
Centre		3.0062	0.0850
Lower Control Limit, LCL		2.9572	0.0000

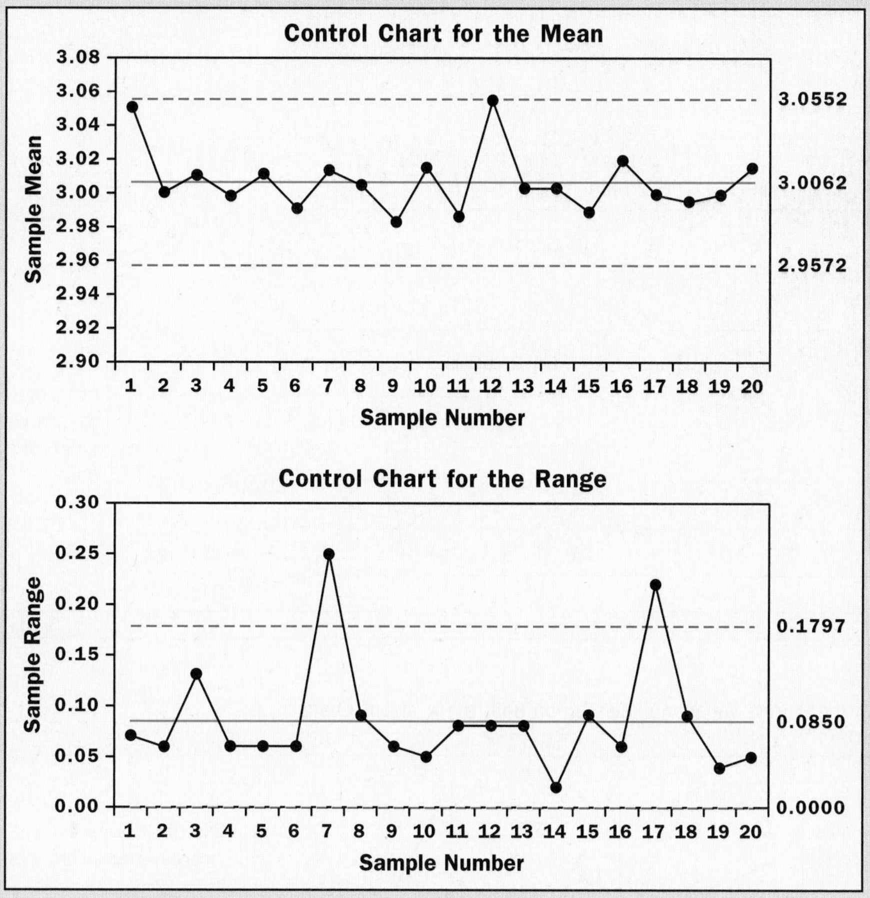

Control Chart for the Mean

Control Chart for the Range

Since D_3 is not listed in Table 17.3 for a subgroup size of $n = 5$, the R chart does not have a lower control limit. Figure 17.4 presents the MegaStat output of the $\bar{x}$ and R charts for the hole location data. Note that the centre lines and control limits that we have just calculated are shown on the $\bar{x}$ and R charts.

Control limits such as those computed in Example 17.3 are called **trial control limits**. Theoretically, control limits are supposed to be computed using subgroups collected while the process is in statistical control. However, it is impossible to know whether the process is in control until we have constructed the control charts. If, after we have plotted the $\bar{x}$ and R charts, we find that the process is in control, we can use the charts to monitor the process.

If the charts show that the process is not in statistical control (for example, there are plot points outside the control limits), we must find and eliminate the assignable causes before we can calculate control limits for monitoring the process. In order to understand how to find and eliminate assignable causes, we must understand how changes in the process mean and the process variation show up on $\bar{x}$ and R charts. To do this, consider Figures 17.5 and 17.6 on the next page. These figures illustrate that, whereas a change in the process mean shows up only on the $\bar{x}$ chart, a change

FIGURE 17.5 A Shift of the Process Mean Shows Up on the $\bar{x}$ Chart

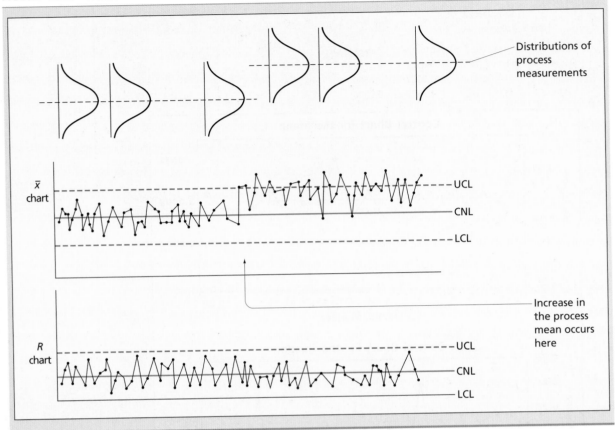

FIGURE 17.6 An Increase in the Process Variation Shows Up on Both the $\bar{x}$ and R Charts

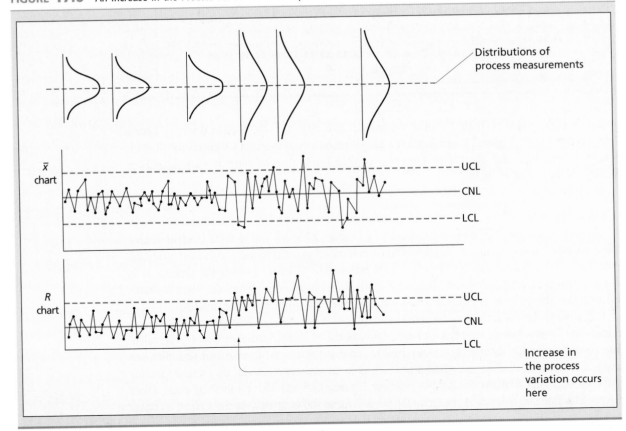

in the process variation shows up on both the $\bar{x}$ and R charts. Specifically, Figure 17.5 shows that when the process mean increases, the sample means plotted on the $\bar{x}$ chart increase and go out of control. Figure 17.6 shows that when the process variation (standard deviation, σ) increases,

1   the sample ranges plotted on the R chart increase and go out of control, and

2   the sample means plotted on the $\bar{x}$ chart become more variable (because, since σ increases, $\sigma_{\bar{x}} = \sigma/\sqrt{n}$ increases) and go out of control.

Since changes in the process mean and the process variation show up on the $\bar{x}$ chart, we do not begin by analyzing the $\bar{x}$ chart. This is because, if there were out-of-control sample means on the $\bar{x}$ chart, we would not know whether the process mean or the process variation had changed. Therefore, it might be more difficult to identify the assignable causes of the out-of-control sample means because the assignable causes that would cause the process mean to shift could be very different from the assignable causes that would cause the process variation to increase. For instance, unwarranted frequent resetting of a machine might cause the process level to shift up and down, while improper lubrication of the machine might increase the process variation.

In order to simplify and better organize our analysis procedure, we begin by analyzing the R chart, which reflects only changes in the process variation. Specifically, we first identify and eliminate the assignable causes of the out-of-control sample ranges on the R chart, and then we analyze the $\bar{x}$ chart. The exact procedure is illustrated in the following example.

Example 17.4   The Hole Location Case ($\bar{x}$ and R Chart Calculations)

Consider the $\bar{x}$ and R charts for the hole location data given in Figure 17.4 (page 605). To develop control limits that can be used for ongoing control, we first examine the R chart. We find two points above the UCL on the R chart. This indicates that excess within-subgroup variability exists at these points. We see that the out-of-control points correspond to subgroups 7 and 17. Investigation reveals that when these subgroups were selected, an inexperienced, newly hired operator ran the operation while the regular operator was on break. We find that the inexperienced operator is not fully closing the clamps that fasten down the compressor shells during the hole-punching operation. This is causing excess variability in the hole locations. This assignable cause can be eliminated by thoroughly retraining the newly hired operator.

Since we have identified and corrected the assignable cause associated with the points that are out of control on the R chart, we can drop subgroups 7 and 17 from the data set. We recalculate centre lines and control limits by using the remaining 18 subgroups. We first recompute (omitting $\bar{x}$ and R values for subgroups 7 and 17)

$$\bar{\bar{x}} = \frac{54.114}{18} = 3.0063 \quad \text{and} \quad \bar{R} = \frac{1.23}{18} = 0.0683.$$

Notice here that $\bar{\bar{x}}$ has not changed much (see Figure 17.4), but $\bar{R}$ has been reduced from 0.085 to 0.0683. Using the new $\bar{\bar{x}}$ and $\bar{R}$ values, revised control limits for the $\bar{x}$ chart are

$$\text{UCL}_{\bar{x}} = \bar{\bar{x}} + A_2\bar{R} = 3.0063 + 0.577(0.0683) = 3.0457,$$
$$\text{LCL}_{\bar{x}} = \bar{\bar{x}} + A_2\bar{R} = 3.0063 - 0.577(0.0683) = 2.9669.$$

The revised UCL for the R chart is

$$\text{UCL}_R = D_4\bar{R} = 2.114(0.0683) = 0.1444.$$

Since D_3 is not listed for subgroups of size five, the R chart does not have an LCL. Here the reduction in $\bar{R}$ has reduced the UCL on the R chart from 0.1797 to 0.1444 and has also narrowed the control limits for the $\bar{x}$ chart. For instance, the UCL for the $\bar{x}$ chart has been reduced from 3.0552 to 3.0457. The MegaStat output of the $\bar{x}$ and R charts employing these revised centre lines and control limits is shown in Figure 17.7 on the next page.

We must now check the revised R chart for statistical control. We find that the chart shows good control: there are no other points outside the control limits or long runs of points on either side of the centre line. Since the R chart is in good control, we can analyze the revised $\bar{x}$ chart.

FIGURE **17.7**   MegaStat Output of Quality Control Process Charts for the Hole Location
Data—Subgroups 7 and 17 Deleted

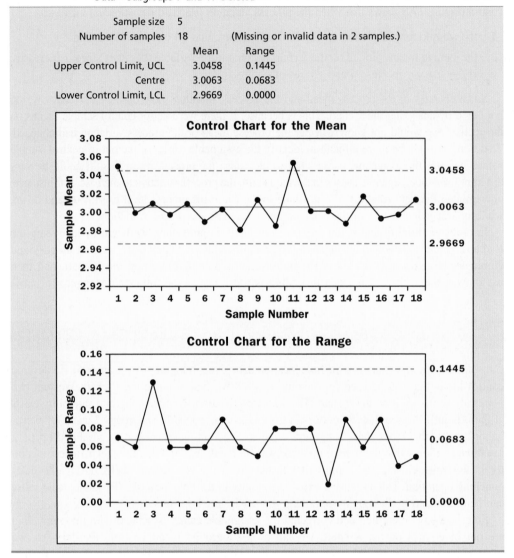

We see that two plot points are above the UCL on the $\bar{x}$ chart. Notice that these points were not outside our original trial control limits in Figure 17.4. However, the elimination of the assignable cause and the resulting reduction in $\bar{R}$ has narrowed the $\bar{x}$ chart control limits so that these points are now out of control. Since the R chart is in control, the points on the $\bar{x}$ chart that are out of control suggest that the process level shifted when original subgroups 1 and 12 (now 1 and 11) were taken. Investigation reveals that these subgroups were observed immediately after start-up at the beginning of the day and immediately after start-up following the lunch break. We find that if we allow a five-minute machine warm-up period, we can eliminate the process level problem.

Since we have again found and eliminated an assignable cause, we must compute newly revised centre lines and control limits. Dropping original subgroups 1 and 12 from the data set, we recompute

$$\bar{\bar{x}} = \frac{48.01}{16} = 3.0006 \quad \text{and} \quad \bar{R} = \frac{1.08}{16} = 0.0675.$$

Using the newest $\bar{\bar{x}}$ and $\bar{R}$ values, we compute newly revised control limits as follows:

$$\text{UCL}_{\bar{x}} = \bar{\bar{x}} + A_2\bar{R} = 3.0006 + 0.577(0.0675) = 3.0396,$$
$$\text{LCL}_{\bar{x}} = \bar{\bar{x}} - A_2\bar{R} = 3.0006 - 0.577(0.0675) = 2.9617,$$
$$\text{UCL}_R = D_4\bar{R} = 2.114(0.0675) = 0.1427.$$

FIGURE **17.8** MegaStat Output of Quality Control Process Charts for the Hole Location
Data—Subgroups 1, 7, 12, and 17 Deleted. The Charts Show Good Control.

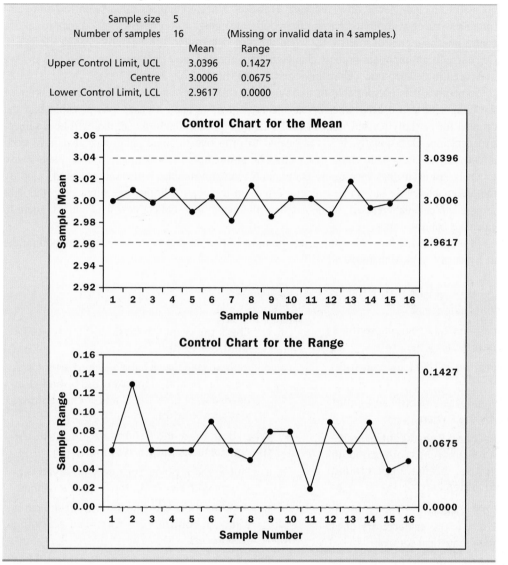

	Mean	Range
Sample size	5	
Number of samples	16	(Missing or invalid data in 4 samples.)
Upper Control Limit, UCL	3.0396	0.1427
Centre	3.0006	0.0675
Lower Control Limit, LCL	2.9617	0.0000

Again, the R chart does not have an LCL. We obtain the newly revised $\bar{x}$ and R charts that are shown in the MegaStat output of Figure 17.8. We see that all the points on each chart are inside their respective control limits. This says that the actions taken to remove assignable causes have brought the process into statistical control. However, it is important to point out that although the process is in statistical control, *this does not necessarily mean that the process is capable of producing products that meet the customer's needs.* That is, while the control charts tell us that no assignable causes of process variation remain, the charts do not (directly) tell us anything about how much common cause variation exists. If there is too much common cause variation, the process will not meet customer or manufacturer specifications. We will talk more about this later.

When both the $\bar{x}$ and R charts are in statistical control, we can use the control limits for ongoing process monitoring. New $\bar{x}$ and R values for subsequent subgroups are plotted with respect to these limits. Plot points outside the control limits indicate the existence of assignable causes and the need for action on the process. The appropriate corrective action can often be taken by local supervision. Sometimes management intervention may be needed. For example, if the assignable cause is out-of-specification raw materials, management may have to work with a supplier to improve the situation. The ongoing control limits occasionally need to be updated to include newly observed data. However, since employees often seem to be uncomfortable working with limits that are frequently changing, it is probably a good idea to update centre lines and control limits only when the new data would substantially change the limits. Of course, if an important process change is implemented, new data must be collected, and we may need to develop new centre lines and control limits from scratch.

Sometimes it is not possible to find an assignable cause, or it is not possible to eliminate the assignable cause even when it can be identified. In such a case, it is possible that the original (or partially revised) trial control limits are good enough to use; this will be a subjective decision. Occasionally, it is reasonable to drop one or more subgroups that have been affected by an assignable cause that cannot be eliminated. For example, the assignable cause might be an event that very rarely occurs and is unpreventable. If the subgroups affected by the assignable cause have a detrimental effect on the control limits, we might drop the subgroups and calculate revised limits. Another alternative is to collect new data and use them to calculate control limits.

In the following box, we summarize the most important points we have made regarding the analysis of $\bar{x}$ and R charts:

Analyzing $\bar{x}$ and R Charts to Establish Process Control

LO5 1 Remember that it is important to use both the $\bar{x}$ chart and the R chart to study the process.

2 Begin by analyzing the R chart for statistical control.

   a. Find and eliminate assignable causes that are indicated by the R chart.

   b. Revise both the $\bar{x}$ and R chart control limits, dropping data for subgroups corresponding to assignable causes that have been found and eliminated in step 2a.

   c. Check the revised R chart for control.

   d. Repeat step 2a, b, and c as necessary until the R chart shows statistical control.

3 When the R chart is in statistical control, the $\bar{x}$ chart can be properly analyzed.

   a. Find and eliminate assignable causes that are indicated by the $\bar{x}$ chart.

   b. Revise both the $\bar{x}$ and R chart control limits, dropping data for subgroups corresponding to assignable causes that have been found and eliminated in step 3a.

   c. Check the revised $\bar{x}$ chart (and the revised R chart) for control.

   d. Repeat step 3a, b, and c (or, if necessary, step 2a, b, and c and step 3a, b, and c) as needed until both the $\bar{x}$ and R charts shows statistical control.

4 When both the $\bar{x}$ and R charts are in control, use the control limits for process monitoring.

   a. Plot $\bar{x}$ and R points for newly observed subgroups with respect to the established limits.

   b. If either the $\bar{x}$ chart or the R chart indicates a lack of control, take corrective action on the process.

5 Periodically update the $\bar{x}$ and R control limits using all relevant data (data that describe the process as it now operates).

6 When a major process change is made, develop new control limits if necessary.

Example 17.5 The Hole Location Case ($\bar{x}$ and R Charts)

We consider the hole location problem and the revised $\bar{x}$ and R charts shown in Figure 17.8 (page 609). Since the process has been brought into statistical control, we may use the control limits in Figure 17.8 to monitor the process. This would assume that we have used an appropriate subgrouping scheme and have observed enough subgroups to give potential assignable causes a chance to show up. In reality, we probably want to collect considerably more than 20 subgroups before setting control limits for ongoing control of the process.

We assume for this example that the control limits in Figure 17.8 are reasonable. Table 17.4 gives four subsequently observed subgroups of five hole location dimensions. The subgroup means and ranges for these data are plotted with respect to the ongoing control limits in the MegaStat output of Figure 17.9. We see that the R chart remains in control, while the mean for subgroup 24 is above the UCL on the $\bar{x}$ chart. This tells us that an assignable cause has increased the process mean. Therefore, action is needed to reduce the process mean.

TABLE 17.4   Four Subgroups of Five Hole Location Dimensions Observed after Developing Control Limits for Ongoing Process Monitoring

	Measurement (Centimetres)					Mean,	Range,
Subgroup	1	2	3	4	5	$\bar{x}$	R
21	2.98	3.00	2.97	2.99	2.98	2.984	0.03
22	3.02	3.06	3.01	2.97	3.03	3.018	0.09
23	3.03	3.08	3.01	2.99	3.02	3.026	0.09
24	3.05	3.00	3.11	3.07	3.06	3.058	0.11

FIGURE 17.9   MegaStat Output of Quality Control Process Charts for the Hole Location Data—Subgroups 1, 7, 12, and 17 Deleted: Ongoing Control

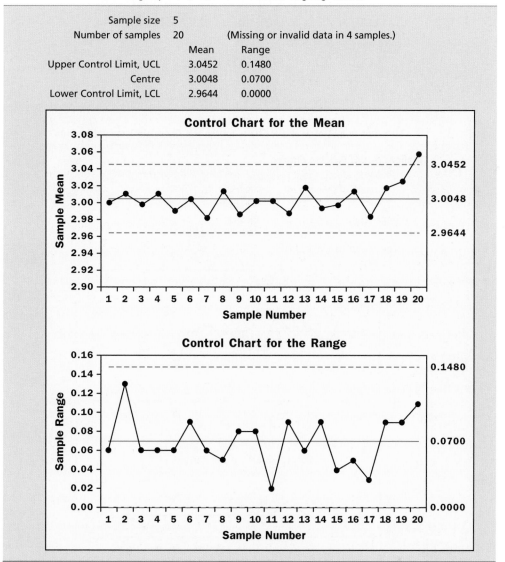

Example 17.6 The Hot Chocolate Temperature Case ($\bar{x}$ and R Charts)

Consider the hot chocolate data given in Table 17.2 (page 599). In order to plot $\bar{x}$ and R charts for these data, we compute

$$\bar{\bar{x}} = \text{the average of the 24 subgroup means}$$
$$= \frac{60.17 + 59.83 + \cdots + 60.17}{24} = 60.710$$

and

$$\bar{R} = \text{the average of the 24 subgroup ranges}$$
$$= \frac{1.70 + 1.70 + \cdots + 2.3}{24} = 2.767.$$

Looking at Table 17.3 (page 603), we see that the $\bar{x}$ and R control chart constants for the subgroup size $n = 3$ are $A_2 = 1.023$ and $D_4 = 2.574$. It follows that we calculate centre lines and control limits as follows:

$$\text{Centre line}_{\bar{x}} = \bar{\bar{x}} = 60.710,$$
$$\text{UCL}_{\bar{x}} = \bar{\bar{x}} + A_2\bar{R} = 60.710 + 1.023(2.767) = 63.5406,$$
$$\text{LCL}_{\bar{x}} = \bar{\bar{x}} - A_2\bar{R} = 60.710 - 1.023(2.767) = 57.8794,$$
$$\text{Centre line}_R = \bar{R} = 2.767,$$
$$\text{UCL}_R = D_4\bar{R} = 2.574(2.767) = 7.1223.$$

FIGURE **17.10**   MegaStat Output of $\bar{x}$ and R Charts for the Hot Chocolate Temperature Data

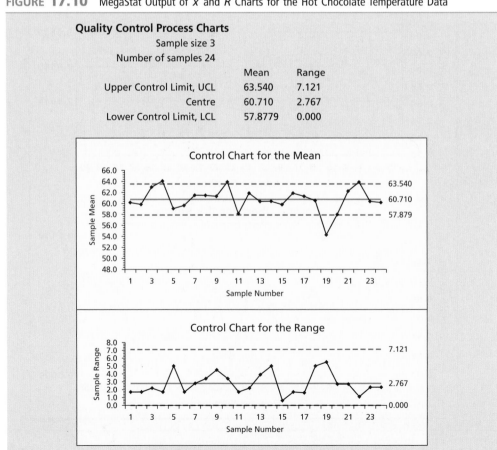

FIGURE **17.11** MegaStat Output of Revised $\bar{x}$ and R Charts for the Hot Chocolate
Temperature Data. The Process Is Now in Control.

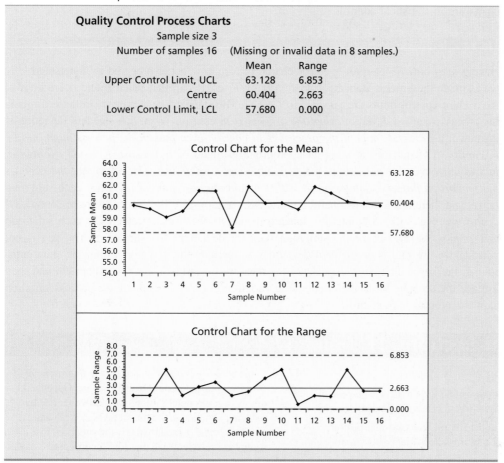

Quality Control Process Charts

Sample size 3

Number of samples 16   (Missing or invalid data in 8 samples.)

	Mean	Range
Upper Control Limit, UCL	63.128	6.853
Centre	60.404	2.663
Lower Control Limit, LCL	57.680	0.000

Since D_3 is not given in Table 17.3 for the subgroup size $n = 3$, the R chart does not have a lower control limit.

The $\bar{x}$ and R charts for the hot chocolate data are given in the MegaStat output of Figure 17.10. We see that the R chart is in good statistical control, while the $\bar{x}$ chart is out of control with three subgroup means above the UCL and one subgroup mean below the LCL. Looking at the $\bar{x}$ chart, we see that the subgroup means that are above the UCL were observed during lunch (note subgroups 4, 10, and 22). Investigation and process documentation reveal that on these days the hot chocolate machine was not turned off between breakfast and lunch. Discussion among members of the dining hall staff further reveals that because there is less time between breakfast and lunch than there is between lunch and dinner or dinner and breakfast, the staff often fail to turn off the hot chocolate machine between breakfast and lunch. Apparently, this is the reason behind the higher hot chocolate temperatures observed during lunch. Investigation also shows that the dining hall staff failed to turn on the hot chocolate machine before breakfast on Thursday (see subgroup 19)—in fact, a student had to ask that the machine be turned on. This caused the subgroup mean for subgroup 19 to be far below the $\bar{x}$ chart LCL. The dining hall staff conclude that the hot chocolate machine needs to be turned off after breakfast and then turned back on 15 minutes before lunch (prior experience suggests that it takes the machine 15 minutes to warm up). The staff also conclude that the machine should be turned on 15 minutes before each meal. In order to ensure that these actions are taken, an automatic timer is purchased to turn on the hot chocolate machine at the appropriate times. This brings the process into statistical control. Figure 17.11 shows $\bar{x}$ and R charts with revised control limits calculated using the subgroups that remain after the subgroups for the out-of-control lunches (subgroups 3, 4, 9, 10, 21, and 22) and the out-of-control breakfast (subgroups 19 and 20) are eliminated from the data set. We see that these revised control charts are in statistical control.

Having seen how to interpret $\bar{x}$ and R charts, we are now better prepared to understand why we estimate the process standard deviation σ by $\bar{R}/d_2$. Recall that when μ and σ are known, the $\bar{x}$ chart control limits are $[\mu \pm 3(\sigma/\sqrt{n})]$. The standard deviation, σ, in these limits is the process standard deviation *when the process is in control*. When this standard deviation is unknown, *we estimate σ as if the process is in control, even though the process might not be in control*. The quantity $\bar{R}/d_2$ is an appropriate estimate of σ because $\bar{R}$ *is the average of individual ranges computed from rational subgroups—subgroups selected so that the chances that important process changes occur within a subgroup are minimized*. Thus, each subgroup range, and therefore $\bar{R}/d_2$, estimates the process variation as if the process were in control. Of course, we could also compute the standard deviation of the measurements in each subgroup and employ the average of the subgroup standard deviations to estimate σ. The key is not whether we use ranges or standard deviations to measure the variation within the subgroups. Rather, the key is that we must calculate a measure of variation for each subgroup and then average the separate measures of subgroup variation in order to estimate the process variation as if the process is in control.

Exercises for Sections 17.3 and 17.4

CONCEPTS

17.5 Explain (1) the purpose of an $\bar{x}$ chart, (2) the purpose of an R chart, and (3) why both charts are needed.

17.6 Explain why the initial control limits calculated for a set of subgrouped data are called "trial control limits."

17.7 Explain why a change in process variability shows up on both the $\bar{x}$ and R charts.

17.8 In each situation, what conclusions (if any) can be made about whether the process mean is changing? Explain your logic.
  a. R chart out of control.
  b. R chart in control, $\bar{x}$ chart out of control.
  c. Both $\bar{x}$ and R charts in control.

METHODS AND APPLICATIONS

17.9 Table 17.5 gives five subgroups of measurement data. Use these data to
  a. Find the values of $\bar{x}$ and R for each subgroup.
  b. Find the values of $\bar{\bar{x}}$ and $\bar{R}$.
  c. Find the values of A_2 and D_4.
  d. Compute $\bar{x}$ and R chart centre lines and control limits.

TABLE **17.5**   Five Subgroups of Measurement Data 🖉

Subgroup	Measurement		
	1	**2**	**3**
1	4	5	6
2	9	7	5
3	4	8	6
4	2	4	3
5	5	6	10

17.10 In the book *Tools and Methods for the Improvement of Quality*, Gitlow, Gitlow, Oppenheim, and Oppenheim discuss a resort hotel's efforts to improve service by reducing variation in the time it takes to clean and prepare rooms. In order to study the situation, five rooms are selected each day for 25 consecutive days, and the time required to clean and prepare each room is recorded. The data obtained are given in Table 17.6.
  a. Calculate the subgroup mean, $\bar{x}$, and range, R, for each of the first two subgroups.
  b. Show that $\bar{\bar{x}} = 15.9416$ minutes and $\bar{R} = 2.696$ minutes.
  c. Find the control chart constants, A_2 and D_4, for the cleaning and preparation time data. Does D_3 exist? What does this say?
  d. Find the centre line and control limits for the $\bar{x}$ chart for these data.
  e. Find the centre line and control limit for the R chart for these data.
  f. Plot the $\bar{x}$ and R charts for the cleaning time data.
  g. Are the $\bar{x}$ and R charts in control? Explain.

17.11 A pizza restaurant monitors the size (measured by the diameter) of the 10-inch pizzas that it prepares. Pizza crusts are made from doughs that are prepared and prepackaged in boxes of 15 by a supplier. Doughs are thawed and pressed in a pressing machine. The toppings are added, and the pizzas are baked. The wetness of the doughs varies from box to box, and if the dough is too wet or greasy, it is difficult to press, resulting in a crust that is too small. The first shift of workers begins work at 4 P.M., and a new shift takes over at 9 P.M. and works until closing. The pressing machine is readjusted at the beginning of each shift. The restaurant takes five

TABLE **17.6** Twenty-five Daily Samples of Five Room Cleaning and Preparation Times 🖈

Sample (Day)	Cleaning and Preparation Time (Minutes)					Mean, $\bar{x}$	Range, R
	1	2	3	4	5		
1	15.6	14.3	17.7	14.3	15.0	—	—
2	15.0	14.8	16.8	16.9	17.4	—	—
3	16.4	15.1	15.7	17.3	16.6	16.22	2.2
4	14.2	14.8	17.3	15.0	16.4	15.54	3.1
5	16.4	16.3	17.6	17.9	14.9	16.62	3.0
6	14.9	17.2	17.2	15.3	14.1	15.74	3.1
7	17.9	17.9	14.7	17.0	14.5	16.40	3.4
8	14.0	17.7	16.9	14.0	14.9	15.50	3.7
9	17.6	16.5	15.3	14.5	15.1	15.80	3.1
10	14.6	14.0	14.7	16.9	14.2	14.88	2.9
11	14.6	15.5	15.9	14.8	14.2	15.00	1.7
12	15.3	15.3	15.9	15.0	17.8	15.86	2.8
13	17.4	14.9	17.7	16.6	14.7	16.26	3.0
14	15.3	16.9	17.9	17.2	17.5	16.96	2.6
15	14.8	15.1	16.6	16.3	14.5	15.46	2.1
16	16.1	14.6	17.5	16.9	17.7	16.56	3.1
17	14.2	14.7	15.3	15.7	14.3	14.84	1.5
18	14.6	17.2	16.0	16.7	16.3	16.16	2.6
19	15.9	16.5	16.1	15.0	17.8	16.26	2.8
20	16.2	14.8	14.8	15.0	15.3	15.22	1.4
21	16.3	15.3	14.0	17.4	14.5	15.50	3.4
22	15.0	17.6	14.5	17.5	17.8	16.48	3.3
23	16.4	15.9	16.7	15.7	16.9	16.32	1.2
24	16.6	15.1	14.1	17.4	17.8	16.20	3.7
25	17.0	17.5	17.4	16.2	17.9	17.20	1.7

Source: H. Gitlow, S. Gitlow, A. Oppenheim, and R. Oppenheim, *Tools and Methods for the Improvement of Quality,* pp. 333–334. Copyright © 1989. Reprinted by permission of McGraw-Hill Companies, Inc.

TABLE **17.7** Ten Samples of Pizza Crust Diameters 🖈

Subgroup	Time	Pizza Crust Diameter (Inches)					Mean, $\bar{X}$	Range, R
		1	2	3	4	5		
1	4 P.M.	9.8	9.0	9.0	9.2	9.2	9.24	0.8
2	5 P.M.	9.5	10.3	10.2	10.0	10.0	10.00	0.8
3	6 P.M.	10.5	10.3	9.8	10.0	10.3	10.18	0.7
4	7 P.M.	10.7	9.5	9.8	10.0	10.0	10.00	1.2
5	8 P.M.	10.0	10.5	10.0	10.5	10.5	10.30	0.5
6	9 P.M.	10.0	9.0	9.0	9.2	9.3	9.30	1.0
7	10 P.M.	11.0	10.0	10.3	10.3	10.0	10.32	1.0
8	11 P.M.	10.0	10.2	10.1	10.3	11.0	10.32	1.0
9	12 A.M.	10.0	10.4	10.4	10.5	10.0	10.26	0.5
10	1 A.M.	11.0	10.5	10.1	10.2	10.2	10.40	0.9

New shift at 9 P.M., pressing machine adjusted at the start of each shift (4 P.M. and 9 P.M.).

consecutive pizzas prepared at the beginning of each hour from opening to closing on a particular day. The diameter of each baked pizza in the subgroups is measured, and the pizza crust diameters obtained are given in Table 17.7. Use the pizza crust diameter data to do the following:

a. Show that $\bar{\bar{x}} = 10.032$ and $\bar{R} = 0.84$.

b. Find the centre lines and control limits for the $\bar{x}$ and R charts for the pizza crust data.

c. Plot the $\bar{x}$ and R charts for the pizza crust data.

d. Is the R chart for the pizza crust data in statistical control? Explain.

e. Is the $\bar{x}$ chart for the pizza crust data in statistical control? If not, use the $\bar{x}$ chart and the information given with the data to try to identify any assignable causes that might exist.

f. Suppose that, based on the $\bar{x}$ chart, the manager of the restaurant decides that the employees do not know how to properly adjust the dough-pressing machine. Because of this, the manager thoroughly

TABLE **17.8**   Fifteen Subgroups of Acid Value Measurements for a Chemical Process

Subgroup (Day)	Acid Value Measurements						Mean, $\bar{x}$	Range, R
	1	2	3	4	5	6		
1	202.1	201.2	196.2	201.6	201.6	201.6	200.717	5.9
2	201.6	201.2	201.2	200.8	201.2	201.2	201.2	.8
3	200.4	200.0	200.8	200.1	198.7	200.4	200.067	2.1
4	200.4	200.4	200.4	200.8	200.4	201.2	200.6	.8
5	200.0	201.6	202.9	201.6	201.2	201.2	201.417	2.9
6	200.0	200.4	200.8	200.8	199.5	200.4	200.317	1.3
7	200.4	200.0	200.4	200.4	200.4	200.4	200.333	.4
8	200.0	200.8	200.0	200.4	200.0	200.0	200.2	.8
9	199.1	200.4	200.4	200.4	200.4	200.0	200.117	1.3
10	201.2	195.3	197.4	201.2	200.0	201.6	199.45	6.3
11	201.6	200.8	200.4	201.2	200.4	199.5	200.65	2.1
12	200.0	199.5	200.4	200.8	200.4	200.8	200.317	1.3
13	201.6	201.6	200.8	201.2	200.8	200.8	201.133	.8
14	200.4	200.0	202.5	200.4	201.2	201.2	200.95	2.5
15	200.0	200.0	201.6	200.8	200.4	200.0	200.467	1.6

trains the employees in the use of this equipment. Because an assignable cause (incorrect adjustment of the pressing machine) has been found and eliminated, we can remove the subgroups affected by this unusual process variation from the data set. We therefore drop subgroups 1 and 6 from the data. Use the remaining eight subgroups to show that we obtain revised centre lines of $\bar{\bar{x}} = 10.2225$ and $\bar{R} = 0.825$.

g. Use the revised values of $\bar{\bar{x}}$ and $\bar{R}$ to compute revised $\bar{x}$ and R chart control limits for the pizza crust diameter data. Plot $\bar{x}$ and R charts using these revised limits. Be sure to omit subgroup means and ranges for subgroups 1 and 6 when plotting these charts.

h. Has removing the assignable cause brought the process into statistical control? Explain.

17.12 A chemical company has collected 15 daily subgroups of measurements of an important chemical property called "acid value" for one of its products. Each subgroup consists of six acid value readings: a single reading was taken every four hours during the day, and the readings for a day are taken as a subgroup. The 15 daily subgroups are given in Table 17.8.

a. Show that for these data, $\bar{\bar{x}} = 200.529$ and $\bar{R} = 2.06$.

b. Plot $\bar{x}$ and R charts for the acid value data. Are these charts in statistical control?

c. On the basis of these charts, is it possible to draw proper conclusions about whether the mean acid value is changing? Explain.

d. Suppose that investigation reveals that the out-of-control points on the R chart (the ranges for subgroups 1 and 10) were caused by an equipment malfunction that can be remedied by redesigning a mechanical part. Since the assignable cause that is responsible for the large ranges for subgroups 1 and 10 has been found and eliminated, we can

remove subgroups 1 and 10 from the data set. Show that using the remaining 13 subgroups gives revised centre lines of $\bar{\bar{x}} = 200.5975$ and $\bar{R} = 1.4385$.

e. Use the revised values of $\bar{\bar{x}}$ and $\bar{R}$ to compute revised $\bar{x}$ and R chart control limits for the acid value data. Plot the revised $\bar{x}$ and R charts, making sure to omit subgroup means and ranges for subgroups 1 and 10.

f. Are the revised $\bar{x}$ and R charts for the remaining 13 subgroups in statistical control? Explain. What does this result tell us to do?

17.13 The data in Table 17.9 consist of 30 subgroups of measurements that specify the location of a tube hole in an air conditioner compressor shell. Each subgroup contains the tube hole dimension measurement for five consecutive compressor shells selected from the production line. The first 15 subgroups were observed on March 21, and the second 15 subgroups were observed on March 22. As indicated in Table 17.9, the die press used in the hole-punching operation was changed after subgroup 5 was observed, and a die repair was made after subgroup 25 was observed.

a. Show that for the first 15 subgroups (observed on March 21), we have $\bar{\bar{x}} = 15.8$ and $\bar{R} = 6.1333$.

b. Plot $\bar{x}$ and R charts for the 15 subgroups that were observed on March 21 (do not use any of the March 22 data). Do these $\bar{x}$ and R charts show statistical control?

c. Using the control limits you computed by using the 15 subgroups observed on March 21, plot $\bar{x}$ and R charts for all 30 subgroups. That is, add the subgroup means and ranges for March 22 to your $\bar{x}$ and R charts, but use the limits you computed from the March 21 data.

d. Do the $\bar{x}$ and R charts obtained in part c show statistical control? Explain.

TABLE **17.9** Thirty Subgroups of Tube Hole Location Dimensions for Air Conditioner Compressor Shells ✎

Tube Hole Location Measurements

	Subgroup	1	2	3	4	5	Mean, $\bar{x}$	Range, R
March 21	1	15	15	16	15	13	14.8	3
	2	15	20	15	17	19	17.2	5
	3	19	16	15	18	17	17.0	4
	4	17	20	18	18	15	17.6	5
Changed to →	5	20	16	15	9	16	15.2	11
Die Press	6	13	16	20	17	22	17.6	9
#628 Here	7	15	13	9	17	13	13.4	8
	8	13	14	18	17	14	15.2	5
	9	19	12	16	13	15	15.0	7
	10	19	14	12	13	13	14.2	7
	11	17	22	15	14	16	16.8	8
	12	19	17	17	15	9	15.4	10
	13	17	13	14	17	15	15.2	4
	14	15	17	17	17	16	16.4	2
	15	14	16	18	16	16	16.0	4
March 22	16	18	10	14	16	18	15.2	8
	17	12	16	15	18	17	15.6	6
	18	15	19	19	17	17	17.4	4
	19	21	16	17	19	17	18.0	5
	20	20	22	25	18	19	20.8	7
	21	18	18	17	17	19	17.8	2
	22	19	20	19	18	18	18.8	2
	23	13	16	15	17	16	15.4	4
	24	16	15	16	17	17	16.2	2
Die Repair →	25	17	20	13	16	16	16.4	7
Made Here	26	25	23	21	24	21	22.8	4
	27	22	25	21	22	25	23.0	4
	28	26	29	25	26	23	25.8	6
	29	24	25	22	22	27	24.0	5
	30	26	21	27	25	26	25.0	6

e. Does it appear that changing to die press #628 is an assignable cause? Explain. (Note that the die press is the machine that is used to punch the tube hole.)

f. Does it appear that making a die repair is an assignable cause? Explain.

17.14 A Toronto company packages a bulk product in bags with a 50-kg label mass. During a typical day's operation of the fill process, 22 subgroups of five bag fills are observed. Using the observed data, $\bar{x}$ and R are calculated to be 52.9364 kg and 1.6818 kg, respectively. When the 22 $\bar{x}$ values and the 22 R values are plotted with respect to the appropriate control limits, the first six subgroups are found to be out of control. This is traced to a mechanical start-up problem, which is remedied. Using the remaining 16 subgroups, $\bar{\bar{x}}$ and $\bar{R}$ are calculated to be 52.5875 kg and 1.2937 kg, respectively.

a. Calculate appropriate revised $\bar{x}$ and R chart control limits.

b. When the remaining 16 $\bar{x}$ values and 16 R values are plotted with respect to the appropriate revised control limits, they are found to be within these limits. What does this imply?

17.15 In the book *Tools and Methods for the Improvement of Quality*, Gitlow, Gitlow, Oppenheim, and Oppenheim discuss an example of using $\bar{x}$ and R charts to study tuning knob diameters. In their problem description, the authors say this:

> A manufacturer of high-end audio components buys metal tuning knobs to be used in the assembly of its products. The knobs are produced automatically by a subcontractor using a single machine that is supposed to produce them with a constant diameter. Nevertheless, because of persistent final assembly problems with the knobs, management has decided to examine this process output by requesting that the subcontractor keep an x-bar and R chart for knob diameter.

On a particular day, the subcontractor selects four knobs every half hour and carefully measures their diameters. Twenty-five subgroups are obtained, and these subgroups (along with their subgroup means and ranges) are given in Table 17.10 on the next page.

a. For these data, show that $\bar{\bar{x}} = 841.45$ and $\bar{R} = 5.16$. Then use these values to calculate control limits and to plot $\bar{x}$ and R charts for the 25 subgroups of tuning knob diameters. Do these $\bar{x}$ and R charts indicate the existence of any assignable causes? Explain.

TABLE **17.10**   Twenty-five Subgroups of Tuning Knob Diameters

Time	Subgroup Number	Diameter Measurement				Average, $\bar{x}$	Range, R
		1	2	3	4		
8:30 A.M.	1	836	846	840	839	840.25	10
9:00	2	842	836	839	837	838.50	6
9:30	3	839	841	839	844	840.75	5
10:00	4	840	836	837	839	838.00	4
10:30	5	838	844	838	842	840.50	6
11:00	6	838	842	837	843	840.00	6
11:30	7	842	839	840	842	840.75	3
12:00	8	840	842	844	836	840.50	8
12:30 P.M.	9	842	841	837	837	839.25	5
1:00	10	846	846	846	845	845.75	1
1:30	11	849	846	848	844	846.75	5
2:00	12	845	844	848	846	845.75	4
2:30	13	847	845	846	846	846.00	2
3:00	14	839	840	841	838	839.50	3
3:30	15	840	839	839	840	839.50	1
4:00	16	842	839	841	837	839.75	5
4:30	17	841	845	839	839	841.00	6
5:00	18	841	841	836	843	840.25	7
5:30	19	845	842	837	840	841.00	8
6:00	20	839	841	842	840	840.50	3
6:30	21	840	840	842	836	839.50	6
7:00	22	844	845	841	843	843.25	4
7:30	23	848	843	844	836	842.75	12
8:00	24	840	844	841	845	842.50	5
8:30	25	843	845	846	842	844.00	4

Source: H. Gitlow, S. Gitlow, A. Oppenheim, and R. Oppenheim, *Tools and Methods for the Improvement of Quality*, p. 301. Copyright © 1989. Reprinted by permission of McGraw-Hill Companies, Inc.

b. An investigation is carried out to find out what caused the large range for subgroup 23. The investigation reveals that a water pipe burst at 7:25 P.M. and that the mishap resulted in water leaking under the machinery used in the tuning knob production process. The resulting disruption is the apparent cause for the out-of-control range for subgroup 23. The water pipe is mended, and since this fix is reasonably permanent, we are justified in removing subgroup 23 from the data set. Using the remaining 24 subgroups, show that revised centre lines are $\bar{\bar{x}} = 841.40$ and $\bar{R} = 4.88$.

c. Use the revised values of $\bar{\bar{x}}$ and $\bar{R}$ to plot revised $\bar{x}$ and R charts for the remaining 24 subgroups of diameters. Be sure to omit the mean and range for subgroup 23.

d. Is the revised R chart now in statistical control? What does your answer say about whether you can use the $\bar{x}$ chart to decide if the process mean is changing?

e. Is the revised $\bar{x}$ chart in statistical control? What does your answer tell you about the process mean?

f. An investigation is now undertaken to find the cause of the very high $\bar{x}$ values for subgroups 10, 11, 12, and 13. We again quote Gitlow, Gitlow, Oppenheim, and Oppenheim:

The investigation leads to the discovery that . . . a keyway wedge had cracked and needed to be

replaced on the machine. The mechanic who normally makes this repair was out to lunch, so the machine operator made the repair. This individual had not been properly trained for the repair; for this reason, the wedge was not properly aligned in the keyway, and the subsequent points were out of control. Both the operator and the mechanic agree that the need for this repair was not unusual. To correct this problem it is decided to train the machine operator and provide the appropriate tools for making this repair in the mechanic's absence. Furthermore, the maintenance and engineering staffs agree to search for a replacement part for the wedge that will not be so prone to cracking.

Since the assignable causes responsible for the very high $\bar{x}$ values for subgroups 10, 11, 12, and 13 have been found and eliminated, we remove these subgroups from the data set. Show that removing subgroups 10, 11, 12, and 13 (in addition to the previously removed subgroup 23) results in the revised centre lines $\bar{\bar{x}} = 840.46$ and $\bar{R} = 5.25$. Then use these revised values to plot revised $\bar{x}$ and R charts for the remaining 20 subgroups.

g. Are all of the subgroup means and ranges for these newly revised $\bar{x}$ and R charts inside their respective control limits?

17.5 PATTERN ANALYSIS

CHAPTER 5

L06

When we observe a plot point outside the control limits on a control chart, we have strong evidence that an assignable cause exists. In addition, several other data patterns indicate the presence of assignable causes. Precise description of these patterns is often made easier by *dividing the control band into zones—designated A, B, and C.* Zone boundaries are set at points that are one and two standard deviations (of the plotted statistic) on either side of the centre line. We obtain six zones—each zone being one standard deviation wide—with three zones on each side of the centre line. The zones that stretch one standard deviation above and below the centre line are designated as **C zones.** The zones that extend from one to two standard deviations away from the centre line are designated as **B zones.** The zones that extend from two to three standard deviations away from the centre line are designated as **A zones.** Figure 17.12(a) illustrates a control chart with the six zones, and Figure 17.12(b) shows how the zone boundaries for an $\bar{x}$ chart and an R chart are calculated. Part (b) of this figure also shows the values of the zone boundaries for the hole location $\bar{x}$ and R charts shown in Figure 17.9 (page 611). In calculating these boundaries, we use $\bar{\bar{x}} = 3.0006$ and $\bar{R} = 0.0675$, which we computed from

FIGURE **17.12** Zone Boundaries

(a) A control chart with A, B, and C zones

(b) Calculating zone boundaries for $\bar{x}$ and R charts in the hole location case

	Zone Boundaries	$\bar{x}$ Chart	R Chart
(0.135%)	Upper Control Limit:	$\bar{\bar{x}} + A_2\bar{R} = 3.0396$	$D_4\bar{R} = 0.1427$
Zone A (2.145%)	Upper A–B Boundary:	$\bar{\bar{x}} + \frac{2}{3}(A_2\bar{R}) = 3.0266$	$\bar{R} + \frac{2}{3}(D_4\bar{R} - \bar{R}) = 0.1176$
Zone B (13.59%)	Upper B–C Boundary:	$\bar{\bar{x}} + \frac{1}{3}(A_2\bar{R}) = 3.0136$	$\bar{R} + \frac{1}{3}(D_4\bar{R} - \bar{R}) = 0.0926$
Zone C (34.13%)	Centre Line:	$\bar{\bar{x}} = 3.0006$	$\bar{R} = 0.0675$
Zone C (34.13%)	Lower B–C Boundary:*	$\bar{\bar{x}} - \frac{1}{3}(A_2\bar{R}) = 2.9876$	$\bar{R} - \frac{1}{3}(D_4\bar{R} - \bar{R}) = 0.0424$
Zone B (13.59%)	Lower A–B Boundary:*	$\bar{\bar{x}} - \frac{2}{3}(A_2\bar{R}) = 2.9746$	$\bar{R} - \frac{2}{3}(D_4\bar{R} - \bar{R}) = 0.0174$
Zone A (2.145%)	Lower Control Limit:*	$\bar{\bar{x}} - A_2\bar{R} = 2.9617$	$D_3\bar{R} = $ does not exist
(0.135%)			

*When the R chart does not have a lower control limit (n < 7), the lower B–C and A–B boundaries should still be computed, as long as they are 0 or positive.

FIGURE **17.13**
A Plot Point outside the Control Limits

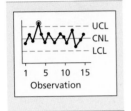

FIGURE **17.14**   Two of Three Consecutive Plot Points in Zone *A* (or beyond)

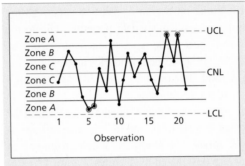

FIGURE **17.15**   Four of Five Consecutive Plot Points in Zone *B* (or beyond)

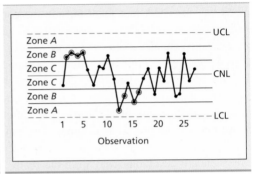

Source: H. Gitlow, S. Gitlow, A. Oppenheim, and R. Oppenheim, *Tools and Methods for the Improvement of Quality,* pp. 191–93, 209–211. Copyright © 1989. Reprinted by permission of McGraw-Hill Companies, Inc.

subgroups 1 through 20 with subgroups 1, 7, 12, and 17 removed from the data set; that is, we are using $\bar{\bar{x}}$ and $\bar{R}$ when the process is in control. For example, the upper *A–B* boundary for the $\bar{x}$ chart has been calculated as follows:

$$\bar{\bar{x}} + \frac{2}{3}(A_2\bar{R}) = 3.0006 + \frac{2}{3}(0.577(0.0675)) = 3.0266.$$

Finally, Figure 17.12(b) shows (based on a normal distribution of plot points) the percentages of points that we would expect to observe in each zone when the process is in statistical control. For instance, we would expect to observe 34.13 percent of the plot points in the upper portion of zone *C*.

For an $\bar{x}$ chart, if the distribution of process measurements is reasonably normal, then the distribution of subgroup means will be approximately normal, and the percentages shown in Figure 17.12 apply. That is, the plotted subgroup means for an in-control $\bar{x}$ chart should look like they have been randomly selected from a normal distribution. Any distribution of plot points that looks very different from the expected percentages will suggest the existence of an assignable cause.

Various companies (for example, Western Electric (AT&T) and Ford Motor Company) have established sets of rules for identifying assignable causes; use of such rules is called **pattern analysis**. We now summarize some commonly accepted rules. Note that many of these rules are illustrated in Figures 17.13, 17.14, 17.15, and 17.16, which show several common out-of-control patterns.

Pattern Analysis for $\bar{x}$ and *R* Charts

LO6   If one or more of the following conditions exist, it is reasonable to conclude that one or more assignable causes are present:

1   One plot point beyond zone *A* (that is, outside the three standard deviation control limits)—see Figure 17.13.

2   Two of three consecutive plot points in zone *A* (or beyond) on one side of the centre line of the control chart. Sometimes a zone boundary that separates zones *A* and *B* is called a **two standard deviation warning limit**. It can be shown that if the process is in control, then the likelihood of observing two of three plot points beyond this

warning limit (even when no points are outside the control limits) is very small. Therefore, such a pattern signals an assignable cause. Figure 17.14 illustrates this pattern. Specifically, note that plot points 5 and 6 are two consecutive plot points in zone *A* and that plot points 19 and 21 are two of three consecutive plot points in zone *A*.

3   Four of five consecutive plot points in zone *B* (or beyond) on one side of the centre line of the control chart. Figure 17.15 illustrates this pattern. Specifically, note that plot points 2, 3, 4, and 5 are four consecutive plot points in zone *B* and that plot points 12, 13, 15, and 16 are four

of five consecutive plot points in zone *B* (or beyond).

4 A run of at least eight plot points. Here we define a **run** to be a sequence of plot points of the same type. For example, we can have a run of points on one side of (above or below) the centre line. Such a run is illustrated in part (a) of Figure 17.16, which shows a run above the centre line. We might also observe a run of steadily increasing plot points (a **run up**) or a run of steadily decreasing plot points (a **run down**). These patterns are illustrated in parts (b) and (c) of Figure 17.16. Any of the above types of runs consisting of at least eight points is an out-of-control signal.

5 A **nonrandom pattern** of plot points. Such a pattern might be an **increasing** or **decreasing trend**. A **fanning-out** or **funneling-in pattern**, a **cycle**, an **alternating pattern**, or any other pattern that is very inconsistent with the percentages given in Figure 17.12 (see parts (d) through (h) of Figure 17.16).

If none of the patterns or conditions in 1 through 5 exists, then the process shows good statistical control or is said to be in control. A process that is in control should not be tampered with. On the other hand, if one or more of the patterns in 1 through 5 exists, action must be taken to find the cause of the out-of-control pattern(s) (which should be eliminated if the assignable cause is undesirable).

It is tempting to use many rules to decide when an assignable cause exists. However, if we use too many rules, we can end up with an unacceptably high chance of a **false out-of-control signal** (that is, an out-of-control signal when there is no assignable cause present). For most control charts, using the rules just described will yield an overall probability of a false signal in the range of 1 to 2 percent.

FIGURE 17.16 Other Out-of-Control Patterns

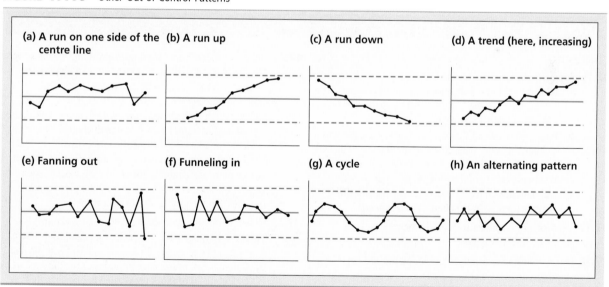

Example 17.7 The Hole Location Case (Pattern Analysis of $\bar{x}$ and *R* Charts)

Figure 17.17 on the next page shows ongoing $\bar{x}$ and *R* charts for the hole location problem. Here the $\bar{x}$ chart includes zone boundaries with zones *A*, *B*, and *C* labelled. Notice that the first out-of-control condition (one plot point beyond zone *A*) exists. Looking at the last five plot points on the $\bar{x}$ chart, we see that the third out-of-control condition (four of five consecutive plot points in zone *B* or beyond) also exists.

FIGURE **17.17**   Ongoing $\bar{x}$ and R Charts for the Hole Location Data—Zones *A*, *B*, and *C* Included

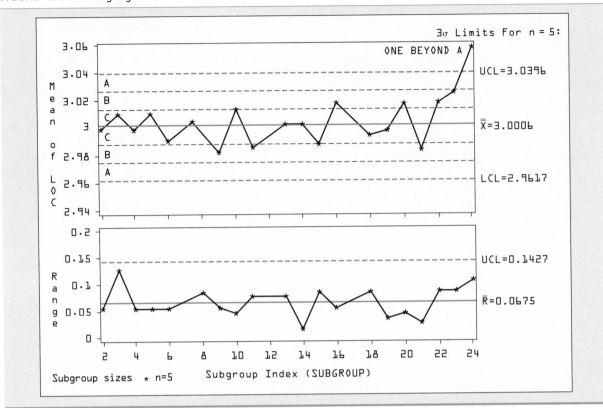

Exercises for Section 17.5

CONCEPTS

17.16 Suppose a process is in statistical control.
  a. What percentage of the plot points on an $\bar{x}$ chart will be found in the *C* zones (that is, in the middle 1/3 of the chart's control band)?
  b. What percentage of the plot points on an $\bar{x}$ chart will be found in either the *C* zones or the *B* zones (that is, in the middle 2/3 of the chart's control band)?
  c. What percentage of the plot points on an $\bar{x}$ chart will be found in the *C* zones, the *B* zones, or the *A* zones (that is, in the chart's control band)?

17.17 Discuss how a sudden increase in the process mean shows up on the $\bar{x}$ chart.

17.18 Discuss how a sudden decrease in the process mean shows up on the $\bar{x}$ chart.

17.19 Discuss how a steady increase in the process mean shows up on the $\bar{x}$ chart. Also, discuss how a steady decrease in the process mean shows up on the $\bar{x}$ chart.

17.20 Explain what we mean by a false out-of-control signal.

METHODS AND APPLICATIONS

17.21 Four control charts are given in Figure 17.18. For each chart, find any evidence of a lack of statistical control (that is, for each chart identify any evidence of the existence of one or more assignable causes). In each case, if such evidence exists, clearly explain why the plot points indicate that the process is not in control.

17.22 In the book *Tools and Methods for the Improvement of Quality*, Gitlow, Gitlow, Oppenheim, and Oppenheim present several control charts in a discussion and exercises dealing with pattern analysis. These control charts, which include appropriate *A*, *B*, and *C* zones, are reproduced in Figure 17.19. For each chart, identify any evidence of a lack of statistical control (that is, for each chart identify any evidence suggesting the existence of one or more assignable causes). In each case, if such evidence exists, clearly explain why the plot points indicate that the process is not in control.

17.23 Consider the tuning knob diameter data given in Table 17.10 (page 618). Recall that the subgroup size is $n = 4$ and that $\bar{\bar{x}} = 841.45$ and $\bar{R} = 5.16$ for these data.
  a. Calculate all of the zone boundaries for the $\bar{x}$ chart.
  b. Calculate all of the *R* chart zone boundaries that are either 0 or positive.

17.24 Given what you now know about pattern analysis, examine each of the following $\bar{x}$ and R charts for evidence of lack of statistical control. In each case, explain any evidence indicating the existence of one or more assignable causes.
  a. The pizza crust diameter $\bar{x}$ and R charts of Exercise 17.11 (pages 614–616).
  b. The acid value $\bar{x}$ and R charts of Exercise 17.12 (page 616).
  c. The tube hole location $\bar{x}$ and R charts of Exercise 17.13 (pages 616–617).

FIGURE 17.18 Charts for Exercise 17.21

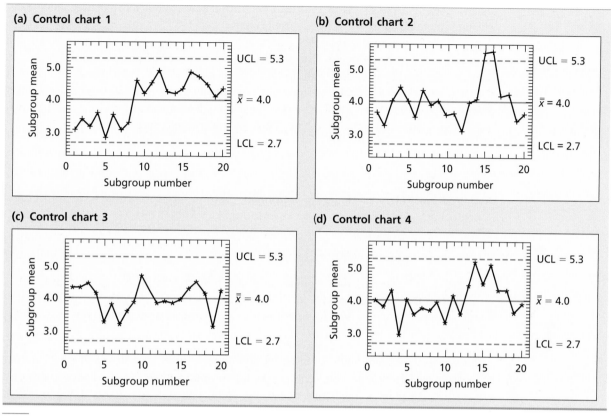

Source: B. Gunter, "Process Capability Studies Part 3: The Tale of the Charts," *Quality Progress* (June 1991), pp. 77–82. Copyright © 1991. American Society for Quality. Used with permission.

FIGURE 17.19 Charts for Exercise 17.22

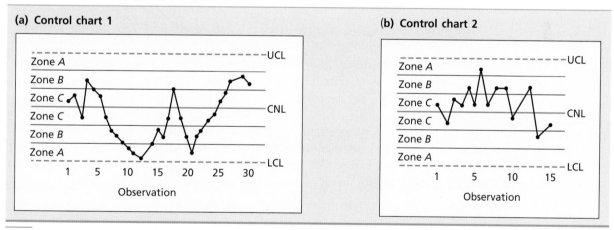

Source: H. Gitlow, S. Gitlow, A. Oppenheim, and R. Oppenheim, *Tools and Methods for the Improvement of Quality*, pp. 191–193, 209–111. Copyright © 1989. Reprinted by permission of McGraw-Hill Companies, Inc.

17.6 COMPARISON OF A PROCESS WITH SPECIFICATIONS: CAPABILITY STUDIES

If we have a process in statistical control, we have found and eliminated the assignable causes of process variation. Therefore, the individual process measurements fluctuate over time with a *constant standard deviation* σ around a *constant mean* μ. It follows that we can use the individual process measurements to estimate μ and σ. Doing this lets us determine if the process is capable of producing output that meets specifications. Specifications are based on fitness-for-use criteria—that is, the specifications are established by design engineers or customers. Even if a process is in statistical control, it may exhibit too much common cause variation (represented by σ) to meet specifications.

As will be shown in Example 17.9, one way to study the capability of a process that is in statistical control is to construct a histogram from a set of individual process measurements. The histogram can then be compared with the product specification limits. In addition, we know that if all possible individual process measurements are normally distributed with mean μ and standard deviation σ, then 99.73 percent of these measurements will be in the interval $[\mu - 3\sigma, \mu + 3\sigma]$. Estimating μ and σ by $\bar{\bar{x}}$ and $\bar{R}/d_2$, we obtain the **natural tolerance limits**[6] for the process.

LO7

> **Natural Tolerance Limits**
>
> The **natural tolerance limits** for a normally distributed process that is in statistical control are
>
> $$\left[\bar{\bar{x}} \pm 3\left(\frac{\bar{R}}{d_2}\right)\right] = \left[\bar{\bar{x}} - 3\left(\frac{\bar{R}}{d_2}\right), \ \bar{\bar{x}} + 3\left(\frac{\bar{R}}{d_2}\right)\right],$$
>
> where d_2 is a constant that depends on the subgroup size, n. Values of d_2 are given in Table 17.3 (page 603) for subgroup sizes $n = 2$ to $n = 25$. These limits contain approximately 99.73 percent of the individual process measurements.

If the natural tolerance limits are inside the specification limits, then almost all (99.73 percent) of the individual process measurements are produced within the specification limits. In this case, we say that the process is **capable** of meeting specifications. Furthermore, if we use $\bar{x}$ and R charts to monitor the process, then as long as the process remains in statistical control, the process will continue to meet the specifications. If the natural tolerance limits are wider than the specification limits, we say that the process is **not capable**. Here some individual process measurements are outside the specification limits.

Example 17.8 The Hot Chocolate Temperature Case (Natural Tolerance Limits)

Consider the $\bar{x}$ and R chart analysis of the hot chocolate temperature data. Suppose the dining hall staff has determined that all of the hot chocolate it serves should have a temperature of between 55°C and 70°C. Recalling that the $\bar{x}$ and R charts of Figure 17.11 (page 613) show that the process has been brought into control with $\bar{\bar{x}} = 60.409$ and $\bar{R} = 2.663$, we find that $\bar{\bar{x}} = 60.404$ is an estimate of the mean hot chocolate temperature, and that $\bar{R}/d_2 = 2.663/1.693 = 1.57$ is an estimate of the standard deviation of all the hot chocolate temperatures. Here $d_2 = 1.693$ is obtained from Table 17.3 (page 603) corresponding to the subgroup size $n = 3$. Assuming that the temperatures are approximately normally distributed, the natural tolerance limits

$$[\bar{\bar{x}} \pm 3(\bar{R}/d_2)] = [60.404 \pm 3(2.663/1.693)]$$
$$= [60.404 \pm 4.719] = [55.685, 65.123]$$

tell us that approximately 99.73 percent of the individual hot chocolate temperatures will be between 55.685°C and 65.123°C. Since these natural tolerance limits are inside the specification limits (55°C to 70°C), almost all the temperatures are within the specifications. Therefore, the hot chocolate–making process is capable of meeting the required temperature specifications. Furthermore, if the process remains in control on its $\bar{x}$ and R charts, it will continue to meet specifications.

---

[6]There are a number of alternative formulas for the natural tolerance limits. Here we give the version that is the most clearly related to using $\bar{x}$ and R charts. At the end of this section, we present an alternative formula.

Example 17.9 The Hole Location Case (Natural Tolerance Limits)

Again consider the hole-punching process for air conditioner compressor shells. Recall that we were able to get this process into a state of statistical control with $\bar{\bar{x}} = 3.0006$ and $\bar{R} = 0.0675$ by removing several assignable causes of process variation.

Figure 17.20 gives a relative frequency histogram of the 80 individual hole location measurements used to construct the $\bar{x}$ and R charts of Figure 17.8 (page 609). This histogram suggests that the population of all individual hole location dimensions is approximately normally distributed.

Since the process is in statistical control, $\bar{\bar{x}} = 3.0006$ is an estimate of the process mean, and $\bar{R}/d_2 = 0.0675/2.326 = 0.0290198$ is an estimate of the process standard deviation. Here $d_2 = 2.326$ is obtained from Table 17.3 (page 603) corresponding to the subgroup size $n = 5$. Furthermore, the natural tolerance limits

$$\left[\bar{\bar{x}} \pm 3\left(\frac{\bar{R}}{d_2}\right) \right] = \left[3.0006 \pm 3\left(\frac{0.0675}{2.326}\right) \right]$$
$$= [3.0006 \pm 0.0871]$$
$$= [2.9135, 3.0877]$$

tell us that almost all (approximately 99.73 percent) of the individual hole location dimensions produced by the hole-punching process are between 2.9135 cm and 3.0877 cm.

Suppose a major customer requires that the hole location dimension meet specifications of 3.00 ± 0.05 cm. That is, the customer requires that every individual hole location dimension be between 2.95 cm and 3.05 cm. The natural tolerance limits, [2.9135, 3.0877], which contain almost all individual hole location dimensions, are wider than the specification limits, [2.95, 3.05]. This says that some of the hole location dimensions are outside the specification limits. Therefore, the process is not capable of meeting the specifications. Note that the histogram in Figure 17.20 also shows that some of the hole location dimensions are outside the specification limits.

FIGURE 17.20 A Relative Frequency Histogram of the Hole Location Data
(Based on the Data with Subgroups 1, 7, 12, and 17 Omitted)

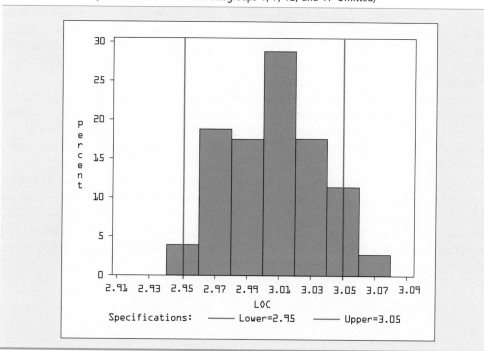

FIGURE **17.21**   Calculating the Fraction out of Specification for the Hole Location Data (Specifications Are 3.00 cm $\pm$ 0.05 cm)

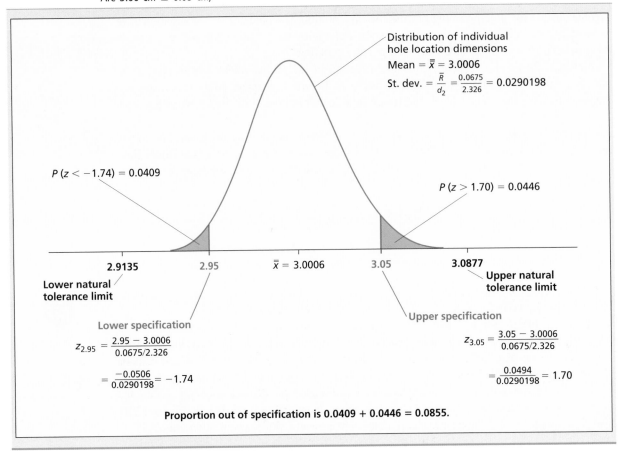

Figure 17.21 illustrates the situation, assuming that the individual hole location dimensions are normally distributed. The figure shows that the natural tolerance limits are wider than the specification limits. The shaded areas under the normal curve make up the fraction of product that is outside the specification limits. Figure 17.21 also shows the calculation of the estimated fraction of hole location dimensions that are out of specification. We estimate that 8.55 percent of the dimensions do not meet the specifications.

Since the process is not capable of meeting specifications, it must be improved by removing common cause variation. This is management's responsibility. Suppose engineering and management conclude that the excessive variation in the hole locations can be reduced by redesigning the machine that punches the holes in the compressor shells. Also suppose that after a research and development program is carried out to do this, the process is run using the new machine and 20 new subgroups of $n = 5$ hole location measurements are obtained. The resulting $\bar{x}$ and R charts (not given here) indicate that the process is in control with $\bar{\bar{x}} = 3.0002$ and $\bar{R} = 0.0348$. Furthermore, a histogram of the 100 hole location dimensions used to construct the $\bar{x}$ and R charts indicates that all possible hole location measurements are approximately normally distributed. It follows that we estimate that almost all individual hole location dimensions are contained within the new natural tolerance limits

$$\left[\bar{\bar{x}} \pm 3\left(\frac{\bar{R}}{d_2}\right) \right] = \left[3.0002 \pm 3\left(\frac{0.0348}{2.326}\right) \right]$$

$$= [3.0002 \pm 0.0449]$$

$$= [2.9553, 3.0451].$$

FIGURE **17.22** A Capable Process: The Natural Tolerance Limits Are within the Specification Limits

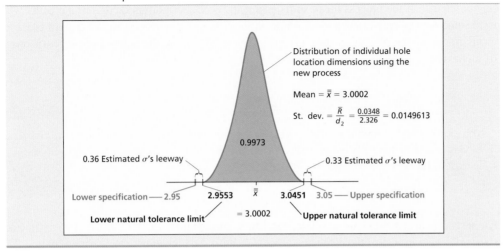

As illustrated in Figure 17.22, these tolerance limits are within the specification limits of 3.00 ± 0.05. Therefore, the new process is now capable of producing almost all hole location dimensions inside the specifications. The new process is capable because the estimated process standard deviation has been substantially reduced (from $\bar{R}/d_2 = 0.0675/2.326 = 0.0290$ for the old process to $\bar{R}/d_2 = 0.0348/2.326 = 0.0149613$ for the redesigned process).

Next, note that (for the improved process) the z value corresponding to the lower specification limit (2.95) is

$$z_{2.95} = \frac{2.95 - 3.0002}{0.0149613} = -3.36.$$

This says that the lower specification limit is 3.36 estimated process standard deviations below $\bar{\bar{x}}$. Since the lower natural tolerance limit is 3 estimated process standard deviations below $\bar{\bar{x}}$, there is a **leeway** of 0.36 estimated process standard deviations between the lower natural tolerance limit and the lower specification limit (see Figure 17.22). Also, note that the z value corresponding to the upper specification limit (3.05) is

$$z_{3.05} = \frac{3.05 - 3.0002}{0.0149613} = 3.33.$$

This says that the upper specification limit is 3.33 estimated process standard deviations above $\bar{\bar{x}}$. Since the upper natural tolerance limit is 3 estimated process standard deviations above $\bar{\bar{x}}$, there is a leeway of 0.33 estimated process standard deviations between the upper natural tolerance limit and the upper specification limit (see Figure 17.22). Because some leeway exists between the natural tolerance limits and the specification limits, the distribution of process measurements (that is, the curve in Figure 17.22) can shift slightly to the right or left (or can become slightly more spread out) without violating the specifications. Obviously, the more leeway, the better.

To understand why process leeway is important, recall that a process must be in statistical control before we can assess the capability of the process. In fact, we have the following:

In order to demonstrate that a company's product meets customer requirements, the company must present

1   $\bar{x}$ and R charts that are in statistical control, and

2   natural tolerance limits that are within the specification limits.

However, even if a capable process shows good statistical control, the process mean and/or the process variation will occasionally change (due to new assignable causes or unexpected recurring problems). If the process mean shifts and/or the process variation increases, a process will need some leeway between the natural tolerance limits and the specification limits in order to avoid producing out-of-specification product. We can determine the amount of process leeway (if any exists) by defining what we call the **sigma level capability** of the process.

> ### Sigma Level Capability
>
> The **sigma level capability** of a process is the number of estimated process standard deviations between the estimated process mean, $\bar{\bar{x}}$, and the specification limit that is closest to $\bar{\bar{x}}$.

For instance, in the previous example, the lower specification limit (2.95) is 3.36 estimated standard deviations below the estimated process mean, $\bar{\bar{x}}$, and the upper specification limit (3.05) is 3.33 estimated process standard deviations above $\bar{\bar{x}}$. It follows that the upper specification limit is closest to the estimated process mean, $\bar{\bar{x}}$, and because this specification limit is 3.33 estimated process standard deviations from $\bar{\bar{x}}$, we say that the hole-punching process has 3.33 sigma capability.

If a process has a sigma level capability of three or more, then there are at least three estimated process standard deviations between $\bar{\bar{x}}$ and the specification limit that is closest to $\bar{\bar{x}}$. It follows that if the distribution of process measurements is normally distributed, then the process is capable of meeting the specifications. For instance, Figure 17.23(a) illustrates a process with three sigma capability. This process is just barely capable—that is, there is no process leeway. Figure 17.23(b) illustrates a process with six sigma capability. This process has three standard deviations of leeway. In general, we see that if a process is capable, the sigma level capability expresses the amount of process leeway. The higher the sigma level capability, the more process leeway. More specifically, for a capable process, the sigma level capability minus three gives the number of estimated standard deviations of process leeway. For example, since the hole-punching process has 3.33 sigma capability, this process has $3.33 - 3 = 0.33$ estimated standard deviations of leeway.

The difference between three sigma and six sigma capability is dramatic. To illustrate this, look at Figure 17.23(a), which shows that a normally distributed process with three sigma capability produces 99.73 percent good quality (the area under the distribution curve between the specification limits is 0.9973). On the other hand, Figure 17.23(b) shows that a normally distributed process with six sigma capability produces 99.9999998 percent good quality. Said another way, if the process mean is centred between the specifications, and if we produce large quantities of product, then a normally distributed process with three sigma capability will produce an average of 2,700 defective products per million, while a normally distributed process with six sigma capability will produce an average of only 0.002 defective products per million.

In the long run, however, process shifts due to assignable causes are likely to occur. It can be shown that if we monitor the process by using an $\bar{x}$ chart that employs a typical subgroup size of four to six, the largest sustained shift of the process mean that might remain undetected by the $\bar{x}$ chart is a shift of 1.5 process standard deviations. In this worst case, it can be shown that a normally distributed three sigma capable process will produce an average of 66,800 defective products per million (clearly unacceptable), while a normally distributed six sigma capable process will produce an average of only 3.4 defective products per million. Therefore, if a six sigma capable process is monitored by $\bar{x}$ and R charts, then, when a process shift occurs, we can detect the shift (by using the control charts), and we can take immediate corrective action before a substantial number of defective products are produced.

FIGURE 17.23 Sigma Level Capability and Process Leeway

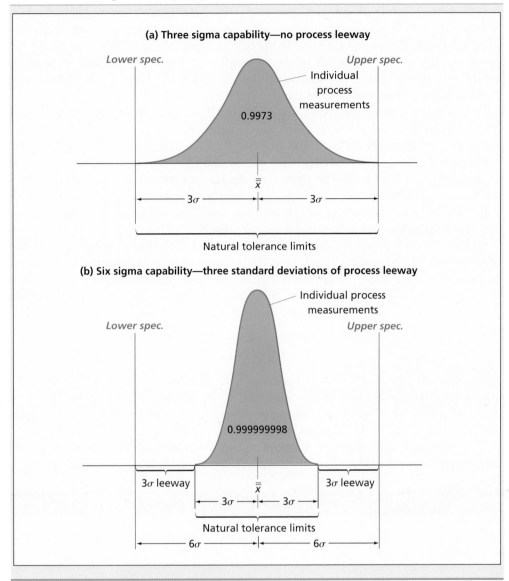

This is, in fact, how control charts are supposed to be used to prevent the production of defective product. That is, our strategy is as follows:

Prevention Using Control Charts

1 Reduce common cause variation in order to create leeway between the natural tolerance limits and the specification limits.

2 Use control charts to establish statistical control and to monitor the process.

3 When the control charts give out-of-control signals, take immediate action on the process to reestablish control before out-of-specification product is produced.

Over the past 25 years, a number of North American companies have adopted a **six sigma philosophy**. In fact, these companies refer to themselves as **six sigma companies**. It is the goal of these companies to achieve six sigma capability for all processes in the entire organization. For instance, Motorola Inc., the first company to adopt a six sigma philosophy, began a five-year quality improvement program in 1987. The goal of Motorola's companywide defect reduction program was to achieve six sigma capability for all processes—for instance, manufacturing processes, delivery, information systems, order completeness, accuracy of transactions records, and so forth. As a result of its six sigma plan, Motorola claims to have saved more than $1.5 billion. The corporation won the Malcolm Baldrige National Quality Award in 1988, and Motorola's six sigma plan has become a model for firms that are committed to quality improvement. Other companies that have adopted the six sigma philosophy are IBM, Digital Equipment Corporation, and General Electric.

To conclude this section, we make two comments. First, it has been traditional to measure process capability by using what is called the C_{p_k} **index**. This index is calculated by dividing the sigma level capability by three. For example, since the hole-punching process illustrated in Figure 17.22 has a sigma level capability of 3.33, the C_{p_k} index for this process is 1.11. In general, if C_{p_k} is at least 1, then the sigma level capability of the process is at least 3 and thus the process is capable. Historically, C_{p_k} has been used because its value relative to the number 1 describes the process capability. We prefer using sigma level capability to characterize process capability because we believe that it is more intuitive.

Second, when a process is in control, then the estimates $\overline{R}/d_2$ and s of the process standard deviation will be very similar. This implies that we can compute the natural tolerance limits by using the alternative formula $[\overline{\overline{x}} \pm 3s]$. For example, since the mean and standard deviation of the 80 observations used to construct the $\overline{x}$ and R charts in Figure 17.8 (page 609) are $\overline{\overline{x}} = 3.0006$ and $s = 0.028875$, we obtain the natural tolerance limits

$$[\overline{\overline{x}} \pm 3s] = [3.0006 \pm 3(0.028875)]$$
$$= [2.9140, 3.0872].$$

These limits are very close to those obtained in Example 17.9, [2.9135, 3.0877], which were computed by using the estimate $\overline{R}/d_2 = 0.0290198$ of the process standard deviation. Use of the alternative formula $[\overline{\overline{x}} \pm 3s]$ is particularly appropriate when there are long-run process variations that are not measured by the subgroup ranges (in which case $\overline{R}/d_2$ underestimates the process standard deviation). Since statistical control in any real application of SPC will not be perfect, some people believe that this version of the natural tolerance limits is the most appropriate.

Exercises for Section 17.6

CONCEPTS

17.25 Write a short paragraph explaining why a process that is in statistical control is not necessarily capable of meeting customer requirements (specifications).

17.26 Explain the interpretation of the natural tolerance limits for a process. What assumptions must be made in order to properly make this interpretation? How do we check these assumptions?

17.27 Explain how the natural tolerance limits compare to the specification limits when
  a. A process is capable of meeting specifications.
  b. A process is not capable of meeting specifications.

17.28 a. Explain why it is important to have leeway between the natural tolerance limits and the specification limits.
  b. Explain what is meant by the sigma level capability for a process.
  c. List two reasons why it is important to achieve six sigma capability.

METHODS AND APPLICATIONS

17.29 Consider the room cleaning and preparation time situation in Exercise 17.10 (page 614). We found that $\overline{x}$ and R charts based on subgroups of size five for these

data are in statistical control with $\overline{\overline{x}} = 15.9416$ minutes and $\overline{R} = 2.696$ minutes.
  a. Assuming that the cleaning and preparation times are approximately normally distributed, calculate a range of values that contains almost all (approximately 99.73 percent) of the individual cleaning and preparation times.
  b. Find reasonable estimates of the maximum and minimum times needed to clean and prepare an individual room.
  c. Suppose the resort hotel wishes to specify that every individual room should be cleaned and prepared in 20 minutes or less. Is this upper specification being met? Explain. Note here that there is no lower specification, since we would like cleaning times to be as short as possible (as long as the job is done properly).
  d. If the upper specification for room cleaning and preparation times is 20 minutes, find the sigma level capability of the process. If the upper specification is 30 minutes, find the sigma level capability.

17.30 Suppose that $\overline{x}$ and R charts based on subgroups of size three are used to monitor the moisture content of a type of paper. The $\overline{x}$ and R charts are found to be in statistical control, with $\bar{\bar{x}} = 6.0$ percent and $\bar{R} = 0.4$ percent. Further, a histogram of the individual moisture content readings suggests that these measurements are approximately normally distributed.

a. Compute the natural tolerance limits (limits that contain almost all of the individual moisture content readings) for this process.

b. If moisture content specifications are 6.0 percent $\pm$ 0.5 percent, is this process capable of meeting the specifications? Why or why not?

c. Estimate the fraction of paper that is out of specification.

d. Find the sigma level capability of the process.

17.31 A grocer in Vancouver has a contract with a produce wholesaler that specifies that the wholesaler will supply the grocer with pineapples that weigh at least 0.75 kg each. In order to monitor the pineapple masses, the grocer randomly selects three pineapples from each of 25 different crates of pineapples received from the wholesaler. Each pineapple's mass is determined and, therefore, 25 subgroups of three pineapple masses are obtained. When $\bar{x}$ and R charts based on these subgroups are constructed, we find that these charts are in statistical control with $\bar{\bar{x}} = 0.8467$ and $\bar{R} = 0.11$. Further, a histogram of the individual pineapple masses indicates that these measurements are approximately normally distributed.

a. Calculate a range of values that contains almost all (approximately 99.73 percent) of the individual pineapple masses.

b. Find a reasonable estimate of the maximum mass of a pineapple that the grocer is likely to sell.

c. Suppose that the grocer's contract with its produce supplier specifies that pineapples are to weigh a minimum of 0.75 kg. Is this lower specification being met? Explain. Note here that there is no upper specification, since pineapples should be as large as possible.

d. If the lower specification of 0.75 kg. is not being met, estimate the fraction of pineapples that weigh less than 0.75 kg. *Hint:* Find an estimate of the standard deviation of the individual pineapple masses.

17.32 Consider the pizza crust diameters for 10-inch pizzas given Exercise 17.11 (pages 614–616). We found that by removing an assignable cause, we were able to bring the process into statistical control with $\bar{\bar{x}} = 10.2225$ and $\bar{R} = 0.825$.

a. Recalling that the subgroup size for the pizza crust $\bar{x}$ and R charts is five, and assuming that the pizza crust diameters are approximately normally distributed, calculate the natural tolerance limits for the diameters.

b. Using the natural tolerance limits, estimate the largest diameter likely to be sold by the restaurant as a 10-inch pizza.

c. Using the natural tolerance limits, estimate the smallest diameter likely to be sold by the restaurant as a 10-inch pizza.

d. Are all 10-inch pizzas sold by this restaurant really at least 10 inches in diameter? If not, estimate the fraction of pizzas that are not at least 10 inches in diameter.

17.33 Consider the bag fill situation in Exercise 17.14 (page 617). We found that the elimination of a start-up problem brought the filling process into statistical control with $\bar{\bar{x}} = 52.5875$ and $\bar{R} = 1.2937$.

a. Recalling that the fill mass $\bar{x}$ and R charts are based on subgroups of size five, and assuming that the fill masses are approximately normally distributed, calculate the natural tolerance limits for the process.

b. Suppose that management wishes to reduce the mean fill mass in order to save money by "giving away" less product. However, since customers expect each bag to contain at least 50 kg of product, management wishes to leave some process leeway. Therefore, after the mean fill mass is reduced, the lower natural tolerance limit is to be no less than 50.5 kg. Based on the natural tolerance limits, how much can the mean fill mass be reduced? If the product costs $2 per kilogram, and if one million bags are sold per year, what is the yearly cost reduction achieved by lowering the mean fill mass?

17.34 Suppose that a normally distributed process (centred at target) has three sigma capability. If the process shifts 1.5 sigmas to the right, show that the process will produce defective products at a rate of 66,800 per million.

17.35 Suppose that a product is assembled using ten different components, each of which must meet specifications for five different quality characteristics. Therefore, we have 50 different specifications that could potentially be violated. Furthermore, suppose that each component possesses three sigma capability (process centred at target) for each quality characteristic. Then, if we assume normality and independence, find the probability that all 50 specifications will be met.

17.7 CHARTS FOR FRACTION NONCONFORMING

Sometimes, rather than collecting measurement data, we inspect items and simply decide whether each item conforms to some desired criterion (or set of criteria). For example, a fuel tank does or does not leak, an order is correctly or incorrectly processed, a batch of chemical product is acceptable or must be reprocessed, or plastic wrap appears clear or opaque. When an inspected unit does not meet the desired criteria, it is said to be **nonconforming** (or **defective**). When an inspected unit meets the desired criteria, it is said to be **conforming** (or **nondefective**). Traditionally, the

LO9

terms *defective* and *nondefective* have been employed. Recently, the terms *nonconforming* and *conforming* have become popular.

The control chart that we plot for this type of data is called a **p chart**. To construct this chart, we observe subgroups of n units over time. We inspect or test the n units in each subgroup and determine the number, d, of these units that are nonconforming. We then calculate for each subgroup

$$\hat{p} = d/n = \text{the fraction of nonconforming units in the subgroup,}$$

and we plot the $\hat{p}$ values versus time on the p chart. If the process being studied is in statistical control and producing a fraction p of nonconforming units, and if the units inspected are independent, then the number of nonconforming units, d, in a subgroup of n units inspected can be described by a binomial distribution. If, in addition, n is large enough so that np is greater than 2,[7] then both d and the fraction, $\hat{p}$, of nonconforming units are approximately described by normal distributions. Furthermore, the population of all possible $\hat{p}$ values has mean $\mu_{\hat{p}} = p$ and standard deviation

$$\sigma_{\hat{p}} = \sqrt{\frac{p(1-p)}{n}}.$$

Therefore, if p is known, we can compute three standard deviation control limits for values of $\hat{p}$ by setting

$$\text{UCL} = p + 3\sqrt{\frac{p(1-p)}{n}} \qquad \text{and} \qquad \text{LCL} = p - 3\sqrt{\frac{p(1-p)}{n}}.$$

However, since it is unlikely that p will be known, we must usually estimate p from process data. The estimate of p is

$$\bar{p} = \frac{\text{Total number of nonconforming units in all subgroups}}{\text{Total number inspected in all subgroups}}.$$

Substituting $\bar{p}$ for p, we obtain the following:

Centre Line and Control Limits for a *p* Chart

Centre line $= \bar{p}$,

LO4

$$\text{UCL} = \bar{p} + 3\sqrt{\frac{\bar{p}(1-\bar{p})}{n}},$$

$$\text{LCL} = \bar{p} - 3\sqrt{\frac{\bar{p}(1-\bar{p})}{n}}.$$

Note that if the LCL is negative, then there is no lower control limit for the p chart.

The control limits calculated using these formulas are considered to be **trial control limits**. Plot points above the upper control limit suggest that one or more assignable causes have increased the process fraction that is nonconforming. Plot points below the lower control limit may suggest that an improvement in the process performance has been observed. However, plot points below the lower control limit may also tell us that an inspection problem exists. Perhaps defective items are still being produced, but for some reason the inspection procedure is not finding them. If the chart shows a lack of control, assignable causes must be found and eliminated and the trial control limits must be revised. Here data for subgroups associated with assignable causes that have been eliminated will be dropped, and data for newly observed subgroups will be added when calculating the revised limits. This procedure is carried out until

---

[7]Some statisticians believe that this condition should be $np > 5$. However, for p charts, many think $np > 2$ is sufficient.

the process is in statistical control. When control is achieved, the limits can be used to monitor process performance. *The process capability for a process that is in statistical control is expressed using $\bar{p}$, the estimated process fraction nonconforming.* When the process is in control and $\bar{p}$ is too high to meet internal or customer requirements, common causes of process variation must be removed in order to reduce $\bar{p}$. This is a management responsibility.

Example 17.10 *p* Chart LCL and UCL Calculations

To improve customer service, a corporation wishes to study the fraction of incorrect sales invoices that are sent to its customers. Every week, a random sample of 100 sales invoices sent during the week is selected, and the number of sales invoices containing at least one error is determined. The data for the last 30 weeks are given in Table 17.11. To construct a *p* chart for these data, we plot the fraction of incorrect invoices versus time. Since the true overall fraction, *p*, of incorrect invoices is unknown, we estimate *p* by (see Table 17.11)

$$\bar{p} = \frac{1 + 5 + 4 + \cdots + 0}{3{,}000} = \frac{69}{3{,}000} = 0.023.$$

Since $n\bar{p} = 100(0.023) = 2.3$ is greater than 2, the population of all possible $\hat{p}$ values has an approximately normal distribution if the process is in statistical control. Therefore, we calculate the centre line and control limits for the *p* chart as follows:

$$\text{Centre line} = \bar{p} = 0.023,$$

$$\text{UCL} = \bar{p} + 3\sqrt{\frac{\bar{p}(1 - \bar{p})}{n}} = 0.023 + 3\sqrt{\frac{0.023(1 - 0.023)}{100}}$$

$$= 0.023 + 0.04497$$

$$= 0.06797,$$

$$\text{LCL} = \bar{p} - 3\sqrt{\frac{\bar{p}(1 - \bar{p})}{n}} = 0.023 - 0.04497$$

$$= -0.02197.$$

Since the LCL is negative, there is no lower control limit for this *p* chart. The MegaStat output of the *p* chart for these data is shown in Figure 17.24 on the next page. We note that none of the plot points are outside the control limits, and we fail to see any nonrandom patterns of

TABLE **17.11** Sales Invoice Data—100 Invoices Sampled Weekly

Week	Number of Incorrect Sales Invoices (d)	Fraction of Incorrect Sales Invoices ($\hat{p} = d/100$)	Week	Number of Incorrect Sales Invoices (d)	Fraction of Incorrect Sales Invoices ($\hat{p} = d/100$)
1	1	0.01	16	3	0.03
2	5	0.05	17	3	0.03
3	4	0.04	18	2	0.02
4	0	0.00	19	1	0.01
5	3	0.03	20	0	0.00
6	2	0.02	21	4	0.04
7	1	0.01	22	2	0.02
8	3	0.03	23	1	0.01
9	0	0.00	24	2	0.02
10	6	0.06	25	5	0.05
11	4	0.04	26	2	0.02
12	3	0.03	27	3	0.03
13	2	0.02	28	4	0.04
14	0	0.00	29	1	0.01
15	2	0.02	30	0	0.00

FIGURE **17.24**   MegaStat Output of a *p* Chart for the Sales Invoice Data

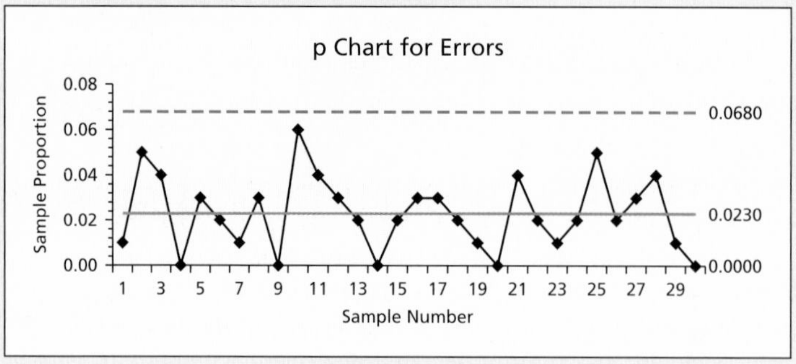

points. We conclude that the process is in statistical control with a relatively constant process fraction nonconforming of $\bar{p} = 0.023$. That is, the process is stable with an average of approximately 2.3 incorrect invoices per 100 invoices processed. Since no assignable causes are present, there is no reason to believe that any of the plot points have been affected by unusual process variations. That is, it will not be worthwhile to look for unusual circumstances that have changed the average number of incorrect invoices per 100 invoices processed. If an average of 2.3 incorrect invoices per 100 invoices is not acceptable, then management must act to remove common causes of process variation. For example, perhaps sales personnel need additional training or perhaps the invoice itself needs to be redesigned.

In the previous example, subgroups of 100 invoices were randomly selected each week for 30 weeks. In general, subgroups must be taken often enough to detect possible sources of variation in the process fraction nonconforming. For example, if we believe that shift changes may significantly influence the process performance, then we must observe at least one subgroup per shift in order to study the shift-to-shift variation. Subgroups must also be taken for a long enough time to allow the major sources of process variation to show up. As a general rule, at least 25 subgroups will be needed to estimate the process performance and to test for process control.

We have said that the size, n, of each subgroup should be large enough so that np (which is usually estimated by $n\bar{p}$) is greater than 2 (some practitioners prefer np to be greater than 5). Since we often monitor a p that is quite small (0.05 or 0.01 or less), n must often be quite large. Subgroup sizes of 50 to 200 or more are common. Another suggestion is to choose a subgroup size that is large enough to give a positive lower control limit (often, when employing a p chart, smaller subgroup sizes give a calculated lower control limit that is negative). A positive LCL is desirable because it allows us to detect opportunities for process improvement. Such an opportunity exists when we observe a plot point below the LCL. If there is no LCL, it would obviously be impossible to obtain a plot point below the LCL. The following can be shown:

A condition that guarantees that the subgroup size is large enough to yield a *positive lower control limit for a p chart* is

$$n > \frac{9(1 - p_0)}{p_0},$$

where p_0 *is an initial estimate of the fraction nonconforming* produced by the process. This condition is appropriate when *three standard deviation control limits* are employed.

For instance, suppose experience suggests that a process produces 2 percent nonconforming items. Then, in order to construct a p chart with a positive lower control limit, the subgroup size employed must be greater than

$$\frac{9(1 - p_0)}{p_0} = \frac{9(1 - 0.02)}{0.02} = 441.$$

As can be seen from this example, for small values of p_0 the above condition may require very large subgroup sizes. For this reason, it is not crucial that the lower control limit be positive.

We have thus far discussed how often—that is, over what specified periods of time (each hour, shift, day, week, or the like)—we should select subgroups. We have also discussed how large each subgroup should be. We next consider how we actually choose the items in a subgroup. One common procedure—which often yields large subgroup sizes—is to include in a subgroup *all (that is, 100 percent) of the units produced in a specified period of time.* For instance, a subgroup might consist of all the units produced during a particular hour. When employing this kind of scheme, we must carefully consider the independence assumption. The binomial distribution assumes that successive units are produced independently. It follows that a *p* chart would not be appropriate if the likelihood of a unit being defective depended on whether other units produced in close proximity are defective. Another procedure is to *randomly select the units in a subgroup from all the units produced in a specified period of time.* This was the procedure used in Example 17.10 to obtain the subgroups of sales invoices. As long as the subgroup size is small relative to the total number of units produced in the specified period, the units in the randomly selected subgroup should probably be **independent**. However, if the rate of production is low, it could be difficult to obtain a large enough subgroup when using this method. In fact, even if we inspect 100 percent of the process output over a specified period, and even if the production rate is quite high, it might still be difficult to obtain a large enough subgroup. This is because (as previously discussed) we must select subgroups often enough to detect possible assignable causes of variation. If we must select subgroups fairly often, the production rate may not be high enough to yield the needed subgroup size in the time in which the subgroup must be selected.

In general, the large subgroup sizes that are required can make it difficult to plot useful *p* charts. For this reason, we sometimes (especially when we are monitoring a very small *p*) relax the requirement that np be greater than 2. Practice shows that even if np is somewhat smaller than 2, we can still use the three standard deviation *p* chart control limits. In such a case, we detect assignable causes by looking for points outside the control limits and by looking for runs of points on the same side of the centre line. In order for the distribution of all possible $\hat{p}$ values to be sufficiently normal to use the pattern analysis rules we presented for $\bar{x}$ charts, $n\bar{p}$ must be greater than 2. In this case, we carry out pattern analysis for a *p* chart as we do for an $\bar{x}$ chart (see Section 17.5), and we use the following zone boundaries:

Upper A–B boundary: $\bar{p} + 2\sqrt{\dfrac{\bar{p}(1-\bar{p})}{n}}$,   Lower B–C boundary: $\bar{p} - \sqrt{\dfrac{\bar{p}(1-\bar{p})}{n}}$,

Upper B–C boundary: $\bar{p} + \sqrt{\dfrac{\bar{p}(1-\bar{p})}{n}}$,   Lower A–B boundary: $\bar{p} - 2\sqrt{\dfrac{\bar{p}(1-\bar{p})}{n}}$.

LO6

Here, when the LCL is negative, it should not be placed on the control chart. Zone boundaries, however, can still be placed on the control chart as long as they are not negative.

Exercises for Section 17.7

CONCEPTS

17.36 In your own words, define a "nonconforming unit."

17.37 Describe two situations in your personal life in which you might wish to plot a control chart for fraction nonconforming.

17.38 Explain why it can sometimes be difficult to obtain rational subgroups when using a control chart for fraction nonconforming.

METHODS AND APPLICATIONS

17.39 Suppose that $\bar{p} = 0.1$ and $n = 100$. Calculate the upper and lower control limits, UCL and LCL, of the corresponding *p* chart.

17.40 Suppose that $\bar{p} = 0.04$ and $n = 400$. Calculate the upper and lower control limits, UCL and LCL, of the corresponding *p* chart.

FIGURE 17.25   A *p* Chart for the Fraction of Orders with Missing Information

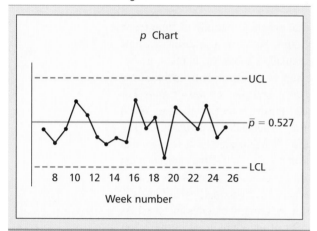

Source: W. J. McCabe, "Examining Processes Improves Operations," *Quality Progress* (July 1989), pp. 26–32. Copyright © 1989 American Society for Quality. Used with permission.

TABLE 17.12   The Number of Erroneous Entries for 24 Daily Samples of 200 Data Entries

Day	Number of Erroneous Entries	Day	Number of Erroneous Entries
1	6	13	2
2	6	14	4
3	6	15	7
4	5	16	1
5	0	17	3
6	0	18	1
7	6	19	4
8	14	20	0
9	4	21	4
10	0	22	15
11	1	23	4
12	8	24	1

Source: H. Gitlow, S. Gitlow, A. Oppenheim, and R. Oppenheim, *Tools and Methods for the Improvement of Quality*, pp. 168–172. Copyright © 1989. Reprinted by permission of McGraw-Hill Companies, Inc.

17.41 In the July 1989 issue of *Quality Progress*, William J. McCabe discusses using a *p* chart to study a company's order entry system. The company was experiencing problems meeting the promised 60-day delivery schedule. An investigation found that the order entry system frequently lacked all the information needed to correctly process orders. Figure 17.25 gives a *p* chart analysis of the percentage of orders having missing information.

a. From Figure 17.25 we see that $\bar{p} = 0.527$. If the subgroup size for this *p* chart is $n = 250$, calculate the upper and lower control limits, UCL and LCL.

b. Is the *p* chart of Figure 17.25 in statistical control? That is, are there any assignable causes affecting the fraction of orders having missing information?

c. On the basis of the *p* chart in Figure 17.25, McCabe says,

> The process was stable and one could conclude that the cause of the problem was built into the system. The major cause of missing information was salespeople not paying attention to detail, combined with management not paying attention to this problem. Having sold the product, entering the order into the system was generally left to clerical people while the salespeople continued selling.

Can you suggest possible improvements to the order entry system?

17.42 In the book *Tools and Methods for the Improvement of Quality*, Gitlow, Gitlow, Oppenheim, and Oppenheim discuss a data entry operation that makes a large number of entries every day. Over a 24-day period, daily samples of 200 data entries are inspected. Table 17.12 gives the number of erroneous entries per 200 that were inspected each day.

a. Use the data in Table 17.12 to compute $\bar{p}$. Then use this value of $\bar{p}$ to calculate the control limits for a

p chart of the data entry operation, and plot the *p* chart. Include zone boundaries on the chart.

b. Is the data entry process in statistical control, or are assignable causes affecting the process? Explain.

c. Investigation of the data entry process is described by Gitlow, Gitlow, Oppenheim, and Oppenheim as follows:

> In our example, to bring the process under control, management investigated the observations which were out of control (days 8 and 22) in an effort to discover and remove the special causes of variation in the process. In this case, management found that on day 8 a new operator had been added to the workforce without any training. The logical conclusion was that the new environment probably caused the unusually high number of errors. To ensure that this special cause would not recur, the company added a one-day training program in which data entry operators would be acclimated to the work environment.
>
> A team of managers and workers conducted an investigation of the circumstances occurring on day 22. Their work revealed that on the previous night one of the data entry consoles malfunctioned and was replaced with a standby unit. The standby unit was older and slightly different from the ones currently used in the department. The repairs on the regular console were not expected to be completed until the morning of day 23. To correct this special source of variation, the team recommended purchasing a spare console that would match the existing equipment and disposing of the outdated model presently being used as the backup. Management then implemented the suggestion.

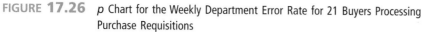

FIGURE **17.26** *p* Chart for the Weekly Department Error Rate for 21 Buyers Processing Purchase Requisitions

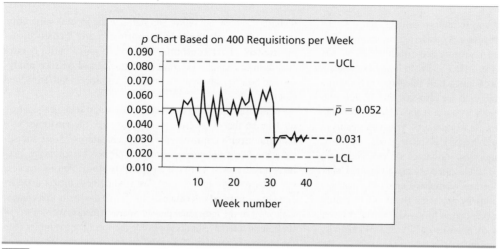

Since the assignable causes on days 8 and 22 have been found and eliminated, we can remove the data for these days from the data set. Remove the data and calculate the new value of $\bar{p}$. Then plot a revised *p* chart for the remaining 22 subgroups.

d. Did the actions taken bring the process into statistical control? Explain.

17.43 In the July 1989 issue of *Quality Progress*, William J. McCabe discusses using a *p* chart to study the percentage of errors made by 21 buyers processing purchase requisitions. The *p* chart presented by McCabe is shown in Figure 17.26. In his explanation of this chart, McCabe says,

> The causes of the errors . . . could include out-of-date procedures, unreliable office equipment, or the perceived level of management concern with errors. These causes are all associated with the system and are all under management control.
>
> Focusing on the 21 buyers, weekly error rates were calculated for a 30-week period (the data existed, but weren't being used). A *p*-chart was set up for the weekly department error rate. It showed a 5.2 percent average rate for the department. In week 31, the manager called the buyers together and made two statements: "I care about errors because they affect our costs and delivery schedules," and "I am going to start to count errors by individual buyers so I can understand the causes." The *p*-chart . . . shows an almost immediate drop from 5.2 percent to 3.1 percent.
>
> The explanation is that the common cause system (supervision, in this case) had changed; the improvement resulted from eliminating buyer sloppiness in the execution of orders. The *p*-chart indicates that buyer errors are now stable at

3.1 percent. The error rate will stay there until the common cause system is changed again.

a. The *p* chart in Figure 17.26 shows that $\bar{p} = 0.052$ for weeks 1 through 30. Noting that the subgroup size for this chart is $n = 400$. calculate the control limits, UCL and LCL, for the *p* chart during weeks 1 through 30.

b. The *p* chart in Figure 17.26 shows that after week 30 the value of $\bar{p}$ is reduced to 0.031. Assuming that the process has been permanently changed after week 30, calculate new control limits based on $\bar{p} = 0.031$. If we use these new control limits after week 30, is the improved process in statistical control? Explain.

17.44 The customer service manager of CanSave, a local discount store, monitors customer complaints. Each day, a random sample of 100 customer transactions is selected. These transactions are monitored, and the number of complaints received concerning these transactions during the next 30 days is recorded. The numbers of complaints received for 20 consecutive daily samples of 100 transactions are, respectively, 2, 5, 10, 1, 5, 6, 9, 4, 1, 7, 1, 5, 7, 4, 5, 4, 6, 3, 10, and 5.

a. Use the data to compute $\bar{p}$. Then use this value of $\bar{p}$ to calculate the control limits for a *p* chart of the complaints data. Plot the *p* chart.

b. Are the customer complaints for this 20-day period in statistical control? That is, have any unusual problems caused an excessive number of complaints during this period? Explain.

c. Suppose CanSave receives 13 complaints in the next 30 days for the 100 transactions that have been randomly selected on day 21. Should the situation be investigated? Explain.

CHAPTER SUMMARY

In this chapter, we studied how to improve business processes by using **control charts**. We began by considering several meanings of quality, and we discussed the history of the quality movement in the United States. We saw that Walter Shewhart introduced statistical quality control while working at Bell Telephone Laboratories during the 1920s and 1930s, and we also saw that W. Edwards Deming taught the Japanese how to use statistical methods to improve product quality following World War II. When the quality of Japanese products surpassed that of U.S.-made goods, and when, as a result, U.S. manufacturers lost substantial shares of their markets, Dr. Deming consulted and lectured extensively in the United States. This sparked an American reemphasis on quality that continues to this day. We also briefly presented **Deming's 14 points**, a set of management principles that, if followed, Deming believed would enable a company to improve quality and productivity, reduce costs, and gain competitive advantage.

We next learned that processes are influenced by **common cause variation** (inherent variation) and by **assignable cause variation** (unusual variation), and we saw that a control chart signals when assignable causes exist. Then we discussed how to sample a process. In particular, we explained that effective control charting requires **rational subgrouping**. Such subgroups minimize the chances that important process variations will occur within subgroups, and they maximize the chances that such variations will occur between subgroups.

Next we studied $\bar{x}$ **and** R **charts** in detail. We saw that $\bar{x}$ charts are used to monitor and stabilize the process mean (level) and

R charts are used to monitor and stabilize the process variability. In particular, we studied how to construct $\bar{x}$ and R charts by using **control chart constants**, how to recognize out-of-control conditions by employing **zone boundaries** and **pattern analysis**, and how to use $\bar{x}$ and R charts to get a process into statistical control.

While it is important to bring a process into statistical control, we learned that it is also necessary to meet the **customer's** or **manufacturer's requirements** (or **specifications**). Since statistical control does not guarantee that the process output meets specifications, we must carry out a **capability study** after the process has been brought into control. We studied how this is done by computing **natural tolerance limits**, which are limits that contain almost all of the individual process measurements. We saw that if the natural tolerance limits are inside the specification limits, then the process is **capable** of meeting the specifications. We also saw that we can measure how capable a process is by using **sigma level capability**, and we learned that a number of major businesses now orient their management philosophy around the concept of **six sigma capability**. In particular, we learned that if a process is in statistical control and if the process has six sigma or better capability, then the defect rate will be very low (3.4 per million or less).

We concluded this chapter by studying p **charts**, which are charts for fraction nonconforming. Such charts are useful when it is not possible (or when it is very expensive) to measure the quality characteristic of interest.

GLOSSARY OF TERMS

acceptance sampling: A statistical sampling technique that enables us to accept or reject a quantity of goods (the lot) without inspecting the entire lot. (page 590)

assignable causes (of process variation): Unusual sources of process variation. Also called **special causes** or **specific causes** of process variation. (page 594)

capable process: A process that can produce products or services that meet customer or manufacturer requirements (specifications). (page 624)

common causes (of process variation): Sources of process variation that are inherent to the process design—that is, sources of usual process variation. (page 594)

conforming unit (nondefective): An inspected unit that meets a set of desired criteria. (page 631)

control chart: A graph of process performance that includes a centre line and two control limits—an upper control limit, UCL, and a lower control limit, LCL. Its purpose is to detect assignable causes. (page 600)

C_{p_k} **index:** A process's sigma level capability divided by 3. (page 630)

ISO 9000: A series of international standards for quality assurance management systems. (page 592)

natural tolerance limits: Assuming a process is in statistical control and assuming process measurements are normally distributed, limits that contain almost all (approximately 99.73 percent) of the individual process measurements. (page 624)

nonconforming unit (defective): An inspected unit that does not meet a set of desired criteria. (page 631)

pattern analysis: Looking for patterns of plot points on a control chart in order to find evidence of assignable causes. (page 620)

p **chart:** A control chart on which the proportion nonconforming (in subgroups of size n) is plotted versus time. (page 632)

quality of conformance: How well a process is able to meet the requirements (specifications) set forth by the process design. (page 589)

quality of design: How well the design of a product or service meets and exceeds the needs and expectations of the customer. (page 589)

quality of performance: How well a product or service performs in the marketplace. (page 589)

rational subgroups: Subgroups of process observations that are selected so that the chances that process changes will occur between subgroups is maximized. (page 596)

R **chart:** A control chart on which subgroup ranges are plotted versus time. It is used to monitor the process variability (or spread). (page 601)

run: A sequence of plot points on a control chart that are of the same type—for instance, a sequence of plot points above the centre line. (page 621)

sigma level capability: The number of estimated process standard deviations between the estimated process mean, $\bar{\bar{x}}$, and the specification limit that is closest to $\bar{\bar{x}}$. (page 628)

statistical process control (SPC): A systematic method for analyzing process data in which we monitor and study the process variation. The goal is continuous process improvement. (page 593)

subgroup: A set of process observations that are grouped together for the purposes of control charting. (page 596)

total quality management (TQM): Applying quality principles to all company activities. (page 591)

variables control charts: Control charts constructed by using measurement data. (page 601)

$\bar{x}$ **chart (x-bar chart):** A control chart on which subgroup means are plotted versus time. It is used to monitor the process mean (or level). (page 601)

IMPORTANT FORMULAS

Centre line and control limits for an $\bar{x}$ chart: page 604

Centre line and control limits for an R chart: page 604

Zone boundaries for an $\bar{x}$ chart: page 619

Zone boundaries for an R chart: page 619

Natural tolerance limits for normally distributed process measurements: page 624

Sigma level capability: page 628

C_{p_k} index: page 630

Centre line and control limits for a p chart: page 632

Zone boundaries for a p chart: page 632

connect Practise and learn online with *Connect*. Questions and tables with online data sets are marked with ✈.

SUPPLEMENTARY EXERCISES

17.45 The makers of a popular brand of orange juice that comes in 1.89-L containers have called in the quality control inspectors. They are concerned about the consistency of the volume of fill of the containers. Every two hours for a three-day period of production, a sample of five containers is randomly selected and the volume of fill is measured. The results are given below:

Sample Number	1	2	3	4	5
1	1.8919	1.8905	1.8900	1.8892	1.8889
2	1.8929	1.8883	1.8910	1.8898	1.8879
3	1.8919	1.8909	1.8908	1.8922	1.8885
4	1.8884	1.8895	1.8909	1.8908	1.8901
5	1.8880	1.8879	1.8887	1.8903	1.8887
6	1.8905	1.8894	1.8924	1.8889	1.8894
7	1.8938	1.8888	1.8920	1.8919	1.8907
8	1.8915	1.8914	1.8899	1.8894	1.8904
9	1.8904	1.8899	1.8874	1.8899	1.8905
10	1.8900	1.8917	1.8898	1.8909	1.8904
11	1.8898	1.8919	1.8892	1.8893	1.8884
12	1.8870	1.8883	1.8902	1.8890	1.8923

Use this information to construct $\bar{x}$ and R charts and comment on any samples that are not in compliance. Is there any cause for concern?

Exercises 17.46 through 17.49 are based on a case study adapted from an example presented in the paper "Managing with Statistical Models" by James C. Seigel (1982). Seigel's example concerned a problem encountered by The Ford Motor Company.

THE CAMSHAFT CASE ✈

An automobile manufacturer produces the parts for its vehicles in many different locations and transports them to assembly plants. In order to keep the assembly operations running efficiently, it is vital that all parts be within specification limits. One important part used in the assembly of V6 engines is the engine camshaft, and one important quality characteristic of this camshaft is the case hardness depth of its eccentrics. A camshaft eccentric is a metal disk positioned on the camshaft so that as the camshaft turns, the eccentric drives a lifter that opens and closes an engine valve. The V6 engine camshaft and its eccentrics are illustrated in Figure 17.32. These eccentrics are hardened by a process that passes the camshaft through an electrical coil that "cooks" or "bakes" the camshaft. Studies indicate that the hardness depth of the eccentric labelled in Figure 17.27 on the next page is representative of the hardness depth of all of the eccentrics on the camshaft. Therefore, the hardness depth of this representative eccentric is measured at a specific location and is regarded to be the *hardness depth of the camshaft*. The optimal or target hardness depth for a camshaft is 4.5 mm. In addition, specifications state that in order for the camshaft to wear properly, the hardness depth of a camshaft must be between 3.0 mm and 6.0 mm.

The automobile manufacturer was having serious problems with the process used to harden the camshaft. This problem was resulting in 12 percent rework and 9 percent scrap, or a total of 21 percent out-of-specification camshafts. The hardening process was automated. However, adjustments could be made to the electrical coil employed in the process. To begin study of the process, a problem-solving team selected 30 daily subgroups of $n = 5$ hardened camshafts and measured the hardness depth of each camshaft. For each subgroup, the team calculated the mean, $\bar{x}$, and range, R, of the $n = 5$ hardness depth readings.

FIGURE **17.27**   A Camshaft and Related Parts

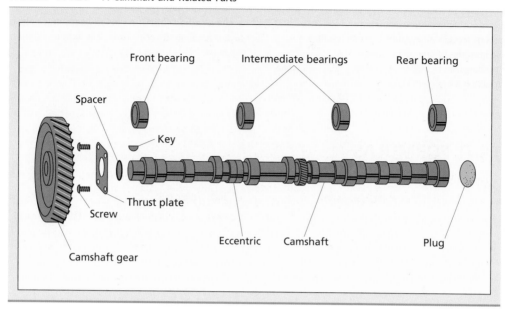

TABLE **17.13**   Hardness Depth Data for Camshafts (Coil #1)

R E A D I N G S		Date	June 7	8	9	10	11	14	15	16	17	18	21	22	23	24	25
	1		3.7	5.5	4.0	4.5	4.7	4.3	5.1	4.3	4.0	3.7	4.4	5.0	7.2	4.9	4.7
	2		4.3	4.0	3.8	4.1	4.7	4.5	4.4	4.1	4.5	4.2	4.6	5.9	6.9	5.1	4.0
	3		5.5	4.3	3.0	3.5	5.0	3.6	4.0	3.7	4.1	4.9	5.4	6.5	6.0	4.5	3.9
	4		4.6	3.5	1.7	4.2	4.3	3.8	3.6	3.9	3.5	5.5	5.5	9.4	5.4	4.0	4.2
	5		4.9	3.6	0	3.9	4.4	4.1	3.7	4.0	3.0	5.9	6.3	10.1	5.5	4.2	3.7
Subgroup Mean $\bar{x}$			4.6	4.2	2.5	4.0	4.6	4.1	4.2	4	3.8	4.8	5.2	7.4	6.2	4.5	4.1
Subgroup Range R			1.8	2.0	4.0	1.0	0.7	0.9	1.5	0.6	1.5	2.2	1.9	5.1	1.8	1.1	1.0

R E A D I N G S		Date	28	29	30	July 1	2	5	6	7	8	9	12	13	14	15	16
	1		3.7	3.5	4.7	4.0	5.0	5.8	3.6	4.0	3.5	4.1	6.2	5.5	4.4	4.0	3.9
	2		3.9	3.8	5.0	3.7	4.1	6.3	3.9	3.6	5.5	4.8	5.1	5.0	4.0	3.6	3.5
	3		3.4	3.6	4.1	3.9	4.2	3.8	4.1	3.5	5.0	3.8	5.4	3.9	3.7	3.7	3.3
	4		3.0	4.1	3.9	4.4	5.2	5.2	3.0	5.5	4.0	3.9	3.9	4.2	3.9	3.5	1.7
	5		0	4.4	4.3	4.2	5.5	3.9	1.7	3.5	3.5	4.4	4.7	4.4	3.6	3.7	0
Subgroup Mean $\bar{x}$			2.8	3.9	4.4	4	4.8	5	3.3	4	4.3	4.2	5.1	4.6	3.9	3.7	2.5
Subgroup Range R			3.9	0.9	1.1	0.7	1.4	2.5	2.4	2.0	2.0	1.0	2.3	1.6	0.8	0.5	3.9

The 30 subgroups are given in Table 17.13. The subgroup means and ranges are plotted in Figure 17.28. These means and ranges seem to exhibit substantial variability, which suggests that the hardening process was not in statistical control; you will compute control limits shortly.

Although control limits had not yet been established, the problem-solving team took several actions to try to stabilize the process while the 30 subgroups were being collected:

1   At point *A*, which corresponds to a low average and a high range, the power on the coil was increased from 8.2 to 9.2.

2   At point *B*, the problem-solving team found a bent coil. The coil was straightened, although at point *B*

the subgroup mean and range do not suggest that any problem exists.

3   At point *C*, which corresponds to a high average and a high range, the power on the coil was decreased to 8.8.

4   At point *D*, which corresponds to a low average and a high range, the coil shorted out. The coil was straightened, and the team designed a gauge that could be used to check the coil spacing to the camshaft.

5   At point *E*, which corresponds to a low average, the spacing between the coil and the camshaft was decreased.

FIGURE **17.28**   Graphs of Performance ($\bar{x}$ and R) for Hardness Depth Data (Using Coil #1)

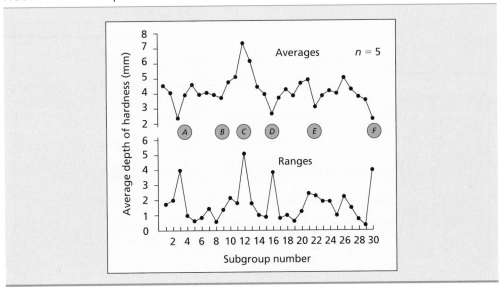

FIGURE **17.29** $\bar{x}$ and R Charts for Hardness Depth Data Using Coil #2 (Same Type as Coil #1)

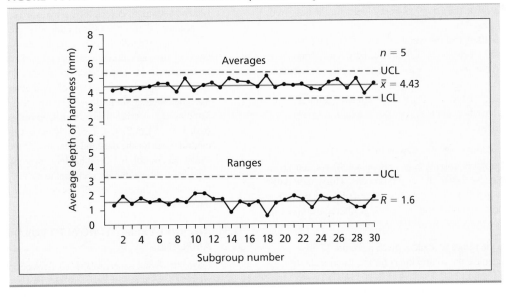

6   At point F, which corresponds to a low average and a high range, the first coil (Coil #1) was replaced. Its replacement (Coil #2) was a coil of the same type.

17.46 Using the data in Table 17.13:

   a. Calculate $\bar{\bar{x}}$ and $\bar{R}$ and then find the centre lines and control limits for $\bar{x}$ and R charts for the camshaft hardness depths.

   b. Plot the $\bar{x}$ and R charts for the camshaft hardness depth data.

   c. Are the $\bar{x}$ and R charts in statistical control? Explain.

Examining the actions taken at points A through E (in Figure 17.28), the problem-solving team learned that the power on the coil should be roughly 8.8 and that it is important

to monitor the spacing between the camshaft and the coil. It also learned that it may be important to check for bent coils. The problem-solving team then (after replacing Coil #1 with Coil #2) attempted to control the hardening process by using this knowledge. Thirty new daily subgroups of $n = 5$ hardness depths were collected. The $\bar{x}$ and R charts for these subgroups are given in Figure 17.29.

17.47 Using the values of $\bar{\bar{x}}$ and $\bar{R}$ in Figure 17.29:

   a. Calculate the control limits for the $\bar{x}$ chart in Figure 17.29.

   b. Calculate the upper control limit for the R chart in Figure 17.29.

   c. Are the $\bar{x}$ and R charts for the 30 new subgroups using Coil #2 (which we recall was of the same type as Coil #1) in statistical control? Explain.

FIGURE **17.30** $\bar{x}$ and R Charts for Hardness Depth Data Using a Redesigned Coil

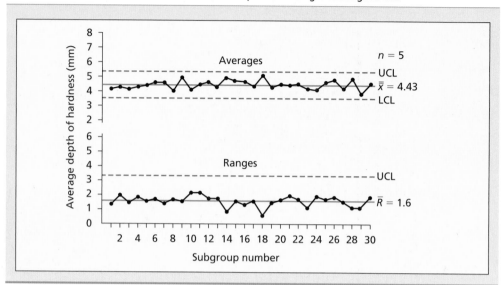

17.48 Consider the $\bar{x}$ and R charts in Figure 17.29.

    a. Calculate the natural tolerance limits for the improved process.

    b. Recalling that the specifications state that the hardness depth of each camshaft must be between 3.0 mm and 6.0 mm, is the improved process capable of meeting these specifications? Explain.

    c. Use $\bar{\bar{x}}$ and $\bar{R}$ to estimate the fraction of hardness depths that are out of specification for the improved process.

Since the hardening process shown in Figure 17.29 was not capable, the problem-solving team redesigned the coil to reduce the common cause variability of the process. Thirty new daily subgroups of $n = 5$ hardness depths were collected using the redesigned coil, and the resulting $\bar{x}$ and R charts are given in Figure 17.30.

17.49 Using the values of $\bar{\bar{x}}$ and $\bar{R}$ given in Figure 17.30:

    a. Calculate the control limits for the $\bar{x}$ and R charts in Figure 17.30.

    b. Is the process (using the redesigned coil) in statistical control? Explain.

    c. Calculate the natural tolerance limits for the process (using the redesigned coil).

    d. Is the process (using the redesigned coil) capable of meeting specifications of 3.0 mm to 6.0 mm? Explain. Also find and interpret the sigma level capability.

17.50 A bank officer wishes to study how many credit card holders attempt to exceed their established credit limits. To accomplish this, the officer randomly selects a weekly sample of 100 cardholders who have been issued credit cards by the bank, and the number of cardholders who have attempted to exceed their credit limit during the week is recorded. The numbers of cardholders who exceeded their credit limit in 20 consecutive weekly samples of 100 cardholders are, respectively, 1, 4, 9, 0, 4, 6, 0, 3, 8, 5, 3, 5, 2, 9, 4, 4, 3, 6, 4, and 0. Construct a control chart for the data and determine if the data are in statistical control. If 12 cardholders in next week's sample of 100 cardholders attempt to exceed their credit limit, should the bank regard this as unusual variation in the process?

17.51 INTERNET EXERCISE: HOW TO BUILD A PAPER AIRPLANE

Go to http://www.paperairplanes.co.uk/planes.php and try your hand at building a paper airplane. There are many designs to choose from. Follow the instructions very carefully, making sure that your folds are accurate and precise. Try this with a friend or group of people and see whose design flies farthest. If your airplane is "out of spec," then it will not fly properly, so take care with your design.

Appendix A
Statistical Tables

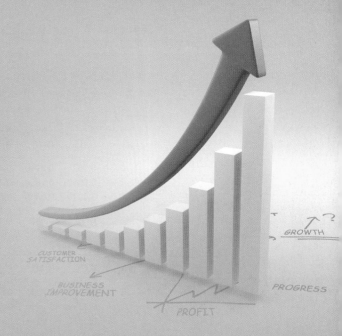

TABLE **A.1**　A Binomial Probability Table:
Binomial Probabilities (n between 2 and 6)

$n = 2$ p

$x\downarrow$	0.05	0.10	0.15	0.20	0.25	0.30	0.35	0.40	0.45	0.50	
0	0.9025	0.8100	0.7225	0.6400	0.5625	0.4900	0.4225	0.3600	0.3025	0.2500	2
1	0.0950	0.1800	0.2550	0.3200	0.3750	0.4200	0.4550	0.4800	0.4950	0.5000	1
2	0.0025	0.0100	0.0225	0.0400	0.0625	0.0900	0.1225	0.1600	0.2025	0.2500	0
	0.95	0.90	0.85	0.80	0.75	0.70	0.65	0.60	0.55	0.50	$x\uparrow$

$n = 3$ p

$x\downarrow$	0.05	0.10	0.15	0.20	0.25	0.30	0.35	0.40	0.45	0.50	
0	0.8574	0.7290	0.6141	0.5120	0.4219	0.3430	0.2746	0.2160	0.1664	0.1250	3
1	0.1354	0.2430	0.3251	0.3840	0.4219	0.4410	0.4436	0.4320	0.4084	0.3750	2
2	0.0071	0.0270	0.0574	0.0960	0.1406	0.1890	0.2389	0.2880	0.3341	0.3750	1
3	0.0001	0.0010	0.0034	0.0080	0.0156	0.0270	0.0429	0.0640	0.0911	0.1250	0
	0.95	0.90	0.85	0.80	0.75	0.70	0.65	0.60	0.55	0.50	$x\uparrow$

$n = 4$ p

$x\downarrow$	0.05	0.10	0.15	0.20	0.25	0.30	0.35	0.40	0.45	0.50	
0	0.8145	0.6561	0.5220	0.4096	0.3164	0.2401	0.1785	0.1296	0.0915	0.0625	4
1	0.1715	0.2916	0.3685	0.4096	0.4219	0.4116	0.3845	0.3456	0.2995	0.2500	3
2	0.0135	0.0486	0.0975	0.1536	0.2109	0.2646	0.3105	0.3456	0.3675	0.3750	2
3	0.0005	0.0036	0.0115	0.0256	0.0469	0.0756	0.1115	0.1536	0.2005	0.2500	1
4	0.0000	0.0001	0.0005	0.0016	0.0039	0.0081	0.0150	0.0256	0.0410	0.0625	0
	0.95	0.90	0.85	0.80	0.75	0.70	0.65	0.60	0.55	0.50	$x\uparrow$

$n = 5$ p

$x\downarrow$	0.05	0.10	0.15	0.20	0.25	0.30	0.35	0.40	0.45	0.50	
0	0.7738	0.5905	0.4437	0.3277	0.2373	0.1681	0.1160	0.0778	0.0503	0.0313	5
1	0.2036	0.3281	0.3915	0.4096	0.3955	0.3602	0.3124	0.2592	0.2059	0.1563	4
2	0.0214	0.0729	0.1382	0.2048	0.2637	0.3087	0.3364	0.3456	0.3369	0.3125	3
3	0.0011	0.0081	0.0244	0.0512	0.0879	0.1323	0.1811	0.2304	0.2757	0.3125	2
4	0.0000	0.0005	0.0022	0.0064	0.0146	0.0284	0.0488	0.0768	0.1128	0.1563	1
5	0.0000	0.0000	0.0001	0.0003	0.0010	0.0024	0.0053	0.0102	0.0185	0.0313	0
	0.95	0.90	0.85	0.80	0.75	0.70	0.65	0.60	0.55	0.50	$x\uparrow$

$n = 6$ p

$x\downarrow$	0.05	0.10	0.15	0.20	0.25	0.30	0.35	0.40	0.45	0.50	
0	0.7351	0.5314	0.3771	0.2621	0.1780	0.1176	0.0754	0.0467	0.0277	0.0156	6
1	0.2321	0.3543	0.3993	0.3932	0.3560	0.3025	0.2437	0.1866	0.1359	0.0938	5
2	0.0305	0.0984	0.1762	0.2458	0.2966	0.3241	0.3280	0.3110	0.2780	0.2344	4
3	0.0021	0.0146	0.0415	0.0819	0.1318	0.1852	0.2355	0.2765	0.3032	0.3125	3
4	0.0001	0.0012	0.0055	0.0154	0.0330	0.0595	0.0951	0.1382	0.1861	0.2344	2
5	0.0000	0.0001	0.0004	0.0015	0.0044	0.0102	0.0205	0.0369	0.0609	0.0938	1
6	0.0000	0.0000	0.0000	0.0001	0.0002	0.0007	0.0018	0.0041	0.0083	0.0156	0
	0.95	0.90	0.85	0.80	0.75	0.70	0.65	0.60	0.55	0.50	$x\uparrow$

(table continued)

TABLE **A.1** *(continued)*
Binomial Probabilities (*n* between 7 and 10)

n = 7 *p*

x↓	0.05	0.10	0.15	0.20	0.25	0.30	0.35	0.40	0.45	0.50	
0	0.6983	0.4783	0.3206	0.2097	0.1335	0.0824	0.0490	0.0280	0.0152	0.0078	7
1	0.2573	0.3720	0.3960	0.3670	0.3115	0.2471	0.1848	0.1306	0.0872	0.0547	6
2	0.0406	0.1240	0.2097	0.2753	0.3115	0.3177	0.2985	0.2613	0.2140	0.1641	5
3	0.0036	0.0230	0.0617	0.1147	0.1730	0.2269	0.2679	0.2903	0.2918	0.2734	4
4	0.0002	0.0026	0.0109	0.0287	0.0577	0.0972	0.1442	0.1935	0.2388	0.2734	3
5	0.0000	0.0002	0.0012	0.0043	0.0115	0.0250	0.0466	0.0774	0.1172	0.1641	2
6	0.0000	0.0000	0.0001	0.0004	0.0013	0.0036	0.0084	0.0172	0.0320	0.0547	1
7	0.0000	0.0000	0.0000	0.0000	0.0001	0.0002	0.0006	0.0016	0.0037	0.0078	0
	0.95	0.90	0.85	0.80	0.75	0.70	0.65	0.60	0.55	0.50	x↑

n = 8 *p*

x↓	0.05	0.10	0.15	0.20	0.25	0.30	0.35	0.40	0.45	0.50	
0	0.6634	0.4305	0.2725	0.1678	0.1001	0.0576	0.0319	0.0168	0.0084	0.0039	8
1	0.2793	0.3826	0.3847	0.3355	0.2670	0.1977	0.1373	0.0896	0.0548	0.0313	7
2	0.0515	0.1488	0.2376	0.2936	0.3115	0.2965	0.2587	0.2090	0.1569	0.1094	6
3	0.0054	0.0331	0.0839	0.1468	0.2076	0.2541	0.2786	0.2787	0.2568	0.2188	5
4	0.0004	0.0046	0.0185	0.0459	0.0865	0.1361	0.1875	0.2322	0.2627	0.2734	4
5	0.0000	0.0004	0.0026	0.0092	0.0231	0.0467	0.0808	0.1239	0.1719	0.2188	3
6	0.0000	0.0000	0.0002	0.0011	0.0038	0.0100	0.0217	0.0413	0.0703	0.1094	2
7	0.0000	0.0000	0.0000	0.0001	0.0004	0.0012	0.0033	0.0079	0.0164	0.0313	1
8	0.0000	0.0000	0.0000	0.0000	0.0000	0.0001	0.0002	0.0007	0.0017	0.0039	0
	0.95	0.90	0.85	0.80	0.75	0.70	0.65	0.60	0.55	0.50	x↑

n = 9 *p*

x↓	0.05	0.10	0.15	0.20	0.25	0.30	0.35	0.40	0.45	0.50	
0	0.6302	0.3874	0.2316	0.1342	0.0751	0.0404	0.0207	0.0101	0.0046	0.0020	9
1	0.2985	0.3874	0.3679	0.3020	0.2253	0.1556	0.1004	0.0605	0.0339	0.0176	8
2	0.0629	0.1722	0.2597	0.3020	0.3003	0.2668	0.2162	0.1612	0.1110	0.0703	7
3	0.0077	0.0446	0.1069	0.1762	0.2336	0.2668	0.2716	0.2508	0.2119	0.1641	6
4	0.0006	0.0074	0.0283	0.0661	0.1168	0.1715	0.2194	0.2508	0.2600	0.2461	5
5	0.0000	0.0008	0.0050	0.0165	0.0389	0.0735	0.1181	0.1672	0.2128	0.2461	4
6	0.0000	0.0001	0.0006	0.0028	0.0087	0.0210	0.0424	0.0743	0.1160	0.1641	3
7	0.0000	0.0000	0.0000	0.0003	0.0012	0.0039	0.0098	0.0212	0.0407	0.0703	2
8	0.0000	0.0000	0.0000	0.0000	0.0001	0.0004	0.0013	0.0035	0.0083	0.0176	1
9	0.0000	0.0000	0.0000	0.0000	0.0000	0.0000	0.0001	0.0003	0.0008	0.0020	0
	0.95	0.90	0.85	0.80	0.75	0.70	0.65	0.60	0.55	0.50	x↑

n = 10 *p*

x↓	0.05	0.10	0.15	0.20	0.25	0.30	0.35	0.40	0.45	0.50	
0	0.5987	0.3487	0.1969	0.1074	0.0563	0.0282	0.0135	0.0060	0.0025	0.0010	10
1	0.3151	0.3874	0.3474	0.2684	0.1877	0.1211	0.0725	0.0403	0.0207	0.0098	9
2	0.0746	0.1937	0.2759	0.3020	0.2816	0.2335	0.1757	0.1209	0.0763	0.0439	8
3	0.0105	0.0574	0.1298	0.2013	0.2503	0.2668	0.2522	0.2150	0.1665	0.1172	7
4	0.0010	0.0112	0.0401	0.0881	0.1460	0.2001	0.2377	0.2508	0.2384	0.2051	6
5	0.0001	0.0015	0.0085	0.0264	0.0584	0.1029	0.1536	0.2007	0.2340	0.2461	5
6	0.0000	0.0001	0.0012	0.0055	0.0162	0.0368	0.0689	0.1115	0.1596	0.2051	4
7	0.0000	0.0000	0.0001	0.0008	0.0031	0.0090	0.0212	0.0425	0.0746	0.1172	3
8	0.0000	0.0000	0.0000	0.0001	0.0004	0.0014	0.0043	0.0106	0.0229	0.0439	2
9	0.0000	0.0000	0.0000	0.0000	0.0000	0.0001	0.0005	0.0016	0.0042	0.0098	1
10	0.0000	0.0000	0.0000	0.0000	0.0000	0.0000	0.0000	0.0001	0.0003	0.0010	0
	0.95	0.90	0.85	0.80	0.75	0.70	0.65	0.60	0.55	0.50	x↑

(table continued)

TABLE **A.1** *(continued)*
Binomial Probabilities (*n* equal to 12, 14, and 15)

n = 12

p

x↓	0.05	0.10	0.15	0.20	0.25	0.30	0.35	0.40	0.45	0.50	
0	0.5404	0.2824	0.1422	0.0687	0.0317	0.0138	0.0057	0.0022	0.0008	0.0002	12
1	0.3413	0.3766	0.3012	0.2062	0.1267	0.0712	0.0368	0.0174	0.0075	0.0029	11
2	0.0988	0.2301	0.2924	0.2835	0.2323	0.1678	0.1088	0.0639	0.0339	0.0161	10
3	0.0173	0.0852	0.1720	0.2362	0.2581	0.2397	0.1954	0.1419	0.0923	0.0537	9
4	0.0021	0.0213	0.0683	0.1329	0.1936	0.2311	0.2367	0.2128	0.1700	0.1208	8
5	0.0002	0.0038	0.0193	0.0532	0.1032	0.1585	0.2039	0.2270	0.2225	0.1934	7
6	0.0000	0.0005	0.0040	0.0155	0.0401	0.0792	0.1281	0.1766	0.2124	0.2256	6
7	0.0000	0.0000	0.0006	0.0033	0.0115	0.0291	0.0591	0.1009	0.1489	0.1934	5
8	0.0000	0.0000	0.0001	0.0005	0.0024	0.0078	0.0199	0.0420	0.0762	0.1208	4
9	0.0000	0.0000	0.0000	0.0001	0.0004	0.0015	0.0048	0.0125	0.0277	0.0537	3
10	0.0000	0.0000	0.0000	0.0000	0.0000	0.0002	0.0008	0.0025	0.0068	0.0161	2
11	0.0000	0.0000	0.0000	0.0000	0.0000	0.0000	0.0001	0.0003	0.0010	0.0029	1
12	0.0000	0.0000	0.0000	0.0000	0.0000	0.0000	0.0000	0.0000	0.0001	0.0002	0
	0.95	0.90	0.85	0.80	0.75	0.70	0.65	0.60	0.55	0.50	x↑

n = 14

p

x↓	0.05	0.10	0.15	0.20	0.25	0.30	0.35	0.40	0.45	0.50	
0	0.4877	0.2288	0.1028	0.0440	0.0178	0.0068	0.0024	0.0008	0.0002	0.0001	14
1	0.3593	0.3559	0.2539	0.1539	0.0832	0.0407	0.0181	0.0073	0.0027	0.0009	13
2	0.1229	0.2570	0.2912	0.2501	0.1802	0.1134	0.0634	0.0317	0.0141	0.0056	12
3	0.0259	0.1142	0.2056	0.2501	0.2402	0.1943	0.1366	0.0845	0.0462	0.0222	11
4	0.0037	0.0349	0.0998	0.1720	0.2202	0.2290	0.2022	0.1549	0.1040	0.0611	10
5	0.0004	0.0078	0.0352	0.0860	0.1468	0.1963	0.2178	0.2066	0.1701	0.1222	9
6	0.0000	0.0013	0.0093	0.0322	0.0734	0.1262	0.1759	0.2066	0.2088	0.1833	8
7	0.0000	0.0002	0.0019	0.0092	0.0280	0.0618	0.1082	0.1574	0.1952	0.2095	7
8	0.0000	0.0000	0.0003	0.0020	0.0082	0.0232	0.0510	0.0918	0.1398	0.1833	6
9	0.0000	0.0000	0.0000	0.0003	0.0018	0.0066	0.0183	0.0408	0.0762	0.1222	5
10	0.0000	0.0000	0.0000	0.0000	0.0003	0.0014	0.0049	0.0136	0.0312	0.0611	4
11	0.0000	0.0000	0.0000	0.0000	0.0000	0.0002	0.0010	0.0033	0.0093	0.0222	3
12	0.0000	0.0000	0.0000	0.0000	0.0000	0.0000	0.0001	0.0005	0.0019	0.0056	2
13	0.0000	0.0000	0.0000	0.0000	0.0000	0.0000	0.0000	0.0001	0.0002	0.0009	1
14	0.0000	0.0000	0.0000	0.0000	0.0000	0.0000	0.0000	0.0000	0.0000	0.0001	0
	0.95	0.90	0.85	0.80	0.75	0.70	0.65	0.60	0.55	0.50	x↑

n = 15

p

x↓	0.05	0.10	0.15	0.20	0.25	0.30	0.35	0.40	0.45	0.50	
0	0.4633	0.2059	0.0874	0.0352	0.0134	0.0047	0.0016	0.0005	0.0001	0.0000	15
1	0.3658	0.3432	0.2312	0.1319	0.0668	0.0305	0.0126	0.0047	0.0016	0.0005	14
2	0.1348	0.2669	0.2856	0.2309	0.1559	0.0916	0.0476	0.0219	0.0090	0.0032	13
3	0.0307	0.1285	0.2184	0.2501	0.2252	0.1700	0.1110	0.0634	0.0318	0.0139	12
4	0.0049	0.0428	0.1156	0.1876	0.2252	0.2186	0.1792	0.1268	0.0780	0.0417	11
5	0.0006	0.0105	0.0449	0.1032	0.1651	0.2061	0.2123	0.1859	0.1404	0.0916	10
6	0.0000	0.0019	0.0132	0.0430	0.0917	0.1472	0.1906	0.2066	0.1914	0.1527	9
7	0.0000	0.0003	0.0030	0.0138	0.0393	0.0811	0.1319	0.1771	0.2013	0.1964	8
8	0.0000	0.0000	0.0005	0.0035	0.0131	0.0348	0.0710	0.1181	0.1647	0.1964	7
9	0.0000	0.0000	0.0001	0.0007	0.0034	0.0116	0.0298	0.0612	0.1048	0.1527	6
10	0.0000	0.0000	0.0000	0.0001	0.0007	0.0030	0.0096	0.0245	0.0515	0.0916	5
11	0.0000	0.0000	0.0000	0.0000	0.0001	0.0006	0.0024	0.0074	0.0191	0.0417	4
12	0.0000	0.0000	0.0000	0.0000	0.0000	0.0001	0.0004	0.0016	0.0052	0.0139	3
13	0.0000	0.0000	0.0000	0.0000	0.0000	0.0000	0.0001	0.0003	0.0010	0.0032	2
14	0.0000	0.0000	0.0000	0.0000	0.0000	0.0000	0.0000	0.0000	0.0001	0.0005	1
15	0.0000	0.0000	0.0000	0.0000	0.0000	0.0000	0.0000	0.0000	0.0000	0.0000	0
	0.95	0.90	0.85	0.80	0.75	0.70	0.65	0.60	0.55	0.50	x↑

(table continued)

TABLE **A.1** (continued)
Binomial Probabilities (n equal to 16 and 18)

n = 16   p

x↓	0.05	0.10	0.15	0.20	0.25	0.30	0.35	0.40	0.45	0.50	
0	0.4401	0.1853	0.0743	0.0281	0.0100	0.0033	0.0010	0.0003	0.0001	0.0000	16
1	0.3706	0.3294	0.2097	0.1126	0.0535	0.0228	0.0087	0.0030	0.0009	0.0002	15
2	0.1463	0.2745	0.2775	0.2111	0.1336	0.0732	0.0353	0.0150	0.0056	0.0018	14
3	0.0359	0.1423	0.2285	0.2463	0.2079	0.1465	0.0888	0.0468	0.0215	0.0085	13
4	0.0061	0.0514	0.1311	0.2001	0.2252	0.2040	0.1553	0.1014	0.0572	0.0278	12
5	0.0008	0.0137	0.0555	0.1201	0.1802	0.2099	0.2008	0.1623	0.1123	0.0667	11
6	0.0001	0.0028	0.0180	0.0550	0.1101	0.1649	0.1982	0.1983	0.1684	0.1222	10
7	0.0000	0.0004	0.0045	0.0197	0.0524	0.1010	0.1524	0.1889	0.1969	0.1746	9
8	0.0000	0.0001	0.0009	0.0055	0.0197	0.0487	0.0923	0.1417	0.1812	0.1964	8
9	0.0000	0.0000	0.0001	0.0012	0.0058	0.0185	0.0442	0.0840	0.1318	0.1746	7
10	0.0000	0.0000	0.0000	0.0002	0.0014	0.0056	0.0167	0.0392	0.0755	0.1222	6
11	0.0000	0.0000	0.0000	0.0000	0.0002	0.0013	0.0049	0.0142	0.0337	0.0667	5
12	0.0000	0.0000	0.0000	0.0000	0.0000	0.0002	0.0011	0.0040	0.0115	0.0278	4
13	0.0000	0.0000	0.0000	0.0000	0.0000	0.0000	0.0002	0.0008	0.0029	0.0085	3
14	0.0000	0.0000	0.0000	0.0000	0.0000	0.0000	0.0000	0.0001	0.0005	0.0018	2
15	0.0000	0.0000	0.0000	0.0000	0.0000	0.0000	0.0000	0.0000	0.0001	0.0002	1
	0.95	0.90	0.85	0.80	0.75	0.70	0.65	0.60	0.55	0.50	x↑

n = 18   p

x↓	0.05	0.10	0.15	0.20	0.25	0.30	0.35	0.40	0.45	0.50	
0	0.3972	0.1501	0.0536	0.0180	0.0056	0.0016	0.0004	0.0001	0.0000	0.0000	18
1	0.3763	0.3002	0.1704	0.0811	0.0338	0.0126	0.0042	0.0012	0.0003	0.0001	17
2	0.1683	0.2835	0.2556	0.1723	0.0958	0.0458	0.0190	0.0069	0.0022	0.0006	16
3	0.0473	0.1680	0.2406	0.2297	0.1704	0.1046	0.0547	0.0246	0.0095	0.0031	15
4	0.0093	0.0700	0.1592	0.2153	0.2130	0.1681	0.1104	0.0614	0.0291	0.0117	14
5	0.0014	0.0218	0.0787	0.1507	0.1988	0.2017	0.1664	0.1146	0.0666	0.0327	13
6	0.0002	0.0052	0.0301	0.0816	0.1436	0.1873	0.1941	0.1655	0.1181	0.0708	12
7	0.0000	0.0010	0.0091	0.0350	0.0820	0.1376	0.1792	0.1892	0.1657	0.1214	11
8	0.0000	0.0002	0.0022	0.0120	0.0376	0.0811	0.1327	0.1734	0.1864	0.1669	10
9	0.0000	0.0000	0.0004	0.0033	0.0139	0.0386	0.0794	0.1284	0.1694	0.1855	9
10	0.0000	0.0000	0.0001	0.0008	0.0042	0.0149	0.0385	0.0771	0.1248	0.1669	8
11	0.0000	0.0000	0.0000	0.0001	0.0010	0.0046	0.0151	0.0374	0.0742	0.1214	7
12	0.0000	0.0000	0.0000	0.0000	0.0002	0.0012	0.0047	0.0145	0.0354	0.0708	6
13	0.0000	0.0000	0.0000	0.0000	0.0000	0.0002	0.0012	0.0045	0.0134	0.0327	5
14	0.0000	0.0000	0.0000	0.0000	0.0000	0.0000	0.0002	0.0011	0.0039	0.0117	4
15	0.0000	0.0000	0.0000	0.0000	0.0000	0.0000	0.0000	0.0002	0.0009	0.0031	3
16	0.0000	0.0000	0.0000	0.0000	0.0000	0.0000	0.0000	0.0000	0.0001	0.0006	2
17	0.0000	0.0000	0.0000	0.0000	0.0000	0.0000	0.0000	0.0000	0.0000	0.0001	1
	0.95	0.90	0.85	0.80	0.75	0.70	0.65	0.60	0.55	0.50	x↑

(table continued)

TABLE **A.1** *(concluded)*
Binomial Probabilities (*n* equal to 20)

n = 20					*p*						
x↓	0.05	0.10	0.15	0.20	0.25	0.30	0.35	0.40	0.45	0.50	
0	0.3585	0.1216	0.0388	0.0115	0.0032	0.0008	0.0002	0.0000	0.0000	0.0000	20
1	0.3774	0.2702	0.1368	0.0576	0.0211	0.0068	0.0020	0.0005	0.0001	0.0000	19
2	0.1887	0.2852	0.2293	0.1369	0.0669	0.0278	0.0100	0.0031	0.0008	0.0002	18
3	0.0596	0.1901	0.2428	0.2054	0.1339	0.0716	0.0323	0.0123	0.0040	0.0011	17
4	0.0133	0.0898	0.1821	0.2182	0.1897	0.1304	0.0738	0.0350	0.0139	0.0046	16
5	0.0022	0.0319	0.1028	0.1746	0.2023	0.1789	0.1272	0.0746	0.0365	0.0148	15
6	0.0003	0.0089	0.0454	0.1091	0.1686	0.1916	0.1712	0.1244	0.0746	0.0370	14
7	0.0000	0.0020	0.0160	0.0545	0.1124	0.1643	0.1844	0.1659	0.1221	0.0739	13
8	0.0000	0.0004	0.0046	0.0222	0.0609	0.1144	0.1614	0.1797	0.1623	0.1201	12
9	0.0000	0.0001	0.0011	0.0074	0.0271	0.0654	0.1158	0.1597	0.1771	0.1602	11
10	0.0000	0.0000	0.0002	0.0020	0.0099	0.0308	0.0686	0.1171	0.1593	0.1762	10
11	0.0000	0.0000	0.0000	0.0005	0.0030	0.0120	0.0336	0.0710	0.1185	0.1602	9
12	0.0000	0.0000	0.0000	0.0001	0.0008	0.0039	0.0136	0.0355	0.0727	0.1201	8
13	0.0000	0.0000	0.0000	0.0000	0.0002	0.0010	0.0045	0.0146	0.0366	0.0739	7
14	0.0000	0.0000	0.0000	0.0000	0.0000	0.0002	0.0012	0.0049	0.0150	0.0370	6
15	0.0000	0.0000	0.0000	0.0000	0.0000	0.0000	0.0003	0.0013	0.0049	0.0148	5
16	0.0000	0.0000	0.0000	0.0000	0.0000	0.0000	0.0000	0.0003	0.0013	0.0046	4
17	0.0000	0.0000	0.0000	0.0000	0.0000	0.0000	0.0000	0.0000	0.0002	0.0011	3
18	0.0000	0.0000	0.0000	0.0000	0.0000	0.0000	0.0000	0.0000	0.0000	0.0002	2
	0.95	0.90	0.85	0.80	0.75	0.70	0.65	0.60	0.55	0.50	*x*↑

Source: Computed by D. K. Hildebrand. Found in D. K. Hildebrand and L. Ott, *Statistical Thinking for Managers*, 3rd ed. (Boston, MA: PWS-KENT Publishing Company, 1991).

TABLE **A.2**　A Poisson Probability Table
Poisson Probabilities (μ between 0.1 and 2.0)

					μ					
x	0.1	0.2	0.3	0.4	0.5	0.6	0.7	0.8	0.9	1.0
0	0.9048	0.8187	0.7408	0.6703	0.6065	0.5488	0.4966	0.4493	0.4066	0.3679
1	0.0905	0.1637	0.2222	0.2681	0.3033	0.3293	0.3476	0.3595	0.3659	0.3679
2	0.0045	0.0164	0.0333	0.0536	0.0758	0.0988	0.1217	0.1438	0.1647	0.1839
3	0.0002	0.0011	0.0033	0.0072	0.0126	0.0198	0.0284	0.0383	0.0494	0.0613
4	0.0000	0.0001	0.0003	0.0007	0.0016	0.0030	0.0050	0.0077	0.0111	0.0153
5	0.0000	0.0000	0.0000	0.0001	0.0002	0.0004	0.0007	0.0012	0.0020	0.0031
6	0.0000	0.0000	0.0000	0.0000	0.0000	0.0000	0.0001	0.0002	0.0003	0.0005

					μ					
x	1.1	1.2	1.3	1.4	1.5	1.6	1.7	1.8	1.9	2.0
0	0.3329	0.3012	0.2725	0.2466	0.2231	0.2019	0.1827	0.1653	0.1496	0.1353
1	0.3662	0.3614	0.3543	0.3452	0.3347	0.3230	0.3106	0.2975	0.2842	0.2707
2	0.2014	0.2169	0.2303	0.2417	0.2510	0.2584	0.2640	0.2678	0.2700	0.2707
3	0.0738	0.0867	0.0998	0.1128	0.1255	0.1378	0.1496	0.1607	0.1710	0.1804
4	0.0203	0.0260	0.0324	0.0395	0.0471	0.0551	0.0636	0.0723	0.0812	0.0902
5	0.0045	0.0062	0.0084	0.0111	0.0141	0.0176	0.0216	0.0260	0.0309	0.0361
6	0.0008	0.0012	0.0018	0.0026	0.0035	0.0047	0.0061	0.0078	0.0098	0.0120
7	0.0001	0.0002	0.0003	0.0005	0.0008	0.0011	0.0015	0.0020	0.0027	0.0034
8	0.0000	0.0000	0.0001	0.0001	0.0001	0.0002	0.0003	0.0005	0.0006	0.0009

(table continued)

TABLE **A.2**   *(continued)*
Poisson Probabilities (μ between 2.1 and 5.0)

					μ					
x	2.1	2.2	2.3	2.4	2.5	2.6	2.7	2.8	2.9	3.0
0	0.1225	0.1108	0.1003	0.0907	0.0821	0.0743	0.0672	0.0608	0.0550	0.0498
1	0.2572	0.2438	0.2306	0.2177	0.2052	0.1931	0.1815	0.1703	0.1596	0.1494
2	0.2700	0.2681	0.2652	0.2613	0.2565	0.2510	0.2450	0.2384	0.2314	0.2240
3	0.1890	0.1966	0.2033	0.2090	0.2138	0.2176	0.2205	0.2225	0.2237	0.2240
4	0.0992	0.1082	0.1169	0.1254	0.1336	0.1414	0.1488	0.1557	0.1622	0.1680
5	0.0417	0.0476	0.0538	0.0602	0.0668	0.0735	0.0804	0.0872	0.0940	0.1008
6	0.0146	0.0174	0.0206	0.0241	0.0278	0.0319	0.0362	0.0407	0.0455	0.0504
7	0.0044	0.0055	0.0068	0.0083	0.0099	0.0118	0.0139	0.0163	0.0188	0.0216
8	0.0011	0.0015	0.0019	0.0025	0.0031	0.0038	0.0047	0.0057	0.0068	0.0081
9	0.0003	0.0004	0.0005	0.0007	0.0009	0.0011	0.0014	0.0018	0.0022	0.0027
10	0.0001	0.0001	0.0001	0.0002	0.0002	0.0003	0.0004	0.0005	0.0006	0.0008
11	0.0000	0.0000	0.0000	0.0000	0.0000	0.0001	0.0001	0.0001	0.0002	0.0002

					μ					
x	3.1	3.2	3.3	3.4	3.5	3.6	3.7	3.8	3.9	4.0
0	0.0450	0.0408	0.0369	0.0334	0.0302	0.0273	0.0247	0.0224	0.0202	0.0183
1	0.1397	0.1304	0.1217	0.1135	0.1057	0.0984	0.0915	0.0850	0.0789	0.0733
2	0.2165	0.2087	0.2008	0.1929	0.1850	0.1771	0.1692	0.1615	0.1539	0.1465
3	0.2237	0.2226	0.2209	0.2186	0.2158	0.2125	0.2087	0.2046	0.2001	0.1954
4	0.1733	0.1781	0.1823	0.1858	0.1888	0.1912	0.1931	0.1944	0.1951	0.1954
5	0.1075	0.1140	0.1203	0.1264	0.1322	0.1377	0.1429	0.1477	0.1522	0.1563
6	0.0555	0.0608	0.0662	0.0716	0.0771	0.0826	0.0881	0.0936	0.0989	0.1042
7	0.0246	0.0278	0.0312	0.0348	0.0385	0.0425	0.0466	0.0508	0.0551	0.0595
8	0.0095	0.0111	0.0129	0.0148	0.0169	0.0191	0.0215	0.0241	0.0269	0.0298
9	0.0033	0.0040	0.0047	0.0056	0.0066	0.0076	0.0089	0.0102	0.0116	0.0132
10	0.0010	0.0013	0.0016	0.0019	0.0023	0.0028	0.0033	0.0039	0.0045	0.0053
11	0.0003	0.0004	0.0005	0.0006	0.0007	0.0009	0.0011	0.0013	0.0016	0.0019
12	0.0001	0.0001	0.0001	0.0002	0.0002	0.0003	0.0003	0.0004	0.0005	0.0006
13	0.0000	0.0000	0.0000	0.0000	0.0001	0.0001	0.0001	0.0001	0.0002	0.0002

					μ					
x	4.1	4.2	4.3	4.4	4.5	4.6	4.7	4.8	4.9	5.0
0	0.0166	0.0150	0.0136	0.0123	0.0111	0.0101	0.0091	0.0082	0.0074	0.0067
1	0.0679	0.0630	0.0583	0.0540	0.0500	0.0462	0.0427	0.0395	0.0365	0.0337
2	0.1393	0.1323	0.1254	0.1188	0.1125	0.1063	0.1005	0.0948	0.0894	0.0842
3	0.1904	0.1852	0.1798	0.1743	0.1687	0.1631	0.1574	0.1517	0.1460	0.1404
4	0.1951	0.1944	0.1933	0.1917	0.1898	0.1875	0.1849	0.1820	0.1789	0.1755
5	0.1600	0.1633	0.1662	0.1687	0.1708	0.1725	0.1738	0.1747	0.1753	0.1755
6	0.1093	0.1143	0.1191	0.1237	0.1281	0.1323	0.1362	0.1398	0.1432	0.1462
7	0.0640	0.0686	0.0732	0.0778	0.0824	0.0869	0.0914	0.0959	0.1002	0.1044
8	0.0328	0.0360	0.0393	0.0428	0.0463	0.0500	0.0537	0.0575	0.0614	0.0653
9	0.0150	0.0168	0.0188	0.0209	0.0232	0.0255	0.0281	0.0307	0.0334	0.0363
10	0.0061	0.0071	0.0081	0.0092	0.0104	0.0118	0.0132	0.0147	0.0164	0.0181
11	0.0023	0.0027	0.0032	0.0037	0.0043	0.0049	0.0056	0.0064	0.0073	0.0082
12	0.0008	0.0009	0.0011	0.0013	0.0016	0.0019	0.0022	0.0026	0.0030	0.0034
13	0.0002	0.0003	0.0004	0.0005	0.0006	0.0007	0.0008	0.0009	0.0011	0.0013
14	0.0001	0.0001	0.0001	0.0001	0.0002	0.0002	0.0003	0.0003	0.0004	0.0005
15	0.0000	0.0000	0.0000	0.0000	0.0001	0.0001	0.0001	0.0001	0.0001	0.0002

(table continued)

TABLE **A.2**   *(concluded)*
Poisson Probabilities (μ between 5.5 and 20.0)

					μ					
x	5.5	6.0	6.5	7.0	7.5	8.0	8.5	9.0	9.5	10.0
0	0.0041	0.0025	0.0015	0.0009	0.0006	0.0003	0.0002	0.0001	0.0001	0.0000
1	0.0225	0.0149	0.0098	0.0064	0.0041	0.0027	0.0017	0.0011	0.0007	0.0005
2	0.0618	0.0446	0.0318	0.0223	0.0156	0.0107	0.0074	0.0050	0.0034	0.0023
3	0.1133	0.0892	0.0688	0.0521	0.0389	0.0286	0.0208	0.0150	0.0107	0.0076
4	0.1558	0.1339	0.1118	0.0912	0.0729	0.0573	0.0443	0.0337	0.0254	0.0189
5	0.1714	0.1606	0.1454	0.1277	0.1094	0.0916	0.0752	0.0607	0.0483	0.0378
6	0.1571	0.1606	0.1575	0.1490	0.1367	0.1221	0.1066	0.0911	0.0764	0.0631
7	0.1234	0.1377	0.1462	0.1490	0.1465	0.1396	0.1294	0.1171	0.1037	0.0901
8	0.0849	0.1033	0.1188	0.1304	0.1373	0.1396	0.1375	0.1318	0.1232	0.1126
9	0.0519	0.0688	0.0858	0.1014	0.1144	0.1241	0.1299	0.1318	0.1300	0.1251
10	0.0285	0.0413	0.0558	0.0710	0.0858	0.0993	0.1104	0.1186	0.1235	0.1251
11	0.0143	0.0225	0.0330	0.0452	0.0585	0.0722	0.0853	0.0970	0.1067	0.1137
12	0.0065	0.0113	0.0179	0.0263	0.0366	0.0481	0.0604	0.0728	0.0844	0.0948
13	0.0028	0.0052	0.0089	0.0142	0.0211	0.0296	0.0395	0.0504	0.0617	0.0729
14	0.0011	0.0022	0.0041	0.0071	0.0113	0.0169	0.0240	0.0324	0.0419	0.0521
15	0.0004	0.0009	0.0018	0.0033	0.0057	0.0090	0.0136	0.0194	0.0265	0.0347
16	0.0001	0.0003	0.0007	0.0014	0.0026	0.0045	0.0072	0.0109	0.0157	0.0217
17	0.0000	0.0001	0.0003	0.0006	0.0012	0.0021	0.0036	0.0058	0.0088	0.0128
18	0.0000	0.0000	0.0001	0.0002	0.0005	0.0009	0.0017	0.0029	0.0046	0.0071
19	0.0000	0.0000	0.0000	0.0001	0.0002	0.0004	0.0008	0.0014	0.0023	0.0037
20	0.0000	0.0000	0.0000	0.0000	0.0001	0.0002	0.0003	0.0006	0.0011	0.0019
21	0.0000	0.0000	0.0000	0.0000	0.0000	0.0001	0.0001	0.0003	0.0005	0.0009
22	0.0000	0.0000	0.0000	0.0000	0.0000	0.0000	0.0001	0.0001	0.0002	0.0004
23	0.0000	0.0000	0.0000	0.0000	0.0000	0.0000	0.0000	0.0000	0.0001	0.0002

					μ					
x	11.0	12.0	13.0	14.0	15.0	16.0	17.0	18.0	19.0	20.0
0	0.0000	0.0000	0.0000	0.0000	0.0000	0.0000	0.0000	0.0000	0.0000	0.0000
1	0.0002	0.0001	0.0000	0.0000	0.0000	0.0000	0.0000	0.0000	0.0000	0.0000
2	0.0010	0.0004	0.0002	0.0001	0.0000	0.0000	0.0000	0.0000	0.0000	0.0000
3	0.0037	0.0018	0.0008	0.0004	0.0002	0.0001	0.0000	0.0000	0.0000	0.0000
4	0.0102	0.0053	0.0027	0.0013	0.0006	0.0003	0.0001	0.0001	0.0000	0.0000
5	0.0224	0.0127	0.0070	0.0037	0.0019	0.0010	0.0005	0.0002	0.0001	0.0001
6	0.0411	0.0255	0.0152	0.0087	0.0048	0.0026	0.0014	0.0007	0.0004	0.0002
7	0.0646	0.0437	0.0281	0.0174	0.0104	0.0060	0.0034	0.0019	0.0010	0.0005
8	0.0888	0.0655	0.0457	0.0304	0.0194	0.0120	0.0072	0.0042	0.0024	0.0013
9	0.1085	0.0874	0.0661	0.0473	0.0324	0.0213	0.0135	0.0083	0.0050	0.0029
10	0.1194	0.1048	0.0859	0.0663	0.0486	0.0341	0.0230	0.0150	0.0095	0.0058
11	0.1194	0.1144	0.1015	0.0844	0.0663	0.0496	0.0355	0.0245	0.0164	0.0106
12	0.1094	0.1144	0.1099	0.0984	0.0829	0.0661	0.0504	0.0368	0.0259	0.0176
13	0.0926	0.1056	0.1099	0.1060	0.0956	0.0814	0.0658	0.0509	0.0378	0.0271
14	0.0728	0.0905	0.1021	0.1060	0.1024	0.0930	0.0800	0.0655	0.0514	0.0387
15	0.0534	0.0724	0.0885	0.0989	0.1024	0.0992	0.0906	0.0786	0.0650	0.0516
16	0.0367	0.0543	0.0719	0.0866	0.0960	0.0992	0.0963	0.0884	0.0772	0.0646
17	0.0237	0.0383	0.0550	0.0713	0.0847	0.0934	0.0963	0.0936	0.0863	0.0760
18	0.0145	0.0255	0.0397	0.0554	0.0706	0.0830	0.0909	0.0936	0.0911	0.0844
19	0.0084	0.0161	0.0272	0.0409	0.0557	0.0699	0.0814	0.0887	0.0911	0.0888
20	0.0046	0.0097	0.0177	0.0286	0.0418	0.0559	0.0692	0.0798	0.0866	0.0888
21	0.0024	0.0055	0.0109	0.0191	0.0299	0.0426	0.0560	0.0684	0.0783	0.0846
22	0.0012	0.0030	0.0065	0.0121	0.0204	0.0310	0.0433	0.0560	0.0676	0.0769
23	0.0006	0.0016	0.0037	0.0074	0.0133	0.0216	0.0320	0.0438	0.0559	0.0669
24	0.0003	0.0008	0.0020	0.0043	0.0083	0.0144	0.0226	0.0328	0.0442	0.0557
25	0.0001	0.0004	0.0010	0.0024	0.0050	0.0092	0.0154	0.0237	0.0336	0.0446
26	0.0000	0.0002	0.0005	0.0013	0.0029	0.0057	0.0101	0.0164	0.0246	0.0343
27	0.0000	0.0001	0.0002	0.0007	0.0016	0.0034	0.0063	0.0109	0.0173	0.0254
28	0.0000	0.0000	0.0001	0.0003	0.0009	0.0019	0.0038	0.0070	0.0117	0.0181
29	0.0000	0.0000	0.0001	0.0002	0.0004	0.0011	0.0023	0.0044	0.0077	0.0125
30	0.0000	0.0000	0.0000	0.0001	0.0002	0.0006	0.0013	0.0026	0.0049	0.0083
31	0.0000	0.0000	0.0000	0.0000	0.0001	0.0003	0.0007	0.0015	0.0030	0.0054
32	0.0000	0.0000	0.0000	0.0000	0.0001	0.0001	0.0004	0.0009	0.0018	0.0034
33	0.0000	0.0000	0.0000	0.0000	0.0000	0.0001	0.0002	0.0005	0.0010	0.0020

Source: Computed by D. K. Hildebrand. Found in D. K. Hildebrand and L. Ott, *Statistical Thinking for Managers*, 3rd ed. (Boston, MA: PWS-KENT Publishing Company, 1991).

TABLE **A.3**   A Table of Areas under the Standard Normal Curve

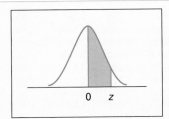

z	.00	.01	.02	.03	.04	.05	.06	.07	.08	.09
0.0	0.0000	0.0040	0.0080	0.0120	0.0160	0.0199	0.0239	0.0279	0.0319	0.0359
0.1	0.0398	0.0438	0.0478	0.0517	0.0557	0.0596	0.0636	0.0675	0.0714	0.0753
0.2	0.0793	0.0832	0.0871	0.0910	0.0948	0.0987	0.1026	0.1064	0.1103	0.1141
0.3	0.1179	0.1217	0.1255	0.1293	0.1331	0.1368	0.1406	0.1443	0.1480	0.1517
0.4	0.1554	0.1591	0.1628	0.1664	0.1700	0.1736	0.1772	0.1808	0.1844	0.1879
0.5	0.1915	0.1950	0.1985	0.2019	0.2054	0.2088	0.2123	0.2157	0.2190	0.2224
0.6	0.2257	0.2291	0.2324	0.2357	0.2389	0.2422	0.2454	0.2486	0.2517	0.2549
0.7	0.2580	0.2611	0.2642	0.2673	0.2704	0.2734	0.2764	0.2794	0.2823	0.2852
0.8	0.2881	0.2910	0.2939	0.2967	0.2995	0.3023	0.3051	0.3078	0.3106	0.3133
0.9	0.3159	0.3186	0.3212	0.3238	0.3264	0.3289	0.3315	0.3340	0.3365	0.3389
1.0	0.3413	0.3438	0.3461	0.3485	0.3508	0.3531	0.3554	0.3577	0.3599	0.3621
1.1	0.3643	0.3665	0.3686	0.3708	0.3729	0.3749	0.3770	0.3790	0.3810	0.3830
1.2	0.3849	0.3869	0.3888	0.3907	0.3925	0.3944	0.3962	0.3980	0.3997	0.4015
1.3	0.4032	0.4049	0.4066	0.4082	0.4099	0.4115	0.4131	0.4147	0.4162	0.4177
1.4	0.4192	0.4207	0.4222	0.4236	0.4251	0.4265	0.4279	0.4292	0.4306	0.4319
1.5	0.4332	0.4345	0.4357	0.4370	0.4382	0.4394	0.4406	0.4418	0.4429	0.4441
1.6	0.4452	0.4463	0.4474	0.4484	0.4495	0.4505	0.4515	0.4525	0.4535	0.4545
1.7	0.4554	0.4564	0.4573	0.4582	0.4591	0.4599	0.4608	0.4616	0.4625	0.4633
1.8	0.4641	0.4649	0.4656	0.4664	0.4671	0.4678	0.4686	0.4693	0.4699	0.4706
1.9	0.4713	0.4719	0.4726	0.4732	0.4738	0.4744	0.4750	0.4756	0.4761	0.4767
2.0	0.4772	0.4778	0.4783	0.4788	0.4793	0.4798	0.4803	0.4808	0.4812	0.4817
2.1	0.4821	0.4826	0.4830	0.4834	0.4838	0.4842	0.4846	0.4850	0.4854	0.4857
2.2	0.4861	0.4864	0.4868	0.4871	0.4875	0.4878	0.4881	0.4884	0.4887	0.4890
2.3	0.4893	0.4896	0.4898	0.4901	0.4904	0.4906	0.4909	0.4911	0.4913	0.4916
2.4	0.4918	0.4920	0.4922	0.4925	0.4927	0.4929	0.4931	0.4932	0.4934	0.4936
2.5	0.4938	0.4940	0.4941	0.4943	0.4945	0.4946	0.4948	0.4949	0.4951	0.4952
2.6	0.4953	0.4955	0.4956	0.4957	0.4959	0.4960	0.4961	0.4962	0.4963	0.4964
2.7	0.4965	0.4966	0.4967	0.4968	0.4969	0.4970	0.4971	0.4972	0.4973	0.4974
2.8	0.4974	0.4975	0.4976	0.4977	0.4977	0.4978	0.4979	0.4979	0.4980	0.4981
2.9	0.4981	0.4982	0.4982	0.4983	0.4984	0.4984	0.4985	0.4985	0.4986	0.4986
3.0	0.4987	0.4987	0.4987	0.4988	0.4988	0.4989	0.4989	0.4989	0.4990	0.4990

Source: A. Hald, *Statistical Tables and Formulas* (New York: Wiley, 1952), abridged from Table 1. Reproduced by permission of the publisher.

TABLE A.4   A Table of Cumulative Areas under the Standard Normal Curve

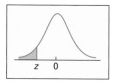

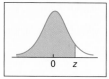

z	.00	.01	.02	.03	.04	.05	.06	.07	.08	.09
−3.4	0.0003	0.0003	0.0003	0.0003	0.0003	0.0003	0.0003	0.0003	0.0003	0.0002
−3.3	0.0005	0.0005	0.0005	0.0004	0.0004	0.0004	0.0004	0.0004	0.0004	0.0003
−3.2	0.0007	0.0007	0.0006	0.0006	0.0006	0.0006	0.0006	0.0005	0.0005	0.0005
−3.1	0.0010	0.0009	0.0009	0.0009	0.0008	0.0008	0.0008	0.0008	0.0007	0.0007
−3.0	0.0013	0.0013	0.0013	0.0012	0.0012	0.0011	0.0011	0.0011	0.0010	0.0010
−2.9	0.0019	0.0018	0.0018	0.0017	0.0016	0.0016	0.0015	0.0015	0.0014	0.0014
−2.8	0.0026	0.0025	0.0024	0.0023	0.0023	0.0022	0.0021	0.0021	0.0020	0.0019
−2.7	0.0035	0.0034	0.0033	0.0032	0.0031	0.0030	0.0029	0.0028	0.0027	0.0026
−2.6	0.0047	0.0045	0.0044	0.0043	0.0041	0.0040	0.0039	0.0038	0.0037	0.0036
−2.5	0.0062	0.0060	0.0059	0.0057	0.0055	0.0054	0.0052	0.0051	0.0049	0.0048
−2.4	0.0082	0.0080	0.0078	0.0075	0.0073	0.0071	0.0069	0.0068	0.0066	0.0064
−2.3	0.0107	0.0104	0.0102	0.0099	0.0096	0.0094	0.0091	0.0089	0.0087	0.0084
−2.2	0.0139	0.0136	0.0132	0.0129	0.0125	0.0122	0.0119	0.0116	0.0113	0.0110
−2.1	0.0179	0.0174	0.0170	0.0166	0.0162	0.0158	0.0154	0.0150	0.0146	0.0143
−2.0	0.0228	0.0222	0.0217	0.0212	0.0207	0.0202	0.0197	0.0192	0.0188	0.0183
−1.9	0.0287	0.0281	0.0274	0.0268	0.0262	0.0256	0.0250	0.0244	0.0239	0.0233
−1.8	0.0359	0.0351	0.0344	0.0336	0.0329	0.0322	0.0314	0.0307	0.0301	0.0294
−1.7	0.0446	0.0436	0.0427	0.0418	0.0409	0.0401	0.0392	0.0384	0.0375	0.0367
−1.6	0.0548	0.0537	0.0526	0.0516	0.0505	0.0495	0.0485	0.0475	0.0465	0.0455
−1.5	0.0668	0.0655	0.0643	0.0630	0.0618	0.0606	0.0594	0.0582	0.0571	0.0559
−1.4	0.0808	0.0793	0.0778	0.0764	0.0749	0.0735	0.0721	0.0708	0.0694	0.0681
−1.3	0.0968	0.0951	0.0934	0.0918	0.0901	0.0885	0.0869	0.0853	0.0838	0.0823
−1.2	0.1151	0.1131	0.1112	0.1093	0.1075	0.1056	0.1038	0.1020	0.1003	0.0985
−1.1	0.1357	0.1335	0.1314	0.1292	0.1271	0.1251	0.1230	0.1210	0.1190	0.1170
−1.0	0.1587	0.1562	0.1539	0.1515	0.1492	0.1469	0.1446	0.1423	0.1401	0.1379
−0.9	0.1841	0.1814	0.1788	0.1762	0.1736	0.1711	0.1685	0.1660	0.1635	0.1611
−0.8	0.2119	0.2090	0.2061	0.2033	0.2005	0.1977	0.1949	0.1922	0.1894	0.1867
−0.7	0.2420	0.2389	0.2358	0.2327	0.2296	0.2266	0.2236	0.2206	0.2177	0.2148
−0.6	0.2743	0.2709	0.2676	0.2643	0.2611	0.2578	0.2546	0.2514	0.2483	0.2451
−0.5	0.3085	0.3050	0.3015	0.2981	0.2946	0.2912	0.2877	0.2843	0.2810	0.2776
−0.4	0.3446	0.3409	0.3372	0.3336	0.3300	0.3264	0.3228	0.3192	0.3156	0.3121
−0.3	0.3821	0.3783	0.3745	0.3707	0.3669	0.3632	0.3594	0.3557	0.3520	0.3483
−0.2	0.4207	0.4168	0.4129	0.4090	0.4052	0.4013	0.3974	0.3936	0.3897	0.3859
−0.1	0.4602	0.4562	0.4522	0.4483	0.4443	0.4404	0.4364	0.4325	0.4286	0.4247
−0.0	0.5000	0.4960	0.4920	0.4880	0.4840	0.4801	0.4761	0.4721	0.4681	0.4641
0.0	0.5000	0.5040	0.5080	0.5120	0.5160	0.5199	0.5239	0.5279	0.5319	0.5359
0.1	0.5398	0.5438	0.5478	0.5517	0.5557	0.5596	0.5636	0.5675	0.5714	0.5753
0.2	0.5793	0.5832	0.5871	0.5910	0.5948	0.5987	0.6026	0.6064	0.6103	0.6141
0.3	0.6179	0.6217	0.6255	0.6293	0.6331	0.6368	0.6406	0.6443	0.6480	0.6517
0.4	0.6554	0.6591	0.6628	0.6664	0.6700	0.6736	0.6772	0.6808	0.6844	0.6879
0.5	0.6915	0.6950	0.6985	0.7019	0.7054	0.7088	0.7123	0.7157	0.7190	0.7224
0.6	0.7257	0.7291	0.7324	0.7357	0.7389	0.7422	0.7454	0.7486	0.7517	0.7549
0.7	0.7580	0.7611	0.7642	0.7673	0.7704	0.7734	0.7764	0.7794	0.7823	0.7852
0.8	0.7881	0.7910	0.7939	0.7967	0.7995	0.8023	0.8051	0.8078	0.8106	0.8133
0.9	0.8159	0.8186	0.8212	0.8238	0.8264	0.8289	0.8315	0.8340	0.8365	0.8389
1.0	0.8413	0.8438	0.8461	0.8485	0.8508	0.8531	0.8554	0.8577	0.8599	0.8621
1.1	0.8643	0.8665	0.8686	0.8708	0.8729	0.8749	0.8770	0.8790	0.8810	0.8830
1.2	0.8849	0.8869	0.8888	0.8907	0.8925	0.8944	0.8962	0.8980	0.8997	0.9015
1.3	0.9032	0.9049	0.9066	0.9082	0.9099	0.9115	0.9131	0.9147	0.9162	0.9177
1.4	0.9192	0.9207	0.9222	0.9236	0.9251	0.9265	0.9279	0.9292	0.9306	0.9319
1.5	0.9332	0.9345	0.9357	0.9370	0.9382	0.9394	0.9406	0.9418	0.9429	0.9441
1.6	0.9452	0.9463	0.9474	0.9484	0.9495	0.9505	0.9515	0.9525	0.9535	0.9545
1.7	0.9554	0.9564	0.9573	0.9582	0.9591	0.9599	0.9608	0.9616	0.9625	0.9633
1.8	0.9641	0.9649	0.9656	0.9664	0.9671	0.9678	0.9686	0.9693	0.9699	0.9706
1.9	0.9713	0.9719	0.9726	0.9732	0.9738	0.9744	0.9750	0.9756	0.9761	0.9767
2.0	0.9772	0.9778	0.9783	0.9788	0.9793	0.9798	0.9803	0.9808	0.9812	0.9817
2.1	0.9821	0.9826	0.9830	0.9834	0.9838	0.9842	0.9846	0.9850	0.9854	0.9857
2.2	0.9861	0.9864	0.9868	0.9871	0.9875	0.9878	0.9881	0.9884	0.9887	0.9890
2.3	0.9893	0.9896	0.9898	0.9901	0.9904	0.9906	0.9909	0.9911	0.9913	0.9916
2.4	0.9918	0.9920	0.9922	0.9925	0.9927	0.9929	0.9931	0.9932	0.9934	0.9936
2.5	0.9938	0.9940	0.9941	0.9943	0.9945	0.9946	0.9948	0.9949	0.9951	0.9952
2.6	0.9953	0.9955	0.9956	0.9957	0.9959	0.9960	0.9961	0.9962	0.9963	0.9964
2.7	0.9965	0.9966	0.9967	0.9968	0.9969	0.9970	0.9971	0.9972	0.9973	0.9974
2.8	0.9974	0.9975	0.9976	0.9977	0.9977	0.9978	0.9979	0.9979	0.9980	0.9981
2.9	0.9981	0.9982	0.9982	0.9983	0.9984	0.9984	0.9985	0.9985	0.9986	0.9986
3.0	0.9987	0.9987	0.9987	0.9988	0.9988	0.9989	0.9989	0.9989	0.9990	0.9990
3.1	0.9990	0.9991	0.9991	0.9991	0.9992	0.9992	0.9992	0.9992	0.9993	0.9993
3.2	0.9993	0.9993	0.9994	0.9994	0.9994	0.9994	0.9994	0.9995	0.9995	0.9995
3.3	0.9995	0.9995	0.9995	0.9996	0.9996	0.9996	0.9996	0.9996	0.9996	0.9997
3.4	0.9997	0.9997	0.9997	0.9997	0.9997	0.9997	0.9997	0.9997	0.9997	0.9998

TABLE A.5   A *t* Table: Values of t_α for *df* = 1 through 48

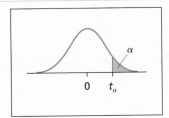

df	$t_{0.100}$	$t_{0.05}$	$t_{0.025}$	$t_{0.01}$	$t_{0.005}$	$t_{0.001}$	$t_{0.0005}$
1	3.078	6.314	12.706	31.821	63.657	318.309	636.619
2	1.886	2.920	4.303	6.965	9.925	22.327	31.599
3	1.638	2.353	3.182	4.541	5.841	10.215	12.924
4	1.533	2.132	2.776	3.747	4.604	7.173	8.610
5	1.476	2.015	2.571	3.365	4.032	5.893	6.869
6	1.440	1.943	2.447	3.143	3.707	5.208	5.959
7	1.415	1.895	2.365	2.998	3.499	4.785	5.408
8	1.397	1.860	2.306	2.896	3.355	4.501	5.041
9	1.383	1.833	2.262	2.821	3.250	4.297	4.781
10	1.372	1.812	2.228	2.764	3.169	4.144	4.587
11	1.363	1.796	2.201	2.718	3.106	4.025	4.437
12	1.356	1.782	2.179	2.681	3.055	3.930	4.318
13	1.350	1.771	2.160	2.650	3.012	3.852	4.221
14	1.345	1.761	2.145	2.624	2.977	3.787	4.140
15	1.341	1.753	2.131	2.602	2.947	3.733	4.073
16	1.337	1.746	2.120	2.583	2.921	3.686	4.015
17	1.333	1.740	2.110	2.567	2.898	3.646	3.965
18	1.330	1.734	2.101	2.552	2.878	3.610	3.922
19	1.328	1.729	2.093	2.539	2.861	3.579	3.883
20	1.325	1.725	2.086	2.528	2.845	3.552	3.850
21	1.323	1.721	2.080	2.518	2.831	3.527	3.819
22	1.321	1.717	2.074	2.508	2.819	3.505	3.792
23	1.319	1.714	2.069	2.500	2.807	3.485	3.768
24	1.318	1.711	2.064	2.492	2.797	3.467	3.745
25	1.316	1.708	2.060	2.485	2.787	3.450	3.725
26	1.315	1.706	2.056	2.479	2.779	3.435	3.707
27	1.314	1.703	2.052	2.473	2.771	3.421	3.690
28	1.313	1.701	2.048	2.467	2.763	3.408	3.674
29	1.311	1.699	2.045	2.462	2.756	3.396	3.659
30	1.310	1.697	2.042	2.457	2.750	3.385	3.646
31	1.309	1.696	2.040	2.453	2.744	3.375	3.633
32	1.309	1.694	2.037	2.449	2.738	3.365	3.622
33	1.308	1.692	2.035	2.445	2.733	3.356	3.611
34	1.307	1.691	2.032	2.441	2.728	3.348	3.601
35	1.306	1.690	2.030	2.438	2.724	3.340	3.591
36	1.306	1.688	2.028	2.434	2.719	3.333	3.582
37	1.305	1.687	2.026	2.431	2.715	3.326	3.574
38	1.304	1.686	2.024	2.429	2.712	3.319	3.566
39	1.304	1.685	2.023	2.426	2.708	3.313	3.558
40	1.303	1.684	2.021	2.423	2.704	3.307	3.551
41	1.303	1.683	2.020	2.421	2.701	3.301	3.544
42	1.302	1.682	2.018	2.418	2.698	3.296	3.538
43	1.302	1.681	2.017	2.416	2.695	3.291	3.532
44	1.301	1.680	2.015	2.414	2.692	3.286	3.526
45	1.301	1.679	2.014	2.412	2.690	3.281	3.520
46	1.300	1.679	2.013	2.410	2.687	3.277	3.515
47	1.300	1.678	2.012	2.408	2.685	3.273	3.510
48	1.299	1.677	2.011	2.407	2.682	3.269	3.505

(table continued)

TABLE **A.5**   *(concluded)*   A *t* Table: Values of t_α for *df* = 49 through 100, 120, and ∞

df	$t_{0.100}$	$t_{0.05}$	$t_{0.025}$	$t_{0.01}$	$t_{0.005}$	$t_{0.001}$	$t_{0.0005}$
49	1.299	1.677	2.010	2.405	2.680	3.265	3.500
50	1.299	1.676	2.009	2.403	2.678	3.261	3.496
51	1.298	1.675	2.008	2.402	2.676	3.258	3.492
52	1.298	1.675	2.007	2.400	2.674	3.255	3.488
53	1.298	1.674	2.006	2.399	2.672	3.251	3.484
54	1.297	1.674	2.005	2.397	2.670	3.248	3.480
55	1.297	1.673	2.004	2.396	2.668	3.245	3.476
56	1.297	1.673	2.003	2.395	2.667	3.242	3.473
57	1.297	1.672	2.002	2.394	2.665	3.239	3.470
58	1.296	1.672	2.002	2.392	2.663	3.237	3.466
59	1.296	1.671	2.001	2.391	2.662	3.234	3.463
60	1.296	1.671	2.000	2.390	2.660	3.232	3.460
61	1.296	1.670	2.000	2.389	2.659	3.229	3.457
62	1.295	1.670	1.999	2.388	2.657	3.227	3.454
63	1.295	1.669	1.998	2.387	2.656	3.225	3.452
64	1.295	1.669	1.998	2.386	2.655	3.223	3.449
65	1.295	1.669	1.997	2.385	2.654	3.220	3.447
66	1.295	1.668	1.997	2.384	2.652	3.218	3.444
67	1.294	1.668	1.996	2.383	2.651	3.216	3.442
68	1.294	1.668	1.995	2.382	2.650	3.214	3.439
69	1.294	1.667	1.995	2.382	2.649	3.213	3.437
70	1.294	1.667	1.994	2.381	2.648	3.211	3.435
71	1.294	1.667	1.994	2.380	2.647	3.209	3.433
72	1.293	1.666	1.993	2.379	2.646	3.207	3.431
73	1.293	1.666	1.993	2.379	2.645	3.206	3.429
74	1.293	1.666	1.993	2.378	2.644	3.204	3.427
75	1.293	1.665	1.992	2.377	2.643	3.202	3.425
76	1.293	1.665	1.992	2.376	2.642	3.201	3.423
77	1.293	1.665	1.991	2.376	2.641	3.199	3.421
78	1.292	1.665	1.991	2.375	2.640	3.198	3.420
79	1.292	1.664	1.990	2.374	2.640	3.197	3.418
80	1.292	1.664	1.990	2.374	2.639	3.195	3.416
81	1.292	1.664	1.990	2.373	2.638	3.194	3.415
82	1.292	1.664	1.989	2.373	2.637	3.193	3.413
83	1.292	1.663	1.989	2.372	2.636	3.191	3.412
84	1.292	1.663	1.989	2.372	2.636	3.190	3.410
85	1.292	1.663	1.988	2.371	2.635	3.189	3.409
86	1.291	1.663	1.988	2.370	2.634	3.188	3.407
87	1.291	1.663	1.988	2.370	2.634	3.187	3.406
88	1.291	1.662	1.987	2.369	2.633	3.185	3.405
89	1.291	1.662	1.987	2.369	2.632	3.184	3.403
90	1.291	1.662	1.987	2.368	2.632	3.183	3.402
91	1.291	1.662	1.986	2.368	2.631	3.182	3.401
92	1.291	1.662	1.986	2.368	2.630	3.181	3.399
93	1.291	1.661	1.986	2.367	2.630	3.180	3.398
94	1.291	1.661	1.986	2.367	2.629	3.179	3.397
95	1.291	1.661	1.985	2.366	2.629	3.178	3.396
96	1.290	1.661	1.985	2.366	2.628	3.177	3.395
97	1.290	1.661	1.985	2.365	2.627	3.176	3.394
98	1.290	1.661	1.984	2.365	2.627	3.175	3.393
99	1.290	1.660	1.984	2.365	2.626	3.175	3.392
100	1.290	1.660	1.984	2.364	2.626	3.174	3.390
120	1.289	1.658	1.980	2.358	2.617	3.160	3.373
∞	1.282	1.645	1.960	2.326	2.576	3.090	3.291

Source: Provided by J. B. Orris using Excel.

TABLE A.6   An *F* Table: Values of $F_{0.10}$

df_2	\ df_1	1	2	3	4	5	6	7	8	9	10	12	15	20	24	30	40	60	120	∞
1		39.86	49.50	53.59	55.83	57.24	58.20	58.91	59.44	59.86	60.19	60.71	61.22	61.74	62.00	62.26	62.53	62.79	63.06	63.33
2		8.53	9.00	9.16	9.24	9.29	9.33	9.35	9.37	9.38	9.39	9.41	9.42	9.44	9.45	9.46	9.47	9.47	9.48	9.49
3		5.54	5.46	5.39	5.34	5.31	5.28	5.27	5.25	5.24	5.23	5.22	5.20	5.18	5.18	5.17	5.16	5.15	5.14	5.13
4		4.54	4.32	4.19	4.11	4.05	4.01	3.98	3.95	3.94	3.92	3.90	3.87	3.84	3.83	3.82	3.80	3.79	3.78	3.76
5		4.06	3.78	3.62	3.52	3.45	3.40	3.37	3.34	3.32	3.30	3.27	3.24	3.21	3.19	3.17	3.16	3.14	3.12	3.10
6		3.78	3.46	3.29	3.18	3.11	3.05	3.01	2.98	2.96	2.94	2.90	2.87	2.84	2.82	2.80	2.78	2.76	2.74	2.72
7		3.59	3.26	3.07	2.96	2.88	2.83	2.78	2.75	2.72	2.70	2.67	2.63	2.59	2.58	2.56	2.54	2.51	2.49	2.47
8		3.46	3.11	2.92	2.81	2.73	2.67	2.62	2.59	2.56	2.54	2.50	2.46	2.42	2.40	2.38	2.36	2.34	2.32	2.29
9		3.36	3.01	2.81	2.69	2.61	2.55	2.51	2.47	2.44	2.42	2.38	2.34	2.30	2.28	2.25	2.23	2.21	2.18	2.16
10		3.29	2.92	2.73	2.61	2.52	2.46	2.41	2.38	2.35	2.32	2.28	2.24	2.20	2.18	2.16	2.13	2.11	2.08	2.06
11		3.23	2.86	2.66	2.54	2.45	2.39	2.34	2.30	2.27	2.25	2.21	2.17	2.12	2.10	2.08	2.05	2.03	2.00	1.97
12		3.18	2.81	2.61	2.48	2.39	2.33	2.28	2.24	2.21	2.19	2.15	2.10	2.06	2.04	2.01	1.99	1.96	1.93	1.90
13		3.14	2.76	2.56	2.43	2.35	2.28	2.23	2.20	2.16	2.14	2.10	2.05	2.01	1.98	1.96	1.93	1.90	1.88	1.85
14		3.10	2.73	2.52	2.39	2.31	2.24	2.19	2.15	2.12	2.10	2.05	2.01	1.96	1.94	1.91	1.89	1.86	1.83	1.80
15		3.07	2.70	2.49	2.36	2.27	2.21	2.16	2.12	2.09	2.06	2.02	1.97	1.92	1.90	1.87	1.85	1.82	1.79	1.76
16		3.05	2.67	2.46	2.33	2.24	2.18	2.13	2.09	2.06	2.03	1.99	1.94	1.89	1.87	1.84	1.81	1.78	1.75	1.72
17		3.03	2.64	2.44	2.31	2.22	2.15	2.10	2.06	2.03	2.00	1.96	1.91	1.86	1.84	1.81	1.78	1.75	1.72	1.69
18		3.01	2.62	2.42	2.29	2.20	2.13	2.08	2.04	2.00	1.98	1.93	1.89	1.84	1.81	1.78	1.75	1.72	1.69	1.66
19		2.99	2.61	2.40	2.27	2.18	2.11	2.06	2.02	1.98	1.96	1.91	1.86	1.81	1.79	1.76	1.73	1.70	1.67	1.63
20		2.97	2.59	2.38	2.25	2.16	2.09	2.04	2.00	1.96	1.94	1.89	1.84	1.79	1.77	1.74	1.71	1.68	1.64	1.61
21		2.96	2.57	2.36	2.23	2.14	2.08	2.02	1.98	1.95	1.92	1.87	1.83	1.78	1.75	1.72	1.69	1.66	1.62	1.59
22		2.95	2.56	2.35	2.22	2.13	2.06	2.01	1.97	1.93	1.90	1.86	1.81	1.76	1.73	1.70	1.67	1.64	1.60	1.57
23		2.94	2.55	2.34	2.21	2.11	2.05	1.99	1.95	1.92	1.89	1.84	1.80	1.74	1.72	1.69	1.66	1.62	1.59	1.55
24		2.93	2.54	2.33	2.19	2.10	2.04	1.98	1.94	1.91	1.88	1.83	1.78	1.73	1.70	1.67	1.64	1.61	1.57	1.53
25		2.92	2.53	2.32	2.18	2.09	2.02	1.97	1.93	1.89	1.87	1.82	1.77	1.72	1.69	1.66	1.63	1.59	1.56	1.52
26		2.91	2.52	2.31	2.17	2.08	2.01	1.96	1.92	1.88	1.86	1.81	1.76	1.71	1.68	1.65	1.61	1.58	1.54	1.50
27		2.90	2.51	2.30	2.17	2.07	2.00	1.95	1.91	1.87	1.85	1.80	1.75	1.70	1.67	1.64	1.60	1.57	1.53	1.49
28		2.89	2.50	2.29	2.16	2.06	2.00	1.94	1.90	1.87	1.84	1.79	1.74	1.69	1.66	1.63	1.59	1.56	1.52	1.48
29		2.89	2.50	2.28	2.15	2.06	1.99	1.93	1.89	1.86	1.83	1.78	1.73	1.68	1.65	1.62	1.58	1.55	1.51	1.47
30		2.88	2.49	2.28	2.14	2.05	1.98	1.93	1.88	1.85	1.82	1.77	1.72	1.67	1.64	1.61	1.57	1.54	1.50	1.46
40		2.84	2.44	2.23	2.09	2.00	1.93	1.87	1.83	1.79	1.76	1.71	1.66	1.61	1.57	1.54	1.51	1.47	1.42	1.38
60		2.79	2.39	2.18	2.04	1.95	1.87	1.82	1.77	1.74	1.71	1.66	1.60	1.54	1.51	1.48	1.44	1.40	1.35	1.29
120		2.75	2.35	2.13	1.99	1.90	1.82	1.77	1.72	1.68	1.65	1.60	1.55	1.48	1.45	1.41	1.37	1.32	1.26	1.19
∞		2.71	2.30	2.08	1.94	1.85	1.77	1.72	1.67	1.63	1.60	1.55	1.49	1.42	1.38	1.34	1.30	1.24	1.17	1.00

Numerator Degrees of Freedom (df_1)

Denominator Degrees of Freedom (df_2)

Source: M. Merrington and C. M. Thompson, "Tables of Percentage Points of the Inverted Beta (*F*)-Distribution," *Biometrika* 33 (1943), pp. 73–88. Reproduced by permission of the Biometrika Trustees.

TABLE A.7   An F Table: Values of $F_{0.05}$

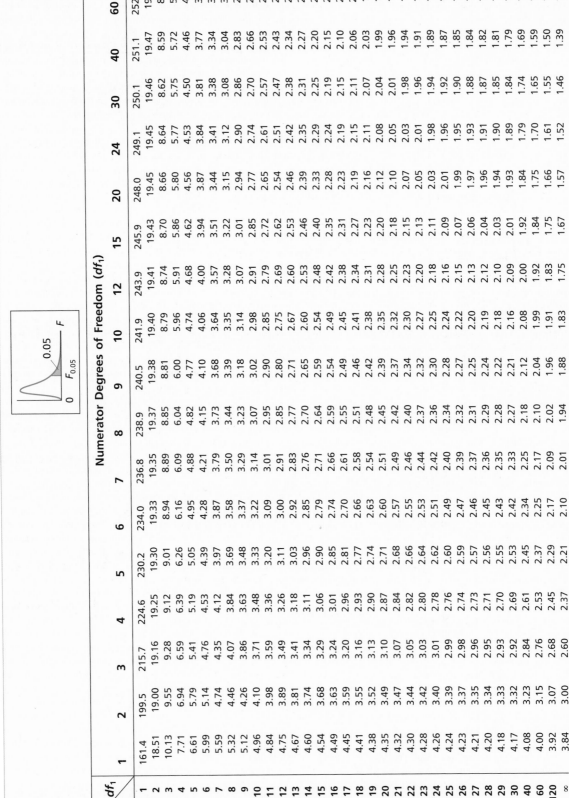

Numerator Degrees of Freedom (df_1)

df_2	1	2	3	4	5	6	7	8	9	10	12	15	20	24	30	40	60	120	∞
1	161.4	199.5	215.7	224.6	230.2	234.0	236.8	238.9	240.5	241.9	243.9	245.9	248.0	249.1	250.1	251.1	252.2	253.3	254.3
2	18.51	19.00	19.16	19.25	19.30	19.33	19.35	19.37	19.38	19.40	19.41	19.43	19.45	19.45	19.46	19.47	19.48	19.49	19.50
3	10.13	9.55	9.28	9.12	9.01	8.94	8.89	8.85	8.81	8.79	8.74	8.70	8.66	8.64	8.62	8.59	8.57	8.55	8.53
4	7.71	6.94	6.59	6.39	6.26	6.16	6.09	6.04	6.00	5.96	5.91	5.86	5.80	5.77	5.75	5.72	5.69	5.66	5.63
5	6.61	5.79	5.41	5.19	5.05	4.95	4.88	4.82	4.77	4.74	4.68	4.62	4.56	4.53	4.50	4.46	4.43	4.40	4.36
6	5.99	5.14	4.76	4.53	4.39	4.28	4.21	4.15	4.10	4.06	4.00	3.94	3.87	3.84	3.81	3.77	3.74	3.70	3.67
7	5.59	4.74	4.35	4.12	3.97	3.87	3.79	3.73	3.68	3.64	3.57	3.51	3.44	3.41	3.38	3.34	3.30	3.27	3.23
8	5.32	4.46	4.07	3.84	3.69	3.58	3.50	3.44	3.39	3.35	3.28	3.22	3.15	3.12	3.08	3.04	3.01	2.97	2.93
9	5.12	4.26	3.86	3.63	3.48	3.37	3.29	3.23	3.18	3.14	3.07	3.01	2.94	2.90	2.86	2.83	2.79	2.75	2.71
10	4.96	4.10	3.71	3.48	3.33	3.22	3.14	3.07	3.02	2.98	2.91	2.85	2.77	2.74	2.70	2.66	2.62	2.58	2.54
11	4.84	3.98	3.59	3.36	3.20	3.09	3.01	2.95	2.90	2.85	2.79	2.72	2.65	2.61	2.57	2.53	2.49	2.45	2.40
12	4.75	3.89	3.49	3.26	3.11	3.00	2.91	2.85	2.80	2.75	2.69	2.62	2.54	2.51	2.47	2.43	2.38	2.34	2.30
13	4.67	3.81	3.41	3.18	3.03	2.92	2.83	2.77	2.71	2.67	2.60	2.53	2.46	2.42	2.38	2.34	2.30	2.25	2.21
14	4.60	3.74	3.34	3.11	2.96	2.85	2.76	2.70	2.65	2.60	2.53	2.46	2.39	2.35	2.31	2.27	2.22	2.18	2.13
15	4.54	3.68	3.29	3.06	2.90	2.79	2.71	2.64	2.59	2.54	2.48	2.40	2.33	2.29	2.25	2.20	2.16	2.11	2.07
16	4.49	3.63	3.24	3.01	2.85	2.74	2.66	2.59	2.54	2.49	2.42	2.35	2.28	2.24	2.19	2.15	2.11	2.06	2.01
17	4.45	3.59	3.20	2.96	2.81	2.70	2.61	2.55	2.49	2.45	2.38	2.31	2.23	2.19	2.15	2.10	2.06	2.01	1.96
18	4.41	3.55	3.16	2.93	2.77	2.66	2.58	2.51	2.46	2.41	2.34	2.27	2.19	2.15	2.11	2.06	2.02	1.97	1.92
19	4.38	3.52	3.13	2.90	2.74	2.63	2.54	2.48	2.42	2.38	2.31	2.23	2.16	2.11	2.07	2.03	1.98	1.93	1.88
20	4.35	3.49	3.10	2.87	2.71	2.60	2.51	2.45	2.39	2.35	2.28	2.20	2.12	2.08	2.04	1.99	1.95	1.90	1.84
21	4.32	3.47	3.07	2.84	2.68	2.57	2.49	2.42	2.37	2.32	2.25	2.18	2.10	2.05	2.01	1.96	1.92	1.87	1.81
22	4.30	3.44	3.05	2.82	2.66	2.55	2.46	2.40	2.34	2.30	2.23	2.15	2.07	2.03	1.98	1.94	1.89	1.84	1.78
23	4.28	3.42	3.03	2.80	2.64	2.53	2.44	2.37	2.32	2.27	2.20	2.13	2.05	2.01	1.96	1.91	1.86	1.81	1.76
24	4.26	3.40	3.01	2.78	2.62	2.51	2.42	2.36	2.30	2.25	2.18	2.11	2.03	1.98	1.94	1.89	1.84	1.79	1.73
25	4.24	3.39	2.99	2.76	2.60	2.49	2.40	2.34	2.28	2.24	2.16	2.09	2.01	1.96	1.92	1.87	1.82	1.77	1.71
26	4.23	3.37	2.98	2.74	2.59	2.47	2.39	2.32	2.27	2.22	2.15	2.07	1.99	1.95	1.90	1.85	1.80	1.75	1.69
27	4.21	3.35	2.96	2.73	2.57	2.46	2.37	2.31	2.25	2.20	2.13	2.06	1.97	1.93	1.88	1.84	1.79	1.73	1.67
28	4.20	3.34	2.95	2.71	2.56	2.45	2.36	2.29	2.24	2.19	2.12	2.04	1.96	1.91	1.87	1.82	1.77	1.71	1.65
29	4.18	3.33	2.93	2.70	2.55	2.43	2.35	2.28	2.22	2.18	2.10	2.03	1.94	1.90	1.85	1.81	1.75	1.70	1.64
30	4.17	3.32	2.92	2.69	2.53	2.42	2.33	2.27	2.21	2.16	2.09	2.01	1.93	1.89	1.84	1.79	1.74	1.68	1.62
40	4.08	3.23	2.84	2.61	2.45	2.34	2.25	2.18	2.12	2.08	2.00	1.92	1.84	1.79	1.74	1.69	1.64	1.58	1.51
60	4.00	3.15	2.76	2.53	2.37	2.25	2.17	2.10	2.04	1.99	1.92	1.84	1.75	1.70	1.65	1.59	1.53	1.47	1.39
120	3.92	3.07	2.68	2.45	2.29	2.17	2.09	2.02	1.96	1.91	1.83	1.75	1.66	1.61	1.55	1.50	1.43	1.35	1.25
∞	3.84	3.00	2.60	2.37	2.21	2.10	2.01	1.94	1.88	1.83	1.75	1.67	1.57	1.52	1.46	1.39	1.32	1.22	1.00

Denominator Degrees of Freedom (df_2)

Source: M. Merrington and C. M. Thompson, "Tables of Percentage Points of the Inverted Beta (F)-Distribution," *Biometrika* 33 (1943), pp. 73–88. Reproduced by permission of the Biometrika Trustees.

TABLE A.8   An *F* Table: Values of $F_{0.025}$

df_2 \ df_1	1	2	3	4	5	6	7	8	9	10	12	15	20	24	30	40	60	120	∞
1	647.8	799.5	864.2	899.6	921.8	937.1	948.2	956.7	963.3	968.6	976.7	984.9	993.1	997.2	1,001	1,006	1,010	1,014	1,018
2	38.51	39.00	39.17	39.25	39.30	39.33	39.36	39.37	39.39	39.40	39.41	39.43	39.45	39.46	39.46	39.47	39.48	39.49	39.50
3	17.44	16.04	15.44	15.10	14.88	14.73	14.62	14.54	14.47	14.42	14.34	14.25	14.17	14.12	14.08	14.04	13.99	13.95	13.90
4	12.22	10.65	9.98	9.60	9.36	9.20	9.07	8.98	8.90	8.84	8.75	8.66	8.56	8.51	8.46	8.41	8.36	8.31	8.26
5	10.01	8.43	7.76	7.39	7.15	6.98	6.85	6.76	6.68	6.62	6.52	6.43	6.33	6.28	6.23	6.18	6.12	6.07	6.02
6	8.81	7.26	6.60	6.23	5.99	5.82	5.70	5.60	5.52	5.46	5.37	5.27	5.17	5.12	5.07	5.01	4.96	4.90	4.85
7	8.07	6.54	5.89	5.52	5.29	5.12	4.99	4.90	4.82	4.76	4.67	4.57	4.47	4.42	4.36	4.31	4.25	4.20	4.14
8	7.57	6.06	5.42	5.05	4.82	4.65	4.53	4.43	4.36	4.30	4.20	4.10	4.00	3.95	3.89	3.84	3.78	3.73	3.67
9	7.21	5.71	5.08	4.72	4.48	4.32	4.20	4.10	4.03	3.96	3.87	3.77	3.67	3.61	3.56	3.51	3.45	3.39	3.33
10	6.94	5.46	4.83	4.47	4.24	4.07	3.95	3.85	3.78	3.72	3.62	3.52	3.42	3.37	3.31	3.26	3.20	3.14	3.08
11	6.72	5.26	4.63	4.28	4.04	3.88	3.76	3.66	3.59	3.53	3.43	3.33	3.23	3.17	3.12	3.06	3.00	2.94	2.88
12	6.55	5.10	4.47	4.12	3.89	3.73	3.61	3.51	3.44	3.37	3.28	3.18	3.07	3.02	2.96	2.91	2.85	2.79	2.72
13	6.41	4.97	4.35	4.00	3.77	3.60	3.48	3.39	3.31	3.25	3.15	3.05	2.95	2.89	2.84	2.78	2.72	2.66	2.60
14	6.30	4.86	4.24	3.89	3.66	3.50	3.38	3.29	3.21	3.15	3.05	2.95	2.84	2.79	2.73	2.67	2.61	2.55	2.49
15	6.20	4.77	4.15	3.80	3.58	3.41	3.29	3.20	3.12	3.06	2.96	2.86	2.76	2.70	2.64	2.59	2.52	2.46	2.40
16	6.12	4.69	4.08	3.73	3.50	3.34	3.22	3.12	3.05	2.99	2.89	2.79	2.68	2.63	2.57	2.51	2.45	2.38	2.32
17	6.04	4.62	4.01	3.66	3.44	3.28	3.16	3.06	2.98	2.92	2.82	2.72	2.62	2.56	2.50	2.44	2.38	2.32	2.25
18	5.98	4.56	3.95	3.61	3.38	3.22	3.10	3.01	2.93	2.87	2.77	2.67	2.56	2.50	2.44	2.38	2.32	2.26	2.19
19	5.92	4.51	3.90	3.56	3.33	3.17	3.05	2.96	2.88	2.82	2.72	2.62	2.51	2.45	2.39	2.33	2.27	2.20	2.13
20	5.87	4.46	3.86	3.51	3.29	3.13	3.01	2.91	2.84	2.77	2.68	2.57	2.46	2.41	2.35	2.29	2.22	2.16	2.09
21	5.83	4.42	3.82	3.48	3.25	3.09	2.97	2.87	2.80	2.73	2.64	2.53	2.42	2.37	2.31	2.25	2.18	2.11	2.04
22	5.79	4.38	3.78	3.44	3.22	3.05	2.93	2.84	2.76	2.70	2.60	2.50	2.39	2.33	2.27	2.21	2.14	2.08	2.00
23	5.75	4.35	3.75	3.41	3.18	3.02	2.90	2.81	2.73	2.67	2.57	2.47	2.36	2.30	2.24	2.18	2.11	2.04	1.97
24	5.72	4.32	3.72	3.38	3.15	2.99	2.87	2.78	2.70	2.64	2.54	2.44	2.33	2.27	2.21	2.15	2.08	2.01	1.94
25	5.69	4.29	3.69	3.35	3.13	2.97	2.85	2.75	2.68	2.61	2.51	2.41	2.30	2.24	2.18	2.12	2.05	1.98	1.91
26	5.66	4.27	3.67	3.33	3.10	2.94	2.82	2.73	2.65	2.59	2.49	2.39	2.28	2.22	2.16	2.09	2.03	1.95	1.88
27	5.63	4.24	3.65	3.31	3.08	2.92	2.80	2.71	2.63	2.57	2.47	2.36	2.25	2.19	2.13	2.07	2.00	1.93	1.85
28	5.61	4.22	3.63	3.29	3.06	2.90	2.78	2.69	2.61	2.55	2.45	2.34	2.23	2.17	2.11	2.05	1.98	1.91	1.83
29	5.59	4.20	3.61	3.27	3.04	2.88	2.76	2.67	2.59	2.53	2.43	2.32	2.21	2.15	2.09	2.03	1.96	1.89	1.81
30	5.57	4.18	3.59	3.25	3.03	2.87	2.75	2.65	2.57	2.51	2.41	2.31	2.20	2.14	2.07	2.01	1.94	1.87	1.79
40	5.42	4.05	3.46	3.13	2.90	2.74	2.62	2.53	2.45	2.39	2.29	2.18	2.07	2.01	1.94	1.88	1.80	1.72	1.64
60	5.29	3.93	3.34	3.01	2.79	2.63	2.51	2.41	2.33	2.27	2.17	2.06	1.94	1.88	1.82	1.74	1.67	1.58	1.48
120	5.15	3.80	3.23	2.89	2.67	2.52	2.39	2.30	2.22	2.16	2.05	1.94	1.82	1.76	1.69	1.61	1.53	1.43	1.31
∞	5.02	3.69	3.12	2.79	2.57	2.41	2.29	2.19	2.11	2.05	1.94	1.83	1.71	1.64	1.57	1.48	1.39	1.27	1.00

Numerator Degrees of Freedom (df_1)

Denominator Degrees of Freedom (df_2)

Source: M. Merrington and C. M. Thompson, "Tables of Percentage Points of the Inverted Beta (*F*)-Distribution," *Biometrika* 33 (1943), pp. 73–88. Reproduced by permission of the Biometrika Trustees.

TABLE A.9 An F Table: Values of $F_{0.01}$

df_2 \ df_1	1	2	3	4	5	6	7	8	9	10	12	15	20	24	30	40	60	120	∞
1	4,052	4,999.5	5,403	5,625	5,764	5,859	5,928	5,982	6,022	6,056	6,106	6,157	6,209	6,235	6,261	6,287	6,313	6,339	6,366
2	98.50	99.00	99.17	99.25	99.30	99.33	99.36	99.37	99.39	99.40	99.42	99.43	99.45	99.46	99.47	99.47	99.48	99.49	99.50
3	34.12	30.82	29.46	28.71	28.24	27.91	27.67	27.49	27.35	27.23	27.05	26.87	26.69	26.60	26.50	26.41	26.32	26.22	26.13
4	21.20	18.00	16.69	15.98	15.52	15.21	14.98	14.80	14.66	14.55	14.37	14.20	14.02	13.93	13.84	13.75	13.65	13.56	13.46
5	16.26	13.27	12.06	11.39	10.97	10.67	10.46	10.29	10.16	10.05	9.89	9.72	9.55	9.47	9.38	9.29	9.20	9.11	9.02
6	13.75	10.92	9.78	9.15	8.75	8.47	8.26	8.10	7.98	7.87	7.72	7.56	7.40	7.31	7.23	7.14	7.06	6.97	6.88
7	12.25	9.55	8.45	7.85	7.46	7.19	6.99	6.84	6.72	6.62	6.47	6.31	6.16	6.07	5.99	5.91	5.82	5.74	5.65
8	11.26	8.65	7.59	7.01	6.63	6.37	6.18	6.03	5.91	5.81	5.67	5.52	5.36	5.28	5.20	5.12	5.03	4.95	4.86
9	10.56	8.02	6.99	6.42	6.06	5.80	5.61	5.47	5.35	5.26	5.11	4.96	4.81	4.73	4.65	4.57	4.48	4.40	4.31
10	10.04	7.56	6.55	5.99	5.64	5.39	5.20	5.06	4.94	4.85	4.71	4.56	4.41	4.33	4.25	4.17	4.08	4.00	3.91
11	9.65	7.21	6.22	5.67	5.32	5.07	4.89	4.74	4.63	4.54	4.40	4.25	4.10	4.02	3.94	3.86	3.78	3.69	3.60
12	9.33	6.93	5.95	5.41	5.06	4.82	4.64	4.50	4.39	4.30	4.16	4.01	3.86	3.78	3.70	3.62	3.54	3.45	3.36
13	9.07	6.70	5.74	5.21	4.86	4.62	4.44	4.30	4.19	4.10	3.96	3.82	3.66	3.59	3.51	3.43	3.34	3.25	3.17
14	8.86	6.51	5.56	5.04	4.69	4.46	4.28	4.14	4.03	3.94	3.80	3.66	3.51	3.43	3.35	3.27	3.18	3.09	3.00
15	8.68	6.36	5.42	4.89	4.56	4.32	4.14	4.00	3.89	3.80	3.67	3.52	3.37	3.29	3.21	3.13	3.05	2.96	2.87
16	8.53	6.23	5.29	4.77	4.44	4.20	4.03	3.89	3.78	3.69	3.55	3.41	3.26	3.18	3.10	3.02	2.93	2.84	2.75
17	8.40	6.11	5.18	4.67	4.34	4.10	3.93	3.79	3.68	3.59	3.46	3.31	3.16	3.08	3.00	2.92	2.83	2.75	2.65
18	8.29	6.01	5.09	4.58	4.25	4.01	3.84	3.71	3.60	3.51	3.37	3.23	3.08	3.00	2.92	2.84	2.75	2.66	2.57
19	8.18	5.93	5.01	4.50	4.17	3.94	3.77	3.63	3.52	3.43	3.30	3.15	3.00	2.92	2.84	2.76	2.67	2.58	2.49
20	8.10	5.85	4.94	4.43	4.10	3.87	3.70	3.56	3.46	3.37	3.23	3.09	2.94	2.86	2.78	2.69	2.61	2.52	2.42
21	8.02	5.78	4.87	4.37	4.04	3.81	3.64	3.51	3.40	3.31	3.17	3.03	2.88	2.80	2.72	2.64	2.55	2.46	2.36
22	7.95	5.72	4.82	4.31	3.99	3.76	3.59	3.45	3.35	3.26	3.12	2.98	2.83	2.75	2.67	2.58	2.50	2.40	2.31
23	7.88	5.66	4.76	4.26	3.94	3.71	3.54	3.41	3.30	3.21	3.07	2.93	2.78	2.70	2.62	2.54	2.45	2.35	2.26
24	7.82	5.61	4.72	4.22	3.90	3.67	3.50	3.36	3.26	3.17	3.03	2.89	2.74	2.66	2.58	2.49	2.40	2.31	2.21
25	7.77	5.57	4.68	4.18	3.85	3.63	3.46	3.32	3.22	3.13	2.99	2.85	2.70	2.62	2.54	2.45	2.36	2.27	2.17
26	7.72	5.53	4.64	4.14	3.82	3.59	3.42	3.29	3.18	3.09	2.96	2.81	2.66	2.58	2.50	2.42	2.33	2.23	2.13
27	7.68	5.49	4.60	4.11	3.78	3.56	3.39	3.26	3.15	3.06	2.93	2.78	2.63	2.55	2.47	2.38	2.29	2.20	2.10
28	7.64	5.45	4.57	4.07	3.75	3.53	3.36	3.23	3.12	3.03	2.90	2.75	2.60	2.52	2.44	2.35	2.26	2.17	2.06
29	7.60	5.42	4.54	4.04	3.73	3.50	3.33	3.20	3.09	3.00	2.87	2.73	2.57	2.49	2.41	2.33	2.23	2.14	2.03
30	7.56	5.39	4.51	4.02	3.70	3.47	3.30	3.17	3.07	2.98	2.84	2.70	2.55	2.47	2.39	2.30	2.21	2.11	2.01
40	7.31	5.18	4.31	3.83	3.51	3.29	3.12	2.99	2.89	2.80	2.66	2.52	2.37	2.29	2.20	2.11	2.02	1.92	1.80
60	7.08	4.98	4.13	3.65	3.34	3.12	2.95	2.82	2.72	2.63	2.50	2.35	2.20	2.12	2.03	1.94	1.84	1.73	1.60
120	6.85	4.79	3.95	3.48	3.17	2.96	2.79	2.66	2.56	2.47	2.34	2.19	2.03	1.95	1.86	1.76	1.66	1.53	1.38
∞	6.63	4.61	3.78	3.32	3.02	2.80	2.64	2.51	2.41	2.32	2.18	2.04	1.88	1.79	1.70	1.59	1.47	1.32	1.00

Numerator Degrees of Freedom (df_1)

Denominator Degrees of Freedom (df_2)

Source: M. Merrington and C. M. Thompson, "Tables of Percentage Points of the Inverted Beta (F)-Distribution," *Biometrika* 33 (1943), pp. 73–88. Reproduced by permission of the Biometrika Trustees.

TABLE **A.10**   A Table of Percentage Points of the Studentized Range
(Note: *r* is the "first value" and *v* is the "second value" referred to in Chapter 10.)

Entry is $q_{0.10}$

											r								
v	2	3	4	5	6	7	8	9	10	11	12	13	14	15	16	17	18	19	20
1	8.93	13.4	16.4	18.5	20.2	21.5	22.6	23.6	24.5	25.2	25.9	26.5	27.1	27.6	28.1	28.5	29.0	29.3	29.7
2	4.13	5.73	6.77	7.54	8.14	8.63	9.05	9.41	9.72	10.0	10.3	10.5	10.7	10.9	11.1	11.2	11.4	11.5	11.7
3	3.33	4.47	5.20	5.74	6.16	6.51	6.81	7.06	7.29	7.49	7.67	7.83	7.98	8.12	8.25	8.37	8.48	8.58	8.68
4	3.01	3.98	4.59	5.03	5.39	5.68	5.93	6.14	6.33	6.49	6.65	6.78	6.91	7.02	7.13	7.23	7.33	7.41	7.50
5	2.85	3.72	4.26	4.66	4.98	5.24	5.46	5.65	5.82	5.97	6.10	6.22	6.34	6.44	6.54	6.63	6.71	6.79	6.86
6	2.75	3.56	4.07	4.44	4.73	4.97	5.17	5.34	5.50	5.64	5.76	5.87	5.98	6.07	6.16	6.25	6.32	6.40	6.47
7	2.68	3.45	3.93	4.28	4.55	4.78	4.97	5.14	5.28	5.41	5.53	5.64	5.74	5.83	5.91	5.99	6.06	6.13	6.19
8	2.63	3.37	3.83	4.17	4.43	4.65	4.83	4.99	5.13	5.25	5.36	5.46	5.56	5.64	5.72	5.80	5.87	5.93	6.00
9	2.59	3.32	3.76	4.08	4.34	4.54	4.72	4.87	5.01	5.13	5.23	5.33	5.42	5.51	5.58	5.66	5.72	5.79	5.85
10	2.56	3.27	3.70	4.02	4.26	4.47	4.64	4.78	4.91	5.03	5.13	5.23	5.32	5.40	5.47	5.54	5.61	5.67	5.73
11	2.54	3.23	3.66	3.96	4.20	4.40	4.57	4.71	4.84	4.95	5.05	5.15	5.23	5.31	5.38	5.45	5.51	5.57	5.63
12	2.52	3.20	3.62	3.92	4.16	4.35	4.51	4.65	4.78	4.89	4.99	5.08	5.16	5.24	5.31	5.37	5.44	5.49	5.55
13	2.50	3.18	3.59	3.88	4.12	4.30	4.46	4.60	4.72	4.83	4.93	5.02	5.10	5.18	5.25	5.31	5.37	5.43	5.48
14	2.49	3.16	3.56	3.85	4.08	4.27	4.42	4.56	4.68	4.79	4.88	4.97	5.05	5.12	5.19	5.26	5.32	5.37	5.43
15	2.48	3.14	3.54	3.83	4.05	4.23	4.39	4.52	4.64	4.75	4.84	4.93	5.01	5.08	5.15	5.21	5.27	5.32	5.38
16	2.47	3.12	3.52	3.80	4.03	4.21	4.36	4.49	4.61	4.71	4.81	4.89	4.97	5.04	5.11	5.17	5.23	5.28	5.33
17	2.46	3.11	3.50	3.78	4.00	4.18	4.33	4.46	4.58	4.68	4.77	4.86	4.93	5.01	5.07	5.13	5.19	5.24	5.30
18	2.45	3.10	3.49	3.77	3.98	4.16	4.31	4.44	4.55	4.65	4.75	4.83	4.90	4.98	5.04	5.10	5.16	5.21	5.26
19	2.45	3.09	3.47	3.75	3.97	4.14	4.29	4.42	4.53	4.63	4.72	4.80	4.88	4.95	5.01	5.07	5.13	5.18	5.23
20	2.44	3.08	3.46	3.74	3.95	4.12	4.27	4.40	4.51	4.61	4.70	4.78	4.85	4.92	4.99	5.05	5.10	5.16	5.20
24	2.42	3.05	3.42	3.69	3.90	4.07	4.21	4.34	4.44	4.54	4.63	4.71	4.78	4.85	4.91	4.97	5.02	5.07	5.12
30	2.40	3.02	3.39	3.65	3.85	4.02	4.16	4.28	4.38	4.47	4.56	4.64	4.71	4.77	4.83	4.89	4.94	4.99	5.03
40	2.38	2.99	3.35	3.60	3.80	3.96	4.10	4.21	4.32	4.41	4.49	4.56	4.63	4.69	4.75	4.81	4.86	4.90	4.95
60	2.36	2.96	3.31	3.56	3.75	3.91	4.04	4.16	4.25	4.34	4.42	4.49	4.56	4.62	4.67	4.73	4.78	4.82	4.86
120	2.34	2.93	3.28	3.52	3.71	3.86	3.99	4.10	4.19	4.28	4.35	4.42	4.48	4.54	4.60	4.65	4.69	4.74	4.78
∞	2.33	2.90	3.24	3.48	3.66	3.81	3.93	4.04	4.13	4.21	4.28	4.35	4.41	4.47	4.52	4.57	4.61	4.65	4.69

(table continued)

TABLE A.10 (continued)

Entry is $q_{0.05}$

v										r									
	2	3	4	5	6	7	8	9	10	11	12	13	14	15	16	17	18	19	20
1	18.0	27.0	32.8	37.1	40.4	43.1	45.4	47.4	49.1	50.6	52.0	53.2	54.3	55.4	56.3	57.2	58.0	58.8	59.6
2	6.08	8.33	9.80	10.9	11.7	12.4	13.0	13.5	14.0	14.4	14.7	15.1	15.4	15.7	15.9	16.1	16.4	16.6	16.8
3	4.50	5.91	6.82	7.50	8.04	8.48	8.85	9.18	9.46	9.72	9.95	10.2	10.3	10.5	10.7	10.8	11.0	11.1	11.2
4	3.93	5.04	5.76	6.29	6.71	7.05	7.35	7.60	7.83	8.03	8.21	8.37	8.52	8.66	8.79	8.91	9.03	9.13	9.23
5	3.64	4.60	5.22	5.67	6.03	6.33	6.58	6.80	6.99	7.17	7.32	7.47	7.60	7.72	7.83	7.93	8.03	8.12	8.21
6	3.46	4.34	4.90	5.30	5.63	5.90	6.12	6.32	6.49	6.65	6.79	6.92	7.03	7.14	7.24	7.34	7.43	7.51	7.59
7	3.34	4.16	4.68	5.06	5.36	5.61	5.82	6.00	6.16	6.30	6.43	6.55	6.66	6.76	6.85	6.94	7.02	7.10	7.17
8	3.26	4.04	4.53	4.89	5.17	5.40	5.60	5.77	5.92	6.05	6.18	6.29	6.39	6.48	6.57	6.65	6.73	6.80	6.87
9	3.20	3.95	4.41	4.76	5.02	5.24	5.43	5.59	5.74	5.87	5.98	6.09	6.19	6.28	6.36	6.44	6.51	6.58	6.64
10	3.15	3.88	4.33	4.65	4.91	5.12	5.30	5.46	5.60	5.72	5.83	5.93	6.03	6.11	6.19	6.27	6.34	6.40	6.47
11	3.11	3.82	4.26	4.57	4.82	5.03	5.20	5.35	5.49	5.61	5.71	5.81	5.90	5.98	6.06	6.13	6.20	6.27	6.33
12	3.08	3.77	4.20	4.51	4.75	4.95	5.12	5.27	5.39	5.51	5.61	5.71	5.80	5.88	5.95	6.02	6.09	6.15	6.21
13	3.06	3.73	4.15	4.45	4.69	4.88	5.05	5.19	5.32	5.43	5.53	5.63	5.71	5.79	5.86	5.93	5.99	6.05	6.11
14	3.03	3.70	4.11	4.41	4.64	4.83	4.99	5.13	5.25	5.36	5.46	5.55	5.64	5.71	5.79	5.85	5.91	5.97	6.03
15	3.01	3.67	4.08	4.37	4.59	4.78	4.94	5.08	5.20	5.31	5.40	5.49	5.57	5.65	5.72	5.78	5.85	5.90	5.96
16	3.00	3.65	4.05	4.33	4.56	4.74	4.90	5.03	5.15	5.26	5.35	5.44	5.52	5.59	5.66	5.73	5.79	5.84	5.90
17	2.98	3.63	4.02	4.30	4.52	4.70	4.86	4.99	5.11	5.21	5.31	5.39	5.47	5.54	5.61	5.67	5.73	5.79	5.84
18	2.97	3.61	4.00	4.28	4.49	4.67	4.82	4.96	5.07	5.17	5.27	5.35	5.43	5.50	5.57	5.63	5.69	5.74	5.79
19	2.96	3.59	3.98	4.25	4.47	4.65	4.79	4.92	5.04	5.14	5.23	5.31	5.39	5.46	5.53	5.59	5.65	5.70	5.75
20	2.95	3.58	3.96	4.23	4.45	4.62	4.77	4.90	5.01	5.11	5.20	5.28	5.36	5.43	5.49	5.55	5.61	5.66	5.71
24	2.92	3.53	3.90	4.17	4.37	4.54	4.68	4.81	4.92	5.01	5.10	5.18	5.25	5.32	5.38	5.44	5.49	5.55	5.59
30	2.89	3.49	3.85	4.10	4.30	4.46	4.60	4.72	4.82	4.92	5.00	5.08	5.15	5.21	5.27	5.33	5.38	5.43	5.47
40	2.86	3.44	3.79	4.04	4.23	4.39	4.52	4.63	4.73	4.82	4.90	4.98	5.04	5.11	5.16	5.22	5.27	5.31	5.36
60	2.83	3.40	3.74	3.98	4.16	4.31	4.44	4.55	4.65	4.73	4.81	4.88	4.94	5.00	5.06	5.11	5.15	5.20	5.24
120	2.80	3.36	3.68	3.92	4.10	4.24	4.36	4.47	4.56	4.64	4.71	4.78	4.84	4.90	4.95	5.00	5.04	5.09	5.13
∞	2.77	3.31	3.63	3.86	4.03	4.17	4.29	4.39	4.47	4.55	4.62	4.68	4.74	4.80	4.85	4.89	4.93	4.97	5.01

(table continued)

TABLE A.10 *(concluded)*

Entry is $q_{0.01}$

v	2	3	4	5	6	7	8	9	10	11	12	13	14	15	16	17	18	19	20
																		r	
1	90.0	135	164	186	202	216	227	237	246	253	260	266	272	277	282	286	290	294	298
2	14.0	19.0	22.3	24.7	26.6	28.2	29.5	30.7	31.7	32.6	33.4	34.1	34.8	35.4	36.0	36.5	37.0	37.5	37.9
3	8.26	10.6	12.2	13.3	14.2	15.0	15.6	16.2	16.7	17.1	17.5	17.9	18.2	18.5	18.8	19.1	19.3	19.5	19.8
4	6.51	8.12	9.17	9.96	10.6	11.1	11.5	11.9	12.3	12.6	12.8	13.1	13.3	13.5	13.7	13.9	14.1	14.2	14.4
5	5.70	6.97	7.80	8.42	8.91	9.32	9.67	9.97	10.2	10.5	10.7	10.9	11.1	11.2	11.4	11.6	11.7	11.8	11.9
6	5.24	6.33	7.03	7.56	7.97	8.32	8.61	8.87	9.10	9.30	9.49	9.65	9.81	9.95	10.1	10.2	10.3	10.4	10.5
7	4.95	5.92	6.54	7.01	7.37	7.68	7.94	8.17	8.37	8.55	8.71	8.86	9.00	9.12	9.24	9.35	9.46	9.55	9.65
8	4.74	5.63	6.20	6.63	6.96	7.24	7.47	7.68	7.87	8.03	8.18	8.31	8.44	8.55	8.66	8.76	8.85	8.94	9.03
9	4.60	5.43	5.96	6.35	6.66	6.91	7.13	7.32	7.49	7.65	7.78	7.91	8.03	8.13	8.23	8.32	8.41	8.49	8.57
10	4.48	5.27	5.77	6.14	6.43	6.67	6.87	7.05	7.21	7.36	7.48	7.60	7.71	7.81	7.91	7.99	8.07	8.15	8.22
11	4.39	5.14	5.62	5.97	6.25	6.48	6.67	6.84	6.99	7.13	7.25	7.36	7.46	7.56	7.65	7.73	7.81	7.88	7.95
12	4.32	5.04	5.50	5.84	6.10	6.32	6.51	6.67	6.81	6.94	7.06	7.17	7.26	7.36	7.44	7.52	7.59	7.66	7.73
13	4.26	4.96	5.40	5.73	5.98	6.19	6.37	6.53	6.67	6.79	6.90	7.01	7.10	7.19	7.27	7.34	7.42	7.48	7.55
14	4.21	4.89	5.32	5.63	5.88	6.08	6.26	6.41	6.54	6.66	6.77	6.87	6.96	7.05	7.12	7.20	7.27	7.33	7.39
15	4.17	4.83	5.25	5.56	5.80	5.99	6.16	6.31	6.44	6.55	6.66	6.76	6.84	6.93	7.00	7.07	7.14	7.20	7.26
16	4.13	4.78	5.19	5.49	5.72	5.92	6.08	6.22	6.35	6.46	6.56	6.66	6.74	6.82	6.90	6.97	7.03	7.09	7.15
17	4.10	4.74	5.14	5.43	5.66	5.85	6.01	6.15	6.27	6.38	6.48	6.57	6.66	6.73	6.80	6.87	6.94	7.00	7.05
18	4.07	4.70	5.09	5.38	5.60	5.79	5.94	6.08	6.20	6.31	6.41	6.50	6.58	6.65	6.72	6.79	6.85	6.91	6.96
19	4.05	4.67	5.05	5.33	5.55	5.73	5.89	6.02	6.14	6.25	6.34	6.43	6.51	6.58	6.65	6.72	6.78	6.84	6.89
20	4.02	4.64	5.02	5.29	5.51	5.69	5.84	5.97	6.09	6.19	6.29	6.37	6.45	6.52	6.59	6.65	6.71	6.76	6.82
24	3.96	4.54	4.91	5.17	5.37	5.54	5.69	5.81	5.92	6.02	6.11	6.19	6.26	6.33	6.39	6.45	6.51	6.56	6.61
30	3.89	4.45	4.80	5.05	5.24	5.40	5.54	5.65	5.76	5.85	5.93	6.01	6.08	6.14	6.20	6.26	6.31	6.36	6.41
40	3.82	4.37	4.70	4.93	5.11	5.27	5.39	5.50	5.60	5.69	5.77	5.84	5.90	5.96	6.02	6.07	6.12	6.17	6.21
60	3.76	4.28	4.60	4.82	4.99	5.13	5.25	5.36	5.45	5.53	5.60	5.67	5.73	5.79	5.84	5.89	5.93	5.98	6.02
120	3.70	4.20	4.50	4.71	4.87	5.01	5.12	5.21	5.30	5.38	5.44	5.51	5.56	5.61	5.66	5.71	5.75	5.79	5.83
∞	3.64	4.12	4.40	4.60	4.76	4.88	4.99	5.08	5.16	5.23	5.29	5.35	5.40	5.45	5.49	5.54	5.57	5.61	5.65

Source: *The Analysis of Variance*, pp. 414–16, by Henry Scheffe, © 1959 by John Wiley & Sons, Inc. Reprinted by permission of John Wiley & Sons, Inc.

TABLE **A.11**   A Table of Critical Values of r ($df = N - 2$ and N Is the Number of Pairs of Scores)

Degrees of Freedom (df)	5%	1%	Degrees of Freedom (df)	5%	1%
1	0.997	1.000	24	0.388	0.496
2	0.950	0.990	25	0.381	0.487
3	0.878	0.959	26	0.374	0.478
4	0.811	0.917	27	0.367	0.470
5	0.754	0.874	28	0.361	0.463
6	0.707	0.834	29	0.355	0.456
7	0.666	0.798	30	0.349	0.449
8	0.632	0.765	35	0.325	0.418
9	0.602	0.735	40	0.304	0.393
10	0.576	0.708	45	0.288	0.372
11	0.553	0.684	50	0.273	0.354
12	0.532	0.661	60	0.250	0.325
13	0.514	0.641	70	0.232	0.302
14	0.497	0.623	80	0.217	0.283
15	0.482	0.606	90	0.205	0.267
16	0.468	0.590	100	0.195	0.254
17	0.456	0.575	125	0.174	0.228
18	0.444	0.561	150	0.159	0.208
19	0.433	0.549	200	0.138	0.181
20	0.423	0.537	300	0.113	0.148
21	0.413	0.526	400	0.098	0.128
22	0.404	0.515	500	0.088	0.115
23	0.396	0.505	1000	0.062	0.081

Source: This table is adapted from Table VII of Fisher and Yates, *Statistical Tables for Biological, Agricultural and Medical Research*, published by Longman Group Ltd, London (previously published by Oliver and Boyd, Edinburgh), and by permission of Pearson Education Limited.

TABLE A.12 A Table of Critical Values for the Durbin–Watson d Statistic ($\alpha = 0.05$)

n	k = 1		k = 2		k = 3		k = 4		k = 5	
	$d_{L,0.05}$	$d_{U,0.05}$	$d_{L,0.05}$	$d_{U,0.05}$	$d_{L,0.05}$	$d_{U,0.05}$	$d_{L,0.05}$	$d_{U,0.05}$	$d_{L,0.05}$	$d_{U,0.05}$
15	1.08	1.36	0.95	1.54	0.82	1.75	0.69	1.97	0.56	2.21
16	1.10	1.37	0.98	1.54	0.86	1.73	0.74	1.93	0.62	2.15
17	1.13	1.38	1.02	1.54	0.90	1.71	0.78	1.90	0.67	2.10
18	1.16	1.39	1.05	1.53	0.93	1.69	0.82	1.87	0.71	2.06
19	1.18	1.40	1.08	1.53	0.97	1.68	0.86	1.85	0.75	2.02
20	1.20	1.41	1.10	1.54	1.00	1.68	0.90	1.83	0.79	1.99
21	1.22	1.42	1.13	1.54	1.03	1.67	0.93	1.81	0.83	1.96
22	1.24	1.43	1.15	1.54	1.05	1.66	0.96	1.80	0.86	1.94
23	1.26	1.44	1.17	1.54	1.08	1.66	0.99	1.79	0.90	1.92
24	1.27	1.45	1.19	1.55	1.10	1.66	1.01	1.78	0.93	1.90
25	1.29	1.45	1.21	1.55	1.12	1.66	1.04	1.77	0.95	1.89
26	1.30	1.46	1.22	1.55	1.14	1.65	1.06	1.76	0.98	1.88
27	1.32	1.47	1.24	1.56	1.16	1.65	1.08	1.76	1.01	1.86
28	1.33	1.48	1.26	1.56	1.18	1.65	1.10	1.75	1.03	1.85
29	1.34	1.48	1.27	1.56	1.20	1.65	1.12	1.74	1.05	1.84
30	1.35	1.49	1.28	1.57	1.21	1.65	1.14	1.74	1.07	1.83
31	1.36	1.50	1.30	1.57	1.23	1.65	1.16	1.74	1.09	1.83
32	1.37	1.50	1.31	1.57	1.24	1.65	1.18	1.73	1.11	1.82
33	1.38	1.51	1.32	1.58	1.26	1.65	1.19	1.73	1.13	1.81
34	1.39	1.51	1.33	1.58	1.27	1.65	1.21	1.73	1.15	1.81
35	1.40	1.52	1.34	1.58	1.28	1.65	1.22	1.73	1.16	1.80
36	1.41	1.52	1.35	1.59	1.29	1.65	1.24	1.73	1.18	1.80
37	1.42	1.53	1.36	1.59	1.31	1.66	1.25	1.72	1.19	1.80
38	1.43	1.54	1.37	1.59	1.32	1.66	1.26	1.72	1.21	1.79
39	1.43	1.54	1.38	1.60	1.33	1.66	1.27	1.72	1.22	1.79
40	1.44	1.54	1.39	1.60	1.34	1.66	1.29	1.72	1.23	1.79
45	1.48	1.57	1.43	1.62	1.38	1.67	1.34	1.72	1.29	1.78
50	1.50	1.59	1.46	1.63	1.42	1.67	1.38	1.72	1.34	1.77
55	1.53	1.60	1.49	1.64	1.45	1.68	1.41	1.72	1.38	1.77
60	1.55	1.62	1.51	1.65	1.48	1.69	1.44	1.73	1.41	1.77
65	1.57	1.63	1.54	1.66	1.50	1.70	1.47	1.73	1.44	1.77
70	1.58	1.64	1.55	1.67	1.52	1.70	1.49	1.74	1.46	1.77
75	1.60	1.65	1.57	1.68	1.54	1.71	1.51	1.74	1.49	1.77
80	1.61	1.66	1.59	1.69	1.56	1.72	1.53	1.74	1.51	1.77
85	1.62	1.67	1.60	1.70	1.57	1.72	1.55	1.75	1.52	1.77
90	1.63	1.68	1.61	1.70	1.59	1.73	1.57	1.75	1.54	1.78
95	1.64	1.69	1.62	1.71	1.60	1.73	1.58	1.75	1.56	1.78
100	1.65	1.69	1.63	1.72	1.61	1.74	1.59	1.76	1.57	1.78

Source: J. Durbin and G. S. Watson, "Testing for Serial Correlation in Least Squares Regression, II," *Biometrika* 30 (1951), pp. 159–78. Reproduced by permission of the Biometrika Trustees.

TABLE A.13 A Table of Critical Values for the Durbin–Watson d Statistic ($\alpha = 0.025$)

n	k = 1		k = 2		k = 3		k = 4		k = 5	
	$d_{L,0.025}$	$d_{U,0.025}$	$d_{L,0.025}$	$d_{U,0.025}$	$d_{L,0.025}$	$d_{U,0.025}$	$d_{L,0.025}$	$d_{U,0.025}$	$d_{L,0.025}$	$d_{U,0.025}$
15	0.95	1.23	0.83	1.40	0.71	1.61	0.59	1.84	0.48	2.09
16	0.98	1.24	0.86	1.40	0.75	1.59	0.64	1.80	0.53	2.03
17	1.01	1.25	0.90	1.40	0.79	1.58	0.68	1.77	0.57	1.98
18	1.03	1.26	0.93	1.40	0.82	1.56	0.72	1.74	0.62	1.93
19	1.06	1.28	0.96	1.41	0.86	1.55	0.76	1.72	0.66	1.90
20	1.08	1.28	0.99	1.41	0.89	1.55	0.79	1.70	0.70	1.87
21	1.10	1.30	1.01	1.41	0.92	1.54	0.83	1.69	0.73	1.84
22	1.12	1.31	1.04	1.42	0.95	1.54	0.86	1.68	0.77	1.82
23	1.14	1.32	1.06	1.42	0.97	1.54	0.89	1.67	0.80	1.80
24	1.16	1.33	1.08	1.43	1.00	1.54	0.91	1.66	0.83	1.79
25	1.18	1.34	1.10	1.43	1.02	1.54	0.94	1.65	0.86	1.77
26	1.19	1.35	1.12	1.44	1.04	1.54	0.96	1.65	0.88	1.76
27	1.21	1.36	1.13	1.44	1.06	1.54	0.99	1.64	0.91	1.75
28	1.22	1.37	1.15	1.45	1.08	1.54	1.01	1.64	0.93	1.74
29	1.24	1.38	1.17	1.45	1.10	1.54	1.03	1.63	0.96	1.73
30	1.25	1.38	1.18	1.46	1.12	1.54	1.05	1.63	0.98	1.73
31	1.26	1.39	1.20	1.47	1.13	1.55	1.07	1.63	1.00	1.72
32	1.27	1.40	1.21	1.47	1.15	1.55	1.08	1.63	1.02	1.71
33	1.28	1.41	1.22	1.48	1.16	1.55	1.10	1.63	1.04	1.71
34	1.29	1.41	1.24	1.48	1.17	1.55	1.12	1.63	1.06	1.70
35	1.30	1.42	1.25	1.48	1.19	1.55	1.13	1.63	1.07	1.70
36	1.31	1.43	1.26	1.49	1.20	1.56	1.15	1.63	1.09	1.70
37	1.32	1.43	1.27	1.49	1.21	1.56	1.16	1.62	1.10	1.70
38	1.33	1.44	1.28	1.50	1.23	1.56	1.17	1.62	1.12	1.70
39	1.34	1.44	1.29	1.50	1.24	1.56	1.19	1.63	1.13	1.69
40	1.35	1.45	1.30	1.51	1.25	1.57	1.20	1.63	1.15	1.69
45	1.39	1.48	1.34	1.53	1.30	1.58	1.25	1.63	1.21	1.69
50	1.42	1.50	1.38	1.54	1.34	1.59	1.30	1.64	1.26	1.69
55	1.45	1.52	1.41	1.56	1.37	1.60	1.33	1.64	1.30	1.69
60	1.47	1.54	1.44	1.57	1.40	1.61	1.37	1.65	1.33	1.69
65	1.49	1.55	1.46	1.59	1.43	1.62	1.40	1.66	1.36	1.69
70	1.51	1.57	1.48	1.60	1.45	1.63	1.42	1.66	1.39	1.70
75	1.53	1.58	1.50	1.61	1.47	1.64	1.45	1.67	1.42	1.70
80	1.54	1.59	1.52	1.62	1.49	1.65	1.47	1.67	1.44	1.70
85	1.56	1.60	1.53	1.63	1.51	1.65	1.49	1.68	1.46	1.70
90	1.57	1.61	1.55	1.64	1.53	1.66	1.50	1.69	1.48	1.71
95	1.58	1.62	1.56	1.65	1.54	1.67	1.52	1.69	1.50	1.71
100	1.59	1.63	1.57	1.65	1.55	1.67	1.53	1.70	1.51	1.72

Source: J. Durbin and G. S. Watson, "Testing for Serial Correlation in Least Squares Regression, II," *Biometrika* 30 (1951), pp. 159–78. Reproduced by permission of the Biometrika Trustees.

TABLE **A.14**   A Table of Critical Values for the Durbin–Watson d Statistic ($\alpha = 0.01$)

	k = 1		k = 2		k = 3		k = 4		k = 5	
n	$d_{L,0.01}$	$d_{U,0.01}$	$d_{L,0.01}$	$d_{U,0.01}$	$d_{L,0.01}$	$d_{U,0.01}$	$d_{L,0.01}$	$d_{U,0.01}$	$d_{L,0.01}$	$d_{U,0.01}$
15	0.81	1.07	0.70	1.25	0.59	1.46	0.49	1.70	0.39	1.96
16	0.84	1.09	0.74	1.25	0.63	1.44	0.53	1.66	0.44	1.90
17	0.87	1.10	0.77	1.25	0.67	1.43	0.57	1.63	0.48	1.85
18	0.90	1.12	0.80	1.26	0.71	1.42	0.61	1.60	0.52	1.80
19	0.93	1.13	0.83	1.26	0.74	1.41	0.65	1.58	0.56	1.77
20	0.95	1.15	0.86	1.27	0.77	1.41	0.68	1.57	0.60	1.74
21	0.97	1.16	0.89	1.27	0.80	1.41	0.72	1.55	0.63	1.71
22	1.00	1.17	0.91	1.28	0.83	1.40	0.75	1.54	0.66	1.69
23	1.02	1.19	0.94	1.29	0.86	1.40	0.77	1.53	0.70	1.67
24	1.04	1.20	0.96	1.30	0.88	1.41	0.80	1.53	0.72	1.66
25	1.05	1.21	0.98	1.30	0.90	1.41	0.83	1.52	0.75	1.65
26	1.07	1.22	1.00	1.31	0.93	1.41	0.85	1.52	0.78	1.64
27	1.09	1.23	1.02	1.32	0.95	1.41	0.88	1.51	0.81	1.63
28	1.10	1.24	1.04	1.32	0.97	1.41	0.90	1.51	0.83	1.62
29	1.12	1.25	1.05	1.33	0.99	1.42	0.92	1.51	0.85	1.61
30	1.13	1.26	1.07	1.34	1.01	1.42	0.94	1.51	0.88	1.61
31	1.15	1.27	1.08	1.34	1.02	1.42	0.96	1.51	0.90	1.60
32	1.16	1.28	1.10	1.35	1.04	1.43	0.98	1.51	0.92	1.60
33	1.17	1.29	1.11	1.36	1.05	1.43	1.00	1.51	0.94	1.59
34	1.18	1.30	1.13	1.36	1.07	1.43	1.01	1.51	0.95	1.59
35	1.19	1.31	1.14	1.37	1.08	1.44	1.03	1.51	0.97	1.59
36	1.21	1.32	1.15	1.38	1.10	1.44	1.04	1.51	0.99	1.59
37	1.22	1.32	1.16	1.38	1.11	1.45	1.06	1.51	1.00	1.59
38	1.23	1.33	1.18	1.39	1.12	1.45	1.07	1.52	1.02	1.58
39	1.24	1.34	1.19	1.39	1.14	1.45	1.09	1.52	1.03	1.58
40	1.25	1.34	1.20	1.40	1.15	1.46	1.10	1.52	1.05	1.58
45	1.29	1.38	1.24	1.42	1.20	1.48	1.16	1.53	1.11	1.58
50	1.32	1.40	1.28	1.45	1.24	1.49	1.20	1.54	1.16	1.59
55	1.36	1.43	1.32	1.47	1.28	1.51	1.25	1.55	1.21	1.59
60	1.38	1.45	1.35	1.48	1.32	1.52	1.28	1.56	1.25	1.60
65	1.41	1.47	1.38	1.50	1.35	1.53	1.31	1.57	1.28	1.61
70	1.43	1.49	1.40	1.52	1.37	1.55	1.34	1.58	1.31	1.61
75	1.45	1.50	1.42	1.53	1.39	1.56	1.37	1.59	1.34	1.62
80	1.47	1.52	1.44	1.54	1.42	1.57	1.39	1.60	1.36	1.62
85	1.48	1.53	1.46	1.55	1.43	1.58	1.41	1.60	1.39	1.63
90	1.50	1.54	1.47	1.56	1.45	1.59	1.43	1.61	1.41	1.64
95	1.51	1.55	1.49	1.57	1.47	1.60	1.45	1.62	1.42	1.64
100	1.52	1.56	1.50	1.58	1.48	1.60	1.46	1.63	1.44	1.65

Source: J. Durbin and G. S. Watson, "Testing for Serial Correlation in Least Squares Regression, II," *Biometrika* 30 (1951), pp. 159–78. Reproduced by permission of the Biometrika Trustees.

TABLE **A.15**   A Wilcoxon Rank Sum Table: Values of T_L and T_U

(a) $\alpha = 0.025$ one-sided; $\alpha = 0.05$ two-sided

n_2 \ n_1	3		4		5		6		7		8		9		10	
	T_L	T_U	T_L	T_U	T_L	T_U	T_L	T_U	T_L	T_U	T_L	T_U	T_L	T_U	T_L	T_U
3	5	16	6	18	6	21	7	23	7	26	8	28	8	31	9	33
4	6	18	11	25	12	28	12	32	13	35	14	38	15	41	16	44
5	6	21	12	28	18	37	19	41	20	45	21	49	22	53	24	56
6	7	23	12	32	19	41	26	52	28	56	29	61	31	65	32	70
7	7	26	13	35	20	45	28	56	37	68	39	73	41	78	43	83
8	8	28	14	38	21	49	29	61	39	73	49	87	51	93	54	98
9	8	31	15	41	22	53	31	65	41	78	51	93	63	108	66	114
10	9	33	16	44	24	56	32	70	43	83	54	98	66	114	79	131

(b) $\alpha = 0.05$ one-sided; $\alpha = 0.10$ two-sided

n_2 \ n_1	3		4		5		6		7		8		9		10	
	T_L	T_U	T_L	T_U	T_L	T_U	T_L	T_U	T_L	T_U	T_L	T_U	T_L	T_U	T_L	T_U
3	6	15	7	17	7	20	8	22	9	24	9	27	10	29	11	31
4	7	17	12	24	13	27	14	30	15	33	16	36	17	39	18	42
5	7	20	13	27	19	36	20	40	22	43	24	46	25	50	26	54
6	8	22	14	30	20	40	28	50	30	54	32	58	33	63	35	67
7	9	24	15	33	22	43	30	54	39	66	41	71	43	76	46	80
8	9	27	16	36	24	46	32	58	41	71	52	84	54	90	57	95
9	10	29	17	39	25	50	33	63	43	76	54	90	66	105	69	111
10	11	31	18	42	26	54	35	67	46	80	57	95	69	111	83	127

Source: F. Wilcoxon and R. A. Wilcox, "Some Rapid Approximate Statistical Procedures" (New York: American Cyanamid Company, 1964), pp. 20–23. Reproduced with the permission of American Cyanamid Company.

TABLE A.16   A Wilcoxon Signed Ranks Table: Values of T_0

One-Sided	Two-Sided	$n = 5$	$n = 6$	$n = 7$	$n = 8$	$n = 9$	$n = 10$
$\alpha = 0.05$	$\alpha = 0.10$	1	2	4	6	8	11
$\alpha = 0.025$	$\alpha = 0.05$		1	2	4	6	8
$\alpha = 0.01$	$\alpha = 0.02$			0	2	3	5
$\alpha = 0.005$	$\alpha = 0.01$				0	2	3
		$n = 11$	$n = 12$	$n = 13$	$n = 14$	$n = 15$	$n = 16$
$\alpha = 0.05$	$\alpha = 0.10$	14	17	21	26	30	36
$\alpha = 0.025$	$\alpha = 0.05$	11	14	17	21	25	30
$\alpha = 0.01$	$\alpha = 0.02$	7	10	13	16	20	24
$\alpha = 0.005$	$\alpha = 0.01$	5	7	10	13	16	19
		$n = 17$	$n = 18$	$n = 19$	$n = 20$	$n = 21$	$n = 22$
$\alpha = 0.05$	$\alpha = 0.10$	41	47	54	60	68	75
$\alpha = 0.025$	$\alpha = 0.05$	35	40	46	52	59	66
$\alpha = 0.01$	$\alpha = 0.02$	28	33	38	43	49	56
$\alpha = 0.005$	$\alpha = 0.01$	23	28	32	37	43	49
		$n = 23$	$n = 24$	$n = 25$	$n = 26$	$n = 27$	$n = 28$
$\alpha = 0.05$	$\alpha = 0.10$	83	92	101	110	120	130
$\alpha = 0.025$	$\alpha = 0.05$	73	81	90	98	107	117
$\alpha = 0.01$	$\alpha = 0.02$	62	69	77	85	93	102
$\alpha = 0.005$	$\alpha = 0.01$	55	61	68	76	84	92
		$n = 29$	$n = 30$	$n = 31$	$n = 32$	$n = 33$	$n = 34$
$\alpha = 0.05$	$\alpha = 0.10$	141	152	163	175	188	201
$\alpha = 0.025$	$\alpha = 0.05$	127	137	148	159	171	183
$\alpha = 0.01$	$\alpha = 0.02$	111	120	130	141	151	162
$\alpha = 0.005$	$\alpha = 0.01$	100	109	118	128	138	149
		$n = 35$	$n = 36$	$n = 37$	$n = 38$	$n = 39$	
$\alpha = 0.05$	$\alpha = 0.10$	214	228	242	256	271	
$\alpha = 0.025$	$\alpha = 0.05$	195	208	222	235	250	
$\alpha = 0.01$	$\alpha = 0.02$	174	186	198	211	224	
$\alpha = 0.005$	$\alpha = 0.01$	160	171	183	195	208	
		$n = 40$	$n = 41$	$n = 42$	$n = 43$	$n = 44$	$n = 45$
$\alpha = 0.05$	$\alpha = 0.10$	287	303	319	336	353	371
$\alpha = 0.025$	$\alpha = 0.05$	264	279	295	311	327	344
$\alpha = 0.01$	$\alpha = 0.02$	238	252	267	281	297	313
$\alpha = 0.005$	$\alpha = 0.01$	221	234	248	262	277	292
		$n = 46$	$n = 47$	$n = 48$	$n = 49$	$n = 50$	
$\alpha = 0.05$	$\alpha = 0.10$	389	408	427	446	466	
$\alpha = 0.025$	$\alpha = 0.05$	361	379	397	415	434	
$\alpha = 0.01$	$\alpha = 0.02$	329	345	362	380	398	
$\alpha = 0.005$	$\alpha = 0.01$	307	323	339	356	373	

Source: F. Wilcoxon and R. A. Wilcox, "Some Rapid Approximate Statistical Procedures" (New York: American Cyanamid Company, 1964), p. 28. Reproduced with the permission of American Cyanamid Company.

TABLE A.17   A Table of Critical Values for Spearman's Rank Correlation Coefficient

n	$\alpha = 0.05$	$\alpha = 0.025$	$\alpha = 0.01$	$\alpha = 0.005$	n	$\alpha = 0.05$	$\alpha = 0.025$	$\alpha = 0.01$	$\alpha = 0.005$
5	0.900	—	—	—	18	0.399	0.476	0.564	0.625
6	0.829	0.886	0.943	—	19	0.388	0.462	0.549	0.608
7	0.714	0.786	0.893	—	20	0.377	0.450	0.534	0.591
8	0.643	0.738	0.833	0.881	21	0.368	0.438	0.521	0.576
9	0.600	0.683	0.783	0.833	22	0.359	0.428	0.508	0.562
10	0.564	0.648	0.745	0.794	23	0.351	0.418	0.496	0.549
11	0.523	0.623	0.736	0.818	24	0.343	0.409	0.485	0.537
12	0.497	0.591	0.703	0.780	25	0.336	0.400	0.475	0.526
13	0.475	0.566	0.673	0.745	26	0.329	0.392	0.465	0.515
14	0.457	0.545	0.646	0.716	27	0.323	0.385	0.456	0.505
15	0.441	0.525	0.623	0.689	28	0.317	0.377	0.448	0.496
16	0.425	0.507	0.601	0.666	29	0.311	0.370	0.440	0.487
17	0.412	0.490	0.582	0.645	30	0.305	0.364	0.432	0.478

Source: E. G. Olds, "Distribution of Sums of Squares of Rank Differences for Small Samples," *Annals of Mathematical Statistics*, 1938, 9. Reproduced with the permission of the editor, *Annals of Mathematical Statistics*.

TABLE A.18   A Chi-Square Table: Values of χ_α^2

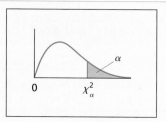

df	$\chi_{0.995}^2$	$\chi_{0.99}^2$	$\chi_{0.975}^2$	$\chi_{0.95}^2$	$\chi_{0.90}^2$
1	0.0000393	0.0001571	0.0009821	0.0039321	0.0157908
2	0.0100251	0.0201007	0.0506356	0.102587	0.210720
3	0.0717212	0.114832	0.215795	0.341846	0.584375
4	0.206990	0.297110	0.484419	0.710721	0.063623
5	0.411740	0.554300	0.831211	1.145476	1.61031
6	0.675727	0.872085	1.237347	1.63539	2.20413
7	0.989265	1.239043	1.68987	2.16735	2.83311
8	1.344419	1.646482	2.17973	2.73264	3.48954
9	1.734926	2.087912	2.70039	3.32511	4.16816
10	2.15585	2.55821	3.24697	3.94030	4.86518
11	2.60321	3.05347	3.81575	4.57481	5.57779
12	3.07382	3.57056	4.40379	5.22603	6.30380
13	3.56503	4.10691	5.00874	5.89186	7.04150
14	4.07468	4.66043	5.62872	6.57063	7.78953
15	4.60094	5.22935	6.26214	7.26094	8.54675
16	5.14224	5.81221	6.90766	7.96164	9.31223
17	5.69724	6.40776	7.56418	8.67176	10.0852
18	6.26481	7.01491	8.23075	9.39046	10.8649
19	6.84398	7.63273	8.90655	10.1170	11.6509
20	7.43386	8.26040	9.59083	10.8508	12.4426
21	8.03366	8.89720	10.28293	11.5913	13.2396
22	8.64272	9.54249	10.9823	12.3380	14.0415
23	9.26042	10.19567	11.6885	13.0905	14.8479
24	9.88623	10.8564	12.4011	13.8484	15.6587
25	10.5197	11.5240	13.1197	14.6114	16.4734
26	11.1603	12.1981	13.8439	15.3791	17.2919
27	11.8076	12.8786	14.5733	16.1513	18.1138
28	12.4613	13.5648	15.3079	16.9279	18.9392
29	13.1211	14.2565	16.0471	17.7083	19.7677
30	13.7867	14.9535	16.7908	18.4926	20.5992
40	20.7065	22.1643	24.4331	26.5093	29.0505
50	27.9907	29.7067	32.3574	34.7642	37.6886
60	35.5346	37.4848	40.4817	43.1879	46.4589
70	43.2752	45.4418	48.7576	51.7393	55.3290
80	51.1720	53.5400	57.1532	60.3915	64.2778
90	59.1963	61.7541	65.6466	69.1260	73.2912
100	67.3276	70.0648	74.2219	77.9295	82.3581

(table continued)

TABLE **A.18**   *(concluded)*
A Chi-Square Table: Values of χ^2_α

df	$\chi^2_{0.10}$	$\chi^2_{0.05}$	$\chi^2_{0.025}$	$\chi^2_{0.01}$	$\chi^2_{0.005}$
1	2.70554	3.84146	5.02389	6.63490	7.87944
2	4.60517	5.99147	7.37776	9.21034	10.5966
3	6.25139	7.81473	9.34840	11.3449	12.8381
4	7.77944	9.48773	11.1433	13.2767	14.8602
5	9.23635	11.0705	12.8325	15.0863	16.7496
6	10.6446	12.5916	14.4494	16.8119	18.5476
7	12.0170	14.0671	16.0128	18.4753	20.2777
8	13.3616	15.5073	17.5346	20.0902	21.9550
9	14.6837	16.9190	19.0228	21.6660	23.5893
10	15.9871	18.3070	20.4831	23.2093	25.1882
11	17.2750	19.6751	21.9200	24.7250	26.7569
12	18.5494	21.0261	23.3367	26.2170	28.2995
13	19.8119	22.3621	24.7356	27.6883	29.8194
14	21.0642	23.6848	26.1190	29.1413	31.3193
15	22.3072	24.9958	27.4884	30.5779	32.8013
16	23.5418	26.2962	28.8454	31.9999	34.2672
17	24.7690	27.5871	30.1910	33.4087	35.7185
18	25.9894	28.8693	31.5264	34.8053	37.1564
19	27.2036	30.1435	32.8523	36.1908	38.5822
20	28.4120	31.4104	34.1696	37.5662	39.9968
21	29.6151	32.6705	35.4789	38.9321	41.4010
22	30.8133	33.9244	36.7807	40.2894	42.7956
23	32.0069	35.1725	38.0757	41.6384	44.1813
24	33.1963	36.4151	39.3641	42.9798	45.5585
25	34.3816	37.6525	40.6465	44.3141	46.9278
26	35.5631	38.8852	41.9232	45.6417	48.2899
27	36.7412	40.1133	43.1944	46.9630	49.6449
28	37.9159	41.3372	44.4607	48.2782	50.9933
29	39.0875	42.5569	45.7222	49.5879	52.3356
30	40.2560	43.7729	46.9792	50.8922	53.6720
40	51.8050	55.7585	59.3417	63.6907	66.7659
50	63.1671	67.5048	71.4202	76.1539	79.4900
60	74.3970	79.0819	83.2976	88.3794	91.9517
70	85.5271	90.5312	95.0231	100.425	104.215
80	96.5782	101.879	106.629	112.329	116.321
90	107.565	113.145	118.136	124.116	128.299
100	118.498	124.342	129.561	135.807	140.169

Source: C. M. Thompson, "Tables of the Percentage Points of the χ^2 Distribution," *Biometrika* 32 (1941), pp. 188–89.
Reproduced by permission of the Biometrika Trustees.

ANSWERS TO MOST ODD-NUMBERED EXERCISES

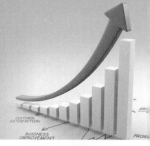

Chapter 1

1.9 0.6

1.15 a. Not in control
b. The plot shows a sharp increase revealing instability. The ice storm had a significant impact on the time needed to process claims. Improvement is needed.

1.17 a. Yes, in control. There is constant variation at a horizontal level.
b. Most breaking strengths will be between 21.3 kg and 24.5 kg.

1.21 Ordinal, nominative, ordinal, nominative, ordinal, nominative

1.35 Nominal, ordinal, ordinal, ordinal, nominal, nominal

1.37 Not in statistical control

Chapter 2

2.3 Distribution is skewed right in 2003; is more normally shaped in 2007.

2.5 a. Class length = 1.6
b. The population of all possible customer waiting times during peak business hours is somewhat positively skewed with a tail to the right.

2.7 The 61 home runs hit by Maris would be considered an outlier.

2.13 a. $N = 10$; mean = 20; median = 20; mode = 20
b. $N = 7$; mean = 503; median = 501; mode = 501

2.15 a. Yes, because $\bar{x} < 6$.
b. Median = 5.25; the mean is slightly larger than the median. The stem-and-leaf display is somewhat skewed right.

2.17 a. Mean = 272.333; median = 68 (Canada's value)
b. U.S. numbers skew the distribution.
c. Histogram probably best for plotting.

2.19 a. Mean = 2201.0000; median = 1,478 (Mexico's value)
b. Mean > median (because of U.S. values)
c. Histogram probably best for plotting.

2.21 a. Here the trick is that Mexico does not have available data, so mean = 467.5 = median.
b. Only two values, so the mean is the median.
c. Histogram probably best for plotting.

2.29 Range = 78,375;
variance = 705,139,612.50;
standard deviation = 26,554.47

2.31 a. Mean = 134.5; variance = 276.7; standard deviation = 16.63
b. $[\bar{x} \pm s] = [134.5 \pm 16.63]$
$= [117.87, 151.13]$
$[\bar{x} \pm 2s] = [134.5 \pm 2(16.63)]$
$= [101.24, 167.76]$
$[\bar{x} \pm 3s] = [134.5 \pm 3(16.63)]$
$= [84.61, 184.39]$

c. Yes, because $190 is not within the 99.73% interval.
d. $z_{157} = 1.353$; $z_{132} = -0.150$; $z_{109} = -1.533$; $z_{145} = 0.631$; $z_{125} = -0.571$; $z_{139} = 0.271$

2.33 a. It is somewhat reasonable.
b. $[\bar{x} \pm s] = [5.46 \pm 2.475]$
$= [2.985, 7.935]$
$[\bar{x} \pm 2s] = [5.46 \pm 2(2.475)]$
$= [.51, 10.41]$
$[\bar{x} \pm 3s] = [5.46 \pm 3(2.475)]$
$= [-1.965, 12.885]$
c. Yes, because the upper limit of the 68.26% interval is less than 8 minutes.
d. 66% fall into $[\bar{x} \pm s]$; 96% fall into $[\bar{x} \pm 2s]$; 100% fall into $[\bar{x} \pm 3s]$. Yes, they are reasonably valid.

2.35 a. It is skewed with a tail to the right.
b. $[\bar{x} \pm s] = [36.56 \pm 4.475]$
$= [32.085, 41.035]$; 73%
$[\bar{x} \pm 2s] = [36.56 \pm 2(4.475)]$
$= [27.61, 45.51]$; 95.23%
$[\bar{x} \pm 3s] = [36.56 \pm 3(4.475)]$
$= [23.135, 49.985]$; 96.83%
c. They are inconsistent with the empirical rule but consistent with Chebyshev's Theorem.
d. The transaction times are positively skewed (to the right).

2.37 a. An estimated 99.73% tolerance interval is $[\bar{x} \pm 3s] = [3.0028 \pm 3(.01437)] = [2.96, 3.046]$.
b. Yes.
c. An estimated 99.73% tolerance interval is $[\bar{x} \pm 3s] = [3 \pm 3(.00786)] = [2.976, 3.024]$.

2.41 a. Mean = 1.740; median = 1.750; standard deviation = 0.246; variance = 0.060; range = 0.8
b. Skewed
c. Mean = 7.690; median = 8.000; mode = 8.000; standard deviation = 1.282; variance = 1.643; range = 3.8
d. fairly normal shape.

2.45 Pie chart is possibly more informative (unless actual dollar values are of interest).

2.47 Pie chart is possibly more informative (unless actual dollar values are of interest).

2.51 Data are scattered around a straight line with negative slope (\).

2.53 a. Yes; the relationship appears to be linear (y increases as x increases).
b. Low sales
c. Not necessarily

2.57 The administration's plot indicates a steep increase over the four years, while the union organizer's plot shows a gradual increase.

2.63 Mean = 9.1627

2.65 Mean = 112.83%; variance = 3780.56; standard deviation = 61.49%

2.67 b. Yes
c. Yes; perhaps those greater than 24 hours

2.73 The graph indicates that Chevy trucks far exceed Ford and Dodge in terms of resale value, but the y-axis scale is misleading.

2.75 The graphs are line graphs.

Chapter 3

3.3 a. Opinions may vary, but the relative frequency approach was used here.
b. If an infinite number of similar weather systems passed over the forecasted region, then you would expect rain to fall 70% of the time.

3.5 a. Relative frequency approach
b. If we had an infinite population of students taking the course, then the proportion of students who would prefer multiple-choice exams to written-question exams would be 82.4%.

3.7 a. .3193
b. .1053

3.9 b. (1) AA
(2) AA, BB, CC
(3) AB, AC, BA, BC, CA, CB
(4) AA, AB, AC, BA, CA
(5) AA, AB, BA, BB
c. Each outcome has probability $\frac{1}{9}$.
(1) $\frac{1}{9}$ (2) $\frac{1}{3}$ (3) $\frac{2}{3}$ (4) $\frac{5}{9}$ (5) $\frac{4}{9}$

3.13 .15

3.17 a. (1) .25   c. (1) .55
(2) .40   (2) .45
(3) .10   (3) .45

3.19 a. .625   d. .5
b. .65   e. .875
c. .35

3.21 a. .75   c. .6
b. .15   d. .6

3.23 a. .3215   c. .278
b. .2519   d. .1597

3.27 a. .2
b. .6
c. Dependent

3.29 .55

3.31 In order to program, the parent must be aware their set has a V-chip. $P(\text{Aware}) = .47$; $P(\text{Prog} \cap \text{Aware}) = P(\text{Aware})P(\text{Prog}|\text{Aware}) = (.47)(.36) = .1692$

3.33 .31

3.35 b. .4
c. Yes, independent.

3.37 a. .874
b. .996
c. .004

3.39 a. .0295   c. Probably not
b. .9705   d. Explanations will vary.

3.43 $P(A_1|B) = .098$; $P(A_2|B) = .610$;
$P(A_3|B) = .293$

3.45 a. .089
b. Opinions may vary. The default rate is 3% in the population to start, and it increases to 8.9% when someone is late. If the store is okay with denying credit to the customers who may never shop there again, then yes. Otherwise, they shouldn't implement the new program.

3.47 P(specialist 1|incorrect) = .247
P(specialist 2|incorrect) = .616
P(specialist 3|incorrect) = .137

3.49 b. P(in|reads "in") = .9863
P(out|reads "in") = .0137
c. P(in|reads "out") = .6667
P(out|reads "out") = .3333

3.51 .4444

3.53 Both stocks rise = 1/9
Both stocks decline = 1/9
Exactly one declines = 4/9

3.57 0.05248

3.59 a. .8586
b. .0534
c. .9445

3.63 a. .2075   c. .105
b. .25   d. .42
e. Yes. Probabilities are not equal; they are not independent events.

3.65 .3077

3.67 a. .08906
b. .8144
c. When $n = 23$, there is about a 50% chance that there will be at least one matched birthday in the group.

3.69 a. .186
b. Explanations will vary, but it doesn't help the case.
c. .625
d. More support than before
e. .833; very strong case

Chapter 4

4.9 a. $\mu_x = .8$
$\sigma_x^2 = .16$
$\sigma_x = .4$
b. $\mu_x = 1.15$; $\sigma_x^2 = .8275$; $\sigma_x = .9097$
c. $\mu_x = 1.6$; $\sigma_x^2 = 4.44$; $\sigma_x = 2.1071$; since the probabilities sum to 1.00, μ_x is the mean of all possible observed values of x.

4.11 a. $\mu_x = .667$; $\sigma_x^2 = .444$; $\sigma_x = .667$; $[-.667, 2.001]$ contains at least $\frac{3}{4}$ of the observed values of x; $[-1.334, 2.668]$ contains at least $\frac{8}{9}$ of the observed values of x.
b. $\mu_x = 1.5$; $\sigma_x^2 = .75$; $\sigma_x = .866$; $[-.232, 3.323]$ contains at least $\frac{3}{4}$ of the observed values of x; $[-1.098, 4.098]$ contains at least $\frac{8}{9}$ of the observed values of x.

c. $\mu_x = 2$; $\sigma_x^2 = 1$; $\sigma_x = 1$; $[0, 4]$ contains at least $\frac{3}{4}$ of the observed values of x; $[-1, 5]$ contains at least $\frac{8}{9}$ of the observed values of x.

4.13 $\mu_x = \$500$; if numerous oil wells were dug, the average profit would be $500.

4.15 a.

x	\$400	$-\$49,600$
$p(x)$	.995	.005

b. $\mu_x = \$150$
c. \$1,250

4.17 $\mu_x = -\$5.60$

4.23 a. $p(x) = \dfrac{6!}{x!(6-x)!}(.3)^x(.7)^{6-x}$
b. (1) .0102
(2) .2557
(3) .7443
(4) .8824

4.25 a. $p(x) = \dfrac{4!}{x!(4-x)!}(.5)^x(.5)^{4-x}$
(1) .0625
(2) .3125
b. (1) .4119
(2) .2517
(3) .0059
c. No, if the claim is true, then the probability of fewer than 5 is very small (.0059).

4.27 a. $P(x = 0) = .9996$
$P(x \geq 1) = .0004$
b. $P(x = 0) = .4845$
$P(x \geq 1) = .5155$
c. $p = \dfrac{1}{35}$
d. .000040019

4.29 a. $P(x \geq 2) = .3446$
b. $P(x = 0) = .2621$
c. $P(x \geq 4) = .01696$

4.33 a. $p(x) = \dfrac{e^{-2}(2)^x}{x!}$ for $x = 0, 1, 2, 3, \ldots$
b.

x	0	1	2	3
$p(x)$	.1353	.2707	.2707	.1804

4	5	6	7	8
.0902	.0361	.0120	.0034	.0009

d. .2707   h. .8120
e. .9473   i. .2706
f. .8571   j. .5774
g. .8647
.3233

4.35 a. .0710
b. .9015
c. .0985

4.37 a. .0498
b. Perhaps not; if the agency's claim is true, the probability of no patrol cars is quite small.
c. .000498

4.39 a. .0190
b. Probably not; the probability of 4 or more defectives is small if the claim is true.

4.41 a .13534
b. .40601
c. .32332

4.45 a. .13333
b. .33333
c. .66667

4.47 a. .026515
b. .95455
c. .97349

4.49 a. .00038670
b. .51651
c. .48349

4.51 a. .16317
b. .093240
c. .99301

4.53 a. .7
b. .3
c. No.

4.55 a.

x	0	1	2
$p(x)$	$\frac{4}{9}$	$\frac{4}{9}$	$\frac{1}{9}$

b.

x	0	1	2
$p(x)$	.49	.42	.09

c.

x	0	1	2
$p(x)$	.54	.42	.04

4.61 a. .7373
b. (1) .0173
(2) .4207
(3) .6129
(4) .0236
c. No; if the claim is true, the probability that 15 or fewer are not satisfied is only .0173.

4.63 a. .2231   c. .9912
b. .9344   d. .0025

4.67 .0037; mean number of failures has increased.

4.69 .3328; not much evidence against the claim.

Chapter 5

5.7 1/125

5.9 a. $\mu_x = 3$; $\sigma_x^2 = 3$; $\sigma_x = 1.732$
b. .5773

5.11 a. $f(x) = \dfrac{1}{b-a} = \dfrac{1}{140-120} = \dfrac{1}{20}$
b. $f(x)$

c. .5
d. .25

5.13 1/6

5.15 a. 4.5 cm
b. $P(2.768 \leq x \leq 6.232)$
$= P(3 \leq x \leq 6) = 1$
$P(3.634 \leq x \leq 5.366)$
$= (5.366 - 3.634)\left(\dfrac{1}{3}\right) = .5773$

5.23 a. $z = -1$; x is one standard deviation below the mean.
b. $z = -3$; x is three standard deviations below the mean.
c. $z = 0$; x is equal to the mean.
d. $z = 2$; x is two standard deviations above the mean.
e. $z = 4$; x is four standard deviations above the mean.

5.25 a. $z_{.01} = 2.33$
b. $z_{.05} = 1.645$
c. $z_{.02} = 2.054$
d. $-z_{.01} = -2.33$
e. $-z_{.05} = -1.645$
f. $-z_{.10} = -1.28$

5.29 a. (1) .9830   b. 947
(2) .0033
(3) .0456

5.31 a. .7257   d. .2877
b. .7257   e. .1379
c. .5478   f. .0384

5.33 a. 10%; 90%; $k = -13.968$
b. Q_1: $k = -1.402$; Q_3: $k = 26.202$

5.35 a. $[\mu \pm 2.33\sigma]$
b. [21.2593 to 24.7207]

5.37 $z = -.44$; therefore $x = \$2,780$

5.39 a. Process B c. Process B
b. Process A d. .5987

5.41 a. .8944
b. .1593, so almost 16% of the class received an A.
c. A student needs to have a perfect score to have scored in the 90th percentile. In fact, better than perfect!

5.47 a. .1915   f. .7099
b. .1093   g. .6883
c. .9265   h. .0436
d. .8554   i. .2789
e. .0012

5.49 a. .1549   f. .7448
b. .0038   g. .0036
c. .9525   h. .3669
d. .7486   i. .3608
e. 0

5.51 a. z that satisfies $P(z < z) = .95$, or $z = 1.645$.
b. z that satisfies $P(z < z) = .975$, or $z = 1.96$.
c. z that satisfies $P(z < z) = .995$, or $z = 2.575$.
d. z that satisfies $P(z < z) = .99$, or $z = 2.326$.
e. z that satisfies $P(z < z) = .05$, or $z = -1.645$.
f. z that satisfies $P(z < z) = .025$, or $z = -1.96$.
g. z that satisfies $P(z < z) = .005$, or $z = -2.575$.

5.55 a. $np = (200)(.4) = 80$; $n(1 - p) = (200)(.6) = 120$; both are ≥ 5
b. (1) .0558   (4) .0025
(2) .9875   (5) .0015
(3) .0125

5.57 a. (1) Both np and $n(1 - p)$ exceed 5.
(2) $\mu = 200$; $\sigma = 12.6491$
(3) less than .0002
b. No.

5.59 443.

5.65 a. $f(x) = 3e^{-3x}$ for $x \geq 0$.
c. .9502
d. .4226
e. .0025
f. $\mu_x = \frac{1}{3}$, $\sigma_x^2 = \frac{1}{9}$, $\sigma_x = \frac{1}{3}$
g. .9502

5.69 a. (1) .1353
(2) .2325
(3) .2212
b. Probably not.

5.71 a. .8944
b. 73.68

5.77 .9306

5.83 a. .0062
b. .6915
c. $k = 3.3275$

5.85 .7745

Chapter 6

6.9 a. Normally distributed; no, because the sample size is large (≥ 30).
b. $\mu_x = 20$; $\sigma_x = .5$
c. .0228
d. .1093

6.11 a. Normal because the sample is large ($n \geq 30$)
b. $\mu_x = 6$; $\sigma_x = .247$
c. .0143
d. 1.43%; conclude that μ is less than 6.

6.13 a. (1) .2206
(2) .0027
b. Yes.

6.15 a. Distribution of $\bar{x}$ is approximately normal.
b. It's very likely that the average salary is greater than $78,425.

6.17 a. Less than .0002.
b. Strong evidence that the eggs are too light.

6.21 a. $\mu_{\hat{p}} = .5$; $\sigma_{\hat{p}}^2 = .001$; $\sigma_{\hat{p}} = .0316$
b. $\mu_{\hat{p}} = .1$; $\sigma_{\hat{p}}^2 = .0009$; $\sigma_{\hat{p}} = .03$
c. $\mu_{\hat{p}} = .8$; $\sigma_{\hat{p}}^2 = .0004$; $\sigma_{\hat{p}} = .02$
d. $\mu_{\hat{p}} = .98$; $\sigma_{\hat{p}}^2 = .000196$; $\sigma_{\hat{p}} = .004427$

6.23 [.4, .6]

6.27 a. $\cong 0$
b. Yes.

6.29 a. (1) .7372
(2) .9756
b. Closer to $\pm 6\%$ because margin of error is usually at 95% probability.

6.31 a. less than .0002
b. Yes.

6.33 Yes; .1977

6.35 .9438

6.37 Yes; $p = .66$ is too high.

6.39 a. .3085
b. .0013
c. More difficult to achieve an average that exceeds $2,150; yes

6.45 a. less than .0002.
b. Yes, conclude that it appears as though $p < .5$.

6.47 a. [22.274 to 23.526]
b. [22.6786 to 23.1214]
c. $n = 5$

6.49 a. .0017
b. Yes, very likely.

6.51 a. less than .0002
b. Yes, exceeds.

Chapter 7

7.5 a. [49.608, 50.392]
b. [49.485, 50.515]
c. [49.566, 50.434]
d. [49.744, 50.256]
e. [49.400, 50.600]

7.7 a. 95%: [4.976, 5.944]; 99%: [4.824, 6.096]
b. Yes
c. No
d. Fairly confident

7.9 a. [3.653, 7.707]
b. 3.653

7.11 a. [548,522.8, 614,263.2]
b. [538,208.94, 624,577.06]
c. Not confident.

7.13 a. [34.901, 41.0990]
b. $n = 97$

7.15 a. Decreases
b. Decreases

7.17 11 $d.f.$: $t_{.10} = 1.363$, $t_{.025} = 2.201$, $t_{.001} = 4.025$
6 $d.f.$: $t_{.10} = 1.440$, $t_{.025} = 2.447$, $t_{.001} = 5.208$

7.19 a. 95%: [4.311, 7.689]; 99%: [3.442, 8.558]
b. Can be 95% confident; cannot be 99% confident.

7.21 a. [13.065, 14.535]
b. Yes

7.23 a. [786.609, 835.391]
b. Yes

7.25 t-based 95% CI: [4.969, 5.951]; at least 95% confident.

7.27 a. [63.6108, 72.3892]
b. [60.7204, 75.2796]
c. Normally distributed

7.29 a. [111.3027, 120.6973]
b. [109.5791, 122.4209]
c. Normally distributed
d. Yes

7.37 $n = 44$

7.43 a. [.304, .496]; [.286, .514]; [.274; .526]
b. [.066, .134]; [.060, .140]; [.055, .145]
c. [.841, .959]; [.830, .970]; [.823, .977]
d. [.464, .736]; [.439, .761]; [.422, .778]

7.45 a. [.473, .610]
b. No, the interval extends below .5

7.47 a. [.3804, .4596]; no
b. [.5701, .6299]; yes
c. 95% margin of error is .03

7.49 a. [.611, .729]
b. Yes

7.51 Yes

7.53 a. [.0077, .0323]
b. [.034, .074]
c. Yes

7.55 $n = 1,425$

7.63 Yes; between 10.216 and 11.784 higher

7.65 $[-1.15, -0.45]$; yes, 95% confident

7.67 [1.124, 1.276]; yes

7.73 [0.508, 0.972]; yes, 95% confident

7.75 [$1.10, $100.90]; no, mean dollar amounts do not differ in a practically important way.

7.81 95%: [100.141, 106.859]; yes
99%: [98.723, 108.277]; no

7.83 1.84 (lower endpoint of 95% CI for μ_d)

7.85 a. [0.40, 0.92].
b. Yes

7.89 $[-.178, -.122]$; yes, entire interval is below zero

7.91 [0.021, 0.111]; yes, 95% confident

7.93 a. $[-.256, -.144]$
b. [.0285, .0915]; proportions have changed

7.95 a. [63.590, 72.490]
b. [52.287, 61.93]
c. Yes, interval is below the lowest value in the CI

7.97 a. $p = 0.82 \pm 0.0199$.
b. True; the sampling allowance we calculated was 1.99%, lower than the 2.6% stated.

7.99 a. [17.195, 18.005]; no, interval contains 18
b. $n \cong 148$

7.101 a. [.686, .806]; no, proportion could be below .7

b. [3.892, 5.868]; yes, interval is above 7

7.103 a. [1.469%, 3.991%]; yes, interval is below 5%

b. [15.259%, 54.261%]; interval is wide because s is large and n is small; increase the sample size

7.105 [523.92, 522.08]

7.107 [1.007, 1.095]; true average mass is likely 1.04 kg

7.111 [$-.30, .46$]

Chapter 8

8.9 a. $H_0: \mu \geq 6$ versus $H_a: \mu < 6$.

b. Type I: decide $\mu < 6$ when μ is really ≥ 6
Type II: decide $\mu \geq 6$ when μ is really < 6

8.11 a. $H_0: \mu = 355$ versus $H_a: \mu \neq 355$

b. Type I: decide $\mu \neq 355$ when $\mu = 355$
Type II: decide $\mu = 355$ when $\mu \neq 355$

8.17 $z_{.10} = 1.28$; since $2.5 > 1.28$, reject H_0 with $\alpha = .10$

8.23 $z = -2$

8.25 $-z_{.05} = -1.645$; since $-2 < -1.645$, reject H_0 with $\alpha = .05$

8.27 $-z_{.001} = -3.09$; since -2 is not less than -3.09, cannot reject H_0 with $\alpha = .001$

8.29 Strong evidence

8.31 $H_0: \mu \geq 6$ versus $H_a: \mu < 6$.

a. Rejection points: $-z_{.10} = -1.28$; $-z_{.05} = -1.645$; $-z_{.01} = -2.33$; $-z_{.001} = -3.09$. Since -2.19 is less than -1.28 and -1.645, reject H_0 with $\alpha = .10$ and .05, but not with $\alpha = .01$ and .001.

b. Since p-value of. 0143 is less than .10 and .05, reject H_0 at those levels of α, but not with $\alpha = .01$ or .001.

c. Strong evidence

8.33 a. $z = 2.41$, reject H_0; shut down and repair.

b. $z = 1.31$, do not reject H_0; do not shut down.

c. $z = 3.09$, reject H_0; shut down and repair.

8.37 $z = -3$

8.39 $z_{.05/2} = 1.96$; since $|-3| > 1.96$, reject H_0 with $\alpha = .05$

8.41 $z_{.001/2} = 3.29$; because $|-3|$ is not greater than 3.29, cannot reject H_0 with $\alpha = .001$

8.43 Strong evidence that H_0 is false

8.47 a. $z = -27.8859$; p-value is less than .001, so reject H_0; estimate $\mu < 4$.

b. $z = 10.16$; p-value is less than .001, so reject H_0; estimate $\mu > 4$.

8.51 Reject H_0 at $\alpha = .10, .05, .01$, but not at $\alpha = .001$

8.53 a. Reject H_0 at $\alpha = .10, .05$ and .01, but not at $\alpha = .001$

b. Very strong evidence

8.57 a. Reject H_0 at $\alpha = .10, .05, .01$, and .001

b. Very strong evidence

8.59 $t = 2.899$; $t_{.05} = 1.669$, so reject H_0; p-value of .0025 means we would reject

at $\alpha = .10, .05$, and .01, but would not reject at $\alpha = .001$.

8.65 a. large enough

b. not large enough

c. large enough

d. large enough

e. large enough

f. not large enough

g. large enough

h. large enough

8.67 a. $z = -2.18$; $-z_{.005} = -2.575$; since $-2.575 < -2.18$, do not reject H_0

b. .0292

c. Reject H_0 at $\alpha = .10$ and .05, but not at $\alpha = .01$ or .001.

8.69 a. $H_0: p \leq .5$; $H_a: p > .50$.

b. $\hat{p} = .5415$; $z = 1.19$; $z_{.10} = 1.28$; since $1.19 < 1.28$, do not reject H_0 for any level of α

c. $\hat{p} = .54$; $z = 2.53$; $z_{.01} = 2.33$; $z_{.001} = 3.09$; since $1.19 < 1.28$, and because $2.33 < 2.53 < 3.09$, reject H_0 at $\alpha = .01$, but not at $\alpha = .001$; very strong evidence

d. $\hat{p} = .54$ based on a much larger sample provides stronger evidence that p is greater than .50.

8.71 a. $H_0: p \leq .18$; $H_a: p > .18$.

b. $\hat{p} = .23$; $z = 1.84$; p-value = .0329; reject H_0 at $\alpha = .10$ and .05, but not at $\alpha = .01$ or .001; strong evidence

c. Perhaps, but this is subjective.

8.73 a. $H_0: p = .95$; $H_a: p < .95$.

b. $\hat{p} = .79$; $z = -14.68$; reject H_0 at each value of α; extremely strong evidence

c. Probably; $\hat{p} = .79$ is far below the claimed .95.

8.75 a. $t = 2.5$; 24 $d.f.$; $t_{.01} = 2.492$; $t_{.001} = 3.467$; since $2.492 < 2.5 < 3.467$, reject H_0 at $\alpha = .10, .05, .01$, but not at $\alpha = .001$; very strong evidence that $\mu > .10$

b. $t = 1.11$; 24 $d.f.$; $t_{.10} = 1.318$; because $1.11 < 1.318$, do not reject H_0 at any of the given values of α; little evidence.

8.77 a. Reject H_0 for $\alpha = .10$ and .05, but not at $\alpha = .01$ and .005

b. Strong evidence

8.81 a. $H_0: p \leq .60$; $H_a: p > .60$

b. $z = 2.58$; $z_{.01} = 2.33$; $z_{.001} = 3.09$; since $2.33 < 2.58 < 3.09$, reject H_0 at $\alpha = .10, .05, .01$, but not at .001; very strong evidence

8.85 $\hat{p} = .8333$; $z = 1.87$; p-value =.0307. At $\alpha = .01$, we would not reject H_0 and conclude that there is no evidence; at $\alpha = .05$, we would reject H_0 and conclude that there is evidence.

Chapter 9

9.3 a. $z = 10$; reject H_0; conclude $\mu_1 > \mu_2$

b. $z = 2$; $z_{.05} = 1.645$; p-value = .0228; reject H_0 at $\alpha = .10, .05$, but not at $\alpha = .01$ or .001

9.7 a. $H_0: \mu_1 - \mu_2 \leq 0$; $H_a: \mu_1 - \mu_2 > 0$

b. $z = 1.41$; $z_{.05} = 1.645$; do not reject H_0; cannot conclude $\mu_1 - \mu_2$

9.9 a. $H_0: \mu_1 - \mu_2 = 0$; $H_a: \mu_1 - \mu_2 > 0$

b. Very strong evidence to reject H_0.

c. Reject H_0; very strong evidence to suggest $\mu_1 > \mu_2$

9.19 a. $t = 2.32$; $t_{.05} = 1.812$; $t_{.01} = 2.764$; 10 $d.f.$; reject H_0 at $\alpha = .05$ but not .01; strong evidence $\mu_1 - \mu_2 > 100$

b. $t = -4.31$; $-t_{.05} = -1.812$; $-t_{.01} = -2.764$; 10 $d.f.$; reject H_0 at $\alpha = .05$ and .01; very strong evidence $\mu_1 - \mu_2 < 110$

9.21 a. $H_0: \mu_A - \mu_B = 0$; $H_a: \mu_A - \mu_B < 0$

b. Reject H_0 at $\alpha = 0.10$ but not at 0.05, 0.01, or 0.001; little evidence to suggest that $\mu_1 < \mu_2$

9.25 $t = 3.39$; $d.f. = 11$; $t_{.005} = 3.106$; $t_{.0005} = 4.437$; reject at $\alpha = .10, .05$, and .01, but not at .001

9.27 a. $H_0: \mu_O - \mu_I = 0$; $H_a: \mu_O - \mu_I \neq 0$

b. 9 $d.f.$; $t_{.025} = 2.262$; $t_{.005} = 3.25$; since $2.262 < 2.31 < 3.25$, reject H_0 at $\alpha = .10$ and .05, but not at .01 or .001; strong evidence that H_0 is false

9.29 a. $t = 5$; $t_{.0005} = 3.505$; reject H_0 at each value of α; extremely strong evidence that μ_1 differs from μ_2

b. $t = 2$; p-value =.0256; reject H_0 at $\alpha = .10$ and .05, but not at .01 or .001; strong evidence that μ_1 and μ_2 differ by more than 3

9.31 $d_1 = 3.25$; $S_d^2 = 2.2143$; $s_d = 1.488$; $t = 6.18$; because $t = 6.18 > t_{.025} = 2.365$, reject $H_0: \mu_d = 0$ in favour of $H_a: \mu_d \neq 0$ by setting $\alpha = .05$

9.35 $z = -2.08$; p-value =.0188 $< \alpha = .05$; reject H_0 at $\alpha = .10$ and .05, but not at .01 or .001; strong evidence

9.37 a. $H_0: p_1 - p_2 = 0$; $H_a: p_1 - p_2 \neq 0$

b. $z = 2.89$; two-sided p-value = .0038; reject H_0 at $\alpha = 0.10, 0.05, 0.01$, but not at 0.001; very little evidence to suggest that $p_1 = p_2$.

9.39 a. Because $5.467 > 1.645$, reject H_0; amount of daily activity has increased

b. $\hat{p} = .265$; $s_{p1-p2} = .01944$; $z = 1.543$; $z_{.025} = 1.96$; since $1.543 < 1.96$, do not reject H_0; amount of time spent watching TV has not increased.

9.43 a. 2.96

b. 4.68

c. 3.16

d. 8.81

9.45 a. $F = 3.24$; $F_{.025} = 8.66$ with $df_1 = 15$ and $df_2 = 4$; do not reject $H_0: \sigma_1^2 = \sigma_2^2$, since $F = 3.24 < F_{.025} = 8.66$

b. $F = 3.24$; $F_{.01} = 14.2$ with $df_1 = 15$ and $df_2 = 4$; do not reject $H_0: \sigma_1^2 \geq \sigma_2^2$, since $F = 3.24 < F_{.01} = 14.20$

9.49 a. $H_0: \mu_T - \mu_B = 0$; $H_a: \mu_T - \mu_B \neq 0$; $t = .42$; cannot reject H_0 at any α value; little or no evidence

9.51 a. $H_0: p_T - p_c \leq 0$; $H_a: p_T - p_c > 0$; $\hat{p} = .085$; $\hat{p}_T = .10$; $\hat{p}_c = .07$; $s_{p1-p2} = .017638027$; $z = 1.7$; $z_{.01} = 2.326$; do not reject H_0 at $\alpha = .01$

b. $z_{.10} = 1.282$; reject H_0 at $\alpha = .10$; result is statistically significant at $\alpha = .10$.

Chapter 10

10.3 Response: time to stabilize emergency condition
Factor: display panels
Treatments: panels A, B, C
Experimental units: controllers.

10.9 a. $F = 184.57$, p-value $= .000$; reject H_0; shelf location has different effects on sales.
b. Middle shelf maximizes the differences.

10.11 a. $F = 43.36$, p-value $= .000$; reject H_0; bottle design does have an impact on sales.
b. $\mu_B - \mu_A$: [11.56, 20.84]
$\mu_C - \mu_A$: [3.56, 12.84]
$\mu_C - \mu_B$: [−12.64, −3.36]
c. (1) [12.41, 19.99]
(2) [4.41, 11.99]
(3) [−11.79, −4.21]
d. μ_A:16.60, [13.92, 19.28]
μ_B:32.8, [30.12, 35.48]
μ_C:24.8, [22.12, 27.48]

10.13 **Pairwise comparisons:**
Divot − Alpha: [38.41, 127.59];
Divot − Century: [50.21, 139.39];
Divot − Best: [−14.39, 74.79];
Century − Alpha: [−56.39, 32.79];
Century − Best: [−109.19, −20.01];
Best − Alpha: [8.21, 97.39];
Best and Divot appear to be the most durable.
95% CI: Divot: [313.26, 359.94];
Best: [283.06, 329.74];
Alpha: [230.26, 276.94];
Century: [218.46, 265.14]

10.17 a. $F = 36.23$; p-value $= .000$; reject H_0. There is a difference in sales methods.
b. $F = 12.87$; p-value $= .007$; reject H_0. Salespeople do have an effect on sales.
c. Method 1 − Method 2: [−2.30, 2.96];
Method 1 − Method 3: [2.37, 7.63];
Method 1 − Method 4: [3.70, 8.96];
Method 2 − Method 3: [2.04, 7.30];
Method 2 − Method 4: [3.37, 8.63];
Method 3 − Method 4: [−1.30, 3.96];
it appears that Methods 1 and 2 maximize mean weekly sales.

10.19 a. $F(2, 6) = 441.75$; $p < .001$. Therefore keyboard brands do have an impact on the mean number of words entered.
b. $F(3, 6) = 107.69$; $p < .001$. Therefore the specialist does have an impact on the mean number of words entered.
c. AB: [8.55, 11.45]; AC: [12.05, 14.95]; BC: [2.05, 4.95]; keyboard A maximizes the mean number of words entered per minute.

10.21 a. $F = 5.78$; p-value $= .0115$; reject H_0. The soft drinks differ in terms of mean sales.
b. Coke Classic − New Coke: [7.99, 68.01]; Coke Classic − Pepsi: [−.21, 59.81]; New Coke − Pepsi: [−38.21, 21.81]; **from MegaStat output:**
Coke Classic − New Coke = 3.23, $p < .01$; Coke Classic − Pepsi = 2.53, $p < .05$; New Coke − Pepsi = 0.70; $p > .40$

c. Yes; mean sales for New Coke are less than Pepsi, even though Tukey test indicates this difference is not significant.

10.23 a. When lines are plotted, they intersect.
b. When lines are plotted, they are parallel.

10.25 a. Panel B requires less time to stabilize the emergency condition.
$F(\text{int}) = .66$; p-value $= .681$; cannot reject H_0: no interaction exists.
b. $F = 26.49$; p-value $= .000$; reject H_0
c. $F = 100.80$; p-value $= .000$; reject H_0
d. $u_A - u_B$: [.49, 5.91]; $u_A - u_C$: [−6.81, −1.39]; $u_B - u_C$: [−10.01, −4.59];
from output: A vs. B = 3.20, $p < .01$; A vs. C = 4.06, $p < .01$; B vs. C = 7.26, $p < .001$
e. **From output:** 1 vs. 2 = 6.25, $p < .001$; 1 vs. 3 = 12.79, $p < .001$; 1 vs. 4 = 3.27, $p < .01$; 2 vs. 3 = 6.54, $p < .001$; 2 vs. 4 = 9.52, $p < .001$; 3 vs. 4 = 16.06, $p < .001$
f. Panel B. There is no interaction.
g. $\bar{y}_{B4} = [6.37, 12.63]$

10.27 a. Interaction is present: $F = 24.73$, p-value $= .001$
Reject H_0; interaction exists.
b. House design C–foreman 1; 95% CI: [17.72, 19.88]

10.29 $F = 40.79$, p-value $< .0001$; conclude treatment means differ. All pairwise differences are significant with p-values less than .01; **from output:** X vs. $Y = 5.23$; X vs. $Z = 3.77$; Y vs. $Z = 8.99$ (.01 critical value $= 3.42$)

10.35 At $\alpha = .05$, the treatment means differ, no interaction exists, fertilizer type effects differ, and wheat type effects differ.

Chapter 11

11.3 $s_{xy} = .4447$; $r_{xy} = .9678$; very strong positive relationship

11.7 $t = 3.34$, t_{critical} at $\alpha = .001$ is 3.09; therefore x and y are strongly related.

11.13 The straight-line appearance on this data plot suggests that the simple linear regression model with a positive slope might be appropriate.

11.15 The plot looks reasonably linear.

11.17 b. Yes, the plot looks linear; positive slope.

11.19 b. Yes, the relationship looks to be linear with a positive slope.

11.27 $s^2 = 21.3002$; s = 4.61521

11.29 $s^2 = 74.67624$; s = 8.64154

11.31 $s^2 = 27.8530$; s = 5.2776

11.33 a. $b_0 = 11.4641$; $b_1 = 24.6022$
$b_0 − 0$ copiers; 11.46 minutes of service.
$b_1 −$ each additional copier adds 24.6022 minutes of service on average. No. The interpretation of b_0 does not make practical sense since it indicates that 11.46 minutes of service would be required for a customer with no copiers.
b. $\hat{y} = 11.4641 + 24.6022(4) = 109.873$, or 109.9 minutes

11.35 b. b_1 is the estimated increase in mean labour cost (10.1463) for every 1 unit

increase in the batch size.
b_0 is the estimated mean labour cost (18.4875) when batch size $= 0$; no.
c. $\hat{y} = 18.4880 + 10.1463x$
d. $\hat{y} = 18.4880 + 10.1463(60) = 627.266$

11.37 a. Strong ($\alpha = .05$) evidence that the regression relationship is significant.
b. Very strong ($\alpha = .01$) evidence that the regression relationship is significant.

11.39 a. $b_0 = 11.4641$; $b_1 = 24.6022$
b. $SSE = 191.7017$; $s^2 = 21.3002$; $s = 4.615$
c. $s_{b_1} = .8045$; $t = 30.580$
d. $df = 9$; $t_{.025} = 2.262$; reject H_0. Strong evidence of a significant relationship between x and y.
e. $t_{.005} = 3.250$; reject H_0. Very strong evidence of a significant relationship between x and y.
f. p-value $= .000$; reject at all α. Extremely strong evidence of a significant relationship between x and y.
g. [22.782, 26.422]
h. [21.987, 27.217]
i. $s_{b_0} = 3.4390$; $t = 3.334$
j. p-value $= .0087$; reject at all α except .001
k. $s_{b_1} = .8045$; $s_{b_0} = 3.439$

11.41 a. $b_0 = 18.488$, $b_1 = 10.1463$
b. $SSE = 746.7624$
c. $s_{b_1} = .0866$, $t = 117.1344$
d. $t = 117.13$; $p < .001$; reject H_0 at .05
e. $t = 117.13$; $p < .001$; reject H_0 at .01
f. p-value $= .000$; reject H_0 at each value of α
g. $[10.1463 \pm 2.228(.0866)] = [9.953, 10.339]$
h. $s_{b_0} = 4.677$, $t = 3.95$
i. p-value $= .003$; fail to reject H_0 at $\alpha = .001$; reject H_0 at all other values of α

11.43 95% C.I. for $\beta_1 = −.87$ to $−.11$

11.47 a. 109.873, [106.721, 113.025]
b. 109.873, [98.967, 120.779]
c. $x = 4$; $\bar{x} = 3.90$; $SS_{xx} = 32.90$; $n = 11$; distance value $= .090657961$; CI = [106.729, 113.016]; this compares (within rounding) to the computer-generated output. For the prediction interval with the same quantities, we get [98.971, 120.775], which also compares within rounding.
d. 113 minutes

11.49 a. 627.26, [621.05, 633.47]
b. 627.26, [607.03, 647.49]
c. $s = 8.642$; $dist = .104000$; 99% CI: [618.42, 636.10]; 99% PI: [598.48, 656.04]

11.55 Explained variation $= 10.653$; $r^2 = 0.792$; $r = 0.890$; 79.2% of the variation in demand can be explained by variation in price differential.

11.57 Explained variation $= 6603.4$; $r^2 = 0.88$; $r = 0.939$; 88% of the variation in sales can be explained by variation in coupons issued.

11.61 a. $F = 106.303$
b. $F_{.05} = 4.20$; reject H_0 ($df_1 = 1$, $df_2 = 28$). Strong evidence of a significant relationship between x and y.

c. $F_{.01} = 7.64$; reject H_0 ($df_1 = 1$, $df_2 = 28$). Very strong evidence of a significant relationship between x and y.

d. p-value = less than .001; reject H_0. Extremely strong evidence of a significant relationship between x and y.

e. $(10.310)^2 = 106.303$ (within rounding error); $(t_{.025})^2 = 4.19 = F_{.05}$

11.63 a. $F = 59.4266$

b. $F_{.05} = 5.32$; $df_1 = 1$; $df_2 = 8$; since $59.43 > 5.32$, reject H_0 at .05

c. $F_{.01} = 11.26$, $df_1 = 1$, $df_2 = 8$; since $59.43 > 11.3$, reject H_0 at .01

d. p-value = .000; reject H_0 at all levels of α

e. $t^2 = 59.44$ (approximately equals $F = 59.43$) $(t_{.025})^2 = 5.32 = F_{.05}$

11.67 Possible violations of the normality and constant variance assumptions.

11.69 a. $\dfrac{3(i) - 1}{3n + 1} = \dfrac{3(4) - 1}{33 + 1} = .3235$

$.5000 - .3235 = .1765, \Rightarrow z = -.46$

$\dfrac{3(i) - 1}{3n + 1} = \dfrac{3(10) - 1}{33 + 1} = .8529$

$.8529 - .5000 = .3529, \Rightarrow z = 1.05$

b. No

11.71 a. $\ln y_t = 2.07012 + 0.25688$; $\ln y_{16} = 2.07012 + 025688(16) = 6.1802$

b. $e^{6.1802} = 483.09$; $e^{5.9945} = 401.22$; $e^{6.3659} = 581.67$

c. $d = 1.87643$; $d_{L,0.05} = 1.08$. Since $d > 1.10$, we fail to reject H_0.

d. Growth rate = $e^{0.25688} = 1.293$. This means the growth rate is expected to be 29.3% per year.

11.73 a. Yes

b. $\hat{y} = 175.048$; 95% CI = [150.0345, 200.0621]; 95% PI = [93.1308, 256.9658]; allow 200 minutes.

11.77 a. $r = .86$, strong relationship between debt and population

b. $R = .86$, same value

c. Smallest = Guatemala; largest = Pakistan

11.79 $r = .875$; strong positive correlation between age and volunteering (older people volunteer more often); $r^2 = .7656$; approximately 76% of the variance in age and volunteering overlaps; $F(1, 4) = 13.09$, $p < .05$; significant linear regression equation; would suggest (if applicable) to target the 65+ group (possibly have more time to volunteer because they are retired).

Chapter 12

12.7 a. The plots show a linear (or somewhat linear) relationship between Price & Demand, IndPrice & Demand, PriceDiff & Demand, and AdvExp & Demand.

b. The mean demand for the large bottle of Fresh when the price of Fresh is $3.70; the average industry price of competitors' similar detergents is $3.90; and the advertising expenditure to promote Fresh is 6.50 ($650,000).

c. β_0 = meaningless in practical terms. β_1 = the mean change in demand for each additional dollar in the price of Fresh holding all other predictor variables constant. β_2 = the mean change in demand for each additional dollar in the average price of competitors' detergents holding all other predictor variables constant. β_3 = the mean change in demand for each additional $100,000 spent on advertising Fresh holding all other predictor variables constant. ε = all other factors that influence the demand for Fresh detergent.

d. The plots for Demand vs. AdvExp and Demand vs. PriceDif appear to be more linear than the other two plots.

12.15 a. $SSE = 1.4318$, $s^2 = .0551$

b. Total variation = 13.4586; explained variation = 12.0268

c. $R^2 = .894$; adjusted $R^2 = .881$; approximately 89% of the variance in demand is predicted by price, average price, and advertising, which drops to 88% when adjusted for the number of predictors.

d. $F = 72.80$

e. at $< .05$, model is significant, F-critical = 2.98

f. at $< .01$, model is significant, F-critical = 4.64

g. output $p = .000000000000888$

12.19 a. $b_0 = 1946.8020$, $b_1 = 0.0386$, $b_2 = 1.0394$, $b_0 = -413.7578$
b_0 = labour hours when x-ray = 0, bed days = 0, and length of stay = 0, which is probably meaningless as the hospital has no patients staying there. b_1 implies that labour hours increase 0.04 for each unit increase in x-rays, when bed days and length of stay remain constant (predicted change). b_2 implies that labour hours increase by 1.04 for each unit of increase in bed days when x-rays and length of stay remain constant (predicted change). b_3 implies that labour hours decrease by 413.76 when length of stay decreases by one unit and both x-rays and bed days remain constant (predicted change).

b. $\hat{y} = 1946.802 + .0386(56194) + 1.0394(14077.88) - 413.7578(6.89) = 15897.65$

c. Therefore, actual hours were $17207.31 - 15896.25 = 1311.06$ hours greater than predicted.

12.29 $y = 17207.31$ is above the upper limit of the interval [14906.2, 16886.3]; this y-value is unusually high.

12.33 The shorter interval is from the model using x_4. This model is better.

12.35 Multiply: $x_1 x_2$

12.37 $\hat{y} = -2.3497 + 2.3611x_1 + 4.1831x_2 - 0.3489x_1x_2$
x_1 = radio / TV; x_2 = print
a. $x_2 = 1$, slope = 2.0122; $x_2 = 2$, slope = 1.6633; $x_2 = 3$, slope = 1.3144; $x_2 = 4$, slope = 0.9655; $x_2 = 5$, slope = 0.6166. These slopes

are the estimated average sales volume increase (in units of $10,000) for every $1,000 increase in radio and TV ads.

b. $x_1 = 1$, slope = 3.8342; $x_1 = 2$, slope 3.4853; $x_1 = 3$, slope = 3.1364, $x_1 = 4$, 2.7875; $x_1 = 5$, slope = 2.4386. These slopes are the estimated average sales volume increase (in units of $10,000) for every $1,000 increase in print ads.

c. The smallest print slope is bigger than the largest radio/TV slope.

12.39 An independent variable, the levels of which are defined by describing them.

12.41 The effect of the qualitative independent variable on the dependent variable.

12.45 a. No interaction since p-values are so large.

b. $\hat{y} = 8.61178$ (861,178 bottles); 95% prediction interval = [8.27089, 8.95266] — slightly bigger

12.47 $(k - g)$ denotes the number of regression parameters we have set equal to zero in H_0. $[n - (k + 1)]$ denotes the denominator degrees of freedom.

12.49 Model 3 — complete
Model 1 — reduced
$H_0 : \beta_4 = \beta_5 = \beta_6 = \beta_7 = 0$

$$F = \dfrac{\frac{1.4318 - .5347}{4}}{\frac{.5347}{22}} = 9.228$$

$F_{.05} = 2.82$ based on 4 and 22 degrees of freedom.
$F_{.01} = 4.31$ based on 4 and 22 degrees of freedom.
Since $9.228 > 4.31$, reject H_0 at $\alpha = .05$ and .01; because the null hypothesis was that the equations have the same slope and intercept, rejecting the H_0 means that at least one of these claims is false.

12.51 $\hat{y} = 30{,}626 + 3.893(28000) - 29{,}607(1.56) + 86.52(1821.7) \cong 251{,}056$

12.53 a. Significant regression model. Price is the only significant predictor.

b. Models are significant for both men and women. For men, Age has a slight negative relationship with interest (younger more interested, $p < .10$). For women, Price is the significant predictor (greater interest with lower prices, $p < .01$).

12.55 a. Interaction term is not a significant predictor ($p > .10$).

b. Introducing the interaction term decreases the F-value but increases the Multiple R slightly.

12.57 a. β_5: $b_5 = 0.2137$, CI = [0.0851, 0.3423], p-value = .0022, significant at 0.01 but not 0.001, so we have very strong evidence.
β_5: $b_6 = 0.3818$, CI = [0.2551, 0.5085], p-value $< .001$, significant at 0.001, so we have extremely strong evidence.

b. $b_6 = .1681$, CI = [.0363, .29], p-value = .0147, strong evidence.

c. $\mu_{[d, a, C]} - \mu_{[d, a, A]} = .408$
$\mu_{[d, a, C]} - \mu_{[d, a, B]} = .18118$
Both differences increased with the larger value of a.

d. The prediction interval for the third model is slightly shorter. The differences between campaign A and campaigns B and C change as volume level changes.

Chapter 13

13.5 a. Significant at $p < .05$
b. Calculated median is 5.

13.7 a. $S_1 = 4$, $S_2 = 5$, $S = 5$
b. p-value = 1.0; do not reject H_0 at any given value of α; conclude no difference in preference for Coke and Pepsi.

13.9 Independent samples z or t test; normal distribution

13.11 $T_1 = 120.5$
$T_2 = 89.5$
$T_1 \not\geq T_U = 131$ and $T_1 \not\leq T_L = 79$; do not reject H_0 and conclude no difference between plants.

13.13 Men and women do differ in their opinions regarding the frequency in which people become sick consuming food prepared at outdoor fairs and festivals.

13.15 Paired-difference t test; when normally distributed

13.17 $z = -0.36$; suggests no difference.

13.19 Post-exposure attitudes are significantly higher at $p < .05$

13.21 One-way ANOVA

13.23 Reject H_0; there is a difference.

13.25 $H = 13.35$; reject H_0. There is a difference in sales based on shelf location. Median sales for the middle shelf have increased.

13.29 a. $r_S = 1 - \dfrac{6 \sum d_i^2}{n(n^2 - 1)}$
b. For each tie, calculate an average rank and assign that value to the tied cases.

13.31 $r_s = .986$, reject H_0 if $r_s > r_a$; since $.986 > .523, .623, .736,$ and $.818$, reject H_0.

13.35 We use the Wilcoxon signed-rank test for paired differences. There is a significant decrease in the ages of its customers' accounts from 2009 to 2010.

13.37 Reject H_0; the loan rates do differ.

13.39 At $\alpha = .05$, (and even .10) we would not reject H_0. There is strong evidence to suggest that the distances for air-filled and helium-filled footballs are the same, statistically speaking.

Chapter 14

14.9 a. Each expected value is ≥ 5.
b. $X^2 = 880.22$
$X^2_{.05} = 12.592$
Since $880.22 > 12.592$, reject H_0; not consistent.

14.11 $X^2(1) = 6.89$, $p < .01$; significantly different; better than the expected.

14.13 a. $\chi^2 = 12.8325$; reject H_0
b. Differences between brand preferences

14.21 a. $\chi^2(1) = 611.55$ which is much greater than χ^2 critical of 3.84; reject H_0;

conclude that sex and unemployment are dependent.
b. Women are more likely to be employed part-time

14.23 a. $\chi^2 = 16.385$; critical chi-square at .05 = 7.815, $df = 3$; reject H_0: independence
b. $[-.216, -.072]$

14.25 $\chi^2 = 65.91$. Since $65.91 > \chi^2_{.05} = 9.48773$ (with $5 - 1 = 4$ degrees of freedom), we reject H_0: $p_1 = p_2 = p_3 = p_4 = p_5 = .2$; entrances not equally used; 95% CI = $[.27, .376]$

14.27

27.69	151.31
28.31	154.69

$X^2 = .04$; since $.04 < \chi^2_{.05} = 3.84146$ (with 1 degree of freedom), we do not reject H_0: independence.

14.31 Test H_0: P(American League wins a game) = P(National League wins a game) = $p = 0.5$ vs. H_a: the previously stated null hypothesis is not true. Determine the probabilities of the series being won (either American or National League) in 4, 5, 6, and 7 games. There were $n = 97$ series played from 1903 to 2005.
p(series being won in 4 games) = .125; observed value = 19; expected value = 12.125.
p(series being won in 5 games) = .25; observed value = 21; expected value = 24.25.
p(series being won in 6 games) = .3125; observed value = 22; expected value = 30.3125.
p(series being won in 7 games) = .3125; observed value = 35; expected value = 30.3125.
$X^2 = 7.34$
With 3 df, we see that $\chi^2_{0.05} = 7.81473$. It appears that the data do support the null hypothesis at $\alpha = 5\%$.

14.33 $\chi^2 = 33.03$, with $7 - 1 = 6$ df, we see that $\chi^2_{0.05} = 12.5916$. At $\alpha = 5\%$ reject H_0 and conclude that it appears that the crimes are not uniformly distributed throughout the days of the week.

14.35 $\chi^2 = 50.206$; with $49 - 1 = 48$ df; at $\alpha = 5\%$ do not reject H_0 and conclude that it appears that the numbers are all coming up with equal probability.

Chapter 15

15.11 a. Location C at $4M
b. Location A at $14M

15.21 a. P("economist says up") = .485; posterior probabilities: .8247, .0928, .0825
b. P("economist says flat") = .300; posterior probabilities: .1667, .7000, .1333
c. P("economist says flat") = .215; posterior probabilities: .2326, .2093, .5581
d. Decision tree not listed in this manual.

15.23 a. EPS = 821.96
b. EPNS = 580
c. EVSI = 241.96
d. $242.00

15.27 a. P("reads in") = .730; posterior probabilities: .9863, .0137
b. P("reads out") = .270; posterior probabilities: .6667, .3333

15.29 a. Test equipment "reads in": EMV(Not Send) = 14,958.90; EMV(Send) = 14,500; Choose: do not send engineer
b. Test equipment "reads out": EMV(Not Send) = 14,000; EMV(Send) = 14,500; Choose: send engineer

15.37 Expected Utility (investing) = .66; Expected Utility (Not investing): .70; Decision maker should not invest.

15.39 a. Research project should continue
b. Should be licensed; slightly better return: $23 license vs. $22.9 develop

15.41 Build Large: $62M; EV(small) = 49; EV(large) = 62

15.43 P(offered internship | good interview) = .5455

15.47 b. EMV(Renew Lease) = 2775; EMV(Relocate) = 1815; using the maximum expected value, management should renew the lease; expected payoff = $2.775M
c. Management should sign the lease; EVPI = 1575

Chapter 16

16.5 a. The data plot suggests that there is a long-run straight-line growth. Therefore, the linear trend model $y_t = \beta_0 + \beta_1 t + \varepsilon_t$ is reasonable.
b. $\hat{y} = 290.089474 + 8.667669(21) = 472.1$; 95% prediction intervals are for y_{21}: $[421.5, 522.7]$

16.7 Predicted values for 2009 = 592,215.0; 2010 = 598,847.2

16.11 $d = 0.43$. Appendix table only goes to $k = 5$, but d is very small. Positive correlation exists.

16.15 The seasonal factors for quarters 1, 2, 3, and 4 are $sn_1 = 1.192$, $sn_2 = 1.521$, $sn_3 = 0.804$, and $sn_4 = 0.484$.

16.25 Forecast = 35,438; used to compare forecasting methods.

16.33 a. 91.10
b. For 2008: 102.70; for 2009: 91.10; sales were up 11.6% in 2008, compared to 2009.
c. Huge drop in sales in 2009 (year 5).

16.37 a. Yes
b. Predicted values for 2009 = 18.2; 2010 = 17.4; 2011 = 16.6; 2012 = 15.8; 2013 = 15.0

16.39 a. Increasing trend
b. Predicted value for 2010 = 7,721,399.7

Chapter 17

17.9 a.

Subgroup	1	2	3	4	5
Mean, $\bar{x}$	5	7	6	3	7
Range, R	2	4	4	2	5

b. $\bar{\bar{x}} = 5.6$; $\bar{R} = 3.4$

c. $A_2 = 1.023$, $D_4 = 2.574$

d. $\bar{\bar{x}} = 5.6$; $\bar{R} = 3.4$; $UCL_{\bar{x}} = 9.0782$; $LCL_{\bar{x}} = 2.1218$; $UCL_R = 8.7516$; no LCL_R

17.13 a. $\bar{\bar{x}} = 15.8$; $\bar{R} = 6.1333$

b. Yes, both charts are in control.

c. Some of the subgroup means exceed the upper control limit.

d. The $\bar{x}$ chart is not in control.

e. No, both charts remain in control after die change.

f. Yes, $\bar{x}$ chart is badly out of control after die repair.

17.15 a. $\bar{\bar{x}} = 841.45$; $\bar{R} = 5.16$; yes, both charts are out of control

b. $\bar{\bar{x}} = 841.45$; $\bar{R} = 4.88$

d. R chart is in control; yes, can use the $\bar{x}$ chart.

e. No, the $\bar{x}$ chart is out of control; process mean is changing.

f. $\bar{\bar{x}} = 840.46$; $\bar{R} = 5.26$

g. Yes, all $\bar{x}$ and R values are within the control limits.

17.21 a. Evidence of lack of control; run of 8 points below centre line; run of 12 points above centre line

b. Evidence of lack of control; two points above UCL

c. No evidence of assignable causes (except for possible cycle)

d. Evidence of lack of control; 2 out of 3 points in zone A or beyond (subgroups 14 and 16)

17.31 a. [.6518, 1.0416]

b. 1.0416 kg

c. No, grapefruit weights might be as low as .6518 kg.

d. .0681

17.35 .8736

17.39 UCL = .19; LCL = .01

17.41 a. UCL = .6217; LCL = .4323

b. In control; no assignable causes

c. Make salespeople responsible for order information

17.43 a. UCL = .0853; LCL = .0187

b. UCL = .057; LCL = .005; the improved process is in control.

17.45 All samples in compliance; no cause for concern.

17.47 a. UCL = 5.3532; LCL = 3.5068

b. $UCL_R = 3.3824$; no LCL_R

c. In control

Ashton, Robert H., John J. Willingham, and Robert K. Elliott. "An Empirical Analysis of Audit Delay." *Journal of Accounting Research* 25, no. 2 (Autumn 1987), pp. 275–92.

Bayus, Barry L. "The Consumer and Durable Replacement Buyer." *Journal of Marketing* 55 (January 1991), pp. 42–51.

Beattie, Vivien, and Michael John Jones. "The Use and Abuse of Graphs in Annual Reports: Theoretical Framework and Empirical Study." *Accounting and Business Research* 22, no. 88 (Autumn 1992), pp. 291–303.

Blodgett, Jeffrey G., Donald H. Granbois, and Rockney G. Walters. "The Effects of Perceived Justice on Complainants' Negative Word-of-Mouth Behavior and Repatronage Intentions." *Journal of Retailing* 69, no. 4 (Winter 1993), pp. 399–428.

Bowerman, Bruce L., and Richard T. O'Connell. *Linear Statistical Models: An Applied Approach.* 2nd ed. Boston, MA: PWS-KENT Publishing Company, 1990, pp. 457, 460–64, 729–974.

Box, G. E. P., and G. M. Jenkins. *Time Series Analysis: Forecasting and Control.* 2nd ed. San Francisco, CA: Holden-Day, 1976.

Clemen, Robert T. *Making Hard Decisions: An Introduction to Decision Analysis.* 2nd ed. Belmont, CA: Duxbury Press, 1996, p. 443.

Cooper, Donald R., and C. William Emory. *Business Research Methods.* 5th ed. Homewood, IL: Richard D. Irwin, 1995, pp. 434–38, 450–51, 458–68.

Dawson, Scott. "Consumer Responses to Electronic Article Surveillance Alarms." *Journal of Retailing* 69, no. 3 (Fall 1993), pp. 353–62.

Deming, W. Edwards. *Out of the Crisis.* Cambridge, MA: Massachusetts Institute of Technology Center for Advanced Engineering Study, 1986, pp. 18–96, 312–14.

Diekhoff, G. (1992). *Statistics for the Social and Behavioral Sciences: Univariate, Bivariate, Multivariate.* Dubuque, IA: Wm. C. Brown.

Dillon, William R., Thomas J. Madden, and Neil H. Firtle. *Essentials of Marketing Research.* Homewood, IL: Richard D. Irwin Inc., 1993, pp. 382–84, 416–17, 419–20, 432–33, 445, 462–64, 524–27.

Farnum, Nicholas R. *Modern Statistical Quality Control and Improvement.* Belmont, CA: Duxbury Press, 1994, p. 55.

Fitzgerald, Neil. "Relations Overcast by Cloudy Conditions." *CA Magazine,* April 1993, pp. 28–35.

Gibbons, J. D. *Nonparametric Statistical Inference.* 2nd ed. New York: McGraw-Hill, 1985.

Gitlow, Howard, Shelly Gitlow, Alan Oppenheim, and Rosa Oppenheim. *Tools and Methods for the Improvement of Quality.* Homewood, IL: Richard D. Irwin, 1989, pp. 14–25, 533–53.

Kumar, V., Roger A. Kerin, and Arun Pereira. "An Empirical Assessment of Merger and Acquisition Activity in Retailing." *Journal of Retailing* 67, no. 3 (Fall 1991), pp. 321–38.

Magee, Robert P. *Advanced Managerial Accounting.* New York, NY: Harper & Row, 1986, p. 223.

Mahmood, Mo Adam, and Gary J. Mann. "Measuring the Organizational Impact of Information Technology Investment: An Exploratory Study." *Journal of Management Information Systems* 10, no. 1 (Summer 1993), pp. 97–122.

Martocchio, Joseph J. "The Financial Cost of Absence Decisions." *Journal of Management* 18, no. 1 (1992), pp. 133–52.

The Miami University Report. Miami University, Oxford, OH, vol. 8, no. 26, 1989.

Moore, David S. *The Basic Practice of Statistics.* 2nd ed. New York: W. H. Freeman and Company, 2000.

Moore, David S., and George P. McCabe. *Introduction to the Practice of Statistics.* 2nd ed. New York: W. H. Freeman, 1993.

Morris, Michael H., Ramon A. Avila, and Jeffrey Allen. "Individualism and the Modern Corporation: Implications for Innovation and Entrepreneurship." *Journal of Management* 19, no. 3 (1993), pp. 595–612.

Neter, J., M. Kutner, C. Nachtsheim, and W. Wasserman. *Applied Linear Statistical Models.* 4th ed. Homewood, IL: Irwin/McGraw-Hill, 1996.

Nunnally, Bennie H., Jr., and D. Anthony Plath. *Cases in Finance.* Burr Ridge, IL: Richard D. Irwin, 1995, pp. 12–1–12–7.

Scheaffer, R. L., William Mendenhall, and Lyman Ott. *Elementary Survey Sampling.* 3rd ed. Boston, MA: Duxbury Press, 1986.

Scherkenbach, William. *The Deming Route to Quality and Productivity: Road Maps and Roadblocks.* Washington, D.C.: Ceepress Books, 1986.

Seigel, James C. "Managing with Statistical Models." SAE Technical Paper 820520. Warrendale, PA: Society for Automotive Engineers, Inc., 1982.

Silk, Alvin J., and Ernst R. Berndt. "Scale and Scope Effects on Advertising Agency Costs." *Marketing Science* 12, no. 1 (Winter 1993), pp. 53–72.

Stevenson, William J. *Production/Operations Management.* 6th ed. Homewood, IL: Irwin/McGraw-Hill, 1999, p. 228.

Von Neumann, J., and O. Morgenstern. *Theory of Games and Economic Behavior*. 2nd ed. Princeton, N.J.: Princeton University Press, 1947.

Walton, Mary. *The Deming Management Method*. New York, NY: Dodd, Mead & Company, 1986.

Weinberger, Marc G., and Harlan E. Spotts. "Humor in U.S. versus U.K. TV Commercials: A Comparison." *Journal of Advertising* 18, no. 2 (1989), pp. 39–44.

Wright, Thomas A., and Douglas G. Bonett. "Role of Employee Coping and Performance in Voluntary Employee Withdrawal: A Research Refinement and Elaboration." *Journal of Management* 19, no. 1 (1993) pp. 147–61.

CREDITS

CASE INDEX

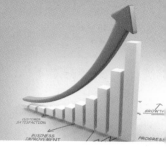